Populated areas (1 or more persons per square mile)

Generalized areas of concentrated population

Courtesy of the American Geographical Society, E. D. Weldon, Cartographer

Man's Role
in
Changing the Face of the Earth

Man's Role in Changing the Face of the Earth

International Symposium
Wenner-Gren Foundation for Anthropological Research

Co-Chairmen of the Symposium

CARL O. SAUER   MARSTON BATES   LEWIS MUMFORD

Participants

WILLIAM A. ALBRECHT

HARRY ALPERT

EDGAR ANDERSON

EUGENE AYRES

A. LESLIE BANKS

H. H. BARTLETT

ALAN M. BATEMAN

DAVID I. BLUMENSTOCK

KENNETH BOULDING

HARRISON BROWN

JOHN C. BUGHER

ALBERT E. BURKE

ANDREW H. CLARK

JOHN T. CURTIS

H. C. DARBY

F. FRASER DARLING

CHARLES GALTON DARWIN

JOHN H. DAVIS

JOHN W. DODDS

FRANK E. EGLER

E. ESTYN EVANS

IAGO GALDSTON

CLARENCE J. GLACKEN

ARTUR GLIKSON

PIERRE GOUROU

EDWARD H. GRAHAM

*MICHAEL GRAHAM

GEORGE W. GRAY

ALAN GREGG

E. A. GUTKIND

CHAUNCY D. HARRIS

EMIL W. HAURY

FRITZ M. HEICHELHEIM

J. A. HISLOP

CHARLES B. HITCHCOCK

SOLIMAN HUZAYYIN

EDAVALETH K. JANAKI AMMAL

STEPHEN B. JONES

LESTER E. KLIMM

FRANK H. KNIGHT

HELMUT LANDSBERG

LUNA B. LEOPOLD

*DONALD H. MC LAUGHLIN

JAMES C. MALIN

ALBERT MAYER

*RADHAKAMAL MUKERJEE

ROBERT CUSHMAN MURPHY

*KARL J. NARR

F. S. C. NORTHROP

SAMUEL H. ORDWAY, JR.

FAIRFIELD OSBORN

GOTTFRIED PFEIFER

*RICHARD J. RUSSELL

CHARLES A. SCARLOTT

VINCENT J. SCHAEFER

PAUL B. SEARS

RODERICK SEIDENBERG

J. RUSSELL SMITH

ALEXANDER SPOEHR

H. BURR STEINBACH

OMER C. STEWART

ARTHUR N. STRAHLER

SOL TAX

*PIERRE TEILHARD DE CHARDIN

HAROLD E. THOMAS

WARREN S. THOMPSON

C. W. THORNTHWAITE

JOHN W. TUKEY

EDWARD L. ULLMAN

JOSEPH H. WILLITS

HERMANN VON WISSMANN

KARL A. WITTFOGEL

*ABEL WOLMAN

*Contributors to Symposium as authors of background papers but not in attendance.

Man's Role
in
Changing the Face of the Earth

Edited by

WILLIAM L. THOMAS, Jr.
Wenner-Gren Foundation

with the collaboration of

CARL O. SAUER
University of California

MARSTON BATES
University of Michigan

LEWIS MUMFORD
University of Pennsylvania

Published for the
WENNER-GREN FOUNDATION FOR ANTHROPOLOGICAL RESEARCH
and the
NATIONAL SCIENCE FOUNDATION

by

THE UNIVERSITY OF CHICAGO PRESS
CHICAGO • ILLINOIS

The INTERNATIONAL SYMPOSIUM ON MAN'S ROLE IN CHANG-ING THE FACE OF THE EARTH was made possible by funds granted by the Wenner-Gren Foundation for Anthropological Research, Incorporated, a foundation endowed for scientific, educational, and charitable purposes. Publication of this volume has been aided by a grant from the National Science Foundation of the United States. Neither Foundation is the author or publisher of this volume, and is not to be understood as endorsing, by virtue of its grant, any of the statements made, or views expressed, herein.

Library of Congress Catalog Number: 56-586

THE UNIVERSITY OF CHICAGO PRESS, CHICAGO 37

Cambridge University Press, London, N.W. 1, England
The University of Toronto Press, Toronto 5, Canada

To

GEORGE P. MARSH

and to the earliest men who
first used tools and fire;
and to the countless generations between
whose skilful hands and contriving brains
have made a whole planet their home
and provided our subject for study

Foreword

On June 16 of this year it was my privilege, as President of the Wenner-Gren Foundation for Anthropological Research, to extend welcome to the seventy illustrious participants assembled in Princeton, New Jersey, for the International Symposium on "Man's Role in Changing the Face of the Earth." The opening ceremonies, which included addresses of welcome from Dr. C. E. Sunderlin, Deputy Director of the National Science Foundation; Dr. Harold W. Dodds, President of Princeton University; and Dr. Axel L. Wenner-Gren, marked the culmination of nearly three years of planning that made possible the Symposium and this volume.

The Wenner-Gren Foundation, ever since its establishment in 1941, has been uniquely concerned with rendering aid in the advancement of anthropology as the study of man. Over the years, the Foundation's program has developed simultaneously along three broad fronts. First, and largely, it has directly assisted (mostly professional anthropologists) through fellowships and grants-in-aid, publication subsidies, and sponsorship of conferences and seminars and by making possible professional stocktaking, as in the International Symposium on Anthropology held in New York in June, 1952, resulting in the three volumes, *Anthropology Today, An Appraisal of Anthropology Today,* and *International Directory of Anthropological Institutions.* Second, the Foundation has been constantly on the search for new ideas and techniques developed in other fields capable of contributing to solutions of anthropological problems; examples of this are the Foundation's postwar program of loans of field equipment and its pioneer aid in the application of the radioactive carbon theory to the problem of absolute dating in archeology and paleoanthropology. Third, the Foundation has been concerned with broadening the bases of public support of anthropology through dissemination of the results of anthropological research and through diffusion of anthropological theory, methods, and knowledge into other fields of science; examples of this have been the organization and publication of such symposium volumes as *The Science of Man in the World Crisis, Ideological Differences and World Order,* and *Most of the World.*

This Symposium and volume on "Man's Role in Changing the Face of the Earth" reflect the second and third facets of our program. The Foundation has long been aware that one of the ways in which scholars move toward theoretical and conceptual ordering of man's knowledge of himself and his world is by synthesis, transcending the limits of present disciplines or branches of science. The Foundation's purpose through the present undertaking has been to further the recombination and synthesis of available and new knowledge, looking toward the development of a more comprehensive science of man.

The subject of the Symposium was the idea of the Foundation's Assistant Director, Dr. William L. Thomas, Jr., who also acted as organizer and is the editor of this volume. The Foundation is indeed grateful for this opportunity to express publicly its appreciation of the vision and zeal of Dr. Thomas. Grateful thanks are also due to him for his devoted and significant contributions and tireless splendid efforts in his multiple activities in connection with this Symposium. We wish to express, too, our feeling of profound gratitude to the three senior scholars—Professors Carl O. Sauer, Marston Bates, and Lewis Mumford—who so willingly and ably aided the Symposium's development. The co-operative assistance of the National Science Foundation, whose grant-in-aid of publication subsidy made possible this volume, is greatly appreciated.

The Foundation was fortunate to encounter a number of persons with alert, able, and active minds interested in a common problem and invited them to come together that they might benefit by stimulation from one another. In a setting that encouraged men to speak easily with one another, many minds learned what others were thinking. The Symposium, in attempting to survey the state of knowledge of a topic touched only in piecemeal fashion by individual disciplines, provided a focus of interest for persons with different theoretical and descriptive backgrounds. The question explored was: What has been, and is, happening to the earth's surface as a result of man's having been on it for a long time, increasing in numbers and skills unevenly, at different places and times?

The story of mankind may be considered as man's own exploration of the various physical and biological conditions on the earth's surface as a result of the elaboration of human needs, capacities, aspirations, and values. Three interrelated factors are involved: (1) the earth's resources; (2) the numerical pressure of population upon, and sustained by, the resources; and (3) man's differing cultures, or ways of life. Understanding these relationships involves knowledge of values, equipment or artifacts, and of the social organizations by which people group themselves, function, and interpret resources and their use. Cultural development may be viewed as man's growing knowledge of, and control over, forces external to himself. By increasing his range of action, man has intervened more and more in the rest of the organic world. Man's evolutionary dominance seems assured—only he himself can threaten it. Man has supplemented organic evolution with a new method of change—the development of culture, the transmission of organized experience, retained, discarded, or altered by further experience.

The Foundation's interest in calling this Symposium, therefore, is anthropology's own—to keep abreast of all the means at man's disposal to affect deliberately or unconsciously the course of his own evolution; in this case, what man has done, and is doing, to change his physical-biological environment on the earth.

PAUL FEJOS

NEW YORK CITY
December 13, 1955

Table of Contents

PART II. PROCESS

List of Illustrations

List of Tables

List of Tables

Introductory

About the Symposium
About the People
About the Theme

"Man's Role in Changing the Face of the Earth" is many things. It is part of the historical reality of the earth during its latest phase, which has witnessed the presence of man. It is an idea or theme of which man, conscious of himself and his activities, has become increasingly aware and which has been touched upon in one or another aspect by scores of scholars through the ages. It was an international symposium, organized by the Wenner-Gren Foundation for Anthropological Research, and held at the Princeton Inn, Princeton, New Jersey, June 16–22, 1955. And, lastly, it is this volume, which treats all the above through the writings of fifty-three contributors and a report on the Symposium discussions of the seventy participants.

ABOUT THE SYMPOSIUM

The development of an interdisciplinary symposium with international participation is a study in organized complexity. Active planning began in the fall of 1952, and a full year was spent in research on the theme, in formulating a statement of the significance of the symposium idea, in drafting a tentative program and roster of possible invitees, and in consultation with more than forty scholars in and out of New York City. In October, 1953, the proposal for a symposium was placed before Professor Carl O. Sauer, then Chairman of the Department of Geog- raphy, University of California, Berkeley, with the request that he serve as Symposium Chairman. We first met for prolonged discussion in Tucson, Arizona, during the annual meeting of the American Anthropological Association in December, 1953. It was agreed that the Symposium's purpose was neither to propose an action program nor to pass resolutions. We did not want it to get lost in elegant verbal acrobatics nor to have it run into the shoals of statistics, except as they might be valid illustrations. The participants were to be selected for their common interest and curiosity about what man has been doing to and with his habitat. To be included was the historical course of action by which man had come to be where he is.

The web of planning and consultation during the winter and spring of 1954 expanded to include sessions with Professors Edgar Anderson, Marston Bates, Stephen Jones, Lewis Mumford, Paul Sears, and Sol Tax. "Round-robin" exchanges of correspondence were voluminous. It was agreed that no effort would be spared in attending to the proper amenities and the comforts of the participants. In seeking to encourage the fullest possible exchange of ideas, there should be a minimum of limitations to communication inherent in group activity. But it was further recognized that the primary objective was not education of the participants through interaction of personalities and ideas but publication of a record of the Symposium in a permanent form, so that the ideas expressed might reach a larger audience and be available to scholars in oncoming generations.

Responsibility for thinking toward this primary objective led to outlining not a conference but a volume. As with *Anthropology Today,* which resulted from the 1952 International Symposium on Anthropology, titles for chapters were suggested. The chapters were to be written as factual accounts, inventories, or data papers. Each chapter was to be oriented around a certain body of subject matter, with the primary intent to "brief" or to inform others who are aware of, but not expert in, the field being surveyed. Taken together, these chapters were to provide a common ground of factual data for persons who, in their approaches to the central theme, had come along many different paths not necessarily with previous intersections. Having been written prior to the Symposium, the chapters were to be preprinted and circulated to all participants for study before their departure from their homes. The objective of these background papers was to free the limited Symposium time for full discussion of ideas and to prevent its being bogged down by formal reading of papers heavily weighted with factual data and intended as exchanges of information.

The Symposium itself was to be structured only loosely. A foundation by planning can provide only opportunity and setting. The creativity of a symposium lies in the hands of its participants. Speakers having the floor could talk about what they wished, regardless of what subject might be listed on a printed program. The Symposium was to be thought of principally in terms of the people whom it would be desirable to bring together for a week; secondly in terms of a handful of chair-

men for the various half-day discussion sessions; and thirdly in terms of a skeletal framework of session themes that would only roughly sketch in a program. This latter would be a guide for the division of effort among chairmen, within which they would have the fullest latitude for the conduct of their respective sessions.

The function of the background papers for the Symposium was to provide common knowledge to all participants in advance of their gathering together. The Symposium, however, could choose to ignore the papers entirely, discuss them all in detail, or pick and choose as it pleased. The background papers simply were to "be there," without any thought that papers rather than people constitute a symposium. The challenge to the Symposium was to rise above the level of the content of the papers into the realm of ideas—the next higher realm of abstraction, as it were—dealing not with the recitation of facts or with the exchange of anecdotes but with the conjunction of thoughts. The resulting publication was to contain two things: first, the background papers, each authored for an audience of non-specialists by a key scholar at home in his field, and, second, an edited version of the Symposium discussions—a report on the thoughts given expression while the group was assembled.

In March, 1954, Sauer proposed a threefold division for the Symposium— "Retrospect," "Process," and "Prospect" —and suggested that there be three co-chairmen corresponding to each of these views of the Symposium theme. Sauer assumed the task for "Retrospect"; Bates and Mumford accepted his invitations to share the co-chairmanships for "Process" and "Prospect," respectively. Once the general outline of the Symposium had been drawn and a roster of invitees had been developed, the Foundation, on behalf of its Board of Directors, began to extend invitations to participants in early June, 1954. The invitations proposed a meeting in June, 1955, outside of New York City, intended as a gathering of some of the world's best minds in a congenial atmosphere for recorded discussion leading to eventual publication for the benefit of the world of scholarship. Expenses of first-class transportation to and from their homes and a sum for personal expenses, as well as provision for the stay during the Symposium, were to be provided by the Foundation. An appendix to the invitation letter listed the invitees and, by way of introduction, their positions, institutional affiliations or addresses, and the titles and dates of several publications of each.

More than two-thirds of those invited were asked to prepare a background or data paper on a suggested topic, such paper to be submitted not later than March 15, 1955. It was pointed out that papers would be published in full and would be distributed to all participants in advance of the Symposium but would not be read aloud. Also, a copy of the published volume and fifty reprints of his chapter would be furnished each author. An appendix to the invitation letter gave additional details about the background papers. Discussion was invited of an author's views of a better phrasing of the proposed title of his paper. (Twenty-three chapters have been retitled in accordance with their authors' suggestions; three authors eventually wrote on subjects other than those proposed.) As guidance for relating each paper to the Symposium theme, the planning group included a list of subjects that each author might consider for inclusion in the content of his paper. An optimum length of eight thousand words (exclusive of a list of "References") was proposed for the papers. With this limitation, obviously no paper could attempt to summarize existing factual

knowledge. Rather, the contributed chapters were to be looked upon as evaluations of the state of knowledge of the topics considered, keeping in mind as a purpose the stimulation of the next generation of research scholars. What are the known problems? What special strategy is called for in planning research? What are the topics and areas principally in urgent need of additional investigation? It was further suggested that, whereas all articles would deal with the qualitative effects of man's working and living in different parts of the world, perhaps some authors would wish to consider the quantitative effects of man on the landscape. How much has man changed the earth's surface? How fast is he changing it? How rapidly can he restore it if his changes have proved unwise or are now considered obsolete and replacement is desired? Perhaps an approach in terms of total amounts and rates of change would produce much more information and insight than would a purely qualitative approach.

Between June, 1954, and March, 1955, ninety-seven invitations were extended, and seventy-six acceptances were received. During the fall of 1954 several memorandums were sent to participants as aids and as reminders of the tasks ahead. In October the place of the Symposium was announced as the Princeton Inn, Princeton, New Jersey, and the dates as June 16–22, 1955; a revised program and roster of participating scholars were included. In November a guide to contributing authors of background papers advised of the format, style for footnotes and bibliography, the inclusion of illustrative material, layout of title page and biographical statement, and manner for ordering author's reprints. In December information was given on the transportation and personal expenses to be furnished each participating scholar.

In December, 1954, through the

award of a grant-for-publication subsidy, the National Science Foundation of the United States joined in the sponsorship of the Symposium. This expression of recognition emphasized the truly broad interest of the Symposium theme for almost all fields of science. Application to the Department of State for designation of the Symposium as an exchange-visitor program in order to facilitate entrance of foreign scholars into the United States was made in December, 1954; notification of such designation and the assignment of serial number P-1974 were received in April, 1955. In May, 1955, a contract was negotiated with the University of Chicago Press for publication of the volume to emanate from the Symposium. Funds received from the National Science Foundation grant were held in a separate account and then transmitted in full to the University of Chicago Press in October, 1955.

The first public announcement of the Symposium meanwhile had appeared in *Science,* on March 11, 1955 (CXXI, No. 3141, 356–57). Other announcements appeared soon after in the British journals *Nature* and *Man.* The first background papers were mailed to all participants in early March; four packages in all were sent by mid-May. Forty-seven of the fifty-three background papers were received by participants for study in advance of the Symposium; four others were distributed upon arrival; the remaining two were reproduced and distributed at Princeton from manuscripts delivered by their authors upon arrival at the Symposium. A special paper on "Princeton and Environs" provided information on travel to Princeton and described the local area and its points of interest. Six scholars who contributed background papers could not attend the Symposium meetings; thus the participants totaled seventy. The Symposium met for six working days, on each of which two three-hour sessions were held. On the evening prior to the Symposium's opening, a dinner in honor of the visiting scholars from outside the United States was attended also by the Symposium co-chairmen and chairmen of the individual half-day discussion sessions. At this pre-Symposium meeting all chairmen had the opportunity to exchange information on the expected nature of their sessions. A briefing was given on the arrangement of the meeting room and on problems of recording, and questions on procedure were answered.

The Symposium program was as follows:

Thursday, June 16

INTRODUCTION

10:15 A.M.   OPENING SESSION: THE SYMPOSIUM THEME

Welcome from the Wenner-Gren Foundation—Dr. PAUL FEJOS, President

Welcome from the National Science Foundation—Dr. C. E. SUNDERLIN, Deputy Director

Welcome to the Princeton Community—Dr. HAROLD W. DODDS, President, Princeton University

Introducing the Symposium Co-Chairmen:

PROFESSOR CARL O. SAUER, University of California

PROFESSOR MARSTON BATES, University of Michigan

PROFESSOR LEWIS MUMFORD, University of Pennsylvania

The Symposium Idea—PROFESSOR SAUER

Remarks of Appreciation—Dr. AXEL L. WENNER-GREN

RETROSPECT

1:30 P.M.   MAN'S TENURE OF THE EARTH
Chairman: F. FRASER DARLING

Friday, June 17
9:00 A.M.   SUBSISTENCE ECONOMIES
Chairman: ALEXANDER SPOEHR

2:00 P.M.   COMMERCIAL ECONOMIES
Chairman: PAUL B. SEARS

Saturday, June 18
9:00 A.M.   INDUSTRIAL REVOLUTION AND URBAN DOMI-
NANCE
Chairman: KENNETH BOULDING

PROCESS

2:00 P.M.   TECHNIQUES OF LEARNING: THEIR LIMITATIONS
AND FIT
Chairmen: EDGAR ANDERSON *and* SOL TAX

Monday, June 20
9:00 A.M.   CHANGES IN PHYSICAL PHENOMENA
Chairman: ALAN M. BATEMAN

2:00 P.M.   CHANGES IN BIOLOGICAL PHENOMENA
Chairman: MARSTON BATES

PROSPECT

Tuesday, June 21
9:00 A.M.   LIMITS OF THE EARTH: MATERIALS AND
IDEAS
Chairmen: JOSEPH H. WILLITS *and* LESTER E. KLIMM

2:00 P.M.   MAN'S SELF-TRANSFORMATION
Chairman: LEWIS MUMFORD

Wednesday, June 22
9:00 A.M.   THE UNSTABLE EQUILIBRIUM OF MAN IN NA-
TURE
Chairman: HARRISON BROWN

SUMMARY REMARKS

2:00 P.M.   RETROSPECT—CARL O. SAUER
PROCESS—MARSTON BATES
PROSPECT—LEWIS MUMFORD

The Symposium "Program and Calendar of Events" listed the daily program, the background papers (by number, title, and author), a roster of Symposium participants (by name, affiliation, and Symposium role), a floor plan of the Princeton Inn, pertinent information concerning Symposium procedure, information on personal arrangements and local facilities, maps of Princeton and of the Princeton University campus, and a roster of the Foundation's Board of Directors, officers and staff, and the Symposium co-chairmen and staff.

The Symposium meeting room and office, rooms for all participants except those living in the immediate vicinity, and meals were provided for within the Princeton Inn. Extracurricular activities in New York City included a theater program on Saturday night and either a sight-seeing cruise around Manhattan Island or a double-header baseball game on Sunday afternoon. The last evening was devoted to a farewell banquet for all Symposium participants, at which Professor Sauer was presented with a silver tea service and an illuminated scroll signed by all who attended.

Prior to the Symposium meeting all background papers had been edited. An editorial office was established at the Princeton Inn, and, during the week of the meeting, two editorial assistants consulted with the authors of background papers, to discuss such matters as amendments in submitted manuscripts, verification of biographical statements, and signing of consent-to-publish agreements. All Symposium discussion for the full six days was recorded; the full transcript of this recording was prepared in mimeographed form totaling 1,093 pages. Bound copies (in three-volume sets) of this transcript are in the Foundation's office and were presented to each of the three Symposium co-chairmen. The co-chairmen edited their "Summary Remarks" of the closing session on the basis of the mimeographed transcript and a tape recording of their remarks that were provided them. A report of the Symposium discussions, based upon the recorded transcript, was prepared by the editor. Each session chairman was provided a copy of the transcript and of the editor's report of his respective session.

The illustrated background papers and the edited report of the discussions together comprise the contents of this volume. The intended audience for this work is nothing less than the vast numbers of the human kind in the "rest of the world," now and to be, outside of the microcosm of Princeton in June, 1955, when those who shared one another's company provided its substance and gave it birth.

ABOUT THE PEOPLE

Any program of such scope and magnitude as has been described could have been made possible only by the enthusiastic co-operation of a host of individuals.

Whatever value this volume may have stems from the combined efforts of the seventy Symposium participants (listed on pp. ii and 1153–55), the fifty-three contributing authors, the thirteen scholars who chaired various parts of the Symposium discussions, and the three Symposium co-chairmen. After the Symposium, and following return to their homes, the participants wrote to us appreciative letters of thanks. But we of the Foundation know that to act as host is to be but a catalytic agent; the active ingredients in the Symposium reaction were the working participants. We look back with fond memory on having met so many interesting and wonderful people. The reader and editor alike are indebted to them for having provided the content of this volume.

The seventy participants, after having been selected for their qualities as individuals, turned out to have backgrounds or specializations in some twenty-four different conventionally defined disciplines, from anthropology to zoölogy. Broadly classified, about 40 per cent were in the field of earth science, 28 per cent in the biological sciences, 12 per cent in the social sciences and the humanities, and 20 per cent in applied fields (administration, city planning, etc.). Fourteen came from nine countries outside the United States (Canada, England, Scotland, Northern Ireland, Belgium, Germany, Egypt, Israel, and India). Sixty-five per cent were associated with universities; 35 per cent represented private institutions, industry, and government.

In their institutional roles, the Board of Directors of the Wenner-Gren Foundation for Anthropological Research and the National Science Board of the

National Science Foundation are to be thanked for their allocations of funds in support of the Symposium—its organization, meeting, and preparation for publication and its publication, respectively. Dr. Axel L. Wenner-Gren, the Founder, and Dr. Paul Fejos, President of the Wenner-Gren Foundation, together with Dr. C. E. Sunderlin, Deputy Director of the National Science Foundation, participated in the opening ceremonies. Professors John W. Dodds and F. S. C. Northrop, members of the Board of Directors of the Wenner-Gren Foundation, and Dr. Harry Alpert, Program Director for Anthropological and Related Sciences of the National Science Foundation, participated in all Symposium sessions.

We are grateful to Dr. David I. Blumenstock, then of Rutgers University, for preparing the special booklet on "Princeton and Environs," from which every Symposium participant benefited with information in advance of arrival. The Princeton University Library, through the good offices of Dr. William S. Dix, loaned many reference volumes on New Jersey and the Princeton community which were available for consultation by all participants. Dr. Robert Cushman Murphy made memorable one evening at Princeton by presenting color slides and film on "The Guano Islands of Peru."

From the very inception of the planning of the Symposium, the editor has had the secretarial assistance of Mrs. Jean S. Stewart. She is the only person other than the editor who daily has witnessed and tended the transformation of an intangible idea into this massive volume. During the past year, since the arrival of manuscripts of the background papers, she has doubled as editorial assistant. The completion of this volume is a monument in testimony to her faithful and steadfast devotion over the last three and a half years. Assisting during brief stages in the planning phase were Misses Susan Davis and Nancy Silbowitz.

The Symposium staff at Princeton drew in part upon those regularly employed by the Foundation. Miss Alice Uchida (now Mrs. Wasserman) supervised the reception desk and acted as office manager, while Miss Joyce De Podesta and Mrs. Joyce Mendelsohn served as meeting-room attendants and assisted in office duties. Needless to say, behind the scenes, the entire staff of the Foundation contributed directly or indirectly to the development of the Symposium and the realization of its goal.

From June through August, 1955, we were fortunate to have the services of Mr. Frederick J. Simoons, a doctoral candidate in the Department of Geography at the University of California, Berkeley. His co-operative assistance during the course of the meetings was invaluable and his functions many; principally, though, he insured the accuracy of the discussion transcripts by identifying speakers and checking the spelling of proper names, foreign words, and technical phrases. After the Symposium and back at the Foundation's offices, the transcript of all the discussion sessions was corrected before mimeographing by playback of the tape recordings; also, he spent considerable time in library research on the material presented in the section that follows: "About the Theme."

The editorial assistants at Princeton were Mrs. Stewart and Miss Anna M. Pikelis, formerly a Foundation staff member and at that time at the University of Chicago and an editorial assistant for the *American Anthropologist*. Together with the editor, they had previously read and marked all background papers; between them they conferred with all the authors present at Princeton and arranged for the approval of the corrected edited version of the manuscripts to be forwarded to the publisher, the University of Chicago Press.

Miss Nancy Silbowitz spent part of the summer months of 1955 at various libraries in New York City checking and completing bibliographic entries. Mrs. Wasserman, Mrs. Jean Shulman, and Miss Silbowitz have served variously as post-Symposium clerks and secretaries, copyreaders, and proofreaders. The skill of Mr. Felix M. Eger in arranging the microphones and controlling the recording devices insured that faithful and complete tape recordings were made of all remarks presented in the meeting room during all six days of discussion.

Throughout the volume, credits for permission to reproduce certain illustrative material appear immediately beneath the respective illustrations. We are especially indebted to Dr. David Lowenthal, of Vassar College, for the loan of the portrait of George P. Marsh reproduced in Figure 49 and for reading and suggesting corrections and additional remarks to our account of the work of Marsh. In undertaking background reading for the following section, "About the Theme," we have had the assistance in German translation of Mrs. Katherine Klein and Ilona Schenk and in Russian translation of Dr. David Sopher and Mr. Albert E. Burke.

The American Geographical Society has been most helpful in many ways. The end-paper map for this volume originally appeared as an inset on one of the Society's maps in the series "Atlas of Diseases." The equal-area elliptical projection is by William Briesemeister, chief cartographer, with population overlay compiled and drafted by E. D. Weldon. Some 40 of the 180 figures for this volume were redrawn for publication by the Society's cartographic staff. The chart of "Conversion Scales" (p. 1156) originally appeared in *Pioneer Settlement* (Special Publication No. 14), published by the Society in 1934. Two Councilors of the Society, Drs. Lester E. Klimm and Robert Cushman Murphy, and the Director, Mr.

Charles B. Hitchcock, were participants in the Symposium. A review of the Symposium, prepared by Murphy and Hitchcock, appeared in the *Geographical Review*, XLV, No. 4 (October, 1955), 583–86.

ABOUT THE THEME

The intellectual fonts in the modern period in developing the theme, "Man's Role in Changing the Face of the Earth," were the American statesman and scholar George Perkins Marsh and the Russian geographer Alexander Ivanovich Woeikof.[1] It is to these two that many contemporary writers refer and from whom they take their inspiration.

Marsh (1801–82) grew up in the stimulating atmosphere of a nineteenth-century New England family which belonged to the intellectual aristocracy. He carefully observed the changes that men had brought about in the forested hills and valleys of New England and maintained his interest in man's modification of the earth's surface throughout his career of service as a lawyer, member of the Congress of the United States, and minister to Turkey and Italy. In 1864, when he was in his sixties, Marsh set forth his ideas about man's alteration of the earth in his greatest work, *Man and Nature; or, Physical Geography as Modified by Human Action.*[2] He pointed out (p. vii) "the dan-

1. Also variously rendered as Aleksandr Voeykov or Voeĭkov.

2. Prior to his major work, Marsh had in 1847 prepared an address on man's alteration of the landscape, intentional and unintentional, desirable and dangerous ("Address Delivered before the Agricultural Society of Rutland County, September 30, 1847" [Rutland, Vermont, 1848], esp. pp. 17–19). His *Report on the Artificial Propagation of Fish* (Burlington, 1857) and his essay, "Study of Nature" (*Christian Examiner*, LXVIII [January, 1860], 33–62), also dealt largely with this theme.

In 1869 and 1872 Marsh brought out Italian

gers of imprudence and the necessity of caution in all operations which, on a large scale, interfere with the spontaneous arrangements of the organic and inorganic world." Further, he suggested (p. 7) "the possibility and the importance of the restoration of the disturbed harmonies and the improvement of waste and exhausted regions."

For Marsh, man was a dynamic force, often irrational in his treatment of the environment. Because of this irrationality, man created a danger to himself that he would destroy his base of subsistence. Marsh decried the environmentalism of many of his contemporaries, who regarded man simply as a passive being acted on by the environment. One of his main objects was to show that, far from being will-less and impotent, man was a free agent "working independently of nature"; it was not the earth that made man, but man who made the earth (Lowenthal, 1953). By understanding the nature of his impact on the environment, man might learn to change the face of the earth in rational, constructive fashion.

Marsh was concerned with man's influence on nature not in an abstract or theoretical sense but in terms of practical changes to improve the lot of mankind. His solution for the problems of Western Europe and the United States was that man should moderate his activities and develop a morality in respect to his use of the earth. He had some very concrete proposals, such as the maintenance of certain proportions of land in forest and the national control of natural resources. Above all, he

editions of *Man and Nature*, published in Florence and incorporating new material. Based upon the Italian work, a new English-language edition, *The Earth as Modified by Human Action*, was published in 1874. A final edition was published posthumously in 1885, though reprintings occurred at least as late as 1898. All English-language editions had both London and New York imprints.

thought it important to ascertain the probable effects of action before acting.

Marsh's work bears the indelible stamp of his experiences in the forests of the New World and his observations in the scrub and desert regions of the Mediterranean. The largest chapter of *Man and Nature* is entitled "The Woods" and comprises more than one-third of the entire volume. Though man's alteration of the forests in the mid-latitudes thus is extensively treated, Marsh did not touch upon the modification of mid-latitude grasslands, a subject that is receiving considerable attention today.

Another even more noteworthy omission in Marsh's work was his lack of concern with the exhaustion of mineral resources. He considered mining only as it disturbed the beauty of the landscape, not in terms of the depletion of reserves of minerals. Still further, although Marsh was living in a period of booming populations all over the world, his emphasis was on maintaining standards of living in Western Europe and the United States. The specter of overpopulation raised by Malthus finds little place in Marsh's work; it is the injury to the earth by man that dominates his writing.

Like most scholars of the mid-nineteenth century, Marsh's focus in space was on Western civilization and in time on the experiences of the Western world, beginning with classical antiquity. This ethnocentric view was more understandable in Marsh's era, because knowledge of the preclassical world, of the high civilizations of Asia and the New World, and of the strange and distant lands and their peoples and cultures was still limited and unreliable.

Man and Nature, despite its shortcomings, was the first great work of synthesis in the modern period to examine in detail man's alteration of the face of the globe. Marsh's eloquent style and copious footnotes revealed the broad scope of his reading; his work attracted wide attention at the time. The early conservationists acknowledged their indebtedness to him; every important figure in forestry, both in America and abroad, testified to the impact of Marsh's work. Nevertheless, the period in which he wrote was dominated by an almost unlimited faith in the possibilities of material progress. Those responding to the alarm for the destruction of nature were far fewer than those who were actively engaged in spreading the railroads, producing new agricultural machinery, expanding world commerce, and opening up the grasslands. Interest in Marsh's work was rekindled in this century when man's destructiveness became so evident that it could no longer be ignored and when the problems that Marsh so vividly pictured loomed large before us. [3]

Another important contributor to the theme of man's influence on the earth was Alexander Ivanovich Woeikof (1842–1914), professor of physical geography at the University of St. Petersburg in Russia. Woeikof's writings, which were published in Russian, German, and French, received wider attention on the continent of Europe than did those of Marsh. Moreover, though Woeikof apparently traveled widely, even visiting the United States, there is no indication in his writings that he was familiar with Marsh's work. The chain of influence from Marsh to Woeikof led through Élisée Reclus, the French geographer who corresponded with Marsh while preparing his own great work, *La Terre* (published in New York in 1874 as *A New Physical Geography*), and whose works were cited by Woeikof.

Woeikof considered the surface of the earth to be composed of movable

bodies (*corps meubles*) of soil and subsoil, sands and gravels on the land, vegetation, materials suspended in the water or carried by it, dust and sand moved by the wind, and snow. Man influenced the surface of the earth especially through an intermediary—vegetation. In modifying natural vegetation and in replacing wild plants by cultivated plants, man augmented the movable bodies, diminished their quantity, or changed their distribution. Among such activities, Woeikof recognized the important part that fire played as a weapon of man.

Woeikof cited cases of the destruction of vegetation by irrational cattle-grazing, of man-made canyons in the chernozem belt of Russia, and of the destruction of chernozem due to shallow plowing. Woeikof thought that man should strive to achieve a certain harmony both within and in his relation to nature. He found examples of such a harmonious activity of man in the irrigation projects of ancient civilizations, in modern Egypt, in arid states of America, and in Russian Central Asia.

Like Marsh, Woeikof was interested in improving the conditions of human life. Among his interests were land improvement in Russia, the relations between climate and the national economy, the use of water, the problems of sand, irrigation of the Transcaucasian districts, the problems of draining swamps, the problems of colonizing the north, changes in level of rivers, the disappearance of the forest, and the cultivation of new plants in Russia.

Woeikof believed that man had an influence on climate through his modification of vegetation; that is, the deforestation that had gone on so extensively in Russia had affected the temperature of the air, the winds, the rains, and the snows. He considered forests to be desirable and urged the restoration of forests that had been destroyed. The view that forests have a significant effect on

3. For the rediscovery of Marsh see Lewis Mumford's *The Brown Decades: A Study of the Arts in America, 1865–1895* (New York: Harcourt, Brace & Co., 1931).

climate is in disfavor in the Western world today, where climatologists believe that, at best, vegetation influences climate on a local scale and to an insignificant degree. Woeikof was an ardent disciple of the use of irrigation and believed that the control and mastery of the water supply was one of the main tasks man had yet to accomplish.

Like many a contemporary romantic, Woeikof was appalled at the expansion of urban areas. He said (1901, p. 208), "This grouping in cities, under conditions unhealthy to body and mind, this dissociation of man and the earth is proof of a sickly state." This theme—that urban civilization is somehow not good, that urban conditions are unhealthy, and even that cities are parasitic on the countryside—is one that is still very much with us today, though Marsh did not consider it.

The effect of warfare on the landscape was considered by Woeikof too, and he cited examples of the decrease in numbers of sedentary populations and the expansion of forests during times of war.

In dealing with the population problem, Woeikof was apparently interested more in the absolute number of people the world could support than in the limitations of resources and the desirability of developing and maintaining high standards of living. His conclusions about the possibilities of expanding population were optimistic, as would be expected from someone who had experience in the rapidly developing areas of the United States and of Russia. He believed that the direct utilization of the light and the heat of the sun as well as the use of the water of the earth could make possible a tremendous expansion in production. Thus, though Woeikof raised questions regarding the nature and effect of man's past use of the earth, he believed (1901, p. 215) that a rational approach to development of our resources could

lead to "des perspectives de progrès si vaste s'ouvrent devant nous qu'on a peine à les croire possible." Thus he was essentially an optimist with a utilitarian approach, while Marsh, though he took a guardedly optimistic note, was more impressed with the enormous damage done in his native New England and in the Mediterranean lands, where he spent his later life, and recognized the need for more than a utilitarian approach—the fostering in Western man of a love of the earth.

Many of the omissions of Marsh's work are apparent in Woeikof's too: the latter's emphasis was on contemporary and Western societies, with particular attention to Russia rather than on man everywhere and through time; his lack of concern about the depletion of mineral resources was also apparent; and his treatment of the world's population growth was perhaps too optimistic.

In the English-speaking world Marsh had no successor until Nathaniel Southgate Shaler, professor of geology at Harvard University, took up the theme of man's destructive activities in his book *Man and the Earth* (1905). His plea was that of a conservationist, and, like Marsh's *Man and Nature*, his writing had a moral tone (p. 1) that "we may be sure that those who look back upon us and our deeds from the centuries to come will remark upon the manner in which we use our heritage, and theirs, as we are now doing, in the spend-thrift's way, with no care for those to come." Shaler pointed out that primitive man and the lower animals made no drain on the stores of the earth but that, the more advanced the economy becomes, the more destructive it is of animals, plants, and mineral resources. He reported that, since the coming of the Iron Age, the consumption of mineral resources had increased to a frightening degree. Whereas in 1600 there were relatively few substances (mostly precious stones) for which men looked to the underground, now there were several hundred substances which were being used by man.

Shaler suggested that, with increasing consumption, mineral resources would be depleted in the foreseeable future. He observed that there are really only two minerals of absolute importance: iron and copper. While others are useful, they are not essential. In view of the gradually decreasing supply of high-grade iron and copper ores, he concluded that production costs of these ores gradually would rise and that eventually iron ore would be concentrated from rocks, a feat which only today is being spoken of as economically feasible.

Shaler went on to discuss the destruction of soil as a result of agricultural practices and the problems of a rapidly expanding population. However, unlike Woeikof, who was concerned with possible limits of population, Shaler was concerned with the limits of the resource base. Thus he said (p. 13): "In a word, we may estimate that in a historic sense very soon the world will be near its food-producing limit." He concluded that already the planet's resources were taxed to support the people who lived on it. How could a population three times as dense be supported and the fertility of the earth be maintained, he demanded. We should try to prevent soil erosion and restore nutrients to the land that are removed by cultivated plants.

Despite his ominous warning, Shaler thought (p. 19) that there is "every reason to believe that our science is ready for the task and that within two centuries of peaceful endeavor we may prepare the place for it." Shaler's book was concerned with future power sources and the use of coal and oil, which he considered temporary energy sources. But he believed the waters, the winds, and the tides to be the permanent resources of supply of power and that man would need to develop these resources of power as well as available supplies of solar energy.

Shaler then turned to the possibility of expanding cultivation into the unwon lands of the earth and of reclaiming land from lakes, rivers, and the sea. He examined the resources of the sea and stated his belief that the sea might be made to contribute "far more than it does now to the needs of man."

Shaler urged (p. 228) that we "awaken a sense of the nobility and dignity of the relation man bears to this wonderful planet and the duty that comes therefrom." He went on to point out that, though many consider the universe to be simply an extension of the individual man, there are also many others who believe that the world is essentially related to us and part of us. It was Shaler's hope (p. 229) that man would come to realize that "whatever else he may be, he is the sum of a series of actions linked with all that goes on upon this earth." He thus emphasized (p. 230) the "oneness of nature and intelligence as its master."

But Shaler's approach to the earth, like Marsh's, was more than one of stark utility. He questioned our plans for the earth as a place to live. Do we envisage an earth that is completely covered with men or, as Shaler put it (p. 172), "an intensely humanized earth, so arranged as to afford a living to the largest possible number of men"? It was Shaler's contention that if this is what we do envisage—a completely domesticated earth—we could obtain a fairly accurate impression as to what it might be like by visiting those centers in Holland and England where there are many people and where there is intensive land use. Shaler did recognize (p. 189) that in Holland and England there was "beauty of a high order"; but in a completely domesticated earth, we could expect that beauty would be ordered and that much of the charm of primitive nature would be lost through replacement by artificial, controlled nature. The aesthetic appreciation of the earth was important in Shaler's thinking, and it is involved, at least implicitly, too, in much contemporary thought about the future of man on the earth.

Shaler was not concerned with changes in the biotic community. Moreover, he limited his consideration to Western society during the industrial revolution, ignoring both the previous efforts of man during the long span of human time and the present-day effects of non-industrial peoples on the earth.

Shaler's place of importance in the development of thought about man and nature is that (1) he focused attention on the destruction of mineral resources and gave thoughtful consideration to impending shortages; (2) he feared that resource bases might be insufficient to provide for the very rapidly increasing populations all over the world; and (3) he added the thought that a new human attitude was necessary toward the earth.

In 1915 an article by a young German geologist, Ernst Fischer, was published posthumously, in which he objected to the clear distinction between *Geisteswissenschaften* and *Naturwissenschaften*. He called attention to the neglect in studying the role of man as a geologic agent and presented examples of man's direct activities on the earth's crust and his influence on water bodies, on the plant world, and on the animal world. By learning how to employ the powers of nature, man has been of considerable indirect influence. Small happenings can have widespread, unplanned, and unsuspected effects; the human being is the youngest of the geologic factors.

Other geologists have followed this line of thought. R. L. Sherlock (1922, 1923, 1931) wrote about man as a geologic agent of denudation and accumulation in the physical landscape of Great Britain; he foresaw a period when man's

destructiveness would be greatly diminished, a prophecy that has not been borne out by subsequent events. Stanisław Pawłowski (1923) described the lowering of hills and erosion in his native Poland and recognized that man's activities involved changes in the direction of the forces of nature.

During the twentieth century the theme of man's transformation of the earth has been given consideration by geographers of many countries—those from England, France, Austria, Germany, and Italy are cited in the "References" that follow. This literature, to which we are indebted, demonstrates that most human activities advance by virtue of contributions from many different types of individuals, with varying backgrounds, working at different levels. We mention those investigators whose work we know best, fully realizing that other selections could be made. Our concern is with concepts rather than persons—to identify lines of work rather than to attribute credit. If injustices are done—as inevitably they must be—the important interest is not the workers but the work.

In France, Paul Vidal de la Blache, to whom the establishment of modern scientific geography in French university life was largely due, recognized (1913) the great part of man in modifying his basic environment as one of the six distinctive characteristics of geography. Jean Brunhes, a student of Vidal de la Blache, published his *Géographie humaine* in 1910 (revised and enlarged editions in 1912, 1925, and 1934; editions in English in 1920 and 1952). He described and analyzed the many patterns of man's occupancy of the earth as expressed in housing types, in village and town sites, and in changing forms of communication. He discussed man's conquest and adaptation of the vegetable and animal kingdoms by his various agricultural techniques; and he was concerned with man's extraction of minerals. All these matters were examined from a holistic and comparative point of view. Brunhes held (1913, p. 312) that the potency of man in transforming the earth is not due to "superiority in strength, but universality of range" and "synthesis of a series of small achievements." Brunhes pushed the discussion of the influence of man on nature beyond the bounds of Western civilization, to consider man's alterations of the earth by other cultures in a variety of environments from tropical rain forest to desert. Cultural differences were important facts for understanding man's activities on the earth. In the first essay of his posthumous *Problèmes de géographie humaine* (1942) Albert Demangeon laid emphasis on the work of man in modifying his environment by means of communication, artesian wells, the control of rivers, and the evolution of new plants for human food. André Allix in 1948 forcefully stated that it was not the economic motives of "crude interest" that determine man's actions on the earth. Indeed, man has many choices to make, and he chooses according to "traditions and taboos," which are a matter of "rite, breeding, and of sentiment." That to study any subject involving man requires an awareness of man in all his complexity —his attitudes and prejudices—is an idea which follows the teachings of Brunhes.

In England, Marion Isabel Newbigin's textbook, *Man and His Conquest of Nature* (1912), emphasized that man has become almost the master of his fate by the progress of human civilization. Man can live only by destroying the balance of nature, by favoring some animals and plants at the expense of others, by forcing those useless to him to give way to those he needs. But many elements, such as rats, crickets, cockroaches, and weeds, have been favored by man without any intention on his part to do so. Miss Newbigin ac-

knowledged indebtedness to the French geographers for material on which her book was based. P. W. Bryan (1933, p. 372) took the approach that "human activity undertaken to satisfy human desires is the motivating force" in man's changes of the surface of the earth and that man "takes products and utilizes natural surfaces to satisfy those desires." The result is the cultural landscape.

In Italy, Giovanni Negri (1930) examined the general characteristics of human action on vegetation. He agreed that man's action on vegetation is not recent but was important even in Paleolithic Europe and that primitive man with his limited technology was nonetheless effective in changing vegetation. Man, he contended, must be considered the head of a great, complex harmony formed by vegetation and as (p. 216) "the momentum that disturbed the balance." Interestingly, Negri acknowledged the writings of Woeikof and Brunhes but did not mention Marsh, although *Man and Nature* had two Italian editions. Others who considered the theme were E. Migliorini (1936) and Aldo Sestini (1938).

In Germany, Paul Schultze-Naumburg (1928) considered the changes to the surface of the earth by man's cultural work. His volume explored the conflict between economics and ethics; it was a plea for counteraction to thoughtless and unnecessary devastation by a money economy and an exposition of the beauty of cultivated nature. He recognized that only very few places in Germany look the same as they did prior to man's interference. In his Introduction he traced the changes in the German landscape, from the time of Tacitus to the twentieth century, brought about as a result of paths and roads, utilization of the flora, mining of minerals, the water economy, industrial plants and railroads, and buildings of all kinds. He asked whether it is paramount to destroy the beauty of the landscape to step up profit. Is it not in the end to the disadvantage of the general and national well-being?

In 1933 Nikolaus Creutzberg published a pictorial atlas with magnificent illustrations (many of them air views) to show the changes to the surface of the earth caused by man in developing a cultured landscape. Man is living nearly everywhere in a cultured landscape which, during centuries, has been shaped in accordance to his needs, his taste, and his personal peculiarities. The forming of the landscape by man is an artistically unconscious process and therefore reflects the personality of a culture far more than it reflects conscious art. In almost all parts of the earth today, the penetration of machine civilization and the coexistence of forms of original cultures represent the main characteristics of the present cultural landscape.

Edwin Fels, professor of geography and director of the Geographical Institute in the Free University of Berlin, for twenty-five years has consistently developed the theme, as a part of economic geography, of man's influence in transforming the earth. In 1934 he pointed to the work of Sherlock (1922) as having been overlooked in Germany. In his 1935 text he explained that in many works the influence of nature upon man had been considered carefully but that the return consequences of man's actions on nature had not been treated very thoroughly; no German text in economic geography up to 1930 had explored this reciprocal action. His work was to fill this gap. Fels's 1954 volume, *Der wirtschaftende Mensch als Gestalter der Erde,* is a thoroughly revised and enlarged edition of his 1935 work; it comprises Part V of a series on the earth and world economy; and it is the most recent predecessor to the present volume. He considers the transformations of the solid surface of the earth, transformation of water bodies, man as a shaper of climate, changes of flora, influence on fauna, man in the pattern of nature (population growth and migration, effects on health), and, finally, the economic landscape. Man is inclined by sentiment and habit to consider his earth-transforming force as small in comparison with nature's. This self-underestimation has been justified in the past but is not in the present. However small the physical strength of the individual man may be, it is tremendous when pooled and guided by the human mind. The process has increased extraordinarily rapidly since about 1800, when man entered the machine age and human strength began to multiply through mechanization techniques.

In 1953 David Lowenthal called attention once again to the fact that American geographers have devoted a great deal of attention to the frontier but little to the historical past. George P. Marsh was hailed as the forerunner of historical geography in the United States, and attention was drawn to Marsh's contributions to the subject. Lowenthal (p. 212) brought up the interesting point that, "unlike Thoreau, who also loved nature, but wished to keep it wild, Marsh wanted it tamed; Thoreau appealed to esthetic sentiment, Marsh to economic practicality." Thus attention is focused once again on the premises behind our relations with nature, behind our desires to modify nature and our desires to plan for the future. Shall we have a wild nature or a tamed nature? What is the impact of domestication and civilization on animals and on human beings? What shall man's goals be for his future relations with the earth?

The organized complexity of modern existence is a new phenomenon in man's experience. Considering what has happened in the United States during the last century, one is tempted to ask whether we are living in a moment of great progress or of great aberration in the human adventure.

When George P. Marsh's *Man and Nature* appeared in 1864, President Lincoln was in office by virtue of having received a total of just over two million popular votes; the total annual receipts of the federal government amounted to less than 4 per cent of the current annual *interest* on the public debt; and the urban shift had only begun, for only one-fifth of the population lived in urban places of 2,500 or more. Since then, our population has increased four and a half times, and farm production through mechanization has more than kept pace. There are now annually produced seven and a half times more cotton, five and a half times more wheat, and four and a half times more corn, even though the farm force has increased only slightly in numbers. The cultivated acreage is about what it was in 1920, but there are now some 4,500,-000 tractors at work upon it.

Mechanization, industrialization, urbanization, and transportation have meant the harnessing of energy in fantastic quantities. The United States alone in the last forty years has consumed more minerals and fossil fuels (coal and petroleum) than all mankind used in the previous millenniums of existence. So far in the twentieth century, 70,000 square miles of land in the United States have been absorbed by towns, cities, and urban industrial developments, with another 16,000 square miles covered by artificially impounded water. And service occupations (government, trade, transportation and utilities, finance, etc.) now surpass, in total persons employed, the production occupations (agriculture, manufacturing, construction, mining).

With more people on the earth than at any time in the past, this is really a most extraordinary period in which to be living. Can we, the participants, pull aside enough to read the plot of the spectacle that we are in? Perspective is required to apprehend the uniqueness of the present and the significance of that uniqueness.

Within the last century man has developed the idea that change is continuous and includes himself. Conceptions of fossil man (prior to present man), of biological evolution (in which man is included with all other living phenomena), and of the vast duration of earth history are but a few examples of ideas developed by science and become part of the public consciousness since the mid-nineteenth century. Can the uniqueness of the present be made clearer for those within it by focusing on the role of man in altering the earth's surface, keeping in mind the longevity of the period in which he has been doing so? This Symposium is intended to contribute to such an understanding.

The efforts of small populations of the past have been by no means negligible; their time scale was that of millenniums. The story of man's role in changing the face of the earth begins with the invention of fire-making and the domestication of plants and animals; continues through his trade, warfare, migrations, and the spread of transportation facilities, fields, and settlements; and culminates in the development of modern mining and manufacturing.

Every human group has had to evaluate the potential of the area it inhabits and to organize its life about its environment in terms of available techniques and the values accepted as desirable. The identification, use, and care of resources is in the end a problem of human values and behavior. Cultural differences in techniques and values, and hence in utilization of the physical-biological environment and its conversion into a human habitat, have distinguished one human group from another. The effects of man on the earth are geographically varied and are historically cumulative. Many changes wrought by man have not been destructive; many were unplanned; and many of the results have been unanticipated and have gone undetected.

Man, the ecological dominant on the planet, needs the insights of scholars in nearly all branches of learning to understand what has happened and is happening to the earth under man's impress. This Symposium is a first attempt to provide an integrated basis for such an insight and to demonstrate the capacity of a great number of fields of knowledge to add importantly to our understanding. What the soil scientist, climatologist, geomorphologist, and others are doing are direct contributions to man's understanding of himself. By expressly not setting the study of man and his behavior apart from other fields of knowledge, by recognizing that man is a part, and an active part, of nature and has been so from earliest times, the Symposium theme lays the groundwork for more meaningful formulation of research designs to learn more about what and how environmental factors influence man's development and behavior.

Nature has always contained man, but all the while is being changed by man in the course of his own self-transformation. The dichotomy of man and nature is thus seen as an intellectual device and as such should not be confused with reality; no longer can man's physical-biological environment be treated, except in theory, as "natural."

The most striking symbol of the new scale in time and space that has been brought into being since the time of Marsh is the airplane. The view from the air that it has provided—the ability to look down upon man's work in a new perspective—has been a great stride toward synthesis. The introduction to this volume continues with an analysis of the significance of our new ability to view "Our World from the Air," accompanied by forty-eight striking illustrations.

And with these words by way of introductory, please to begin.

WILLIAM L. THOMAS, JR.

NEW YORK CITY
March 1, 1956

REFERENCES

ALLIX, ANDRÉ
  1948 "Man in Human Geography," *Scottish Geographical Magazine,* LXIV, 1–8.

BRUNHES, JEAN
  1913 "The Specific Characteristics and Complex Character of the Subject-Matter of Human Geography," *Scottish Geographical Magazine,* XXIX, 304–22, 358–74.
  1925 *La Géographie humaine.* 3d ed. (1st ed., 1910.) Paris: Felix Alcan. 974 pp.
  1952 *Human Geography.* Abridged ed. by MME M. JEAN-BRUNHES DELAMARRE and PIERRE DEFFONTAINES; trans. by ERNEST F. Row. London: George G. Harrap & Co., Ltd. 256 pp.

BRYAN, P. W.
  1933 *Man's Adaptation of Nature:* *Studies of the Cultural Landscape.* New York: Henry Holt & Co. 386 pp.

CREUTZBURG, NIKOLAUS
  1933 *Kultur im Spiegel der Landschaft: Das Bild der Erde in seiner Gestaltung durch den Menschen. Ein Bilderatlas.* Leipzig: Bibliographisches Institut. 218 pp.

FELS, EDWIN
  1932 "Der Einfluss des Verkehrs auf Naturlandschaft und Lebewelt," pp. 288–94 in *Festschrift für Carl Uhlig.* Öhringen: Verlag der Hohenloheschen Buchandlung F. Rau. 345 pp.
  1934 "Der Mensch als Gestalter der Erdoberflache: Hinweis auf ein vergessenes Buch," *Petermanns geographische Mitteilungen,* LXXX, No. 2, 50–51.
  1935 *Der Mensch als Gestalter der Erde: Ein Beitrag zur allgemeinen*

Wirtschafts- und Verkehrsgeographie.
Leipzig: Bibliographisches Institut.
206 pp.
1954 *Der wirtschaftende Mensch als Gestalter der Erde.* Stuttgart: Franckh'sche Verlagshandlung. 258 pp.

FISCHER, ERNST
1915 "Der Mensch als Geologischer Faktor," *Zeitschrift der Deutsches Geologisches Gesellschaft,* LXI, 106–48.

HALTENBERGER, MICHAEL
1937 "Die Technik als umgestaltender Faktor in der geographischen Landschaft," *Comptes-Rendus du Congrès International de Géographie, Varsovie, 1934,* III, 9–15. Warsaw.

LOWENTHAL, DAVID
1953 "George Perkins Marsh and the American Geographical Tradition," *Geographical Review,* XLIII, No. 2, 207–13.

MARSH, GEORGE PERKINS
1864 *Man and Nature; or, Physical Geography as Modified by Human Action.* New York: Scribners; London: Sampson Low. 560 pp. (Two Italian editions, published in Florence, Italy, 1869 and 1872.)
1874 *The Earth as Modified by Human Action: A New Edition of "Man and Nature."* New York: Scribner, Armstrong & Co. 656 pp. (Revised posthumous edition in 1885.)

MIGLIORINI, E.
1936 "L'Uomo come agente che modifica la terra, secondo una recente opera tedesca," *Revista geografica italiana,* XLIII, 36–47.

NEGRI, GIOVANNI
1930 "Caratteri generali dell'azione umana sulla vegetazione," *Atti dello XI Congresso Geografico Italiano, Napoli,* I, 215–33.

NEWBIGIN, MARION ISABEL
1912 *Man and His Conquest of Nature.* London: Adam & Charles Black. 183 pp.

PAWŁOWSKI, STANISŁAW
1923 "Zmiany w ukształtowaniu powierzchni ziemi wywołane przez człowieka (Modifications apportées par l'homme à la surface terrestre)," *Przeglad Geograficzny,* IV, 48–64.

SCHULTZE-NAUMBURG, PAUL
1928 *Die Gestaltung der Landschaft durch den Menschen,* Vol. VII. Munich: Georg D. W. Callwey Verlag. 487 pp.

SESTINI, ALDO
1938 "Intorno all'opera dell'uomo come agente modificatore della superficie terrestre," *Revista geografica italiana,* XLV, 231–43.

SHALER, NATHANIEL SOUTHGATE
1905 *Man and the Earth.* New York: Duffield & Co. 240 pp.

SHERLOCK, ROBERT LIONEL
1922 *Man as a Geological Agent: An Account of His Action on Inanimate Nature.* London: H. F. & G. Witherby. 372 pp.
1923 "The Influence of Man as an Agent in Geographical Change," *Geographical Journal,* LXI, No. 4, 258–73.
1931 *Man's Influence on the Earth.* London: Home University Library of Modern Knowledge. 256 pp.

VIDAL DE LA BLACHE, PAUL
1913 "Des Caractères distinctifs de la géographie," *Annales de géographie,* XXII, 289–99.

WOEIKOF (VOEĬKOV), ALEXANDER (ALEKSANDR) IVANOVICH
1901 "De l'Influence de l'homme sur la terre," *Annales de géographie,* X, 97–114, 193–215.
1949 *Vozdeĭstvie cheloveka na prirodu: Izbrannye stat'i* ("Influence of Man upon Nature: Selected Articles"). Edited, with an Introductory Article and Notes, by V. V. POKSHISHEVSKII. Moscow: Gos. izdvo geografich. lit-ry. 254 pp. (In Russian.) (A collection of articles mostly published in the late nineteenth century.)

Our World from the Air: Conflict and Adaptation

E. A. GUTKIND[*]

THE PERENNIAL REVOLUTION

Man and nature are the twin agents of the perennial revolution which shapes and reshapes the face of the earth and the character of man's activities. This struggle, at times violent and sporadic, at others gentle and consistent, but forever demanding a new response to a new challenge, activates the potential energies of man and nature, molding them into a grand pattern of advance or retreat, of creative interaction or disastrous antagonism, and of promise or failure.

The conquest of the air enables mankind for the first time in its history to experience this interaction in all its innumerable ramifications. A new scale in time and space has been added to our mental and material equipment. Before this conquest we were winding our way like worms through narrow passages and seeing only more or less un-

* Dr. Gutkind, M.T.P.I., F.R.G.S., Dr.Ing., Dipl.Arch., Member MARS–CIAM, was, after World War I, adviser to the Armistice Commission on Physical Reconstruction, then worked as private architect and town planner. During World War II he was head of the Demographic Survey and Plan, then member of the Control Commission for Germany, in charge of physical planning. His numerous works include: *Revolution of Environment*, 1946; *Our World from the Air: An International Survey of Man and His Environment*, 1952; *Community and Environment: A Discourse on Social Ecology*, 1953; and *The Expanding Environment: The End of Cities, the Rise of Communities*, 1953.

related details. Today we can look at the world with a God's-eye view, take in at a glance the infinite variety of environmental patterns spread over the earth, and appreciate their dynamic relationships. We can see this great variety condensed in time and space and can shed the still-lingering ideas of stable and isolated societies. We can see side by side the different scales in time and space and the tensions arising out of the neighborly proximity of seemingly incompatible transformations of the earth's surface. The whole field of human activities and of nature's gifts and refusals unfolds before our eyes and senses, ranging from the most primitive to the most up-to-date interference with nature, from unconscious, isolated, and small-scale activities to the conscious remaking of the environment in vast parts of the world. All these different stages exist today, and in many parts of the world they overlap.

The airplane has given us the synoptic view. This coincides with the general trend away from the overestimation of the purely analytical approach to numerous problems toward synthesis and unitary ideas. Both analysis and synthesis are needed and should be applied to every problem on equal terms. The advent of the airplane and the air view is, therefore, of symbolic significance. Since the beginning of the scientific revolution, analysis has been paramount. In the ages preceding this event humanity found protection and

1

guidance in a unifying faith and symbolism—or at least believed that it would find them in these manifestations of its essence as far as it affected its spiritual and mental aspirations. But these guides have lost their power ever since science began systematically to analyze nature and to help to transform the environment on a perpetually widening scale, with growing intensity and at a steadily increasing pace. The revolt against analysis is not new. Goethe was perhaps its most determined and outspoken exponent. In *Die Farbenlehre* he wrote: "A century which relies only on analysis and seems to be afraid of synthesis is not on the right way; for only both together, like breathing in and breathing out, form the essence of science."

It is not mere coincidence that the synoptic view which the airplane offers us emerged as an indispensable instrument of our growing understanding, knowledge, and insight. This change contains a double challenge: It forces us to see the transformations which man has wrought from the earth as a perennial revolution and to experience their dynamic unity as a whole. Without the synoptic view from the air this would be impossible, and without the trend toward unitary ideas we would fail to interpret correctly what we now can see. We are at one of the decisive turning points in the history of humanity comparable to the domestication of animals, the invention of the earliest tools, the foundation of the first cities, and the conception of the heliocentric universe. At this turning point we can look back and take stock of man's past achievements and failures. But we can also perceive the great perspectives in which future generations must make their contributions.

No transformation produces a static and lasting result. Hence our environment is at any moment of human history the product of a perennial revolution, of a continuous process of change. Man's adjustments to his environment are not a series of unrelated stages of development, each more or less accomplished and self-contained entities, but an organic and integrated chain of events. Thus permanency exists only in the uninterrupted *continuity* of change and in the dynamic relations among all aspects of human activities. In other words, permanency without synthesis is a delusion. To these two criteria a third has to be added: the growing scale of the transformations, expanding from small and individual to large and collective operations. This Trinity—permanency of change, synthesis of relations, and the increase of scale—forms the yardstick by which the interaction of man and environment should be judged.

In general, individual efforts are now out of tune, in time and space, with the dynamics of social needs and aspirations. The unity between the individual scale and the totality of the environment has broken down. Something new must be put in its place. The right scale depends on the awareness of relations—of the relations between individual and group, between the functional and personal life, between the man-made landscape and the natural landscape, between all parts of the immediate environment and the wider world around us and, finally, the universe. The old scale has been destroyed, and man as an individual being is cut loose from the totality of the forces which play on the environmental field.

Are these demands not too great or—as the hard-boiled realist will say—too vague? The answer is definitely "No," for in reality they merely repeat the age-old longings of man as a social being, though not as an economic animal. Every primitive tribe was nearer this universal scale than we are today. But we are not a primitive tribe—at least we pretend not to be—and we must, therefore, find a new solution to this eternal problem, the total oneness of relations; and with it we must develop a new adaptation to this new scale. The conquest of the air forces us into this adventure. The airplane is the instrument which has introduced this new scale as an inescapable reality, bridging the gap between the smallest social unit, the individual human being, and the largest unit, the universe—between, as it were, the social microscope and the social telescope. However, let there be no mistake. This has nothing to do with the mock-heroic flights into space or the megalomaniac idea of launching artificial satellites which would revolve around the earth. The solution lies somewhat nearer home and is less expensive. It lies within ourselves, but it may cost more effort than to discover the brave new world in the outer spaces of the heavens.

No structure can grow beyond its organic size, for, if it does, it destroys the internal coherence and functional efficiency. Therefore, the results of every human interference with nature should be evaluated with relation to the entire variety of environmental conditions, not to one condition only. Or to put it in another way: If we want to find out the optimum structure of an individual human work and its optimum relation to other works, we must investigate not merely the conditions of the immediate environment in which the work actually takes place but also its relations and reactions to the world at large. We must think not only in terms of processes but also in terms of groups of environments, for this alone can get us out of the rut of daily and narrow routine and ennoble our works beyond mere utilitarian efficiency.

Consequently, the comparative study of man's transformations which the airplane makes possible opens the way toward a re-evaluation of what man has done and what he can do to the earth.

Above all, the widening scale of the reassessment of the work of previous generations and of the great possibilities which the future holds in store leads us to an increased awareness of the all-embracing unity of mankind and of the absurdity of all spiritual and political frontiers. It makes us aware of the inescapable fact that only *differences of degree, not of principle, distinguish nations.* This is especially evident if we think in terms of generations instead of years. Then the distinction between the uneven development of different civilizations which today exist side by side shrinks almost to nothing.

No structure can grow beyond its organic size without impairing its coherence and efficiency. This is only too painfully obvious when we look down at our cities, towns, villages, and industrial districts. It is not only their unsystematic growth and their excessive size but also their amorphous structure in general and in detail which destroy the dynamic equilibrium of their functions and, consequently, their productive and balanced relations to the surrounding region and the country as a whole. What driving power is behind this lopsided development? It is the same lack of balance which pervades our life in general One function—work—is paramount, and all other activities of our functional as well as of our personal life are subordinated to this devouring obsession. Work means industry, and industry means industrial buildings, districts, and countries. This one-sided overestimation of one function has created the urban deserts, has upset the fertile relations between urban and rural life, and has debased human dignity to the level of a soulless machine. The human scale has been lost in the turmoil of an illusory progress toward the "great know-how."

All this can be seen in unerring clarity from the air. The landscape which spreads before our eyes and mind is like a seismograph recording the finest oscillations of man's role in changing the face of the earth. On the vast screen of this seismograph of the world the genuinely great revolutions which mark the real turning points in the history of mankind are recorded. In the nomads' tracks through the deserts leading to oases settlements we can still experience the revolution from a migratory to a sedentary way of life. In the contrast between the empty fields of the prairies and the nearest town (Fig. 1) we can still relive the tremendous impact of the urban revolution. In the minute fields of Old China tilled by men as their own living tools (Fig. 2) and in the large fields of the New World (Fig. 3) and Russia worked by tractors the revolution of the machines is still present. In the small and compact village of an African tribe (Fig. 4), in a collective settlement of Israel (Fig. 5), in a walled town of Iran (Fig. 6), and in the sprawling cities of the "progressive" countries (Fig. 7) there is retold the tremendous drama of the social revolution, from closely knit communities

THE URBAN REVOLUTION

Courtesy of the Department of Mines and Resources, Canada

Fig. 1.—Canada, Saskatchewan, Regina. The compact space of the town is cut out from the vastness of the surrounding countryside and separated as a space in its own right, as a rebellious protest against nature. Social proximity within the orbit of the town and social isolation of the outlying farms are the antagonistic results. A new dimension, uncommensurable with nature, has been thrown open to human life, creating a realm of its own in opposition to the country.

to atomized societies, from the coherence and self-sufficiency of clan homogeneity to the fellowship based on elective affinity, and, finally, to the hollow conformity of the uprooted urban multitudes. The great seismograph reveals all these landmarks of the perennial revolution. But only if we can sense the deep unity in the world-wide diversity of the innumerable features which the struggle between man and nature has imprinted on the earth can we hope to understand the intensity and variety, the interdependence, and the true significance of what the past has to teach us. We must work out a new relationship to the external world and conceive it as an ever changing pattern of phenomena and events all intimately connected with one another as an expanding environment abounding in inspiring possibilities. The synoptic view demands the appreciation of the whole nexus of relations in every detail and of the creative potentiality of every detail within the whole. In a more precise way

THE REVOLUTION OF THE MACHINES

FIG. 2.—China, farmland. The small scale of the agricultural landscape of China transformed by the work of millions of peasants as their own living tools is clearly visible in this air view taken from an altitude of 4,500 feet.

this can be expressed once more as the simultaneous need for analysis and synthesis. And for those who are never happy without a new pigeonhole it may be added that something like a new discipline is needed, which for want of a better name might be called "social ecology." This new discipline would include those branches of the social and natural sciences which have a more or less direct bearing upon the role of man in re-forming his habitat.

But there should be no mistake: This does not mean an amorphous new discipline. On the contrary, it means a systematic selection of the really instrumental forces which shape man's social aspirations and transform his environ-ment accordingly. The goal of social ecology is wholeness and not a mere adding-together of innumerable details. This is not the place to enter into a detailed description of the exact meaning, scope, and character of social ecology. This would lead us too far, for in the last instance environment is everything, from the suits we wear to the universe —the whole of the external world. The natural and the man-made environ-ments coalesce, and no clear demar-cation line can be drawn between the two. However, we should always re-member that we are influenced by an unlimited variety of environmental con-ditions and that our immediate envi-ronment in all its ramifications is itself

THE REVOLUTION OF THE MACHINES

Courtesy of the U.S. Soil Conservation Service

FIG. 3.—United States, Arizona, Pinal County, fields. Many of the original fields have been com-bined in a geometrical transformation of nature on a large scale and in one continuous sweep for the mechanization of agriculture and the rational use of irrigation.

always part of the greater whole. Ecology, in its original sense, is the study of the relation of animals to their habitat. It deals with "chain reactions" of influences caused by the character and workings of environmental factors and the way in which they affect a particular species and vice versa. These are the same problems which face human civilizations. The main lesson we can learn from animal ecology is the need for studying human communities as a *whole* and in their *total* relationship to their physical and social environment.

These demands are, like all generalizations, open to an easy criticism. But this should not deter us from adapting our thinking to a new and bewildering situation. Admittedly quite a number of cherished ideas and ideals will have to be revised, and even the seemingly unassailable basis of a scientific approach, the analytical and pragmatic method, will have to be re-examined. But our fear of abstract notions or, for that matter, of the deductive method should not stand in the way of finding a new synthesis between science and philosophy, between slow, step-by-step experiments and brilliant, artistic short cuts. For how else can wholeness be achieved than by the unity of the practical and speculative mode of thinking. We may quote in this connection Whitehead, when he says in *Adventures of Ideas:*

THE SOCIAL REVOLUTION

Courtesy of the Agence Économique des Colonies

Fig. 4.—French West Africa, Senegal, Presqu'île du Cap Vert, village of Yof. The compact village is inhabited by Mohammedan fishermen of the same tribe. It consists of a few families, each compound occupied by the same consanguinous group and surrounded by a fence. Social coherence and co-operation bind all inhabitants intimately together in life and work.

Courtesy of Keren Hayesod, Jerusalem

FIG. 5.—Israel, Nahalal. The social and economic structure of this co-operative smallholder's settlement in the Valley of Jezreel is based on four cardinal principles: equal distribution of land, mutual aid, equal work for all, and co-operative purchasing and marketing. The central area is occupied by communal buildings and gardens, while the fields extend behind each farm. The whole is one integrated social and economic unit.

Courtesy of the Oriental Institute, University of Chicago

FIG. 6.—Iran, Bustam. This place of pilgrimage in northern Iran is protected by a fortress wall and surrounded by its fields, forming a compact oasis in the desert plain. The exclusion of the outside world creates social coherence and economic self-sufficiency and co-operation.

In each age of the world distinguished by high activity there will be found at its culmination, some profound cosmological outlook, implicitly accepted, impressing its own type upon current springs of action. This ultimate cosmology is only partly expressed, and the details of such expression issue into derivative specialized questions of secondary generality which conceal a general agreement upon first principles almost too obvious to need expression, and almost too general to be capable of expression. In each period there is a general form of the forms of thought; and, like the air we breathe, such a form is so translucent, and so pervading, and so seemingly necessary, that only by extreme effort can we become aware of it.

It is these "first principles" which we must try to understand, to formulate, and to apply. Then what appeared abstract and vague before will become concrete and precise. If we fail to grasp the particular "form of the forms of thought" which is characteristic of our time, if we fail to sense the translucent atmosphere which pervades our lives, we remain, at best, helpless and confused wanderers on this earth and, at worst, irresponsible tinkers who squander the riches intrusted to them by nature.

To calm the doubts of the eternal realists, we may also cite Kant. Although they may regard him as an utterly impracticable and useless phenomenon in the harsh world of what they call "hard facts," they might yet be induced to ponder over what he says

THE SOCIAL REVOLUTION

Courtesy of the Ministry of Town and Country Planning

FIG. 7.—England, Somerset, Bath. The extremes of two different periods confront each other: culture, masterful restriction and unity, and imaginative town planning, on the one hand; ruthlessness, confusion, and unimaginative "sprawl," on the other. Social disintegration and chaos are the result.

in the *Critique of Judgment:* "We can imagine an intellect which, while it is not discursive like our own but intuitive, proceeds from the general synthesis, from the idea as a whole as such, to the particular, that is from the whole to the parts."[1] A supreme effort is needed to reconcile this new approach with our accustomed methods of transforming our environment. People are afraid of ideas. They prefer the dry facts of daily life. But those who are afraid of ideas lose their meaning in the end. This is perhaps the greatest danger which surrounds this new chapter in the history of mankind. And yet this chapter will be opened not by the many but by the few, as it has always happened in the past. But today the danger is infinitely greater, for the many, united in mediocrity by the pressure of conformity and reduced to the dead level of utter complacency and political immaturity, are far more decisive than ever in times past, because the media of mass communications take hold of their conscience before they are even aware of what is going on. They distrust, moreover, the unusual, the far-reaching, and the defiant passion of the clearsighted rebels. It is so much easier and so much more comforting to rely on what is known, on what can be seen and touched, and to bridge the gap between the old and the new by a flight into romanticism. The responsibility which rests on the few is tremendous. It is a burden of social awareness and scientific integrity, of moral insight and fearless adherence to the highest ethical standards. But there is no need for despondency. On the contrary, there is every reason for a hopeful expectancy and even optimism. In the chain of the perennial revolutions the most important one is still missing: the revolution which will lead to the discovery of man.

1. Author's translation.

This revolution is being carried forward by the double attack of the social and natural sciences. This course has been outlined most brilliantly by Dr. E. D. Adrian in his presidential address to the 1954 meeting of the British Association for the Advancement of Science. He said:

It may be optimistic to think that we should be better off if we had a better understanding of human reactions. . . . But an increased knowledge of how the mind can be influenced could certainly forestall many of the influences which might be used to undermine our integrity. Discoveries about our own nature may disturb our peace of mind, but our own generation has already faced the theories of Freud as our grandfathers faced those of Charles Darwin. There was the same passionate resentment of the idea that our thoughts were more moulded by unconscious forces; but we have recovered our balance and we are not downhearted at finding ourselves less rational than we thought. . . . Now we can look to the many branches of social sciences to make a dispassionate study of what actually happens in our society without regard to what might be expected to happen if we are to believe all we have been told. The picture of human behaviour which the social scientist has to draw is of a system in which the units are men and women. . . . Scientists who work in laboratories have a far easier task in selecting what they should observe and in making measurements and checking theories by experiments. But in spite of our hesitations we can see that there are facts to be found out about our usefulness in society and about our relations with one another and with the group to which we belong. It is too early to be cautious in encouraging these unfamiliar lines of research. We must do what we can to develop the sciences which deal with human behaviour, even though we cannot always see what can come out of them. But human beings, when we consider them as material for the biologist, are not to be thought of as incapable of improvement.

These lofty goals cannot be reached by the accumulation of knowledge alone. Insight and vision are the indispensable counterparts without which pure knowledge remains the doubtful privilege of the ivory towers, now called "laboratories." In the words of two philosophers, Whitehead and Kant, and of a great scientist, Dr. Adrian, the way toward a synthesis of philosophy and science, of the speculative and rational mind, and of the deductive and inductive methods has been charted. The air has been conquered, and with this conquest a new freedom of ideas and insights has been given us. Here lies the field of the new unitary vision which will hold together the innumerable aspects of the dialogue between man and nature. When we look down from the airplane at the earth with an open mind freed from the fetters of preconceived ideas and outworn methods of appreciation, everything falls into a true perspective—even man himself as an integral part of the whole. Man has done tremendous things in his wrestling with nature, but the results are only too often questionable because they lack social responsibility. We can see the general mess he has made of many great opportunities; we can see the decaying ant heaps of our cities, the rural isolation and backwardness in many areas of the world, excluding millions from the main currents of life; we can see the misuse of the natural resources and vast parts of the earth's surface still unused. The new role of man in changing the face of the earth will lead to a different and higher standard of control over his physical environment and, above all, over his social surroundings. This will be the greatest and noblest phase of the perennial revolution, and its outcome will decide whether the social sciences were equal to this occasion—or failed. The leadership in the next stage of transformation belongs to the social sciences. All other

sciences must be subordinated to their guidance, for in the realm of learning they represent the moral conscience of mankind. The recent developments are an only too painful reminder that this conscience is not wide awake.

CHAINS OF TRANSFORMATIONS

Our world from the air is a kaleidoscopic jumble of natural and man-made features. And yet in this seemingly inextricable chaos there can be discerned a few trends, a few principles, and a few indications which bind all parts together in one grand pattern of transformations similar in essence and sequence. This veneer, spread by a divine designer over the earth and inlaid with an infinite variety of shapes, materials, and colors, reflects the finest oscillations of man's aspirations and achievements, of his failures and frustrations, and of his understanding but also of his ruthless disregard for nature.

The underlying trends form an indivisible unity in space and time if we apply the right yardstick, that is, a long-term and a large-scale evaluation. Then chains of transformation become visible, and something like an organic and integrated process of development emerges from the ever renewed adaptation of the environment to human needs and of man to his environment.

In broad outlines three principal chains of transformation can be distinguished. The most general is the change in the interaction of man and environment from an "I-Thou" to an "I-It" relationship. The second chain of transformation is more explicit in character; it shows man's reactions to his environment in successive stages, ranging from fear and defense to confidence and aggressiveness and, finally, to growing understanding and responsibility, always guided by the two complementary forces of instinct and reason and resulting in unconscious or conscious control of man's efforts toward systematization.

The third chain represents the widening scale and the changing experience of space, the latter intimately related to the notion of the universe. These three chains of transformation illustrate together and each in its own right the fulfilment of the basic human needs of shelter, food, work, and social intercourse. Consequently, the significance of each chain of transformation should be evaluated in relation to these four basic needs. These three principal chains of transformation and these four basic needs of human nature form an insoluble whole, and, as human nature is everywhere fundamentally the same, they produce in similar conditions also similar results, though for an inexperienced eye these may seem to differ considerably.

There are of course still other possibilities of systematizing the transformations through which the interaction of man and nature has passed and is likely to pass in the future. But those suggested above are, as will be seen, the most comprehensive and the most formative relations between the two contestants.

1. The transformation from an "I-Thou" to an "I-It" relationship is evident in the changing interdependence of man and nature and of group and individual. These two aspects belong together, and the results of this unity and of this change can still be seen today. The layout of tribal villages (Figs. 8 and 9), of old towns in Europe (Figs. 10 and 11) and Asia, the ancestral graves interspersed between the settlements of the living generation in China (Figs. 12 and 13), the pyramids and temples of Egypt, Mexico, and the Far East (Figs. 14 and 15), the rival symbols of church and castle dominating the skyline of medieval towns (Figs. 16 and 17)—all these bear witness to the intimate and direct "I-Thou" relationship between man and nature and man and man. When this relationship be-

came indirect and estranged, when it turned into an "I-It" relationship, disintegrating the symbolic and magical bonds between man and environment and upsetting the oneness of man's functional and personal life, the growing abstractness and the ensuing disunity produced the amorphous character of all modern towns (Fig. 18) and villages and the harsh and purely utilitarian attitude toward nature. Today the transformation from the hesitant and whispered dialogue between man and nature to the aggressive and loud exploitation of nature and from closely knit communities to atomized societies is complete. A juxtaposition of air views of the "I-Thou" and the "I-It" periods reveals at a glance the tremendous impact of this changed state of mind upon all present works of man: The anonymous despotism of modern society has destroyed the organic interdependence of villages and fields and the organic clarity of all places where human beings congregate. The only unity that still exists is a unity of disorder.

If we want to open a new chapter in the history of mankind's relationship to nature, we should try to understand the fundamental character of the change from an "I-Thou" to an "I-It" attitude. How can we rediscover the genuinely creative force which should guide our activities in the future? It is for this reason that we must pause for a consideration of the influences which have brought this transformation about.

We have dealt with these problems in more detail in our *Community and Environment*. On the next few pages we have made use, to a certain extent, of some of the ideas discussed in this work.

As long as man was deeply imbedded in nature and every natural phenomenon had a symbolic significance, the man-environment relationship was more a mutual adaptation than a one-sided conquest of nature by man. The re-

Courtesy of the American Geographical Society, New York

FIG. 8.—Sudan, Bari Village. A closely knit social group occupies the compact and fenced-in space of this village. Here life is immediate, and the traditional huts are part of the landscape. The relationship between man and man and man and nature is intimate and direct. It is an "I-Thou" and reciprocal contact.

Ewing Galloway

FIG. 9.—Belgian Congo, copper-miners' village. Unity through repetition is the characteristic note of this cantonment for the workers in the copper mines. The pathetic attempt to retain something of the indigenous style by putting thatched roofs on the standardized huts is an outward symbol of the helplessness and confusion of an atomized society which has spread its tentacles to this remote part of the world. The workers and their families living in these cells are uprooted and depersonalized beings and trained as human automata. They are estranged from nature and from each other. Life in this regimented agglomeration of huts has lost its immediacy and imposed all the prerequisites of an indirect and impersonal existence, of an "I-It" relationship.

13

Compagnie Aérienne Française

FIG. 10.—France, Aude, Carcassonne. The ancient part of the town is inclosed by two *enceintes* within which a large number of houses are closely huddled together. The perplexities which threatened to overwhelm medieval man and to disrupt his religious and worldly loyalties drove him into fraternal associations. The shells of the family and the guilds, confraternities, and religious orders enfolded the individual being. The walls were the ever present and bodily manifestations of these all-embracing loyalties. The towns of the Middle Ages were communities in which elected affinities and family bonds were merged into each other and where life was immediate and personal, a perfect "I-Thou" relationship.

FIG. 11.—Anywhere. In these sprawling towns the last vestiges of a community have disappeared. They are hardly anything else than an agglomeration of innumerable and isolated details, of human atoms, and of rows of boxes, called houses, interspersed between industries. It is a total victory of laissez faire insensibility and recklessness over organic growth and even over organized development. Our towns are work-centered power stations of the national state. They are the precursors of the ant state and deliver the vast army of experts. The "I-It" relationship is paramount.

Photo Graf zu Castell

FIG. 12.—China, Kansu, Lanchow, graves. These graves near Lanchow cover many square miles of the plain, although it is only here that the land can be fruitfully cultivated, and are symbols of the impact of the past on the present. The ancestor cult and the general reverence for ancestral graves were stronger even than the pressing need for careful preservation of the soil, which is insufficient for the great number of Chinese peasants. Life in Old China was lived retrospectively, guided by the cult of the dead, which introduced an ever present and powerful element of intimate family coherence and unitedness with the environment within an all-pervading "I-Thou" relationship.

Courtesy of the American Geographical Society, New York

FIG. 13.—Argentina, Buenos Aires, city of the dead. There are worlds between the pious devotion of the peasant of Old China who sacrificed to the dead a valuable part of his barely sufficient soil and the contemporary solution with its rigidly lined-up monuments for the wealthier families and the regimented similarity of the humbler graves. Depersonalization extends to life after death. The dead are cut loose from any direct contact with the living. Impersonal and abstract relations invade even the revered atmosphere of this "city" of the dead.

Courtesy of the Agence Économique des Colonies

FIG. 14.—Indochina, Cambodia, Angkor Wat. The temple lies near the royal city of Angkor Thom within a park surrounded by a moat. Five walls, in ever narrowing rectangles and on rising terraces, encircle the innermost sanctuary, removing it from the mortal ken and yet absorbing the worshipers into its all-embracing holiness. The temple is isolated from the hustle and bustle of the daily life in the near-by town, and yet this isolation is the very source of its emotional appeal to the awareness of the unity of man and the universe and of the individual and the community to which he belongs. Here the "I-Thou" relationship is demonstrated on a grand scale and with the utmost intensity.

Courtesy of the Ministère des Travaux Publics

FIG. 15.—France, Pas-de-Calais, mining town. "Homes and gardens" for the workers living directly above the pit where they work form the basic pattern of this mining town. Two toy churches are inserted into this disingenious and degrading travesty of a town destined for human beings whose only common bond is the identity of their abodes. This rigid layout and the unity by repetition, these unfailing symptoms of massification, are the overt sign of an "I-It" relationship. Although places of worship are included directly in the precincts of the town, apparently as the expression of a "community spirit," they are in reality more isolated from the life of the inhabitants than the isolated temple of Angkor Wat.

FIG. 16.—Spain, Toledo. Church and castle are the rival symbols of the Middle Ages. Here in Toledo, as in many other towns, both dominate the skyline. The houses rise as a compact mass in terraces to the highest plateau. They are "introvert," their rooms arranged around an inner courtyard; only a few windows and doors open onto the streets. The natural features of the site compress the town to a compact unit which, just like the "introvert" houses, forces the whole place into a determined seclusion that increases the personal contact of the inhabitants.

Courtesy of the Ministère des Travaux Publics

FIG. 17.—France, Paris, Billancourt. The industrial district is situated on an island in the Seine. It forms an inseparable unit with the residential quarters. Factory chimneys are the characteristic feature of the skyline. Everywhere they are the symbols of modern society and of its demon, industry. They are the expression of the one-sided preoccupation with work, an attitude which has made the existence of modern man lopsided, destroyed the unity of his personal and functional life, undermined his intimate and personal relations, and produced the dangerous conditions in which a machine-centered managerial revolution can develop placement of natural features was rather a modification in defense against external dangers than a deliberate attempt at dominating nature in a spirit of aggressiveness. If nature threatened to get out of hand, magic was expected to help. It was an "I-Thou" relationship, with all the ups and downs inherent even in the closest association; and it was also a total relationship in which man was dependent on the universal character of the environment, being himself an integral part of nature and dimly aware that there was nothing which could not influence in one way or another his own existence and his attitude to the surrounding world. Since the scientific revolution, nature has been depersonalized, and the awareness of the total relationship between man and nature has been fading out.

During the first three thousand years of recorded history, man remained deeply imbedded in his natural environment. Nature and man, human and cosmic events, are merged into one, and man's experience is immediate and personal. The symbolic significance of events and phenomena is equated with actual reality. This produces a particular concept of causality and of space and time which establishes between man and the phenomenal world an intimate and reciprocal dependence. The external world is a great "Thou" to early man. He does not search for impersonal laws behind the goings-on of the universe. Consequently, his approach is not analytical.

The world of primitive man is still a living reality today and is still immersed in magic and animism. It is a

TRANSFORMATION FROM AN "I-THOU" TO AN "I-IT" RELATIONSHIP

Compagnie Aérienne Française

FIG. 18.—France, Haute-Garonne, Toulouse. The final result of the misguided "I-It" relationship: the canyon street as the life-artery of urban existence, purposeless, meaningless, joyless, and as the expression of the growing abstractness and the amorphous character of modern cities.

world which has no development as we understand it. Change means a break in the established and reciprocal relationship between man and environment and would destroy the unity between him and the natural phenomena. Two spheres pervade each other: the macrocosm and the microcosm. The effort of primitive man is directed toward a fusion of the two through magical contacts which make the universal and the social space coalesce.

Greek thought is still permeated by an experience of nature which, as Professor Butterfield has expressed it, somewhat controversially, in *The Origins of Modern Science,* "has the door halfway open to spirits," though man's interpretation of the universe has shifted from unquestioning belief to the search for truth. In spite of all progress in logical reasoning and mathematics, the Greek relationship to nature has remained tinged with the conviction that it is an eminently personal world in which one has to find his way. The great "Thou" still lingers on in spite of the brilliant unfolding of individualistic thought and reason. The legacy of the past is still too strong for the Greeks. They have not completely shaken off the fetters of mythical limitations. Macrocosm and microcosm are firmly interwoven, and man symbolizes the general in his individual being. Greek symbolism is very concrete, very direct; it comes to life in visible form, not through complicated analogies. Thus the classical and even the Hellenistic *polis* is the symbolic expression of the ideal structure of society and the only correct form of its synthesis with the supermathematical cosmic order. When created, the *polis* was limited in size and character, and its scale was fixed by human standards. Thus life has not become abstract, and the relations of men to their town remain concrete.

Something similar applies to the towns of Old China. The walls were the most sacred part of the town and were erected first. The town was conceived as a whole from the very beginning, and the space created by the inclosure of the walls was only gradually filled with houses and official buildings. Although quite a number of Chinese towns extend over a large area and their streets and houses seem to form an inextricable mess, they are yet systematic and attuned to the human scale. Life was not deprived of its immediate and personal character. Magical considerations played an important part: The layout of a town was not only based on practical conditions; it was dependent on geomantic rules, as part of the magical ideas which have dominated Chinese thinking from early times. If we look from the air at a Chinese town which has retained its old character, we see the sharp line of the walls inclosing a seemingly chaotic agglomeration of houses in their protecting embrace. The direct and intimate relation between man and nature is still at work.

The burgher of the medieval town was the direct successor of the citizen of the *polis:* The narrow living space of his town was the center where his whole life converged. His spiritual and practical activities were confined to this limited sphere. Family, guilds, religious orders, and confraternities enfolded the individual. The town was a community, a union in the sense of brotherhood.

Christianity tended to break up the magical and taboo links on which blood relationship largely rests in China, India, Japan, and Islamic countries. Elective affinities assumed equal rights with consanguinous relationships. It is this voluntary association which gave a new security and created essential preconditions from which an urban community could grow. Religion was the great "uniter" of medieval life; it guided men into the spirit of genuine communities and made life direct and personal. Work and family life were one and proceeded under the same roof. Man-made and natural environments retained their intimate character, and man still felt that he was the center, like the earth, of the universe. Nature is on a par with man. In the words of Pico della Mirandola, which he puts into the mouth of the Creator when he is speaking to Adam: "In the middle of the world have I placed thee that thou mayst the more easily look about thee and see all that is therein contained."

Since the scientific revolution, the awareness of the total relationship between man and nature has been fading out. Life became gradually more abstract, and the relations between men lost their personal directness. Religious man receded into the shadows of the past, and economic man appeared on the horizon. Group-consciousness weak-

ened, and the interaction of the general and the individual will melted away until it led in the Baroque to the supremacy of a small minority and to the leveling-down of the majority to an inarticulate mass of obedient subjects of the rising state. The strong social and religious bonds which had enveloped and held together the small communities and which had created a unison of individual spontaneity and communal spirit—these bonds were broken, and the way was open to the social disintegration of the present. The new order had a far-reaching effect on the relationship between the places in which men lived, worked, and traded. Family life and business life fell apart. Work became the center around which everything else rotated until it swallowed up the whole of man's thinking and feeling

TRANSFORMATION FROM AN "I-THOU" TO AN "I-IT" RELATIONSHIP

Compania Mexicana Aerofoto

Fig. 19.—Mexico, Guanajuato, Salvatierra. Although the countryside extends far into the town, a genuine and organic relationship between the urban and rural structures is missing. It is difficult to say whether the town or the country is the cause of this lack of systematic unity and dynamic balance between the two settings. The whole complex is a mongrelized paradox with the pretensions of a big city and the purely utilitarian attitude toward nature.

and dictated the cycle of his daily life; until fragmented man, the finished and dangerous product of our time, was the result.

This growing disintegration can be seen in the loss of homogeneity of urban and rural settings (Fig. 19) and in the unrelated attempts at the exploitation of the natural resources. The new "I-It" relationship between man and nature has destroyed the continuity of the intimate and personal contact between man and environment and also the unity of thought linking the everyday events and the immediate environment to the order of the universe. Only about ten generations separate us from the beginning of the scientific revolution. But this short period has created conditions of life which challenge the very essence of our existence. We face the disruptive impact of an "I-It" relationship which extends not only to things but also to persons.

2. The second chain of transformation consists of four stages in man's changing attitude to his environment, all of which can be observed today sometimes in close proximity to one another. The first stage is one of fear and the longing for security—of fear of the unpredictable and unknown forces of nature and of protection against these forces and the hostility of men. Particularly in primitive conditions, careless displacement of the natural features is the result. These activities lead often to collective work and are accompanied by the gradual formation of integrated groups. Man feels himself a part of nature, and cosmic and earthly events are for him inextricably interwoven. His orientations in space and time are concrete, not abstract, concepts. He solves his practical problems in an empirical manner, and his attitude to the external world of things and men is permeated by an "I-Thou" relationship full of symbolic and personal meaning. All this is evident in the works of early and primitive man and can be observed today in the windscreen settlements of the Bushmen, in the pile dwellings of the South Seas and of other parts of the world (Fig. 20), in the careless displacement of the natural conditions for shifting agriculture, in the kraals of the Bantu Negroes (Fig. 21), in the *zadrugas* of Old Bulgaria (Fig. 22), and in many other institutions and works.

The second stage is one of growing self-confidence and increasing observation, leading to a more rational adaptation of the environment to differentiated needs. Elementary protection develops into purposeful reshaping of the environment, and displacement of nature is followed by replacement. The objectives are complex and interrelated and widen in scope and character. Man accepts the challenge of nature as a disciple and re-former, and the "I-Thou" relationship persists, though fashioned by man in a different way, and remolds the interrelationship of individual and group and the appreciation of the cosmic and earthly phenomena correspondingly. During this stage all activities bear the same mark of immediacy and reciprocal adjustment. This is manifest in such works as the rice terraces and fields of China (Fig. 23), in the geomantic adaptation of Chinese towns to environmental conditions (Fig. 24), in the regulation of the rivers and the irrigation of the fields (Fig. 25), and in the social and religious significance of the layout of Indian, African, and other towns, to mention only a few of the innumerable examples.

The third stage which had led to our present situation is one of aggressiveness and conquest. Adjustment to the environment develops into exploitation. The objectives are unlimited and grow in diversity but also in disunity (Fig. 26). With the ruthlessness of a pioneer, man expands his living space, and, with a complete disregard of the danger of a

Copyright Avianca

FIG. 20.—Colombia, Ciénaga Grande, fishing village. The village stands in the Caribbean coastal lowlands, where little habitable ground is available. It is a compact settlement: home and work-place in one and providing economic security and physical protection against the hazards of life in the middle of the swamps fed by the waters of four rivers.

Courtesy of the American Geographical Society, New York

FIG. 21.—British Mandated Territory of Tanganyika, fields behind windbreaks. Security of food supply has been achieved by the protection of the fields behind windbreaks adapted to the terrain and serving as inclosures of the individual kraals.

FIG. 22.—Bulgaria, *zadruga* village. In this loosely grouped village each family farm is surrounded by a low wall. Narrow lanes give access to every single farmstead. The village is built on the *zadruga* principle, a social unit comprising one joint family. Hamlets develop by subdivision of the joint family and by addition of new buildings. In the course of time these hamlets grow into large villages where the *zadruga* units, forming compact groups, can be clearly discerned from the other parts interspersed between them.

CONFIDENCE AND ADJUSTMENT

Photo Graf zu Castell

FIG. 23.—China, Hunan, rice terraces. The northern slopes of the mountains separating Kwangtung from Hunan sweep down from a height of 6,000 feet to a gigantic sea of rice fields, above which rise, like islands, hillocks with woods and settlements. Every field can be irrigated and properly drained. The village in the foreground consists of only a few houses covering a minimum of space—no more than can be spared from cultivation.

Photo Graf zu Castell

FIG. 24.—China, Hopeh, Peiping. The "Forbidden City," the emperor's residence, symbolizes the very heart of the Chinese Empire. It is situated right in the center of the outer city, like the yamen, the residence of the representative of the ruler, in any other town. The whole plan is oriented to this center, which, physically and psychologically, is the focal point. The "Forbidden City" is a town within a town. It is perhaps the only architectural work whose actual execution corresponds entirely with the ideal conception. Religious-geomantic considerations play an essential part in the layout of the city in general and in detail.

Courtesy of the Oriental Institute, University of Chicago

Fig. 25.—Iran, Province of Fars, irrigation system. The picture shows the head of an irrigation system developed by an enlightened Buyide prince who during the second half of the tenth century A.D. built the dam to raise the water of the Kur River below its junction with the Pulvar. Ten great wheels raised the water to such a high level that three hundred villages were supplied; each wheel also worked a flour mill. The dam is still in use, and many villages of the Marv Dasht today profit from this old system.

Aggressiveness and Disintegration

Courtesy of the Ministère des Travaux Publics

Fig. 26.—Belgium, Liége. The town of Liége extends along the banks of the Meuse River, including an island which is connected with both banks by numerous bridges. It is an old town with many remarkable buildings, but the modern age, with its ruthless disregard of organic growth, has contributed to its disintegration and unsystematic expansion.

FIG. 27.—Somewhere

"I'm Mrs. Edward M. Barnes. Where Do I Live?"

FIG. 28.—Anywhere

primarily quantitative expansion, he deludes himself into the role of an omnipotent remaker of his environment (Figs. 27 and 28). Neglect and exploitation of the natural resources, rural isolation and urban expansion, have produced an unexampled disunity of the social and economic structure (Fig. 29). The physical expression of this third stage is evident in practically all works of modern man. They are perhaps the most conspicuous features which meet the eye from the air.

This phase is drawing to a close. The fourth stage of the interaction of man and environment is slowly taking shape. Faintly the outlines of this new epoch are discernible. It will be an age of responsibility and unification (Figs. 30, 31, and 32). Expansive ruthlessness is gradually merging into a careful adjustment to environmental conditions and new possibilities. Man begins to be aware of his real responsibility and of the limitations which the closing frontiers of the world impose upon him. The objectives are gaining in precision, foresight, and co-ordination. Unity in diversity and unification are emerging as the main tasks in the next stage of development in which man must act as a co-ordinator, guided by social awareness and insight into the workings of nature.

3. The third chain of transformation represents the changing experience of space in relation to the conception of the universe and the widening scale of human activities. Through the whole of known history the ideas of space which

AGGRESSIVENESS AND DISINTEGRATION

Courtesy of the Ministère des Travaux Publics

Fig. 29.—France, Pas-de-Calais, coal mine and homes. The inhuman blending of work and living place is part of the mining region in the north of France. The dumps are the most conspicuous landmarks of the exploitation of the natural resources and of the exploitation of the human "material."

man put on the universe were the reflection of his changing attitude toward the environment and vice versa. And with these different ideas the scale widened, and large and comprehensive operations replaced small and isolated activities. Roughly three phases can be distinguished.

a) During the first phase man is the center of life on earth, and the earth is the center of the universe, which is conceived as finite and consisting of concentric spheres. This is the system of Aristotle which dominated man's thought for two thousand years. Similar conceptions, though slightly modified, developed in other parts of the world. While this lasted, all activities of man were undertaken in the same spirit: They aimed at stability and were limited in scope and character. Nature was experienced as a multitude of concrete orientations, and, therefore, a concrete, body-like property was the essential quality of all human works. As far as these conceptions still exist

RESPONSIBILITY AND UNIFICATION

Courtesy of the U.S. Soil Conservation Service

Fig. 30.—United States, Texas, Bell County, contour plowing. Creative adaptation to nature is gaining momentum through the application of scientific knowledge and deeper insight into the work of nature. A new responsibility toward the soil is emerging. Although different in many aspects from the streamlined terraces of China, the effects produced are nevertheless similar in their spirit of close adaptation to nature. In this picture of an individual farm, the upper slopes are controlled with terracing and strip cropping and the lower slopes with strip cropping alone. This produces a visual effect which differs from the old field systems as much as does an abstract from a Renaissance painting.

Courtesy of the U.S. Bureau of Reclamation

FIG. 31.—United States, Arizona, Boulder Dam, the hub of a large region. It is a long way from the earliest regulations of rivers, when a dam served as a protecting screen for the surrounding country, or from the primitive water control of African tribes, to the gigantic modern structures. To mere protection is added generation of power; to the needs of agriculture, those of industry; and to the mimicry with which early works copied natural features, the self-conscious originality of today, beautiful in its simplicity and decisive in its grandeur. The dam is part of the great scheme which is shown on the map (Fig. 32). The electric-power plant supplies hydroelectric power and irrigation water to a large area with a highly developed economy. It is the main source of energy which has enabled Los Angeles and the surrounding region to increase its population to a very considerable degree and at an unprecedented pace.

today, this conformity of the conception of the universal space and of the earthly works of man is unmistakable. This identity is not the result of a deliberate and conscious adaptation of the environment to the ideas of the universal space—such a notion would belong to the dream world of retrospective fabri- cations—but the expression of the latent spiritual forces which unite all thoughts and all works of man in one great scheme. As Whitehead, whose words we repeat in this connection, said, it is the "profound cosmological outlook, implicitly accepted, impressing its own type upon the current springs of ac-

RESPONSIBILITY AND UNIFICATION

Courtesy of the U.S. Bureau of Reclamation

FIG. 32.—The area benefited by control of the Colorado River tion." Works which can still be appreciated as evidence of this particular notion of space during this period reveal their characteristic features best from the air, for only then can they show most clearly their limitations and the belief of their creators in the possibility of stable conditions. The erection of fortified walls, protecting and inclosing the great empires of the Incas, the Romans, and the Chinese (Fig. 33), is an outstanding example of this spirit. The towns within these empires, as are also those of the European Middle Ages, though with some modifications, and other parts of the world, are built from outside inward (Fig. 34). They are conceived as limited units for a self-contained and stable life (Figs. 35–39).

b) The heliocentric universe of Copernicus is still finite, terminating in the sphere of the fixed stars, with the sun instead of the earth as the center. A new feeling of space develops, and the relegation of the earth to a secondary role in the universal system engenders tensions which made the ancient conception of the universe meaningless. Man is moved, with the earth, to the periphery. Slowly but irresistibly the whole outlook of man changes. He and his earth lose their central position, and

THE CHANGING SCALE

FIG. 33.—China, the Great Wall. The discovery of the third dimension, the conquest of the air, has made all national frontiers obsolete and their defense senseless. Frontiers have been revealed for what they are in reality—historical incidents. The Great Wall of China is the most expressive manifestation of the faith of a people in protection by walls. It is a grandiose reminder of the past and of the utmost limits to which the security of a national state can be identified with fixed frontiers. The Great Wall, begun about 500 B.C., served as protection against Mongol invaders from the steppes. Its fortlike watchhouses for the soldiers and the numerous towers form, together with the wall itself, a formidable defense system.

Exclusive News Agency

FIG. 34.—France, French Flanders, Bergues. The pedestrian scale is the standard of measurement. The town was encompassed by a circular wall, now replaced by a road. Gardens are interspersed between the houses. The church occupies the center, while the town hall with the belfry, a watchtower with an alarm bell, stands at the end of the town near the wall.

Courtesy of the Ministère des Travaux Publics

FIG. 35.—France, Gard, Aiguesmortes. The place was founded by St. Louis as one of the fortified towns, the bastides. A single uniform idea inspired the layout, which consists of a rectangular pattern of streets and a central square. This was typical of the Middle Ages wherever a new town was founded as a coherent unit. In return for the plots alloted to them the settlers helped in the building of the walls. Aiguesmortes is not more than 596 yards by 149 yards in extent. It served as a strong-point in a sparsely inhabited region. It is situated in an isolated position in the marshy plain of the Rhone Delta.

Courtesy of the Oriental Institute, University of Chicago

FIG. 36.—Iran, Isfahan, the Maidan-i-Shah. The town was the capital of the kingdom during the period from 1499 to 1736. The maidan, the "King's Square," is dominated by the most impressive structure in the town, the mosque of the shah. Although the circuit of the town extends over 30 miles, this architectural group is clearly the center, surpassing in importance and brilliance the vast mass of other buildings and gardens. The precincts of this complex include the religious center, the mosque, and the secular center, the palace of the king.

Swiss Air Photo

FIG. 37.—Switzerland, Canton of Zürich, Regensberg. The characteristic feature of the small town is the castle. In former times it was the all-important center of social and economic life. The situation on the top of the hill acts as a natural restriction to the size of the town.

Aerofilms, Ltd. K.L.M.

FIG. 38.—Netherlands, Overijssel, Elburg. In this old fortress-town on the shores of the Zuider Zee, each house has preserved its individuality as a clearly defined entity. Life within the town, limited physically by the wall and spiritually by the self-restraint imposed by social and economic bonds, achieved unity in diversity partly because the town never grew beyond pedestrian use and partly by the elimination of everything outside the experience of the community.

FIG. 39.—Italy, Venice, St. Mark's Square. The Square is the center of life in Venice. It is one of the most perfect examples of an open-air festival hall surrounded on three sides by uniform buildings and on the fourth closed by the Church of St. Mark. The *piazzetta*, a smaller square of similar proportions, opens the main square to the waterfront.

he is forced into the acceptance of a totally different view—a view from the periphery toward a new center, the sun. A more dynamic and wider outlook is the result. The compact empires of the first period are superseded by scattered possessions. An outburst of expansion sets in. The towns of Europe begin to expand. The simple walls are replaced by complicated fortifications for defense against long-range firearms (Figs. 40, 41). The perspective view is introduced as an element of town planning (Fig. 42), and the external appearance of the houses gains in importance. The extrovert dwelling place becomes the general rule. A new feeling of space and spaciousness is expressed in all works of man. Of this period we still have numerous examples which bear witness to the tremendous tensions arising out of this new attitude toward life and of thinking and planning on a larger scale.

c) The third phase leads eventually in our time to a conception of space which, like the universe, is unbounded and yet not infinite (Fig. 43), as a sphere is without a boundary and yet is not infinite, for it has a definite size conditioned by its radius. In the same way, the size of the universe depends on its average curvature. The first rudiments of this modern cosmology can be traced back to the Renaissance. Giordano Bruno was the first to assert that the universe has no limits but is infinite, without a creator, for an infinite uni-

THE IMPACT OF COPERNICUS

Aerofilms Ltd. K.L.M.

FIG. 40.—Netherlands, North Holland, Naarden. The fortress stands between the shores of the Zuider Zee and the Naardermeer as a protection of Amsterdam from the west. It is one of the finest examples of Renaissance fortifications. With the appearance of long-range firearms, the simple walls were replaced by a complicated system of bastions and ramparts surrounded by moats. This coincided with a new conception of town planning and especially with the introduction of perspective—the result of the changed conception of the universe originated by Copernicus and Giordano Bruno. In Naarden the church occupies the center while in Italy the center was mostly reserved for the *piazza d'armi*, the meeting place of the defenders.

verse cannot be created from outside. During this period, from the beginning of the seventeenth century to modern times, the evolution of the feeling of space is more or less identical with a quest for expansion, with the breaking-down of limitations, and with the belief in an almost automatic progress. Today we are face to face with the confused results of this mode of thinking. The limits of expansion have been reached. The earth is fully known. Frontiers and walls as protection are recognized as historical incidents and as useless demonstrations. Our towns are shapeless, flowing over into the country.

At present we are in a particularly dangerous but also particularly formative period of transformation. The old ideas of space are still strong, and the

THE IMPACT OF COPERNICUS

Courtesy of the Ministère des Travaux Publics

FIG. 41.—France, Pyrénées-Orientales, Montlouis. Founded in 1681 by Vauban, the French military engineer, the place exhibits the starlike form which has made his fortifications famous. It stands on a plateau encircled by the deep valley of the Têt River and served as a frontier fortress against Spain. Small fields, owing to the mountainous character of the country and to repeated subdivisions, surround the two villages; one laid out compactly and the other as a roadside settlement.

new conceptions have not yet found a concrete expression. This confused state of mind is visible in all parts of the world. The illusion of infinite spread and the conviction that individual and unrelated actions will produce a coherent whole are fading away. When we look down at the earth and at the results of man's transformations, we may be impressed by the quantitative change—although this should not be overrated—but the qualitative aspects can hardly command the same positive tribute. The general picture is one of disintegration, disorder, and irresponsibility. Only here and there a few beginnings of co-ordination, systematic development, and responsibility can be discovered. The new feeling of space seems so far merely to be a cult of bigness. Its true implications still await their consummation in a language of form which grows out of the deep layers of human creativeness.

d) The widening scale of man's transformations suffers from the same and facile deception that bigness is identical with large enterprises. The problem is much more complex and will not be solved by the immature and blind boosters of quantity or by adherence to the dogma that quantity turns into quality, if and when the quantitative increase of change has reached an overwhelming scale.

Moreover, scale, like many other notions, is relative. When we fly from England to Japan, the gradual change of scale is perhaps the most striking impression. Scale is small in the British

THE IMPACT OF COPERNICUS

FIG. 42.—Italy, Rome, St. Peter's Square. The church has been placed at the end of the perspective view which corresponds to the new heliocentric idea of the universe. Like two enormous tentacles, the Colonnades of Bernini encompass the forecourt, linking the ensemble of the church and the gently rising square to the opposite end, where originally a continuation of the perspective layout was planned by Carlo Fontana.

Isles, increases over Europe, grows to large dimensions over Russia, only to decrease again over Japan. This is not exclusively the result of geographical factors, though these play a not entirely negligible role. It is more the outcome of the changing attitude of the inhabitants toward their respective environments. However, the varying scale is manifest in many things which are far removed from the direct and physical influence of the environment. Here are a few examples. For the West European, his garden is a collection of beautiful flowers and plants arranged as pleasingly as possible, or rigidly as the ornamental gardens of Spain or France, or with modest variety as the peasant gardens of Austria and Switzerland. For the Japanese, the garden is a microcosm consciously created out of nature's overwhelming diversity as a "concentrated" nature within a limited space. Or something quite different:

THE IMPACT OF THE AIRPLANE

Courtesy of the U.S. Air Force Photo Reconnaissance Laboratories

FIG. 43.—Region between Boston and New York. The scale of the airplane sweeps away boundaries and limitations. Railways, motorcars, and airplanes, all together, if sensibly used and co-ordinated, open up the remotest and almost forgotten parts of the world. The introduction of the helicopter will complete this development. Regional integration on a large scale and physical and, above all, cultural decentralization will result from this tremendous transformation. Within the wide and elastic

The size of the paper on which we write is generally smaller in England than in Middle Europe and Russia, while it is smaller still in Japan. Or the houses: Broadly speaking, they are smaller in England, in general larger in Europe and Russia, but distinctly smaller in Japan. This applies of course only to the indigenous and old buildings, not to the Europeanized monstrosities dotted over the whole route.

What, then, is the correct assessment of scale and its gradually widening character? The answer can be given succinctly. Today we must reconcile two diametrically opposite aspects: the infinitely large and the infinitely small. This means, therefore, not merely an extension but, at the same time, also a limitation in space. The new scale is more than the expression of a transformed environment as such. It is an intellectual adventure into the totality of phenomena and conditions which

framework of regional unity new communities will come into being, and the oppressive dominance of the big cities will give way to a balanced structure of settlement in which every community will have its rightful place.

The shrinking of the world which the airplane accelerates with every new improvement means the approaching end of the sovereign national states. It opens the way to life-centered communities. It marks the beginning of the end of the work-centered cities and towns.

surround us. As a matter of fact, this has always been so. It is evident in a Zulu kraal, every part of which is within easy walking distance and which can be taken in as a whole at a glance (Fig. 44); in the small fields of Europe (Fig. 45); in the small and compact settlements in oases (Fig. 46); in hilltop towns of Italy, Spain, and Switzerland (Fig. 47); or in medieval towns of Europe and even in the large cities of Old China (Fig. 48).

And what is the characteristic of this widening scale? It is the atunement of the human scale to the universal scale, the simultaneous and willing experience of the infinite, and the acceptance of the safety which the human scale provides. Only if both these scales are joined together on the same level of

importance can we hope to regain something of the old unity between the two. Mere bigness crushes the human scale and creates diffidence and finally social disintegration.

It would be a wrong assessment of the significance of the airplane if we regarded it solely as an instrument that brings home most dramatically the shrinking of the globe. This is only one side of this new venture. The airplane enables us for the first time to look down—in the truest sense of the word—on man's works from above and to see them as a still very imperfect attempt at reshaping the natural environment. It imposes upon us forcibly the insignificance of what man has done so far to the earth and the challenge of the human scale which we almost lost

THE HUMAN SCALE PRESERVED

Fig. 44.—British East Africa, Kenya, Kisumu, Kavirondo kraals. The Kavirondo are agriculturists and dairymen. Their area is relatively closely settled, and kraals cover the countryside in unending succession. The cattle pen is sometimes in the center, where it is well protected. The ring fence gives a feeling of limitation and helps to preserve the human scale.

through the childish adoration of the big and yet so inadequate buildings and structures erected by man.

In a recent lecture to the European Management Conference, Ortega y Gasset had the courage to tell this audience of managerial pundits that productivity alone was not identical with the economy of a society but that the economy was intimately connected with the social characer of that society. He argued that the social nexus, in spite of an increase in productivity—he referred only to Europe, but his argument applies, of course, to other countries—has been disintegrating. Since the war there had developed a new social phenomenon which, taken together with the social disintegration in general, was an ominous sign of bewilderment and fear. He called this phenomenon "nationalism turned inward." What he meant by this is that the war marked the end of expansive nationalism and that since its end countries had begun to pay increasing attention to their own national customs and had become consequently more parochial. Instead of fighting each other and admiring the courage of their enemies, they denigrated each other, vilified each other's way of life and institutions, and hated each other more than ever before. And he concluded his argument by suggesting that this "nationalism turned inward" was a sign of the refusal to find a replacement for war. We may add that it is also a symbol of the rivaling forces of nationalism

THE HUMAN SCALE PRESERVED

Fig. 45.—Finland, Gulf of Bothnia, Liminka. Farms are clustered around a church in a small wood; others are widely dispersed over the countryside, and fields are laid out in strips. The physical structure of the whole area is only loosely knit together. In spite of this wide dispersion, the human scale is a living reality expressed in the small fields and in the numerous single farms dotted over the land as an ever present reminder of man as the measure of all things.

Literary Services (Mondiale)

Fig. 46.—Aden Protectorate, The Hadhramaut, Shibam. The town consists of only five hundred houses remarkable for their height: the skyscrapers of the desert. It stands on a slight eminence in the valley. The houses are close together, and there is no further building space. Shibam is a representative example of the intensive use of the small site to which all oases are restricted. The result of this compactness is close social and economic contact, protection against the desert and hostile outsiders, and a feeling of security heightened by the preservation of the human scale.

Courtesy of the Italian Embassy, London

Fig. 47.—Italy, Latium, Montecompatri. The town represents an ideal form of a hilltop settlement focused on the church, which stands right in the center. At the farther end is a palace. The outer street follows the contours of the hill. The whole is an extraordinarily beautiful architectural composition in which everything, man-made works and nature alike, is adapted to human proportions.

Photo Graf zu Castell

FIG. 48.—China, Shensi, Sian. Sian is the provincial capital of Shensi. It is one of the oldest towns of China and has repeatedly been the capital of the Chinese Empire. It is situated on the Wei River. The main arteries lead straight through the town from one gate to the other. Between them is an inextricable maze of lanes and side streets. Chinese towns are laid out mostly on a rectangular ground plan within the inclosure of the walls which were built first in accordance with religious ritual. Gradually the inner space was filled with buildings. The towns of Old China combined growth and organization. They solved this seemingly irreconcilable problem because life, and also such practical works as building, was deeply imbedded in religion and magical symbolism. The bonds of the family and the clan were of primary importance. Especially within the maze of the secondary streets the human scale was preserved, and life retained its immediate and personal character.

43

and universalism and of the apparent incompatibility between the chores of a daily life-routine within the parochial narrowness of a national state and the latent yearning for universal oneness.

What has this to do with the new scale which the airplane—and the modern means of mass communications—has given us? The answer is plain: The new scale has outrun our political and social comprehension and brought matters to a head. The inverted nationalism is merely an escape, because national frontiers have become meaningless, and yet the unity of the world evades us. This helplessness is a product of fear—but it could also be the very beginning of a new departure, for it can release the forces of self-examination and introspection which are still hidden in the soul of confused and irritated nations.

Ideas are more potent forces than material achievements. They are the real driving power behind our actions. This is the reason why this paper has been written with a strong emphasis on the imponderables which are at work behind the discovery of the third dimension, the conquest of the air, and the reshaping of our environment. It may be expected that this approach is not to the liking of the eternal realists and the hosts of pygmies who call themselves experts. For them, only that counts which can be seen and touched and used directly and practically. For them ideas are thin air, "such stuff as dreams are made of." They will, let us hope, dismiss the tenor of this paper as abstract and almost useless, for they are so preoccupied with their pet subjects that they never see the woods for the trees.

Today the whole world is our unit of thinking and acting. Nothing can develop in isolation, and the transformation in one country produces direct reactions on the physical and social structure of all the others. This awareness is perhaps the greatest triumph of the conquest of the air. It depends exclusively on the spirit in which we take up this challenge, not on our material achievements, whether our independence of the surface of the earth which the airplane has made possible will be a blessing or a curse.

Part I
Retrospect

Man's Tenure of the Earth

Man's Tenure of the Earth

The Agency of Man on the Earth

CARL O. SAUER[*]

THE THEME

As a short title for the present conference we have spoken at times and with hope of a "Marsh Festival," after the statesman-scholar, George Perkins Marsh, who a century ago considered the ways in which the Earth has been modified by human action (Marsh, 1864, 1874). The theme is the capacity of man to alter his natural environment, the manner of his so doing, and the virtue of his actions. It is concerned with historically cumulative effects, with the physical and biologic processes that man sets in motion, inhibits, or deflects, and with the differences in cultural conduct that distinguish one human group from another.

Every human population, at all times, has needed to evaluate the economic potential of its inhabited area, to organize its life about its natural environment in terms of the skills available to it and the values which it accepted. In the cultural *mise en valeur* of the environment, a deformation of the pristine, or prehuman, landscape has been initiated that has increased with length of occupation, growth in population, and addition of skills. Wherever men live, they have operated to alter the aspect of the Earth, both animate and inanimate, be it to their boon or bane.

The general theme may be described, therefore, in its first outline, as an attempt to set forth the geographic effects, that is, the appropriation of habitat by habit, resulting from the spread of differing cultures to all the *oikoumene* throughout all we know of human time. We need to understand better how man has disturbed and displaced more and more of the organic world, has become in more and more regions the ecologic dominant, and has affected the course of organic evolution. Also how he has worked surficial changes as to terrain, soil, and the waters on the land and how he has drawn upon its minerals. Latterly, at least, his urban activities and concentrations have effected local alterations of the atmosphere. We are trying to examine the processes of terrestrial change he has entrained or originated, and we are attempting to ask, from our several interests and experiences, relevant questions as to cultural behaviors and effects. Thus we come properly also to consider the qualities of his actions as they seem to affect his future well-being. In this proper study of mankind, living out the destiny ascribed in Genesis—"to have dominion over all the earth"—the concern is valid as to whether his organized energies (social behavior) have or should have

[*] Dr. Sauer is Professor of Geography at the University of California, Berkeley, and was chairman of the Department of Geography (1923–54). He is a member of the advisory board of the John Simon Guggenheim Memorial Foundation; was president for 1940 of the Association of American Geographers and is its honorary president (1955–56); and recipient in 1940 of the Charles P. Daly Medal of the American Geographical Society. His publications include: *Aboriginal Population of Northwestern Mexico,* 1935; *Colima of New Spain in the Sixteenth Century,* 1948; and *Agricultural Origins and Dispersals,* 1952.

a quality of concern with regard to his posterity.

ON THE NATURE OF MAN

The primordial condition of man setting our kind apart from other primates involved more than hands, brain, and walking upright. Man owes his success in part to his digestive apparatus, which is equaled by none of his near-kin or by few other similarly omnivorous animals as to the range of potential food which can sustain him on a mixed, vegetarian, or flesh diet. The long, helpless infancy and the dependence through the years of childhood have forged, it would seem, *ab origine* a maternal bond that expresses itself in persistence of family and in formal recognition of kinship, system of kinship being perhaps the first basis of social organization. When humans lost the oestrous cycle is unknown; its weakening and loss is probably a feature of domestication, and it may have occurred early in the history of man, eldest of the domesticated creatures.

Built into the biologic nature of man therefore appear to be qualities tending to maximize geographic expansiveness, vigorous reproduction, and a bent to social development. His extreme food range favored numerical increase; I question, for instance, any assumptions of sporadic or very sparse populations of Paleolithic man in any lands he had occupied. The dominant and continuous role of woman in caring for the family suggests further inferences. Maternal duties prescribed as sedentary a life as possible. Her collecting of food and other primary materials was on the short tether of her dependent offspring. Hers also was the care of what had been collected in excess of immediate need, the problem of storage, hers the direction toward homemaking and furnishing. To the "nature" of woman we may perhaps ascribe an original social grouping, a cluster of kindred house-holds, in which some stayed home to watch over bairns and baggage while others ranged afield. Baby-sitting may be one of the most ancient of human institutions.

Implicit in this interpretation of the nature of man and primordial society, as based on his trend to sedentary life and clustering, are territoriality, the provision of stores against season of lack, and probably a tendency to monogamy. These traits are familiar enough among numerous animals, and there is no reason for denying them to primitive man. Shifts of population imposed by seasons do not mean wandering, homeless habits; nomadism is an advanced and specialized mode of life. Folk who stuffed or starved, who took no heed of the morrow, could not have possessed the Earth or laid the foundations of human culture. To the ancestral folk we may rather ascribe practical-minded economy of effort. Their success in survival and in dispersal into greatly differing habitats tells of ability to derive and communicate sensible judgments from changing circumstances.

The culture of man is herewith considered as in the main a continuum from the beginning; such is its treatment by archeology. The record of artifacts is much greater, more continuous, and begins earlier than do his recovered skeletal remains. Thereby hangs the still-argued question of human evolution, about which divergent views are unreconciled. If culture was transmitted and advanced in time and space as the archeologic record indicates, there would appear to be a linked history of a mankind that includes all the specific and generic hominid classifications of physical anthropology. Man, *sensu latiore*, therefore may conceivably be one large species complex, from archaic to modern forms, always capable of interbreeding and intercommunication. Variation occurred by long geographic isolation, blending usually when different stocks met. The former is accepted; the latter seems assured to some and is rejected by others, the Mount Carmel series of skulls being thus notoriously in dispute.

Neanderthal man, poor fellow, has had a rough time of it. He invented the Mousterian culture, a major advance which appears to have been derived from two anterior culture lines. The Abbé Breuil has credited him with ceremonial cults that show a developed religious belief and spiritual ceremonial (Breuil and Lantier, 1951, chap. xviii). Boyd, in his serologic classification of mankind (1950), the only system available on a genetic basis, has surmised that Neanderthal is ancestral to a Paleo-European race. There is no basis for holding Neanderthal man as mentally inferior or as unable to cope with the late Pleistocene changes of European climate. Yet there remains aversion to admitting him to our ancestry. The sad confusion of physical anthropology is partly the result of its meager knowledge of hereditary factors, but also to *Homo's* readiness to crossbreed, a trait of his domestication and a break with the conservatism of the instinctive.

We are groping in the obscurity of a dim past; it may be better to consider cultural growth throughout human time as proceeding by invention, borrowing, and blending of learning, rather than by evolution of human brain, until we know more of biological evolution in man. The little that we have of skeletal remains is subject to unreconciled evaluations; the record of his work is less equivocal. The question is not, could Peking man have left the artifacts attributed to him, as has been the subject of debate, but did he, that is, do the bones belong with the tools?

When primordial man began to spread over the Earth, he knew little, but what he had learned was by tested and transmitted experience; he cannot have been fear-ridden but rather, at least in his successful kinds, was venturesome, ready to try out his abilities in new surroundings. More and more he imposed himself on his animal competitors and impressed his mark on the lands he inhabited. Wherever he settled, he came to stay unless the climate changed too adversely or the spreading sea drove him back.

CLIMATIC CHANGES AND THEIR EFFECTS ON MAN

The age of man is also the Ice Age. Man may have witnessed its beginning; we perhaps are still living in an interglacial phase. His growth of learning and his expansion over the Earth have taken place during a geologic period of extreme instability of climates and also of extreme simultaneous climatic contrast. His span has been cast within a period of high environmental tensions. Spreading icecaps caused the ocean to shrink back from the shallow continental margins, their waning to spread the seas over coastal plains. With lowered sea levels, rivers trenched their valley floors below coastal lowlands; as sea level rose, streams flooded and aggraded their valleys. Glacial and Recent time have been governed by some sort of climatic pendulum, varying in amplitude of swing, but affecting land and sea in all latitudes, and life in most areas. The effects have been most felt in the Northern Hemisphere, with its large continental masses, wide plains, high mountain ranges, and broad plateaus. Millions of square miles of land were alternately buried under ice and exposed; here, also, the shallow seas upon the continental shelf spread and shrank most broadly.

This time of recurrent changes of atmosphere, land, and sea gave advantage to plastic, mobile, and prolific organisms, to plants and animals that could colonize newly available bodies of land, that had progeny some of which withstood the stresses of climatic change. The time was favorable for biologic evolution, for mutants suited to a changed environment, for hybrids formed by mingling, as on ecologic frontiers. To this period has been assigned the origin of many annual plant species dependent on heavy seed production for success (Ames, 1939). Adaptive variations in human stocks, aided by sufficiently isolating episodes of Earth history, have also been inferred.[1]

The duration of the Ice Age and of its stages has not been determined. The old guess of a million years over all is still convenient. The four glacial and three interglacial stages may have general validity; there are doubts that they were strictly in phase in all continents. In North America the relations of the several continental icecaps to the phases of Rocky Mountain glaciation, and of the latter to the Pacific mountains, are only inferred, as is the tie-in of pluvial stages in our Southwest. That great lakes and permanent streams existed in many of the present dry lands of the world is certain, that these pluvial phases of intermediate latitudes correspond to glacial ones in high latitudes and altitudes is in considerable part certain, but only in a few cases has a pluvial state been securely tied to a contemporaneous glacial stage. The promising long-range correlation of Pleistocene events by eustatic marine terraces and their dependent alluvial terraces is as yet only well started. Except for northwestern Europe, the calendar of the later geologic past is still very uncertain. The student of farther human time, anxious for an absolute chronology, is at the moment relying widely on the ingenious astronomical calendar of Milankovitch and Zeuner as an acceptable span for the Ice Age as a whole and for its divisions. It is not acceptable, however, to meteorology and climatology.[2] Slowly and bit by bit only are we likely to see the pieces fall into their proper order; nothing is gained by assurance as to what is insecure.

The newer meteorology is interesting itself in the dynamics of climatic change (Shapley, 1953; Mannerfelt *et al.*, 1949). Changes in the general circulation pattern have been inferred as conveying, in times of glacial advance, more and more frequent masses of moist, relatively warm air into high latitudes and thereby also increasing the amount of cloud cover. The importance now attached to condensation nuclei has directed attention again to the possible significance of volcanic dust. Synoptic climatological data are being examined for partial models in contemporary conditions as conducive to glaciation and deglaciation (Leighly, 1949, pp. 133–34). To the student of the human past, reserve is again indicated in making large climatic reconstructions. Such cautions I should suggest, with reserve also as to my competence to offer them, with regard to the following:

It is misleading to generalize glacial stages as cold and interglacial ones as warm. The developing phases of glaciation probably required relatively warm moist air, and decline may have been by the dominance of cold dry air over the ice margins. The times of climatic change may thus not coincide with the change from glacial advance to deglaciation. We may hazard the inference that developing glaciation is associated with low contrast of regional climates; regression of ice and beginning of an interglacial phase probably are connected (although not in each case) with accentuated contrast or "continentality" of climates. One interglacial did not repeat necessarily the features of another; nor must one glacial phase du-

1. As most recently by Coon, 1953.

2. Shapley, 1953; Willett, 1950; Simpson, G. C., 1934, 1940.

plicate another. We need only note the difference in centers of continental glaciation, of direction of growth of ice lobes, of terminal moraine-building, of structure of till and of fluvioglacial components to see the individuality of climates of glacial stages. In North America, in contrast to Europe, there is very little indication of a periglacial cold zone of tundra and of permafrost in front of the continental icecaps. Questionable also is the loess thesis of dust as whipped up from bare ground and deposited in beds by wind, these surfaces somehow becoming vegetated by a cold steppe plant cover.

The events of the last deglaciation and of the "postglacial" are intelligible as yet only in part. A priori it is reasonable to consider that the contemporary pattern of climates had become more or less established before the last ice retreat began. Lesser later local climatic oscillations have been found but have been improperly extended and exaggerated, however, in archeological literature. In the pollen studies of bogs of northwestern Europe, the term "climatic optimum" was introduced innocently to note a poleward and mountainward extension of moderate proportions for certain plants not occurring at the same time over the entire area. Possibly this expansion of range means that there were sunnier summers and fall seasons, permitting the setting and maturing of seed for such plants somewhat beyond their prior and present range, that is, under more "continental" and less "maritime" weather conditions. This modest and expectable variation of a local climate in the high latitudes and at the changing sea borders of North Atlantic Europe has been construed by some students of prehistory into a sort of climatic golden age, existent at more or less the same time in distant parts of the world, without regard to dynamics or patterns of climates. We might well

be spared such naïvely nominal climatic constructions as have been running riot through interpretations of prehistory and even of historic time.

The appearance or disappearance, increase or decrease, of particular plants and animals may not spell out obligatory climatic change, as has been so freely inferred. Plants differ greatly in rate of dispersal, in pioneering ability, in having routes available for their spread, and in other ways that may enter into an unstable ecologic association, as on the oft-shifted stage of Pleistocene and Recent physiography. The intervention of man and animals has also occurred to disturb the balance. The appearance and fading of pines in an area, characteristic in many bog pollen columns, may tell nothing of climatic change: pines are notorious early colonizers, establishing themselves freely in mineral soils and open situations and yielding to other trees as shading and organic cover of ground increase. Deer thrive on browse; they increase wherever palatable twigs become abundant, in brush lands and with young tree growth; ecologic factors of disturbance other than climate may determine the food available to them and the numbers found in archeologic remains.

The penetration of man to the New World is involved in the question of past and present climates. The origin and growth of the dominant doctrine of a first peopling of the Western Hemisphere in postglacial time is beyond our present objective, but it was not based on valid knowledge of climatic history. The postglacial and present climatic pattern is one of extremes rarely reached or exceeded in the past of the Earth. Passage by land within this time across Siberia, Alaska, and Canada demanded specialized advanced skills in survival under great and long cold comparable to those known to Eskimo and Athabascan, an excessive postulate for many of the primitive peoples of the New World. Relatively mild climates did prevail in high latitudes at times during the Pleistocene. At such times in both directions between Old and New World, massive migrations took place of animals incapable of living on tundras, animals that are attractive game for man. If man was then living in eastern Asia, nothing hindered him from migrating along with such non-boreal mammals. The question is of fundamental interest, because it asks whether man in the New World, within a very few thousand years, achieved independently a culture growth comparable and curiously parallel to that of the Old, which required a much greater span. There is thus also the inference that our more primitive aborigines passed the high latitudes during more genial climes rather than that they lost subsequently numerous useful skills.

FIRE

Speech, tools, and fire are the tripod of culture and have been so, we think, from the beginning. About the hearth, the home and workshop are centered. Space heating under shelter, as a rock overhang, made possible living in inclement climates; cooking made palatable many plant products; industrial innovators experimented with heat treatment of wood, bone, and minerals. About the fireplace, social life took form, and the exchange of ideas was fostered. The availability of fuel has been one of the main factors determining the location of clustered habitation.

Even to Paleolithic man, occupant of the Earth for all but the last 1 or 2 per cent of human time, must be conceded gradual deformation of vegetation by fire. His fuel needs were supplied by dead wood, drifted or fallen, and also by the stripping of bark and bast that caused trees to die and become available as fuel supply. The setting or escape of fire about camp sites cleared away small and young growth, stimulated annual plants, aided in collecting, and became elaborated in time into the fire drive, a formally organized procedure among the cultures of the Upper Paleolithic *grande chasse* and of their New World counterpart.

Inferentially, modern primitive peoples illustrate the ancient practices in all parts of the world. Burning, as a practice facilitating collecting and hunting, by insensible stages became a device to improve the yield of desired animals and plants. Deliberate management of their range by burning to increase food supply is apparent among hunting and collecting peoples, in widely separated areas, but has had little study. Mature woody growth provides less food for man and ground animals than do fire-disturbed sites, with protein-rich young growth and stimulated seed production, accessible at ground levels. Game yields are usually greatest where the vegetation is kept in an immediate state of ecologic succession. With agricultural and pastoral peoples, burning in preparation for planting and for the increase of pasture has been nearly universal until lately.

The gradually cumulative modifications of vegetation may become large as to selection of kind and as to aspect of the plant cover. Pyrophytes include woody monocotyledons, such as palms, which do not depend on a vulnerable cambium tissue, trees insulated by thick corky bark, trees and shrubs able to reproduce by sprouting, and plants with thick, hard-shelled seeds aided in germination by heat. Loss of organic matter on and in the soil may shift advantage to forms that germinate well in mineral soils, as the numerous conifers. Precocity is advantageous. The assemblages consequent upon fires are usually characterized by a reduced number of species, even by the dominance of few and single species. Minor elements in a natural flora, originally mainly confined to accidentally disturbed and exposed situations, such as windfalls and eroding slopes, have opened to them by recurrent burning the chance to spread and multiply. In most cases the shift is from mesophytic to less exacting, more xeric, forms, to those that do not require ample soil moisture and can tolerate at all times full exposure to sun. In the long run the scales are tipped against the great, slowly maturing plants—the trees (a park land of mature trees may be the last stand of what was a complete woodland). Our eastern woodlands, at the time of white settlement, seem largely to have been in process of change to park lands. Early accounts stress the open stands of trees, as indicated by the comment that one could drive a coach from seaboard to the Mississippi River over almost any favoring terrain. The "forest primeval" is exceptional. In the end the success in a land occupied by man of whatever cultural level goes to the annuals and short-lived perennials, able to seed heavily or to reproduce by rhizome and tuber. This grossly drawn sketch may introduce the matter of processes resulting in what is called ecologically a secondary fire association, or subclimax, if it has historical persistence.

The climatic origin of grasslands rests on a poorly founded hypothesis. In the first place, the individual great grasslands extend over long climatic gradients from wet to dry and grade on their driest margins into brush and scrub. Woody growth occurs in them where there are breaks in the general surface, as in the Cross Timbers of our Southwest. Woody plants establish themselves freely in grasslands if fire protection is given: the prairies and steppes are suited to the growth of the trees and shrubs native to adjacent lands but may lack them. An individual grassland may extend across varied parent-materials. Their most common quality is that they are upland plains, having periods of dry weather long enough to dry out the surface of the ground, which accumulate a sufficient amount of burnable matter to feed and spread a fire. Their position and limits are determined by relief; nor do they extend into arid lands or those having a continuously wet ground surface. Fires may sweep indefinitely across a surface of low relief but are checked shortly at barriers of broken terrain, the checking being more abrupt if the barrier is sunk below the general surface. The inference is that origin and preservation of grasslands are due, in the main, to burning and that they are in fact great and, in some cases, ancient cultural features.

In other instances simplified woodlands, such as the pine woods of our Southeast, *palmares* in tropical savannas, are pyrophytic deformations; there are numerous vegetational alternatives other than the formation of grassland by recurrent burning. Wherever primitive man has had the opportunity to turn fire loose on a land, he seems to have done so, from time immemorial; it is only civilized societies that have undertaken to stop fires.

In areas controlled by customary burning, a near-ecologic equilibrium may have been attained, a biotic recombination maintained by similarly repeated human intervention. This is not destructive exploitation. The surface of the ground remains protected by growing cover, the absorption of rain and snow is undiminished, and loss of moisture from ground to atmosphere possibly is reduced. Microclimatic differences between woodland and grassland are established as effect if not as cause, and some are implicit in the Shelter Belt Project.

Our modern civilization demands fire control for the protection of its property. American forestry was begun as a remedy for the devastation by careless lumbering at a time when dreadful holocausts almost automatically followed logging, as in the Great Lakes states. Foresters have made a first principle of fire suppression. Complete protection, however, accumulates tinder year by year; the longer the accumulation, the greater is the fire hazard and the more severe the fire when it results. Stockmen are vociferous about the loss of grazing areas to brush under such protection of the public lands. Here and there, carefully controlled light burning is beginning to find acceptance in range and forest management. It is being applied to long-leaf pine reproduction in Southeastern states and to some extent for grazing in western range management. In effect, the question is now being raised whether well-regulated fires may not have an ecologic role beneficent to modern man, as they did in older days.

PEASANT AND PASTORAL WAYS

The next revolutionary intervention of man in the natural order came as he selected certain plants and animals to be taken under his care, to be reproduced, and to be bred into domesticated forms increasingly dependent on him for survival. Their adaptation to serve human wants runs counter, as a rule, to the processes of natural selection. New lines and processes of organic evolution were entrained, widening the gap between wild and domestic forms. The natural land became deformed, as to biota, surface, and soil, into unstable cultural landscapes.

Conventionally, agricultural origins are placed at the beginning of Neolithic time, but it is obvious that the earliest archeologic record of the Neolithic presents a picture of an accomplished domestication of plants and animals, of peasant and pastoral life reresembling basic conditions that may still be met in some parts of the Near East.

Three premises as to the origin of agriculture seem to me to be necessary:

(1) That this new mode of life was sedentary and that it arose out of an earlier sedentary society. Under most conditions, and especially among primitive agriculturists, the planted land must be watched over continuously against plant predators. (2) That planting and domestication did not start from hunger but from surplus and leisure. Famine-haunted folk lack the opportunity and incentive for the slow and continuing selection of domesticated forms. Village communities in comfortable circumstances are indicated for such progressive steps. (3) Primitive agriculture is located in woodlands. Even the pioneer American farmer hardly invaded the grasslands until the second quarter of the past century. His fields were clearings won by deadening, usually by girdling, the trees. The larger the trees, the easier the task; brush required grubbing and cutting; sod stopped his advance until he had plows capable of ripping through the matted grass roots. The forest litter he cleaned up by occasional burning; the dead trunks hardly interfered with his planting. The American pioneer learned and followed Indian practices. It is curious that scholars, because they carried into their thinking the tidy fields of the European plowman and the felling of trees by ax, have so often thought that forests repelled agriculture and that open lands invited it.

The oldest form of tillage is by digging, often but usually improperly called "hoe culture." This was the only mode known in the New World, in Negro Africa, and in the Pacific islands. It gave rise, at an advanced level, to the gardens and horticulture of Monsoon Asia and perhaps of the Mediterranean. Its modern tools are spade, fork, and hoe, all derived from ancient forms. In tropical America this form of tillage is known as the *conuco*, in Mexico as the *milpa*, in the latter case a planting of seeds of maize, squash, beans, and perhaps other annuals. The conuco is stocked mainly by root and stem cuttings, a perennial garden plot. Recently, the revival of the Old Norse term "swithe," or "swidden," has been proposed (Izikowitz, 1951, p. 7 n.; Conklin, 1954).

Such a plot begins by deadening tree growth, followed toward the end of a dry period by burning, the ashes serving as quick fertilizer. The cleared space then is well stocked with a diverse assemblage of useful plants, grown as tiers of vegetation if moisture and fertility are adequate. In the maize-beans-squash complex the squash vines spread over the ground, the cornstalks grow tall, and the beans climb up the cornstalks. Thus the ground is well protected by plant cover, with good interception of the falling rain. In each conuco a high diversity of plants may be cared for, ranging from low herbs to shrubs, such as cotton and manioc, to trees entangled with cultivated climbers. The seeming disorder is actually a very full use of light and moisture, an admirable ecologic substitution by man, perhaps equivalent to the natural cover also in the protection given to the surface of the ground. In the tropical conuco an irregular patch is dug into at convenient spots and at almost any time to set out or collect different plants, the planted surface at no time being wholly dug over. Digging roots and replanting may be going on at the same time. Our notions of a harvest season when the whole crop is taken off the field are inapplicable. In the conucos something may be gathered on almost any day through the year. The same plant may yield pot and salad greens, pollen-rich flowers, immature fruit, and ripened fruit; garden and field are one, and numerous domestic uses may be served by each plant. Such multiple population of the tilled space makes possible the highest yields per unit of surface, to which may be added

the comments that this system has developed plants of highest productivity, such as bananas, yams, and manioc, and that food production is by no means the only utility of many such plants.

The planting systems really do not deserve the invidious terms given them, such as "slash and burn" or "shifting agriculture." The abandonment of the planting after a time to the resprouting and reseeding wild woody growth is a form of rotation by which the soil is replenished by nutriments carried up from deep-rooted trees and shrubs, to be spread over the ground as litter. Such use of the land is freed from the limitations imposed on the plowed field by terrain. That it may give good yields on steep and broken slopes is not an argument against the method, which gives much better protection against soil erosion than does any plowing. It is also in these cultures that we find that systems of terracing of slopes have been established.

Some of the faults charged against the system derive from the late impact from our own culture, such as providing axes and machetes by which sprouts and brush may be kept whacked out instead of letting the land rest under regrowth, the replacement of subsistence crops by money crops, the worldwide spurt in population, and the demand for manufactured goods which is designated as rising standard of living. Nor do I claim that under this primitive planting man could go on forever growing his necessities without depleting the soil; but rather that, in its basic procedure and crop assemblages, this system has been most conservative of fertility at high levels of yield; that, being protective and intensive, we might consider it as being fully suited to the physical and cultural conditions of the areas where it exists. Our Western know-how is directed to land use over a short run of years and is not the wisdom of the primitive peasant rooted to his ancestral lands.

Our attitudes toward farming stem from the other ancient trunk whence spring the sowers, reapers, and mowers; the plowmen, dairymen, shepherds, and herdsmen. This is the complex already well represented in the earliest Neolithic sites of the Near East. The interest of this culture is directed especially toward seed production of annuals, cereal grasses in particular. The seedbed is carefully prepared beforehand to minimize weed growth and provide a light cover of well-worked soil in which the small seeds germinate. An evenly worked and smooth surface contrasts with the hit-or-miss piling of earth mounds, "hills" in the American farm vernacular, characteristic of conuco and milpa. Instead of a diversity of plants, the prepared ground receives the seed of one kind. (Western India is a significant exception.) The crop is not further cultivated and stands to maturity, when it is reaped at one time. After the harvest the field may lie fallow until the next season. The tillage implement is the plow, in second place, the harrow, both used to get the field ready for sowing. Seeding traditionally is by broadcasting, harvesting by cutting blades.

Herd animals, meat cattle, sheep, goats, horses, asses, camels, are either original or very early in this system. The keeping of grazing and browsing animals is basic. All of them are milked or have been so in the past. In my estimation milking is an original practice and quality of their domestication and continued to be in many cases their first economic utility; meat and hides, the product of surplus animals only.

The over-all picture is in great contrast to that of the planting cultures: regular, elongated fields minimize turning the animals that pull the plow; fields are cultivated in the off season, in part to keep them free of volunteer growth;

fields are fallowed but not abandoned, the harvest season is crowded into the end of the annual growth period; thereafter, stock is pastured on stubble and fallow; land unsuited or not needed for the plow is used as range on which the stock grazes and browses under watch of herdboys or herdsmen.

This complex spread from its Near Eastern cradle mainly in three directions, changing its character under changed environments and by increase of population.

1. Spreading into the steppes of Eurasia, the culture lost its tillage and became completely pastoral, with true nomadism. This is controversial, but the evidence seems to me to show that all domestication of the herd animals (except for reindeer) was effected by sedentary agriculturists living between India and the Mediterranean and also that the great, single, continuous area in which milking was practiced includes all the nomadic peoples, mainly as a fringe about the milking seed-farmers. It has also been pointed out that nomadic cultures depend on agricultural peoples for some of their needs and, thus lacking a self-contained economy, can hardly have originated independently.

2. The drift of the Celtic, Germanic, and Slavic peoples westward (out of southwestern and western Asia?) through the northern European plain appears to have brought them to their historic seats predominantly as cattle- and horse-raisers. Their movement was into lands of cooler and shorter summers and of higher humidity, in which wheat and barley did poorly. An acceptable thesis is that, in southwestern Asia, rye and probably oats were weed grasses growing in fields of barley and wheat. They were harvested together and not separated by winnowing. In the westward movement of seed farmers across Europe, the weed grains did better and the noble grain less well. The

cooler and wetter the summers, the less wheat and barley did the sower reap and the more of rye and oat seeds, which gradually became domesticated by succeeding where the originally planted kinds failed.

Northwestern and Central Europe appear to be the home of our principal hay and pasture grasses and clovers. As the stock-raising colonists deadened and burned over tracts of woodland, native grasses and clovers spontaneously took possession of the openings. These were held and enlarged by repetition of burning and cutting. Meadow and pasture, from the agricultural beginnings, were more important here than plowland. Even the latter, by pasturing the rye fields and the feeding of oat straw and grain, were part of animal husbandry. Here, as nowhere else, did the common farmer concern himself with producing feed for his stock. He was first a husbandman; he cut hay to store for winter feed and cured it at considerable trouble; he stabled his animals over the inclement season, or stall-fed them through the year; the dung-hill provided dressing for field and meadow. House, barn, and stable were fused into one structure. The prosperity of farmstead and village was measured by its livestock rather than by arable land.

The resultant pattern of land use, which carries through from the earliest times, as recovered by archeology in Denmark and northern Germany, was highly conservative of soil fertility. The animal husbandry maintained so effective a ground cover that northern Europe has known very little soil erosion. Animal manure and compost provided adequate return of fertility to the soil. Man pretty well established a closed ecologic cycle. It was probably here that man first undertook to till the heavy soils. Clayey soils, rich in plant food but deficient in drainage, are widespread in the lowlands, partly due to climatic conditions, partly a legacy of the Ice Age. The modern plow with share, moldboard, and colter had either its origin or a major development here for turning real furrows to secure better aeration and drainage. Beneficial in northwestern and Central Europe, it was later to become an instrument of serious loss elsewhere.

3. The spread of sowing and herding cultures westward along both sides of the Mediterranean required no major climatic readjustment. Wheat and barley continued to be the staple grains; sheep and goats were of greater economic importance than cattle and horses. Qualities of the environment that characterized the Near East were accentuated to the west: valleys lie imbedded in mountainous terrain, the uplands are underlain by and developed out of limestone, and, to the south of the Mediterranean, aridity becomes prevalent. The hazard of drought lay ever upon the Near Eastern homeland and on the colonial regions to the west and south. No break between farmer and herdsman is discernible at any time; as the village Arab of today is related to the Bedouin, the environmental specialization may have been present from the beginning: flocks on the mountains and dry lands, fields where moisture sufficed and soil was adequate.

That the lands about the Mediterranean have become worn and frayed by the usage to which they have been subjected has long been recognized, though not much is known as to when and how. The eastern and southern Mediterranean uplands especially are largely of limestone, attractive as to soil fertility but, by their nature, without deep original mantle of soil or showing the usual gradation of subsoil into bedrock and thus are very vulnerable to erosion. The less suited the land was or became to plow cultivation, the greater the shift to pastoral economy. Thus a downslope migration of tillage characterized, in time, the retreating limits of the fields, and more and more land became range for goats, sheep, and asses. Repeatedly prolonged droughts must have speeded the downslope shift, hillside fields suffering most, and with failing vegetation cover becoming more subject to washing when rains came.

Thus we come again to the question of climatic change as against attrition of surface and increased xerophytism of vegetation by human disturbance and, in particular, to what is called the "desertification" of North Africa and the expansion of the Sahara. A case for directional change in the pattern of atmospheric circulation has been inferred from archeology and faunal changes. I am doubtful that it is a good case within the time of agricultural and pastoral occupation. Another view is that the progressive reduction of plant cover by man has affected soil and ground-surface climate unfavorably. Largely, and possibly wholly, the deterioration of the borders of the dry lands may have been caused by adverse, cumulative effects of man's activities. From archeologic work we need much more information as to whether human occupation has been failing in such areas over a long time, or whether it has happened at defined intervals, and also whether, if such intervals are noted, they may have a cultural rather than an environmental (climatic) basis.

No protective herbaceous flora became established around the shores of the Mediterranean on pastures and meadows as was the case in the north. Flocks and herds grazed during the short season of soft, new grass but most of the year browsed on woody growth. The more palatable feed was eaten first and increasingly eliminated; goats and asses got along on range that had dropped below the support levels required by more exacting livestock. As is presently true in the western United States, each prolonged drought must have left the range depleted, its carrying capacity reduced, and recovery of cover less likely. Natural balance between plants and animals is rarely reestablished under such exploitation, since man will try to save his herd rather than their range. A large and long deterioration of the range may therefore fully account for the poor and xerophytic flora and fauna without postulating progressive climatic desiccation, for the kinds of life that survive under overuse of the land are the most undemanding inhabitants.

Comparative studies of North Africa and of the American Southwest and northern Mexico are needed to throw light on the supposed "desiccation" of the Old World. We know the dates of introduction of cattle and sheep to the American ranges and can determine rate and kind of change of vegetation and surface. The present desolate shifting-sand area that lies between the Hopi villages and the Colorado River was such good pasture land late in the eighteenth century that Father Escalante, returning from his canyon exploration, rested his travel-worn animals there to regain flesh. The effects of Navaho sheep-herding in little more than a century and mainly in the last sixty years are well documented. Lower California and Sonora are climatic homologues of the western Sahara. Against the desolation of the latter, the lands about the Gulf of California are a riot of bloom in spring and green through summer. Their diversity, in kind and form, of plant and of animal life is high, and the numbers are large. When Leo Waibel came from his African studies to Sonora and Arizona, he remarked: "But your deserts are not plant deserts." Nor do we have hammadas or ergs, though geologic and meteorologic conditions may be similar. The principal difference may be that we have had no millennial, or even centuries-long, overstocking of our arid, semiarid, and subhumid lands. The scant life and even the rock and sand surfaces of the Old World deserts may record long attrition by man in climatic tension zones.

IMPACT OF CIVILIZATION IN ANTIQUITY AND THE MIDDLE AGES

Have the elder civilizations fallen because their lands deteriorated? Ellsworth Huntington read adverse climatic change into each such failure; at the other extreme, political loss of competence has been asserted as sufficient. Intimate knowledge of historical sources, archeologic sites, biogeography and ecology, and the processes of geomorphology must be fused in patient field studies, so that we may read the changes in habitability through human time for the lands in which civilization first took form.

The rise of civilizations has been accomplished and sustained by the development of powerful and elaborately organized states with a drive to territorial expansion, by commerce in bulk and to distant parts, by monetary economy, and by the growth of cities. Capital cities, port cities by sea and river, and garrison towns drew to themselves population and products from near and far. The ways of the country became subordinated to the demands of the cities, the *citizen* distinct from the *miserabilis plebs*. The containment of community by locally available resources gave way to the introduction of goods, especially foodstuffs, regulated by purchasing, distributing, or taxing power.

Thereby removal of resource from place of origin to place of demand tended to set up growing disturbance of whatever ecologic equilibrium had been maintained by the older rural communities sustained directly within their metes. The economic history of antiquity shows repeated shifts in the areas of supply of raw materials that are not explained by political events but raise unanswered questions as to decline of fertility, destruction of plant cover, and incidence of soil erosion. What, for instance, happened to Arabia Felix, Numidia, Mauretania, to the interior Lusitania that has become the frayed Spanish Extremadura of today? When and at whose hands did the forests disappear that furnished ship and house timbers, wood for burning lime, the charcoal for smelting ores, and urban fuel needs? Are political disasters sufficient to account for the failure of the civilizations that depended on irrigation and drainage engineering? How much of the wide deterioration of Mediterranean and Near Eastern lands came during or after the time of strong political and commercial organization? For ancient and medieval history our knowledge as to what happened to the land remains too largely blank, except for the central and northern European periphery. The written documents, the testimony of the archeologic sites, have not often been interpreted by observation of the physical condition of the locality as it is and comparison with what it was.

The aspect of the Mediterranean landscapes was greatly changed by classical civilization through the introduction of plants out of the East. Victor Hehn first described Italy as wearing a dress of an alien vegetation, and, though he carried the theme of plant introduction out of the East too far, his study (1886) of the Mediterranean lands through antiquity is not only memorable but retains much validity. The westward dispersal of vine, olive, fig, the stone fruits, bread wheat, rice, and many ornamentals and some shade trees was due in part or in whole to the spread of Greco-Roman civilization, to which the Arabs added sugar cane, date palm, cotton, some of the citrus fruits, and other items.

EUROPEAN OVERSEAS COLONIZATION

When European nations ventured forth across the Atlantic, it was to trade or raid, the distinction often determined by the opportunity. In Africa and Asia the European posts and factories pretty well continued in this tradition through the eighteenth century. In the New World the same initial activities soon turned into permanent settlement of Old World forms and stocks. Columbus, searching only for a trade route, started the first overseas empire. Spain stumbled into colonization, and the other nations acquired stakes they hoped might equal the Spanish territorial claim. The Casa de Contratación, or House of Trade, at Seville, the main Atlantic port, became the Spanish colonial office. The conquistadores came not to settle but to make their fortunes and return home, and much the same was true for the earlier adventurers from other nations. Soldiers and adventurers rather than peasants and artisans made up the first arrivals, and few brought their women. Only in New England did settlement begin with a representative assortment of people, and only here were the new communities transplanted from the homeland without great alteration.

The first colony, Santo Domingo, set in large measure the pattern of colonization. It began with trade, including ornaments of gold. The quest for gold brought forced labor and the dying-off of the natives, and this, in turn, slave-hunting and importation of black slaves. Decline of natives brought food shortages and wide abandonment of conucos. Cattle and hogs were pastured on the lately tilled surfaces; and Spaniards, lacking labor to do gold-placering, became stock ranchers. Some turned to cutting dyewoods. Of the numerous European plants introduced to supply accustomed wants, a few, sugar cane, cassia, and ginger, proved moderately profitable for export, and some of the hesitant beginnings became the first tropical plantations. One hope of fortune failing, another was tried; the stumbling into empire was under way by men who had scarcely any vision of founding a new homeland.

What then happened to the lands of the New World in the three colonial centuries? In the first place, the aboriginal populations in contact with Europeans nearly everywhere declined greatly or were extinguished. Especially in the tropical lowlands, with the most notable exception of Yucatán, the natives faded away, and in many cases the land was quickly repossessed by forest growth. The once heavily populous lands of eastern Panama and northwestern Colombia, much of the lowland country of Mexico, both on the Pacific and Gulf sides, became emptied in a very few years, was retaken by jungle and forest, and in considerable part remains such to the present. The highlands of Mexico, of Central America, and of the Andean lands declined in population greatly through the sixteenth and perhaps well through the seventeenth century, with slow, gradual recovery in the eighteenth. The total population, white and other, of the areas under European control was, I think, less at the end of the eighteenth century than at the time of discovery. Only in British and French West Indian islands were dense rural populations built up.

It is hardly an exaggeration to say that the early Europeans supported themselves on Indian fields. An attractive place to live for a European would ordinarily have been such for an Indian. In the Spanish colonies, unlike the English and French, the earlier grants were not of land titles but of Indian communities to serve colonist and crown. In crops and their tillage the colonists of all nations largely used the Indian ways, with the diversion of part of the field crop to animal feed. Only in the Northeast, most of all in our Middle Colonies, were native and European crops fused into a conservative plow-and-animal husbandry, with field rotation, manuring, and marl dressing. The Middle Colonies of the eighteenth century appear to have compared favorably with the best farming practices of western Europe.

Sugar cane, first and foremost of the tropical plantations, as a closely planted giant grass, gave satisfactory protection to the surface of the land. The removal of cane from the land did reduce fertility unless the waste was properly returned to the canefields. The most conservative practices known are from the British islands, where cane waste was fed to cattle kept in pens, and manuring was customary and heavy. Bagasse was of little value as fuel in this period because of the light crushing rollers used for extracting cane juice; thus the colonial sugar mills were heavy wood users, especially for boiling sugar. The exhaustion of wood supply became a serious problem in the island of Haiti within the sixteenth century.

Other plantation crops—tobacco, indigo, cotton, and coffee—held more serious erosion hazards, partly because they were planted in rows and given clean cultivation, partly because they made use of steeper slopes and thinner soils. The worst offender was tobacco, grown on land that was kept bared to the rains and nourished by the wood ashes of burned clearings. Its cultivation met with greatest success in our Upper South, resulted in rapidly shifting clearings because of soil depletion, and caused the first serious soil erosion in our country. Virginia, Maryland, and North Carolina show to the present the damages of tobacco culture of colonial and early post-colonial times. Southern Ohio and eastern Missouri repeated the story before the middle of the nineteenth century.

As had happened in Haiti, sharp decline of native populations brought elsewhere abandonment of cleared and tilled land and thereby opportunity to the stockman. The plants that pioneer in former fields which are left untilled for reasons other than because of decline of fertility include forms, especially annuals, of high palatability, grasses, amaranths, chenopods, and legumes. Such is the main explanation for the quick appearance of stock ranches, of *ganado mayor* and *menor*, in the former Indian agricultural lands all over Spanish America. Cattle, horses, and hogs thrived in tropical lowland as well as in highland areas. Sheep-raising flourished most in early years in the highlands of New Spain and Peru, where Indian population had shrunk. Spanish stock, trespassing upon Indian plantings, both in lowland and in highland, afflicted the natives and depressed their chances of recovery (Simpson, L., 1952). In the wide savannas stockmen took over the native habits of burning.

The Spaniards passed in a few years from the trading and looting of metals to successful prospecting, at which they became so adept that it is still said that the good mines of today are the *antiguas* of colonial working. When mines were abandoned, it was less often due to the working-out of the ore bodies than to inability to cope with water in shafts and to the exhaustion of the necessary fuel and timber. A good illustration has been worked out for Parral in Mexico (West, 1949). Zacatecas, today in the midst of a high sparse grassland, was in colonial times a woodland of oak and pine and, at lower levels, of mesquite. About Andean mines the scant wood was soon exhausted, necessitating recourse to cutting mats of *tola* heath and even the clumps of coarse *ichu* (stipa) grass. Quite commonly the old mining *reales* of North and South America are surrounded by a broad zone of reduced and impoverished vegetation. The effects were increased by the concentration of pack and work animals in the mines, with resultant overpasturing. Similar attrition took place about towns and cities, through timber-cutting, charcoal- and lime-burning, and overpasturing. The first viceroy of New Spain warned his successor in 1546 of the depletion of wood about the city of Mexico.

I have used mainly examples from Spanish America for the colonial times, partly because I am most familiar with this record. However, attrition was more sensible here because of mines and urban concentrations and because, for cultural and climatic reasons, the vegetation cover was less.

LAST FRONTIERS OF SETTLEMENT

The surges of migration of the nineteenth century are family history for many of us. Never before did, and never again may, the white man expand his settlements as in that brief span that began in the later eighteenth century and ended with the first World War. The prelude was in the eighteenth century, not only as a result of the industrial revolution as begun in England, but also in a less heralded agricultural revolution over Western and Central Europe. The spread of potato-growing, the development of beets and turnips as field crops, rotation of fields with clover, innovations in tillage, improved livestock breeds—all joined to raise agricultural production to new levels in western Europe. The new agriculture was brought to our Middle Colonies by a massive immigration of capable European farmers and here further transformed by adding maize to the small grains–clover rotation. Thus was built on both sides of the North Atlantic a balanced animal husbandry of increased yield of human and animal foods. Urban and rural growth alike went into vigorous upswing around the turn of the eighteenth century. The youth of the countryside poured into the rising industrial

cities but also emigrated, especially from Central Europe into Pennsylvania, into Hungarian and Moldavian lands repossessed from the Turks and into South Russia gained from the Tartars. The last *Völkerwanderung* was under way and soon edging onto the grasslands.

The year 1800 brought a new cotton to the world market, previously an obscure annual variant known to us as Mexican Upland cotton, still uncertainly understood as to how it got into our South. Cleaned by the new gin, its profitable production rocketed. The rapidly advancing frontier of cotton-planting was moved westward from Georgia to Texas within the first half of the century. This movement was a more southerly and even greater parallel to the earlier westward drive of the tobacco frontier. Both swept away the woodlands and the Indians, including the farming tribes. The new cotton, like tobacco, a clean cultivated row crop and a cash crop, bared the fields to surface wash, especially in winter. The southern upland soils gradually lost their organic horizons, color, and protection; gullies began to be noted even before the Civil War. Guano and Chilean nitrate and soon southern rock phosphate were applied increasingly to the wasting soils. Eugene Hilgard told the history of cotton in our South tersely and well in the United States Census of 1880. As I write, across from my window stands the building bearing his name and the inscription: TO RESCUE FOR HUMAN SOCIETY THE NATIVE VALUES OF RURAL LIFE. It was in wasting cotton fields that Hilgard learned soil science and thought about a rural society that had become hitched wholly to world commerce. Meantime the mill towns of England, the Continent, and New England grew lustily; with them, machine industries, transport facilities, and the overseas shipment of food.

The next great American frontier may

be conveniently and reasonably dated by the opening of the Erie Canal in 1825, provisioning the cities with grain and meat on both sides of the North Atlantic, first by canal and river, soon followed by the railroad. The earlier frontiers had been pushed from the Atlantic Seaboard to and beyond the Mississippi by the cultivation of tropical plants in extratropical lands, were dominantly monocultural, preferred woodlands, and relied mainly on hand labor. For them the term "plantation culture" was not inapt. The last thrust, from the Mohawk Valley to the Mississippi, was West European as to agricultural system, rural values, settlers, and largely as to crops.

By the time of the Civil War, the first great phase of the northern westward movement had crossed the Missouri River into Kansas and Nebraska. New England spilled over by way of the Great Lakes, especially along the northern fringe of prairies against the North Woods. New York and Baltimore were gateways for the masses of Continental emigrants hurrying to seek new homes beyond the Alleghenies. The migrant streams mingled as they overspread the Mississippi Valley, land of promise unequaled in the history of our kindred. These settlers were fit to the task: they were good husbandmen and artisans. They came to put down their roots, and the gracious country towns, farmsteads, and rural churches still bear witness to the homemaking way of life they brought and kept. At last they had land of their own, and it was good. They took care of their land, and it did well by them; surplus rather than substance of the soil provided the foodstuffs that moved to eastern markets. Steel plows that cut through the sod, east-west railroads, and cheap lumber from the white-pine forests of the Great Lakes unlocked the fertility of the prairies; the first great plowing-up of the grasslands was under way.

Many prairie counties reached their maximum population in less than a generation, many of them before the beginning of the Civil War. The surplus, another youthful generation, moved on farther west or sought fortune in the growing cities. Thus, toward the end of the century the Trans-Missouri grassy plains had been plowed up to and into the lands of drought hazard. Here the Corn Belt husbandry broke down, especially because of the great drought of the early nineties, and the Wheat Belt took form, a monocultural and unbalanced derivative. I well remember parties of landlookers going out from my native Missouri county, first to central Kansas and Nebraska, then to the Red River Valley, and finally even to the Panhandle of Texas and the prairies of Manitoba. The local newspapers "back home" still carry news from these daughter-colonies, and still those who long ago moved west are returned "home" at the last to lie in native soil.

The development of the Middle West did exact its price of natural resources. The white-pine stands of the Great Lakes were destroyed to build the farms and towns of the Corn Belt; the logged-over lands suffered dreadful burning. As husbandry gave way westward to wheat-growing, the land was looked on less as homestead and more as speculation, to be cropped heavily and continuously for grain, without benefit of rotation and manuring, and to be sold at an advantageous price, perhaps to reinvest in new and undepleted land.

The history of the extratropical grasslands elsewhere in the world is much like our own and differs little in period and pace. Southern Russia, the Pampas, Australia, and South Africa repeat largely the history of the American West. The industrial revolution was made possible by the plowing-up of the great non-tropical grasslands of the world. So also was the intensification of agriculture in western Europe, benefiting from the importation of cheap overseas feedstuffs, grains, their by-products of milling (note the term "shipstuff"), oil-seed meals. Food and feed were cheap in and about the centers of industry, partly because the fertility of the new lands of the world was exported to them without reckoning the maintenance of resource.

At the turn of the century serious concern developed about the adequacy of resources for industrial civilization. The conservation movement was born. It originated in the United States, where the depletion of lately virgin lands gave warning that we were drawing recklessly on a diminishing natural capital. It is to be remembered that this awareness came, not to men living in the midst of the industrial and commercial centers of the older country-sides, but to foresters who witnessed devastation about the Great Lakes, to geologists who had worked in the iron and copper ranges of the Great Lakes and prospected the West in pioneer days, to naturalists who lived through the winning of the West.

THE EVER DYNAMIC ECONOMY

As a native of the nineteenth century, I have been an amazed and bewildered witness of the change of tempo that started with the first World War, was given an additional whirl on the second, and still continues to accelerate. The worry of the earlier part of the century was that we might not use our natural resources thriftily; it has given way to easy confidence in the capacities of technologic advance without limit. The natural scientists were and still may be conservation-minded; the physical scientists and engineers today are often of the lineage of Daedalus, inventing ever more daring reorganizations of matter and, in consequence, whether they desire it or not, of social institutions. Social science eyes the attainments of physical science enviously and hopes

for similar competence and authority in reordering the world. Progress is the common watchword of our age, its motor-innovating techniques, its objective the ever expanding "dynamic economy," with ever increasing input of energy. Capacity to produce and capacity to consume are the twin spirals of the new age which is to have no end, if war can be eliminated. The measure of progress is "standard of living," a term that the English language has contributed to the vernaculars of the world. An American industrialist says, roundly, that our principal problem now is to accelerate obsolescence, which remark was anticipated at the end of the past century by Eduard Hahn (1900) when he thought that industrialization depended on the production of junk.

Need we ask ourselves whether there still is the problem of limited resources, of an ecologic balance that we disturb or disregard at the peril of the future? Was Wordsworth of the early industrial age farsighted when he said that "getting and spending we lay waste our powers"? Are our newly found powers to transform the world, so successful in the short run of the last years, proper and wise beyond the tenure of those now living? To what end are we committing the world to increasing momentum of change?

The steeply increasing production of late years is due only in part to better recovery, more efficient use of energy, and substitution of abundant for scarce materials. Mainly we have been learning how to deplete more rapidly the resources known to be accessible to us. Must we not admit that very much of what we call production is extraction?

Even the so-called "renewable resources" are not being renewed. Despite better utilization and substitution, timber growth is falling farther behind use and loss, inferior stands and kinds are being exploited, and woodland deterioration is spreading. Much of the world is in a state of wood famine, without known means of remedy or substitution.

Commercial agriculture requires ample working capital and depends in high degree on mechanization and fertilization. A late estimate assigns a fourth of the net income of our farms to the purchase of durable farm equipment. The more farming becomes industry and business, the less remains of the older husbandry in which man lived in balance with his land. We speak with satisfaction of releasing rural population from farm to urban living and count the savings of man-hours in units of farm product and of acres. In some areas the farmer is becoming a town dweller, moving his equipment to the land for brief periods of planting, cultivating, and harvest. Farm garden, orchard, stable, barn, barnyards, and woodlots are disappearing in many parts, the farm families as dependent as their city cousins on grocer, butcher, baker, milkman, and fuel services. Where the farm is in fact capital in land and improvements, requiring bookkeeping on current assets and liabilities, the agriculturist becomes an operator of an outdoor factory of specialized products and is concerned with maximizing the profits of the current year and the next. Increasing need of working capital requires increased monetary returns; this is perhaps all we mean by "intensive" or "scientific" farming, which is in greater and greater degree extractive.

The current agricultural surpluses are not proof that food production has ceased to be a problem or will cease to be the major problem of the world. Our output has been secured at unconsidered costs and risks by the objective of immediate profit, which has replaced the older attitudes of living with the land. The change got under way especially as motors replaced draft animals. Land formerly used for oats and other feed crops became available to grow more corn, soybeans, cotton, and other crops largely sold and shipped. The traditional corn-oats-clover rotation, protective of the surface and maintaining nitrogen balance, began to break down. Soybeans, moderately planted in the twenties and then largely for hay, developed into a major seed crop, aided by heavy governmental benefit payments as soil-building, which they are not. Soil-depleting and soil-exposing crops were given strong impetus in the shift to mechanized farming; less of the better land is used for pasture and hay; less animal and green manure is returned to fields. The fixation of nitrogen by clover has come to be considered too slow; it "pays better" to put the land into corn, beans, and cotton and to apply nitrogen from bag or tank. Dressing the soil with commercial nitrogen makes it possible to plant more closely, thus doubling the number of corn and other plants to the acre at nearly the same tillage cost. Stimulation of plant growth by nitrogen brings increased need of additional phosphorus and potash. In the last ten years the Corn Belt has more or less caught up with the Cotton Belt in the purchase of commercial fertilizer. The more valuable the land, the greater the investment in farm machinery, the more profitable the application of more and more commercial fertilizers.

The so-called row crops, which are the principal cash crops, demand cultivation during much of their period of growth. They give therefore indifferent protection to the surface while growing and almost none after they are harvested. They are ill suited to being followed by a winter cover crop. The organic color is fading from much of our best-grade farm lands. Rains and melting snow float away more and more of the top soil. There is little concern as long as we can plow more deeply and buy more fertilizer. Governmental restriction of acreage for individual crops has been an inducement to apply more fertilizer to the permitted acreage and to plant the rest in uncontrolled but usually also cash crops. Our commercial agriculture, except what remains in animal husbandry such as dairying, is kept expanding by increasing overdraft on the fertility of our soils. Its limits are set by the economically available sources of purchased nitrogen, phosphorus, potassium, and sulfur.

Since Columbus, the spread of European culture has been continuous and cumulative, borne by immediate self-interest, as in mercantilist economy, but sustained also by a sense of civilizing mission redefined from time to time. In the spirit of the present, this mission is to "develop the underdeveloped" parts of the world, material good and spiritual good now having become one. It is our current faith that the ways of the West are the ways that are best for the rest of the world. Our own ever growing needs for raw materials have driven the search for metals and petroleum to the ends of the Earth in order to move them into the stream of world commerce. Some beneficial measure of industry and transport facility thereby accrues to distant places of origin. We also wish to be benefactors by increasing food supply where food is inadequate and by diverting people from rural to industrial life, because such is our way, to which we should like to bring others.

The road we are laying out for the world is paved with good intentions, but do we know where it leads? On the material side we are hastening the depletion of resources. Our programs of agricultural aid pay little attention to native ways and products. Instead of going out to learn what their experiences and preferences are, we go forth to introduce our ways and consider backward what is not according to our pattern. Spade and hoe and mixed plantings are an affront to our faith in progress. We promote mechanization. At the least, we hold, others should be taught to use steel plows that turn neat furrows, though we have no idea how long the soil will stay on well-plowed slopes planted to annuals. We want more fields of maize, rice, beans of kinds familiar to us, products amenable to statistical determination and available for commercial distribution. To increase production, we prescribe dressing with commercial fertilizers. In unnoticed contrast to our own experience these are to be applied in large measure to lands of low productivity and perhaps of low effectiveness of fertilizers. Industrialization is recommended to take care of the surplus populations. We present and recommend to the world a blueprint of what works well with us at the moment, heedless that we may be destroying wise and durable native systems of living with the land. The modern industrial mood (I hesitate to add intellectual mood) is insensitive to other ways and values.

For the present, living beyond one's means has become civic virtue, increase of "output" the goal of society. The prophets of a new world by material progress may be stopped by economic limits of physical matter. They may fail because people grow tired of getting and spending as measure and mode of living. They may be checked because men come to fear the requisite growing power of government over the individual and the community. The high moments of history have come not when man was most concerned with the comforts and displays of the flesh but when his spirit was moved to grow in grace. What we need more perhaps is an ethic and aesthetic under which man, practicing the qualities of prudence and moderation, may indeed pass on to posterity a good Earth.

REFERENCES

AMES, OAKES
 1939 *Economic Annuals and Human Cultures.* Cambridge, Mass.: Botanical Museum of Harvard University. 153 pp.
BOYD, W. C.
 1950 *Genetics and the Races of Man.* Boston: Little, Brown & Co. 453 pp.
BREUIL, HENRI, and LANTIER, RAYMON
 1951 *Les Hommes de la pierre ancienne.* Paris: Payot. 334 pp.
CONKLIN, HAROLD C.
 1954 "An Ethnoecological Approach to Shifting Agriculture," *Transactions of the New York Academy of Sciences,* Series II, XVII, No. 2, 133–42.
COON, CARLETON
 1953 "Climate and Race," pp. 13–34 in SHAPLEY, HARLOW (ed.), *Climatic Change.* Cambridge, Mass.: Harvard University Press. 318 pp.
HAHN, EDUARD
 1900 *Wirtschaft der Welt am Ausgang des neunzehuten Jahrhunderts.* Heidelberg: C. Winter. 320 pp.
HEHN, VICTOR
 1888 *Wanderings of Plants and Animals from Their First Home.* Ed. JAMES S. STALLYBRASS. London: Swan Sonnenschein & Co. 523 pp.
IZIKOWITZ, KARL GUSTAV
 1951 *Lamet: Hill Peasants in French Indochina.* ("Etnologiska Studier," No. 17.) Göteborg: Etnografiska Museet. 375 pp.
LEIGHLY, JOHN B.
 1949 "On Continentality and Glaciation," pp. 133–46 in MANNERFELT, CARL M:SON, et al. (eds.), *Glaciers and Climate (Symposium Dedicated to Hans W:son Ahlmann as a Tribute from the Swedish Society for Anthropology and Geography).* (*Geografiska Annaler,* Vol. XXXI, Häfte 1–4.) 383 pp.

MANNERFELT, CARL M:SON, *et al.* (eds.)
 1949 *Glaciers and Climate (Symposium Dedicated to Hans W:son Ahlmann as a Tribute from the Swedish Society for Anthropology and Geography).* (*Geografiska Annaler,* Vol. XXXI, Häfte 1–4.) 383 pp.
MARSH, GEORGE P.
 1864 *Man and Nature.* New York: Charles Scribner & Co.; London: Sampson, Low & Son. 577 pp.
 1874 *The Earth as Modified by Human Action.* New York: Scribner, Armstrong & Co. 656 pp. (2d ed., 1885. New York: C. Scribner's Sons. 629 pp.)
SHAPLEY, HARLOW (ed.)
 1953 *Climatic Change.* Cambridge, Mass.: Harvard University Press. 318 pp.
SIMPSON, G. C.
 1934 "World Climate during the Quaternary Period," *Quarterly Journal of the Royal Meteorological Society,* LX, No. 257 (October), 425–78.
 1940 "Possible Causes of Change in Climate and Their Limitations," *Proceedings of the Linnean Society of London,* CLII, Part II (April), 190–219.
SIMPSON, LESLEY B.
 1952 *Exploitation of Land in Central Mexico in the Sixteenth Century.* ("Ibero-Americana," No. 36.) Berkeley: University of California Press. 92 pp.
WEST, ROBERT C.
 1949 *The Mining Community in Northern New Spain: The Parral Mining District.* ("Ibero-Americana," No. 30.) Berkeley: University of California Press. 169 pp.
WILLETT, H. C.
 1950 "The General Circulation at the Last (Würm) Glacial Maximum," *Geografiska Annaler,* XXXII, Häfte 3–4, 179–87.

Changing Ideas of the Habitable World

CLARENCE J. GLACKEN[*]

The reason that Attica in former times could support a soldiery exempt from the toil of farming, says Plato in his *Critias,* was that its soil—as is proved by the remnant now left—surpassed all others in fertility. Deluges, however, washed the soil down from the mountains, and it was lost because the land dropped abruptly into the sea. Attica became a "skeleton of a body wasted by disease." Long ago, Plato continues, there were abundant forests in the mountains which provided fodder for the animals and storage for water, which could then issue forth in springs and rivers. "The water was not lost, as it is today, by running off a barren ground to the sea." The extent of these forests, many of which had been cut down, was revealed in the traces still remaining and by the sanctuaries which were situated at the former sources of springs and rivers (Plato, 1929, *Critias* 111, A–D).

Plato reconstructs the prehistory of Attica by showing how the relict soils reveal ancient conditions of the plains and how the relict trees reveal the ancient conditions of the mountains, suggesting that human history was in part the history of environmental changes induced by natural catastrophes and

* Dr. Glacken is Assistant Professor of Geography at the University of California, Berkeley. An abstract of his doctoral dissertation, "The Idea of the Habitable World," was published in 1952, and his book, *The Great Loochoo: A Study in Okinawan Village Life,* in 1955.

human activities. Perhaps if this view had found more elaborate expression in the *Laws,* in which Plato discusses the origin and development of society, an awareness of the philosophical implications of man's activities in changing the environment might have at that time entered the main stream of Western thought (1926, iii. 677–86D).

Across the Eurasian continent, Mencius, the Chinese philosopher, described the beautiful trees of the new mountain which were hewn down with axes. When they began growing again, buds and sprouts appeared, and cattle and goats browsed upon them. "To these things is owing the bare and stripped appearance of the mountain, and when people now see it, they think it was never finely wooded. But is this the nature of the mountain?" Few statements have summed up more lucidly than has this question of Mencius the difficulties of distinguishing a natural from a cultural landscape (1933, vi. 1. 8).

In the third century B.C. Eratosthenes described the manner in which the island of Cyprus was made habitable. Formerly its plains could not be used for agriculture because they were covered with forests. Felling trees in order to provide fuel for smelting copper and silver mined there helped to clear the forests, and, "as the sea was now navigated with security and by a large naval force," additional clearings were made for ship timber. These cuttings were not sufficient to clear the forests, and the people therefore were allowed to cut down the trees "to hold the land thus cleared as their own property, free from all payments" (Strabo xiv. 6. 5). Eratosthenes thus relates the changes in the landscape to mining, navigation, and governmental land policy.

Early observations such as these failed to inspire men to study the environmental changes made by human cultures as a part of human history. The reason for this failure is not that human modifications of the environment were so inconsequential as to be unworthy of remark but that the emphasis was on human society, its origin, and the manner of its changing through historical time.

THE GOLDEN AGE AND THE IDEA OF CYCLES

In the Greek notion of a past golden age with its "golden race of mortal men," nature which had not felt the intrusions of human art was considered more perfect and fruitful. "The bounteous earth," Hesiod said, "bare first for them of her own will, in plenty and without stint." Similar statements were made centuries later by Lucretius, Varro, and Ovid (Hesiod, 1879, p. 80; Lucretius, 1947, ii. 1155–60; Varro, 1912, ii. 2. 3–4; Ovid *Metam.* i. 101–5). The praise of the fertile soils of the golden age, which did not require cultivation, was probably a reflection of contemporary dissatisfaction with the modest yields obtained by hard work.

The idea of a cycle in the course of history, or in the growth of states and institutions—an analogy derived from the life-cycle of an organism—was in antiquity an alternative conception to the notion of degeneration from a golden age. Epicurus and Lucretius applied the cyclical theory to the earth itself, which in its prime spontaneously yielded crops, vines, fruits, and pastures that now even with toil could not be made to grow. A son should not complain about his father's good luck or rail at heaven because of his old and wilted vines: "nor does he grasp that all things waste away little by little and pass to the grave fordone by age and the lapse of life" (Lucretius, 1947, ii. 1165–74).[1]

Later in the poem, however, Lucretius, following Epicurus, traces the origin of metallurgy to the accidental smelting of ores heated by forest fires which may have been started by lightning, or by men who wished to frighten enemies concealed in the woods, to enlarge their fields or pastures, or to kill the wild animals for profit, for hunting by the use of pitfalls and fire was an earlier development than driving game with dogs into fenced-in glades (*ibid.*, v. 1245–50).

The landscapes of inhabited lands were created by imitating nature; man had learned how to domesticate nature by sowing, grafting, and experimenting with plants. "And day by day they would constrain the woods more and more to retire up the mountains, and to give up the land beneath to tilth" to have meadows, pools, streams, crops, vineyards, and olive orchards (*ibid.*, 1370–75). Lucretius clearly is describing here, in poetical language and without any suggestion of decay and death, the manner in which a people transforms the landscape.

ANOTHER NATURE

The early history of the idea of man as a modifier of his environment is also related to the broader conception, similar to the cyclical theory, of a teleology existent in a single organism or in all nature—a conception fully developed by Aristotle in his discussion of the four causes. The fruit of the tree was inherent in the seed; so was a design implicit

1. The author is grateful to the Oxford University Press for permission to quote from *Tit: Lucreti Cari De rerum natura,* as translated by Cyril Bailey.

in the living creation. Since man was the highest creature, all nature must have been created for him, an idea which must be one of the oldest of which there is a written record, for it is clearly expressed in ancient Egyptian creation myths (Frankfort *et al.*, 1951, p. 64).

In the idea of a design in nature, as it was developed by the Greeks and their Roman disciples, a pleasant and harmonious relation between man and nature is either expressed or implied, for human art improves the natural advantages of an earth which has been created as a home for man. This idea is discussed by Aristotle (*Politics* i. 8), Cicero, Seneca (1912, iv. 5), and Pliny (1938–52, vii. Pref.), Cicero's exposition being the most detailed. The earth endowed with living nature, said Cicero, is the proper home both for the gods and for man, man taking an active part in the care of nature by cultivating the earth so that its fertility would not be choked with weeds. There is an order of nature existing on earth—which is eternal—an order in which the great variety of organic species is arranged in an ascending scale. Man, as the highest being in the scale, changes nature by using his hands, with which, guided by the intellect, he has created the art of agriculture and the techniques of fishing, animal domestication, mining, clearing, and navigation (Cicero, 1894, *Nature of the Gods* ii. 39, 45, 53).

We are the absolute masters of what the earth produces. We enjoy the mountains and the plains. The rivers are ours. We sow the seed, and plant the trees. We fertilize the earth. . . . We stop, direct, and turn the rivers: in short by our hands we endeavor, by our various operations in this world, to make, as it were, another Nature [*ibid.* 60; cf. 30–67].

The concept of "another," the man-made nature, thus seems a fusion of two elements: the design inherent in nature and the improvements of nature which are interpreted as the effects brought about by human art in fulfilment of the design.

SOIL AND AGRICULTURE

In the technical agricultural writings of antiquity, comments regarding human changes of nature also appear in discussions of land use and of soil fertility. These writings, from Hesiod through Vergil and Pliny, are concerned for the most part with technical details, the Roman writers particularly emphasizing farm management and the cultivation of the olive and the vine. One significant fact about them is the association of soil conservation with agriculture—an association which has persisted in modern, even contemporary, times in discussions regarding population and food supply, in which the chief emphasis has been on the care and fertilization of arable land.

Perhaps the earliest idea is that the soils must be allowed to rest, because cultivation tires them. "Fallow-land," said Hesiod, "is a guardian-from-death-and-ruin, and a soother of children" (1879, p. 99). There is a similar idea in the Old Testament (Exod. 23:10–11; Lev. 25:1–7, 21–22), the Lord commanding that every seventh year be a "sabbath of rest unto the land."

Two Roman writers, Varro and Columella, are significant in this history, because their writings, revealing the influence of Stoic philosophy, dealt with questions which transcended the technical details of agriculture.

Varro said that human life had developed from the original state of nature "when man lived on those things which the virgin earth produced spontaneously"—another reminder of the strength of the idea that soil fertility was characteristic of a golden age. From the state of nature mankind passed through a pastoral stage of gathering and animal domestication followed by the agricultural stage that lasted until the rise of contemporary civilization (1912, ii. 1. 4–5).

This theory and its modern successors diverted attention from the actual historical events, since cultural development presumably took place regardless of the nature of the physical environment. The first serious challenge to this sequence was delayed, as Carl Sauer (1952, p. 20) has said, until Alexander von Humboldt attacked the theory, because pastoral nomadism was not found in the New World. Since Varro's time, however, abstract theories of cultural development have evaded the question of how man was changing his environment as he marched through these stages.

Varro was far more sensible than his latter-day imitators, for he saw an exception to his theory in his own time and in his own country: heads of families have deserted the land for the cities and have imported corn and wine from foreign countries. "And so in that country where the city's founders were shepherds and taught agriculture to their descendants, these descendants have reversed the process, and through covetousness and in despite of laws, have turned corn-land into meadow, not knowing the difference between agriculture and grazing" (1912, ii. Introd.). Agriculture was creative; grazing, extractive. "Grazing cattle do not help to produce what grows on the land; they remove it with their teeth" (*ibid.*).

In his work on agriculture Columella comments approvingly on the opinions of a certain Tremelius that the productivity of land declines rapidly after a clearing; plows break the roots of the plants, and the trees no longer provide organic materials for fertilizer—a sentence reminding one of current discussions of the exhaustion of tropical soils a few years after they have been cleared and cultivated (1941, ii. 1. 6–7). Columella is significant as a thinker, how-

ever, because he objected to the analogy of the earth as a mortal being; his work begins with an attack, probably aimed at the Epicureans and Lucretius, on the popular view that the earth had a life-cycle: "It is not, therefore, because of weariness, as very many have believed, nor because of old age, but manifestly because of our own lack of energy that our cultivated lands yield us a less generous return. For we may reap greater harvests if the earth is quickened again by frequent, timely, and moderate manuring" (*ibid.* 1. 7; cf. i. Pref.).[2] Instead of a philosophy of the earth as a mortal being, the practical Columella substitutes manuring.

The *Natural History* of Pliny gives further evidence of a lively awareness in antiquity of the effects of human activities on the earth. Pliny says, too, that a soil should not be regarded as old in a mortal sense. Soils would last with care, and in cultivating hillsides it was not necessary to denude them if the digging were done skilfully. He also describes how the emptying of a lake in the Larissa district of Thessaly lowered the temperature of the vicinity, causing the olive to disappear and the vines to be frostbitten, how the climate of Aenos on the Maritza became warmer when the river was diverted near it, and how Philippi altered its climate when its land under cultivation was drained (1938–52, xvii. 29–30).

INFLUENCE OF THE PHYSICAL ENVIRONMENT

Another influential body of thought, the theory of the influence of the physical environment on human cultures, owes its origin to the thinkers of antiquity. This literature, both in antiquity and in modern times, has dealt with the influence of climate, soils, and geo-

2. The author is grateful to the Harvard University Press for permission to quote from *On Agriculture*, as translated by Harrison Boyd Ash.

graphical location on individuals and on cultures. Its main outlines may be traced[3] through the Hippocratic writings, Herodotus, Thucydides, Aristotle, Polybius, Pliny, and Vitruvius, although the ancient writers on the whole were far less rigid in their determinism than many thinkers of the eighteenth and nineteenth centuries.

The significance of these theories is that they led to a one-sided preoccupation with environmental influences, largely ignoring the significance of man as an agent in changing the environment; in ancient and modern times both ideas were often expressed by the same writer without any realization of an implied contradiction.

THE BOOK OF GENESIS

Ideas derived from the Old Testament have also been important elements in the formulation of modern conceptions of man's relation to the earth. All beings which existed before the flood were commanded by the Creator to be fruitful and to multiply, man receiving in addition the command to take possession of the earth. After the flood the Lord gave similar commands to Noah and his sons, making a covenant with them that he would not again destroy the living things on earth. Man by divine command assumes a powerful control over nature (Gen. 1:21–22, 27–28; 8:17, 21–22; 9:1–3). The fusion of these Old Testament ideas with the classical and Stoic idea of a design in nature provided a strong stimulus to the seventeenth-century study of living nature in order to find there proofs of the wisdom of God.

The ideas of antiquity which have had the most influence on modern con-

ceptions of the relation of man to the earth were the idea of a design in nature and the various theories of environmental influence. The cyclical idea has been of great importance in the history of social and political thought and in the philosophy of history—Vico and Spengler are modern examples—but does not seem to have had a lasting influence in modern conceptions of man's relation to nature. The agricultural writings were very influential in early modern times but only as a technical literature. The idea of man as a modifier of the earth does not seem to have been transmitted as an idea, probably because it was not well formulated in antiquity and because notices of man's activities were absorbed as descriptions or as elements of well-established ideas.

FELLING OF TREES

Men in early modern times became aware of their power to change nature mostly because they observed the effects of cutting down trees, for comments on the consequences of clearing have been traced to Carolingian times (Maury, 1856, pp. 71–80). Concern over the consequences of deforestation was very marked in the late seventeenth century, as the provisions of Colbert's *Forest Ordinance* (1669) (see Brown, 1883*b*) and the discussions in Evelyn's *Silva* (1664) clearly show. The provisions of the *Forest Ordinance* reveal an awareness of the relation of forest care to such practices as grazing, mast feeding, and the gathering of forest litter. In Evelyn's *Silva* the idea that economic objectives may act at cross-purposes with desirable arrangements in nature is revealed in the discussion of agriculture, industry, and forestry. Evelyn thought the prosperity of the glass-making, iron-smelting, and naval-building industries often was inconsistent with the existence of forests because of the heedless consumption of wood for fuel, resources like woods and iron ore having a capri-

---

3. See the Hippocratic writings (*Airs, Waters, Places*); Herodotus (*Hist.* ix. 122); Thucydides (*Pelop. War* i. 1); Aristotle (*Pol.* vii. vi. 1–3); Polybius (*Hist.* iv. 19–21); Pliny (*Nat. Hist.* ii. 80); Vitruvius (*On Arch.* i. iv–vi; ii. i).

cious and unfortunate distribution: "But nature has thought fit to produce this wasting Ore more plentifully in wood-land than in any other ground, and to enrich our forests to their own destruction" (1786, II, 265; cf. p. 214 on succession; p. 269). Evelyn's main censure, however, was reserved for the encroachments of agriculture on the forests—for the "disproportionate spread of tillage" (*ibid.*, I, 1–2).

THE WISDOM OF GOD

In the late seventeenth century a grand conception of nature as a divinely created order for the well-being of all life was formulated. It was a time of great interest in philosophy, population theory, botany, geology, and astronomy and of great activity in the drainage of swamps, fens, and bogs. The key ideas in this conception, which is closely related to the idea of a great chain of being whose importance in the history of Western thought has been so profoundly elucidated by Arthur Lovejoy, are fully discussed in John Ray's *The Wisdom of God Manifested in the Works of the Creation* (first edition, 1691) and William Derham's *Physicotheology*. A disciple of Ray, Derham based his work on the Boyle Lectures which he delivered in 1711–12.

Although the conception was closely related to contemporary theological and philosophical thinking, particularly that of the Cambridge Platonists, we must content ourselves here with pointing out several attitudes which were held toward the earth as a habitable planet. (1) Men like Ray and Derham ardently tried to refute the ideas of Thomas Burnet, whose *Sacred Theory of the Earth* contained many unflattering references to the planet as it was constituted after the flood (1753, I, 65). According to Burnet, it was poorly fashioned as a living place for man, and nature was hard and niggardly. Furthermore, the earth was unreasonably tilted

twenty-three and a half degrees from the plane of the ecliptic, there was altogether too much sea, and the haphazard distribution of mountains and valleys could not be compared with the advantages of the smooth-surfaced antediluvian world (*ibid.*, pp. 178–89).

In rebuttal, Ray, Derham, and others of like mind pointed out the great advantages of the earth's tilting on its axis to all life, the inclination being responsible for the seasons and for preventing climatic excess. The sea, far from being superfluous, supplied rain for the land. The hand of a wise Providence was seen also in the washing-down of earth from the mountains to be spread on the meadows, in the running water carrying soil in suspension to nourish plants, and in the winds which moved the clouds in the sky, providing a more "commodius watering." They commented too on the beauties created by the happy distribution of landforms, lakes, and streams on the earth, making life both convenient and enjoyable. (2) The distribution of climates and the production of plants and animals in the various zones were too advantageous to life and too well reasoned to be accepted as fortuitous circumstances. (3) The task of human art was to improve the primeval aspect of the earth through tillage and in other ways. (4) Although the Creator had bestowed great gifts on man, all ranks of being in the world had their place in nature and were not created for man alone. Man in this conception is a mighty but not omnipotent being on earth; he is at the top of the scale, but with responsibilities, for he is a caretaker, or, in the words of Sir Mathew Hale, a steward of God (Ray, 1759, pp. 79–91 *et passim*; Derham, 1798, pp. 60–64 *et passim*).

These thinkers rejected both the idea of the world as a machine and the Baconian view that scientific and religious inquiry should be separate. They saw man living in a world—which he could change and improve—where the order and beauty of nature, manifestations of the Creator's skill and wisdom, could be seen everywhere (Ray, 1759, pp. 31–37; Derham, 1798, pp. 116, 131–32). There was no patience with primitivism: a man, said Ray, would be wanting in sense if he preferred the existence of a Scythian to the polished life and the beautifully tilled fields of Europe (1759, pp. 164–65).

More than a century before Alexander von Humboldt's famous phrases about the unity of nature amid its diversity, these men spoke of a balance and a harmony in nature which had been so wonderfully designed by the Creator.[4] The classical notion of a design in nature, the Old Testament ideas, and the seventeenth-century passion for science had come together and provided the stimulus for the enthusiastic study of living nature.[5]

In the later development of the idea of a harmony in nature, the role of the Creator recedes somewhat, and nature becomes an entity itself—often it is personified—and the idea of man as a being co-operating in the improvement of nature is expanded. In the nineteenth century, especially in the works of Marsh, the idea creeps in that man has failed in his appointed role as a steward of God and that man's vast changes are upsetting the balance and the harmony of nature and are ruining the earth.

INHABITED AND UNINHABITED COUNTRIES

In the stately and eloquent writings of Buffon, which reveal a deep study of the scientific literature of England, man plays a very active role in changing the surface of the earth. Buffon contrasts the appearance of inhabited with uninhabited lands: the anciently inhabited countries have few woods, lakes, or marshes, but they have many heaths and scrub, their mountains are bare, and their soils are less fertile because they lack the organic matter which woods—felled in inhabited countries—supply, and the herbs are browsed. "Men destroy woods, drain marshes and lakes, and in process of time, give an appearance to the surface of the earth totally different from that of uninhabited or newly peopled countries" (Buffon, 1866, I, 38).

The French naturalist also was interested in climatic change brought about by clearing and cited instances from travel accounts of Quebec, Cayenne, and the Guianas. Lands with forests are cold, and, when the forests are cut, the climate becomes warmer. It is more difficult for man to cool than to heat the earth, for it is easier to cut trees in Guiana than to plant them in Arabia (*ibid.*, pp. 45–46, 73; II, 183; 1799, IV, 21–23). In countries which are too small to support polished societies, the surface of the land is more rugged and unequal, and the river channels are more interrupted by cataracts (Buffon, 1866, I, 7).

Buffon stresses the profound effects which man has made in nature by the domestication of animals and plants. The domestication of the dog made man's peaceable possession of the earth possible because it was the means by which wild animals were tracked down, captured, and domesticated. The domestication of animals, in turn, was the basis both of hunting and of agriculture, so that men and animals could multiply; in this manner, an environment was refashioned in the course of time by human art. With the multiplication and dispersal of man and his animals, the days of the wild animals were numbered. "Time fights against them." In words like those Darwin used in the first chapter of the *Origin of*

---

4. On the balance of animals and a seventeenth-century food chain see Derham, 1798, pp. 257–70; cf. Ray, 1759, pp. 371–75.

5. On Ray's influence see Raven, 1942, pp. 452–76.

Species, Buffon describes the control man has acquired over plants through breeding and artificial selection (*ibid.,* p. 365, essay on the dog; II, 35, on mules; pp. 184–86).

Occasionally, Buffon indignantly criticizes the acts of man, observing, for example, that he would destroy all nature "if by a fecundity superior to his depradations she did not repair the havock he makes" (*ibid.,* I, 392, on carnivorous animals), but in the main Buffon has an optimistic outlook. Like John Ray, he has no patience with the supposed glories of a golden age or with the beauties of a state of nature, but he had praise for nature which had been and would continue to be improved through human art. In the "Epochs of Nature," composed toward the end of a long life, Buffon divides the history of the earth into seven periods, the last of which is called "when the power of man assisted the works of nature." To Buffon, man through his ability to modify nature had now become a force in the evolution of the earth (*ibid.,* II, 184; 1799, IV, 40–41).

The importance of Buffon's thought lay in the recognition of the historical relation between the growth and dispersal of plant, animal, and human populations and the modifications of the earth which this growth and dispersal had brought about both in old settlements and in new colonies.

THE ALPINE TORRENTS

Studies of the torrents of the French and the Austrian Alps undertaken in the late eighteenth and early nineteenth centuries deepened immeasurably the realization of man's power to change the earth. As the century wore on, the field of inquiry had broadened to encompass the relation of human cultures to the forests, climate, soils, and agriculture.

In 1797 a French engineer named Fabre announced that the causes of the sudden and overwhelming Alpine torrents which flooded the farms and settlements of the lowlands were clearing and deforestation in the high Alps. The cutting of trees in the high mountain fastnesses, Fabre said, permitted the formation of torrents which brought about seven kinds of disaster: the ruin of the forests; the erosion of the mountain soils and the consequent destruction of mountain pastures; the ruin of dwellings situated along the streams; the divisions of watercourses in their lower reaches caused by floods; litigation over riparian rights as a consequence of the division of the watercourses; silting of the mouth of streams; and the diminution of the water sources which fed the streams and rivers (extract in Brown, 1880, pp. 55–58).

Fabre's work was the beginning of a long series of French studies, pursued by foresters, engineers, and agronomists, whose work is so intimately associated with the great project of reforestation (*reboisment*) which the French government undertook in the Hautes-Alpes during the nineteenth century (Anonymous, 1911). Fabre's successor, Surell, continued the study, announcing that Alpine torrents appeared when forests disappeared and that they disappeared when forests were restored (extracts in Brown, 1880, pp. 30–47). Similar works on the Austrian Alps, possibly anticipating that of Fabre, appeared about the same time, three of them being published, significantly, in the city of Innsbruck. The Italians also had interested themselves in torrents, control of watercourses, and soil erosion, their interest in these subjects going back at least to Leonardo, who had noted that streams were muddier when they passed through populated districts (*ibid.,* pp. 131–34; Leonardo da Vinci, 1954, p. 310).

The theme running through the specialized studies which appeared in the early-nineteenth-century literature was that clearing, grazing and transhumance, torrents, and shifting agriculture were all parts of the greater problem of Alpine deforestation. Observations made of the levels of Alpine lakes further broadened the inquiry to include study of the relation of deforestation to climate. Horace-Bénedict de Saussure aroused considerable interest when he published, in his *Voyage dans les Alpes,* measurements of the water levels of Lake Neuchâtel, Lake Bienne, and Lake Morat; the French chemist Boussingault studied De Saussure's materials and came to the conclusion that water levels had lowered in modern times owing to the cutting of woods (De Saussure, 1779, I, 324; cf. p. 150).

The prestige and the industry of Alexander von Humboldt also stimulated inquiry into the question, for he had devoted much time to the study of the relation of forest clearance to climatic change, using the lakes both of the New World and of Central Asia as examples. After studying the lake in the valley of Aragua in Venezuela, von Humboldt concluded that the lake level in 1800, the year of his visit, had lowered in recent times and that deforestation, clearing of plains, and the cultivation of indigo were, in addition to evaporation and the dryness of the atmosphere, the causes of the gradual drying-up of the lake. "By felling the trees which cover the tops and sides of mountains," von Humboldt said (1852, II, 9), in a widely quoted sentence, "men in every climate prepare at once two calamities for future generations: want of fuel and scarcity of water."

Twenty-five years later Boussingault visited the same valley in order to see if any changes had occurred since von Humboldt's visit and found that the level of the lake had been rising so fast that people feared the possibility of floods. His explanation for this reversal of conditions was that the country was devastated in the wars of independence, the newly freed slaves had joined the army, agriculture was largely abandoned, and the forest again covered the ground; natural conditions, being easily restored in a tropical environment, had re-established the flow of waters in a region which now approximated virgin conditions (Boussingault, n.d., p. 499).

Alexander von Humboldt's writings are an important landmark in the history of the idea of man as a geographic agent, even though many environmentalistic ideas are scattered throughout his works. Like Mencius and Buffon, von Humboldt had an eye for the distinction between a cultural and a natural landscape. A traveler to Italy, Spain, or the African coasts of the Mediterranean, he said, might "easily be led to adopt the erroneous inference that absence of trees is a characteristic of hot climates." But southern Europe was different at the time of the Pelasgian or Carthaginian colonization; civilization sets bounds to the increase of forests, and the youthfulness of a civilization is proved by the existence of its woods (Humboldt, 1849, p. 232, essay on physiognomy of plants).

Both von Humboldt and Boussingault were influential in promoting scientific investigation of the relation of agriculture and forest clearance to climatic change. Boussingault summarized the results of his investigation of the relation of man's cultural activities to his environment: (1) extensive forest destruction diminishes the amount of running water; (2) the diminution might be owing to less average annual rainfall or more active evaporation or both; (3) the quantity of running water of countries having no agricultural improvement is regular and does not seem to change perceptibly; (4) forests regularize stream flow by impeding evaporation; (5) agriculture in a dry country which lacks forests dissipates an additional portion of running water; and (6) limited clearings of forests cause a diminution of springs (Boussingault, n.d., p. 507).

Early-nineteenth-century American writers also discussed questions relating to the effects of agriculture on the forests; a paper on the subject written by Thomas Jefferson was translated into French by the Abbé Morellet (Becquerel, 1871, p. 408). The early American writers were particularly alarmed at soil exhaustion and soil erosion and suggested many different methods of fertilizing or of plowing to preserve the soils. There was in fact a strong continuity of scientific effort in the United States and in Europe throughout the century with relation to the preservation of soils and of forests (Hough, 1878, pp. 278–79; Van Hise, 1910; McDonald, 1941; Bennett, 1944).

Meanwhile, Carl Fraas had published an influential book on the destruction of the vegetation of Persia, Mesopotamia, Palestine, Egypt, and southern Europe as a result of human activities. Fraas argued that the original vegetation of these regions had been a response to climatic conditions and that man, mostly through deforestation, had changed the vegetation—which was now less useful to him—and also the climate, rejecting explanations of climatic change through purely physical causes (1847, pp. 18–124). Fraas's thesis influenced the eminent German historian Ernst Curtius, whose work on the Peloponnesus stressed the role of man as an agent in changing the environment of the Morea (1851, I, 53–55).

The conclusion of these early-nineteenth-century investigators can be summed up in a sentence: Civilization leads to aridity. These theories of climatic change as a result of human activities both in agriculture and in the forests appeared considerably earlier than those of Prince Kropotkin (1904), Raphael Pumpelly (1908), and Ells-

worth Huntington (1915) that the desiccation of Eurasia and the consequent decline of civilizations were the result of climatic change independent of human agency (cf. Gregory, 1914). Recent writings during the last twenty years on soil erosion, destructive grazing, and the like have in fact returned to earlier views that aridity has been caused by man (e.g., Bennett, 1939; Jacks and Whyte, 1939; Lowdermilk, 1943).

MAN AND PLANTS

Botanists and plant geographers also were discussing the effects of culture on the natural vegetation. The Danish plant geographer Frederick Schouw wrote that nature if uninterfered with would remain about the same throughout time; man, however, could change the vegetation, and his power to do so increased with his cultural advancement. The greatest transformations had taken place in Europe; only the European polar regions and the Alps were relatively unchanged. Perhaps had he lived closer to the Alps, Schouw might have included them as a region of change. Curiously, Schouw did not regard grazing as bringing about significant changes in nature. Although he repeats earlier themes that countries with the oldest civilizations have the fewest woods, his faith in science and technology made him optimistic, for civilization had created natural beauty itself, and a "more profound knowledge of natural forces gives a counterpoise to whatever hurtful effects civilisation brings with it" (1852, p. 238; cf. pp. 15–16, 67, 239).

The German botanist Schleiden stressed the great influence man had exerted in altering the world distribution of vegetation. Plant domestication and plant breeding he considered the most beneficial of man's changes, but man had also been a distributor of weeds; rubbish plants—thorns and thistles—"mark the track which Man has proudly traversed throughout the earth" (1848, p. 306; cf. pp. 299–307).

Around the middle of the century Alphonse de Candolle warned scientists who were interested in the evolution of plants and in their distribution in past geological eras that time was running out. "The increasing activity of man effaces these every day, and it is not one of the lesser merits of our civilization to establish a multitude of facts of which our posterity would no longer have any material visible proof" (1855, p. 1340).

Victor Hehn's celebrated work, *The Wanderings of Plants and Animals* (1888), is unique because he emphasized the power of man and rejected the idea that man caused irreversible changes in nature. It could not be denied that, especially since the age of discovery, "the whole physiognomy of life, labour, and landscape in a country may in the course of centuries be changed under the hand of man." European plants and animals had supplanted those of the New World, but the best illustration was the history of organic nature of Greece and Italy, because the known time span was at least two millenniums (Hehn, 1888, p. 7). In essence, Hehn said that the Mediterranean lands were an indirect creation of the Near Eastern peoples, for, in the Near East, plants and animals had been domesticated and had been diffused through the Mediterranean by man. Hehn had no patience, however, with pessimists like Fraas who saw the exhaustion of the earth as a consequence of human activities and who did not emphasize the possibilities of restoration; the depradations of the goat, deforestation, and soil erosion need not be irreparable. For the same reason he objected to the new agricultural chemistry whose disciples "have already passed sentence on the East and the Mediterranean countries and raised their lament over the dead" (*ibid.*, p. 23; on exhaustion of culture, pp. 19–30).

The work of Hehn, a philologist, was in that great scholarly tradition of Jones, Adelung, Bopp, Schlegel, Lassen, and Grimm, which was concerned both with comparative linguistics and with the origin of the Aryans. All civilization had been derived from an Eastern cradle, an idea which was summed up in the phrase *ex oriente lux.* Carl Ritter, Arnold Guyot, and George W. F. Hegel used this idea in their interpretation of history as a geographical march from east to west; Hehn applied the idea to environmental change in the Mediterranean.

THE WEAKNESS OF MAN

In the first edition of his *Principles of Geology* (1830–33), Charles Lyell wrote that man must be considered "among the powers of organic nature" which modified the physical geography of the globe. Although these modifications were considerable, they were to Lyell relatively insignificant. "No application, perhaps, of human skill and labour tends so greatly to vary the state of the habitable surface, as that employed in the drainage of lakes and marshes, since not only the *stations* of many animals and plants, but the general climate of a district, may thus be modified" (1830–33, II, 205). Lyell compared the effects of human modifications to those of brute animals, the only anomaly in the intervention of man being that a single species "would exert, by its superior power and universal distribution, an influence equal to that of hundreds of other terrestrial animals." If one inquired whether man, through his direct removing power or indirect changes, tended to lessen or increase the inequalities of the earth's surface, Lyell said, "we shall incline, perhaps, to the opinion that he is a levelling agent" (*ibid.*, p. 207).

The great geologist subsequently

modified his earlier views and no longer maintained that human modifications were similar in kind to brute action. Man in his progressive development increased his power of change through the accumulation of knowledge and could be expected to make even greater changes in the future. Lyell hoped that any man-made modifications would be in harmony with the orderly evolution which he thought had characterized most of the past history of the earth (1872, I, 170–71). The minor role of man as a geological force is in sharp contrast with the violent role many of Lyell's contemporaries found man playing throughout the world, although Lyell himself describes in a vivid passage a man-made gully he observed during his American tour near Milledgeville, Georgia (1849, II, 23–25; cf. I, 344–45).

THE STRENGTH OF MAN

When President Lincoln appointed George Perkins Marsh to be the first American minister to the Kingdom of Italy in 1861, Marsh had already served as American minister to Turkey and on a diplomatic mission to Greece. In the preparation of *Man and Nature, or Physical Geography as Modified by Human Action* (1864), he had at his disposal not only his own observations but the immense accumulation of European materials whose vastness I have only hinted at in the preceding pages.

Marsh rightly said that his work was the first general and extended study of the subject, although he did not, as the title implies, consider the whole earth; the countries of northwestern Europe and of the Mediterranean Basin were his chief examples. His purpose was to indicate "the character and approximately, the extent of the changes produced by human action, . . . the dangers of imprudence and the necessity of caution in all operations, which on a large scale interfere with the sponta-

neous arrangements of the organic or the inorganic world," to make suggestions for "the restoration of disturbed harmonies," and, in a sentence which shows his kinship with the classical, biblical, and seventeenth-century tradition, "incidentally, to illustrate the doctrine that man is, in both kind and degree, a power of a higher order than any other forms of animated life, which, like him, are nourished at the table of bounteous nature" (1864, p. iii). *Man and Nature* may be described as a philosophical treatise documented with technical materials. In his work the technical ideas of men like Evelyn, Fabre, and their successors converge with the seventeenth-century conception of nature as a divinely designed balance and harmony. Marsh attacked the idea that man was a weak geological agent whose power, as Lyell at first thought, is of the same order as brute animals, as well as the environmentalistic ideas, which he ascribed to Ritter, Guyot, and von Humboldt, that human cultures were molded in large part by the physical environment.

Marsh organized his book topically according to "the chronological succession in which man must be supposed to have extended his sway over the different provinces of his material kingdom": first on animal and vegetable life, and then on the woods, the waters, and the sands. The effects of deforestation, however, are given by far the greatest prominence because of the intense preoccupation of the early-nineteenth-century scientists with this subject (*ibid.*, pp. v–vi).

In *Man and Nature* Marsh discussed many themes relating to human cultures and the environments transformed by them: the need of restoring the old lands and of caring for the new in a great era of international migration (*ibid.*, p. 26); the balance of nature, human activities being considered as disturbances of that balance (p. 27);

Courtesy of Professor Dr. Franz Termer

Alexander von Humboldt (1769–1859)

Courtesy of David Lowenthal

George Perkins Marsh (1801–82)

Courtesy of the American Geographical Society, New York

Élisée Reclus (1830–1905)

Courtesy of the American Geographical Society, New York

P. Vidal de la Blache (1845–1918)

FIG. 49

the idea that every plant, animal, and human being is a geographical agent, man being destructive, plants—and animals to some extent—being restorative (pp. 57–58); the revolution accomplished by man in plant distributions throughout the world (pp. 59–60); the idea that a domestic animal, like the goat or the camel, is an agent of man in modifying the environment (p. 79); the effects of wars, revolutions, and changes of fashion on physical geography (p. 84); modern agriculture as a feeding and breeding ground for insects and the consequent increase of insect life at the expense of vegetable life, birds, and the smaller quadrupeds (p. 104); the increase in climatic contrasts resulting from deforestation (pp. 153, 210); man's use of fire in clearing and in shifting agriculture (p. 136); the changes resulting from the drainage of bogs, reclamation of polders (chap. iv), and the fixation of sand dunes (chap. v); and the importance of conserving ground water, including proposals for water storage (pp. 449–50).

Marsh was a famous and widely recognized man both in Europe and in America; his works were referred to in the House of Commons in connection with the alarming deforestation of India; he was a recognized authority in America; and he helped compile the irrigation laws of France, Italy, and Spain and to assist the state of California in the development of its irrigation law. Yet his work was submerged in the tide of opinion which saw progress everywhere in the beneficent command which man had attained over nature. While Marsh was writing of the deterioration of the earth as a habitable planet, Herbert Spencer, for example, spoke of the inevitable march of civilization, its population approaching equilibrium as it advanced, until at the end of the evolution the whole world would be cultivated like a garden (1866–67, II, 506–7).

More than twenty years ago Lewis Mumford (1931, pp. 72–78) reminded us of the great contributions of the forgotten American minister to Italy. Marsh brought together materials which had been discussed in Europe for two generations, but his work was no mere compilation. He looked behind the doctrine of man's control over nature through science and technology and emphasized the unplanned, unanticipated, and uncontrolled changes which man had made in his environment, an approach which was responsible for both the pessimism and the urgency of his writings. He did not deny that there was a favorable side to the picture, but restorations had been inconsequential compared with the great accumulation of devastating changes.

Marsh did more than make a plea for conservation; he gave the world a deeper insight into the nature of human history. Our greatest debt to him is that he studied the technical works of European foresters, meteorologists, agronomists, drainage engineers and hydrologists, botanists and plant geographers, and scientific travelers and for the first time placed the results of their investigations where they belonged—in the forefront of human history.

THE WIDE WORLD

The late-nineteenth-century literature is extremely voluminous, and it is possible to give only a few examples which illustrate various points of view regarding the relation of human cultures to environmental change. The studies and observations were world wide, particularly in Europe, the United States, Africa south of the Sahara, China, and India. The great changes which the Europeans were making in the environment of Australia and New Zealand also had been of great interest since Lyell's time.

Baron von Richthofen described the desiccation of the Tarim Basin, a consequence, he thought, of the diversion of water for oasis agriculture resulting in the drying-up of other lands which were then subject to wind erosion, the sand thus blown by the wind ultimately covering the fertile soil of the oases (1877–1912, I, 124–25); he saw a close relation between the deforestation and soil erosion in Shansi Province (*ibid.*, II, 479) and noted the irrigation system of Szechwan (*ibid.*, III, 232–34) and the deforestation of southeastern China (*ibid.*, pp. 414–15).

The French geographer Élisée Reclus, whose nineteen-volume work on the earth and its inhabitants was the most impressive of the nineteenth-century geographical surveys of the world, was torn between a belief in inevitable progress and a pessimism derived in part from Marsh, in part from his own observations. It was difficult to predict the possible course of civilization, for one could be optimistic regarding the impressive land reclamation, as in the Haarlem polder of Holland, but pessimistic regarding the world-wide deforestation and the indifference of minds of a "so-called positive tendency" to changes which man was making in nature (Reclus, 1873, pp. 522–30).

In the late seventies and eighties John Croumbie Brown published a remarkable series of works on forestry which are of great value because they contain extensive extracts of contemporary literature published in out-of-the-way places (see "References," *sub nomine*). Although Brown was interested primarily in the forests, related subjects like shifting agriculture, transhumance, cattle- and sheep-grazing, and the problem of the goat were discussed at length. Equally remarkable was the report which Franklin B. Hough made for the United States Commissioner of Agriculture in 1877, including material on environmental change in the United States and in Europe, with frequent references to the works of von Humboldt, Becquerel, Boussingault, Brown, and Marsh. The works of Brown and Hough—even more than Marsh's—reveal the breadth, variety, and historical depth of the study of environmental change in the nineteenth century.

In the United States, Nathaniel S. Shaler explored many of the themes which Marsh had mentioned. Geologists everywhere, Shaler wrote, recognized changes man had made on the earth, especially in the pursuit of agriculture. "The old view that the earth was firm set and that on it we could build for 'aye' has gone the way of ancient opinions" (1896, p. 328). In his monograph on soils—a landmark in the history of soil concepts—Shaler stressed the importance of maintaining the "tillage values" of a country, for human cultures depend on the soil for their existence and must devise means for its continued preservation. Shaler took many of his illustrations regarding deforestation and soil erosion from both sides of the Atlantic (*ibid.*, pp. 369–71).

Shaler discussed the dependence of civilization on metals and minerals and the problems posed by their accelerated use. Although he gave serious consideration to the possibility of their exhaustion, he had faith in technology and in the power of man to use the falling waters, the winds, and the tides. (The German geologist Fischer also wrote a penetrating analysis [1915] of the effects of civilization on mineral resources.) New resources created by invention would replace exhausted ones; Shaler matter-of-factly predicted the deforestation of the globe by the twenty-third century (1905b, p. 31), leaving only a few forests to insure the flow of streams. Man will not disappear from the earth but will master it; his intellect enables him to combat the agents that destroy other forms of organic life. "The limits set to him are not those set by the death of his species, but by the endurance of the earth to the demands his progressive desires make upon it" (1904–5, p. 234).

In 1904 the German geographer Ernst Friedrich tried to give theoretical expression to the great changes which had been made throughout the world—changes which were accelerating because of the expansion of the European peoples. Friedrich distinguished between the simple exploitative economy which did no permanent harm and the characteristic exploitative economy which destroyed so much of the environment that it led to impoverishment of a people. The stages of this economic development were (1) intensive, prolonged, and heedless characteristic exploitation, followed by (2) impoverishment, which in turn led to (3) self-consciousness and awareness of the need for conservation. The need which followed exploitation in the environment of Europe had led to the discovery of soil fertilizers. "We see before our eyes processes going on in the new lands whose completed results may be observed in old Europe" (Friedrich, 1904, p. 72). Exploitative economy (*Raubwirtschaft*), reprehensible as its excesses—apparent in the slaughter of the seal, the bison, the elephant, and the whale—might be from a moral point of view, was the way of progress. Mining, for example, was purely extractive, yet "in many cases we have to seek in mining an explanation for the geographical expansion of mankind on earth" (*ibid.*). *Raubwirtschaft* was temporary, a characteristic of the youth of colonization; the earth gradually would be rationally exploited under the leadership of the European peoples (*ibid.*, p. 95). Friedrich's essay was influential because many of his ideas, which stressed the active force of man, were adopted by the French school of geographers, the possibilists, whose writings

in turn have had a wide influence on twentieth-century concepts of man's relation to his environment.

The Russian geographer and climatologist Alexander Woeikof, whose writings also influenced the French school, thought that the power of man lay in his ability to divide and rule nature; by interfering with vegetation, for example, man permitted the wasting-away of soils by wind and rain. The task of mankind was to control vegetation which held the soil in place, otherwise destruction of soils would lead to the extinction of civilization. Woeikof (1901, pp. 105–6) ascribed the origin of the silt in the Hwang Ho to the activities of man which had induced soil erosion. He thought the great expansion of cities, inclosing man on all sides, contributed to his growing ignorance of the processes of nature (*ibid.*, pp. 207–8). Woeikof was optimistic with qualifications: if the disharmonies were corrected, there were "vast perspectives of progress" ahead (p. 215). There were also the tropical lands between the fifteenth parallels of North and South latitude which could if necessary hold ten billion people (p. 211).

After a century of study of man's activities throughout the world, it is not surprising that a group of French thinkers with interests in geography and history announced the doctrine of possibilism: human cultures were not molded by their environment; environment merely offered various possibilities which different cultures might use in different ways. This doctrine was a fusion of three sets of ideas: (1) the idea of man as a geographic agent, emphasizing, that is, the role of man in changing the physical environment; (2) the significance of historical factors in the development of a culture; and (3) a concept of resources based on the idea of plant and animal associations, derived from the growing science of plant ecology. Possibilism, however, was a weak tea compared with the strong brews of yesteryear.[6]

By the first decade of the twentieth century—scarcely seventy years after Lyell had described man as a weak geological agent—several geologists were calling man the dominant geological force of the planet. Terms like the "psychozoic era," "anthropozoic era," and the "mental era" were used to characterize this new geological period, anticipating Vernadsky's thesis, a generation later, that the world was no longer a biosphere but a noösphere. After reviewing the favorable and alarming aspects of man's power, Chamberlin and Salisbury expressed the newer point of view: "It is to be observed that the mental era has but just begun, and that its effects are increasing with a rapidity quite phenomenal when measured by the slow pace of most geological change" (1904, I, 619; cf. Vernadsky, 1944, pp. 487–88).

ENVIRONMENT AND PROGRESS

This rich and vivid literature concerning environmental change brought about by human cultures was completely ignored by the large majority of the students of man both in the eighteenth and in the nineteenth centuries. How is one to explain this neglect? In the first place, the subject of man's changes of the earth was widely scattered in scientific and technical literature, where the philosophers, moral philosophers, and students of human society would be unlikely to turn for inspiration. In the second place, other ideas, especially environmental determinism and the idea of progress, dominated the thinking of men who wrote history or who attempted a theoretical reconstruction of human development.

Environmental determinism has had an astonishing vitality in modern times,

6. On possibilism see Brunhes, 1920; Febvre, 1925; Vidal de la Blanche, 1926.

especially in the nineteenth century—when one would expect it least—an age of international migration, colonization of new lands, and far-reaching environmental changes throughout the world. There were two general kinds of environmental theory: (1) the older tradition concerned with the influence of such factors as climate, location, and relief which originated in antiquity and was revived in modern times by such thinkers as Bodin, Montesquieu, and Carl Ritter, followed by (2) a more rigid determinism owing to the application of the Darwinian theory to human society. Cultures succeeded in the struggle for existence because of their ability to adapt themselves to limitations enforced by the physical environment. It was the Malthusian theory applied to human society, but in the form which Darwin in the *Origin of Species* had given it by applying Malthus' principle of population to the whole realm of organic nature. The older environmentalism led to an emphasis on geographical factors, influences, and controls, and the newer to an emphasis on the survival value of environmental adaptations. Environmentalism completely overshadowed the idea of man as a geographic agent, and the subject, instead of becoming a vital part of the study of man, was relegated to the technical and scientific literature.

The idea of a progressive cultural development through an ideal series of stages was a dominant one from the eighteenth century until the beginning of World War I. It is true that many writers defined progress in terms of man's increasing control over nature, but this was a control, acquired by a mastery of theoretical science and a knowledge of natural law, which was conscious and purposive in its application. Mankind dutifully marched through the stages of its cultural evolution guided by the philosophers and the schoolmasters. The earth—if it was considered at all—was the stage on which the drama was acted out. The idea that the haphazard, accidental, undesired, unintended, and unforeseen changes which were brought about by man in the pursuit of his economic and social goals might have a place in the histories of civilization and in the study of contemporary peoples was absent from this point of view.

THE LEGACY AND THE PROM-
ISE OF THE PAST

The ancient idea of a unity and design in nature and the Old Testament conception of the role of man on earth provided the basis for the impressive contributions of the seventeenth-century thinkers, like Ray, who gave a fuller meaning to the idea of a balance in nature. The works of French naturalists of the eighteenth century, like Buffon's, von Humboldt's study of plant associations in the different climatic regions of the earth, and Darwin's idea of a web of life, were in the same tradition. Ecological studies since Darwin have in the main adhered to the idea of a balance in nature. Today the concept, a fundamental one in the conservation philosophy, is involved in one of the most important controversies of our time: the influence of world population growth and of theoretical and applied science on the physical geography of the earth. Optimists have faith in the conscious and purposive power of science; pessimists see the destruction of the earth as a consequence of the haphazard and heedless disturbances of the balance of nature.

If human activities, however, are considered—or defined—as interferences with this balance, we assume the existence of a nature which is an abstraction, and we neglect the effects of prehistoric and historic cultures on the natural environment. These effects are historical events, and, if not regarded as such, the study of human cultures, with

their mass of customs and traditions, and the study of physical environments will go their separate ways, and the gap between the two will be bridged with metaphors.

If the problem is regarded as a historical one, we will attain a better understanding of the processes of cultural growth and the processes of nature. The themes mentioned by Buffon, Hehn, and Marsh have been enriched in our times by thinkers who have taken advantage of historical materials. Sauer's emphasis on historical periods like the Neolithic, the age of discovery, and modern industrial times as eras of great environmental change and his stress on the antiquity of human changes in the environment through the use of fire show the importance of studying environmental change throughout history (1938, 1950, 1952). Vavilov's studies (1951) of original areas of plant domestication and his conception of man as a strong force in the evolution of plants create a similar impression. British scholars have linked the study of nature with the study of history, for the British have long been interested in local history and in the changes which long settlement has brought about in their small island. Ritchie's study (1920) of the influence of man on the animal life of Scotland and Sherlock's study (1922) of man as a geological force in England are excellent illustrations of the use of historical materials. In Tansley's history (1939, pp. 147–210) of vegetational change in the British Isles, we see man maintaining or altering the vegetation, sometimes consciously, sometimes unconsciously, to suit the economic demands or the social goals of each historical period.

In this historical essay I have confined the discussion almost exclusively to ideas which have been developed in the Western tradition, because most of them owe their existence to two unique achievements of Western thought: science and critical scholarship. In looking back on the past, it seems that the thinkers of ancient and early modern times saw only the changes that appeared in localities known to them, that those of the eighteenth century realized these changes were world wide, and that the thinkers of the nineteenth recognized both their extent and their cumulative effect, while contemporary thinkers are impressed with the acceleration of change as a consequence of population growth and technological advance.

Today, with all our awareness of the power of man, many thinkers still regard this as a planned and purposefully applied power. The testimony of the past, in all its richness and variety, reminds us that this is a false view. The earth has felt the touch of man in ways which can be understood only by following the devious paths he has taken. The ideas and observations of the past suggest what these paths were—and where they led—and therefore will be a continuing source of new insights into the historical processes which have brought the earth to its present condition.

REFERENCES

Anonymous
  1911   *Restauration et conservation des terrains en montagne.* (Ministère de l'Agriculture: Direction Générale des Eaux et Forêts.) 3 vols. Paris: Imprimerie Nationale. (Historical and regional; contains many excellent illustrations.)

Becquerel, Antoine César
  1871   "Forests and Their Climatic Influence," *Annual Report of the Smithsonian Institution for the Year 1869*, pp. 394–416. Washington, D.C.: Government Printing Office. (Reviews ideas of climatic change.)

Bennett, Hugh Hammond
  1939   *Soil Conservation.* New York and London: McGraw-Hill Book Co. 993 pp.
  1944   *Thomas Jefferson, Soil Conservationist.* (U.S. Department of Agriculture Miscellaneous Publications, No. 548.) Washington, D.C.: Government Printing Office. 15 pp.

Boussingault, J. B.
  N.d.   *Rural Economy, in Its Relations with Chemistry, Physics, and Meteorology; or, Chemistry Applied to Agriculture.* Trans. with an Introduction and Notes, by George Law. New York: O. Judd & Co. 507 pp.

Brown, John Croumbie
  1877   *Forests and Moisture; or Effects of Forests on Humidity of Climate.* Edinburgh: Oliver & Boyd; London: Simpkin, Marshall & Co. 308 pp.

(All of Brown's works are valuable because of their extensive extracts.)
  1878   *Pine Plantations on the Sand-Wastes of France.* Edinburgh: Oliver & Boyd; London: Simpkin, Marshall & Co. 172 pp.
  1880   *Reboisment in France: Or Records of the Replanting of the Alps, the Cevennes, and the Pyrenees with Trees, Herbage and Bush, with a View To Arresting and Preventing the Destructive Consequences and Effects of Torrents.* London: Kegan Paul & Co. 351 pp.
  1883a   *The Forests of England and the Management of Them in Bye-Gone Times.* Edinburgh: Oliver & Boyd; London: Simpkin, Marshall & Co. 263 pp.
  1883b   *French Forest Ordinance of 1669; with Historical Sketch of Previous Treatment of Forests in France.* Edinburgh: Oliver & Boyd; London: Simpkin, Marshall & Co. 180 pp.
  1884   *Introduction to the Study of Modern Forest Economy.* Edinburgh: Oliver & Boyd; London: Simpkin, Marshall & Co. and William Rider & Son; Montreal: Dawson Bros. 228 pp.

Brunhes, Jean
  1920   *Human Geography, an Attempt at a Positive Classification: Principles and Examples.* Trans. from the French by T. C. Le Compte; ed. Isaiah Bowman and Richard El-

WOOD DODGE. Chicago and New York: Rand McNally & Co. 648 pp (Many references.)

BUFFON, COUNT DE (GEORGE LOUIS LE CLERC)
1799 "Époques de la nature," *Histoire générale et particulière*, III, 157–447; IV, 5–164. Paris: F. Dufart.
1866 *A Natural History, General and Particular: Containing the History and Theory of the Earth, a General History of Man, the Brute Creation, Vegetables, Minerals, &c. &c.* Trans. from the French by WILLIAM SMELLIE. 2 vols. London: Thomas Kelly & Co. (Volume II [pp. 151–86] contains a partial translation of "Époques de la nature.")

BURNET, THOMAS
1753 *The Sacred Theory of the Earth.* 2 vols. Glasgow: R. Urie.

CANDOLLE, ALPHONSE DE
1855 *Géographie botanique raisonnée; ou exposition des faits principaux et des lois concernant la distribution géographique des plantes de l'époque actuelle.* 2 vols. Paris: V. Masson.

CHAMBERLIN, THOMAS C., and SALISBURY, ROLLIN D.
1904 *Geology*, Vol. I: *Geologic Processes and Their Results.* New York: Henry Holt & Co. 684 pp.

CICERO
1894 *Tusculan Disputations; Also Treatises on the Nature of the Gods and on the Commonwealth.* Literally Trans. from the Latin, Chiefly by C. D. YONGE. ("Harper's New Classical Library.") New York: Harper & Bros. 466 pp.

COLUMELLA, LUCIUS JUNIUS MODERATUS
1941 *On Agriculture.* Trans. from the Latin by HARRISON BOYD ASH. ("Loeb Classical Library," Vol. I.) Cambridge, Mass.: Harvard University Press. 461 pp.

CURTIUS, ERNST
1851 *Peloponnesos: Eine historisch-geographische Beschreibung der Halbinsel.* 2 vols. Gotha: Justus Perthes.

DERHAM, WILLIAM
1798 *Physico-theology: Or a Demonstration of the Being and Attributes of God, from His Works of Creation.*
New ed. 2 vols. London: A. Strahan, T. Cadell Jun & W. Davies; Edinburgh: W. Creech. (Valuable notes by the editor.)

EVELYN, JOHN
1786 *Silva: Or a Discourse of Forest Trees, and the Propagation of Timber in His Majesty's Dominions.* New ed. 2 vols. York: A. Ward. (Many references to contemporary materials.)

FEBVRE, LUCIEN, in collaboration with LIONEL BETAILLON
1925 *A Geographical Introduction to History.* Trans. from the French by E. G. MOUNTFORD and J. W. PAXTON. London: K. Paul, Trench, Trubner & Co.; New York: Alfred A. Knopf. 388 pp.

FELS, EDWIN
1935 *Der Mench als Gestalter der Erde: Ein Beitrag zur allgemeinen Wirtschafts- und Verkehrsgeographie.* Leipzig: Bibliographisches Institut. 206 pp. (Many references; interesting historical introduction.)

FISCHER, ERNST
1915 "Der Mensch als geologischer Faktor," *Zeitschrift der Deutsche Geologische Gesellschaft*, LXVII, 106–48. (A remarkable work, including discussions of antiquity of man's role as a geologic agent, mineral exhaustion, and civilization and water.)

FRAAS, C.
1847 *Klima und Pflanzenwelt in der Zeit, ein Beitrag zur Geschichte Beider.* Landshut: Verlag von J. G. Wölfle. 137 pp. (Many references to contemporary materials.)

FRANKFORT, HENRI; FRANKFORT, MRS. HENRI; WILSON, JOHN A.; and JACOBSEN, THORKILD
1951 *Before Philosophy: The Intellectual Adventure of Ancient Man.* Harmondsworth: Penguin Books. 275 pp.

FRIEDRICH, ERNST
1904 "Wesen und geographische Verbreitung der 'Raubwirtschaft,'" *Petermanns Mitteilungen*, L, 68–79, 92–95. (Many references to contemporary materials.)

GREGORY, J. W.
1914 "Is the Earth Drying Up?" *Geographical Journal*, XLIII, 148–72,

293–318. (Discussion of theories of desiccation; many references.)

HEHN, VICTOR
1888 *The Wanderings of Plants and Animals from Their First Home.* Ed. JAMES S. STALLYBRASS. London: Swan Sonnenschein & Co. 523 pp.
1902 *Kulturpflanzen und Hausthiere in ihrem Übergang aus Asien nach Griechenland und Italien sowie in das Übrige Europa.* 7th ed. Berlin: Gebrüder Bornträger. 651 pp.

HESIOD
1879 *The Works of Hesiod, Callimachus, and Theognis.* Trans. from the Greek by J. BANKS. ("Bohn's Classical Library.") London: George Bell & Sons. 495 pp.

HOUGH, FRANKLIN B.
1878 *Report upon Forestry: Prepared under the Direction of the Commissioner of Agriculture, in Pursuance of an Act of Congress Approved August 15, 1876.* Washington, D.C.: Government Printing Office. 650 pp. (Like Brown's works, an excellent source for nineteenth-century ideas of climatic change and deforestation. Many quotations and extracts.)

HUMBOLDT, ALEXANDER DE, and BONPLAND, A.
1807 *Essai sur la géographie des plantes, accompagné d'un tableau physique des régions équinoxiales.* Paris: F. Schoell. 155 pp.

HUMBOLDT, ALEXANDER VON
1849 *Aspects of Nature in Different Lands and Different Climates; with Scientific Elucidations.* Trans. from the French by MRS. SABINE. Philadelphia: Lea & Blanchard. 475 pp.
1852 *Personal Narrative of Travels to the Equinoctial Regions of America, during the Years 1799–1804.* Trans. and ed. from the French by THOMASINA ROSS. 3 vols. London: Henry G. Bohn.

HUNTINGTON, ELLSWORTH
1915 *Civilization and Climate.* New Haven, Conn.: Yale University Press. 333 pp.

JACKS, G. V., and WHYTE, R. O.
1939 *Vanishing Lands: A World Survey of Soil Erosion.* New York: Doubleday, Doran & Co. 332 pp.

KROPOTKIN, PRINCE
1904 "The Desiccation of Eur-Asia," *Geographical Journal,* XXIII, 722–41.

LEONARDO DA VINCI
1954 *The Notebooks of Leonardo da Vinci.* Arranged, Rendered into English, and Introduced by EDWARD MacCURDY. New York: Georges Braziller & Co. 1,247 pp.

LOVEJOY, ARTHUR O.
1948 *The Great Chain of Being: A Study of the History of an Idea.* (William James Lectures Delivered at Harvard University, 1933.) Cambridge, Mass.: Harvard University Press. 382 pp.

LOWDERMILK, WALTER CLAY
1943 "Lessons from the Old World to the Americas in Land Use," *Annual Report of the Smithsonian Institution, 1943,* pp. 413–27. Washington, D.C.: Government Printing Office.

LUCRETIUS
1947 *Titi Lucreti Cari De rerum natura.* Ed. with Prolegomena, Critical Apparatus, Translation, and Commentary, by CYRIL BAILEY. Oxford: Clarendon Press. 581 pp. (Vol. I contains text and translation.)

LYELL, CHARLES
1830–33 *Principles of Geology, Being an Attempt To Explain the Former Changes of the Earth's Surface, by Reference to Causes Now Operating.* 3 vols. London: J. Murray.
1849 *A Second Visit to the United States of North America.* 2 vols. London: J. Murray.
1872 *Principles of Geology; or, The Modern Changes of the Earth and Its Inhabitants Considered as Illustrative of Geology.* 11th rev. ed. 2 vols. New York: D. Appleton & Co.

McDONALD, ANGUS
1941 *Early American Soil Conservationists.* (U.S. Department of Agriculture Miscellaneous Publications, No. 449.) Washington, D.C.: Government Printing Office. 62 pp. (Full bibliography.)

MARSH, GEORGE P.
1864 *Man and Nature, or Physical*

Geography as Modified by Human Action. New York: Charles Scribner & Co.; London: Sampson, Low & Son. 577 pp. (All of Marsh's works are richly documented.)

1874   *The Earth as Modified by Human Action: A New Edition of "Man and Nature."* New York: Scribner, Armstrong & Co. 656 pp.

1885   *The Earth as Modified by Human Action: A Last Revision of "Man and Nature."* New York: C. Scribner's Sons. 629 pp.

MAURY, ALFRED

1856   *Les Forêts de la France dans l'antiquité et au moyen âge: Nouveaux essais sur leur topographie, leur histoire et la legislation qui les régissait.* Paris: Imprimerie Impériale. 270 pp. (Many references to ancient and medieval sources.)

MENCIUS

1933   *The Four Books: Confucian Analects, The Great Learning, The Doctrine of the Mean, and The Works of Mencius.* Trans. from the Chinese with Notes by JAMES LEGGE. Shanghai: Chinese Book Co. 1,014 pp.

MUMFORD, LEWIS

1931   *The Brown Decades: A Study of the Arts in America, 1865–1895.* New York: Harcourt, Brace & Co. 266 pp.

PLATO

1926   *Laws.* Trans. from the Greek by R. G. BURY. ("Loeb Classical Library.") 2 vols. London: Heinemann; New York: G. P. Putnam's Sons.

1929   *Plato: Timaeus and Critias.* Trans. from the Greek by A. E. TAYLOR. London: Methuen & Co. 133 pp.

PLINY THE ELDER (GAIUS PLINIUS SECUNDUS)

1938–52   *Natural History.* Trans. from the Latin by H. RACKHAM. ("Loeb Classical Library.") Cambridge, Mass.: Harvard University Press. (Vols. I–VI, IX.)

PUMPELLY, RAPHAEL

1908   *Explorations in Turkestan: Expedition of 1904, and Prehistoric Civilizations of Anau: Origins, Growth, and Influence of Environment.* 2 vols. Washington D.C.: Carnegie Institution.

RAVEN, CHARLES E.

1942   *John Ray, Naturalist: His Life and Works.* Cambridge: Cambridge University Press. 502 pp.

RAY, JOHN

1759   *The Wisdom of God Manifested in the Works of the Creation.* 12th ed. corrected. London: John Rivington, John Ward, Joseph Richardson. 405 pp.

RECLUS, ÉLISÉE

1873   *The Ocean, Atmosphere, and Life: Being the Second Series of a Descriptive History of the Life of the Globe.* New York: Harper & Bros. 534 pp.

RICHTHOFEN, FERDINAND FREIHERR VON

1877–1912   *China: Ergebnisse eigener Reisen und darauf gegründeter Studien.* 5 vols. Berlin: D. Reimer.

RITCHIE, JAMES

1920   *The Influence of Man on Animal Life in Scotland: A Study in Faunal Evolution.* Cambridge: Cambridge University Press. 550 pp.

SAUER, CARL O.

1938   "Theme of Plant and Animal Destruction in Economic History," *Journal of Farm Economics,* XX, 765–75.

1950   "Grassland Climax, Fire, and Man," *Journal of Range Management,* III, 16–21.

1952   *Agricultural Origins and Dispersals.* (Bowman Memorial Lectures, Series Two.) New York: American Geographical Society. 110 pp.

SAUSSURE, HORACE-BÉNÉDICT DE

1779   *Voyages dans les Alpes, précédés d'un essai sur l'histoire naturelle des environs de Genève.* 2 vols. Neuchâtel: Chez Samuel Fauche Imprimeur et Libraire du Roi.

SCHLEIDEN, M. J.

1848   *The Plant: A Biography.* Trans. from the German by ARTHUR HENFREY. London: Hippolyte Baillière. 365 pp.

SCHOUW, JOACHIM FREDERIC

1852   *The Earth, Plants, and Man.* Trans. and ed. from the Danish by ARTHUR HENFREY. ("Bohn's Scientific Library.") London: Henry G. Bohn. 402 pp.

SENECA, L. ANNAEUS
1912 *On Benefits.* Trans. from the Latin by AUBREY STEWART. London: George Bell & Sons. 227 pp.

SHALER, NATHANIEL S.
1891 "The Origin and Nature of Soils," *Twelfth Annual Report of the United States Geological Survey, 1890–1891,* Part I: *Geology,* pp. 213–345. Washington, D.C.: Government Printing Office.
1896 "The Economic Aspects of Soil Erosion," *National Geographic Magazine,* VII, 328–30, 368–77.
1904–5 "Earth and Man: An Economic Forecast," *International Quarterly,* X, 227–39.
1905*a* "The Future of Power," *ibid.,* XI, 24–38.
1905*b* "The Exhaustion of the World's Metals," *ibid.,* pp. 230–47.
1912 *Man and the Earth.* New York: Duffield & Co. 240 pp. (Some chapters are reprinted from the *International Quarterly* articles.)

SHERLOCK, ROBERT L.
1922 *Man as a Geological Agent: An Account of His Action on Inanimate Nature.* London: H. F. & G. Witherby. 372 pp.

SPENCER, HERBERT
1866–67 *The Principles of Biology.* 2 vols. New York: D. Appleton & Co.

TANSLEY, A. G.
1939 *The British Islands and Their Vegetation.* Cambridge: Cambridge University Press. 930 pp.

UNWIN, A. H.
N.d. *Goat-grazing and Forestry in Cyprus.* London: Crosby Lockwood & Son. 163 pp. (Contains many extracts regarding goat devastation throughout the world.)

VAN HISE, CHARLES RICHARD
1910 *The Conservation of Natural Resources in the United States.* New York: Macmillan Co. 413 pp.

VARRO, MARCUS T.
1912 *On Farming.* Trans. from the Latin by LLOYD STORR-BEST. London: George Bell & Sons. 375 pp.

VAVILOV, NIKOLAI IVANOVICH
1951 *The Origin, Variation, Immunity and Breeding of Cultivated Plants.* Trans. from the Russian by K. STARR CHESTER. (*Chronica botanica,* Vol. XIII, Nos. 1–6.) Waltham, Mass.: Chronica Botanica Co. 366 pp.

VERNADSKY, W. I.
1944 "Problems of Biogeochemistry. II. The Fundamental Matter-Energy Difference between the Living and the Inert Natural Bodies of the Biosphere," *Transactions of the Connecticut Academy of Arts and Sciences,* XXXV, 483–517.

VIDAL DE LA BLACHE, PAUL
1926 *Principles of Human Geography.* Ed. EMMANUEL DE MARTONNE; trans. from the French by MILLICENT TODD BINGHAM. New York: Henry Holt & Co. 511 pp.

WHITAKER, J. R.
1940 "World View of Destruction and Conservation of Natural Resources," *Annals of the Association of American Geographers,* XXX, 143–62. (Late-nineteenth-century writers.)

WOEIKOF, ALEXANDER
1901 "De l'influence de l'homme sur la terre," *Annales de géographie,* X, 97–114, 193–215. (Excellently documented; includes materials relating to France, Poland, Russia, China.)

Cultural Differences in the Interpretation of Natural Resources

ALEXANDER SPOEHR[*]

An examination of the interpretation that different peoples have placed on the natural resources on which they depend falls in the more general field of human ecology. The relation of any human population to its natural resources is only part of a more inclusive set of relationships between such a population and its total natural environment. "Human ecology," though variously and often vaguely defined as a field of specific subject matter, emphasizes relationships with the environment and, as Bates (1953) has said, achieves its greatest usefulness as a point of view. The subject of this paper, therefore, is a part of human ecology, and the following remarks will stress a point of view rather than attempt a synthesis of a body of scientific literature.

I am indebted to Carl Sauer for pointing out that the concept "natural resources" is largely derived from our own society's ceaseless attempt at finding new and more intensive uses for the raw materials of nature. It is doubtful that many other societies, most of which are less involved with technological development, think about natural resources in the same way as we do. It is probable that the term itself, with the feeling tones that it carries, is primarily a product of our own industrial civilization. For this reason it is not possible to take the body of ethnographic accounts of different peoples and obtain a clear-cut view as to exactly what interpretation has been placed on their natural resources by non-Western societies in different places and at different times. In ethnographic accounts chapters dealing with such peoples are seldom written quite that way.

In the following review it has been necessary to tie a cross-cultural comparison of the interpretation of natural resources to several rather arbitrarily selected reference points. Three have been chosen and will be examined in turn: (1) natural resources in relation to technology; (2) natural resources in relation to social structure; and (3) natural resources and the interpretation of habitat. Of these three reference points, the first is most restricted in scope. The remaining two involve a progressively wider range of subject matter.

NATURAL RESOURCES AND TECHNOLOGY

It is a truism that every society must adapt itself to its environment to survive. This adaptation is largely effected through the particular technology that a given society has developed and main-

*Dr. Spoehr is Director of the Bernice P. Bishop Museum, Honolulu, Hawaii, a position to which he was appointed in 1953. From 1940 to 1952 he was a member of the staff of the Department of Anthropology, Chicago Natural History Museum. He has conducted anthropological field work among the Indians of the southeastern United States and in the Marshall, Mariana, and Palau island groups of Micronesia. His publications include: *Majuro: A Village in the Marshall Islands*, 1949, and *Saipan: The Ethnology of a War-devastated Island*, 1954.

tains. Viewed in world perspective and from the vantage point of man's history on earth, the variety of technical systems is very great, ranging from the simple technology of food-collectors such as the Australian aborigines or the Great Basin Indians of North America to the highly complex technology of Western industrial civilization. Various classifications of technologies have been devised, and no attempt will be made here to extend them (Forde, 1934). The point is rather that, regardless of the degree of complexity of a given technology, every technology is necessarily based on a thorough knowledge of the natural resources which are utilized through the working of the technology. A food-collecting technology may be of a very simple order, but the men who practice it must of necessity have a sound empirical knowledge of that sector of the natural environment that provides the food they seek.

This point is made merely to emphasize that so-called "primitive" peoples do not exist in a state of ignorance of the natural world about them. It is true that the knowledge they possess is essentially empirical and that the over-all characteristics of a people's technology tend to direct their interest to those particular resources of nature on which they depend. Thus the population densities of some of the Micronesian atolls are so high in relation to their few square miles of dry-land area that these communities could not possibly survive without the fish resources of the atoll lagoons. A large sector of the technology of these atoll dwellers is comprised of skills and techniques associated with fishing, the building of canoes, and seamanship, which in turn is related to an intimate knowledge of fish species, the habits and relative abundance of various species, whether or not they are poisonous, and similar matters. A given technology, by making possible a particular kind of adaptation, tends to crystallize interest and knowledge around that segment of natural resources on which the technology depends.

Anthropological literature abounds also in examples of different peoples inhabiting the same or very similar habitats but who have made use of different sectors of the resources of their habitat. There may be a high degree of selectivity of particular resources around which the technology is centered. An interesting example can be given from Hawaii. In the days when the Hawaiians had their islands to themselves, they were fishermen and farmers. Their agricultural economy was built particularly on the cultivation of taro, which was grown chiefly in irrigated plots in the bottom-land areas of coastal valleys, usually with very high rainfall. Such a valley, famous in local history, is that of Waipio on the island of Hawaii. It is estimated that at one time from three to four thousand people lived in Waipio. During the nineteenth and twentieth centuries the economy of Hawaii completely changed. With the influx of immigrants from America, Europe, and Asia, the economy of the island of Hawaii changed to large-scale agriculture, centered on sugar cane, coffee, and cattle-raising, for none of which Waipio is suitable. The valley's population today has dwindled to twenty-six persons, and a great part of it has been abandoned. Its soil resources are neglected, for present-day large-scale agricultural technology in use on the island is not suited to them, and they have been by-passed.

The example from Hawaii again illustrates the point that interest in specific natural resources and the uses to which they are put is greatly conditioned by the nature of the technology imposed upon such resources. Technology is in itself a part of man's culture, and the interpretation of specific resources cannot be understood except as a facet of human culture.

To a considerable degree, the interest of our own society in the availability, renewability, and exploitability of natural resources springs from our singular bent toward technological invention. It is true that technological invention has been a potent force throughout man's long history on earth. Yet, viewed against the background of human history, our industrial civilization of the twentieth century has developed in a very short time. One of its characteristics, related, of course, to the growth of science, is its concern with invention. This concern the anthropologist does not find to be shared with all societies. Among many, once an adaptation to a given environment has been made through the medium of a particular technology, the manner of thought imbedded in the culture of these societies may actually militate against the inventive process. One of the best examples is given by Raymond Firth in his outstanding study of the economy of Tikopia, a very isolated small island in the southwestern Pacific. Firth (1939) notes that the material culture and the technology of Tikopia are very closely adjusted to the resources of the island environment. He notes further that the Tikopians are in no way loath to accept trade goods in the form of useful tools. However, the Polynesian people of this small island "have formulated no particular doctrine of technical invention" (*ibid.*, p. 86). Their interest is centered on legendary origins of how they themselves came to be rather than on technological origins and on the technical processes of invention and change.

Although the variety of cultures possessed by non-literate, non-Western societies is so great that the appellation "primitive" is usually a misnomer, it is true that such societies are generally small and tied to a local habitat. Every local habitat imposes certain limitations on a purely local technology. The people of a Pacific atoll must of necessity exist within the limitations of an atoll environment. It is true that as taro-raisers the Marshall Islanders have challenged the natural limitations of their atoll environment by excavating large pits in the coral lime sands of the atoll islets and, by creating humus, through filling these pits with decaying vegetable matter, are able to raise taro. This is a small-scale example of how one society has successfully challenged environmental restrictions. Yet the contrast is great when compared with the manner in which contemporary Western industrial civilization has freed itself from local environmental bonds and through its technology is world wide in scope. Chapple and Coon (1942, p. 249) have pointed out that technologically less complex societies tend to exploit single landscapes, whereas "we . . . live in all environments, not by exploiting single landscapes, separately, but by pooling and redistributing the products of all types of environment." A marked difference in the cultural interpretation of natural resources among different peoples follows from this fact. In small-scale preliterate societies concern with natural resources tends to be local; ours is world wide.

NATURAL RESOURCES AND SOCIAL STRUCTURE

So far we have touched on the relation of resources to technology, which in the last analysis comprises the characteristics of a society's tool system for converting raw materials into finished products. The techniques available to a society, however, are but one facet of its total economy. The latter comprehends also a body of generally accepted concepts regarding the control and use of resources, goods, and productive processes—such as those concepts embodied in the terms "income," "capital," and "rent"—and, in addition, the particular manner in which human beings are organized to carry out activities generally labeled as economic. In this latter category are the particular ways in which the individuals working in a factory or on a farm are organized, or the manner in which the market of a Mexican town is organized. In each case, interpersonal relations tend to fall in definable patterns, into a system of relationships that tends to persist so long as the common end—such as the exchange of goods—is being pursued. This organization of human beings in economic activity is but part of the total social structure of a society. Economic organization is related at many points to other segments of social structure. Thus, the organization of a craft industry carried out in individual households is closely related to the prevailing characteristics of the system of relations among the kinfolk of the various households. A people's kinship system is only in part an aspect of their economy.

This point is made because the use of natural resources is controlled by the nature of social structure in addition to a body of productive techniques alone. One cannot consider the link between natural resources and man merely as a matter of converting raw materials into goods through a given technology in order to house, feed, and clothe so-and-so many people, essential as these facts are.

For purposes of illustration and contrast, the following example from a technologically less complex society may be useful.

To the atoll dwellers of the Marshall Islands the coconut palm, as well as the fish resources of the sea, is a mainstay of life. A relatively simple body of techniques employing hand labor makes possible the use of the coconut for food, for export as copra, and for a variety of other products. However, the control of the coconut palm as a natural resource, the organization of production whereby it is converted into usable goods, and the distribution of income derived from its production are all linked to Marshallese social structure. The Marshall Islanders retain a feudal-like class system of nobility and commoners. Title to all the land of the atoll nominally rests with the paramount chief. Usufruct rights are apportioned among the lesser chiefs and, in turn, among the commoners. Land is not sold, and our own concepts of ownership of real property are foreign to the system. The commoners cultivate the land, and the nobility receive tribute in the form of produce. Today, a share of cash receipts from the sale of copra is also remitted to the paramount chief as tribute. In addition, land rights are, for the most part, held by lineages of kinfolk who trace descent in the matrilineal line. Each lineage has a head who represents the lineage, and the headship as an office is also passed down in the matrilineal line. Lineages, the class organization, and land tenure are all interrelated elements of a single system. As a result, to the Marshallese, the control and use of land resources are mediated through the particular characteristics of their social structure.

The significance of cultural factors in relation to resources is perhaps most clearly discerned during periods of rapid change. Cultural change is a complex, but not a haphazard, phenomenon. At times it may follow a rigidly defined course that from a biologist's point of view is non-adaptive, in so far as the conservation and use of resources is concerned. An oft-quoted example is found in the cattle-raising peoples of East Africa, among whom cattle are so highly regarded and are so fundamental a basis of status within the community that the greatest resistance to a reduction of herds has been encountered among these people, despite serious depletion of resources (Read, 1938). A somewhat similar case is provided by the resistance of the Navaho to reduction of sheep on their overgrazed ranges.

The purpose of these examples is simply to emphasize that any group "interprets" its natural resources within the framework of its own social structure. The point at which this probably is most apparent is in the organization of production, for it is in production that the manner of control and the use of natural resources are most evident. The initial point in the productive process is the conversion of raw materials into goods. The raw materials are derived from resources in their natural state. If the resources are especially limited, restrictive rights to their use may exist. Our own concepts of "ownership" may be viewed as the conjunction of our own particular social system and limited resources. Yet Western ideas of ownership are by no means universal and are but one example of how an exclusive right may be culturally defined. The Pacific islands provide examples of differently conceived rights to resources, where Western concepts of ownership are not applicable. Yet, among these peoples, rights controlling how resources, particularly land, are to be used and who is entitled to exercise control can also be viewed as the conjunction of social structure and habitat. The case of the Marshallese has been noted. For more extensive analyses of other island societies the reader is referred to Firth (1929, 1939), to Hogbin (1939), and to Herskovits' recent (1952) general review of the problem of ownership and land tenure.

NATURAL RESOURCES AND HABITAT

Natural resources are physically a part of habitat, and habitat is but one aspect of that complex of physical, chemical, and biological processes, with their resultant products, which we call "nature." Modern man has conceptually isolated natural resources as that segment of the physical world that has a present or potential use for the survival and physical well-being of man, to be developed as far as possible through the application of scientific knowledge. Yet natural resources are still a part of nature.

The title of this paper, with its emphasis on the "interpretation" of natural resources, implies a comparison of attitudes held by different peoples toward natural resources. But, to return to a point made earlier, concern for the development of "natural resources" seems largely a facet of modern civilization. What is necessary is an examination, not merely of culturally conditioned attitudes toward natural resources, but of how various peoples have come to regard their relationship with their respective habitats (of which resources are but a part) and indeed with the entire physical universe in which they exist. It is at this point that the most fundamental contrast can be discerned between the Western industrial world and small-scale, often preliterate, societies.

This subject has been explored and presented, in a much more expert fashion than that of which I am capable, by Robert Redfield in his recent book, *The Primitive World and Its Transformations*. It is a subject that anthropologists have long pondered, though few with the breadth of interest displayed by Redfield. His presentation is the point of departure for the following paragraphs.

For the purpose of this essay there are two questions that are particularly relevant: (1) How have men, in different times and places, regarded nature, and hence the habitats in which they dwell? (2) How have these attitudes affected what men feel they should do about conserving and developing their habitats for human use?

In regard to the first question, the initial point to be made is taken from Redfield and the writers that he in turn draws upon. It is that virtually every people regards the universe in some sort of structured cosmology. The degree to which this cosmology is systematized varies enormously. The points of emphasis vary enormously. But everywhere, and since ancient times, man has pondered his relation to the physical facts of the universe and has attempted to see man, nature, and the supernatural in some sort of understandable relation. In this, my feeling from reading the accounts of ethnologists is the same as Redfield's (1953, pp. 105–6)—that preliterate peoples, in regarding the universe, "think of an orderly system originally set running by divine will and thereafter exhibiting its immanent order." Whether the gods do or can interfere in the machine they have set running is either not thought about or perhaps not reported sufficiently by ethnologists. It seems more probable that preliterate peoples tend to regard the universe as operating under irreversible laws, once these are set in motion.

And how is man's place regarded in this scheme? To what degree is he subject also to an order established under supernatural sanction? Here at least most preliterate societies offer a contrast with our own. The contrast is well exemplified in the opening paragraph of Elsdon Best's monograph, *Forest Lore of the Maori*. The contrast is shown both in Best's point of view and in that of the Maori of whom he was writing:

The outlook of the Maori, as in connection with natural phenomena and nature generally, often differed widely from our own; thus he looked upon the far spread forests of his island home as being necessary to his welfare, and also as being of allied origin. This peculiar outlook was based on the strange belief that man, birds, and trees are descended from a common source; their ultimate origin lay with the primal pair, Rangi the Sky Parent and Papa the Earth Mother, though they were actually brought into being by Tane the Fertilizer, one of the seventy offspring of the above-mentioned primal parents [Best, 1942, p. 1].

Man, to many peoples, is not set apart from nature but is part of a single order, combining man, nature, and the gods. When man utilizes the resources of nature, it is within the framework of this system of ideas. Thus, in writing of the lack of interest in technological invention displayed by the island people of Tikopia, Firth notes (1939, p. 88) that the Tikopia are governed by their theory of natural resources, which "may be described briefly as a theory of the human utilization of resources under supernatural control, which governs not only their fertility, but also the social and economic relationships of those who handle them."

Within this essentially stable system, man and nature are not conceptually opposed but are considered as parts of the same thing. The totemic rites of the Australian Karadjeri, whereby the economically and socially important species of plants and animals were believed to be assured of normal increase, reflected a similar manner of thought (Elkin, 1933). When Gayton, writing of the integration of culture and environment effected through economic activity, ceremony, and myth among the Yokuts Indians, states (1946, p. 262) that "men and animals were peers," much the same idea is expressed.

In his consideration of the involvement of man and nature in the thought of preliterate and ancient societies, Redfield notes (1953, p. 104) that the men of these societies did not "confront" nature. For them, "being already in nature, man cannot exactly confront it." Rather, Redfield suggests, the relation is one of mutuality, existing under a moral order that binds man, nature, and the gods in one.

The modern Western world has undergone a major transformation from this orientation. Man has been conceptually separated from nature, and God from both. Speaking of the development of Western thought since classical times, Redfield (pp. 109–10) states:

The subsequent development of a world view in which God and man are both separated from nature, and in which the exploitation of material nature comes to be a prime attitude, may be attributable to our Western world almost entirely and so might be regarded, as Sol Tax has suggested (Tax, 1944), as a particular "cultural invention." By the seventeenth century in European philosophy God was outside the system as its mere clockmaker. To the early American, nature was God's provision for man's exploitation. . . . The contemporary Western world, now imitated by the Orient, tends to regard the relation of man to nature as a relation of man to physical matter in which application of physical science to man's material comfort is man's paramount assignment on earth.

These observations may appear overdrawn to some, but they illustrate what I believe is a fundamental contrast in the thinking of the Western world, as contrasted to preliterate and ancient peoples. It is a contrast that in itself is a least a partial answer to our second question posed earlier—namely, how has this contrasting attitude affected what men feel they should do about developing their habitats for human use? Certainly the tenor of contemporary American thought holds that habitat is something apart from man and is to be manipulated to his advantage. In the world of today, with the ever growing millions of human beings to clothe, feed, and house, this attitude has a very immediate and practical import.

On the other hand, despite the long history of the growth of technology, throughout which some men as far back as the earliest periods of human history must have been concerned with improving tools to develop resources for human use, preliterate societies lack the pervading instrumental attitude toward nature generally characteristic of ourselves. The difference probably accounts for the significance of magic associated with technology, which Malinowski long ago reported for the Trobriand Islands. Among these people, although their full technological skill is called upon in an enterprise, such as gardening, fishing, or voyaging, recourse to magic is had to fill the inevitable gap between the application of human skill and the certainty of success.

The contrasting attitudes of Western and preliterate thought lead to another question. For several decades anthropologists have been attempting to observe the changes that take place in small scale, for the most preliterate, societies, when they come in contact with Western industrial civilization. In so far as the interpretation of natural resources is concerned, is not the contrast just discussed at the root of the change that takes place? I suspect it is. To review all the evidence is beyond the scope of this paper, but I quote an anthropological colleague, John Gillin, comparing the Indian and the Ladino cultures (crystallized out of contact with Spain) of Guatemala:

The principal and fundamental goal of Indian cultures is to effect a peaceful adjustment or adaptation to the universe. In contrast, the main goal of Ladino culture is to effect control of the universe by man. The Indian wishes to come to terms with the universe, the Ladino wishes to dominate it. . . . The Indian attitude is not one of abject submission to natural and supernatural forces. The basic assumptions in Indian cultures, however, do hold that man is in a world which operates according to certain laws or rules ultimately controlled by that part of the universe which we would call the supernatural or unseen, that this general plan of things is ongoing or immutable, that man must learn certain patterns of action and attitude to bring himself into conformity with this scheme of things, and that if he does so he will receive the minimum amount of punishment or misfortune and the maximum rewards of which such a scheme is capable. . . . The Ladino, on the other hand, assumes that the universe, including its supernatural department, can be manipulated by man . . . [Gillin, 1952, p. 196].

The gradual adoption of this attitude could, I believe, be documented from other societies in contact with the West. It seems to have been, for instance, a concomitant of the extension of the copra industry to various islands of the Pacific during the nineteenth and twentieth centuries. The development of the copra industry in the Marshall Islands was almost certainly accompanied by a marked change in attitude toward land, whereby it came to be regarded as a resource to be controlled and manipulated by man to his best advantage, in a fashion comparable to the Ladino point of view described by Gillin. To what degree the extension of this attitude follows the penetration of a money economy into societies such as the Marshallese, together with the growth of trade and a widening in the range of wants, is not clear.

If these contrasting attitudes toward nature, and in consequence toward natural resources, have been correctly described in these paragraphs, I should like to turn to some ramifications in regard to the interpretation of nature by our own society.

To the degree that the Western world is composed of almost completely urbanized individuals, it not merely regards habitat, and consequently natural resources, as an entity that is to be dominated and manipulated by man but tends to relegate the whole matter to a handful of specialists and, in effect, to place nature outside its immediate sphere of concern. Urban man has be-

come so far removed from his biological moorings and so immersed in the immediate problems of urban living that he stands as an "egocentric man in a homocentric world." Despite the millions of Americans who annually visit our national parks each year, it is to be doubted that much change is thereby effected in the basic urban attitude. The aesthetic principles underlying American conservation movements can perhaps best be viewed as a minority reaction to the prevailing urban point of view. Conservation, in the sense of the attempt by the Save-the-Redwoods League to preserve stands of California giant sequoias from extinction, is an effort to protect modern man from himself. Such efforts are not, to my knowledge, found among preliterate peoples living in small communities in close and personal relation to nature. Among most of them, though it is largely unrecorded in the reports of ethnologists, I suspect that the aesthetic appreciation of nature is a common feature of daily life. Yet I should add that most of my own field experience has been in the congenial islands of the Pacific.

If the prevailing mode of thought tends to regard nature as a physical entity apart from man, with the corollary that man's duty is to develop and dominate to the best of his ability the resources of his habitat, there are nevertheless certain countercurrents in contemporary scientific thought that cannot be ignored. These countercurrents are well exemplified by Darwin and Faraday.

Darwin opened our eyes to the functioning of organic nature, and his mode of thought led to discovery of new facts and relationships in the living world. Darwin dealt with man's place in nature and with man as a part of a huge, dynamic biocoenose, of which man was only a small part, actually not very different from the other parts, and subject to the same processes and regularities. In his point of view as to man's integration with the natural world, Darwin might be considered as close to the way in which preliterate peoples regard nature, except for the fundamental difference that the former developed his point of view on the basis of observed reality; the latter, on recourse to the sanction of man-created legend and myth. Darwin left to his successors the concept of man as a part of nature, whatever qualities man may possess that distinguish him from other forms of life.

Faraday, on the other hand, introduced us to inanimate forces which could be made to serve man's needs and wants. He stimulated the invention of new devices and the formation of a great new technology based on the use of natural forces. He also stimulated the creation of a homocentric world, a modern, mechanized, exploiting world of men whose contemplating largely centers about themselves and who attempt to plan, arrange, and administer in their own name. Whereas the heritage of Darwin has provided the fascination of biological revelation, that of Faraday has brought the excitement attending the accomplishment and application of the physical sciences.

In a modern world where men are dedicated to exploiting to the utmost the natural resources of this planet— a dedication that is stimulated by the very numbers of men on earth—the point of view exemplified by Faraday is necessarily uppermost. It could hardly be otherwise. Yet one cannot forget the bearded figure of Darwin watching quietly from the shadows.

REFERENCES

BATES, MARSTON
  1950 *The Nature of Natural History.* New York: Charles Scribner's Sons. 309 pp.
  1953 "Human Ecology," pp. 700–714 in KROEBER, A. L. (Chairman), *Anthropology Today: An Encyclopedic Inventory.* Chicago: University of Chicago Press. 966 pp.
BEST, ELSDON
  1925 *Maori Agriculture.* (Bulletin No. 9.) Wellington, N.Z.: Dominion Museum. 172 pp.
  1942 *Forest Lore of the Maori.* (Bulletin No. 14.) Wellington, N. Z.: Dominion Museum. 503 pp.
BEWS, J. W.
  1935 *Human Ecology.* London: H. Milford. 312 pp.
CHAPPLE, E. D., and COON, C. S.
  1942 *Principles of Anthropology.* New York: Henry Holt & Co. 718 pp.
DARWIN, SIR FRANCIS (ed.)
  1950 *Charles Darwin's Autobiography.* New York: Henry Schuman. 266 pp.
ELKIN, A. P.
  1933 *Studies in Australian Totemism.* ("Oceania Monographs," No. 2.) Sydney. 131 pp.

EVANS-PRITCHARD, E. E.
  1940 *The Nuer: A Description of the Modes of Livelihood and Political Institutions of a Nilotic People.* Oxford: Clarendon Press. 271 pp.
FIRTH, RAYMOND
  1929 *Primitive Economics of the New Zealand Maori.* London: G. Routledge & Sons; New York: E. P. Dutton & Co. 505 pp.
  1939 *Primitive Polynesian Economy.* London: G. Routledge & Sons. 387 pp.
  1946 *Malay Fishermen: Their Peasant Economy.* London: Kegan Paul, Trench, Trubner & Co. 354 pp.
FORDE, C. D.
  1934 *Habitat, Economy and Society: A Geographical Introduction to Ethnology.* London: Methuen & Co.; New York: Harcourt, Brace & Co. 500 pp.
GAYTON, A. H.
  1946 "Culture-Environment Integration: External References in Yokuts Life," *Southwestern Journal of Anthropology,* II, 252–68.
GILLIN, JOHN
  1952 "Ethos and Cultural Aspects of Personality," pp. 193–222 in TAX, SOL

(ed.), *Heritage of Conquest.* Glencoe, Ill.: Free Press. 312 pp.

HERSKOVITS, M. J.
1948   *Man and His Works.* New York: Alfred A. Knopf. 678 pp.
1952   *Economic Anthropology.* New York: Alfred A. Knopf. 547 pp.

HOGBIN, H. I.
1939   *Experiments in Civilization: The Effects of European Culture on a Native Community of the Solomon Islands.* London: G. Routledge & Sons. 268 pp.

KLUCKHOHN, CLYDE, and LEIGHTON, DOROTHEA
1946   *The Navaho.* Cambridge, Mass.: Harvard University Press. 258 pp.

MALINOWSKI, BRONISLAW
1935   *Coral Gardens and Their Magic.* 2 vols. London: Allen & Unwin.

MEAD, MARGARET
1940   *Mountain Arapesh. II. Supernaturalism.* ("Anthropological Papers," Vol. XXXIV, Part III.) New York: American Museum of Natural History.

READ, MARGARET
1938   *Native Standards of Living and African Culture Change.* (Supplement to *Africa,* Vol. XI, No. 3.) 56 pp.

REDFIELD, ROBERT
1953   *The Primitive World and Its Transformations.* Ithaca, N.Y.: Cornell University Press. 185 pp.

SEARS, P. B.
1950   *Charles Darwin: The Naturalist as a Cultural Force.* New York: Charles Scribner's Sons. 124 pp.

SPOEHR, ALEXANDER
1949   *Majuro: A Village in the Marshall Islands.* ("Fieldiana: Anthropology," Vol. XXXIX.) Chicago: Chicago Natural History Museum. 266 pp.

TAX, SOL
1941   "World View and Social Relations in Guatemala," *American Anthropologist,* XLIII, 27–42.
1953   *Penny Capitalism: A Guatemalan Indian Economy.* (Smithsonian Institution, Institute of Social Anthropology, Publication No. 10.) Washington, D.C.: Government Printing Office. 230 pp.

TAX, SOL (ed.)
1952   *Heritage of Conquest: The Ethnology of Middle America.* Glencoe, Ill.: Free Press. 312 pp.

THURNWALD, R.
1932   *Economics in Primitive Communities.* London: Oxford University Press. 314 pp.

The Antiquity and World Expansion of Human Culture

PIERRE TEILHARD DE CHARDIN[*]

PLANETARY NATURE OF MAN: A PRESENTATION OF THE NOÖSPHERE

How and how much does man, by his presence and his activities, transform the face of the earth? As a common background to the various technical answers, dealing with soil conservation, water distribution, city building, etc., we should like to mention and to emphasize a still deeper and more general change which our zoölogical group has brought to the terrestrial world. This change would betray and characterize the presence of man on earth to an observer on Sirius, namely, the progressive expansion of a special layer of thinking and cultured substance all around the globe.

More than a half-century ago the great geologist Suess took a bold and lucky step when, in addition to describing our planet by the classical sequence of concentrical, spherical shells (barysphere, lithosphere, atmosphere, etc.), he decided to add the biosphere, in order to affirm, in a concise and vivid way, that the frail but superactive film of highly complex, self-reproducing matter spread around the world was of decided geological significance and value. Since Suess's times, the notion of a special planetary envelope of organic matter distinct from the inorganic lithosphere has been accepted as a normal basis for the fast-growing structures of geobiology (a new branch of science). But, then, why not take one step more and recognize the fact that, if the appearance of the earth has undergone a major alteration by turning chlorophyll-green or life-warm since the Paleozoic period, an even more revolutionary transformation took place at the end of Tertiary time, when our planet developed the psychically reflexive human surface, for which, together with Professor Édouard Le Roy and Professor Vernadsky, we suggested in the 1920's the name "noösphere"?[1]

Ultimately, neither earth nor man can be fully understood except with regard to the marvelous sheet of humanized and socialized matter, which, despite its incredibly small mass and its incredible thinness, has to be regarded positively as the most sharply individualized and the most specifically distinct of all the planetary units so far recognized.

As a natural introduction to the problem, devoted precisely to the study

* Dr. Teilhard de Chardin's paper appears posthumously. Father Teilhard was Research Associate of the Wenner-Gren Foundation for Anthropological Research at the time of his death on April 10, 1955. During his lifetime he was an adviser to the National Geological Survey of China and a member of the French Academy of Sciences. He was primarily a geologist and vertebrate paleontologist whose interests ultimately led him to the problems concerning the origins of man both in Southeast Asia and in Africa south of the Sahara.

1. From the Greek noos, "mind," and sphaera, "sphere."

of the relations existing between earth and man in the course of their respective developments, let us therefore summarize the essence of what can be scientifically stated today concerning (1) the historical establishment of the noösphere; (2) the cultural structure; and, finally, (3) the present comportment, as well as the possible future, of mankind considered as a biological whole on a planetary scale.

HISTORICAL DEVELOPMENT OF THE NOÖSPHERE

Scarcely more than a century has elapsed since living man, realizing that he, too, was a product of biological evolution, began to hunt not only for animal fossils but also and predominantly for "fossil man." In spite of intensive research, we are still far from having gained a complete vision of the history of our zoölogical group. Yet, as we consider its main features (Fig. 50), the reconstruction of our past is by now sufficiently advanced to have taken what may be regarded as its *final general shape*. The main lines of the picture gradually have come to light through the joint efforts of prehistory and paleoanthropology.

Most surely, for stringent geological and paleontological reasons, the mysterious phenomenon of initial "hominization" (that is, the mutational emergence in nature of a reflexive, or "self-conscious," type of consciousness) must have taken place, by the end of the Pliocene, within the tropical or subtropical areas of the Old World in which there happened to be concentrated, at the closing of the Tertiary,

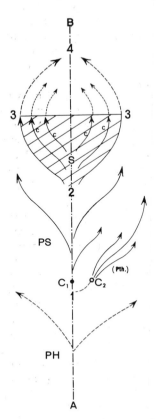

PH = Pre-Hominians (Australopithecines, *Meganthropus*, etc.), branching, diverging

PS = Pre- and para-*sapiens* types of Hominians (Neanderthaloids, Pithecanthropians, etc.), branching, slightly converging

S = *Homo sapiens*, not branching; first expanding, then fast converging

c, c, c = Various cultural units

1 = First emergence of eu-Hominians (critical point, or threshold of reflexion)

2 = Emergence of *Homo sapiens*, and beginning of the formation of the noösphere (through co-reflexion)

$3, 3$ = Division at present, between expansional and compressional phases in the development of the noösphere

$4(?)$ = Upper limit, and critical point of co-reflexion (conjectured)

C_1 = African center of hominization

C_2 = Indo-Malaysian center of hominization (*Pth.* = Pithecanthropians)

AB = Ideal axis of hominization

Approximate time elapsed between *1* and *2*, more than half a million years; between *2* and *3* (Upper Paleolithic, Neolithic, historical times), about fifty thousand years

FIG. 50.—A symbolic expression of the successive phases of hominization the most advanced representatives of the higher, tail-less chimpanzee- or gorilla-like primates presently included by the zoölogists in the Pongidae family.

What were the number, the physical appearance, and the comportment of these first true Hominians? That, we perhaps shall never know. Owing to the fact that the first stages of any organized system are constitutionally of a fragile structure, the traces of any "beginning" are selectively erased by the passage of time. There is still, and probably there will almost always remain, a blank in our vision of the past at the place occupied by the origins of man, though no more or less, in fact, than in the case of the birth of any other animal species or of any human civilization.

The presence of recognizable para- or pre-Hominians, anatomically comparable with the Pleistocene Australopithecines of Africa recently has been detected as early as the Upper Miocene of Italy (*Oreopithecus bamboli*). But no "eu-Hominians" were likely to have wandered on the surface of the earth before the Basal Pleistocene (Villafranchian), that is, earlier than approximately a million years ago.

In so far as we can guess, the initial hominization must have developed along an extensive west-east South Himalayan belt, ranging from equatorial Africa to Malaysia. But at a very early stage in the process it seems that this elongated "mutational front" was ruptured in the middle; the result of this segmentation was the individualization of two distinct centers of hominization: Center 1, located in Central Africa (C_1, Fig. 50, p. 104), and Center 2 (C_2, Fig. 50, p. 104), located somewhere in Indo-Malaysia.

Zoölogically speaking, Center 1 and Center 2 were remarkably symmetrical in their structures. Each of them shows a core of eu-Hominian type, surrounded by a cluster of para-Hominian forms (Australopithecines of Africa [?], *Meganthropus* of Java, etc.).

But in so far as their evolutive power is concerned, they were in fact of quite different values. Whereas the pithecanthropians (*Pithecanthropus, Sinanthropus, Homo soloensis*) of the Far East never exceeded the dimensions of a marginal branch of humanity, or ever rose above a low anatomical stage comparable with that of Neanderthal man of Middle Pleistocene of Europe, evidence is growing that in the heart of Africa, and nowhere else, there originated what has become the bulk, if not the totality, of modern mankind.

To be sure, bony remains of ancient man still are very scarce in Africa south of the modern Sahara, and so far they consist mostly of the pithecanthropian-like (and relatively late) skulls of Rhodesia and Saldanha. But hidden behind this outer envelope of "neanderthaloid" or "para-*sapiens*" appearance, the presence in Africa of an exceptionally progressive subphylum of proto-*sapiens* type (perhaps actually represented by the modern-looking, yet heavily fossilized, Kanam jaw from Kenya) becomes more and more probable. Without this assumption, it would be extremely difficult either to explain the unique development in the Lower Pleistocene of Africa of a hand-ax culture which is the oldest and the richest of the world or to understand the sudden outburst of "modern man" throughout Eurasia (apparently from south to north) at the dawn of Upper Paleolithic time.

For the greater part of the Pleistocene (that is, during the whole Prelithic[?] and early Paleolithic times), facts force us to admit that man has remained strangely limited, geographically, within the original boundaries of his zoölogical birth. Except for some marked peripheral advance of the hand-ax industry in southwestern Europe and Southeast Asia (as far as Indonesia[?]), the territory occupied by our ancestors some fifty thousand years ago was still substantially the same tropical and subtropical "Pongids belt" on which the first hominization occurred hundreds of thousands of years before at the end of the Pliocene. It is as though, during an enormous span of time, man, still immature, was kept busy by some organic adjustment at the innermost part of himself.

But subsequently, by the end of the Middle Pleistocene, a general movement of populations resulted in a fundamental redistribution of man on the surface of the earth. At that time a definitely modernized type of man, radiating apparently from a Mediterranean base, succeeded for the first time in invading those expanded northern parts of the continents where the Old and the New Worlds come into close contact, or even weld, along a boreal belt. To some extent, Africa, despite its size, had been for millenniums a closed container for man or even a blind corner. Once having reached the vast free spaces, first, of northern Eurasia and, somewhat later, of North America, man, endowed at last both anatomically and culturally with his full expansive force, seems to have progressed quickly, like an irresistible tide, over the newly open land: only a few thousands of years later he had already reached Patagonia!

This was a true "second hominization," indeed: the rise out of Africa and the world-wide spreading of *Homo sapiens,* the "universal man."

As a result of this Upper Paleolithic expansion, Mesolithic man was no longer merely a tropical and subtropical animal. At last he had become what we are now: a pan-terrestrial form of advanced life. But his hold on the earth at this early stage was still most precarious and very loose. And it was to require the continuous and intensive ef-

fort of many more millenniums of agricultural and proto-industrial cultures to fill the gaps and to establish a first satisfactory net of connections between men and men all over the world.

Several hundred thousand years had been spent on the mere *preparation,* mainly in Africa, of a human planetary invasion. Some thirty thousand years more had been required for the actual *occupation* of the extra-African lands. Approximately ten thousand years (that is, the whole combined Neolithic and historical times) were necessary before a preliminary *consolidation* of the human envelope had been realized all around the earth.

But today, after so many eons of hominization, the great accomplishment pursued by life since its first emergence on earth two or three billion years ago is over; namely, the achievement of an unbroken, co-conscious organism, coextensive with the entire area of the globe. Definitely cemented on itself in the course of the last century by the powerful forces of industry and science, the newborn noösphere is now spread right before our eyes and is caught already in the first grip of an irresistible *totalization.*

Before trying to investigate this final phase of the development of the noösphere, let us first analyze the secret of its internal structure in order to discover the deep reasons why man represents so obviously (judging merely from his biological success) a *revolution* in the very process of natural *evolution.*

CULTURAL NATURE OF THE NOÖSPHERE

By human culture, I refer to the manifold process according to which any human population, whenever left to itself, immediately starts spontaneously to arrange itself at a social level into an organized system of ends and means, in which two basic components are always present: First, a material component, or "increase in complexity," which includes both the various types of implements and techniques necessary to the gathering or the production of all kinds of food or supplies and the various rules or laws which provide the best conditions for an optimum birth rate or for a satisfactory circulation of goods and resources within the limits of the population under consideration. Second, a spiritual component, or "increase in consciousness," namely, some particular outlook on the world and life (an approach which is at once philosophical, ethical, aesthetic, and religious), the function of which is to impart a meaning, a direction, and an incentive or stimulus to the material activities and development of the community.

For the many fragments of mankind that have become isolated or have gained their independence in the course of time, just so many tentative technicomental systems of the world as a whole —that is, just so many *cultures*—have gradually come into existence. This is one of the major lessons taught by the universal history of man, from the earliest known stages until the present time.

Understood thus as a collective answer to the general biological problem of survival and growth, the typically human phenomenon of culture is of course foreshadowed, to some extent, at the prehuman levels of life. In the case of animals, too, the struggle for life leads each different species forcibly toward the discovery of some constructive adjustment between germinal forces of reproduction and multiplication, on the one hand, and quasi-social forces of collective arrangement, on the other.

But whereas, in the case of non-reflexive life, *social* and *germinal* persistently have been unable to combine into a definite and unlimited creative process,[2] in the case of man, on the contrary

(and clearly in some sort of connection with the newly acquired human power of "thinking"), both social and germinal have given rise, by their conjunction, to a decidedly superior type of evolution—a "new evolution" in fact[3]—special to the noösphere and characterized at the same time by a new and more efficient form of invention, by a new and more efficient form of heredity, and by a new and more efficient form of speciation.

A New and More Efficient Form of Invention

Since its earliest beginnings, life has never stopped "inventing" and perfecting new organic contraptions along the most amazing variety of lines. But for a very long time this continuous advance seems to have been achieved much more through a patient expectation and utilization than by a positive pursuit and control of chances. Before man, the evolution of animal life was unquestionably directional and preferential. But in its mechanism it did not show any real *purpose*. Since the appearance of man, however, the living individual being becomes able to *plan*. And this power of planning, when focused on research and when brought socially to the dimensions of a concerted effort for discovery, opens a new era in the development of terrestrial life. Without escaping the general conditions and "servitudes" of every organic substance in the universe, man has introduced, and is gradually expanding at the very core of nature through his collective power of reflexive invention, a new method for arranging matter: no longer the old random arrangement but

2. Either the social is lagging behind in the animal world, or, as it happens for the insects, society chokes the development of the individual.

3. This expression is from George Gaylord Simpson's *The Meaning of Evolution*, 1951.

an active arrangement through *self-evo-lution.*

A New and More Efficient Form of Heredity

Germinal heredity, so deeply investi-gated by our modern geneticists, proved to be a marvelous instrument of prog-ress during the earlier, prehuman stages of the development of life. But owing to the very nature of its chromo-somic mechanism, germinal heredity is affected, in fact, with a triple basic weakness which makes it unable to in-sure, if left to itself, any further advance of evolution in the case of such a com-plicated and fast-changing type of or-ganism as man, especially *collective* man. First, the characters transmitted by genes are by their very nature re-stricted to a category of rather ele-mentary features; namely, those which control the material arrangement of the cells in the course of embryogenesis. Second, the number of these elementary characters is drastically limited in the germ by the exiguous size of the chro-mosomes. Third (if we except the pos-sible case of some social instincts among the insects), there is no observable chromosomic transmission to the species of the characters eventually *acquired* by the industrious activity of each in-dividual in the course of its life.

Now, remarkably enough, it is pre-cisely on these three different grounds that a decided improvement becomes manifest in the *cultured* zones of life, in so far as the registration and the transmission of human experience are concerned. Thanks to language, to in-formation, and to education, an un-limited number of unlimitedly complex ideas or techniques accumulate continu-ously, and organize themselves perma-nently, in the unlimited capacity of col-lective human memory.

Thus, duplicating the history of the old *chromosomic heredity*, an incom-parably more sensitive and receptive *educational heredity* is now at work in the noösphere. This is precisely the more-needed power to collect the over-abundant products and to feed the con-stantly accelerated progress of a self-evolving process.

A New and More Efficient Form of Speciation

Considered over a sufficiently pro-tracted span of time, every animal pop-ulation shows a tendency to split, under a statistical effect of genetic mutations, into branching systems of varieties, sub-species, and, ultimately, true, new, spe-cific forms. In the case of man, things proceed in much the same way, except that, as a consequence of the specifically human association between germinal and social, the splitting and branching operation results in the formation of new, *mainly cultural,* instead of new, *mainly anatomical,* types.

Fundamentally, according to my point of view, culturation is nothing but a "hominized" form of speciation. Or to express the same thing different-ly: *cultural units* are for the noösphere the mere equivalent and the true suc-cessors of *zoölogical species* in the bio-sphere. True successors, we insist. And how much better fitted than their prede-cessors to satisfy the new requisites of an advanced type of evolution!

Let us briefly dwell on this important point. Considered as an instrument for evolution, zoölogical speciation, in addi-tion to being very much slowed down by the non-inheritance of acquired characters, is seriously handicapped by the fast-increasing estrangement ob-servable between the products of its operation. In the very process of be-coming itself, each newly formed zoölogical type becomes more and more separated and isolated from the other surrounding species in the process of its inner development. Growing aloneness, mutual impermeability, and consequent basic incapacity for any sort of interspecific synthesis were the common fate of animal phyla under the "old" regime of evolution.

In contrast, with the rise of self-evolution, not only does the speed of transformation increase rapidly, because of the cumulative transmission of planned inventions, but, and more important, a remarkable capacity emerges among the socialized offsprings of the new evolution for keeping in close inner touch with one another—and even for fusing with one another—in the course of their development. On the one hand, the various human cultural units spread all over the world at a given time never cease (even during the most acute phases of their differentiation) to react mutually on one another at the depth of their individual growth. Whatever may be the degree of their mutual divergence, they still form, when taken together, an unbroken sheet of organized consciousness. And, moreover, on the other hand, they prove able (provided they happen to be sufficiently active and sufficiently compressed on one another) to penetrate, to metamorphose, and to absorb one another into something fundamentally new. This is the well-known process of *acculturation*—a process possibly bound to culminate some day in a complete "mono-culturation" of the human world, but a process, in any case, without which no formation of any continuous human shell would ever have been physically possible on the surface of the earth.

From the preceding analysis of the cultural nature of human expansion one might conclude erroneously that the so-called "noösphere" is nothing more than an uninteresting kind of pseudo- or para-organism, since, according to a widespread opinion, it would be dangerously confusing to identify what is really *natural* and what is simply *cultural* (that is, "artificial") in the world. Here, we confess to touch upon a point still hotly debated even among anthropologists; namely, to decide whether the word "biological" can or cannot be applied correctly (in a non-allegoric way) to the workings and to the products of human culture. And yet, in our opinion, a decisive and final positive answer to the problem is already forced upon our mind by the three following joint considerations:

1. Whatever may be the ultimate physical nature of psychological awareness, increasing consciousness—traceable by increasing cerebration—is overwhelmingly proved by general paleontology and comparative zoölogy to be a safe and absolute parameter (or index) of biological evolution.

2. Aside from any undue anthropocentrism, but from the inescapable evidence derived from the revolutionary effects of hominization, *reflexive awareness* must be held, not as a mere variety, but as a *superstage* of consciousness.

3. Judging from the very mechanism of its operation, which is ultimately reducible to a process of *co-cerebration* and *co-reflexion*, culturation cannot be regarded as anything less than a direct prolongation of hominization.

Obviously, if they are linked with one another in their natural order, these three successive steps scientifically detected in the terrestrial development of life—(1) direct (or simple) consciousness; (2) reflexion (consciousness raised to its second power; for man, *to know that he knows*); and (3) culture (co-reflexion)—have one, and only one, possible meaning. They show in an unmistakable way by their mere natural sequence that man, through culturation, is not drifting away along some side path and toward some blind corner of the universe but that he is still moving directly along the major axis of cosmic development. From all that we know most certainly from the entire history of the past, culturation, because it biologically expresses a collective advance in reflexion, decidedly is not an inferior or reduced form of evolution but rather represents a supertype. This evidence, far from being of merely speculative interest, turns out to be of the utmost importance, both for our power of vision and for our power of action.

It is of importance for our power of action, of course, because it is tremendously necessary to the security of man and to his sense of values to be sure at last, in his effort to become more human ("ultra-human"), that he is responsible for, and supported by, the main and most central forces of a growing universe. It is important for our power of vision too, because, if the full impact of evolution is actually concentrating at present on the achievement of the noösphere, then we can understand better the terrific energies at work and the incredible potentialities still awaiting us in the process and in the progress of human acculturation.

PRESENT STATUS AND POSSIBLE FUTURE OF THE NOÖSPHERE

A common attitude today, one repeatedly expressed in the statements of highly intellectual and religious people, is that man and mankind are regarded as being a practically stabilized product of evolution and even as a disintegrating and decaying one. Under the influence of science and techniques, man is supposedly not improving but even regressing biologically. Hence "progress" is a myth and an illusion. In many quarters this is the new and fashionable way of thinking "realistically."

For anyone who is aware of the basic evolutive significance of any *increase of consciousness through complexity* inside the noösphere, such a pessimistic view of the present status of the world is so incredibly wrong scientifically, and at the same time so dangerously depressing psychologically, that we believe that the time has come to react against

it openly and vigorously. And this can best be done, it seems to us, by presenting a more objective and more comforting interpretation of the major crisis which we have been going through since the beginning of the twentieth century.

Something very deep and very wide is certainly taking place, these days, at the core of the humanized zones of the planet. But *what?* To this question the only satisfactory answer, in our opinion, is as follows.

Up to a very recent date the phenomenon of "hominization," because it was continuing (for perhaps about a million years) to operate on a relatively unpopulated world, was predominantly a process of *expansional and diverging* directions. Just as in any given animal species the main rule of life is to propagate and to differentiate at a maximum, so the chief occupation of man during this first period was to invade all the free parts of the earth and, at the same time, to attempt every possible form of cultural arrangement.

At present, however (that is, for less than a century!), owing to the coincidence of a sharp demographic jump with an incredible progress in intercommunication, the development of mankind has suddenly become *compressional and converging* in its direction.[4] The movement has completely reversed its phase, with the result that, under a tremendous and incoercible *rapprochement* and compression of both human bodies and human minds, co-arrangement and co-reflexion are now rising toward astronomical values at the interior of the noösphere. Even if humanity is not becoming either better or happier in the course of the process,

4. Very much in the same way as a pulsation entering a globe through the lower pole would first expand, up to the level of the equator, and then, in moving farther on toward the upper pole of the sphere, would become more and more compressed (cf. Fig. 50, p. 104).

it is today forced, more than ever, in its entirety and under two irresistible factors (that is, by the double curvature of our rounded mother-planet and of our converging minds) to move toward unheard-of and unimaginable degrees of organized complexity and of reflexive consciousness.

To become ultra-reflexive (that is, "ultra-human") by reaching some stage of mono-culturation—or else to resign and to die on the way—this, aside from any temperamental or philosophical considerations, must on purely scientific grounds be regarded as the biological fate of man.

For conventional and conservative reasons we dislike, and we try to weaken, the growing evidence that, judged by the best standards of biological evolution, our species is still far from being zoölogically mature. Instead of closing our eyes to the stupendous technico-mental acceleration of anthropogenesis in our modern times, why not rather try to face the situation and to guess how far the process is likely to carry us and how it is going to end eventually?

Whenever we speculate on the future of civilization, we generally assume that, except for the unlikely case of some physical, physiological, or psychological accident of planetary dimensions, man will survive practically unchanged as long as the earth will supply him with a sufficiency of food and energy. But, in our opinion, we should consider another idea that is both more interesting and more probable; namely, that the whole human adventure, in so far as it turns out to represent *a fast-converging process,* is bound to end some day, not by exhaustion from *external* causes, but climactically for *internal* reasons, just because *there is* a critical upper limit (or threshold) to the planetary development of co-reflexion.

If we follow this line of thought to the end, we are led to the suspicion that every "thinking planet" in the universe (like a psychical nova) must culminate sooner or later, through protracted inner maturation, in some implosive concentration of its cultural noösphere. And this specific event should possibly coincide with some escape of the fully "co-reflected" parts of the *Weltstoff* outside and beyond the apparent boundaries of time and space. Strangely enough, such a wild hypothesis of a transhuman universe conforms perfectly to the general pattern of a physical world in which absolutely nothing can grow indefinitely without meeting ultimately some critical level of emergence and transformation. From the inflexible point of view of energetics, the process fulfils, we believe, a condition *sine qua non* for the steady continuation of human effort during the next million years toward an ever greater culture and acculturation.

So far, man has accepted blindly (just as the industrial workers of a century ago) the pushing-ahead of the terrestrial development of life, without asking himself whether it was a paying game to play at being Atlas. But this phase of instinctive co-operation is decidedly over. The time can be foreseen when the human drive for climbing always higher toward consciousness through complexity will die out, unless it is stimulated by growing scientific evidence that, through ever intensified hominization, we are really moving *somewhere* and *forever.*

That some definite Everest should really be there ahead of us, behind the clouds, an Everest from which there is no return to the plain; that through a stubborn confluence of our minds and hearts we should eventually succeed in breaking the barrier of darkness and mutual exteriority which still separates life as we know it from some higher and more stable form of knowledge and unanimity; and to become actually and acutely conscious of the imperative craving of our deepest ego for some definitely *irreversible* type of achieve-ment—might well be, we venture to say, the next step which man will take (very soon, perhaps) in the process of his co-reflexive self-evolution.

REFERENCES

BLUM, HAROLD F.
  1951 *Time's Arrow and Evolution.* Princeton, N.J.: Princeton University Press. 222 pp.
BOYD, WILLIAM C.
  1950 *Genetics and the Races of Man.* Boston: Little, Brown & Co. 453 pp.
BRIDGMAN, P. W.
  1949 "The Potential Intelligent Society of the Future," pp. 229–50 in NORTHROP, F. S. C. (ed.), *Ideological Differences and World Order.* New Haven, Conn.: Yale University Press. 486 pp.
DARWIN, CHARLES GALTON
  1953 *The Next Million Years.* New York: Doubleday & Co. 210 pp.
HUXLEY, JULIAN S.
  1953 *Evolution in Action.* New York: Harper & Bros. 177 pp.
NEEDHAM, JOSEPH
  1943 *Time, the Refreshing River.* New York: Macmillan Co. 280 pp.

REDFIELD, ROBERT
  1953 *The Primitive World and Its Transformations.* Ithaca, N.Y.: Cornell University Press. 183 pp.
SEIDENBERG, RODERICK
  1950 *Post-historic Man.* Chapel Hill: University of North Carolina Press. 246 pp.
SIMPSON, GEORGE GAYLORD
  1951 *The Meaning of Evolution.* ("New American Library.") Rev. ed. New York: Mentor Books. 192 pp.
TEILHARD DE CHARDIN, PIERRE
  1951 "La Structure phylétique du groupe humain," *Annales de paléontologie,* XXXVII, 77–106.
WHITE, LESLIE
  1949 *The Science of Culture.* New York: Farrar & Straus. 444 pp.
WIENER, NORBERT
  1954 *The Human Use of Human Beings: Cybernetics and Society.* Boston: Houghton Mifflin Co. 199 pp.

Through the Corridors of Time

Through the Corridors of Time

Fire as the First Great Force Employed by Man[1]

OMER C. STEWART*

EVIDENCE FROM ARCHEOLOGY AND ETHNOLOGY

Use of fire and manufactured implements of stone are the cultural achievements recorded in ancient strata of the earth as indicators of the beginning of humanity. Language, stone tools, and control of fire probably distinguished mankind from other primates by the beginning of the Pleistocene, which we might place at one million years ago. The actual evidence for the use of fire by the first humans is as scarce and indefinite as the evidence of the origin of man himself.

The oldest hearths geologically were those discovered about 1920 by J. Reid Moir near Ipswich, England (Osborn, 1927). Some doubt about them has persisted, and may increase, owing to the fact that Moir attributed the hearths to Piltdown man of recent infamy. On the other hand, the rostrocarinates of Moir, assigned to the preglacial age of England, have gained acceptance in spite of the abandonment of the notion of "Eolithic age" and "Pliocene man" in Continental Europe. The paucity of fireplaces from open sites of early Pleistocene age limits the direct evidence of the date of man's first control of fire but does not subtract from the value of fire as a diagnostic trait for human origins.

Cave sites offer more certain data on the control of fire by man, because there is little chance of ash or charcoal from lightning fires entering caves. A layer of ash in an open site could be attributed to fires of a non-human agency. It might be assumed that lightning has occurred for millions of years and that vegetation could have been ignited during all the eons that it has existed on the earth's surface. The recognition of such a possibility does not establish the fact that vegetation has been burned during all its history. Geologists have identified little wood ash or partly burned wood in pre-Pleistocene deposits (Plummer, 1912b, p. 7), and its presence in Pleistocene strata is usually accepted by geologists and paleontologists, as well as by archeologists, as evidence of human occupation. Thus, notwithstanding the admitted possibility of forest fires set by lightning in prehuman times, the failure to find much evidence of pre-Pleistocene vegetation burning permits us to minimize its role. Lightning fires were presumably of importance in the early Pleistocene, however, since they provide the most rea-

* Dr. Stewart is Professor of Anthropology at the University of Colorado, Boulder, Colorado, and from 1952 to 1954 was chairman of the Department of Social Sciences (Anthropology, Economics, Political Science, and Sociology). In 1940–41 he was a Post-doctoral Fellow of the Social Science Research Council. His publications include: *The Northern Paiute Bands*, 1939; *Culture Elements Distribution: XVIII—Ute, Southern Paiute*, 1942; and *Ute Peyotism*, 1948.

1. Research on which this paper is based has been supported by grants from the University of Colorado Graduate School Committee on Research and Creative Work.

sonable source for man's knowledge of fire. With fire, as with all aspects of Paleolithic and even Neolithic culture, however, we are dependent largely upon imagination and pure logic to explain ultimate origins.

The cause of prehuman fires and the source of man's first knowledge of fire may be considered together. Evidence with which to substantiate theories of such origins is about as plentiful for us as it was for Aeschylus when he wrote *Prometheus Bound* about 470 B.C. (Osborn, 1927, pp. 16–17). In seeking to explain the origin of fire as a tool of man, I recognize my kinship with aboriginal mythmakers as well as with the scientific optimists of a century ago who expected to learn of cultural beginnings from surviving Stone Age peoples. We continue to speculate nevertheless. In 1926 Hough in his monograph *Fire as an Agent in Human Culture* stated (p. 5) that "natural ignitions may be divided into volcanic, chemical, electrical, frictional due to earth movements, and frictional on wood."

Of the natural agencies which start fires, only volcanoes and lightning are frequently observed igniting vegetation. Molten lava could have served as a recurrent source of fire in the vicinity of the proper types of active volcanoes.

If volcanoes were the only source of new fire by fire-using people otherwise unable to make fire, however, great sections of the world would have remained unoccupied.

Lightning is at present much more nearly universal than volcanoes. Fires started by lightning are widespread over the earth and occur regularly. Although we can imagine lightning as a fundamental factor in man's initiation into the mysteries of fire, its relative importance throughout human history must be carefully evaluated and will be considered at some length later in this paper.

The chemical agent for natural igni-

tion proposed by Hough (*ibid.*) is spontaneous combustion of seams of coal and coal dust. Burning seams of coal possibly spontaneously ignited in prehistoric times are reported for New Zealand, the Mackenzie River, and Borneo. Other examples of burning coal in West Virginia and Russia are of questionable natural origin. However, the world distribution of exposed seams of coal which might have become lighted by spontaneous combustion or by friction is too limited to have helped teach many ancient men the usefulness of fire. Spontaneous combustion may have occurred in the marshes of Louisiana in prehuman times, according to the botanist Roland M. Harper (1943, p. 32) and to Viosca (1931).

Equally difficult to verify is the theory that flames may have resulted from dead branches being rubbed together by winds. Hough (1926, p. 7) quotes this observation made by François Bernier in Kashmir in 1663: "Some of the trees were scorched and burnt, either blasted by the thunderbolt, or, according to the traditions of the peasantry, set on fire in the heat of summer by rubbing against each other when agitated by fierce, burning winds." Also unverified is the belief that sparks from contact of boulders falling on rocks may have ignited fires (Chipp, 1926, p. 228).

Whatever may have been its start, fire must have been known to man and have been controlled by him before he learned to manufacture it. The discovery of a method to ignite vegetable matter looms as one of humanity's greatest acts. Yet, before that momentous event, hominids may well have guarded and transported fire for hundreds of thousands of years. *Australopithecus prometheus* of South Africa now stands up to proclaim that a small-brained ape-man had the ability to tend fire. Professor Raymond Dart (1948) of the University of the Witwatersrand has declared that this peculiar primate, intermediate between apes and man, kept fire in his caves. Few anthropologists are willing to accept the proposition that this small-brained man-ape could have controlled fire, and the evidence Dart used to justify naming his fossil *prometheus* has been carefully scrutinized and generally rejected. However, Dart and his few supporters confidently expect additional evidence confirming use of fire by *Australopithecus* to be discovered soon.

Although exciting because of its morphology, *Australopithecus* is not generally accepted as the most ancient hominid fossil geologically. The *Australopithecus* deposits have been assigned to such diverse periods as Upper Pliocene and Middle Pleistocene. Most geological opinion seems to favor the more recent date. The geologic dating of *Australopithecus* is as disputed as the question of his tool-using and fire-making. Nevertheless, *Australopithecus* may yet prove to be the progenitor of mankind and force us to admit that half a brain was enough to get fires started and to push us forever onto the hominid sidetrack.

Sinanthropus pekinensis is the earliest man known to have controlled fire. Extensive excavations at Choukoutien, near Peking, brought to light fifteen individual skulls and skull fragments which indicate a human type much nearer to modern man than *Australopithecus*. In the cave with the hundreds of pieces of fossilized bones of human type were crudely chipped stone tools and large quantities of solidified wood ash, charcoal, seeds, animal bones, and other material distinct from the rocks of the limestone caves. There is no doubt that Peking man tended the fire in his cave home and must have carried it with him when he moved abroad.

The deposits in the Choukoutien cave have been variously assigned to late Middle, early Middle, and Lower Pleis-

tocene. *Sinanthropus* has been placed from a quarter- to a half-million years ago. In any event, man's use of fire as a powerful tool capable of tremendous influence on his environment has continued for at least a quarter-million years.

As important as the fact of the first control of fire is for our thesis, we are forced to reason by analogy with modern aborigines to get some idea of what happened during most of the time of human occupation of and influence upon the earth. The few bits of archeological evidence, outside of ashes in cave dwellings, of primitive man's role in changing his geographic environment come from Upper Paleolithic and Neolithic times, not more than twenty-five thousand years ago, and will be mentioned later. The difficult problem we face is to reconstruct man's use of fire outside his family hearth during the hundreds of thousands of years of his development from the protoanthropic stage of *Sinanthropus* and *Pithecanthropus* to his appearance as *Homo sapiens*. During those millenniums this new primate moved out from his natural habitat in the tropical rain forests and came to occupy virtually all the earth. Use of fire was certainly essential for man's life away from the tropics, and it may have played an important role wherever he settled. Domestic fires, however, are pertinent for consideration only as they may have had wider influence. Although our archeological evidence of most ancient fires comes from the rock shelters and caves occupied by man from the time of *Sinanthropus*, it is reasonable to suppose that campfires were made during hunting trips away from caves and during migrations. It is fair to assume that man has used fire from the time he gained control over it, much as it has been used by the culturally most primitive aborigines up to the present.

Since modern aborigines carry hot

coals, punk, and slow matches, so that they can make fire to prepare meals during the day and at temporary overnight stops, I assume this practice has been customary since man acquired the use of fire. Hough (1926, pp. 3–4) recorded means of carrying fire from areas as scattered as New Guinea, the Mississippi Valley, Patagonia, Arizona, Australia, and China. It was probably universal among natives who had only the simple hand fire drill with which to manufacture fire. Almost all tribes of western North America, listed in the Culture Element Distribution survey of the University of California (Kroeber, 1939), reported carrying some sort of slow match, so that they could easily start a campfire while away from home.

As humans spread out from the tropical zone, within which they were by nature equipped to live without artificial protection or supplementary heat, preservation and transportation of fire must have been a major concern for the entire group. Before the manufacture of fire was discovered, and even when the simple fire drill or fire saw was used to ignite new fire, there must have been much more thought and energy given to preserving fire than to extinguishing it. Indians of western America reported lighting bushes and trees, so that the roots would become ignited and yet burn very slowly underground for days or weeks, in order that a light could be obtained if necessary without using the fire drill.

Would earliest man traveling with fire across the countryside carefully extinguish each campfire? More likely, would he not put on a big log and bank his fire to preserve it against the chance of his return, even though he carried a spark in a horn or carried a bark slow match? If an accident occurred and the portable spark were put out, it would be comforting to know that logs or roots had been left burning and that a return trip might find a glowing spark.

Reason suggests that the first fire users, while migrating or hunting far from home base, intentionally left campfires burning and whenever possible tried to leave them smoldering slowly, so that they might burn for days. The analogy with modern natives supports this reasoned conclusion. Europeans, as well as Indians from Alaska, California, Kansas, and Virginia, have been reported leaving campfires unextinguished. In a very extensive search of the literature I discovered almost no reference that natives anywhere carefully extinguished fires.

This brings me to my first important deduction about the beginning of fire as a factor of significance in modifying the surface of the earth. Everywhere that man traveled, he made campfires and left them to ignite any and all the vegetation in the vicinity. Campfires of a sparse population might not do much igniting in many regions. In flat country which dried out at certain seasons and where strong winds occurred with the drought, a few abandoned campfires might influence the vegetation of a large area. It is my opinion that native peoples have rarely been careful to extinguish their campfires when made in the open country and that primitive hunting and gathering peoples from the time they acquired fire have allowed their fires to ignite the landscape, because it did not occur to them to protect the vegetation from fire.

We may project back to the beginning of human culture other historically known burning practices which would have extensive effect on the landscape. In fact, except for the use of fire in connection with agriculture and grazing, all the reasons given by modern natives for setting vegetation on fire may also have motivated our most remote ancestors. Wild animals and plants now existing, with few exceptions, are those with which man has competed and to which he has adjusted during his entire history. We may assume that the interrelationships of life-forms have been in general fairly uniform during the last million years. Local variations of tremendous proportions have indeed occurred, like the glacial advances. Even the glaciers, however, were relatively restricted, and beyond their limits man lived with the animals and plants we know. Hunting and gathering folk hundreds of thousands of years ago may be presumed to have developed many of the techniques for exploiting the natural environments which people at the hunting level of culture still employ.

Not only did ancient man abandon his campfires to ignite vegetation but he probably deliberately started conflagrations which swept over the country. In ancient times, as in recent ones, thick forests and dense jungles of brush offered very little use to the hunter or collector. On the contrary, narrow trails through tangled and heavy growth were dangerous because of the concealment provided to human, as well as animal, enemies. Whenever possible, aborigines have set fire to jungles and thick woods in order to "open them up." Widely spaced trees and clear meadows and plains offer better and safer hunting.

Klamath Indians in forested southern Oregon and Pomo Indians in the redwood country of northern California complained to me that modern forestry, which allows brush and trees to grow rank and uncontrolled, was depriving the Indians of much hunting territory. The Klamath Indian said: "Now I just hear the deer running through the brush at places we used to kill many deer. When the brush got as thick as it is now, we would burn it off." There are many other references to intentional burning to thin or remove brush and trees in order to improve visibility for hunting and to facilitate travel. Clearing to get an advantage for hunting

would also reduce the danger from enemies.

Aubréville, in his exhaustive work (1949, p. 323) on the forests and savannas of French Equatorial Africa, also concluded that aborigines would have burned for the advantages afforded by open woods and plains. Werner in British Central Africa observed (1906, pp. 9–12) that, "where there are no trees or bushes, the grass is usually tall . . . and has to be burned off at the end of every dry season—otherwise it would become an impenetrable jungle." Werner noted that brush fires were set purposely "or accidentally by some travellers' campfire," and he added:

These fires have from the earliest ages formed one of the characteristic features of African travel. One of the oldest records of exploration [from about 500 B.C.]—the *Periplus* of Hanno—describes them, ". . . by day we saw nothing but woods, but by night we saw many fires burning . . . going along four days, we saw by night the land full of flame and in the midst was a lofty fire, greater than the rest and seemed to touch the stars."

Historic aborigines tell us of a number of other reasons for broadcast burning which may also have motivated primeval man. To rouse or drive game during hunting was the reason most frequently recorded over the world. A hundred different Indian groups of North America as well as natives of South America, Africa, Tasmania, Australia, New Guinea, China, and Turkestan set fire to drive game. Birket-Smith (1929) believes Europeans have used fire for hunting since Solutrean times, or during the last fifteen thousand years. Sauer (1944) and Eiseley (1954) interpret the evidence of late Pleistocene man in America to mean that fire drives were used here ten to twenty thousand years ago. Lucretius (1908, p. 212) in 55 B.C. assumed that the practice was very ancient and had, possibly, contributed to the discovery of smelting thousands of years before his time. It seems reasonable to assume that fire as an aid to hunting would have been used with greater frequency as one extended further and further into the past. In the most ancient times the weapons, traps, and other hunting tools would be less efficient. In other words, during the Lower Paleolithic for approximately nine hundred thousand years, while the hunting tools consisted only of sharpened sticks and the stone fist ax or *coup de poing,* fire would have been a relatively greater aid to hunting than in the Neolithic, when the bow and arrow were perfected. Fire also would be used in the collection of various insects, like crickets, whenever they were used as food.

Burning of grasslands and forests to improve pasture for game has been widely reported. This practice includes burning off year-old dry stocks in order to make new growth available, burning to produce greener and more tender grass, burning to remove brush and trees, and burning to speed the appearance of new grass in the spring. To improve pasture has been given as the reason for setting fire to vegetation by hunting peoples from the Atlantic to the Pacific in the United States, as well as in Argentina, Manchuria, and South Africa.

It has long been realized that even the poorest hunting and gathering peoples who appeared to be on the lowest level of material culture had a very thorough knowledge of the characteristics of the wild plants in their homelands. Aborigines not only knew growth patterns and the geographic conditions favored by each plant species; they were well aware also of various means to assist different plants in the struggle with other plants. That they understood the value of fire as a tool to procure and maintain the yield of certain wild plants they desired has been much in evidence. This knowledge was displayed,

as noted above, through deliberate burning to improve grazing conditions for game. In addition, throughout the western United States, Indians from about fifty tribes reported intentional broadcast burning in order to increase the yield of seeds of wild grasses and weeds which were collected for food. Several forest-dwelling tribes, among them the Iroquois and Powhatan of the Atlantic seaboard, the Kwakiutl of British Columbia, and several California tribes, as well as the Yahgan of Tierra del Fuego, burned woods and bushes to improve the berry harvest. Fire has also been widely used to make vegetable food more available, as when forest litter was ignited to uncover acorns or nuts. Furthermore, fire has been used to aid growth of tobacco and to produce willows for basketry weaving.

The practical motivations for incendiarism listed above would lead to repeated and regular application of flame to vegetation. The benefits obtained during recent years could have been obtained equally well hundreds of thousands of years ago. Although there is no way to determine at what period in human history natives applied the torch for which reason, there is, nevertheless, no basis for thinking that any one of the motives so far listed is of recent origin. All of them have probably influenced mankind to set fires since the beginning of humanity.

Of less general applicability and of more specialized use is the setting of vegetation on fire as an act of war. It is logical to suppose that small populations at war would have readily recognized that fire could be a weapon. The first men to see the value of flame to rouse or drive game would quite certainly have realized that the same tool could be helpful to flush an enemy from dry brush or grass.

Herodotus in 447 B.C. (1936, p. 240) provides the earliest apparent documentation of the scorched-earth method of defense on the Russian grasslands. When the Scythians retreated before the army of Darius, they left "the whole country bare of forage . . . destroying all that grew on the ground." Lucretius (1908, p. 212) also mentions fire as an implement of war. American Indians from the prairies of the United States, the pampas of Argentina, and the grasslands of California report using fire as a weapon. It was even a practice of the Papuans of New Guinea.

In addition to the references which specify the reasons for intentional broadcast burning, there are a number of sources which state simply that such fires occurred in particular areas. There are records of natives firing the vegetation for unspecified reasons for nearly all the separate states of the United States. Similar reports of incendiarism for undetermined reasons have come from Mexico, the Antilles, Argentina, Brazil, Venezuela, India, China, Ceylon, Sumatra, Lapland, Sweden, Russia, and Africa. I must believe, with Sauer (1952), Hough (1926), Shantz (1947), and Kuhnholtz-Lordat (1939), that aborigines the world over since time immemorial have set vegetation on fire. In recognizing that the preagricultural populations of the world had good and sufficient reasons for clearing lands and also had the means to do so, we add many thousands of years to the period that man has been an important ecological factor on the earth.

I am aware that some scholars appear reluctant to grant that the hunters and collectors had any influence on the geographic environment. Clark (1952, pp. 91–92), introducing his chapter on Neolithic farming in Europe, asserted that prior to clearing by the early agriculturalists Europe was covered by a great primeval forest. Clark (*ibid.*, p. 94) draws his conclusion from the increase in herb pollen and charcoal at the Neolithic level of Danish peat bogs analyzed by Iversen. The fact that there were significant amounts of both charcoal and herb pollen and that the amounts fluctuated markedly before the Neolithic should have suggested that intentional burning preceded the Neolithic farmers. It is true, of course, that damp forests of pre-Neolithic times could not be ignited easily. However, Stefansson (1913, p. 10) tells of intentional burning of forests by American Indians to improve hunting in the subarctic coniferous forest of the lower Mackenzie River, and Seifriz (1934, p. 307) gives an account of Lapps burning their pine forests, indicating that hunters may go to great trouble to burn moist forests at those rare and irregular periods when the forests would carry fire.

It seems certain that forest-burning expanded in Europe during Neolithic times, as indicated by the amount of the charcoal and herb pollen in the Neolithic peat deposits. A sharp rise in population was made possible by improved and stabilized food supply resulting from the introduction of farming and herding. Agriculturalists with good axes, whether made of stone or steel, and with the milpa or slash-and-burn system of land preparation, would surely clear more damp forest than would hunters. Notwithstanding the increase of open lands in Europe brought about by cultivation, fire as a tool without agriculture should not be minimized. Whether in Europe, Africa, Asia, or the Americas, the record is clear that burning for hunting preceded as well as accompanied the use of fire with agriculture and grazing. It is not always clear which is the strongest motivation —hunting, agriculture, or herding— where there is a mixed economy. The importance of the agricultural motive is clear and dominant in the moist northern forests and the tropical rain forests, where cutting of some brush and trees and stripping the bark from others are necessary to allow the area to become dry enough to burn. Where broadcast wild fires are impossible, the work of opening a section is justified only where a crop can be grown in the fertilizing ash. Extreme tropical rain forests, however, have been removed initially for planting but have been maintained in grass by annual burning. Tansley and Chipp (1926), Aubréville (1949), and Kuhnholtz-Lordat (1939) abundantly document this sequence for historic peoples and project its occurrence into the distant past. Clark (1952, p. 95) briefly summarizes the relationship of plants to prehistoric burning in Europe and concludes that extensive meadows, grasslands, and heaths were formed with the aid of fire during the Neolithic. Some grasslands have continued until the present and are only now being returned to forest. The generalization that all primitive hoe-and-dibble planters the world over used fire as a tool in cultivation seems justified.

Gordon M. Day (1953) carefully and thoroughly documented vegetation burning by Iroquois and Algonkin Indians to clear fields for agriculture and to open forests for hunting in New England at the time of European discovery. All the aboriginal maize farmers of the eastern United States employed similar methods. Furthermore, the Maya of Yucatan were forced to move their towns, according to Hough (1926, p. 67) and Lundell (1934, p. 265), after milpa cultivation had degraded the soil and established sod in place of trees. The New Zealand grasslands, although ancient and pre-European, are now attributed to the old Maori custom of clearing forests for planting with the aid of fire. Repeated burning maintains grass on ancient fields (Allen, 1937, p. 27). The same process was observed in 1952 on Guadalcanal. Annual fires maintained grass on old fields, while new fields were acquired by cutting and burning forests (Johnson, personal communication). I have received personal reports of similar practices leading to comparable results in New Guinea, Alor, and Sumatra, and I have found in the literature references to the same customs in South America, Africa, Madagascar, China, Ceylon, and Indochina.

Some antiquity for the slash-and-burn agriculture in Korea is implied by its being designated by special terms: *hwajon* (Japanese: *kaden*) for the fire field, and *hwajommin* (Japanese: *kadenmin*) for the fire-field farmer. In 1944 Grajdanzev (p. 95) wrote of Korea that *kaden* "consists of the burning of grasses and bushes in the forest area and planting cereals or potatoes there for a few seasons and then moving to another place when the fertility of the ground has been exhausted." Over 100,000 acres were said to have been cultivated in 1938 by *kadenmin,* who constituted 2.4 per cent of Korean farmers (*ibid.,* p. 109).

There are numerous examples of the passage of land from cultivation into pasture and thereafter of the maintenance of the grazing area by fire. Several scholars tell of the renewal of the heath by burning after the brush grows beyond a certain height. Young shoots provide better feed for cattle, sheep, and goats.

In 1931 the American geographer Ellen Churchill Semple presented an excellent summary of the role of fire and grazing in the deforestation of the Mediterranean. I quote Dr. Semple's classic study at some length (pp. 290–91):

Denudation of the forests made such inroads upon the wood supply of Italy that by the fifth century Roman architectural technique had become modified to meet the growing scarcity and increased price of wood.

Clearing for tillage land and the legitimate consumption of wood as lumber were only part of the process of destruction.

The long dry summers and the resinous character of Mediterranean *maqui* shrubs made forest fires frequent and disastrous, while the high winds of the hot season fanned the flames. Such fires were a commonplace event in ancient Palestine. Isaiah describes one in a metaphorical passage: "It shall devour the briers and thorns, and shall kindle in the thickets of the forest, and they shall mount up like the lifting up of smoke." Homer knows the effect of protracted drought and strong summer winds upon such a conflagration. "Through deep glens rageth fierce fire on some parched mountain side and the deep forest beneath, and the wind, driving it, whirleth everywhere the flame. . . ."

Fires were often started, either intentionally or accidentally, by the herdsmen who ranged the mountain forests with their sheep and goats in the dry season. Burning improved the pasturage, because the ashes temporarily enriched the soil, and the abundant shoots from the old roots furnished better fodder. The forests once destroyed were hard to restore.

Dr. Semple could have used also quotations from Lucretius (1908, p. 213) and Vergil (1947, pp. 14, 51).

Burning to improve grazing was also reported for the steppes of the lower Volga during a trip in spring of 1794 by Pallas (1803, p. 115, with footnote): "The nights, however, still continue cold, and we saw fire on the steppe, at a considerable distance. . . . The steppes are frequently fired, either by the negligence of travellers, or willfully by the herdsmen, in order to forward the crops of grass."

Kuhnholtz-Lordat (1939, pp. 191–241) devoted a fifty-page section of his book *La Terre incendiée* to "Fire and Herding." He discovered that fire was used as a tool to help prepare pastures in Madagascar, French North Africa (by Berbers), South Africa, Rhodesia, the Congo, France, Switzerland, the Malay Peninsula, the Balkans, and other lands of the Mediterranean.

All the reasons for burning over the landscape already enumerated, except for farming and herding, could have existed generally during all the history of man. I have considered also the practices of ancient animal and plant husbandry, in so far as these used fire as a tool, but I wish to emphasize that most of the motivations of the primitive hunters and gatherers continued to activate some of the simple agriculturists as well as the modern farmers, mechanics, doctors, and other specialists of all kinds who hunt as a sport.

Dr. Marion Kingston, professor of English at the University of Colorado, wrote me that "the deer burn still comprises a thick chapter in the Maine poacher's handbook." Kuhnholtz-Lordat (1939, pp. 245–47) also wrote of the importance of the use of fire in hunting by those who have agriculture and herds. This is true in tropical Africa, Indochina, Madagascar, the Baltic, and America.

The most ancient reasons for burning persist and are joined to the motives of the planter and the herder. With the domestication of plants and animals, commencing about 8000 B.C., all the known motives for using fire as a tool were operative. From the earlier hunting stage the change was very slight in some instances, as with the shift from preparing pasture for wild game to doing so for domestic herds. The sample of archeological and ethnological evidence presented seems sufficient to sustain the opinion that man has set fire to the landscape during his entire history. It may be worth while, nevertheless, to review some of the botanical material which supports and bolsters the above opinion. Although the anthropological and botanical data combine and strengthen the structure of evidence of man's influence on his geographic environment, plant distributions and other knowledge gained from botany appear more complete and more certain in some respects.

Botanical evidence for the antiquity and universality of burning falls into three general categories. (1) Exact dating of burns by means of fire scars and tree-ring analysis is possible and provocative in a few localities. (2) Some studies in plant succession indicate clearly and immediately that the normal plant succession of the area has been disturbed. Many species are known as *pyrophytes* (Kuhnholtz-Lordat, 1939, pp. 31–34) or fire plants and indicate frequent burning-over. (3) Related to plant succession but more complicated in analysis is a comparison of plant potential from an analysis of soil, moisture, temperature, etc., with the actual plant cover. This is of particular importance where very extensive regions, such as the American prairies and plains, the Argentine pampas, the Russian steppes, and the African sudan and veld, present an appearance of being entirely natural and climatically determined.

To discover the impact of man and his cultural tools on nature from a study of plant cover, it is always necessary to weigh man's potential against similar effects which could be produced by other means, such as by lightning. Whenever we find botanical evidence that an area has been burned over, there is always the question whether the fire was from natural or from human cause. American botanists, plant ecologists, and geographers as a group appear to favor the idea that all prehistoric fires were due to natural causes, and, by so doing, they greatly minimize human influence. I know of no study of lightning-caused fires which permits such a conclusion to be drawn with confidence.

In the tree rings and fire scars of giant sequoias is the history of their survival against regular attacks by flames throughout their entire lives of two thousand years. Were these fires set by Indians or lightning? There is no sure answer. Yet, in the Sierra Nevada, where the sequoias are located, authenticated lightning fires occur annually by the hundreds and could certainly account for all the scars made during the last two millenniums. However, redwoods of the Coast Range of northern California and lightning statistics for that region tell a very different story. Fritz (1932, pp. 2–3) wrote that fires ignited by lightning are extremely rare.

Analysis of burned tissue and growth rings shows that forests in Oregon (Keen, 1940, p. 498) and in Pennsylvania (Lutz, 1930, pp. 1–29) were also repeatedly subjected to fire during the last thousand years. Relatively few lightning fires are recorded for Pennsylvania; it would seem that the majority of the scars in these forests were from man-made fire. Within the time limits imposed by the trees themselves, the record of the trees may be interpreted to mean that Indians certainly caused fires for about two thousand years. Moreover, if hunters and gatherers in California and Pennsylvania are certainly known to have used fire as a tool for two thousand years, there is no reason not to suppose that the practice has been carried on for many more thousands of years.

From regions widely distributed over the world come reports of ancient and extensive burning, as evidenced by the types of plants growing under various particular climatic conditions. Let me first cite the material for the southern pine area of the United States. Shantz and Zon (1924, p. 14 and their Fig. 2) designated the region "Longleaf-Loblolly-Slash Pines (Southeastern Pine Forest)" and wrote that this forest, which is like that of the drought-resistant western yellow pine, occurs where there is heavy precipitation, because of the sandy soil and evaporation.

The first Europeans in the area reported game drives by means of fire and also reported that some open prairies, such as the Shenandoah Valley, became tree-covered as soon as burning was curtailed (Maxwell, 1910). Weaver and Clements (1929, p. 512) wrote of the area as follows: "The extent of this great pine belt has naturally led to the assumption that it is climax in nature, but its ecological character, as well as actual successional studies at widely separated points, leaves little or no doubt that it is essentially a fire subclimax."

H. H. Chapman, of Yale University, directed extensive observations and experiments for about thirty years and established beyond doubt that the longleaf pine forest was dependent upon fire for its very existence. Early in the thirties Chapman (1932a, p. 603) wrote that "if complete fire protection must be enforced . . . the long-leaf pine will disappear as a species." Later he proposed (1950a, 1950b) that the longleaf pine had made a fundamental genetic, probably evolutionary, adjustment to fire. The longleaf can survive being defoliated several times and still quickly produce a remarkably large and healthy tree. Chapman thought lightning fires responsible for the genetic adjustment, but there are too few cases of lightning starting fires in the southeastern pine forest for that natural agent to have stimulated special adaptation. In this area lightning almost inevitably occurs with rain, which extinguishes any fire due to lightning strikes. Harper (1943, p. 32) suggested spontaneous combustion as the natural agent in antiquity, which over the millenniums maintained the pine forest in a hardwood area.

If ten to twenty-five thousand years would suffice for the genetic adjustment of the southern pines, the adjustment could be due to man-made fires. The Vero and Melbourne, Florida, sites, at which human skeletons were found in association with mastodon bones, suggest that the southeastern section of the United States has been inhabited by man as long as any in the New World. If it were thought that a longer time—say, a hundred thousand years—was required for evolutionary development of longleaf pine peculiarities, I believe this evidence could be taken as support for placing man's occupancy of the New World in the third interglacial.

Daubenmire (1947, pp. 331–34) lists a number of other fire plants, including the lodgepole pine, which are encouraged and multiplied by fire. Troup (1926, pp. 308–9) wrote that Burmese teak forests need fire to exist, and Gorrie (1935) reported that the cheer pine of the Himalayas was likewise dependent upon fire for survival. There are other examples of extensive forests, such as the Douglas fir of the Pacific Coast of the northwestern United States, which appear to be subclimax, and possibly dependent upon fire, in an area where lightning fires are almost unknown.

In summary, the botanical evidence just outlined leaves little doubt that fire has played a decisive role on the landscape during many thousands of years. And it seems reasonable to believe with Braun-Blanquet (1932, p. 278) that human rather than atmospheric agents were responsible:

While prairie and forest fires may occasionally be caused by lightning, that is the exception rather than the rule. In 90 out of 100 cases they are caused by man, either willfully or accidentally. Contrary to the opinion of some American investigators, therefore, fire is to be classed among the anthropogenous factors.

Additional botanical analysis as an aid to understanding man's primeval influence on the face of the earth may be introduced by a quotation from Farmer (1953, pp. 115–17):

"The savanna is one of the most wide-spread landscapes of Africa. . . . It results from the tropical climate with a moderate amount of rainfall and a long spell of drought." Many of us were brought up at school to believe this statement from M. E. Hardy's *Geography of Plants* (Oxford, 1920). But few would now agree that African savanna, at least in its present aspect, is a true climax vegetation, and the same might be said of other tropical grass-lands, such as the *llanos* and *campos* of South America and the *cogonales* of the Philippines. The conviction has grown that such grasslands, as we see them today, are wholly or partly man-made, the product of shifting cultivation and peri-odic burning. Savanna, in this view, is a fire-climax. . . . A careful study . . . is C. H. Holmes's valuable and well illustrated paper "The Grass, Fern, and Savannah Lands of Ceylon.". . . Holmes analyzes the climate of Ceylon and concludes that the climax vegetation of all seven present types [of Ceylon vegetation] is a closed forest . . . all seven types as they stand today are secondary, the result of clearing, burning, cultivation, and thereafter, peri-odic burning.

Troup (1926, p. 310) would add the grasslands of India to the list of those made by man.

Even though the human cause of tropical wet grassland may be estab-lished beyond doubt, the question of the prairies and plains of the temperate zone is still challenging. These are the world's greatest continuous areas of pure grass. Their size and the fact that they have been in all historic time es-sentially uniform and unchanged lead almost inevitably to the conclusion that they are climatically and geographical-ly determined. Many scientists who have studied them have been steadfast in their belief that the extensive grass-lands of Argentina, Russia, and North America resulted solely from the re-sponse of vegetation to precipitation, evaporation, temperature, and soil. The American prairies have been the home, training ground, and object of mature

research for the leading plant ecologists of the United States. For over fifty years botanists, geographers, ecologists, geologists, and other scientists attached to the large and respected state univer-sities of Nebraska, Illinois, Indiana, Kansas, Iowa, Wisconsin, Ohio, Minne-sota, and Missouri have studied the prairies. World-famous scholars, such as F. E. Clements, B. Shimek, and J. E. Weaver, have spent their lives analyz-ing the vegetation of American prairies and plains and have maintained their belief that the peculiar purity of plant cover over the whole area resulted from the fact that grass was its climax vege-tation. Weaver's recent book, *North American Prairie* (1954), which pre-sents the essence of his own forty years of research and the results obtained by many of his colleagues and students may well serve as an example of the views of American plant ecologists. Ac-cording to Weaver (1954, p. 21), "cli-max prairie is the outcome of thousands of years of sorting out of species and adaptations to the soil and climate." Fire as a factor is dismissed with a few passing references.

Weaver (1954, p. 273) summarized his three-page section on "Effects of Burning" partly by quoting the Minne-sota geographer Borchert (1950) as follows:

Fire is less destructive to grasses than to woody vegetation and it may sometimes benefit prairie where debris has accumu-lated over several years. This undoubtedly occurred where fires were set by light-ning. The prairie and indeed the entire area of North American Grassland at time of settlement consisted of a climax vege-tation, the extent of which was controlled by climate. Fire was only one of the many environmental factors. The grasses pro-duced large amounts of dead, dry, inflam-mable material. Lightning often started fires. "Thus the Grassland climates favor fire, just as they favor grass whether there are fires or not. . . . Fire, if not primitive man, himself, would simply have been one part of the ecological complex of a region with the climate of the Grassland. . . . Also, the precipitation pattern of eastern America during major drought years can explain why the influence of fire was restricted to the grassland. The climate of the forests generally did not favor burning" (Borchert, 1950, pp. 38–39). After extended study of the climate of Central North America, Borchert concludes: "The geographical pattern of postulated postglacial fluctuation of the Grassland fits the facts of the recorded climate. The pattern of the Grassland at the time of white settlement also fits those facts. The patterns, themselves, suggest very strongly that they were, in the words of an earlier author, dictated by the master hand of climate."

It is the very stability and size of the temperate grasslands which make them of special value for evaluating man's influence on his environment. If the evidence would allow for a strong presumption that the great mid-latitude plains and prairies had been dependent on man's fire for their existence, then we could give much more weight to fire as the first tool with which man changed his geographic environment. Both the extent and the uniformity of the herbaceous plant cover would require a tremendous time period to achieve. And, if the temperate as well as tropical grasslands should be attributed to man, we must say that it was the hunters and gatherers, in ages before agriculture and herding, who produced such profound and permanent modification of the landscape. I believe there is considerable evidence for such a conclusion notwithstanding the contrary opinions of the many American ecologists and geographers.

There is, of course, room for differences of opinion even when the same raw data are evaluated. For example, the experiments conducted by Clements, Weaver, and Hanson (1929), cited by Weaver (1954, p. 189), demonstrated that shrubs could and did invade prairie sod. To Weaver, however,

they showed only how slow such an invasion would be. There is involved here a difference of time-and-space perspective An advance of forest onto prairie of a few feet a year may be interpreted to allow forests to replace grass only if viewed as continuing thousands of years. Not all studies confirm such a slow rate of invasion into tall-grass prairie: Chavennes (1941, p. 80) discovered that there had been a decrease of 60 per cent of Wisconsin prairie in the twenty-five years from 1829 to 1854, owing to the invasion of trees and brush following the cessation of fires and preceding cultivation. Gleason (1922, pp. 80–82) wrote of Illinois that "barrens were converted into forests as by magic when fires that had maintained them were stopped." Gleason went on to say that forests advanced into Illinois grasslands one to two miles in thirty years and also that northwestern Illinois and southwestern Wisconsin, now heavily forested where not cultivated, was 80–90 per cent prairie grassland when first visited by Europeans. And elsewhere (1913, p. 181) he wrote that "prairie fires have been the deciding factor in determining the distribution of forests in the Middle West."

Whereas Weaver (1954, p. 190) minimized the "extension of forest into prairie" by saying it "occurred in a limited manner following settlement and the cessation of prairie fires," there is abundant evidence to show that brush and trees, if given a chance, would invade virtually all the tall-grass moist prairie. The Kentucky barrens and the prairies of Ohio, Michigan, and Indiana have all been invaded by woods. The 75,000,000 acres of grassland of Texas and neighboring states have become covered with mesquite jungles. Sagebrush and juniper have invaded parts of the drier grasslands from the west, and aspen forests have crept hundreds of miles into the northern prairie as a prelude to pine.

We cannot judge from observations whether forest would eventually spread over all the grasslands, because there does not yet exist an opportunity for a fair and free competition between prairie grass and weeds, on the one hand, and brush and trees, on the other. Cultivation, overgrazing, and mowing interfere. Also, fires still sweep over vast sections of the prairie and plains so frequently that they are declared the greatest barrier to the establishment of forests and shelter belts in the Midwest. However, the fact that throughout the tall-grass prairie planted groves of many species have flourished and have reproduced seedlings during moist years and, furthermore, have survived the most severe and prolonged period of drought in the 1930's suggests that there is no climatic barrier to forests in the area. Also the success, at the driest western edge of the tall-grass prairie, of the Shelter Belt Project, made up of 16,000 miles of tree plantings extending from Canada to Texas, shows that soil and moisture are sufficient for tree growth (Anonymous, 1942, p. 456).

The Nebraska National Forest was planted in the sand hills at the driest extreme of the prairie zone in 1903, but a prairie fire spread into the planted area in 1910, destroying most of the trees. Replanted in 1911 and protected by firebreaks, the 20,000 acres of conifers have developed mature trees and true forest conditions where natural reproduction is taking place (Davis, 1951). The firebreaks have stopped several large outside grass fires from spreading into the planted area, but there is no mention of lightning igniting the forest itself.

Let us consider this question of lightning on the North American grasslands. Weaver (1954, p. 273), as quoted above, repeats an assertion frequently made that "lightning often started fires" on the prairies. I have found no evidence that lightning ignited vegetation on the plains and prairies at times and places to cause widespread grass fires. Lightning increases with elevation, and most of the fires it starts in plant cover are in the Rocky Mountains and the Sierra Nevada–Cascade ranges of western America. Even in the forests of the Wichita Mountains of Oklahoma, only twenty-six fires in four years were attributed to lightning. Plummer (1912*a*), in the monograph entitled *Lightning in Relation to Forest Fires,* stated that there are very few records of fires being started on the plains and prairies, and even then he is not really explicit. In fact, I have been able to discover no authentic record of any grass fire ever being ignited by lightning. This agrees with the experience of Gleason (1913, p. 176), the famous plant geographer, already quoted, who wrote that he could find "no record of a prairie fire produced by lightning."

Borchert's misconception, apparently accepted by Weaver in 1954, that in aboriginal times "the influence of fire was restricted to the grassland," may be passed over without further comment, since the record for Indian burning of all woodlands of the eastern United States is so complete (Maxwell, 1910; Day, 1953; Chapman, 1932, 1944, 1947, 1950). Another point made by Borchert (1950, pp. 38–39) and cited by Weaver is frequently found in publications of American plant ecologists. I refer to the idea that fire and primitive man as influences on the physical environment can be passed over by the simple statement that they were "one part of the ecological complex of a region."

If the geographers and ecologists really acted on this expressed view, how different might be their conclusions! Unfortunately, this statement of principle is as far as they go. Whereas rainfall, snowfall, evaporation, wind, frost, temperature, etc., are measured, correlated, analyzed, and charted for each month and for many years, and these are applied to each plant and then to plant complexes, fire is treated only in a passing reference. Borchert (1950) himself gave "The Effect of Fire" one paragraph of a half-page length in his thirty-nine-page article on the climate of the American grassland. I found no other record, measurement, or analysis of the effects of fire in the dozens of Vestal's publications. Stating the principle that fire should be treated as any other part of the natural environment is not enough. It should in fact be treated and studied as fully as other ecological factors.

It is the record of vegetation burning by American Indians throughout the hemisphere from Alaska to Tierra del Fuego and from coast to coast which has led me to consider fire an ancient and powerful force in the hand of man in America. Archeology supports the opinion that fire was employed to drive game on the plains by America's first inhabitants and has been so used to the present. The American grasslands were regularly and frequently burned over at the time of European discovery and exploration.

In summarizing the effect of fire on the North American grassland, it seems reasonable to assume that, since the moist prairies can support true forests and the dry plains can support xeric brush and scattered trees, and since the trees are capable of invading the sod, some non-geographic force is critical for the formation and maintenance of grasslands in America. Fires set by man have been present for thousands of years, and lightning-set fires have been rare. Burning by primitive peoples may thus be considered a determining factor.

Although the matter has been debated for the last century, a number of scientists have preceded me in this conclusion: Marsh (1864), Christy (1892), Cook (1908), Gleason (1913, 1932), Sauer (1920, 1952), and Humphrey (1958), to name a few. Schmieder (1927) came to the same conclusion regarding the pampas of Argentina, and it appears that the evidence regarding the Russian steppes would justify a similar view. For example, Pallas (1803) saw several grass fires and implied that they occurred regularly; Mirov (1935) and Vyssotsky (1935) reported the success of shelter-belt planting on the steppes. The data on grasslands of the tropical and temperate zones of the world support the view that they have been formed and have undoubtedly been maintained by man by means of fire. The implication that man used fire as a tool in remote prehistoric times is strong.

The unrestricted burning of vegetation appears to be a universal culture trait among historic primitive peoples and therefore was probably employed by our remote ancestors. Archeology indicates that extensive areas of the Old and New Worlds were being burned over ten thousand years ago. It is logical to assume that some of the reasons which motivated historic and Neolithic men would also have motivated our remote ancestors to set vegetation on fire. One may conclude that fire has been used by man to influence his geographic environment during his entire career as a human. Furthermore, it is impossible to understand clearly the distribution and history of vegetation of the earth's land surfaces without careful consideration of fire as a universal factor influencing the plant geography of the world.

REFERENCES

ALLEN, H. H.
1937 "Origin and Distribution of the Naturalized Plants of New Zealand," *Proceedings of the Linnean Society of London,* CL, Part I, 25–47.

ANONYMOUS
1942 "Record Survival Made by Shelterbelt Trees," *Journal of Forestry,* XL, No. 6, 456.

AUBRÉVILLE, A.
1949 *Climats, forêts et désert:fication de l'Afrique tropicale.* Paris: Société d'Éditions Géographiques, Marit:mes et Coloniales. 351 pp.

BIRKET-SMITH, KAJ
1929 *The Caribou Eskimos: Report of the Fifth Thule Expedition 1921–1924,* Vol. V, Part II. Copenhagen: Gyldendal. 419 pp.

BORCHERT, JOHN R.
1950 "The Climate of the Central North American Grassland," *Annals of the Association of American Geographers,* XL, No. 1, 1–39.

BRAUN-BLANQUET, J.
1932 *Plant Sociology.* New York: McGraw-Hill Book Co. 439 pp.

CHAPMAN, H. H.
1932a "Some Further Relations of Fire to Longleaf Pine," *Journal of Forestry,* XXX, No. 5, 602–5.
1932b "Is the Longleaf Type a Climax?" *Ecology,* XIII, 328–34.
1944 "Fire and Pines," *American Forests,* L, 62–63, 91–93.
1947 "Natural Areas," *Ecology,* XXVIII, 193–94.
1950a "Lightning in the Longleaf," *American Forests,* LVI, No. 1, 10–12.
1950b "An Unknown Pioneer in Prescribed Burning in Burma," *Journal of Forestry,* XLVIII, No. 2, 131–32.

CHAVENNES, ELIZABETH
1941 "Written Records of Forest Succession," *Scientific Monthly,* LIII (July), 76–77.

CHIPP, T. F.
1926 "Aims and Methods of Study of Tropical Countries, with Special Reference to West Africa," pp. 194–237 in TANSLEY, A. G., and CHIPP, T. F. (eds.), *Aims and Methods in the Study of Vegetation.* London:

British Empire Vegetation Committee and the Crown Agents for the Colonies. 383 pp.

CHRISTY, MILLER
1892 "Why Are the Prairies Treeless?" *Proceedings of the Royal Geographical Society and Monthly Record of Geography,* XIV, 78–100. London.

CLARK, J. G. D.
1945 "Farmers and Forests in Neolithic Europe," *Antiquity,* XIX, No. 74, 57–71.
1952 *Prehistoric Europe, the Economic Basis.* London: Methuen & Co. 349 pp.

CLEMENTS, FREDERIC E.; WEAVER, JOHN E.; and HANSON, HERBERT C.
1929 *Plant Competition.* (Publication No. 398.) Washington, D.C.: Carnegie Institution. 340 pp.

COOK, O. F.
1908 *Change of Vegetation on the South Texas Prairies.* (Bureau of Plant Industries Circular No. 14.) Washington, D.C.: U.S. Department of Agriculture. 7 pp.

DART, R. A.
1948 "The Makapansgat Proto-human *Australopithecus prometheus,*" *American Journal of Physical Anthropology,* VI, 259.

DAUBENMIRE, R. F.
1947 *Plants and Environment.* New York: John Wiley & Sons. 424 pp.

DAVIS, WILFRED S.
1951 "Nebraska Firebreaks," *Fire Control Notes,* XII, No. 1, 40–46. Washington, D.C.: U.S. Department of Agriculture Forest Service.

DAY, GORDON M.
1953 "The Indian as an Ecological Factor in the Northeastern Forest," *Ecology,* XXXIV, 329–46.

EISELEY, LOREN C.
1954 "Man the Fire-maker," *Scientific American,* CXCI, 52–57.

FARMER, B. H.
1953 "Tropical Grasslands of Ceylon," *Geographical Review,* XLIII, No. 1, 115–17.

FLANNERY, REGINA
1939 *An Analysis of Coastal Algonquian Culture.* ("Anthropological Se-

ries," No. 7.) Washington, D.C.: Catholic University of America Press. 219 pp.

FRIEDERICI, G.

1925 *Der Charakter der Entdeckung und Eroberung Amerikas durch die Europäer.* 3 vols. Stuttgart: Gotha.

1930 "Der Grad der Durchdringbarkeit Nordamerikas im Zeitalter der Entdeckungen und ersten Durchforschung des Kontinents durch die Europäer," *Petermanns geographische Mitteilungen,* CCIX, 223–26.

FRITZ, EMANUEL

1932 *The Role of Fire in the Redwood Region.* (Circular No. 323.) Berkeley: University of California Agriculture Extension Service. 22 pp.

GLEASON, HENRY ALLEN

1913 "The Relation of Forest Distribution and Prairie Fires to the Middle West," *Torreya,* XIII, 173–81.

1932 "The Vegetational History of the Middle West," *Annals of the Association of American Geographers,* XII, 39–85.

GORRIE, R. MACLAGAN

1935 "Protective Burning in Himalayan Pine," *Journal of Forestry,* XXXVIII, 807–11.

GRAJDANZEV, ANDREW J.

1944 *Modern Korea.* New York: John Day Co. 330 pp.

HARPER, ROLAND M.

1943 *Forests of Alabama.* (Monograph No. 10.) University, Ala.: Geologic Survey of Alabama. 230 pp.

HERODOTUS

1936 *History.* Trans. GEORGE RAWLINSON; ed. MANUEL KOMROFF. New York: Tudor Publishing Co. 544 pp.

HOLMES, C. H.

1951 *The Grass, Fern, and Savannah Lands of Ceylon: Their Nature and Ecological Significance.* (Institute Paper No. 28.) Oxford: University of Oxford Imperial Forestry Institute. 95 pp.

HOUGH, WALTER

1926 *Fire as an Agent in Human Culture.* (Bulletin No. 139.) Washington, D.C.: United States National Museum. 270 pp.

HUMPHREY, R. R.

1953 "The Desert Grassland, Past and Present," *Journal of Range Management,* VI, 159–64.

KEEN, F. P.

1940 "Longevity of Ponderosa Pine," *Journal of Forestry,* XXXVIII, 597–98.

KROEBER, A. L.

1939 "Culture Element Distributions, XI: Tribes Surveyed," *University of California Anthropological Records,* I, No. 7, 435–40.

KUHNHOLTZ-LORDAT, G.

1939 *La Terre incendiée.* Nîmes, France: Éditions de la Maison Cairée Ateliers Bruguier. 361 pp.

LUCRETIUS

1908 *On the Nature of the Universe.* Trans. from the Latin by H. A. J MUNRO. London: George Bell & Sons. 267 pp.

LUNDELL, CYRUS LONGWORTH

1934 *Preliminary Sketch of the Phytogeography of the Yucatan Peninsula.* (Publication No. 436.) Washington, D.C.: Carnegie Institution. 355 pp.

LUTZ, H. J.

1930 "The Vegetation of Heart's Content: A Virgin Forest in Northwestern Pennsylvania," *Ecology,* XI, 1–29.

MARSH, G. P.

1864 *Man and Nature.* New York: C. Scribner & Co. 560 pp.

MAXWELL, HU

1910 "The Use and Abuse of Forests by the Virginia Indians," *William and Mary College Historical Magazine,* XIX, 86–104.

MIROV, N. T.

1935 "Two Centuries of Afforestation and Shelterbelt Planting on the Russian Steppes," *Journal of Forestry,* XXXIII, 971–73.

MOIR, J. REID

1919 *Pre-Palaeolithic Man.* Ipswich: W. E. Harrison; London: Simpkin, Marshall, Hamilton, Kent & Co. 67 pp.

OSBORN, HENRY FAIRFIELD

1927 *Man Rises to Parnassus.* Princeton, N.J.: Princeton University Press. 216 pp

PALLAS, P. S.

1803 *Travels through the Southern Provinces of the Russian Empire in*

the Years 1793 and 1794. 2 vols.
London: A. Strahan.

PLUMMER, FRED G.

1912a *Lightning in Relation to Forest Fires.* (Bulletin No. 111.) Washington, D.C.: U.S. Department of Agriculture Forest Service. 39 pp.

1912b *Forest Fires.* (Bulletin No. 117.) Washington, D.C.: U.S. Department of Agriculture Forest Service. 39 pp.

SAUER, CARL O.

1920 *Geography of the Ozark Highland of Missouri.* Chicago: University of Chicago Press (for the Geographical Society of Chicago). 245 pp.

1927 *Geography of the Pennyroyal.* ("Kentucky Geological Survey," Series VI, Vol. XXV.) Frankfort. 299 pp.

1944 "A Geographic Sketch of Early Man in America," *Geographical Review,* XXXIV, 529–73.

1947 "Early Relations of Man to Plants," *ibid.,* XXXVII, 1–25.

1950 "Grassland Climax, Fire, and Man," *Journal of Range Management,* III, 16–22.

1952 *Agricultural Origins and Dispersals.* (Bowman Memorial Lectures, Series Two.) New York: American Geographical Society. 110 pp.

SCHMIEDER, O.

1927 "The Pampa," *University of California Publications in Geography,* II, No. 8, 255–70.

SEIFRIZ, WILLIAM

1934 "The Plant Life of Russian Lapland," *Ecology,* XV, 306–18.

SEMPLE, ELLEN CHURCHILL

1931 *The Geography of the Mediterranean Region.* New York: Henry Holt & Co. 737 pp.

SHANTZ, H. L.

1947 *The Use of Fire as a Tool in the Management of the Brush Ranges of California.* Sacramento: California State Board of Forestry. 156 pp.

SHANTZ, H. L., and ZON, RAPHAEL

1924 *Atlas of American Agriculture: Natural Vegetation.* Washington, D.C.: U.S. Department of Agriculture. 29 pp.

SHIMEK, B.

1911 "The Prairies," *Contributions from the Laboratories of Natural History,* VI, No. 2, 169–224. (Bulletin No. 35.) State University of Iowa.

STEFANSSON, VILHJALMUR

1913 *My Life with the Eskimo.* New York: Macmillan Co. 538 pp.

STEWART, O. C.

1943 "Notes on Pomo Ethnogeography," *University of California Publications in American Archeology and Ethnology,* XL, 29–62.

1951 "Burning and Natural Vegetation in the United States," *Geographical Review,* XLI, 317–20.

1953 "Why the Great Plains Are Treeless," *Colorado Quarterly,* II, 40–50. Boulder.

1954 "The Forgotten Side of Ethnogeography," pp. 221–48 in SPENCER, R. (ed.), *Methods and Perspectives in Anthropology: Essays in Honor of Wilson D. Wallis.* Minneapolis: University of Minnesota Press. 323 pp.

STOECKELER, JOSEPH H.

1945 "Narrow Shelterbelts for the Southern Great Plains," *Soil Conservation,* XI, No. 1, 16–20. Washington, D.C.: U.S. Department of Agriculture.

TANSLEY, A. G., and CHIPP, T. F. (eds.)

1926 *Aims and Methods in the Study of Vegetation.* London: British Empire Vegetation Committee and the Crown Agents for the Colonies. 383 pp.

TROUP, R. S.

1926 "Problems of Forest Ecology in India," pp. 283–313 in TANSLEY, A. G., and CHIPP, T. F. (eds.), *Aims and Methods of the Study of Vegetation.* London: British Empire Vegetation Committee and the Crown Agents for the Colonies. 383 pp.

VERGIL

1947 *Georgics.* Trans. from the Latin by C. DAY LEWIS. New York: Oxford University Press. 83 pp.

VIOSCA, PERCY, JR.

1931 "Spontaneous Combustion in the Marshes of Southern Louisiana," *Ecology,* XII, 439–42.

VYSSOTSKY, G. N.
1935 "Shelterbelt in the Steppes of Russia," *Journal of Forestry*, XXXIII, 781–88.

WEAVER, J. E.
1954 *North American Prairie*. Lincoln, Neb.: Johnsen Publishing Co. 348 pp.

WEAVER, J. E., and CLEMENTS, F. E.
1929 *Plant Ecology*. New York: McGraw-Hill Book Co. 601 pp.

WERNER, A.
1906 *The Natives of British Central Africa*. London: A. Constable. 303 pp.

Early Food-producing Populations

KARL J. NARR[*]

Man's contest with external nature is expressed in two different ways: *adaptation* to and *changing* of a given environment. Adaptation may be a matter of organic evolution as well as of intellectual power. To meet the rigors of a cold climate, for instance, some animals developed a coat of hair as the result of a change in the germ plasm. But man can adapt himself to life in the same environment by inventing and making coats. Creative spiritual actions thus form an exclusively human way of adaptation, man's compensation for his relatively poorly endowed body being his superior intellect, which brought

* Dr. Narr is Scientific Assistant at the Seminar für Ur- und Frühgeschichte of the Georg-August University at Göttingen, Germany. Primarily a prehistorian, he focuses his research on problems which concern the synthesis of archeological work with geological, environmental, anthropological, and ethnological studies. His publications include contributions to the international manual, *Historia mundi:* "Das höhere Jägertum: Jüngere Jagd- und Sammelstufe" ("Developed Hunting: the Later Stage of Hunting and Gathering") and "Hirten, Pflanzer, Bauern: Produktionsstufe" ("Herdsmen, Plant Cultivators, and Peasants: The Stage of Food Production"), 1952–53; and "Formengruppen und Kulturkreise im europäischen Paläolithikum: Stand und Aufgaben der Altsteinzeitforschung" ("Form Complexes and Culture Areas in the European Paleolithic: State and Tasks of Researches into the Old Stone Age"), 1954. His book, *Das rheinische Jungpaläolithikum: Zugleich ein Beitrag zur Chronologie der späten Altsteinzeit Mittel- und Westeuropas* ("The Rhenish Upper Paleolithic: A Contribution to the Chronology of the Upper Paleolithic of Middle and Western Europe"), is in press.

forth the typical human phenomenon of culture. In the course of history man created new industries and new economies that have furthered the increase of his species. With growth of population and addition of skills, he did not confine himself to mere adaptation but changed more and more of the surrounding world until he became in many regions the ecologic dominant. Man also affected the course of organic evolution, in particular, when he began to control his food supply by cultivating plants and breeding animals, finally displacing both from their original biome and habitat, either subsequently transforming an environment by that artificial exotic invasion or previously preparing the new area for the reception of the exotic plants and/or animals in question. Thus the growing intensity of new economies answering the want for food exhibits a logical relation to man's increasing role in changing the face of the earth.

PRELUDE: COLLECTORS AND HUNTER-FISHERS

Among populations whose economy is confined to mere hunting and gathering, adaptation to the environment evidently plays a far greater part than change. Variations of climate and the appearance and disappearance, increase and decrease, of particular plants and animals are able to stimulate new demands which can be appeased only by the invention of new methods of hunting and new weapons and implements.

134

This has already been conjectured for some groups as early as the Lower Paleolithic (Narr, 1953*b*). On the other hand, cultures of this simple kind, once adapted to a particular biome, showed a general tendency to cling to the latter. This, too, is almost certainly true for the earliest times, but the rich evidence of the Upper Paleolithic provides examples which can be far better demonstrated than those from the poorly documented Lower Paleolithic. Thus we see, for instance, that the East Gravettian mammoth hunters extended the limits of their area of distribution with the progressing loess steppe in full glacial times (but apparently avoided the completely treeless loess tundra—a phenomenon that might be explained by requirement of wood for fire and, perhaps, for the construction of the well-known semisubterranean dwellings). Also, we see that the West Magdalenian hunters of reindeer, horse, and red deer preferred life in the park tundra and followed the pioneering pines and birches (and the animals attached to this environment) when they entered the plains of northwestern Germany and the Netherlands at the end of the Ice Age (Narr, 1954). Nevertheless, a certain amount of new, though eventually minor, adaptations were required. The plains north of the German and Belgian central range of mountains completely lack the caves and rock shelters which facilitated the life of the Magdalenian hunters in their Franco-Cantabrian homeland. Huts and tents (like those fortunately discovered by Rust [1948, 1951] in northern Germany and the Netherlands) must have played a far greater part and been of different type, perhaps, than those in southwestern France and northern Spain. To be sure, the attachment of certain cultures to a particular environment must not be overestimated or made a general and unconditional rule. Regarding the early spread of mankind over the whole *oiku-*

mene, we can postulate that Paleolithic man was able to overcome the barriers of nature. But we need not insist on that problem. The critical question for our theme is whether, or to what degree, the activities of hunting and gathering populations altered or did not alter the aspect of the earth.

There can be no doubt that early hunting and food-gathering people possessed certain means of altering their environment. At first thought, one may be tempted to consider hunters specialized in a distinct species of animals as having disturbed the ecologic equilibrium by diminishing the number of their prey, until finally destroying the hunters' very base of sustenance. (See also Darling, pp. 778–87.) But it is very improbable that even Upper Paleolithic and Mesolithic man killed more game with his still-primitive weapons than could be replenished by annual increase under normal ecologic conditions. Moreover, it may be thought that prehistoric hunters preserved game to a certain degree, as many of our primitive contemporaries also do. Among recent hunting populations it is a general rule not to kill more game than is needed, and, frequently, this is sanctioned by ethical codes and religious beliefs.

Certainly there was also a tendency toward the making of clearings of a sort by collectors and hunters of the Old and Middle Stone Age. Around their more or less temporary camps, shrubs, brushes, and small trees needed for the construction of windbreaks and huts and as fuel were removed. Clearing an area caused changes of vegetation around the camps, such as the stimulation of chenopods, by the accumulation of organic refuse. This has been demonstrated for the northern Mesolithic by pollen analytical work (Iversen, 1941), but similar processes can be supposed for other times and regions. (See also Sears, p. 475.) To be sure, the way of life of shifting hunters and collectors prevented permanent changes. Moreover, they affected but small patches.

If one could have flown over northern Europe in Mesolithic times, it is doubtful whether more than an occasional wisp of smoke from some campfire, or maybe a small cluster of huts or shelters by a river bank or an old lake bed, would have advertised the presence of man: in all essentials the forest would have stretched unbroken, save only by mountain, swamp and water, to the margins of the sea [Clark, 1952, pp. 91–92].

Indeed, the damp forests of Mesolithic northern Europe could not be ignited easily. But what about less dense, coniferous woods, park tundras, and savannas, especially in plains, with dry seasons or in periods of a generally drier climate? Under such conditions, campfires which had been left unwatched or fire drives, which almost certainly must have been practiced during the Old Stone Age (Soergel, 1922), or even the setting of fires to burn off the brushwood could have done extensive work in clearing the forests. Fortunately, this is no mere deduction. During the Allerødian climatic period the flatlands north of the German and Belgian central range of mountains were occupied by forests of pines and birches. At the very end of that period, in the transitional so-called "Usselo horizon," when the climate again was becoming colder and drier, the existence of great forest fires is documented by rather thick layers of charcoal and even carbonized trunks, at several sites in the Netherlands and in northern Germany. These strata frequently contain artifacts, fireplaces, and other refuse of the camps of late Magdalenian hunters. The best-explored sites are Usselo, Twente (as yet unpublished excavations by Hijszeler; see also Schwabedissen, 1954),[1] and Rissen near Hamburg (Schwabedissen, 1951, 1954). There is no proof, of course, that it was Paleolithic man who, either by carelessness

or to improve hunting and the berry harvest (e.g., Stewart, pp. 118–24, 125), set fire to the forests. But the possibility, or even probability, thereof cannot be denied. With this restriction in mind, we may suppose that the sudden decrease of pines and birches which marks the beginning of the colder and drier Later Dryas period is due partially to the activities of man. We may suppose that comparable phenomena would also be revealed in other periods and regions, for instance, in the French "Paradise of Early Man," if similar conditions of preservation had prevailed there (or, perhaps, if excavations were not so exclusively confined to the easily discoverable and most promising cave sites).

NEOLITHIC AGRICULTURE AND PASTORALISM

Adhering to the approved advice of Aristotle that the essentials of a phenomenon are best understood if one tries to explore their rise from the very beginnings, we first should inquire about the *origins of food production* and its bearing on changes of environment. Alas! The state of our knowledge does not permit such an inquiry, for the question of agricultural and pastoral origins is still controversial. One theory favors the view that, from a common cradle of mixed farming, which is to be located in the lands of the Fertile Crescent, the new food-producing economy spread in different directions. One of these led into the steppes of Eurasia, where the culture was altered into a completely pastoral and nomadic one— a process which was furthered by environmental factors. A second theory hinges on different origins of plant cultivation and stock-raising, respectively. Spreading into the other continents of

1. From economical and environmental points of view the site of Usselo is especially interesting because of the great amount of crowberries found there.

the Old World, the two economies met each other and intermingled in the region of the Fertile Crescent or adjacent countries, thus giving rise to mixed farming.

A few years ago the author tried to evaluate the different arguments (Narr, 1953a). In the meantime fresh evidence and new reconsiderations have been brought forward in favor of both theories (Jettmar, 1953, 1954; Pohlhausen, 1954a, 1954b). On the whole, however, the evidence available today does not permit a definite decision. No doubt the archeological record proves that mixed farming (full agriculture combined with stock-raising) was already in existence at the latest by the fifth millennium B.C. (Some sites between northern Iran and Nubia seem to hint that transhumance may have been an early, or perhaps the earliest, form of mixed farming.) But the archeological record still is very meager or nonexistent for the centers of full nomadic pastoralism and semiagriculture (in the sense of Hatt in Curwen and Hatt, 1953), respectively. (Moreover, nomadic herdsmen, living in tents and using implements of perishable material, are less likely to leave recognizable traces than full agriculturists; roots and tuberous plants cultivated by semiagriculturists will be found among cultural refuse only under exceptionally favorable conditions of preservation.)

On completely theoretical foundations we can establish several levels of food production based upon the relation of the respective domesticated plants and/or animals to the original environment.

STAGE 1.—*Domesticated plants and animals remain within the biome and habitat of their wild ancestors.* The newly found capacity to domesticate certain kinds of animals spread over parts, or the whole, of the region of natural distribution of the species in question but did not surpass the ecologic limits of the species. Examples: The tame reindeer inhabits only the same regions as its wild cousins do or did. Several plants of primitive agriculture in the southern woodlands remained therein.

STAGE 2.—*Man brings domesticated plants and animals out of their original biome and habitat.* This can be done in two different ways:

SUBSTAGE 2a.—*Plants and animals are transplanted into, and accustomed to, a new environment.* The new area subsequently is altered by the effects of that exotic invasion. Examples: Selection of more resistant sorts of cultivated plants can allow the introduction of cultivation into regions where agriculture hitherto had been impossible. Man also was capable of moving domesticated animals into habitats devoid of their wild ancestors. Goats are brought from the mountainous countries into valleys and plains and sheep from the slopes of high hills. Grazing pressure (and protection against predators) may then alter the ecosystem of the newly occupied area.

SUBSTAGE 2b.—*Plants and animals are transplanted into an artificially prepared area.* The environment has previously been adjusted to the exotic invaders. Examples: Woodland is cleared to suit it for the sowing of grains and thus is transformed into a kind of artificial steppe. Brush and trees are removed by burning, to promote or make possible growth of grass and herbs, thereby improving pasture for animals originally adapted (or accustomed by man) to grassland.

The above classification shows an intensification of change in the physical-biological environment by the activities of man. Perhaps it should be stressed that it is only a classification of phenomena which must not be mistaken for an established historic sequence. While it undoubtedly contains elements of a true evolutionary sequence, nevertheless this cannot be taken as a decision a priori but has to be established by careful historical inquiry for each separate case. Confusion of a theoretical evolutionary system (like that constructed by H. L. Morgan and E. B. Tylor, which even today is not yet overcome completely) with a historical sequence of cultural and economic levels has caused trouble enough. *Vestigia terrent!*

Consequently, it is our task, as culture historian, to examine whether the historic changing of the face of the earth by early food-producing populations affords a picture which can be related to the above classification. As already indicated, this is as yet impossible to do completely. At present we can but select some examples from times and regions where the state of research provides sufficient evidence. But even that is practically impossible for the earliest decisive periods of food-producing economies. Mixed farming, for instance, was practiced very early in the valleys of the Nile, the Euphrates, and the Tigris. Yet the oldest sites where mixed farming, probably transhumance, can be affirmed are not situated near the banks of these great rivers, as has been believed previously, but rather on some of the adjacent plains and foothills. In the streamlands of the Fertile Crescent the face of the earth was deeply changed by the irrigation activities of man, yet it cannot even be decided whether or not irrigation began to be practiced by some rather early communities of farmers during the fifth millennium B.C. Was irrigation eventually the "Response" to the menacing "Challenge" of the encroaching desert (expressed in layers of drift sand in the refuse of occupation sites, such as the Faiyûm and Merimde)? Or was it invented only in connection with the "Urban Revolution" of the late fourth or early third millennium B.C.?

Examples which give a satisfactory picture of the economic system of an early food-producing population and its bearing on changes of the environment can be selected only from the better explored regions of Europe. But such regions are far removed in space and time from the supposed cradle, or cradles, of plant cultivation and stock-raising. Nevertheless, it seems more useful to consider some food-producing populations of the European Neolithic than to lose our way in a labyrinth of mere theoretical deductions.

Danubian Farmers of the Early Neolithic: Clearance in the Wooded Loess Lands of Middle Europe

The so-called "Danubian" culture represents the earliest definitely known farming population in Middle Europe. To be sure, the name "Danubian" is somewhat misleading, for the bulk of Danubian sites lies north of the Danube, stretching from Hungary into the southern fringes of the northern German plains and from the Vistula to Belgium (and by a few spurs even into the region of Paris). The term "Danubian" customarily is used in a wide sense to include some rather different Neolithic groups of Central Europe and the Balkans. But here it will be used only in the strict sense of *Bandkeramik* (as defined by Milojčić, 1951, and roughly corresponding to the "Danubian I" of Childe, 1950*a*). Though the Danubian is related to some early Neolithic groups of Hungary and the Balkans, this relation is almost exclusively confined to rather general economic elements, namely, similar cereals and domesticated animals. The typological elements, in particular the ceramics, show quite distinct patterns. The Danubian, therefore, may best be classified as a civilization that, by its basic economic traits, ultimately comes from the great "oriental drift" (Schachermeyr, 1954) but which also has developed many elements of its own (perhaps by action of an indigenous pre-Neolithic substratum as yet practically unknown). This justifies our speaking of a quite distinct and particular culture, the origin of which lies in Moravia, Bohemia, and the adjacent parts of central Germany.

The absolute age of the Danubian is still controversial. There is convincing archeological evidence that the closing stage of its older part is contemporaneous with the Starčewo III–Vinča A horizons of the Balkanic sequence, which, in their turn, by correlation with Mediterranean groups, can be dated in the older centuries of the third millennium B.C., perhaps stretching to the middle of the latter (Milojčić, 1949, 1951). The beginning of the Danubian is a crucial question, for we cannot say with certainty whether it parallels the older levels within the "oriental drift" or of what age these are. Natural science seems to favor a rather early date, perhaps around 4000 B.C.[2] As yet we cannot state much more than that the commencement of the Danubian can be placed somewhere between the closing of the fifth and the beginning of the third millennium B.C. The Later Danubian lasted until its replacement by other Neolithic cultures within the centuries around 2000 B.C.

The archeological record of the Danubian consists mainly of domestic sites. This is a happy circumstance for our theme, because it provides us with a sufficiently complete picture of the general way of life of that ancient farming population (Buttler, 1938; Childe, 1950a; Tackenberg, 1953; Danthine, 1954). The Danubian economy was

2. Radiocarbon datings suggest a date within the centuries around 4000 B.C.; but, as this method is still in its infancy, one has to be careful not to infer too much from its results. Pollen-analysis examinations show an amount of grain pollen, which has to be ascribed to Danubian grain cultivation, in the middle of the Atlantic period. The Atlantic period has been dated by indirect correlation with varve series as between about 5500 and 2500 B.C. (Munthe, 1940) or about 4600 and 2000 B.C. (Florin, 1944), respectively.

based on the cultivation of barley, one-grained wheat (*Einkorn*), emmer, at least in some regions, and, perhaps, bread wheat,[3] beans, peas, lentils, and flax. Stock-breeding was apparently practiced on a rather small scale, for only relatively few bones of dogs, oxen, sheep, and pigs turn up in the settlement refuse. The Danubian peasants preferred the well-drained and fertile loess soils, which are exceptionally easy to work (see the instructive map of Clark, 1952, p. 96). Moreover, in some regions they seem to have selected particular kinds of loess. In the northern Rhineland, for instance, Danubian set-

FIG. 51.—Soils and Neolithic sites in the northern Rhineland, showing the Danubian. (After Tackenberg and Mückenhausen.)

tlements (as well as those of the peasants of the late Bronze Age) are restricted to the southern parts of the loess region, where the loess layers are less thick than in the northern parts (Steeger, 1932; Uslar, 1951) and where the brown earth (centuries earlier and more intensely tilled) shows a higher degree of basal saturation (Mückenhausen, 1952). (See Fig. 51.)

It is quite unlikely that the Danubian peasants knew the plow. Because of the lack of corresponding traces on the

3. Emmer is reported from the Rhineland and Belgium; bread wheat, from Poland (Childe, 1950a, p. 97).

tools in question, it must be denied that rather clumsy axes and other stone implements were used as plowshares, as has been suggested by some authors. We must suppose that the agricultural technique of the Danubians was a kind of hoe cultivation, though the implements for tilling the soil are still unknown, with the possible exception of kinds of perforated "maceheads" which, in reality, may have been used as charging stones for digging sticks. The Danubian hoes seem to have been made of wood,[4] since the so-called "flat hoes" and "shoe-last celts" of stone were almost certainly not used for cultivation but as carpenters' implements (Rieth, 1949–50). Carpentry played a great part in the life of the Danubian peasants, because they lived in great rectangular wooden buildings, up to more than 40 meters in length (Paret, 1946; Stieren, 1951), which were grouped together in villages surrounded by palisades. The quest for wood of a Danubian community must have covered a considerable area.

Hoe cultivators who, by lack of a corresponding degree of stock-breeding, did not have a sufficient resource of animal dung almost certainly must have practiced shifting cultivation. When, after a few easy crops, the available ground within easy reach had been exploited, the Danubians passed on to fresh grounds not too far distant. Eventually, after this procedure occurred several times, and the soil of the earlier sites had regenerated sufficiently, the people returned to their old dwelling places, or these areas were occupied by a kindred group. There is convincing evidence that the famous settlement of Köln-Lindenthal near Cologne was abandoned and resettled at least seven times within a period of a few hundred

4. Among recent primitive hoe cultivators also, the use of tilling implements of stone is almost unknown (Hoeltker, 1947; for one of the rare exceptions see Purse-Stanek, 1953).

years (Sangmeister, 1951; Buttler and Haberey, 1936).

The loess lands were once hailed as an open corridor through the hostile forest. This view is rather incompatible with the great need for wood among the Danubians. Moreover, the general picture of the Central European vegetation in Atlantic times shows that the loess soils supported a friendly, mixed-oak forest. This is also verified by the examination of soil profiles (Tüxen, 1931; Garnett, 1945; Schwarz, 1948). This forest must have allowed a growth of foliage in addition to the fattening acorns on which cattle and swine could feed. The assumption of settlement in wooded countries implies a deduction which is most important for our theme, namely, that the Danubian peasants cleared the forests. "Slash and burn" (*Brandwirtschaft*) is the method which could easily have been practiced by Neolithic man. Recent experiments have shown that extensive clearings could have been made with Neolithic stone tools and that felled mixed-oak forests could successfully have been burned even while the wood was still green. Moreover, these experiments demonstrate that cereals grew luxuriantly in the burned area, in contrast to an unburned one (P., E., 1954). Thus, at first, small patches and, gradually, greater parts of the Central European woodland were transformed into a kind of artificial steppe. To be sure, this procedure slackened by the shifting of settlements, which allowed the forest to regenerate without serious depredations of grazing animals. On the other hand, the newly regenerated plots may have remained attractive, compared with the original virgin forests. Because of the probably long duration of the Danubian culture and the shifting of settlements, the density of the Danubian population may not have been so great as one is tempted to assume when regarding the densely dotted distribution maps. But our knowledge of sites certainly reflects only a small part of the true settlement. The pressure of population on the desirable loess soils in the closing stages of Danubian civilization may indeed have been great enough to permit J. G. D. Clark to say (1952, p. 97) that "new communities have continually hived off from the old ones, so that ultimately the point was reached when clearance outstripped the capacity of the woodlands to regenerate themselves."

The Loess Lands of Northwestern Europe: The Problem of the Campignian (Hunter-Collectors or Clearing Farmers[?])

A very interesting problem is posed in the loess lands of France and Belgium. The westernmost compact Danubian province is formed by the settlements in the Belgian Hesbaye, where penetration seems to have been rather short and late. The Belgian Danubian ("Omalien"), which shows close affinities to the Rhenish styles of Plaidt and Cologne, corresponds only to the later stages (III–IV, and perhaps II, of the sequence at Köln-Lindenthal near Cologne) and, therefore, is to be placed within the centuries around the middle and before the end of the third millennium B.C. Only a scanty offshoot is represented by a few finds in the loess regions of northwestern France. The same country is occupied by a very interesting, though highly problematic, civilization, namely, the Campignian. The bulk of the typical Campignian (the "facies d'habitation" of the "Campignien classique" of Nougier, 1950), lies in northwestern France, where the Danubian is very poorly represented, whereas in Belgium only a few sites attest the presence of the Campignian (Fig. 52, p. 142).

The Campignian is known mainly through its industry of chipped (not polished!) silex with predominance of picks and tranchets. Its typological relations to the Mesolithic forest cultures of northern Germany, the Baltic lands, and Scandinavia are so close that it almost certainly is to be interpreted as a genetic connection. There is as yet no convincing and well-established third group which could claim to be the common ancestor of both, but this may be partially due to a certain lack of archeological research in some of the countries in question. Nevertheless, on the evidence available today, one may be justified in trying to derive the one from the other: the Campignian from the northern Mesolithic forest cultures, or vice versa. This latter possibility has been denied by some historians, because some aspects of the Campignian industry occur only in the later stages of the northern sequence[5] (Oldesloe-Gudenaa and Ertebölle), which belong to the Atlantic climatic period of the postglacial. In the northern woodland cultures these can be derived from the older stages, whereas a possible comparable ancestor is completely lacking in the Campignian region. However, it is very troubling that no continental group is known which might establish a sufficiently direct link between both. The "Præ-Campignian" of Nougier (1950) has, at least partially, to be taken cautiously, for its sites are very doubtful or, as in the case of the Belgian sites in the vicinity of Aubel, represent a lateral (and late) offshoot. On the other hand, the Mesolithic forest cultures extended to England by the only possible way—over land which today is covered by the North Sea (Schwabedissen, 1952). This land route must still have been in existence at the beginning of the Atlantic period. (Its submergence may have pushed people from the North Sea land to the east and

5. See also the review of Nougier's book (1950) by Schwabedissen, 1952.

southwest, respectively.) The distribution of the typical Campignian gives the impression, in fact, of a bridgehead attached to the English Channel (see the map of Nougier, 1950, p. 541, where the "Præ-Campignian" has to be held in question). Moreover, the typical Campignian shows close affinities to the Mesolithic cultures of England in Atlantic times, in particular, the Lower Halstow group.

The question of the age of the Campignian is intimately linked with its origins. If the typological and genetic connection with the northern forest cultures is taken for granted, one conse-

quently has to assume the beginning of the Atlantic period as a *terminus post quem* for the Campignian development, say, a date about the middle of the sixth or fifth millennium B.C.[6] On the other hand, the later stage of the Campignian (the "Post-Campignian" of Nougier, 1950) shows admixtures of the "Western Neolithic" ("Neolithic lacustre" or "Robenhausien," of an antiquated terminology still used by some

6. The middle of the Atlantic period has been dated at 5500 and 2500 B.C. (Munthe, 1940) and 4600 and 1950 B.C. (Florin, 1944) by indirect correlation with varve series. See also n. 2, p. 139.

|||||| Westernmost Danubian

Campignian of Northern France

Greatest Density of Campignian sites

● Campignian sites in Belgium

⊔⊔⊔⊔⊔ Approximate limits of loess

Fig. 52.—Loess lands of northwestern Europe, showing Danubian and Campignian. (After Buttler, Destexhe-Jamotte, Hamal-Nandrin, and Nougier, with additions.)

authors) and ultimately merged with the latter, giving rise to some special technical facies. Thus the introduction of the "Western Neolithic," which has to be placed in the centuries around 2000 B.C., provides us with a *terminus ante quem*. In Belgium the "Western Neolithic" is later than the Danubian. The Campignian's being closely connected in time with the "Western Neolithic" but showing no marked influences of the Danubian[7] prompts some Belgian prehistorians to place it into a supposed lag of time between the Danubian and the "Western Neolithic" (Destexhe-Jamotte, 1953; Philippe, 1953). That might be true for Belgium, where the pure Campignian is very rare, but does not exclude a greater, though as yet not exactly determined, age of the latter in the other parts of its area of distribution, namely, in northwestern France, where the Danubian, for the most part, is very poorly represented. Because of the general chronological position of both cultures, a partial contemporaneousness of the Campignian and Danubian seems highly probable, though it must be admitted that archeologically verified connections are extremely scanty and by no means cogent.[8]

The Campignians are considered by many authors to be a plant-cultivating population even in the early stages of that civilization. An extreme theory regards them as "the first to put their seal on the landscape, which is henceforth 'humanized,' . . . the founders of [the] Western rural life, . . . the first peasants of the West" (Nougier, 1950, p. 534). If this point of view is granted, one has to assume that the Campignians were the first to clear the forests on the French loess lands (there being no reasonable evidence that eventually these countries were not wooded in Atlantic times). No doubt, the Campignian stone tools were fitted to deal with trees and wood, though the polished ax is superior to the chipped ax.

If one takes the Mesolithic peoples of the northern woodlands who were hunter-collectors and fishers attached to the postglacial forest as the probable ancestors of the Campignian, at once the question rises whence the assumed peasant life of the "typical" Campignian took its origins. Did those early Campignians themselves invent a food-producing culture of their own, or did they learn it from an already existing farming population with which they may have been in contact? In the latter respect one might think of the Danubians, as do Stokar (1942, p. 11) and Corbeil (1949).

But, first of all, we must ask whether the assumption of peasant life of the "typical" Campignians is really substantiated. Finds of some grinding stones and a few bones of dogs, cattle, and pigs form the only direct evidence. Even if the context with the "typical" Campignian implements of the sites in question is proved, that does not demon-

7. However, one could ask whether several Campignian picks which, by their general shape and, in particular, by their cross-section (but not by technique and material!), closely resemble the Danubian "shoe-last celts" (e.g., Nougier, 1950, Fig. 35) are not possibly signs which indicate that a foreign principle of form was taken over by indigenous workers using their old technique and accustomed material. A parallel may be demonstrated by "maceheads" of Campignian tradition, which also seem to copy those of true Neolithic civilizations by applying the inherited technique of chipping flint to the borrowed form (Nougier, 1949, 1950).

8. Picks with a triangular and subtriangular cross-section also turned up in some domestic sites of the Danubian and the "Western Neolithic" (Hamal-Nandrin and Servais, 1928). A formidable pick has also been found at Köln-Lindenthal in a pit of the Later Danubian (Buttler and Haberey, 1936, Pl. 69 14). However, this form occurs also in the "Western Neolithic" of Campignian tradition, though an overlap in time of the latter with the Danubian is as yet unproved but not unreasonable, since these groups preferred different soils.

strate that these "early" Campignians themselves practiced farming and stock-breeding. The findings are too sporadic to rule out the possibility, or even probability, that they belong to a relatively late occurrence which already had undergone influences by penetration of true Neolithic peasants. (The same is valid also for the whole question of the Campignian ceramics.) Moreover, isolated finds of that kind, within a culture that lived in the neighborhood of (or even overlapped spatially and chronologically) a well-established farming population (such as the Danubians), can also be explained in terms of symbiosis and barter or like possibilities.

Furthermore, it has been argued that a kind of indirect evidence is given by the predilection for loess soils, which, by this theory, are regarded as open "prairies" inviting the early plant-cultivators (Nougier, 1950). But that new infusion of the old theory of a natural late postglacial steppe heath (*Steppenheidetheorie*) is certainly not in conformity with modern views of the vegetational picture of postglacial, in particular, "Atlantic," Europe. Therefore we must ask ourselves whether the "typical" Campignians were not a mere hunting and collecting population (as the people of the northern Mesolithic were, too) who preferred the loess soils because they supported a wooded country of a kind that facilitated their habitual way of life as hunter-collectors attached to a like environment (Forde, 1930; Philippe, 1953).

Thus, the Campignian problem, though of no great direct value for our theme, may stand here as a warning that one must not conclude too much from general, though sometimes attractive, views. Even though the ecologic conditions of an area are well explored, one cannot deduce the economy of its former inhabitants from a densely dotted distribution map. The economic state of a prehistoric population can be established only by sufficient excavations of a kind still lacking for the French Campignian. To study the result of man's activities on the environment, we first have to gain a sufficient conception of these activities themselves. Only then can we hope to understand what happened to a certain environment, even if there is no direct evidence.

"Pastoral Farmers" of the Late Neolithic and Early Bronze Age: The Growth of the Heath

Precious direct evidence for changes of the environment is provided by pollen analysis. An already well-known example is that of Neolithic Denmark, where Iversen (1941) concluded that "(1) connected with settlement there was extensive forest-clearing; (2) trees were felled (by stone axe); (3) extensive scrubby pasture sprang up immediately after forest-clearing; (4) burned areas were sown with cereals; (5) settlements were of short duration and new areas were colonized as soon as the forest regenerated" (P., E., 1954, p. 9). It is the same general scheme which also could be supposed for the Danubian. The Danubian example has been used here because it is much older and, therefore, nearer to the origins of food production than the Neolithic of northern Germany and southern Scandinavia. However, in the "Northern Neolithic" cattle-breeding and grazing pressure played an important part in contrast to the Danubian. Consequently, in the north, and especially on poorer, sandier soils, the temporary clearings of shifting agriculturists quickly became more permanent than on the loess soils of Central Europe (Clark, 1952, p. 97). But the final breakdown of forest regeneration seems to have been completed by the action of some late Neolithic populations. These exhibit so many common traits, in particular corded ware and battle-axes, that they are conveniently treated together as "Battle-ax" cultures, and their emergence is to be explained by immigration rather than by local differentiation. Their distribution stretches from the Pontic steppe to western Germany. In reality, they fall into a series of local and regional groups, such as, for instance, the "Saxo-Thuringian Corded-ware" and the "Sepatate Grave II" cultures of northern Germany and Jutland. On the western fringes these—in particular, the northern group—intermingled with the "Bell-beaker" culture coming from the Iberian Peninsula and formed, together with interacting local substrata, the different "Beaker" cultures of the Rhineland, the Netherlands, and England. These late Neolithic "melting pots" formed the foundations for the Bronze Age populations of the regions in question. Of course the newly arrived techniques of the Bronze Age transformed the picture of civilization, but in some regions it can be observed that the Bronze Age people erected principally the same great burial mounds, and their settlement is restricted to the same parts of the land as before (Marschall *et al.*, 1954; Beck, 1951).

Unfortunately, the different "Corded-ware" and "Beaker" cultures are better known from graves than from settlements, which renders more difficult the reconstruction of their economic systems. Nevertheless, it can be supposed that stock-raising played so great a part that one may speak of "pastoral farmers" (*Weidebauern;* see Tackenberg, 1953, 1954). On the other hand, it would be an unjustified exaggeration to speak of mere "nomadic herdsmen." The cemeteries are too extensive to belong to nomads, and a sort of cultivation is proved by grain imprints on pottery (Childe, 1950*a*). On the whole, the life of the "Battle-ax" people of Central Europe seems to have been sedentary,[9]

though shifting more easily than that of other Neolithic groups and with parts of its population leading the life of herdsmen. Because of like circumstances, we may expect that the "Battle-ax" folk bred pigs only on a very small scale and preferred animals which were more easily driven, such as cattle, sheep, and horses. Bones and crania of horses turn up rather frequently among the grave goods, particularly in the younger stages of that civilization. We may infer that "Battle-ax" people, as do most of the known horse-breeders, observed a certain ritual attitude with reference to the horse. Therefrom, we may deduce that they did not feed upon horses (except for rare ritual purposes) and needed other beasts for substantial meat provisions. Among most of the known horse-breeders, sheep play a great part in this respect. That is precisely the situation which is revealed by some domestic sites of the "Battle-ax" culture in its eastern area of distribution and which, because of the great uniformity of some basic common traits of that culture, may serve as an analogy to the groups farther west. A marked predominance of sheep is shown, exceeding the number of horses, oxen, goats, and the very few pigs.

Many groups of the "Battle-ax" culture preferred the poorer and sandier soils less favorable for agriculture than the loess of Central Europe or the younger moraines of the north (Fig. 53). The great expansion of the "Battle-ax" culture occurred in a time of slightly more humid climate, within the generally drier subboreal period of the postglacial (Overbeck, 1939, 1950). These soils were less densely wooded, but nevertheless, clearings were neces-

9. Great rectangular buildings at Succase and Tolkemit (West Prussia) point in the same direction (Ehrlich, 1936) but are perhaps to be ascribed to the interaction of an older substratum of the local mixed culture (*Haff-Küsten-Kultur*).

sary to prepare the ground for agriculture and pasture. Though the exact method is not known, we may suppose, on the basis of the known general technical level of the late Neolithic populations, that fire played an important part in their activities. The process of making permanent the temporary clearings was doubtless enhanced by the depredations of grazing animals of the "Battle-ax" culture to a higher degree than among the Danubians. Sheep, if locally concentrated, can provide a grazing pressure which exceeds even that of cattle.

Fig. 53.—Soils and Neolithic sites in the northern Rhineland, showing "corded ware" and "Rhenish beakers." (After Tackenberg and Mückenhausen, simplified.)

"Corded-ware–Battle-ax" people penetrated into northern Germany and southern Scandinavia earlier than into the western margins of the great "Battle-ax" province. Perhaps this may explain the observation that, in Jutland, Schleswig-Holstein, and northwestern Germany, clearance and depredation already during Neolithic time seem to have outstripped the capacity of the forests to regenerate themselves, whereas in parts of the Netherlands and the Rhineland this occurred only at the beginning of the Bronze Age (Shwantes, 1939; Giffen, 1930; Marschall *et al.*,

1954; Clark, 1952).[10] The heath has occupied great areas as a result of the activities of man, who, by extensive stock-raising and, eventually also, by intentional burning off the shrubs and seedlings, prevented the regeneration of the forests.

CONCLUSIONS AND PERSPECTIVE

The scarcity of evidence available today makes it very dangerous to infer too much from those examples which tell us the story of man's changing the face of the earth. Nevertheless, one may state that the research of the last two decades has shown that the early food-producers of the Neolithic practiced clearing on far greater a scale than had been hitherto believed. On the other hand, one has to be careful not to exaggerate this result. Neolithic man, too, went the way of less resistance, and there were obstacles which he did not overcome. There are regions, even some of fertile and easily workable soil, which prehistoric man apparently avoided. The small country called "Bergisches Land," which lies east of the Rhine between the Ruhr and the Sieg, on the windward side of a mountain range and, at least in times of prevailing western winds, was always more humid and densely wooded than its counterparts west of the Rhine, was not occupied by the Danubians. Only in the beginning of the somewhat drier subboreal period did it have scanty traces of settlement. The late Neolithic "Battle-ax" and "Beaker" cultures also avoided this region, except for a small western margin, and it remained unoccupied until the period of great clear-

10. In the latter areas the Neolithic burial mounds were made of sand, whereas those of the Bronze Age were commonly built from heath sods. Bronze Age finds are relatively rare in the Rhineland, but, as yet, it cannot be decided whether this is due to progressive deterioration of the habitat caused by a not markedly nomadic pastoralism. (See also Darling, p. 780.)

ances in the Middle Ages (Marschall *et al.*, 1954; Uslar, 1950–51).

Moreover, it seems that some of the observable changes of the environment are but partially due to the activities of man, who, in some cases, only furthered the effects of an ecologic crisis. Such may be the case for the forest fires of the late Allerød, which were followed by the reintroduction of tundra during the drier and colder Later Dryas period. This must not be overlooked even in the case of the well-known clearances at the beginning of the "Northern Neolithic," which coincide with the commencement of the somewhat drier subboreal period and the retreat of the mixed-oak forest. Man's action in that case seems to have been furthered by environmental changes through forces independent of man, who, nevertheless, profited thereby.

All this is apt to inhibit our making general deductions about the historic process. But the above examples allow us to make some conclusions on the archeological work that is needed to explore that process. Splendid results have been obtained where the basic economy of a culture is known and the original environment, as well as its changes caused by man, are verified by pollen analysis or like methods (e.g., Iversen's research [1941] into the "Northern Neolithic"). Where the economy of a

culture (e.g., the Danubian) is known by sufficient excavations of domestic sites and the environment can be reconstructed in its general traits, we can also infer the changes which may have occurred. Where the economy can be deduced only from grave goods (e.g., Western battle-ax groups), the results are less assured. But even approximate conclusions are quite impossible if the economy of a culture (e.g., Campignian) cannot be identified with sufficient assurance.

To be sure, there is another condition besides the demand for carefully excavated domestic sites, namely, a well-defined distribution of the culture in question, expressed in densely dotted maps. Only this can give exact information on the relations between archeologically explored complexes and the geographical and environmental factors. But this aim can hardly be fulfilled by archeological expeditions only. Cooperation of local inhabitants with archeologists is required, and this, in turn, calls for a certain degree of education and consciousness of, and fondness for, the history of one's own country and people. For this reason we remain skeptical about the quick growth in our knowledge of just those regions which are especially interesting because they are the supposed cradle or cradles of origin of food production.

REFERENCES

ANONYMOUS
1948 "The Culture Sequence in the Northern Stone Age Revised after Twelve Years' Research," *University of London, Institute of Archaeology, Annual Report*, IV (1946–47), 46–60.
BECK, HANS
1951 "Zur vor- und frühgeschichtlichen Besiedlung Südwestfalens," *Westfalen*, XXIX, No. 1, 9–26.
BRAIDWOOD, ROBERT J.
1950 "Jarmo: A Village of Early Farmers in Iraq," *Antiquity*, XXIV, No. 96, 189–95.

BUTTLER, WERNER
1931 *Die Bandkeramik in ihrem nordwestlichsten Verbreitungsgebiet.* Marburg an der Lahn: N.G. Elwertsche Verlagsbuchhandlung. 87 pp. (See also the shorter original version in 19. *Bericht der Römisch-Germanischen Kommission 1929* [1930], pp. 146–200.)
1938 *Der donauländische und der westische Kulturkreis der jüngeren Steinzeit.* ("Handbuch der Urgeschichte Deutschlands," Band 2.)

Berlin and Leipzig: Walter de Gruyter & Co. 108 pp.

BUTTLER, WERNER, and HABEREY, WALDEMAR
1936 *Die bandkeramische Ansiedlung bei Köln-Lindenthal.* ("Römisch-Germanische Forschungen," Band 11.) Berlin and Leipzig: Walter de Gruyter & Co. 178 pp.

CASTILLO, ALBERTO DEL
1947 "El Neoeneolítico," pp. 487–714 in MENÉNDEZ PIDAL, RAMÓN (ed.), *Historia de España*, Vol. I: *España prehistórica.* Madrid: Espasa-Calpe, S.A. 896 pp.

CHILDE, V. GORDON
1950a *The Dawn of European Civilisation.* 5th ed. London: Routledge & Kegan Paul. 362 pp.
1950b *Prehistoric Migrations in Europe.* Oslo: H. Aschehoug & Co. (W. Nygaard). 249 pp.
1954 *New Light on the Most Ancient East.* London: Routledge & Kegan Paul. 255 pp.

CLARK, J. G. D.
1952 *Prehistoric Europe: The Economic Basis.* London: Methuen & Co. 349 pp.

COON, CARLETON S.
1951 *Cave Explorations in Iran 1949.* ("Museum Monographs.") Philadelphia: University Museum. 80 pp.

CORBEIL, JEAN
1949 "La Civilisation d'Ertebölle et les origines du Campignien," *Bulletin de la Société Préhistorique Française*, XLVI, Nos. 3–4, 102–10.

CURWEN, CECIL E., and HATT, GUDMUND
1953 *Plough and Pasture: The Early History of Farming.* New York: Henry Schuman. 329 pp.

DANTHINE, HÉLÈNE
1954 "Le 'Danubien,'" *Bulletin de la Société Préhistorique Française*, LI, No. 8, 82–84.

DESTEXHE-JAMOTTE, J.
1952 "Le Gisement Campignien de Latinne (Province de Liège)," *Bulletin de la Société Royale Belge d'Études Géologiques et Archéologiques "Les Chercheurs de la Wallonie,"* XV, 145–57.

EHRLICH, BRUNO
1936 "Bericht *Succase, Kr. Elbing*,"

Nachrichtenblatt für Deutsche Vorzeit, XII, 206–9.

FIRBAS, FRANZ
1949 *Spät- und nacheiszeitliche Waldgeschichte Mitteleuropas nördlich der Alpen*, Vol. I: *Allgemeine Waldgeschichte*, Jena: Gustav Fischer. 480 pp.

FLORIN, ST.
1944 "Havstrandens förskjutningar och bebyggels-eutvecklingen i östra Mellansverige under senkvartär tid," *Geologiska Föreningens Förhandlingar*, LXVI, 551–634.

FORDE, DARYLL
1930 "Early Cultures of Atlantic Europe," *American Anthropologist*, XXXII, 19–100.

GARNETT, A.
1945 "The Loess Regions of Central Europe in Prehistoric Times," *Geographical Journal*, CVI, 132–43.

GIFFEN, A. E. VAN
1930 *Die Bauart der Einzelgräber.* (*Mannus-Bibliothek*, Vol. XLIV–XLV.) Leipzig: Curt Kabitzsch. 208 pp.

HAMAL-NANDRIN, J., and SERVAIS, J.
1928 "Instruments à section triangulaire," *Bulletin de la Société Préhistorique Française*, XXV, No. 12, 28–38.

HANČAR, FRANZ
1937 *Urgeschichte Kaukasiens von den Anfängen seiner Besiedlung bis in die Zeit seiner frühen Metallurgie.* ("Bücher zur Ur- und Frühgeschichte," Vol. VI.) Vienna: Anton Schroll. 448 pp.

HERMANNS, MATHIAS
1949 *Die Nomaden von Tibet: Ursprung und Entwicklung der Viehzucht.* Vienna: Herold Verlag. 325 pp.

HOELTKER, GEORG
1947 "Steinerne Ackerbaugeräte," *Internationales Archiv für Ethnographie*, XVI, Nos. 4–6, 77–156.

IVERSEN, JOH.
1941 "Landnam i Danmarks Stenalder, En pollenanlytisk Undersøgelse over det første Landbrugs Indvirkning paa Vegetationsudviklingen," *Danmarks Geologiske Undersøgelse*, II, No. 66, 7–68.

JETTMAR, KARL
1953 "Neue Beiträge zur Entwicklungsgeschichte der Viehzucht," *Wiener völkerkundliche Mitteilungen*, I, No. 2, 1–14.
1954 "Les plus anciennes civilisations d'éleveurs des steppes d'Asie Centrale," *Cahiers d'histoire mondiale*, I, No. 4, 760–83.

LAVIOSA-ZAMBOTTI, PIA
1943 *Le Più antiche culture agricole Europee*. Milan-Messina: Giuseppe Principato. 514 pp.
1947 *Origini e diffusione della civiltà*. ("Pubblicazzione dell'Istituto di Ricerche Preistoriche e Archeologiche presso la Società Archeologica," Comense 1.) Milan: Dott. Carlo Marzorati. 509 pp.

MARIËN, M. E.
1952 *Oud-België van de eerste landbouwers tot de komst van Caesar*. Antwerp: De Sikkel. 527 pp.

MARSCHALL, ARTHUR; NARR, KARL J.; and USLAR, RAFAEL VON
1954 *Die vor- und frühgeschichtliche Besiedlung des Bergischen Landes*. (3. Beiheft der "Bonner Jahrbücher.") Neustadt an der Aisch: Ph. C. W. Schmidt. 272 pp. (Also *Zeitschrift des Bergischen Geschichtsvereins*, Vol. LXXIII.)

MENGHIN, OSWALD
1931 *Weltgeschichte der Steinzeit*. Vienna: Anton Schroll & Co. 648 pp.

MILOJČIĆ, VLADIMIR
1949 *Chronologie der jüngeren Steinzeit Mittel und Südosteuropas*. Berlin: Gebr. Mann. 137 pp.
1951 "Die Siedlungsgrenzen und Zeitstellung der Bandkeramik im Osten und Südosten Europas," *Bericht den Römisch-Germanischen Kommission*, XXXIII (1943–50), 110–24.

MÜCKENHAUSEN, E.
1952 "Die Böden des linken Niederrheins," *Der Niederrhein* (*Zeitschrift für Heimatpflege und Wandern*), XIX, Nos. 3–4 (Krefeld), 72–77.

MUNTHE, H.
1940 *Om nordens, främst Baltikums, senkvartära utveckling och stenåldersbebyggelse*. ("Kungliga Svenska Vetenkaps akademiens Handlingar," Series III, Vol. XIX, No. 1.) Stockholm. 242 pp.

NARR, KARL J.
1952 "Das höhere Jägertum: Jüngere Jagd- und Sammelstufe," pp. 502–22 in VALJAVEC, F. (ed.), *Historia mundi: Ein Handbuch der Weltgeschichte in Zehn Bänden*, Vol. I: *Frühe Menschheit*. Bern: A. Francke; Munich: Leo Lehnen. 560 pp.
1953a "Hirten, Pflanzer, Bauern: Produktionsstufe," pp. 66–100 in VALJAVEC, F. (ed.), *Historia Mundi: Ein Handbuch der Weltgeschichte in Zehn Bänden*, Vol. II: *Grundlagen und Entfaltung der ältesten Hochkulturen*. Bern: A. Francke; Munich: Leo Lehnen. 655 pp.
1953b "Zur Frage altpaläolithischer Kulturkreise," *Anthropos*, XLVIII, Nos. 5–6, 773–94.
1954 "Formengruppen und Kulturkreise im europäischen Paläolithikum: Stand und Aufgaben der Altsteinzeitforschung," *Bericht der Römisch-Germanischen Kommission*, XXXIV (1951–53), 1–40.

NOUGIER, LOUIS-RENÉ
1949 "La Répartition géographique des casse-têtes discoides," *Bulletin de la Société Préhistorique Française*, XLVI, 428–33.
1950 *Les Civilisations Campigniennes en Europe occidentale*. Le Mans: Ch. Monnoyer. 571 pp.

OVERBECK, FRITZ
1939 *Die Moore Niedersachsens in geologisch-botanischer Betrachtung*. ("Wirtschaftswissenschaftliche. Gesellschaft zum Studium Niedersachsens," Reihe A, Vol. LII.) 54 pp.
1950 "Neue pollenanalytisch-stratigraphische Untersuchungen zum Pflug von Walle," *Nachrichten aus Niedersachsens Urgeschichte*, XIX, 3–30.

P., E.
1954 "A Report on the Conference Held in London, 9th to 11th April, 1954, 'Prehistoric Agriculture,'" *Archaeological News Letter*, V, No. 1, 8–14.

PARET, OSCAR
1946 *Das neue Bild der Vorgeschich-*

te. Stuttgart: August Schröder. 225 pp.

PHILIPPE, JOSEPH
  1953 "Le Campignien occidental et les gisements des environs d'Aubel (Province de Liège)," pp. 165–84 in SOCIÉTÉ ROYALE BELGE D'ANTHROPOLOGIE ET DE PRÉHISTOIRE (ed.), *Mélanges en hommage au professeur Hamal-Nandrin*. Brussels: Imprimerie Administrative. 216 pp.

PITTIONI, RICHARD
  1950 *Beiträge zur Geschichte des Keramikums in Afrika und im Nahen Osten: Prähistorische Forschungen*, Vol. II. Horn-Vienna: Ferdinand Berger. 50 pp.

POHLHAUSEN, HENN
  1954a *Das Wanderhirtentum und seine Vorstufen: Eine ethnographisch-geographische Studie zur Entwicklung der Eingeborenenwirtschaft: Kulturgeschichtliche Forschungen*, Vol. IV. Braunschweig: Albert Limbach. 176 pp.
  1954b *Nachweisbare Spuren des Wanderhirtentums in der südkaspischen Mittelsteinzeit*. Lund: Berlingska Boktryckeriet. 15 pp.

PURSE-STANEK, ERIKA
  1953 "Stone Implements and Their Use in the Agriculture of Taiwan," *Wiener völkerkundliche Mitteilungen*, I, No. 2, 22–31.

RIETH, ADOLF
  1949–50 "Geschliffene bandkeramische Steingeräte zur Holtzbearbeitung," *Prähistorische Zeitschrift*, XXXIV–XXXV, Part I, 230–32.

RUST, ALFRED
  1948 "Jungpaläolithische Wohnanlagen bei Hamburg," *Hammaburg, vor- und frühgeschichtliche Forschungen aus dem niederelbischen Raum*, I, 33–38.
  1951 "Über die Kulturentwicklung des endglazialen Jungpaläolithikums in Nordwesteuropa," pp. 48–58 in KERSTEN, KARL (ed.), *Festschrift für Gustav Schwantes*. Neumünster: Karl Wachholtz. 233 pp.

SANGMEISTER, EDWARD
  1951 "Zum Charakter der bandkeramischen Siedlung," *Bericht der Römisch-Germanischen Kommission*, XXXIII (1943–50), 89–109.

SAUER, CARL O.
  1952 *Agricultural Origins and Dispersals*. (Bowman Memorial Lectures, Series Two.) New York: American Geographical Society. 110 pp.

SCHACHERMEYR, FRITZ
  1954 "Die vorderasiatische Kulturtrift," *Saeculum: Jahrbuch für Universalgeschichte*, V, No. 3, 268–91.

SCHWABEDISSEN, HERMANN
  1951 "Das Magdalénien im nordwesteuropäischen Flachland," *Eiszeitalter und Gegenwart*, I, 152–65.
  1952a "Zur Besiedlung des Nordseeraums in der älteren und mittleren Steinzeit," pp. 59–77 in KERSTEN, KARL (ed.), *Festschrift für Gustav Schwantes*. Neumünster: Karl Wachholtz. 233 pp.
  1952b Review of L. R. NOUGIER, *Les Civilisations Campigniennes en Europe occidentale*, *Germania*, XXX, 399–405.
  1954 *Die Federmesser-Gruppen des nordwesteuropäischen Flachlandes: Zur Ausbreitung des Spät-Magdalénien*. ("Offa-Bücher," N.F., Vol. IX.) Neumünster: Karl Wachholtz. 104 pp.

SCHWANTES, GUSTAV
  1939 *Die Vorgeschichte Schleswig-Holsteins (Stein- und Bronzezeit)*. Neumünster: Karl Wachholtz. 589 pp.

SCHWARZ, KLAUS
  1948 "Lagen die Siedlungen der linearbandkeramischen Kultur Mitteldeutschlands in waldfreien oder bewaldeten Landschaften," pp. 1–28 in SCHWARZ, KLAUS (ed.), *Strena praehistorica*. Halle an der Saale: Max Niemeyer. 253 pp.

SOERGEL, W.
  1922 *Die Jagd der Vorzeit*. Jena: Gustav Fischer. 149 pp.

STEEGER, ALBERT
  1932 "Studien zur Siedlungsgeschichte des Niederrheinischen Tieflandes," *Rheinische Vierteljahrsblätter*, II, 278–95.

STIEREN, AUGUST
  1951 "Bandkeramische Grossbauten bei Bochum und ihre Parallelen in

Mitteleuropa," *Bericht der Römisch-Germanischen Kommission,* XXXIII (1943–50), 61–88.

STOKAR, WALTER VON
1942 "Phylogenie und Vorgeschichts-forschung," *Praehistorische Zeitschrift,* XXXII–XXXIII (1941–42), 3–15.

TACKENBERG, KURT
1953 "Die jüngere Steinzeit Europas: Das Neolithikum," pp. 11–65 in VAL-JAVEC, F. (ed.), *Historia mundi,* Vol. II. Bern: A. Francke; Munich: Leo Lehnen. 655 pp.
1954 *Fundkarten zur Vorgeschichte der Rheinprovinz.* (Beiheft 2 der "Bonner Jahrbücher.") Bonn: Rudolf Habelt. 107 pp.

TÜXEN, REINHOLD
1931 "Die Grundlagen der Urland-schaftsforschung," *Nachrichten aus Niedersachsens Urgeschichte,* V, 59–96.

USLAR, RAFAEL VON
1950–51 "Zur vor- und frühgeschicht-lichen Besiedlung des Bergischen Landes," *Rheinische Vierteljahrsblätter,* XV–XVI, 8–18.
1951 "Zur vorgeschichtlichen Besied-lung des Niederrheins," *Niederrhein-isches Jahrbuch,* III, 54–56.

ZEUNER, F. E.
1951 "A Postglacial Period of Dry Summers Expressed in Soils, and Its Archaeological Date," *University of London, Institute of Archaeology, Annual Report,* VII (1949–50), 46–53.

The Hydraulic Civilizations

KARL A. WITTFOGEL[*]

THE HYDRAULIC AND THE URBAN REVOLUTION

A great deal has recently been said about the "urban revolution"—a process of differentiation that split an originally village-centered agrarian society into an urban and a rural sector: town and village. The distinction between town and village considerably interested certain classical economists (Smith, 1937, pp. 373 ff.), including Marx (1953, pp. 381, 382 ff.; 1919, I, 317; III, Part I, 318). Properly employed, it opens up important sociohistorical vistas.

However, those who use it today, either as part of a general developmental scheme or as a means for juxtaposing urban and rural ("folk") culture, tend to disregard two essential methodological precautions. Stress on the revolutionary character of the rise of the town one-sidedly accents what at the most is only one among several features of cultural change. For instance, Childe, who is eager to accustom his readers to the idea of revolution (1952, p. 19), thus promotes historical views that are highly problematic. And his unqualified emphasis on urbanization as a develop-

mental feature bulwarks the thesis of a general evolution in agrarian civilization that is manifestly false. This thesis, which culminates in the concept of a unilinear and necessarily progressive development of society, clearly contradicts the facts of history. It also contradicts the views of the classical economists, who with varying consistency recognized that the higher agrarian civilizations of the "Orient" and their urban and rural conditions followed a pattern of development decidedly unlike that of the West.

A juxtaposition of rural and urban institutions will promote our analysis of agrarian history to the extent to which we realize that there are at least two major types of rural-urban agrarian civilizations—hydraulic and non-hydraulic—and that the primitive farmers who started on an agrohydraulic course initiated a revolution that, structurally and for a whole epoch, split the higher civilizations into two different parts. Prior to the urban revolution and with extraordinary consequences, the fate of agricultural man was profoundly shaped by what may be suitably called the "hydraulic revolution."

MAJOR EFFECTS OF THE HYDRAULIC REVOLUTION

Hydraulic Agriculture

The peculiarities of agrohydraulic civilization become apparent as soon as we realize the role that the management of water has played in the subsistence economy of certain agrarian societies.

* Dr. Wittfogel is Professor of Chinese History, University of Washington, Seattle, and Director of the Chinese History Project, co-sponsored by the University of Washington and Columbia University. He is author of *Wirtschaft und Gesellschaft Chinas*, 1931, and co-author, with Fêng Chia-shêng, of *History of Chinese Society, Liao (907–1125)*, 1949. A recently completed book, *Oriental Despotism and Hydraulic Society* is scheduled for publication in 1956.

To be sure, water is no more essential to agriculture than several other basic factors, such as temperature, the lay of the land, the fertility of the soil, and the character of the cultivable plants. But water is specific in that, among the manipulative essentials, it is the only element which tends to agglomerate in bulk (Wittfogel, 1956, chap. ii). In its agriculturally most precious occurrence —as the water of rivers and large streams in arid or semiarid regions—it therefore defied the small-scale approach which, under preindustrial conditions, was so effective in the treatment of soil and plants. In order to bring fertility to large water-deficient areas by the management of substantial sources of water supply, man had to create large-scale enterprises that usually were operated by the government. The emergence of big productive water works (for irrigation) was frequently accompanied by the emergence of big protective water works (for flood control), and at times the latter even surpassed the former in magnitude and urgency. I suggest that this type of agrarian economy be called "hydraulic agriculture" to distinguish it from rainfall farming and hydroagriculture.

It is customary to apply the term "rainfall agriculture" to a situation in which a favorable climate permits cultivation on the basis of natural precipitation. The term "hydroagriculture" may be applied to a situation in which the members of a farming community resort to irrigation but, because of the scarcity and fragmentation of the available moisture, to irrigation on a small scale only. The term "hydraulic agriculture" may be applied to a situation in which the dimension of the available water supply leads to the creation of large productive and protective water works that are managed by the government.

Institutional Essence of Hydraulic Civilization

Irrigation was practiced in parts of Greece to compensate for the deficiencies of a semiarid climate and in Japan for the cultivation of an aquatic plant— rice. But in both countries a broken terrain permitted the growth of only small irrigation works, which could be handled without government direction. This fact has had far-reaching sociohistorical consequences. Japan established a simple variant of the same feudal society which, in a more complex form, emerged in medieval Europe (Wittfogel, 1956, chap. x). And Greece, prior to the Hellenistic period, developed aristocratic and democratic ways of life. In each case hydroagriculture encouraged the evolution of a multicentered society, an institutional conformation that assumed great significance in the rainfall-based civilizations of feudal Europe.

The contrast between this development and that of the agrohydraulic world is striking. Where agriculture required substantial and centralized works of water control, the representatives of the government monopolized political power and societal leadership, and they dominated their country's economy. By preventing the growth of strong competitive forces, such as a feudal knighthood, an autonomous church, or self-governing guild cities, they were able to make themselves the sole masters of their society. It is this combination of a hydraulic agriculture, a hydraulic government, and a single-centered society that constitutes the institutional essence of hydraulic civilization.

Differentiations

Within the orbit of hydraulic civilization immense cultural differences occur; but this essay cannot elaborate on them.

An inquiry dealing with man's impact upon his natural environment may content itself with discussing certain subdivisions of the general institutional order that concern this man-nature relation.

Development in political structure is most consequential when the primitive governments of hydraulic tribes, managed largely by part-time functionaries, evolve into statelike organizations, managed by a body of full-time officials. The hydraulic state provides more comprehensive opportunities for imposing hydraulic installations upon the natural environment, but it also gives the men of the state apparatus the opportunity to neglect water works which will benefit the people, in order to build huge palaces and tombs and process precious organic and inorganic materials which will benefit the rulers.

Development in the patterns of property may lead from a predominance of state control over land and over professional handicraft and trade (simple hydraulic society) to a configuration in which mobile property in industry and trade is largely private, while land remains government controlled (semicomplex hydraulic society), or to a configuration in which private property in land is also widespread (complex hydraulic society). The rise of a semicomplex hydraulic order tends to differentiate the individual producer's interaction with nature; and it furthers the processes of locomotion which overcome difficulties of space and terrain. The rise of private property in land (tenancy as well as ownership) tends to stimulate careful agriculture. The intensive farmers of the ancient Near East were mainly tenants of public (state and temple) lands or of private estates. In China the transition to private landownership evoked the comment that the peasants worked less carefully on the public fields than on their own land (Lü, 1936, ch. 17). Chinese peasant farming, which for over two thousand years has been based on private property of land, represents perhaps the most advanced form of intensive agriculture prior to the machine age.

Development in the spatial expansion of the hydraulic state is equally consequential. It is a historical fact that certain non-hydraulic *constructional* patterns and the major *organizational* and *acquisitive* patterns of hydraulic ("Oriental") despotism advanced far beyond the area of hydraulic economy proper. In "loose" hydraulic civilizations, such as China, India, and pre-Spanish Mexico, the monopolistic state apparatus controlled wide areas that had no comprehensive water works and in some cases not even small-scale irrigation.

This aspect was readily accepted by earlier analysts of "Asiatic" society, from the classical economists to Max Weber. But little effort has been made to explain the underlying mechanics of power. Still less analytic attention has been given to the fact that, either through a breakoff from a hydraulic regime proper (later Byzantium) or through institutional transfer (Mongol and post-Mongol Russia and probably Maya society), there may be governments which fulfil few or no agrohydraulic functions but which utilize the organizational methods of hydraulic despotism (such as record-keeping, census-taking, centralized armies, a state system of post and intelligence) as well as its acquisitive methods (such as general labor service, general and heavy taxation, and periodic confiscations) and its legal and political methods (such as fragmentary laws of inheritance and the suppression of independent political organizations) to keep private property weak and the non-bureaucratic forces of society politically impotent.

In fact, so strong were the devices of hydraulic statecraft and social control that they operated successfully in "marginal" areas without those large-scale water works which persisted in the hydraulic core areas and which apparently were an essential feature in the genesis of all historically relevant agrarian monopoly despotisms. From the standpoint of man's relation to man, the institutional periphery of the hydraulic world has been important in that it enormously widened the range of this despotic order. From the standpoint of man's relation to nature, it has been important in that, like the hydraulic core area, it frustrated the development of a big mechanized industry—the most profound recent change in man's attitude toward his natural environment.

MAN AND NATURE IN HYDRAULIC CIVILIZATION

Having considered the institutional setting of hydraulic civilization, we are now ready to contemplate more closely the specific relations between man and nature within it. These relations involve a peculiar system of mass labor in one segment of the economic order and a peculiar system of intensive work in another.

Government-directed Preparatory Operations: Division of Labor and Co-operation, Bureaucracy, Astronomical and Mathematical Sciences

Hydraulic civilization came into being not through a technological but through an organizational revolution. Its rise necessitated the establishment of a new system of division of labor and co-operation.

Economic historians, when dealing with this matter, frequently assert that until recent times agriculture, in contrast to industry, involved little division of labor and no significant co-operation (Seligman, 1914, p. 350; Sombart, 1927, II, 825 ff.; Marshall, 1946, p. 290; for pioneer formulations see Smith, 1937, p. 6; and Marx, 1919, I, 300, 322 ff.). By

and large, this view is justified with regard to the conditions of non-hydraulic farming. But it does not fit the operational pattern of hydraulic agriculture. A major separation between "preparatory labor" (for this term see Mill, 1909, p. 31) and production proper is held to have occurred first in the industrial revolution. Actually, it took place much earlier and on an enormous scale in the hydraulic revolution.

Comprehensive preparatory activities were necessary to make cultivation either possible (in arid areas) or safe and rewarding (in semiarid areas) or specific (in humid areas suitable for the growth of aquatic plants, such as rice and wet taro). The difference between this type of preparatory labor and the preparatory labor employed in modern industry is obvious. In industry preparatory labor provides the ultimate producer with raw material, with auxiliary material (e.g., coal for fuel and oil for lubrication), and also with special tools (machinery). In hydraulic economy preparatory labor consisted essentially in the gathering, conducting, and distributing of one auxiliary material—water. In modern industry the workers who engage in preparatory activities, such as mining, the making of machinery, etc., tend to work full time at their various jobs. In agrohydraulic economy division of labor proceeded differently. The great mass of the men who made and maintained the canals and dikes and who watched for floods did not do so full time and for the greater part of the year but part time and for as short a period as possible. In their overwhelming majority they were farmers, and the very authorities who mobilized them for hydraulic and other *corvée* duties were eager to have them return in good time to their villages to attend properly to the cultivation of their fields.

Thus, like modern industry, hydraulic agriculture involves significant division of labor; but, unlike modern industry, it involves no significant division of laborers. And while the organizers of preparatory work in industry endeavor to achieve their purpose with as small a labor force as possible, the organizers of the hydraulic *corvée* are interested in mobilizing as large a labor force as circumstances permit.

In hydraulic tribes, such as the Suk and Chagga of East Africa and the Pueblo Indians of New Mexico, all ablebodied males participated as a matter of course in the ditch work. In small, state-centered hydraulic civilizations, such as Bali and the early Mesopotamian and Indian city-states, the same mobilization pattern seems to have been customary (Wittfogel, 1956, chap. ii). A list of canal workers in ancient Lagash includes one corviable person from each commoner family (Schneider, 1920, pp. 108 ff.). In an irrigation conflict which, according to a pious legend, led to the Buddha's personal interference, the whole laboring population of the towns involved is said to have engaged in the hydraulic work (Anonymous, n.d., *Jātakam*, p. 441). Even clusters of territorial states may, at times, have gathered their combined populations to execute a big hydraulic task. This appears to have been the case in the Mexican federation prior to the arrival of the Spaniards. And it may have been a recurring trend in countries such as Egypt, where all villages depended on one huge source of irrigation water and where, therefore, their labor forces could be called up, either simultaneously or in shifts, to dig, dam, and watch for floods (Wittfogel, 1956, chap. ii).

In larger hydraulic civilizations varying regional conditions suggested varying patterns of state-directed *corvée* labor, but its mass character remained unchanged. The underlying mobilization principle is drastically formulated by a historian of Mogul economy, Pant (1930, p. 70): "The King by his *firman* (order) could collect any number of men he liked. There was no limit to his massing of labourers, save the number of people in his Empire." Pant was speaking of Mogul India, but his statement is valid for all analogous periods and countries. In hydraulic economy man extended his power over the arid, the semiarid, and certain humid parts of the globe through a government-directed division of labor and a mode of co-operation not practiced in agrarian civilizations of the non-hydraulic type.

The development of such a work pattern meant more than the agglomeration of large numbers of men. To have many persons co-operate periodically and effectively, there had to be planning, record-keeping, communication, and supervision. There had to be organization in depth. And above the tribal level this involved permanent offices and officials to man them—bureaucrats.

Of course, there were scribes in the city-states of ancient Greece and Rome and on the manorial estates, at the courts, and in the church centers of medieval Europe. But there was no national managerial network. In the great Oriental civilizations a hydraulic bureaucracy (*Wasserbau-Bureaukratie* [Weber, 1921–22, p. 117]) emerged together with the new type of organization in depth.

It was in these same Oriental (hydraulic) civilizations that man, in seeking a more rational approach to nature, laid the foundations for several sciences: astronomy, algebra, and geometry. Significantly, Greek mathematics and astronomy drew their early inspiration from the Oriental Near East, and they reached their climax under Euclid, Heron, and Ptolemy, not in Greece, but in one of the foremost centers of hydraulic culture—Egypt (Wittfogel, 1931, p. 682).

To be sure, neither the bureaucratic nor the scientific possibilities of hydraulic civilization were always exhausted. Some simpler hydraulic civilizations did not advance far. But the major hydraulic centers created elaborate administrations, and their astronomical and mathematical accomplishments were impressive. Thus any attempt to define hydraulic man's relation to nature must also consider the organizational (bureaucratic) and the scientific aspects of hydraulic economy.

Irrigation Farming with Intensive Labor and Special Operations of Tillage

Government management of the great hydraulic works is supplemented by intensive farming based on irrigation. As stated above, irrigation farming also occurs in certain non-hydraulic societies, and to this extent the subsequent statements have validity beyond the borders of hydraulic civilization. But, while irrigation farming occurs occasionally in the non-hydraulic agricultural world, it is essential in the core areas of hydraulic civilization.

Irrigation demands a treatment of soil and water that is not customary in rainfall farming. The typical irrigation peasant has (1) to dig and re-dig ditches and furrows; (2) to terrace the land if it is uneven; (3) to raise the moisture if the level of the water supply is below the surface of the fields; and (4) to regulate the flow of the water from the source to the goal, directing its ultimate application to the crop. Tasks (1) and (4) are essential to all irrigation farming proper (inundation farming requires damming rather than ditching). Task (3) is also a frequent one, for, except at the time of high floods, the level of water tends to lie below that of the cultivated fields.

The type and amount of work involved in these operations become clear when we contrast the labor budget of an Oriental irrigation farmer with that of a rainfall farmer of medieval Europe. The medieval peasant usually plowed his field once or twice, then he sowed

(Farain, 1942, p. 142; cf. Maitland, 1921, pp. 398 ff.; Lamprecht, 1886, p. 557), and he harvested his crop at the end of the season. As a rule he spent no time watering.

The irrigation farmer, who, of course, plows, sows, and harvests, is in addition burdened with a number of other chores. In regions like Egypt, which depended mainly on inundation, these activities were insignificant, yet such regions were not very numerous. In others, such as ancient Mesopotamia, inundation was supplemented by canal irrigation. In this case a considerable amount of time was devoted to the watering of the fields (Meissner, 1920, pp. 192, 194). In modern India the husbandmen of a Punjab village spend much time irrigating their crops, wheat receiving three to four waterings in January, February, and March during more than twenty days. This work period is the most time-consuming item listed in the year's agricultural calendar (Singh, 1928, pp. 33–36, 38). Sugar cane is an old Indian crop, requiring a great deal of water. In certain Deccan villages favoring its cultivation, the total cost of plowing, harrowing, planting, harvesting, and related operations is about 97 rupees as against 157 rupees for watering (Mann and Kanitkar, 1920, p. 86). In a South Gujarat village, studied by Mukhtyar (1930, p. 96), watering is by far the heaviest expense item in the labor budget of the grower of sugar cane.

Concerning Chinese traditional irrigation economy, Buck has provided us with valuable numerical data. In 1923, 152 farms in Pinghsiang (in present Hopeh Province) grew wheat as their main crop. Of the time devoted to this crop, the peasant spent 10.2 per cent in plowing, 1.7 per cent in harrowing, 9.2 per cent in harvesting, or altogether 21.1 per cent, as against 58.5 per cent in irrigating (Buck, 1930, p. 306). In 1924 two groups of farmers in Kiangsu Province spent 21 and 25.1 per cent, respectively, in plowing, harrowing, and harvesting their main rice crop, as against 18.1 and 39.6 per cent in its irrigation (*ibid.*, p. 310). As may be expected, the labor budgets show great variation in detail, but they all reveal that the amount of work involved in watering operations is commonly far in excess of the combined operations of a non-irrigation farmer.

Repeated preparatory tillage—plowing or hoeing—was also undertaken by the rainfall farmers of feudal Europe (Cole and Mathews, 1938, pp. 324 ff.). But it was primarily on the manorial domain that the fields were "worked" three or four times, while the "poor peasants could often only work their land once to the detriment of the yield" (Parain, 1942, p. 141; cf. Lamprecht, 1886, p. 557).

Except for some cutting of thistles (Parain, 1942, pp. 144 ff.; Kulischer, 1928, p. 160), intertillage was then, as now, technically impossible for grain crops, because, under conditions of rainfall farming, these "can be grown satisfactorily and most economically by planting them in solid stands so that they cover all the ground equally." As a rule, they are today "given no tillage while they are growing" (Cole and Mathews, 1938, p. 327).

Plants grown in rows are easily approached and easily cultivated. But the most important of these, corn and potatoes, appeared in Europe only after the discovery of America, and even after the sixteenth century their economic importance remained definitely secondary to that of the cereals. In the West the modern dry farmer still hesitates to cultivate grain crops in rows. After an early harrowing he frequently lets nature take its course (Widtsoe, 1913, pp. 163 ff.).

Irrigation agriculture requires a rowlike arrangement of the seeds not only for crops such as corn and potatoes but also for cereals. Plants can be watered by ditches only if proper space for the distributing furrows is provided. The layout of the fields differs in accordance with economic experience, crops, and terrain, but all patterns aim at making the plants accessible to the irrigation farmer, who may work the soil and the crop as thoroughly as he wishes.

Intensive techniques are not limited to the period between sowing and harvesting. Frequently the soil is plowed or harrowed several times before the sowing. Nor are these techniques limited to the fields for which irrigation water is available. In semiarid areas (under conditions of full aridity cultivation ends where the water supply ends) the farmers are eager to grow not only crops which they can water but also crops which may mature without the benefit of irrigation.

Chinese farmers in the province of Kiangsu who had sufficient water for two main crops only, rice and vegetables, used to grow wheat and barley without irrigation. However, they treated the last two as intensively as the first two. Of all labor devoted to wheat, intertillage accounted for over 20 per cent; in the case of barley, it accounted for almost 33 per cent; and in the case of kaoliang, which in some parts of Hopeh is grown without irrigation, it accounted for more than 40 per cent (Buck, 1930, p. 306).

In India certain Deccan villages grow their main cereal crop, *bajri,* also without irrigation. But, like the irrigated cereals, it is planted in rows and intensively cultivated. It gets one plowing and four harrowings before sowing and further treatment after sowing (Mann and Kanitkar, 1920, pp. 72 ff.).

The good Aztec farmer made beds for his corn, pulverized the soil, and kept his crop free of weeds (Sahagun, 1938, p. 39). He irrigated whenever this was possible, but he obviously was expected to farm intensively under any circumstances. The Mayan peasants of Yucatán, who did not water their crops, weeded them as carefully as did the inhabitants of the highland regions in which irrigation farming was customary.

Thus, as the political patterns of hydraulic civilization spread far beyond the areas of hydraulic economy, so the techniques of irrigation farming spread far beyond the irrigated fields. These techniques established an agronomical relation among man, soil, and plants that, in terms of a given amount of land, was much more rewarding than the agriculture of preindustrial Europe. Early in the twentieth century a European agronomist found the Indian peasants, who by and large followed their traditional pattern of cultivation, quite as good as the average modern British farmer and in some respects better (Anonymous, 1909, p. 6). The father of organic chemistry, Justus von Liebig, in comparing nineteenth-century German agriculture with contemporary Chinese farming, viewed the former as the procedure of "a child compared to that of a mature and experienced man" (Liebig, 1878, p. 453).

Demographic Consequences

In some ways Liebig's statement touches upon problems that lie outside the concern of the biochemist. But he was quite right in noting the greater refinement—and better results—of hydraulic agriculture as practiced in China. Whatever its deficiencies, this method of farming produced great quantities of food on a given acreage, and it permitted the individual peasant to support his family on a very small farmstead. For this reason the areas of intensive hydraulic farming came to support extremely dense populations.

In preconquest America relatively small hydraulic regions comprised about 75 per cent of America's total population (Kroeber, 1939, p. 166; Ro-

senblat, 1945, pp. 188 ff., 202 ff.; Kubler, 1946, p. 339; for a considerably higher estimate of the population of the Inca Empire see Rowe, 1946, p. 185). Beloch's classical estimates (1886, p. 507) for the time of Augustus assume a much greater density for the Asian provinces of the Roman Empire (thirty persons per square kilometer) than for the European provinces (ten persons per square kilometer). The contrast becomes even more spectacular when we juxtapose his figures for Augustan Greece (eleven) and Italy (twenty-four) with those of Egypt (one hundred and seventy-nine). More recent studies (Premerstein, 1936, p. 56; Rostovtzeff, 1941, II, 1138; III, 1605) suggest a still higher figure for Egypt, namely, about two hundred and eighty persons per square kilometer.

The population distribution in contemporary Han China was not unlike that of the Roman Empire. The old Chinese territories of the north seem to have been as densely populated as Rome's eastern provinces, while the hydraulic core areas of the Han world showed demographic trends similar to those of their western counterparts, Egypt and Babylonia (Lao, 1935, pp. 216 ff.).

The dimension of the Oriental cities expresses both the productivity of hydraulic agriculture and the acquisitive power of its administrative centers. While, in classical days, Athens may have had 120,000 inhabitants, Corinth 70,000, and the majority of all Greek cities between 5,000 and 10,000 persons (Beloch, 1886, p. 478), Hellenistic Ephesus may have harbored 225,000 people (*ibid.*, p. 231), Antioch 500,000 (*ibid.*, p. 479; Kahrstedt, 1924, p. 663; Rostovtzeff, 1941, I, 498), Seleuceia 600,000 (Beloch, 1886, p. 479; Rostovtzeff, 1941, I, 498; II, 1140), and Alexandria at the end of the Hellenistic period the same number (Rostovtzeff, 1941, II, 1139 ff.). The recently published "gerusia acts" lead Rostovtzeff (*ibid.,* p. 1139; cf. Premerstein, 1936, p. 56) to conclude that for A.D. 37 the total population of the Egyptian capital "must be estimated at one million at least."

It is also illuminating to compare these figures with estimates for metropolitan populations in pre-Spanish America and feudal Europe. Prevailing expert opinion credits Cuzco with 200,-000 and Mexico City with 300,000 inhabitants (Rosenblat, 1945, pp. 205, 191). Some cities of Moorish Spain may have housed several hundred thousand persons, and the capital, Cordova, at its peak, a million (Wittfogel, 1956, chap. vi; cf. also al-Makkari, 1840, pp. 214 ff.). In contrast, in the fourteenth century the most populous city north of the Alps seems to have had 35,000 inhabitants (London), while other major English cities comprised 11,000 (York), 9,500 (Bristol), or between 7,000 and 5,000 persons (Rogers, 1884, p. 117). At the beginning of the fifteenth century the foremost city of the Hanseatic League, Lübeck, had 22,300 inhabitants and Frankfurt 10,000. Other big German towns of this century sheltered between 20,000 and 10,000 persons, Leipzig 4,000 and Dresden 3,200 (Büchner, 1922, p. 382).

Chinese census data have been discussed at length. What should be remembered is that these data were compiled primarily for fiscal reasons. Since tax payments had to agree with the announced population, the census records tended to represent not the actual but the admitted population, that is, the lowest figures the regional officials dared to submit (Wittfogel and Fêng, 1949, p. 53). Weak regimes got understatements, and tougher and more effective governments more realistic accounts. Two decades ago Buck, on the basis of a comprehensive rural survey, obtained population figures about 23 per cent higher than the official data.

He hesitated to press his findings, but he stated that, if his higher figures were used, "the total would be over 600 million" (1937, p. 363). The first census taken by the new Communist government claims a total mainland population of almost 600 million persons.

Much more could be said on this subject. But the just-cited data fit with our other information on Oriental demography. Obviously, the hydraulic way of life permitted an accumulation of rural and urban populations which, though paralleled in a few non-hydraulic territories of small-scale irrigation, such as Japan, has not been matched by the higher agrarian civilizations based on rainfall farming.

DIMENSIONS OF HYDRAULIC CIVILIZATION
IN TIME, SPACE, AND MANPOWER

According to conservative estimates, hydraulic civilizations took shape in the ancient Near East not later than the fourth millennium B.C., and they persisted until very recent times. It may therefore be said safely that in this area hydraulic civilization endured for about five millenniums.

The great hydraulic civilizations of India and China maintained themselves for some three or four millenniums. And recent archeological finds suggest that in certain areas of the Western Hemisphere, such as Peru, hydraulic civilizations may have existed at least since the first millennium B.C., that is, for more than two millenniums prior to the arrival of the Spaniards.

Neither ancient Greece nor feudal Europe nor Japan can equal these figures. Greek agrarian civilization seems to have lasted for a millennium until Hellenistic despotism put an end to its non-Oriental pattern. The societies of feudal Europe and Japan had an even shorter duration.

The core areas and the margins of the hydraulic civilizations covered the greater part of western, southern, and eastern Asia. The Hellenistic regimes, the Orientalized Roman Empire, the Arab conquests of Spain and Sicily, and the Byzantine, Turkish, and Russian expansions imposed Orientally despotic regimes on large areas of Europe.

In Africa north of the Sahara, a hydraulic way of life prevailed for millenniums. A thousand years ago it seems to have spread temporarily from Lake Tanganyika and Kenya to Rhodesia (Huntingford, 1933, pp. 153, 159 ff.; Wilson, 1932, pp. 252 ff.; Hall and Neal, 1904, pp. 356 ff.; Randall-MacIver, 1906, pp. 12 ff.). In recent times it was observed among the Chagga and a few other tribes of central East Africa.

Hydraulic agriculture and government persisted in some major Pacific islands, such as Hawaii. In pre-Columbian America hydraulic developments spread beyond the Rio Grande in the north. In the Meso-American highlands and in the lowlands of Yucatán, clusters of loose and marginal hydraulic civilizations emerged. And in the south hydraulic expansion reached its maximum on the eve of the Spanish conquest. Early in the sixteenth century the Inca Empire stretched from Peru to Ecuador in the north and to Bolivia and Chile in the west and south. It co-ordinated practically all important centers of higher agrarian development in South America. Clearly, hydraulic civilizations covered a vastly larger proportion of the surface of the globe than all other significant agrarian civilizations taken together.

The demographic dimension of the hydraulic world has already been indicated. According to our present information, it would seem that, prior to the commercial and industrial revolution, the majority of all human beings lived within the orbit of hydraulic civilization.

COSTS AND PERSPECTIVES OF HYDRAULIC CIVILIZATION

Manifestly, then, this civilization was an eminently successful "going concern." It stimulated organization in depth. It gave birth to certain sciences. And it refined farming and handicraft. Yet, in terms of human affairs, it was as costly as it was tenacious. While such scientific aids to counting and measuring as astronomy and mathematics emerged, these developments eventually stalled, and the experimental sciences never gained significance. Masses of men were co-ordinated for public works and warfare, but the patterns of integration were crude, and they improved little throughout the centuries. Farming techniques were subtle, but from the standpoint of the main protagonist, the peasant, their one-sidedly labor-intensive development was frustrating. Hydraulic agriculture made the cultivator till his fields with a minimum of labor-saving tools and animals and with a maximum of human labor. Being politically without influence, the hydraulic farmer maintained a man-nature relation that involved unending drudgery on a socially and culturally depressing level.

Aristotle's vision of a society of free men based on the advance of the mechanical arts is increasingly being realized in the multicentered industrial societies of the West. It never materialized in hydraulic society. For reasons inherent in this institutional conformation, the masters of hydraulic civilization succeeded in perpetuating the economic and technological order which was the *raison d'être* for their existence.

The stationary character of the great Oriental civilizations was noted incisively in the eighteenth and nineteenth centuries, when the expanding commercial and industrial societies of the West began to loosen up what had previously seemed to be an indestructible societal edifice. The Western impact on man-nature relations in the countries of Oriental despotism was as varied as the forms in which it occurred. No fair-minded observer will deny its destructive aspects. But he will also point to the positive and non-totalitarian innovations that not infrequently accompanied it. And he will submit that, even in its most predatory and aggressive manifestations, Western colonialism, which today is subsiding, is more superficial than the new totalitarian colonialism, which is spreading so rapidly.

Hydraulic ("Oriental") civilization has been in transition for generations. It continues to change in a global situation dominated, on the one hand, by the forces of the totalitarian revolution and, on the other hand, by the forces of the multicentered Western world, in which the growth of an increasingly open society is enhanced by the democratic version of a second industrial revolution. The future of hydraulic civilization and of man's relation to nature and man everywhere ultimately depends on the relative strength of these two competing revolutions.

REFERENCES

ANONYMOUS
  1909 *Imperial Gazetteer of India*, Vol. III. Oxford: Clarendon Press. 520 pp.
  N.d. *Jātakam: Das Buch der Erzählungen aus früheren Existenzen Buddhas*, Vol. V. Trans. by JULIUS DUTOIT. Munich: Oskar Schloss. 608 pp.
BELOCH, JULIUS
  1886 *Die Bevölkerung der griechisch-römischen Welt*. Leipzig: Duncker & Humblot. 520 pp.
BUCK, JOHN LOSSING
  1930 *Chinese Farm Economy*. Nanking: University of Nanking; Chicago: University of Chicago Press. 476 pp.
  1937 *Land Utilization in China*. Chicago: University of Chicago Press. 494 pp.
BÜCHER, KARL
  1922 *Die Entstehung der Volkswirtschaft*, Vol. I. Tübingen: H. Laupp. 475 pp.
CHILDE, V. GORDON
  1952 *Man Makes Himself*. New York: Mentor Books. 192 pp.
COLE, JOHN S., and MATHEWS, O. R.
  1938 "Tillage," pp. 321–28 in U.S. DEPARTMENT OF AGRICULTURE, *Soils and Men: Yearbook of Agriculture*. Washington, D.C.: Government Printing Office. 1232 pp.
HALL, RICHARD NICKLIN, and NEAL, W. S.
  1904 *The Ancient Ruins of Rhodesia*. London: Methuen & Co. 404 pp.
HUNTINGFORD, G. W. B.
  1933 "The Azanian Civilization of Kenya," *Antiquity*, VII, No. 26, 153–65.
KAHRSTEDT, ULRICH
  1924 "Die Bevölkerung des Altertums," *Handwörterbuch der Staatswissenschaften*, II, 655–70. 4th ed. Jena.
KROEBER, A. L.
  1939 *Cultural and Natural Areas of Native North America*. Berkeley: University of California Press. 242 pp.
KUBLER, GEORGE
  1946 "The Quechua in the Colonial World," pp. 331–410 in STEWARD, JULIAN H. (ed.), *Handbook of South American Indians*, Vol. II. (Smithsonian Institution, Bureau of American Ethnology, Bulletin No. 143.) Washington, D.C.: Government Printing Office. 976 pp.
KULISCHER, JOSEF
  1928 *Allgemeine Wirtschaftsgeschichte des Mittelalters und der Neuzeit*, Vol. I: *Das Mittelalter*. Munich and Berlin: R. Oldenbourgh. 351 pp.
LAMPRECHT, KARL G.
  1886 *Deutsches Wirtschaftsleben im Mittelalter: Untersuchungen über die Entwicklung der materiellen Kultur des platten Landes auf Grund der Quellen zunächst des Mosellandes*, Vol. I, No. 1. Leipzig: Alphons Dürr. 663 pp.
LAO KAN
  1935 "Liang Han chün-kuo mien-chi chih ku-chi chi k'ou-shu tsêng-chien

chih t'ui-ts'ê," *Academia sinica*, V, No. 2, 215–40. Peking.

LIEBIG, JUSTUS VON
   1878   *Chemische Briefe*. 6th ed. Leipzig and Heidelberg: Carl Winters. 479 pp.

[LÜ]
   1936   *Lü-shih ch'un-ch'iu* ("Mr. Lü's Spring and Autumn Annals"), in *Ssŭ-pu Pei-yao*. Chung-hua ed. Shanghai. 770 pp.

MAITLAND, FREDERIC WILLIAM
   1921   *Domesday Book and Beyond*. Cambridge: Cambridge University Press. 527 pp.

AL-MAKKARI, AHMED IBN MOHAMMED
   1840   *The History of the Mohammedan Dynasties in Spain: extracted from the "Nafhu-t-tíb min Ghosni-l-Andalusi-r-rattíb wa Tárikh Lisánu-d-dín Ibni-l-khattíb,"* Vol. I. Trans. from the Arabic by PASCUAL DE GAYANGOS Y ARCE. London: Oriental Translation Fund. 548 pp.

MANN, HAROLD H., and KANITKAR, N. V.
   1920   *Land and Labour in a Deccan Village*. ("University of Bombay Economic Series," No. III.) London and Bombay: H. Milford and Oxford University Press. 182 pp.

MARSHALL, ALFRED
   1946   *Principles of Economics*. London: Macmillan & Co. 871 pp.

MARX, KARL
   1919   *Das Kapital*, Vols. I and III, Part I. Hamburg. Otto Meissner. 739+ 448 pp.
   1953   *Grundrisse der Kritik der politischen Oekonomie (Rohentwurf)*. Berlin: Dietz. 1,102 pp.

MEISSNER, BRUNO
   1920   *Babylonien und Assyrien*, Vol. I. Heidelberg: Carl Winters. 466 pp.

MILL, JOHN STUART
   1909   *Principles of Political Economy*. London and New York: Longmans, Green & Co. 1,013 pp.

MUKHTYAR, G. C.
   1930   *Life and Labour in a South Gujarat Village*. Ed. C. N. VAKIL. London and New York: Longmans, Green & Co. 304 pp.

PANT, D.
   1930   *The Commercial Policy of the Moguls*. Bombay: D. B. Taraporevala Sons & Co. 281 pp.

PARAIN, CHARLES
   1942   "The Evolution of Agricultural Technique," pp. 118–68 in CLAPHAM, J. H. and POWER, E, (eds.), *Cambridge Economic History*, Vol. 1. 2 vols. Cambridge: Cambridge University Press.

PREMERSTEIN, ANTON VON
   1936   *Alexandrinische Geronten vor Kaiser Gajus*. ("Mitteilungen der Papyrussammlung der Giessener Universitätsbibliothek," Monograph V.) Giessen. 71 pp.

RANDALL-MACIVER, DAVID
   1906   *Mediaeval Rhodesia*. London and New York: Macmillan & Co. 106 pp.

ROGERS, JAMES E. THOROLD
   1884   *Six Centuries of Work and Wages*. New York: G. P. Putnam's Sons. 591 pp.

ROSENBLAT, ÁNGEL
   1945   *La Población indígena de América desde 1492 hasta la actualidad*. Buenos Aires: Institución Cultural Española. 295 pp.

ROSTOVTZEFF, M.
   1941   *The Social and Economic History of the Hellenistic World*. 3 vols. Oxford: Clarendon Press. 1,779 pp.

ROWE, JOHN HOWLAND
   1946   "Inca Culture at the Time of the Spanish Conquest," pp. 183–330 in STEWARD, JULIAN H. (ed.), *Handbook of South American Indians*, Vol. II. (Smithsonian Institution, Bureau of American Ethnology, Bulletin No. 143.) Washington, D.C.: Government Printing Office. 976 pp.

SAHAGUN, BERNARDINO DE
   1938   *Historia general de las cosas de Nueva España*, Vol. III. Mexico, D.F.: Pedro Robredo. 390 pp.

SCHNEIDER, ANNA
   1920   *Die Anfänge der Kulturwirtschaft: Die sumerische Tempelstadt*. Essen: G. D. Baedeker. 120 pp.

SELIGMAN, EDWIN R. A.
   1914   *Principles of Economics*. New York and London: Longmans, Green & Co. 711 pp.

SINGH, SARDAR GIAN
   1928   *An Economic Survey of Gaggar*

Bhana, a Village in the Amritsar District of the Punjab. (Board of Economic Inquiry, Punjab, Conducted by . . . under the Supervision of M. KING . . . [Rural Section Publication No. 16], "Punjab Village Survey," Vol. I.) Lahore. 235 pp.

SMITH, ADAM
1937 *An Inquiry into the Nature and Causes of the Wealth of Nations.* New York: Modern Library. 976 pp.

SOMBART, WERNER
1927 *Das Wirtschaftsleben im Zeitalter des Hochkapitalismus.* 2 vols. Munich and Leipzig: Duncker & Humblot. 1,064 pp.

WEBER, MAX
1921–22 *Wirtschaft und Gesellschaft: Grundriss der Sozialökonomik.* 2 vols. Tübingen: J. C. B. Mohr. 840 pp.

WIDTSOE, JOHN A
1913 *Dry-Farming: A System of Agriculture for Countries under a Low Rainfall.* New York: Macmillan Co. 445 pp.

WILSON, G. E. H.
1932 "The Ancient Civilization of the Rift Valley," *Man,* XXXII, No. 298, 250–57.

WITTFOGEL, KARL A.
1931 *Wirtschaft und Gesellschaft Chinas.* Leipzig: C. L. Hirschfeld. 768 pp.
1956 *Oriental Despotism and Hydraulic Society.* (In press.)

WITTFOGEL, KARL A., and FÊNG CHIA-SHÊNG
1949 *History of Chinese Society, Liao (907–1125).* (*Transactions of the American Philosophical Society,* Vol. XXXVI.) New York: Macmillan Co. 752 pp.

Effects of Classical Antiquity on the Land

FRITZ M. HEICHELHEIM[*]

* Dr. Heichelheim is Assistant Professor in Greek and Roman History at the University of Toronto, Canada; Honorary Full Professor for Ancient Economic History at Hochschule Giessen, Westdeutsche Bundesrepublik; and Secretary of the Joint Papyrus Project of Toronto University and University Library Giessen. His works include: *Wirtschaftliche Schwankungen der Zeit von Alexander bis Augustus*, 1929; *Wirtschaftsgeschichte des Altertums* (2 vols.), 1939 (soon to be published in English); "Roman Syria," in T. Frank, *An Economic Survey of Ancient Rome*, Vol. IV, 1938; and "Roemische und byzantinische Sozial- und Wirtschaftsgeschichte," *Historia mundi*, Vol. IV, 1955.

THE THEMA

This survey is concerned with Greco-Roman civilization from about 1100 B.C. to A.D. 565 as far as it influenced the over-all geophysical structure of the Mediterranean lands and their neighboring regions. We exclude from our inquiry the Minoan, Mycenaean, Helladic, and the Italian prehistoric third and second millenniums B.C. Italy was an essential part of prehistoric western Europe during this time, and Greece was not essentially different in social and economic conditions from the contemporary ancient Oriental Bronze Age civilizations as far as we are able at present to ascertain such matters.

Similarly, the Byzantine development from the death of Justinian I in A.D. 565 to the Turkish conquest of Constantinople in A.D. 1453 has closer affinities, on the whole, with the contemporary medieval Western, medieval Islamic, and medieval Russian structural alterations in social and economic patterns and technical know-how than it has with the ages of Pericles, Cicero, and Tribonianus. Two rather unique and violent population and language changes appear near the beginning and the end of classical antiquity as we define it. About 1100 B.C. the incipient Iron Age led to Indo-European, Semitic, and other migrations and to language changes of great intensity from Britain to India, probably surpassing in historic importance and revolutionary impact the much-discussed and powerful Germanic, Slav, Arabic, and related migrations before and after A.D. 565.

In addition, a terrible plague, from A.D. 542 or so, depopulated the world from Wales to Central Asia, eliminating for good the genes of between one-third and one-half of the population groups and races of classical antiquity proper. Under these circumstances, it is not surprising that, after A.D. 565, Latin and Greek ceased to be living languages, giving way to the Romance, Germanic, Celtic, and Western Slav languages and literatures of the medieval West and to Middle Greek, Slavic, Armenian, Syriac, Coptic, Persian, and especially Arabic literary development in the medieval East.

FROM *ca.* 1100 TO *ca.* 560 B.C.

The world of the early Iron Age, after the Dorian, Italic, and the many other migrations of this period had come to an end, looked essentially different from that of the ancient Oriental Bronze Age. The new Iron Age villages, from India to Spain and Britain, maintained political autonomy, or even independence, and a higher standard of technical civilization for the lower classes (i.e., for at least 90 per cent of the world population) than the ancient Oriental Bronze Age cities had been able to offer. The invention of the iron plowshare alone, not to speak of numerous other improved or novel agricultural iron tools, brought about an agricultural revolution, for the wooden prehistoric and ancient Oriental plowshares could be worked only in so-called "light soils."

When the heavy soils, the most fertile of our globe, were taken under the plow for the first time in human history, enormous population increases outside of Egypt, Babylonia, and other territories of "hydraulic" civilizations were the consequence. Similarly, owing to new Iron Age techniques, mining production throughout the world was intensified considerably. Greece, about 800 B.C. or so, gradually began to take the lead in improving the potentialities of the new Iron Age civilizations. First, a new type of city settlement developed, the Greek *polis*, originally mainly an agrarian settlement of aristocrats, their dependents and retainers, some craftsmen, merchants, small farmers, and priests.

Thereafter the Greek colonization movement planted such Hellenic *poleis* in large numbers from Naucratis in Egypt and the Cyrenaica to the Crimea and the Taman Peninsula of southern Russia and from Poseidion and the Karatepe of the "Danuna" on the Syrian coast to the shores of the Iberian Peninsula. Everywhere, with the help of iron plowshares and the other new agricultural tools, the heavy soils were opened to the growing of grain. The Hellenic vineyard and olive plantations on hilly terraces and viticulture on high trees were introduced; some forests were transformed into more open park landscapes for aesthetic reasons; fishing and piracy intensified. The agricultural plants and animals of Greece, especially vines, olives, certain grain species, certain breeds of dogs, donkeys, horses, bees, horned cattle, sheep, pigs, goats, spread to all new Greek settlements and those of neighboring natives, as far as the climate from Spain to Syria and from North Africa to southern Russia permitted. In exchange, new domestic breeds were brought to Greece from abroad. The domestic fowl in its advance from India and the Orient reached the Greek settlements during the eighth century B.C.

The Etruscans, a proto-Indo-European nation, whose upper class hailed from northwestern Asia Minor and originally from the Caucasus, founded semiagricultural towns (similar to those of the Greeks) in the Toscana and Latium, among them Rome (probably between 650 and 575 B.C.). Greeks and Etruscans were soon imitated by the so-called *oppida* of the native Italic tribes.

During the last decades of the eighth century B.C., Phoenician and Greek inventors in shipbuilding intensified Mediterranean communications. Phalanx infantry, a pattern of battle formation and armament which had originally been brought by the Assyrians to their Phrygian and Lydian allies, finally spread to the Greek motherland from southwestern Asia Minor. This tactic, adapted by the Greeks, gradually made the small, free Hellenic infantryman more important politically and strategically than the horsed aristocrat of the preceding centuries.

The Greek invention of the coin, near 650 B.C., first being struck in electrum, then in silver and gold, and the subsequent rise of early Greek coin economy revolutionized capital investment in agriculture, mining, craftsman's workshops, trade, and banking operations. The output of Corinthian, Attic, and other pottery for export throughout the Mediterranean area was stimulated and greatly increased. The issues of small silver denominations, which began in Aegina and Corinth slightly before 600 B.C., made possible small savings and, especially, domestic trade without clumsy and wasteful barter operations. By these means, the hardworking and thrifty mass of free Greek *polis* citizens gradually was made independent in their economic aims from their ruling aristocratic families. The Greek phalanx and the Greek coin economy became, in fact, the main forces which stimulated the nascent Greek democracy and small farming.

FROM *ca.* 560 TO 333 B.C.

The earlier structural revolution of Hellenic town and agricultural societies was imitated intensively by non-Greeks from the time of King Croesus of Lydia. The Greeks themselves advanced to a period of classical refinement in all spheres of human life, especially by introducing the principles of reason, logic, and the analysis of cause and effect into all suitable patterns of human activity. The capital which could be invested by society in changing the appearance of cities and countryside increased, mainly because of the creation of world currencies, such as the Attic silver money, which was accepted from Spain to India, but also owing to professional bankers, nautical loans, and *Giro* transfers in bookkeeping that made their appearance in Greece and Babylonia.

The prices of agricultural products rose not only in Hellas between the sixth and the fourth centuries B.C. but also in Babylonia, an indication of increased demand from growing city populations in West and East. The Greek *poleis* of the period were characterized by scientific and rational town building and town planning and by well-made harbor and dock buildings, aqueducts, roads, light-fires, and large workshops of craftsmen with some division of labor (*ergasterion*). We even find the Athenian *deigma*, a clearing-house and exchange for samples of import goods, or the Athenian agora, a permanent and large market with stands for the traders in accordance with their goods. Agorai of this kind were to be the models for the similarly organized bazaars of the Hellenistic-Roman era and those of the Oriental Middle East in our own time. Even artificial harbor basins were excavated. Sailing ships were as quick then as they were until A.D. 1500 or so.

As recent excavations in Austria have made certain, the Celtic inhabitants of the Alps invented the horseshoe about 400 B.C., gradually to be accepted in western Europe during the following centuries as an assistance to overland transport. Earlier, this revolutionary transport invention enabled Celtic cavalry to annihilate a Roman army on the Allia, to sack Rome in 387 B.C., and to annihilate the cavalry and phalanx of Macedonia in 278 B.C. The carefully excavated silver mines of Laurium in Attica and the contemporary Attic inscriptions which are concerned with this mining district are witnesses to numerous technical and economic improvements and well-thought-out legal provisions in this important field of primary production.

Agriculture in Greek *polis* territory also was made more logical and more rational. The use of manure in various forms and of special seeds and breeds of animals, the timing of plowing, seeding, and harvesting, the administration of and the bookkeeping for small and large agricultural estates were treated as a fine art and, during the fourth century B.C., stimulated mankind's first scientific agricultural treatises. Three-field crop rotation, which was generally made use of during the Hellenistic age, appears to be alluded to, in a much-discussed inscriptional rent contract from Euboea, as early as the fourth century B.C.

In Italy, Roman colonization began systematically and permanently during the second quarter of the fourth century B.C. In its gradual advance it revolutionized agriculture throughout the peninsula. As early as the sixth and fifth centuries B.C., the wet, but fertile, soils near the mouth of the Tiber and throughout central Italy had been drained and opened for intensive agriculture, especially with the help of the so-called *cuniculi*. The cat, originally only a domesticated animal of Egypt, appeared then in Etruria also, to spread into Greece and over the whole world during the following period.

The structural changes in the Greek *polis* territories of the period would not have been possible without an enormous increase in the number of slaves for agricultural, industrial, and mining employment. Slavery, however, with the exception of mining and a few other fields of labor, was still comparatively humane. Free men were permitted to take residence wherever they wished, to go to law on their own responsibility, and to work as long and in whatever field of activity they wished, and they were protected against seizure as property. As Professor Westermann proved in an illuminating analysis of Delphic inscriptions (1943), the Greek master could give his slaves three of the "four freedoms" without legally freeing them. Even Roman slavery was still rather patriarchal. Freed slaves of Roman masters could expect their children to be treated as full citizens. Only during the subsequent period and under the influence of a strict interpretation of Roman law was slavery to become that scourge of mankind which was to destroy the happiness and even the lives of millions between 201 and 31 B.C. and to menace the population structure of classical antiquity.

FROM 333 TO 31 B.C.

Alexander the Great established Macedonian government and Hellenic influence as far to the east as the Indus region and present-day Chinese Turkestan. The Ganges region in India was subjected temporarily by Indo-Bactrian kings of Greek descent after 200 B.C. or so. Ptolemaic kings of the third century B.C. had occupied Zanzibar, parts of the coasts of East Africa and southern Arabia, and parts of the Sudan. The seaway to India had been discovered in 117–116 B.C. with the help of the monsoon. Finally, Rome began to conquer and colonize Spain (from 209 B.C. onward), North Africa (from 146 B.C. onward), the central and northern Balkan Peninsula (from 229 B.C. onward), and Gaul (from 125 B.C. onward). By these means was the geographical and anthropogeographical structural revolution, characteristic of early Greco-Roman development, intensified over a comparatively large part of the earth.

A central region of refined civilization (from Babylonia to Italy and Sicily) was surrounded by a larger, outer zone (from the Ganges to the Atlantic) of assimilated barbarian kingdoms, Greek colonial states, and Roman outer provinces and subject allies, in which there were islands of *polis* economy or Roman municipal settlements from which the know-how of Hellenistic and Roman agriculture was gradually appropriated by the native villagers. This was not a period of capital growth pure and simple; there also were considerable capital destruction and waste of capital, owing mainly to the Roman wars of conquest after 201 B.C., the civil wars, the slave-hunting, and the exploitation which characterized Roman provincial administration from 201 to 31 B.C.

World currencies like the "Attic" currency of Alexander the Great and most of his successors, the "Phoenician" currency of the Ptolemies, and, finally, the "Attic" Roman denarius and its many subject currencies made capital transfers easy. The first two coin issues were trimetallic, gold, silver, and bronze being comparatively well adjusted to one another, a pattern of refinement reached by Rome as late as the time of Julius Caesar. For the surprisingly modern capital-investing and generally economic planning of the Hellenistic empires in town, agricultural, and mining production, we have very instructive evidence from the kingdom of Syracuse, from Ptolemaic Egypt (with the largest banking organization of antiquity), from the Seleucid Empire, and from the Hellenistic India of the Arthashastra of Kautilya.

During the third century B.C. much capital was brought to the Middle East, where the interest rate for capital investments was at least three times as high as in the Greek motherland. The capital destruction during the two subsequent centuries of Roman supremacy was cushioned by new colonization and town foundations in Italy and the West. In addition, a new type of money appeared, the bill of exchange, payable to any bearer, quite possibly rejuvenated and Hellenized from unknown ancient Oriental survivals of the cuneiform bearer instruments of the second millennium B.C. Three such documents are known from Ptolemaic Egypt during the second and first centuries B.C. (*Strassburg Ostraka* 510; *Papiri di Regale Università di Milano I*, No. 25 and especially *Papyrus Rylands Library IV*, No. 580); a number of much-discussed references about capital transfer transactions in Plautus and Cicero now have to be reinterpreted in the light of this new evidence.

Planned colonization, general economic planning, world currencies, and the novel bills of exchange made possible a changed appearance of the cities and even more of the countryside from Spain and Gaul to India and Turkestan. The coastal cities, especially in the Mediterranean area, came under the influence of an intensive foreign trade, with cheap mass products, an intensi-

fied market and domestic trade, and comparatively large workshops, with, in some cases, as many as three hundred or so employees and slaves, which often produced for trade over large distances. Campanian bronze vessels and iron tools of the period are found in Scandinavia, for instance, and Mediterranean textiles in Mongolia. Port, dock, and harbor buildings, well-constructed light-fires, *deigmata*, permanent markets for trade and political assemblies, aqueducts, splendid private buildings of the rich, and the use of bricks and concrete for the dwellings of the poor characterized this brilliant and often well-planned Greco-Roman town development, the center of which moved from Greece and the Middle East to Italy during the second century B.C.

From the late fourth century B.C. onward, improved caravan routes in the Middle East and especially the famous network of Roman military roads made the still rather expensive overland communications of the world of classical antiquity more profitable than before. Hellenistic and Roman agriculture from Spain and Gaul to India owed much to Greek, Carthaginian, and, eventually, Roman agricultural science, but perhaps even more to Greek applied mathematics. Not only the Archimedian screw but also the *sakye*, and practically all other irrigation machines and devices which we now call typically Oriental, were, in fact, invented during the third century B.C. as a consequence of Hellenistic progress in mathematics. The *norag*, a new threshing device, was similarly useful, as were improved plows, sickles, and other agricultural tools.

Enormous territories, from the Middle East and North Africa to India and, perhaps, China, which could not be irrigated by the few already ancient Oriental devices for canals and irrigation, now were opened for agriculture and destined to remain in cultivation, on the whole, up to the present day. Mathematically improved water mills, wine and olive-oil presses, and other such devices had a similar importance for the agricultural production of Roman Italy and the Roman provinces from North Africa to the Rhine.

In addition, the agricultural plants and domesticated animal breeds of the whole enormous region from India to Spain and Gaul were now gradually exchanged, as far as the local climate permitted. Cotton came to Egypt, to Babylonia, and even occasionally to Aegean Greece. Apricot trees, lemon trees, melons, Asiatic cattle, and Egyptian cats, ducks, and geese appeared in Greece and Italy. Italy received, in addition, sesame, several clover species, nut, cherry, peach, certain plum, certain fig, quince, almond, chestnut, walnut, and other fruit and nut trees, cypresses, radish, flax, and beetroot. Still more important were the improvements of the period in breeding scientifically or importing superior breeds of horses, donkeys, camels, horned cattle, sheep, goats, pigs, dogs, cats, chickens, ducks, geese, pigeons, pheasants, peacocks, rabbits (from Spain), bees, and even outlandish fish and oysters, special vines, date and fig trees, olive plants, and grain varieties from everywhere in the world where climatic and market conditions made this possible.

Even China participated in this exchange of animals and plants to a smaller extent, receiving, during this period and that of the Roman principate, bloodstock horses, lucerne clover, vines, walnut seeds, pomegranates, peas, certain cucumbers and onions, coriander, and other plants and animals in exchange for the apricot tree, perhaps the peach tree, and goldfish. The reason for these revolutionary changes in the agricultural pattern of the countryside from the Atlantic to the Yellow Sea was that a change-over from subsistence to market farming characterized enormous territories of the globe during the Hellenistic age and that of the Roman Republic.

Wherever market economy had become profitable, the small and almost self-sufficient peasant estates of earlier centuries were on the retreat. In Egypt, Sicily, Hellenistic India, and large provinces of the Seleucid kingdom, economic agricultural planning by the state bureaucracy treated, to a very far degree, the small and the (not much freer) large agricultural units of the regions in question as subordinated economic entities of a centrally organized, provincial state agriculture. In those regions of the Carthaginian Empire, of Italy, and of the Roman provinces where the new agricultural market economy was profitable, large independent slave estates, the much-discussed latifundia, took the place of numerous small, free peasant homesteads. In both groups of territories scientific, rational agriculture was promoted and was expounded simultaneously in textbooks like those of Theophrastus, the Carthaginian Mago, and the Latins Cato and Varro.

Agricultural tools, agricultural methods (manure, two crops in one year, three-field crop rotation, summer and winter grazing of cattle, vegetable production, wine and olive production, and much more), estate and territorial planning, training of especially qualified servants, and the building of complementary estate workshops for products of craftsmanship were carefully adapted to the most recent and most profitable textbook advices. Destructive tendencies were not wholly missing during this period. The population of the Mediterranean area decreased between 201 and 31 B.C., owing to the Roman wars of conquest, civil wars, social revolutions, and slave-hunting. In Greece and Egypt a reduction of the area under agriculture and of the size of village and town settlements appears from archeological excavations. This temporary loss was more than made good by the population growth and colonial activity in the *imperium Romanum* of the first and second centuries A.D.

The fertility potential of the soil was, however, rarely endangered in classical antiquity. The plows and other agricultural tools of the period were not strong enough to cause what we now call soil destruction. A visit to any museum where Greco-Roman agricultural instruments are preserved will bear this out. In Greece proper and in similar hilly and mountainous subtropical regions which were conquered by Rome and depopulated by slave-hunting, the hillsides, which were steep but still suitable for vineyards, olive plants, vegetable gardens, or modest fruit trees, became barren wasteland. These artificial terraces, which had replaced forest and undergrowth during the Bronze and especially the earlier Iron ages, were no longer protected by the farmer's watchfulness against rain, which gradually washed away the small amount of subsoil held in place by human endeavors.

Malaria was introduced into Sicily during the fourth century B.C. and into Italy during the Second Punic War, in both cases by Carthaginian soldiers from North Africa. Thereafter, this endemic disease of the Apennine Peninsula is the probable reason why the Maremma of Etruria and the Pontine marshes in the Romagna were abandoned by peasant homesteaders from the early second century B.C. onward. However, the main part of Italy, with the exception of these and some other fertile fenlands, was not seriously affected before the Middle Ages by this much-discussed scourge of mankind. Neither did the latifundia, as we know now for certain, destroy the natural soil fertility of any part of Italy, although

damage from overgrazing on estates devoted to cattle-breeding would have been imaginable in theory.

That this is so can be proved irrefutably, to our surprise, in opposition to majority opinions of modern experts, with the help of the aerial survey of practically the whole of Italy taken during World War II by the Royal Air Force of Great Britain; the negatives of this strategic survey are now preserved in Oxford and are accessible to interested scholars. According to these air photographs, the fertility and the extent of the originally cultivated agricultural soil, even in now desolate Apulia, were never impaired in antiquity.

There appear in these photographs evidences of the primitive round huts of the pre-Roman natives of the Bronze and Iron ages. The numerous ditches and walls of the agricultural *centuriatio* of the simultaneously Roman military and agricultural *coloniae*, in the times of the so-called Second and Third Samnite Wars, can be outlined. The second century B.C., the time of the changeover from subsistence to market farming in many parts of Italy, brought into being larger units of land, yet practically all the earlier peasant plots remained in cultivation under old and new owners. Even during the thirteen or so centuries of the periods of the Roman principate, the late Roman Empire, and the earlier Middle Ages, Apulia and other now desolate regions of southern Italy and Sicily remained fertile peasant country. The British air photographs, supporting trial excavations, and documents forgotten in Italian archives until a few years ago have now irrefutably made obvious this conclusion. Spanish destructive methods of sheep-breeding after A.D. 1300, and not Roman or early medieval agricultural mismanagement and maladministration, are the real cause for the present emptiness of many regions of the southern Italian country-side.

FROM 31 B.C. TO A.D. 284

The period of the Roman principate from Augustus to Carinus is Janus-faced. The enormous Empire territory, from the Wall of Hadrian in Britain to the Euphrates and from the Sahara, the first Nile cataract, Aden, and Zanzibar to the eastern banks of the Rhine, the southern banks of the Danube, the Carpathians of modern Romania, and the regions to the north, east, and west of the Black Sea, was filled with more city settlements than ever before, far into the third century A.D. On the other hand, as early as the reign of Emperor Hadrian these cities began to shrink in size and population, a gradual process which was accelerated during the troubles of the third century A.D., to the point when hundreds, if not thousands, of such town settlements had to be abandoned forever.

The intellectuals of the period were proud of the splendor, the standard of life, and the civilization which manifested itself in the cities of the Roman Empire. They did not realize that the permanent structural changes of their age were to be found not in the cities but in the despised agricultural sector of the Roman world, where more than 90 per cent of the inhabitants of the Roman Empire found employment and livelihood. The reason for the striking and unintentional shrinking of the cities was that the capital and labor potential at the disposal of the Roman Empire authorities for urbanizing their world was totally insufficient.

The Roman silver and gold currency, which Augustus finally reorganized, and its subsidiary provincial currencies were sadly depleted during the three centuries from Augustus to Carinus as a consequence of the generally passive trade balance of the Empire. Contemporary authors and numerous Roman coin hoards from northern Germany, Scandinavia, southern Russia, Scotland, Ireland, southern Arabia, Iran, the Russian Caucasus, western Siberia, and especially India bear witness to this. From Augustus to Marcus Aurelius, the ratio of copper to silver was stabilized at 1:56 or so; that of silver to gold fluctuated between 1:12 and 1:9 or so. In the fourth century A.D., on the other hand, we find a ratio of copper to silver of 1:125; of silver to gold fluctuating at between 1:14 and 1:18. According to these figures, much more than half of the silver and much more than two-thirds of the gold which had circulated in Roman territory during the reign of Augustus had left the Mediterranean world, mainly during the time from Nero to Carinus.

The canals, roads, harbor works, and docks which were constructed from Britain to the Euphrates during the first, second, and even the troubled third centuries A.D. were very numerous. Many of them were never destroyed or could be restored easily, proving to be very useful in maintaining the standards of the mainly agricultural and the nascent town economies of the early Middle Ages. Nevertheless, these means of communication were not sufficiently numerous and not sufficiently well planned to maintain free trade, with cheap mass products, between the town communities of the Empire from Britain to the Euphrates in the same intensity as had been characteristic for the centuries from *ca.* 560 to 31 B.C. As early as about A.D. 100 most of the colonized Roman provinces in the east and west and even much smaller subdivisions of some Roman provinces had become practically self-sufficient economic units as far as the production and trade of cheap mass products were concerned.

From the reign of Emperor Hadrian onward, interprovincial free trade was largely restricted, owing to the unbeatable local competition in cheap goods, to the valuable and luxury products, and to government transports, for which captains and merchants had to be bound to their professions for an increasing number of cheap goods. For government transports overland the *cursus publicus,* the imperial government's permanent courier and transport service over the Roman road system, became such a terrible burden, owing to its increased use by the army and the bureaucracy, that settlements close to imperial relay stations were abandoned occasionally. On the other hand, trade inside of the more or less recently urbanized provinces, like Britain, Gaul, much of Spain and North Africa, the Alpine and Danubian provinces, eastern Asia Minor, and the province of Arabia, reached a relative intensity which, on the whole, was to be permanent and was never again to decline to pre-Roman and prehistoric levels, even under the impact of the most destructive migration waves of the early Middle Ages.

Local trade inside of and between the old and new villages of the Empire reached a similar intensity, which was to remain permanent in post-Roman times. During the second and third centuries A.D. the local trade and especially professional banking throughout the shrinking town settlements became so unprofitable, however, that the government authorities had to bind many such specialized traders and bankers to their professions to maintain all essential services for army. court, and Empire administration and to uphold, for the troubled town populations, at least an appearance of the intensity of local trade and banking transactions which had been characteristic of the Empire towns of the first century A.D.

As a consequence of the gradual strengthening of the new provinces and the efflorescence of the agricultural districts everywhere in the Empire, the considerable know-how of Hellenistic-Roman craftsmanship spread to all new towns and to villages and estates in the countryside from Britain to Arabia. The colonization efforts, which filled the Empire with towns, villages, country villas, and the redoubtable *limes* fortifications, signal systems, and strategic roads, which protected the peaceful settlers against foreign enemies, would not have been possible without concrete and the brickworks which sprang up throughout the provinces. More than that, new inventions, mostly connected with technical methods of using air for economic purposes, made Greco-Roman craftsmanship more efficient than ever.

Improved bellows not only made mining safer but led eventually to the production of true steel for the first time in human technical history, probably about the third century A.D. Windmills in suitable regions supplemented the earlier water mills, from the first or second centuries A.D. More important still was the invention of glass-blowing between 40 and 30 B.C., which occurred on the Mediterranean coast of either Egypt or Syria-Palestine. Cast glass had been known from the third millennium B.C., but its production costs had been too high to permit inexpensive use for non-luxury purposes. Henceforth, vessels made of cheap blown glass were to be found also in the village huts of the poor.

Glass sarcophagi and especially glass windows were used by the upper and even the middle classes of the Empire. Roman administration and proper town life would not have been possible in Britain, on both sides of the Rhine, and on the Danube without the imperial administrators and the well-to-do being protected against the Central European winter by glass windows, which permitted office work and reading at all times of the year. A completely novel industry of glass-making sprang up during the first century of the principate, mainly concentrated in Cologne, some other cities of Gaul, Rome and other Italian towns, Alexandria, Antioch, and several smaller cities of Syria and Asia Minor, achieving a permanent and most important contribution of classical antiquity to the well-being of medieval and modern mankind.

In the newly colonized and urbanized territories of the Roman Empire, the Hellenistic-Roman know-how in craftsmanship had been appropriated first by the city settlements, as is only natural. When these shrank in size again during the second and third centuries A.D., the government had, in the more ancient centers of civilization and in trade and banking, to bind many professional workers to their jobs to prevent endangering the safety of the Roman armies and the imperial administration. What happened simultaneously in the countryside was, however, of far greater historic importance than this process of decay in the cities.

Throughout the Empire the large estates which worked for foreign and local markets gradually expanded their own workshops for those crafts whose production was profitable and suitable for their economic pattern. The competition from the sale of the surplus of these estate workshops in near-by free markets endangered the livelihood of many city craftsmen throughout the Empire from the second century A.D. onward and induced many insufficiently employed town-dwelling craftsmen to take service on countryside estates. Through such newcomers the simple villagers, freeborn or slaveborn, were gradually instructed in all technical inventions and devices of classical antiquity which were apt to improve the peasant's standard of life and income.

The beauty of Samian and other pottery, of bronze, iron, steel, and glass tools, and some technical niceties of earlier mechanical devices were sacrificed to local cheap production by village and estate craftsmen. As a result,

however, the average villager throughout the Empire of the Roman principate had more technical comfort at his disposal than had the Athenian *polis* proletarian during the period from the Persian Wars to Pericles or than had the Roman city proletarian at the time of the Gracchan brothers. More important still, the difference between the standards of life of a small and dependent farmer in the countryside of the Empire of the Roman principate and that of the contemporary city proletarian had become negligible, except if in Rome, Alexandria, Antioch, and two or three other famous centers which were well cared for by the government.

This process was intensified by the agricultural changes of the period, which took place, in regional variation, during different decades of the first, second, and third centuries A.D. With the help of the fully developed methods of Greco-Roman agricultural science and technique, large new territories were permanently taken into cultivation. In England the fertile fenlands of East Anglia were drained, and the Fosse and other still existing canals were constructed to transport grain from these and other imperial and private estates to the garrisons and camp followers in northern England and the Scottish Lowlands. Vineyards producing local and world-famous beverages were to be characteristic of the hilly countryside of Gaul and the Rhineland for all the future. The regions on both sides of the Danube were similarly opened up. In Holland the sea was brought under control as never before with the help of well-planned ditches and drainage systems. In the fenlands of East Anglia the Roman drainage works and many Romano-British villages survived beyond the time of Roman occupation, to be given up readily under the earlier and later Anglo-Saxon kings and, anyway, before the *Domesday Book* was compiled. In Holland the Roman ditches and canals were preserved and kept in good order by the Salian Franks but were unable to withstand the rising water levels of the early Middle Ages.

In regions bordering the deserts of North Africa and the Middle East, methods of agriculture were used which were successfully imitated by French colonizers in Algeria, Tunisia, and Morocco during the nineteenth and twentieth centuries. In these semiarid regions with slight soil moisture, olive plantations were kept alive for two or three years by transporting water from afar to new plantations. Once the roots of the olive plants reached the subsurface water, the very desert became habitable and profitable agricultural soil. In Egypt careful Roman flood-control measures and new irrigation canals made productive again those territories of the Nile country which had been given up as desert or marshlands during the last two centuries of Ptolemaic rule. In Transjordania, the Negev, and the Syrian Desert regions numerous new cisterns and irrigation systems preserved the life-giving water of heavy rainfalls for years and, exactly as at present again in the state of Israel, made settlements possible everywhere. The small Roman province of Mesopotamia, which was of the highest strategic importance, was most thoroughly colonized during the third century A.D. Here and in Britain urban decline was delayed up to the fifth century A.D.; in Roman Arabia, even into the sixth century A.D. In Italy and elsewhere there occurred a novel wheeled plow.

The agricultural plants and domestic animals which had been adapted to the countries from Babylonia and Syria to Italy during the preceding period were now used everywhere in the Roman Empire, as far as the climate permitted, first on large estates and on agricultural soil annexed to the new town settlements and thereafter by the simple villagers. The slave estates of the preceding period vanished, however, as early as the period of Augustus and his immediate successors. The *pax Romana*, which the world owed to the first princeps, made slave-hunting of the earlier profitable *en gros* pattern impossible, and the numbers of cheap slaves from victorious campaigns of conquest were reduced to a trickle. In consequence, the market price of slaves soon rose so high that to employ menial agricultural slaves in large numbers became unprofitable.

Only rump estates, therefore, were cultivated scientifically with the help of a comparatively small number of unfree agricultural and household servants and a library containing the main agricultural textbooks of the past and present. The largest part of the latifundia of the republican centuries and of their successors in the provinces were instead farmed out to small peasants, in modern times all usually called *coloni*. They had to pay a contractual rent and took over some contractual work on the main estate. They received some technical agricultural advice from the experts on the main estate, and were gradually offered contracts on imperial and private estates which covered not only the lifetime of an individual farmer but even those of his sons and grandsons.

Furthermore, it was now profitable for many estate owners and imperial estates to free experienced agricultural slaves, permit them to marry, and to provide them contractually with land as *coloni*. Germanic and Eastern prisoners of war were similarly settled on imperial and private estate soil, although with some police supervision and without the legal protection given to Roman citizens and provincials in good standing. On many of the plots of the *coloni*, subsistence farming more or less gradually replaced market farming again, but without the agricultural production potential and the technical comfort of the Roman Empire peasantry, relapsing to pre-Hellenic, pre-Roman, or pre-historic levels.

Owing to the troubles of the third century A.D., the latifundia of the time of the principate, with their rump estates and *coloni,* often changed over from imperial administration or from a rich city-dwelling owner to proper *patrocinia.* Army officers retired to such estates as their permanent abode, maintained mercenary, private guard units (*bucellarii*), and protected their lands and those of their *coloni* not only against foreign invaders and inimical and friendly army units appearing in their region but also against visits from the imperial tax-collectors. Gradually, numerous free villagers, unbearably oppressed by plundering soldiers and the tax-collectors, voluntarily ceded their lands to owners of neighboring *patrocinia,* to be protected as *coloni.* The *patrocinium* owners, as a rule, knew how to use their influence at the imperial court and, with the provincial administration, to obtain permission to collect all taxes from their *coloni* directly and to pay no more than a fixed lump sum from the whole *patrocinium* territory into the imperial treasury.

The native barbarians everywhere outside of the Empire's frontiers, with the exception of the inhabitants of the Parthian kingdom, had so far been completely unable to transplant and adapt to their own needs the pattern of the Greco-Roman city settlements without becoming Roman allies. The new Empire peasantry, however, with their semiscientific technical know-how, village craftsmanship, and use of a wide variety of agricultural tools, plants, and domesticated animals, could be imitated more easily, especially as prisoners of war from all neighboring barbarian countries had been trained as *coloni* in Roman agricultural production by Roman masters. It is not surprising under these circumstances that, from the

second century A.D., agriculture in Ireland, Scotland, free Germany, Scandinavia, eastern Europe, and western Siberia began to include the tools, plants, animals, and technical methods of classical antiquity.

The coasts of East and West Africa, the Sudan, Abyssinia, the more backward regions of the Middle East, the Arabian Peninsula, and Iran had been subject to similar trends from the third century B.C. and continued their agricultural refinement with stronger intensity than before. This is borne out by the results of excavations and by the thousands of technical words which are early intruders from Latin and Greek into practically all languages of Europe, North Africa, and western Asia and are connected with Greco-Roman agriculture and simple craftsmanship. A revolution of village life and village production began in a territory many times larger than the Roman Empire. Gradually, in this way, the agricultural foundations for the Western, Islamic, and Russian medieval civilizations were laid.

The population of the Roman Empire under the principate at the time of Augustus amounted to between fifty and seventy millions, an estimate which has been accepted tentatively by the overwhelming majority of experts. The shrinking of the city settlements (with the exceptions mentioned on p. 175). almost everywhere throughout the Roman Empire during the third century A.D. has led many scholars to the assumption that this was a period of considerable population decrease, similar to that which has been guessed for those late Roman centuries during which comparably troubled conditions prevailed. especially in Gaul, Britain, Spain, and North Africa. Unfortunately, our sources do not permit absolutely certain conclusions to this difficult question.

Excavations show that, different from the urban development, the number of peasant plots and villages certainly did not decrease during the third century A.D., as Germanic and other prisoners of war replaced in large numbers possible losses from the serious civil wars and foreign invasions of this period. In addition, the Greco-Roman practice of exposing newborn babies to die was virtually discontinued wherever the population masses turned to Christianity. Therefore, it seems rather likely that the population of the Roman Empire, if it did not increase, at least held its own during the third century A.D., as the late Professor Delbrueck maintained (1921) from mainly strategic considerations. Recent research by Professor Kahrstedt (1954), on the population numbers on estates which had taken the place of some small earlier *poleis* in Greece proper, leads to similar conclusions for the second and third centuries A.D., as far as the province of Achaia is concerned. At any rate, the Roman Empire seems to have gained in the agricultural sector at least as much during the third century A.D. as it lost in the town settlements.

FROM A.D. 284 TO 565

The late Roman period, from our point of view, cannot be classified as a time of outright decline. It is true that the great Emperor Diocletian and his successors, during the fourth and fifth centuries A.D., were able only to strengthen and maintain city life in their dominions by asking for very serious sacrifices from practically all inhabitants of the Roman Empire. The help of extensive and permanent state assistance given to most towns of the Empire and state control over the agricultural sector upheld a minimum for Empire defense and civilized Empire administration. In the subsequent eastern Roman Empire, however, city life recovered and came into its own again as early as the fifth and sixth centuries A.D. Constantinople and other eastern Roman town centers continued to increase in size.

Even in territories, like Britain, which were lost to the Empire, money economy and local money trade remained to a noticeable extent, at least regionally. Our museums today include the so-called *minimi* and *minimissimi*, tiny bronze coins issued by local, and probably private, mints for small shopping transactions of the population after the Roman administration had left Britain in the early fifth century A.D. and all Roman mints had closed down. Diocletian and Constantine the Great, early in our period, were able to create a gold currency, that of the solidus, or the later bezant, which was essential for trade transactions of the world from Scotland and Scandinavia to India and from Russia to Abyssinia for more than a full millennium and which was not adulterated or diminished in weight for almost a thousand years.

For bills of exchange, known for the later part of the period from Alexander to Augustus, we cannot prove, on the basis of present evidence, that they survived into the earlier or later centuries of the time of the principate. Since the fifth century A.D., however, bearer documents are mentioned again in the Talmuds, Iranian, Arabic, and Byzantine sources, indicating a rejuvenation of money and town economy in the eastern Mediterranean area. These late Roman and Oriental bearer documents are the models for the bills of exchange in Latin, which initiated medieval conditions in this field in Frankish western Europe.

Foreign trade in cheap mass products was almost exclusively organized by the Roman state during the first two centuries of the period but gradually stood again on its own feet in the eastern Roman Empire from the fifth and sixth centuries A.D. onward. Only to the west of Constantinople, in the same period, was local city trade and banking on the downgrade. Trade in luxury products increased in intensity during the late Roman period in the west and east, and new products, like Asiatic and Mediterranean silk, supplemented the earlier valuable products. Naval transport conditions and overland transport on most Roman roads were inferior only in times of war to those of the second and third centuries A.D. Overland transport was even improved during the Byzantine centuries when the originally Chinese inventions of saddle and stirrup gradually became known in the eastern Mediterranean area and subsequently farther west. Many technical peculiarities of Greco-Roman craftsmanship came more and more to be used in villages. Special skills which were not profitable in the agricultural sector were kept alive and often improved in the famous imperial factories, mainly of Constantinople, where privileged craftsmen worked for the requirements of the imperial court, the army and navy, the administration, and occasionally private buyers.

Neither were technical inventions and new professions of craftsmen missing. Better steel was now made. The earliest chemical formulas preserved on papyrus are known from the early fourth century A.D. The first reference to Greek fire, a potent mixture of unburned chalk, petrol, and saltpeter, belongs to approximately A.D. 500. An independent silk weavers' craft began to develop after A.D. 552–53. Numerous craftsmen of various professions were resident on the soil of the *patrocinia* and worked for local needs. More important, still, was a completely novel, late Roman type of economic unit which combined many professions of craftsmanship with agriculture.

In Egypt of the early fourth century A.D., monasteries sprang up in which manual labor was considered to be a religious duty. In large Egyptian units of this kind, like the "White Monastery," there were more craftsmen at work in a co-ordinated manner than in any Greek *ergasterion* or Roman *fabrica* of earlier centuries. As far as agriculture was concerned, such monasteries had access to all Greek and Latin works on agricultural science or related subjects, either in the original or in translations into an oriental language of the Middle East. These monasteries proved especially able in making desert lands or, from the sixth century A.D. onward in the West, forest, fen, and other waste lands as fertile as the climate and the agricultural knowledge of their time permitted. Many monasteries even specialized in this backbreaking work of agricultural colonization.

It is well known that, after tentative experiments in Italy, the Provence, Spain, and North Africa, the Benedictine monasteries of the sixth century A.D. finally found the pattern by which this originally Egyptian form of religious community life could become an integral stimulus for the western Middle Ages. They prevented any real collapse of civilization in the countryside and even the earliest cities, any far-reaching agricultural deterioration even in troubled times, or any permanent abandonment of potentially fertile soil. Here, in this and in many other fields of activity, it is obvious that late Roman agriculture was as active and open to improvements as in earlier ages, in spite of all the difficulties and troubles of the time of migrations in West and East.

The silkworm and the specialized, intensive cultivation of the mulberry plant were introduced into the eastern Roman Empire from Central Asia in A.D. 553 or so. New types of cucumber, better breeds of dogs, "Arabic" horses, camels, and hunting birds were produced, and the number and specialization of agricultural tools further increased. The inherited agricultural textbooks were supplemented by new works and by more or less modernized and embellished translations. Modern authors often have expressed severe judgments about late Roman agricultural conditions, because serfdom of the originally free *coloni*, which had begun during the third century A.D., became practically universal during the fourth and the early fifth centuries A.D., swallowing up most of the free villagers also.

But one usually forgets that this development was only temporary as far as the eastern Roman Empire was concerned. Feudalism was suppressed to a very marked degree, and the binding of the peasant to an estate was lifted or mitigated from the sixth century A.D. onward, a change which was strongly supported by the Christian church. In the seventh century A.D., Byzantine peasantry was organized, as a rule, into military (*themata*) and civilian villages and was practically free again. The beginnings of this structural change of great world historic importance appear as early as the sixth century A.D., in the papyrus evidence from Egypt, in Chalcedonian and monophysitic church authors of the sixth and early seventh centuries A.D., and in the much-discussed agricultural reform legislation of Pope Gregory the Great.

Only the West, under Visigothic, Frankish, Burgundian, and Lombard rule, remained dedicated to peasant serfdom for political reasons during these centuries. But, even so, the population of the countryside certainly did not, as a rule, decrease, nor was soil fertility undermined. In the Frankish, Burgundian, and Alemannic territories and in Anglo-Saxon Britain, modern excavations have revealed numerous Germanic villages on the soil of earlier imperial and private Roman estates, evidence of numerous families making a living where only a small agricultural and administrative staff of servants had

dwelt before. Recently discovered Latin documents from Vandalic North Africa show that life was certainly not as much disturbed as Latin and Greek authors report for this area.

In Italy air photography has proved that, whatever damage Ostrogoths, Lombards, and Byzantine generals may have done to agriculture in the fifth and sixth centuries A.D., during temporary warlike operations, was repaired quickly, the Benedictine monasteries even improving regionally on the earlier state of affairs. Egyptian agriculture, as Professor Johnson recently has pointed out (Johnson and West, 1949), and likewise the agriculture of Syria and Palestine do not seem to have suffered at all, except from temporary Persian invasions. Transjordania and other semidesert territories of the Roman Middle East flourished more than ever, especially as these regions were a favorite haunt of eremites and monasteries and experienced, in addition, an enormous population increase from Arabic immigrants. This occurred long before Islam, a migration movement which was especially intensified after a dam break of Marib in A.D. 450, and the final collapse of the artificial irrigation system of southern Arabia between A.D. 542 and 570 diminished enormously the agricultural productivity of southern Arabia.

Asia Minor and the Greek-speaking, southern part of the Balkan Peninsula were made the center of the eastern Roman Empire during this period and experienced in consequence a sizable increase in their town and village populations. The political weakness of the late Roman Empire in the east and west and the final loss of Italy, the western Roman provinces, the Roman Middle East, and the North Balkan regions was not caused by a permanent economic decline of the Empire structure or a population decrease. The main reason for this far-reaching political change was that the *imperium Romanum*, and also the Persian kingdom, had ceased to be the only civilized territories of the world outside of India and China.

The technical methods and the essentials of Greco-Roman civilization in their Christian reformulation were taken over during the last period of classical antiquity by practically the whole of Europe, large parts of western and Central Asia, East Africa, and Arabia. As a result, the military superiority of the Roman army was undermined, and Empire defense became more difficult and often impossible.

Finally, new civilizations arose in what is now the Islamic Middle East, in Abyssinia, in the Romance, Germanic, Celtic, and Western Slavic-speaking West, and in eastern Europe. These daughter-civilizations were, in the course of time, to surpass by far their Greco-Roman mother-civilization, albeit bringing, during their later history, soil destruction to more than one region which had flourished during classical antiquity.

REFERENCES

Where no special references are given below, the problems touched upon in this survey have been discussed in detail in:

HEICHELHEIM, FRITZ M.
   1939   *Wirtschaftsgeschichte des Altertums*, Vols. I and II. Leiden: Sijthoff. 1240 pp.

Of general surveys not mentioned in the pertinent notes of the above work, see especially:

ANONYMOUS
   1924–39   *Cambridge Ancient History.* 12 vols. Cambridge: Cambridge University Press.

BENGTSON, HERMANN
   1950   *Griechische Geschichte von den Anfängen bis in die römische Kaiserzeit.* ("Handbuch der Altertumswissenschaft," Vol. III, No. 4.) Munich: Beck. 592 pp.

BURY, JOHN B., and MEIGGS, RUSSEL
   1951   *A History of Greece to the Death of Alexander the Great.* 3d ed. London: Macmillan & Co. 926 pp.

CARY, MAX
   1954   *A History of Rome Down to the Reign of Constantine.* 2d ed. London: Macmillan & Co. 820 pp.

FRANK, TENNEY
   1933–40   *An Economic Survey of Ancient Rome.* 5 vols. Baltimore: Johns Hopkins University Press.

MICHELL, H.
   1940   *The Economics of Ancient Greece.* Cambridge: Cambridge University Press. 416 pp.

OSTROGORSKY, GEORG
   1940   *Geschichte des byzantinischen Staats.* ("Handbuch der Altertumswissenschaft," Vol. XII, Nos. 1–2.) Munich: Beck. 448 pp.

PREAUX, CLAIRE
   1939   *L'Economie royale des Lagides.* Brussels: Fondation Reine Élisabeth. 646 pp.

ROSTOVTZEFF, MICHAEL
   1951   *The Social and Economic History of the Hellenistic World.* 3 vols. Oxford: Clarendon Press. 1780 pp.

STEIN, ERNST
   1928   *Geschichte des spaetroemischen Reiches.* Vienna: Seidel. 592 pp.
   1949   *Histoire du Bas Empire.* Paris and Brussels: Desclée de Brouwer. 900 pp.

REFERENCES ON SPECIAL PROBLEMS

AGRICULTURE OF BYZANTINE EGYPT
AND VANDALIC AFRICA

COURTALS, CH.; LESCHI, L.; PERAT, CH.; and SAUMAGNE, CH.
   1952   *Tablettes Albertini: Actes privés de l'époque vandale (fin du Ve siècle),* Vols. I and II. Paris: Arts et métiers graphiques. 344 pp.

JOHNSON, ALLAN CH., and WEST, LOUIS C.
   1949   *Byzantine Egypt.* ("Princeton

University Studies in Papyrology," No. 6.) Princeton, N.J.: Princeton University Press. 344 pp.

AIR PHOTOGRAPHS OF ITALY

BRADFORD, JOHN
1947 "A Technique for the Study of Centuriation," *Antiquity*, XXI, 197–204.
1949 "Buried Landscapes in Southern Italy," *ibid.*, XXIII, 65–72.
1950 "The Apulia Expedition: An Interim Report," *ibid.*, XXIV, 84–95.
1955 *Ancient Landscapes in Europe and Asia: Studies in Archaeology and Photography.* Oxford: Oxford University Press. 164 pp.

BEGINNINGS OF COINAGE

ROBINSON, E. S. G.
1951 "The Coins from the Ephesian Artemision Reconsidered," *Journal of Hellenic Studies*, LXXI, 156–67.

COINAGE IN POST-ROMAN BRITAIN

SUTHERLAND, C. H. V.
1938 "Minimi, Radiate and Diademed," *Transactions of the International Numismatic Congress, 1936*, pp. 252–61. London: Quaritch.
1950 "The Canterbury Minimissimi Again," *Numismatic Chronicle*, 6th ser., IX, 242–44.

DATE OF THE FOUNDING OF ROME

GJERSTADT, EINAR
1952a "Stratigraphic Excavations in the Forum Romanum," *Antiquity*, XXVI, 60–64.
1952b "Scavi stratigrafici nel Foro Romano e problemi ad essi relativi," *Bulletino di Commissione Archeologica Communale di Roma*, LXXIII, 13–29.

HORSESHOE IN PREMEDIEVAL TIMES

HELL, MAX
1950 "Keltische Hufeisen aus Salzburg," *Archaeologia Austriaca*, VII, 92–95.
1953 "Weitere keltische Hufeisen aus Salzburg und Umgebung," *ibid.*, XII, 44–49.

MONASTERIES

HEICHELHEIM, FRITZ M.
1955a "Art Domaene," in KLAUSER, H. (ed.), *Reallexikon für Antike und Christentum*, Vol. III. 3 vols. Stuttgart: Hiersemann Verlag.
1955b "Roemische Sozial- und Wirtschaftsgeschichte," in VALJAVEC, F. (ed.), *Historia mundi: Ein Handbuch der Weltgeschichte in Zehn Bänden*, Vol. IV. Bern: A. Franke; Munich: Leo Lehnen.

PHALANX

STIER, HANS ERICH
1950 "Probleme der frühgriechischen Geschichte und Kultur," *Historia*, I, 195–230.

PLANNING ECONOMY OF THE HELLENISTIC MONARCHIES FROM INDIA TO SICILY

HEICHELHEIM, FRITZ M.
1938 "New Light on the Influence of Hellenistic Financial Administration in the Near East and India," *Economic History*, February, pp. 1–12.
1953 "The Wilbour Papyrus," *Historia*, II, 129–35.

POPULATION OF THE ROMAN EMPIRE UNDER THE PRINCIPATE AND DOMINATE

BOAK, ARTHUR E. A.
1955 *Manpower Shortage and the Fall of the Roman Empire in the West.* Ann Arbor: University of Michigan Press. 164 pp.

DELBRUECK, HANS
1921 *Geschichte der Kriegskunst*, Vol. II. 3d ed. Berlin: Stilke. 508 pp.

KAHRSTEDT, ULRICH
1954 *Das wirtschaftliche Gesicht Griechenlands in der Kaiserzeit.* ("Dissertationes Bernenses," Vol. I, No. 7.) Bern: A. Francke. 296 pp.

SLAVERY IN CLASSICAL GREECE

WESTERMANN, WILLIAM L.
1943 "Slavery and the Elements of Freedom in Ancient Greece," *Quarterly Bulletin of the Polish Institute of*

Arts and Sciences in America, January, pp. 1–16.

1955 *The Slave Systems of Greek and Roman Antiquity.* ("Memoirs of the American Philosophical Society," Vol. XL.) Philadelphia. 180 pp.

SOUTH ARABIAN IRRIGATION COLLAPSE

GROHMANN, ADOLF

1930 In PAULY-WISSOWA, *Realencyklopaedie der klassischen Altertumswissenschaft,* XIV, 1736–44. Stuttgart: Metzler. 2,584 pp.

The Clearing of the Woodland in Europe

H. C. DARBY*

Perhaps the greatest single factor in the evolution of the European landscapes has been the clearing of the wood that once clothed almost the entire continent. The presence of woodland, and the effort to use it or subdue it, has been a constant motif throughout the history of successive centuries; and the struggle has left a mark, often upon the form and intensity of human settlement, and always upon the general character of the landscape. The attack, begun in prehistoric times, has been continued from innumerable centers, and, little by little, as population has grown, the wood has given way to pasture and to arable land. But the clearing has not been a continuous or sustained process, for at times the forest has reasserted itself and crept back. Nor has the clearing been complete, for substantial tracts of wood still remain. But the net result has been ever more open space; and man, driven by economic motives, and as if relenting at the success of his attack, is now seeking to stay, or at any rate to regulate, the clearing and to place the care of forests upon a rational basis. "The woods"—their de-struction and its consequences and the need for a policy of conservation—was one of the main themes of George P. Marsh's *Man and Nature,* which first appeared in 1864.

Broadly speaking, the clearing has had its own characteristics in each of the three regions of European history—Southern Europe, Central and Western Europe, and Eastern Europe. Although this division into three is not very precise, it is a convenient one. In Southern Europe, under Mediterranean conditions of climate and soil, the forest was open in character and was composed largely of evergreen oaks and pines. Once cleared, it showed less regenerative power than did the forests to the north; already by classical times much of it seems to have disappeared, leaving behind scrub and, in places, bare surfaces exposed to soil erosion. In the second region, in Western and Central Europe, the temperate forest zone is dominated by the oak, mixed with a variety of other deciduous trees, including the beech, but giving way to conifers on the higher ground. It was not until the Middle Ages that the main outlines of the clearing of this dense woodland were sketched, and the story of that clearing is relatively much better documented than the story elsewhere in Europe. The third region is that of Eastern Europe, with which the north may be linked. The mixed forest of Central Europe stretched into this region, but without the beech, which may be regarded as an indicator of the

* Dr. Darby is Professor of Geography in the University of London and Head of the Department of Geography at University College, London. He is a member of the Royal Commission on Historical Monuments (England). He edited *An Historical Geography of England before A.D. 1800,* 1936, and his publications include: *The Medieval Fenland,* 1940; *The Draining of the Fens,* 1940; and *The Domesday Geography of Eastern England,* 1952.

contrast between peninsular and continental Europe (Fig. 54). In the south lie the steppes which, if they ever bore forests (and they may well have), must have been cleared in preclassical times. In the north lies the coniferous belt where agriculture is restricted and where man's impression has been relatively slight.

Fig. 54.—Europe: limits of certain trees

THE MEDITERRANEAN LANDS

Classical Times

The difference between the climate of the Mediterranean Basin and that of the rest of Europe is striking. The rainfall of the three summer months (June, July, August) rarely exceeds six inches, and in many areas it is less than two. The northward limit of the olive follows very closely that of truly Mediterranean conditions (Fig. 54). As a result of this climate, the characteristic Mediterranean forest grows in open formation and is largely evergreen in character; it comprises such species as the Aleppo pine and various kinds of evergreen oak, particularly the holm oak and the valonia oak. To what extent the Mediterranean lowlands were originally covered by forest is uncertain, but it is clear that there was, and is, much local variation, with gradations northward into the dense deciduous woodlands of Central and Western Europe and south-

ward into the scatter of solitary, thorny, and spiny shrubs of steppe and desert. In the mountainous areas within the basin, the characteristic open forest gives way to a wood cover that resembles that to the north; here are the beech, the Spanish chestnut, and species of deciduous oak, and these, in turn, merge higher up into various kinds of fir mixed with, or dominated by, the black pine. This is so in the Pyrenees, the Alps, the Apennines, and the Balkan Mountains. The same succession in varying degrees is encountered in the higher parts of Sicily, the Peloponnesus, Crete, and Cyprus.

Classical writers provide abundant indications of the existence of wood (Semple, 1931). Homer, maybe as early as the ninth century B.C., spoke of "wooded Samothrace," of "wooded Zacynthos," of the "tall pines and oaks" of Sicily, and of other "wooded country." He told how Sarpedon fell in battle "as falls an oak or silver poplar, or a slim pine tree, that on the hills the shipwrights fell with whetted axes, to be timber for shipbuilding." And he described the noise of battle as "the din of woodcutters in the glades of a mountain." In another metaphor he compared the press of battle with the consequences of fire in this land of parched summers: "Through deep glens the fierce fire rages on some parched mountain-side, and the deep forest burns, and the driving wind whirls the flame every way."[1] Thucydides also knew of the consequences of forest fires and wrote of "spontaneous conflagrations sometimes known to occur through the wind rubbing the branches of a mountain forest together."[2] Once destroyed, whether by chance fire or by the hand

1. The references from Homer are as follows: *Iliad* xiii. 13; xvi. 482–84; xvi. 643–46; xx. 490–92 (see also x. 154–57; xxi. 340–49); *Odyssey* i. 246; ix. 186 (see also xiii. 243–46; xiv. 1–2).

2. Thucydides *History of the Peloponnesian War* ii. 77.

of man, the forest could regenerate itself only with difficulty, for the new growth found an implacable enemy in the goat. By the fifth century B.C. the destructive nibble of the goat up the mountainsides was already well advanced. Plato in the *Critias* provides us with a theory of the consequences of the destruction of wood. Not long since, he wrote, the soil of Attica was deep and carried "much forest-land." But its trees had disappeared, some to provide rafters for the roofs of Athenian buildings; and, as he wrote, Attica was a naked upland: "What now remains compared with what then existed is like the skeleton of a sick man, all the fat and soft earth having been wasted away, and only the bare framework of the land being left."[3]

But, although Attica was thus laid bare by the fifth century B.C., much of Greece, and indeed of the whole basin of the Mediterranean, was still well wooded. It was Theophrastus, who, in the following century, wrote the *Enquiry into Plants*, which provides us with considerable information about the forests of his time. He referred to the forests of the plains, but it is about the more important forests of the uplands that he gave us most detail. It was they that best produced "serviceable timber"; the trees, he wrote, "that grow on the level parts of the mountains are specially fair and vigorous; next to these come those which grow on the lower parts and in the hollows; while those that grow on the heights are of the poorest quality," presumably because of their stunted nature. He repeatedly referred to the timber of many parts of Greece and of western Crete. Beyond Greece, he noted the fir and pine of Latium and southern Italy, but he added that these were "said to be nothing to the trees of Corsica." Various species of trees were discussed and their suitability noted for shipbuilding and for housebuilding—for

rafters and beams, for yardarms, masts and keels, for making charcoal, and for "the carpenter's various purposes."[4]

In the centuries that followed, a variety of other classical authors fill out the picture of the Mediterranean forests, giving details about this locality or that. Strabo, in his *Geography*, at the beginning of the Christian Era, showed that the woods of many Mediterranean uplands still survived in abundance. In the west, the mountains of southeastern Spain were described as "covered with thick woods and gigantic trees," and these furnished timber for shipbuilding as well as other forest products, such as pitch and kermes berries. In the north the Spanish slopes of the Pyrenees were likewise "covered with forests containing numerous kinds of trees and evergreens," which yielded excellent hams (equal to those of the Cantabrians), presumably from the swine that fed in their shade. Marseilles was famous for shipbuilding; and, eastward, in the hinterland of Genoa, the Ligurian Mountains furnished "plenty of wood for the construction of ships." In the Po Basin the woods contained "such an abundance of mast, that Rome was principally supplied from the swine fed there"; the pitch works were "amazing," and so were the large casks produced for wine. The central Apennines and the hills of Etruria provided wood for the "ceaseless building" that went on in the Eternal City itself. In the southern Apennines the Sila Mountains yielded "fine trees" and the excellent pitch that was noted by many writers. Across the Straits of Messina, in Sicily, there were "woods and plantations of all kinds."[5] The Alps and Corsica, although Strabo

3. Plato *Critias* 111BC.

4. The references are from Theophrastus *Enquiry into Plants* Books iii, iv, and v, *passim.*

5. The references from Strabo's *Geography* are as follows: 3. 4. 2; 3. 2. 6; 3. 4. 11; 4. 1. 5; 4. 6. 2; 5. 1. 12; 5. 2. 5; 5. 3. 7; 6. 1. 9.

does not say so, were also prominent lumber regions at this time.[6]

Strabo's references to the forests of the eastern Mediterranean Basin are not so numerous, but he tells a story of Cyprus that may well have exemplified what had also happened elsewhere:

Eratosthenes says that anciently the plains abounded with timber, and were covered with forests, which prevented cultivation; the mines were of some service towards clearing the surface, for trees were cut down to smelt the copper and silver. Besides this, timber was required for the construction of fleets, as the sea was now navigated with security and by a large naval force; but when even these means were insufficient to check the growth of timber in the forests, permission was given to such as were able and inclined, to cut down the trees and to hold the land thus cleared as their own property, free from all payments.

Yet, even in Strabo's time, the western promontory of Acamus was covered by "a large forest." That the Macedonian forests were still in existence is evident from Strabo's references to "dockyards for shipbuilding" along the northern coast of the Aegean; Crete, too, could still be described as wooded.[7] That the Peloponnesus was also well wooded at this time we may assume from the fact that Pausanias' *Description of Greece,* written in the second century A.D., refers to trees (cypress, oak, and pine) on the plains as well as in the higher mountain regions. It was the same to the north of the Gulf of Corinth and in Boeotia.[8]

The general impression left by these and other classical authors is that the Mediterranean lands were then more densely wooded than they are today

but that already there had been considerable clearing and that the extensive forests which remained were for the most part in the mountainous areas. Toward the end of the classical period, in the economic crisis that befell the Roman Empire during the third and fourth centuries, the progress of clearing was halted. What is more, land that had once been tilled became derelict and overgrown. Lactantius, writing in about A.D. 300, said tersely: "The fields were neglected; cultivated land became forest" (Koebner, 1941, p. 24). By the end of the fourth century, in 395, large tracts of the once-fertile province of Campania, for example, were derelict, and this even before the war bands of the Goths and Vandals had set foot in the peninsula of Italy.[9]

Postclassical Times

It is difficult to construct, even in outline, a narrative of the vicissitudes of clearing in postclassical times. The conditions were so varied, and the record is incomplete; but the general facts are not in doubt (George, 1933; Parain, 1936; Turrill, 1929). When the Mediterranean region emerged from the confusion of the barbarian impact, we see men at work once more cutting down trees to satisfy the demands of agriculture, pasture, and industry and also for a variety of miscellaneous purposes.

In medieval Italy, for example, the cultivated area was extended slowly and laboriously, partly by diking and draining but also by clearing forest, and landowners encouraged such pioneering by offering favorable terms (Caggese, 1907–8, I, 157 ff.; II, 216 ff.). Not only were the lands of existing communities extended but new communities were founded in the wilderness by both lay and ecclesiastical land-

6. Pliny *Natural History* 16. 15, 16, 18, 29; 13. 15, 16.

7. The references from Strabo's *Geography* are as follows: 14. 6. 5; 14. 6. 2; Frags. 33 and 36; 10. 4. 4.

8. Pausanias *Description of Greece* **5. 6.** 4; 7. 26. 10; 8. 1. 6; 8. 11. 1; 8. 12. 1; 8. 38. 5; 8. 54. 5; 9. 24. 5; 10. 38. 9.

9. J. B. Bury (ed.), *Edward Gibbon's The History of the Decline and Fall of the Roman Empire* (London: Methuen & Co., 1897), II, 194.

lords. In this way was the fruitfulness of such places as inland Tuscany created.

The wood found an enemy not only in the cultivator but in the pastoralist. The practice of transhumance, so common in Mediterranean lands, meant that destruction by animals was extended over wide areas. In Spain the powerful organization of the Mesta, which controlled the large-scale annual migrations of Castilian flocks, was able to safeguard pasturage at the expense of the woodland; and, wrote Klein (1920, p. 307), "there can be no doubt that the Castilian forests suffered severely from the regular visits of the millions of migrating sheep." Various conservation measures adopted in the thirteenth century seem to have had some effect, but sixteenth-century descriptions contrast the naked desolation of Castile with the dense forests of the northern coast (*ibid.*, p. 321). In varying degrees, woodland elsewhere also suffered from the moving flocks and their shepherds. It was the same in Mediterranean France, in the hill country of the Apennines, and throughout the Balkans. Patsch gives instances (1922, pp. 23–26) of the deliberate destruction of forests and brushwood to provide new pasture throughout the Balkans. The havoc wrought by grazing lay not only in its destruction but also in its prevention of new growth. Even much of the bare karstlands were once wooded and could be made to carry trees once more if grazing animals were excluded.

Industry also took a heavy toll. The demands of tanning and of charcoal-making were important locally, and Patsch (*ibid.*, p. 28) has shown how destructive were the efforts of charcoal-burners in Herzegovina. The silver and copper mines of Serbia and Bosnia, the silver and quicksilver of Guadalcanal and Almaden in southern Spain, the iron of the Basque provinces, the iron

and the alum of the Italian Peninsula—all needed much timber. The coming of the railway brought new demands for its own purposes and also facilitated the transport of sawn timber elsewhere. But the greatest of the wood-devouring industries in the Mediterranean area may well have been shipbuilding. The medieval fleets of the Byzantine Empire, of Venice, Genoa, and other Italian maritime states, and of Catalonia were launched at the expense of the Mediterranean forest. The Venetian Republic might once have held "the gorgeous east in fee," but part of the price of this sovereignty was the bareness of the Adriatic coastlands; and during the fifteenth and sixteenth centuries Venice had to face the problem of diminishing timber supplies (Lane, 1934, p. 217; Turrill, 1929, p. 197). Along the eastern Adriatic shore was the city-republic of Ragusa, which has given us the word "argosy"; shipbuilding here was always an important industry, and its grand fleet denuded the forests of the mountains behind and of the islands near by. One of the complaints in her last dispute with Venice in 1754 was that the Venetians had illegally cut down wood in Ragusan territory (Villari, 1904, p. 328). Farther south timber was also being cut at this time, and Lord Broughton, who traveled here with Lord Byron, noted that "the woods of Albania, before the French revolution, furnished Toulon with timber for ship-building."[10] It was the same elsewhere in the Mediterranean area. Even Spain, in the days of the Armada, looked as far away as the Baltic for suitable timber (Albion, 1926, p. 183).

Warfare, both regular and irregular, increased the pace of destruction. Peter

10. J. C. Hobhouse (Baron Broughton), *A Journey through Albania, and Other Provinces of Turkey in Europe and Asia, to Constantinople, during the Years 1809 and 1810* (London: James Cawthorn, 1813), p. 74.

Mundy, in 1620, observed that "whole woods" of pine trees in western Bosnia were "cutt downe to the ground, To prevent Theeves that usually lurked amonge them."[11] During the Turkish wars of the 1870's and 1880's great stretches of timber were also felled, for strategic reasons, along the Bulgarian and Serbian frontiers.[12] At the other end of the Mediterranean, in Spain, much wood disappeared during the wars of the reconquest from the Moslems (Cánovas del Castillo, 1910, p. 43); and then again, during the Peninsular and Carlist wars, the woods that sheltered rebels and brigands were destroyed.

Much wood has also been cut for building, for fuel, and for a hundred and one domestic purposes. A frequent method of felling trees, in the Balkan Peninsula at any rate, was to make a fire at the base of a tree and burn through the trunk. It is not surprising that accidental forest fires were common in such a dry land. W. M. Leake, for example, recorded an accidental fire in southern Cephalonia: "The bare stems are now," he wrote in 1835, "conspicuous monuments of the misfortune."[13] It was not the first forest fire in Cephalonia, and such blackened monuments were also to be found in other places. Conifers were a source of resin, tar, and pitch, and Leake encountered an example of destructive exploitation in central Greece—"a forest which seems as if it would not long exist, as the greater part of the trees are in a process of destruction for the purpose of collecting their resin to make pitch"; hacked and wounded over a number of years, the trees could not survive.[14] In

the growth that followed the destruction of a pine forest, the beech with its dense shade frequently gained at the expense of the conifers; stumps of conifers are recorded in beech forests in the Shar Planina region on the Serbian-Albanian border. Or, again, Mount Pelion in Thessaly carried conifers in classical times, but they have been largely replaced by beech and oak (Turrill, 1929, p. 195).

The result of this interference, human and animal, coupled with the dry climate and the poor soil, is that much of the Mediterranean lands are covered by seminatural brushwood communities. The names given to this scrub in all its variations are many—*garrigue, maquis, macchie, matorral, monte bajo, phrygana*—and among its constituents are such aromatic shrubs as lavender, myrtle, rosemary, and thyme. The deciduous brushwood of the higher Balkan interior is known by the Serbian name of *shiblyak*. Varied by dwarf evergreens, this scrub is encountered from Portugal to the Dardanelles, and, with its associated pastures, it is the grazing ground of sheep and goats. Where the soil is thin or otherwise unfavorable, the vegetation becomes even more open, and bare rock appears between the stunted shrubs. The menace of soil erosion broods over the whole area. The development of state forest services and of programs of afforestation in the Mediterranean countries is the answer to this challenge, but the difficulties presented by the legacy of bare surfaces are formidable.

CENTRAL AND WESTERN EUROPE

Prehistoric and Roman Times

It has long been recognized that the heavier impervious soils carried great stretches of wood at the dawn of prehistory in Central and Western Europe; and it was thought, until recently, that the lighter soils, on the other hand, were open and treeless. Penck suggested that,

11. *The Travels of Peter Mundy, in Europe and Asia, 1608–1667* (Cambridge: Hakluyt Society, 1907), I, 84.

12. A. Stead, *Servia by the Servians* (London: Heinemann, 1909), p. 255.

13. *Travels in Northern Greece* (London: J. Rodwell, 1835), III, 59.

14. *Ibid.*, II, 380.

for example, Neolithic settlements were concentrated in loess country because it may have been as free from forest "as the prairies of the North American West" (1887, pp. 437–41). This was the thesis developed by Gradmann in a succession of publications (e.g., 1898, 1901, 1906, 1931). He believed that these early communities were almost incapable of clearing woodland and that, as a corollary, the areas which they colonized must have been forest-free, or, at any rate, only lightly forested. This open character he attributed to a dry climatic phase during the subboreal period (between about 2500 and 500 B.C.) that followed an earlier forest phase; it was the spread of steppe-heath conditions over the loess and other light soils that, according to this view, gave the Neolithic farmers their opportunity. It was a view that was widely accepted (e.g., by Hoops, 1905, p. 99).

But the development of the technique of pollen analysis (Godwin, 1934) brought with it the realization that even the lightest soils were not devoid of wood when farming first began and that, for example, so-called "natural heath" had its origin in the clearing of its wood by Neolithic farmers (Godwin, 1944b). The pollen of forest trees in many localities is abruptly replaced by that of other vegetation, and the light soils are revealed not as treeless steppes but as areas of vigorous tree growth (Tüxen, 1931; Garnett, 1945). Even the dry Alföld of the Hungarian plain, noted for its steppelike character in Europe, is said to have been originally wooded (De Soó, 1929, p. 335), although others have thought this view an exaggeration (Rungaldier, 1943, p. 55). Schott (1952, p. 266) likewise thinks that it is an exaggeration to attribute all the heaths along the coast of northwestern Germany to human interference; he believes that, in any case, they would have been formed on the poorest land as a result of a gradual deterioration of the soil.

We must then envisage the primitive landscape of Central and Western Europe as covered by a mantle of forest, broken only where the Alps, the Carpathians, and a few other mountains rose above the tree line, and where occasional stretches of country, for one reason or another, were too sterile or too marshy. It was a broad-leaved forest, where oak generally predominated, but mixed with such other trees as elm, beech, and lime, and with an undergrowth of hazel. In its shade lived some Mesolithic hunters and food-gatherers, opening up small areas for their dwellings, using tree trunks for boats, and finding in the forest both fruit and game (Childe, 1931).

With the advent of agriculture in Neolithic times, the wood in places was cleared partly by the ax and partly by fire. There is abundant evidence of the use of the flint or stone ax in Neolithic times, and modern experiment has shown that trees can be cut down relatively easily with these implements; a polished ax is superior to a chipped ax (Nietsch, 1939, p. 70). Flint mines supplied the material for the axes, and widespread trade contacts disseminated it. Grenier instanced (1930, p. 29) the large number of broken polished axes found when the wood around the spring of Bonnefontaine in Lorraine was cleared; it seems that the spring had attracted settlers who destroyed the wood around it and cultivated the land. In a later age the forest re-established itself, only to be cleared once more to reveal evidence of the earlier effort. The other method of clearing was by fire. Iversen found, in the bog of Ordrup in Denmark, a marked and widespread layer of charcoal at the level where forest pollen abruptly decreased; burning seems to have been followed by cultivation, for it is at this level that the pollen of cereals and of weeds appears. Here, suggests Iversen (1941), is an example of *Brandwirtschaft* and of forest clearance by Neolithic farmers.

Once a wood was cleared, whether by the ax or by fire, grazing by domestic animals must have done much to hinder or prevent regeneration.

Grenier regarded the great achievements of the Neolithic age as "the domestication of animals, the invention of agriculture, and the conquest of land under forest" (1930, p. 28). But we must not think of wholesale and necessarily permanent destruction of large tracts of wood; the stumps, for example, may well have remained for long, as they did in some clearings of a much later age (see below). "What in reality we have to envisage," writes Clark, "is the temporary clearance of restricted areas carried out in successive stretches of forest, many of which re-established themselves as the farmers and their stock moved elsewhere" (1945, p. 67; cf. 1944 and 1947).

During the succeeding prehistoric ages of bronze and iron there was some extension of the areas of settlement, but on the whole such extensions were few, and development seems to have been toward a more intensive utilization of the area already occupied (Gradmann, 1901, p. 374). This is seen, for example, from the maps accompanying Fox's study (1923) of the Cambridge region. Nor is this difficult to explain, for it was not until the close of prehistoric times that the farmer possessed a heavy, wheeled plow with which he could attack the heavier and ill-drained soils. The clay lands, therefore, continued for long in the shade of their dense woods. Certainly at the dawn of history Europe was covered with immense forests. In the first century before our era, the so-called "Hercynian Forest" of the classical authors stretched eastward from the Rhine for a vast distance. Caesar tells of men who had journeyed through it for two months without reaching an end, and other writers commented upon its somber solitude.[15] Yet it seems clear

15. Caesar *Gallic War* 6. 25.

that this forest was not as continuous nor as formidable as some classical allusions suggest, and we hear of clearings and of unforested areas and of the movement of troops through the forest itself (Dopsch, 1937, pp. 30–32). Still, the woodlands of *Germania* were very extensive, and within the Roman Empire, in Gaul and Britain, there were also large wooded tracts. In Britain a good deal of clearing took place locally, but "there is nothing to suggest a wholesale and general destruction" (Fox, 1923, p. 225), and the same is true of Gaul (Jullian, 1920, p. 179).

The Middle Ages (to A.D. 1500)

During the barbarian invasions it is difficult to perceive what happened to the Roman clearings. Documents of the time speak of deserted lands, *vastinae* or *solitudines;* and, although this impression may have been exaggerated (Dopsch, 1937, p. 92), it seems clear that the woods crept back over many neglected fields (Boissonnade, 1927, pp. 24–30). With the advent of more settled times, the attack upon the woodland was begun in earnest and was to gather force with the centuries. Behind the clash of warfare and the noise of political affairs the work of clearing went on in relative silence; but, if the details are obscure, we are, at any rate, able to judge by the results. The circumstances varied from place to place —an isolated clearing here; an enlargement of an existing field there; an inclosure for pasture in another place; maybe the throwing-off of a hamlet elsewhere. Sometimes a clearing was made by a single settler with the permission of his lord, to whom he paid a rent. At other times it was made by a large group of peasants who joined together for the purpose and incorporated the new arable within the regime and economy of their existing field system. But we know all too little of the details.

An echo of this activity in England

comes to us from the Anglo-Saxon poet who described the plowman as the "grey enemy of the wood";[16] and we can obtain some indication of the progress made over the span of six centuries or so (A.D. 450–1086) from the evidence of place names and from the statistics of the *Domesday Book*. The earlier evidence is becoming clear through the work of the English Place-Name Society. The distribution of different types of names in the county of Middlesex, for example, provides a revealing supplement to any deductions from surface geology (Gover *et al.*, 1942). Upon the light gravel and loamy soils of the south of the county, names which do not indicate wood are common (e.g., those ending in "-ham" and "-cote"). They belong to the early phase of the Saxon settlement upon fertile land already open. The wood names, later in date, lie on the intractable London clay to the north. In the extreme northeast there are scarcely any names, for here was a great expanse of unsettled woodland, the memory of which is preserved today in the name of Enfield Chase. The contrast between the distribution of the two groups of names is striking (Fig. 55). The northern woodland, within easy reach of London, could still be described in the twelfth century as "a great forest with wooded glades and lairs of wild beasts, deer both red and fallow, wild boars and bulls" (Stenton *et al.*, 1934, p. 27).

The effects of Anglo-Saxon and Scandinavian pioneering upon the landscape of England were summed up in the Domesday Inquest of 1086 (Darby, 1950). One of the questions asked by the Domesday commissioners was, "How much wood?" The form of the answers varied in different parts of the country. Occasionally, they merely stated that there was enough wood for

16. R. K. Gordon (ed.), *Anglo-Saxon Poetry* (London: Everyman's Library [J. M. Dent & Sons], 1954), p. 295.

fuel, or for repairing the houses, or for making and mending the fences. But, normally, the amount of wood was indicated in one of two ways: either by areal or linear dimensions or in terms of the swine that fed upon the acorns or beech mast. The woodland of Middlesex was measured by the latter method, and Figure 55 shows that some of its villages had wood for as many as two thousand swine; the feeding of swine has always been a great feature of the European forests (Fig. 56a). When the Domesday evidence for all England has been assembled, we shall be able to perceive a number of still heavily wooded tracts (Darby, 1952). But, although clearing was taking place generally, the forest was always ready to assert itself. Land devastated by raiding or by the march of armies soon became overgrown, and on the unsettled Welsh border of England we occasionally hear of plowland that had relapsed into woodland (Darby and Terrett, 1954, p. 85).

It is clear that in post-Domesday times, as in earlier years, throughout the length and breadth of the countryside, the ax was at work cutting down the trees, and the pick was at work grubbing up the roots. Bennett (1937, p. 51) has described the role of the clearing in the life of a medieval village: "For a family burdened with more children than their shares in the common fields would warrant such assart land was a godsend. Here they could utilise their spare labour, and produce something to help fill the many hungry mouths at home." The records of every English county tell their own story of this spreading cultivation, and much of the work must have escaped mention in any document. Some memorial of this activity exists today in the form of field names dating from post-Domesday times, and Middle English elements such as "stubbing" (place where trees have been stubbed) are common. Other names, to be found alike in early documents and on modern maps, are "sarts" from "assarts," "intak" or "intake," and "stokking," a "stump clearing"; a name such as "Brindley," on the other hand, means "clearing (*leah*) caused by fire (*brende*)," and "Brentwood" is "burnt wood." Nor must we forget that the need for arable land was not the only demand upon woodland. Timber for the building of bridges, castles, and cathedrals, for scaffolding as well as for the fabric; wood for the making of utensils and for a hundred and one purposes about a house or farm; and charcoal for the iron forges and for other industrial activity—all took their toll (Darby, 1951).

On the Continent there was even greater scope for the pioneer, and, in the centuries after the breakup of the Roman Empire, we begin to discern the early attack in progress. The Salian Franks in the fourth and fifth centuries avoided the great *Silva Carbonnaria*, the Charcoal-burners' Forest, on what

FIG. 55.—The woodland of Middlesex. (After Gover *et al.*, 1942; Darby and Campbell, in press.)

is now the unwooded plain of southern Brabant, and then began to occupy it in the sixth and seventh centuries (Des Marez, 1926). Elsewhere, we see the newcomers in the Empire making clearings (*Bifänge*), not only on overgrown deserted lands, but in the hitherto undisturbed forests (Dopsch, 1937, pp. 99, 116, 151). By the time of Charlemagne (*ca.* A.D. 800), much had been accomplished; one of his decrees bade his agents, "whenever they found capable men, to give them wood to clear." From widely separate places come indications of the retreat of the wood, and even parts of the great forests (such as that of the Ardennes) were already beginning to lose their primeval charac-

ter. Before A.D. 800 the valleys of the Odenwald, between the Neckar and the Main, were not much cultivated, but shortly afterward there were many clearings in them, and the so-called "forest village" (*Waldhufendorf*) appeared here at an early date (Koebner, 1941. pp. 45–46). Its form differed fundamentally from that of the traditional nucleated village surrounded by "open fields" with intermixed strips. The houses were laid out in a single or double row, usually along a valley bottom, and behind each house stretched its land in a long, narrow belt reaching back into the wood (Niemeier, 1949).

But clearing was not universal, and already in the relatively long-settled

FIG. 56a.—Swine feeding in the wood. (From British Museum, MS Tiberius, B. V, Part I, folio 7; the manuscript comes from the eleventh century A.D.)

FIG. 56b.—Cutting wood. (From British Museum, MS Tiberius, B. V, Part I, folio 6; the manuscript comes from the eleventh century A.D.)

lands of the west a conflict of interests can be observed. Set against the advantage of colonization were the interests of the chase and the wish to preserve forests as hunting parks; the game laws and the penalties for infringement of forest rights were often severe. Also, the wood itself was not without value. It provided timber and fuel, pasture and fruit; and a lord's interest frequently lay in denying his peasants the freedom to destroy it. Licenses were exacted to pasture swine, to fell timber, and to till the cleared land, and a great array of rights to control the use of the forest grew. When the Count of Vendôme found unauthorized clearings in his woods, he had the houses destroyed and the crops cleared away, and the monk who recorded this did so with approval. Thus was progress governed "by the varying balance between a peasantry growing by natural increase and the restrictive policies of its feudal lords" (Koebner, 1941, p. 69).

But the time was soon to be when lords were not so insistent upon their forest rights. From about 1050 onward, for some two hundred years or so, came the great heroic period of reclamation, "l'âge des grands défrichements" of the French writers. The outline has been sketched by Bloch (1931, pp. 1–20), and Flach has shown the earlier pioneers replacing forests by villages (1893, pp. 145 ff.). There are also older accounts of the French forests (Maury, 1850, 1866, 1867), and many detailed studies fill in the picture for this or that locality (e.g., Campagne, 1912; Sclafert, 1926). Among those who took the lead in organizing the new effort were the religious houses. The older Benedictine monasteries had pioneered in the mountains of the Dauphiné and on the plains of the Ile de France and elsewhere; and they were followed in the twelfth century by new monastic orders, above all, by the Cistercians. Their rule laid stress upon manual labor and especially

upon work in the field; they sought the wilderness and became the great farmers of the Middle Ages, and they were to find that solitude was but a poor defender of poverty. By the end of the twelfth century the Cistercian houses alone numbered five hundred, and this figure was to reach seven hundred and fifty in the fifteenth century. Countless other monasteries also took part. Nor were laymen, lords and peasants alike, slow to share in the rewards of this new and peaceful crusade.

There was a widespread extension of the arable land of existing villages, and new fields were brought into being alongside the old. In other places the expansion took the form of subsidiary hamlets and isolated homesteads. Modern topographical maps often indicate how scattered settlements were spread through the forest in small clearings. That the assart (from the French *essarter*, "to grub up," or "to clear") had come to have a definite place in manorial economy is abundantly clear from monastic and other documents. The obituary of Albericus Cornu, who had been a canon of Notre-Dame de Paris, tells us, for example, how he had improved the abbey estates; the woods had "for long been so useless that they were a burden rather than a source of income," and Albericus had been able to free them from the forest jurisdiction of the Count of Champagne and other lords and turn them into arable land (Koebner, 1941, p. 77).

Clearing was also promoted by the establishment of entirely new settlements. Village colonies were organized to bring the near-by waste or forest under cultivation. The *villes neuves* of northern France, the *bourgs* of the west (Koebner, 1941, pp. 71–72), and *bastides* and *sauvetés* of the south (Arqué, 1948; Ourliac, 1949) housed *hospites*, or colonists, who came to invade the waste. The form of many of these settlements reminds us of the *Waldhufen* village of Germany. The names of some of them were taken from the woods upon which they encroached; the names of others include an element such as *sart;* yet other names also tell us something of their story. In the wooded countryside of Puisaye, between the Loire and the Yonne, we find, side by side, a Jerusalem, a Jericho, a Nazareth, and a Bethlehem, which reflect the Crusading age in which they were born (Bloch, 1931, p. 11).

It was the same elsewhere in Western Europe. We hear of clearing operations, of *hospites* and of *villae novae,* in Flanders, Hainault, and Brabant; and French names that end in "-sart" and Flemish names that end in "-rode" indicate the success of the attack (Duvivier, 1859). To the east, the monasteries of the Rhineland endowed with ample lands were no less active. They and their daughter-abbeys between the Rhine and the Elbe were breaking into the woods and heaths of Saxony and Thuringia. Place names that end in "-wald" ("wood") and "-holz" ("grove") indicate the former character of the countryside, and those that end in "-rode" ("grubbed up"), "-schwend" ("burned") and "-hau" ("cut down") bear witness to the clearing (Schlüter, 1952, pp. 23–35). Conditions varied from place to place, but the net result of the Great Reclamation, or *Urbarmachung,* was to change the economy and the appearance of considerable stretches in the broad lowlands and the Alpine zone alike. Upland massifs such as the Harz, the Eifel, the Westerwald, the Thuringian Forest, and the Black Forest were coming to look like great wooded islands in a sea of cultivation; but even their shades were not undisturbed. The copper- and silver-bearing lead ores of the once-wooded Rammelsberg in the Harz were perhaps the most famous metal deposits, but the working both of these metals and of iron, to-

gether with the activity of the charcoal-burner, was widespread (Nef, 1952, p. 435). Moreover, agriculture was being extended in the valleys of these uplands, and the changes can be summed up in the words of Caesarius of Prüm, set in the wooded Eifel. Writing in 1222, and referring to the previous century, he said: "During this long space of time many forests were felled, villages founded, mills erected, taxes ordained, vines planted, and an infinite amount of land reduced to agriculture" (Thompson, 1928a, p. 758).

Great though the efforts in the long-settled regions of Western Europe and the Rhineland were, it was to the east, in the heart of Central Europe, that the most spectacular changes took place. The lands abandoned by the Teutonic peoples as they moved into the Roman provinces had been occupied by the Slavs, who migrated westward across the Vistula and the Oder and southward across the Danube. By about A.D. 600 the frontier between the German and Slav worlds had become roughly the line of the Elbe-Saale in the north, while southward it ran across the Alps toward the head of the Adriatic (Fig. 57). After an interval, and following the setbacks of border warfare, the Germans began to advance southeastward in the tenth century and northeastward across the European plain after about 1100. It was, wrote Lamprecht (1893, p. 349), the great deed of the German people in the Middle Ages. In all its complexity, it has attracted an enormous literature.[17] The advance took place under the impetus of economic and missionary motives, and there arose a contrast between the old western feudal Germany and the new eastern colonial Germany. Analogy has been drawn between this advance and the expansion of the American people west-

17. For some convenient reviews see Aubin, 1941; Kötzschke and Ebert, 1937; and Thompson, 1928b.

ward from the Atlantic seaboard. What the new west meant to young America in the nineteenth century, the new east meant to Germany in the Middle Ages (Thompson, 1928*b*, pp. xviii, 523). Although historical analogies are often misleading, this comparison does emphasize the colonial character of much of medieval Germany. Some parallels between clearing in the Old and New Worlds have also been drawn by Schott (1935).

Fig. 57.—German colonization eastward. (After W. R. Shepherd, *Historical Atlas* [3d ed.; London: University of London Press, 1924], Pl. 80.)

The surface of the northern German plain is covered almost everywhere with deposits laid down by the great ice sheets which spread out from Scandinavia in Quaternary times. Much of the clay is hummocky, and on its ill-drained surface lay marsh and shallow lakes of curious shape; many of the river valleys were also marshy. Elsewhere, stretches of infertile sand and gravel, derived from the glacial de-

posits, formed a type of country known as geest; the landscape that confronted the German colonists was one of wood, marsh, and heath. The wood, or a great deal of it, fell before the ax of the pioneer, and both place names and the *Waldhufen* village testify to the clearing activity. The settlers came from the older parts of Germany, "with horses and oxen, with ploughs and waggons," to transform the countrysides of what are now Mecklenburg, Pomerania, Brandenburg, and Silesia (Thompson, 1928*b*, p. 501). About 1100, we hear, for example, of Count Wiprecht of Groitzsch, to the south of Leipzig between the Saale and the Elbe, bringing colonists from the west to clear his forests (Koebner, 1941, p. 81). Later in the century the ruler of Meissen was settling colonists in the frontier forests of the Erzgebirge (Aubin, 1941, p. 366). Some words of Helmold of Holstein, whose "Chronicle" describes the pioneering life of the time, illustrate not only the vicissitudes of the frontier struggle but also the recuperative power of the forest. Speaking of an earlier Saxon advance and retreat, he said: "There still remain many evidences of that former occupation, especially in the forest which extends from the city of Lütjenburg through the mighty tracts of Schleswig, in whose vast and almost impenetrable solitudes yet may be descried the furrows which once marked out the plowlands" (Thompson, 1928*b*, p. 491). But even as Helmold wrote (*ca.* 1170), the plow was soon to move over the ground once more.

Alongside the clearing of the wood went other transformations. The German colonists with their axes were accompanied and followed by Dutch, Flemish, and Frisians who embanked streams and drained marshes. Into the dry soils of part of the geest they cut irrigation canals, and they gave their name to the district of Fläming that lies to the east of Magdeburg. The changes were urban as well as rural. The dates of the founding of the cities of northern Germany mark the success of the advance. Behind the achievement of the Hanseatic cities in the fourteenth and fifteenth centuries lay a background of some generations of colonial struggle.

By the end of the thirteenth century the advance had spent itself. Poland was penetrated by German colonists and civilization, but only to a limited degree. Yet in the forests and waste of two outlying eastern areas, German missionary zeal and colonizing impulse had found fruitful fields of activity. Early in the thirteenth century the military order of the Brethren of the Sword had planted the country around the Gulf of Riga with German fortified towns; it was, wrote a chronicler of the time, a land of fertile fields and abundant pasture, but with much wood (*ibid.*, p. 526). Later in the century, between this northern outpost and the homeland, a second military order, the Teutonic Knights, more thoroughly occupied the woodland (Schlüter, 1920). It was the last chapter in the history of medieval colonization by the Germans in the north. The consequences were fateful for the affairs of Europe, because this new area of activity, later known as East Prussia, was separated from the main body of German settlement by what was to be called "the Polish Corridor" (Fig. 57).

The activity in northern Germany had been paralleled to the south. In the eastern Alps, the rise of Austria, founded as an outpost against the Magyars in the tenth century, was accompanied by an advance of German-speaking peoples comparable to that across the northern plain, but the information is more scanty. The advance took place partly down the Danube and partly southward into the lands of the southern Slavs. Not only the main valleys, but the side valleys as well, were cleared for tillage below and pasturage

above. Beyond the main frontier of German speech, isolated German settlements appeared as islands in Slav or Magyar territory. One of the characteristic features of the mountain belt as a whole was its mining activity. If the amounts appear small to us and the technology primitive, we must consider them in the context of their time. German mining camps grew into towns on the slopes of the Erzgebirge (Ore Mountains), in the Sudeten Mountains, in Bohemia itself, eastward in Slovakia, southward in Styria, Carinthia, and Carniola, and beyond in Bosnia and Serbia. Still farther east lie the mountains of Transylvania. Its Latin name indicates its forested nature, and its Magyar name, "Edily," comes from *erdö* ("forest"). To these mountains came Germans from the Rhineland, mostly in the twelfth century, at the invitation of the early Magyar kings, to fell the frontier forests and to become farmers and miners; the many place names that end in "-hau" form some memorial to their clearing. Nef, who has discussed the importance of mining in medieval Europe, writes (1952, p. 472) of the demands made upon wood for pit props, for building, for fuel, and for charcoal.

But, in recording the importance of the eastward movement of the German-speaking peoples, we must not forget the work of the Slavonic peoples themselves. Even in Germanized areas, such as Mecklenburg, Slavonic lords and peasants may have been responsible for much clearing (Power, 1932, p. 725). Slav place-name elements, such as *drewa* ("wood") and *trebynja* ("clearing") form memorials of their activity (Trautmann, 1948–49, II, 37, 89). Beyond, in Poland, Bohemia, and elsewhere, they founded new villages and reclaimed the wilderness, sometimes under German law, sometimes under Slavonic. Settlements of a *Waldhufen* type are to be found in the uplands of southern Poland (De Martonne, 1931, p.

629). In Bohemia there are over three hundred place names that include the element *lhota,* and there are eighty more in Moravia. The word, roughly speaking, means "freedom," and it was used in this connection to denote the exemptions from render that were sometimes granted to settlements made on empty or waste land. Its widespread distribution may be taken as some index of the transforming activity of the Czechs. The word in the form of *lêhota* occurs more than forty times in Slovakia farther east, but there it seems to have been associated with German law (Aubin, 1941, pp. 395–96). In this area other place-name elements, such as *kopanice, lazy,* and *paseky,* specifically indicate clearing (Deffontaines, 1932, p. 57). Here, the activity was smaller in amount and maybe later in time, but the phenomenon was fundamentally the same.

This great expansive movement of clearing during the Middle Ages did not continue uninterruptedly into modern times. In places it slowed down; in others it ceased; in yet other places the frontiers of cultivation even retreated. Certainly over most of central and western Europe agrarian effort had passed its maximum by 1300, and the great age of expanding arable land was succeeded in the fourteenth and fifteenth centuries by one of stagnation and contraction. During the hundred years between 1350 and 1450, the decline was especially marked. The causes of this recession are obscure and involved, and among the agencies invoked to explain it are the destruction of war, great pestilences, falling prices, and a basic decline in population (Postan, 1952, pp. 191–216). Abandoned holdings and depopulated or deserted villages were to be found not only in the "old lands" of the south and west but also in Mecklenburg, Pomerania, Brandenburg, and Prussia. In the south and west of Germany the acreage of these *Wüstungen* has been placed as high as one-half of

the area once cultivated; the statistical mode for Germany as a whole has been placed at 25 per cent. These figures probably overemphasize the contraction, because some abandoned holdings may represent no more than temporary withdrawals or changes in the use of land; but, when all reservations are made, the facts are striking enough (Pohlendt, 1950). To what extent the woods advanced upon the untilled fields and unused pastures we cannot say, but there is no doubt that they did in many places, and traces of cultivation are to be found in wooded areas even today. The abandonment took place at various dates, but, says Mortensen (1951, p. 359), in the main it is clearly a medieval phenomenon. Figure 58 shows the oscillation in the area around Hofgeismar in the upper Weser Basin (Jäger, 1951); and, more recently, Jäger has also shown (1954) how many large forests in Germany have come into being since the Middle Ages. From such evidence as this we must not assume that the area under cultivation was at one time greater than it is today, because the phenomenon may in part be due to the more complete separation of forest and farm land. But more investigation is needed before we can be clear about these matters (Mortensen, 1951, p. 359).

The ravages of war and pillage bore particularly hard upon some localities. The cultivated land that had been brought into being in Bohemia was very adversely affected by the Hussite Wars (1419–36), and it has been estimated that one-sixth of the population either perished or left the country. In the west, France suffered grievously during the Hundred Years' War (1337–1453). Thomas Basin, bishop of Lisieux, writing about 1440, described the vast extent of uncultivated land between the Somme and the Loire all "overgrown with brambles and bushes" (Boissonnade, 1927, p. 316). Population fell in places to one-half, even to one-third, of its former level. Some of the accounts may have been exaggerated, but there is no doubt about the widespread desolation and about the growth of wood on the untilled fields (Waddington, 1930). In the southwest, in Saintogne, between the Charente and the Dordogne, for a long time people said that "the forests came back to France with the English."

Modern Times (*after A.D. 1500*)

The clearing that had taken place in the Middle Ages, epic though it was, still left Western and Central Europe with abundant tracts of wood. But soon, in the sixteenth century, in many places there were complaints about a shortage of timber, and the shortage developed into a problem that occupied the attention of statesmen and publicists for many centuries. It was not only that the woods were becoming smaller but that the demand for timber was growing greater. There had been signs toward the end of the fifteenth century that the recession in the economic life of the late Middle Ages was merging into recovery and into a new prosperity that

Fig. 58.—Woodland in the area around Hofgeismar in the upper Weser Basin. *H* = Hofgeismar, *M* = Münden. (After Jäger, 1951.)

brought with it an ever increasing appetite for wood.

The pace of industrial life was quickening. Glassworks and soapworks, for example, needed more and more wood ash. The production of tin, lead, copper, iron, and coal depended upon timber for pit props and charcoal for fuel; the salt industry in the Tyrol and elsewhere also needed wood for evaporating the brine. It was perhaps the iron industry that made the greatest single demand, and, particularly in the wooded valleys of the upland blocks of France and Central Europe, an endless series of small metal establishments were to be found, often run by men who divided their labors between the forge and the field. As the clearing progressed, the huts of the charcoal-burners moved from one locality to another, and there appeared new mounds of small logs, covered with clay to prevent too rapid a combustion.

The fears of a shortage of timber in England can be seen in a commission of 1548 to inquire into the destruction of wood in the ironmaking area of the Weald. But neither its report nor successive Acts of Parliament in the sixteenth century were able to stay the destruction (Straker, 1931, p. 109). The solution to the problem was to find a substitute, and it is not surprising that during the seventeenth century many treatises suggested the use of coal instead of charcoal. It was about the year 1709 that Abraham Darby first smelted ore with coke in Shropshire, and by the middle of the eighteenth century the use of coal for smelting had become common in England. Here, as elsewhere, the growth of the iron and steel industry was linked with coal and not wood, and names such as "Forge Wood" and "Furnace Wood" recall, on modern English maps, the activities and changes of a past age.

The problem was less acute on the Continent, where there was more wood and less industry, and it was not until well into the nineteenth century that smelting with coke became established. But that the problem was not absent here can be seen from a French proposal of 1715 to limit the number of forges; late in the eighteenth century, as in earlier times, we hear of numerous small potteries, glassworks, and forges scattered through the forests of France (Brunhes and Deffontaines, 1926, p. 354; Dion, 1938). In Germany, as late as 1848, Banfield could write (1846–48, II, 65) of the wooded district between the Ruhr and the Sieg: "A rotation of coppice or underwood, cut down every sixteen years, affords both bark for the numerous tanners and charcoal for the metallurgists; and both occupations alternate with the care of small farms belonging to these small manufacturers, as the rye is admitted into the forest rotation the year after the underwood is cut down." This forest-field rotation was known as *Reutbergwirtschaft*, as opposed to the more permanent *Brandwirtschaft*, and it was a feature of many parts of Germany (Schmitthenner, 1923). It has left a memory in the place names of some districts (Mutton, 1938, p. 119); and, even today, there are localities from which it has not entirely disappeared (Fickeler, 1954, p. 27).

With the overseas expansion of Europe, the need for timber for shipbuilding was also greatly increased. The growth of England's mercantile marine and the development of the English navy from the Tudor age onward depended upon an adequate supply of oaks for the hulls of ships; fir trees, for masts, together with such "naval stores" as pitch and tar, were imported from Baltic lands. The Dutch wars of the seventeenth century, the maritime wars of the eighteenth, and the Napoleonic Wars were a heavy and continuous drain upon English oak, and English seamen were only too conscious of their difficulties. Samuel Pepys, employed at the Admiralty, could only write, "God knows where materials can be had" (Albion, 1926, p. ix). English timber never recovered from the strain of the wars with France, and English ships came to rely more and more upon the pine and oak of the New World and the teak of India.

foreign, colonial, commercial, and forest policies as well."

The rise of the Dutch navy was even more dependent upon the Baltic trade; the timber and "naval stores" of these northern lands were as important to sea power in the seventeenth and eighteenth centuries as heavy industry was to be in more modern times. It was certainly so in France. Richelieu and especially Colbert, in the seventeenth cen-

Fig. 59.—Agricultural improvement. (From Andrews, 1853.)

In the meantime, the Admiralty, in its alarm over the timber shortage, consulted the newly formed Royal Society, which in turn asked John Evelyn to report upon the problem. The result was the appearance in 1664 of Evelyn's *Sylva: A Discourse of Forest Trees,* and in the years that followed there were various intermittent attempts at planting. The influence of the timber shortage appeared in many ways, wrote Albion (1926, p. vii), "not only in the Navy itself, but in international law, in naval architecture, and in England's

tury, aimed at the creation of a French navy. Colbert instituted dockyards and naval schools and reorganized the naval service. In 1669 came the famous "Ordonnance des eaux et forêts," which stated that no wood should be cleared without authority; but, as in England, these regulations soon ceased to be observed.

The timber problem remained acute for the navies of Europe until March 9, 1862. It was on that day that the Battle of Hampton Roads in the American Civil War demonstrated the superiority of the iron-clad ship (Albion, 1926, pp. 408–9). The end of the era of wooden ships had come suddenly, and it left a permanent mark upon the countrysides of Europe.

There was yet another and continuing demand upon wood. Although the pioneer age of *défrichement* and *Urbarmachung* was over, agriculture still con-

but it continued and was even accelerated by an edict of 1766, which exempted newly cleared land from taxation for fifteen years (Debien, 1952, p. 45). In mountainous districts, such as the Alps (Blache, 1923) and the Ardennes (Liouville, 1897), temporary clearings for cultivation continued to be made by burning, and the ash fertilized

CENTRAL EUROPE

FOREST c.900

100 Miles

FIG. 60.—Central Europe: forest *ca.* 900. (After Schlüter, 1952.)

tinued to expand at the expense of the forest in this locality or that. It was certainly so in England, as much evidence after 1500, and even after 1800, testifies (Darby, 1951, pp. 78–79). Figure 59, from G. H. Andrews' *Modern Husbandry* of 1853, shows the cutting-down of trees and the tile-draining of the clay soils that had nourished them. It was the same in France. Widespread felling had disquieted the agricultural writer Bernard Palissy in the sixteenth century,

the soil. In other places, too, upland communities of herdsmen, eager for pasturage, regarded trees as their enemies; and their successors have been left to inherit a legacy of soil erosion and inundation (Rabot, 1905, p. 207).

Eastward, in the German realm, the Thirty Years' War (1618–48) left a staggering legacy of devastation. Conservative estimates say that at least one-third of the population perished, but to what extent the forest crept back over the untilled fields we cannot say. Anyway, there was recovery, and German agricultural chemistry was greatly to distinguish itself. But immense stretches of forest continued into the twentieth century; they amounted to over thirty million acres, and about one-half of this was on the large estates of private owners. The plain of Poland had also still remained. In the twentieth century about 18 per cent of Belgium was wooded, 19 per cent of France, 27 per cent of Germany, and 23 per cent of Poland. Southward, the figures rose to 37 per cent for Austria, 33 per cent for Czechoslovakia, and 29 per cent each for Yugoslavia and Bulgaria, and 28 per cent for Rumania. For Hungary, with

CENTRAL
EUROPE

FOREST *c.*1900

100 Miles

FIG. 61.—Central Europe: forest *ca.* 1900. (After Schlüter, 1952.)

been far from cleared, while to the south the clearings and the woodland industries of the Slovakian highlands (Deffontaines, 1932) and the Carpathians recalled those of the upland regions of the west. Looking at Central and Western Europe as a whole in the nineteenth and twentieth centuries, the surprising thing is that, despite the varied demands upon wood and the long centuries of exploitation, so much its plains, the figure fell to 11 per cent (Dietrich, 1928).

The contrast between Figures 60 and 61 shows the net result of clearing as opposed to regeneration and replanting over the thousand years between A.D. 900 and 1900 (Schlüter, 1952). Much of the existing forest bears the mark of long exploitation and differs considerably from the natural forest that would cover almost the whole area had there been no interference by man. The most striking evidence of this interference has been the steady increase during the nineteenth and twentieth centuries in the percentage of conifers. Since about the middle of the nineteenth century, various national forest policies have resulted in the formation of state forest services. To varying degrees, the management of forested areas has been put upon a scientific basis; reasoned programs of felling have been organized, and new methods of seed selection and regeneration have been devised. One feature of the new policies has been the concentration upon soft woods, reflecting the changing demand from fuel to timber and pulpwood. The Scotch fir, the larch, the spruce, and new varieties of fir from abroad—the silver fir and the Douglas fir, for example—are giving a new value to poor hillsides and infertile stretches of sand and gravel. Large areas of heath in northwestern Germany and of sand dunes along the Baltic coast have been planted with conifers. In Belgium extensive planting has altered the appearance of the barren Kempenland (Monkhouse, 1949, p. 93). In Britain the sandy waste of the Breckland has also taken on a new look (Clarke *et al.*, 1938). But perhaps the most striking change has been on the Landes in southwestern France. At the end of the eighteenth century there were only a few scattered maritime pines and some dwarf oaks on this dreary expanse of marsh, gravel, and shifting sand. But the scene has been transformed, by draining and planting, into a vast forest covering some two million acres and forming a conspicuous feature of the woodland map of France (Fig. 62). The trees are mostly maritime pines, and they yield resin, pit props, and a variety of constructional timber (Larroquette, 1924). These are only a few examples of the recent transformations of the European landscape. But great though such changes have

been, they are localized. Could the Roman legionaries tramp the countryside once more, they would be reminded only rarely of the dense shades they had encountered when they left the Mediterranean lands to build an empire.

EASTERN AND NORTHERN EUROPE

From south to north the great vegetation belts of European Russia in historical times have been the steppes, the mixed forest, and the coniferous forest, together with the transitional zones between them (Fig. 63).

The Steppes

Traveler after traveler has described the vast treeless plain of the steppes, and historians have emphasized its role as an open corridor along which nomadic peoples, with their herds, traveled westward from central Asia. But in classical times there was certainly some wood along the lower courses of the rivers that flow into the Black Sea. Herodotus, for example, wrote of "the forest country" along the lower Dnieper. Neumann (1855, pp. 74–99) came to the conclusion that there were substantial stretches of woodland here, but his ideas have been thought by some to be exaggerated (Minns, 1913, p. 1). Looking back beyond the classical age into prehistory, Taliev thought that the grass steppe had been formed on the site of destroyed forest, but, added Keller (1927, p. 232), "this view has not been generally accepted." Since then, Leimbach, in a survey of the Russian literature (1948, p. 255), has thought it "very likely that the Ukraine in the same way as the Hungarian Puszta was once mainly forest land," while Wilhelmy, in another survey (1950, p. 31), is not in agreement. We must await further elucidation of the problem, but it may not be without significance that Keller pointed out (1927, p. 228) that, in the transitional zone between steppe and forest, "the forest often occupies areas which are apparently identical in conditions of soil and land relief with other areas which are occupied by steppe vegetation. And clear evidence of the advance of forest on steppe is not lacking. . . . In the northern parts of the forest-steppe zone this advance is very marked. Burial mounds, which were un-

among the woods, and with projections of woodland southward, especially along the river valleys; but the wooded tracts have grown fewer and smaller, "until nowadays the steppe lands begin farther north than they once did." Kiev, founded in the ninth century, by tradition lay "amongst forests" where now is

FIG. 62.—France: forest *ca.* 1920. (After *Atlas de France*, 1935, Fl. 38 [Paris: Comité National de Géographie].)

doubtedly made in open steppe, are now covered with trees."

But, while the forest may have advanced in places, it is clear that the transitional forest steppe as a whole has been greatly cleared with the advance of colonization southward from the seventeenth century onward. Both steppe and forest have mingled and contested here, with islands of steppe

open steppe (Kluchevsky, 1911–31, V, 233, 241).

The Mixed Forest

The homeland of the Slavs in the early centuries of the Christian Era seems to have lain between the Carpathian Mountains and the middle and upper Dnieper. From this base, according to some scholars, they advanced not only westward and southward but also northward and northeastward into the valleys and plains of the upper Volga and its tributaries. Here, in the mixed oak forest, they seem to have met with but little resistance from the sparse Finno-Ugrian population. There is much est near the river Sheksna (Davies, 1952, p. 119). Some memory of the great woodland through which they passed is preserved in the name of the city of Bryansk. It is difficult to obtain a clear picture of this great epoch of colonization, so silent was it. But in the

Fig. 63.—Russia: vegetation zones. (After Keller, 1927.)

that is controversial about these matters (Paszkiewicz, 1954, p. 255), but it is clear that the agriculture of the area was primitive, apparently migratory, and supplemented by trapping and by the honey of wild bees. From the third and fourth centuries comes evidence of a slash-and-burn husbandry in the for- eleventh and twelfth centuries we hear of new settlements and new principalities in the land between the Volga and the Oka, and some of the princes embarked upon a policy of deliberately attracting new settlers and took pride in the success of their colonization (Kluchevsky, 1911–31, I, 196 ff.).

Moscow itself was first mentioned in 1147 and by the end of the Middle Ages was to establish its control over the other Volga-Oka principalities. The mixed-forest country between the Volga and the Oka has been called the "Ile de France" of Russia, the cradle of the Russian state; and the wedge of colonization, set between the inhospitable north and the insecure steppe, was not only to develop and fill out with the centuries, as forest hamlets and villages were established (Eck, 1933, pp. 55, 275), but also to improve its agriculture. The temporary cultivation of burned clearings gave way by the sixteenth century to more intensive cultivation on a two- or three-field basis, as in the West. Yet the Russians were much slower in clearing the wilderness than the trans-Elbean Germans who moved into the lands of the western Slavs, and the retreat of the wood was more gradual. "Indeed, eighteenth-century Muscovy would have struck a Western European traveller journeying from Smolensk to Moscow as one huge forest, and the towns and villages in it as mere clearings." But the clearing was to continue until the forest land of central Russia became "a mere dwindling reminiscence of the past, and preserved as a luxury" (Kluchevsky, 1911–31, V, 244–45). It had supplied fuel and building material, it had supported a whole range of small-scale forest industries, and it had yielded its soil for agriculture.

The Coniferous Forest

To the north, beyond the upper Volga, the growing season becomes shorter, and the soil more infertile; the mixed forest gives way to the coniferous forest which still covers the greater part of the countryside. The dominant trees are the spruce and the pine, the former on clay, the latter on sand, and everywhere these are mingled with peat moors. It was thinly peopled by Finnish and Lapp tribes and provided an enormous reservoir of fur—sable, marten, fox, and, of lesser value, bear, squirrel, and otter. Fur led the traders northward and eastward along the great rivers linked one to another by portages. It was an economy that anticipated that of the *coureurs de bois* of French Canada. The great part of the trade of this hinterland found an outlet at Novgorod in the west, a Hanse center and a market of renown in medieval Europe; its main commodity was fur, but forest products—tar, pitch, potash, and wax—were also among its exports.

Not only traders but missionaries came north to these trans-Volgan lands. Between 1340 and 1440, especially, there was a great development of monasticism, and the monks sought the untamed wilderness. Bielozersk, founded in 1397, and many other houses, together with their daughter-foundations, became agrarian colonies. We hear of black, impassable, and untilled forests, of the hewing of trees, of newly plowed fields, and of fresh villages and hamlets (Kluchevsky, 1911–31, II, 151 ff.). The opening of the White Sea route from the west by Elizabethan Adventurers in 1533 greatly increased the importance of these northern lands. By this time, the subjection of Novgorod in 1478 had brought her rough trading empire within the sphere of Muscovy, and the new gains of the sixteenth century were to fall to Moscow. Hakluyt's account of the Adventurers' journey from Archangel to Moscow speaks of the very large forests of fir trees, the wooden houses, the flax and hemp, and the great quantity and variety of furs, and it is a description that was echoed by later writers.[18] The effects of the new contact were soon evident. Small settlements developed into prosperous towns between Moscow and

18. Richard Hakluyt, *The Principal Navigations* (London: Everyman's Library [J. M. Dent & Sons], 1907), I, 254, 278–79.

the White Sea, and Yaroslavl, Vologda, and other centers added to the consumption of timber. The pace of exploitation increased as factories for boiling tar, burning potash, and making rope were established; the tanning industry was developed; the salt industry, too, was important. There were also grants of land, in the Kama area in the 1560's, for example, with power to settle immigrants upon them (*ibid.*, p. 224). Metallurgical industries and mining were developed, especially from the time of Peter the Great in the eighteenth century, and they consumed timber both in the coniferous and in the mixed-forest zone. A whole range of traditional forest industries continued to grow, often with considerable specialization between village and village (Roudski and Shafranov, 1893, p. 334).

But we must not endow this northern settlement with an intensity it did not possess. The crops were mostly rye and oats, flax and hemp, and much of the agriculture was primitive. A Russian account from as late as the end of the nineteenth century is interesting because of the light it throws upon earlier practices elsewhere:

The forest-field system means an alternation of agriculture with more or less lasting periods of forest-growing between. Properly speaking, the forest-field system of economy as practised in most parts of the north and north-east districts of Russia, cannot be called a system of economy in the strict sense of the term, because, in most cases, the felling of trees and the clearing of woods for the cultivation of grain, and afterwards, for the re-growing of trees, are practised without any definite plan. This is one of the simplest forms of primitive economy, and in which field-cultivation is of second-rate importance, as portions of improved land, in most cases, are quite insignificant in comparison with the forests among which they are dispersed [Ermolov, 1893, pp. 64–65].

We hear, too, of the burning of trees and undergrowth in connection with the cultivation (Semenov, 1893, p. 82). Manninen has also described (1932, pp. 245, 274–75) the agriculture of the Finno-Ugrian peoples as involving the felling and burning of successive tracts of forest; the rich ash resulted in a yield some three to four times that from ordinary plowland. Frequently, as among the Votyaks of the Volga-Kama region, the tree stumps were left in the ground and the soil tilled between them.

That this was an immemorial practice among the Finnish peoples we may suppose from a passage in the *Kalevala* epic where the voice of the aged Väinä-möinen is said to halt "like the hoe among the pine roots."[19] Traces of this primitive agriculture have also survived among the Baltic Finns. Mead's study of land clearance in Finland shows that "burning might be rotational or casual," and he instances an example of rotational burning in eastern Finland in 1781. The trees were felled in the first year and fired in the second year. Four to six years of crop then followed, often amid the tree stumps, after which the land relapsed to scrub and wood for a span of twenty to thirty years. "Where rotational burning occurred, four cycles in a century was the average. In a hundred years, therefore, the burnt-over land experienced twenty years under grain, perhaps twelve under rough pasture and sixty-eight as woodland grazing" (Mead, 1953, p. 46). Since the eighteenth century, and particularly since the middle of the nineteenth, the practice has declined as methods of agriculture have improved and the value of forests has increased (Figs. 64 and 65). It still occurs, but only occasionally and with caution. On the forests that remain (70 per cent in Finland), it has left a mark, for the first trees to appear on burned-over areas

19. *Kalevala: Or, The Land of Heroes,* trans. W. F. Kirby (London: Everyman's Library [J. M. Dent & Sons], 1907), I, 248.

FIG. 64.—Firing the woodland. (From Mead, 1953; sketches made by Magnus von Wright, 1883.)

FIG. 65.—Plowing the fired land. (From Mead, 1953; sketches made by Magnus von Wright, 1883.)

are birch and alder, not conifers or hardwoods.

Across the Baltic Sea, in Sweden, rotational burning was also found, and it has recently been studied by Montelius, who says (1953) there is no doubt that it has been practiced "since prehistoric times." Medieval evidence indicates the cultivation of rye and turnips in forest clearings over large parts of the country. The practice was greatly stimulated by the immigration of Finns during the sixteenth and seventeenth centuries, and the result was a conflict with mining companies interested in wood for miners and in charcoal for foundries and forges. Attempts made to limit burning in the mining districts resulted in a compromise by which the heavy tree trunks were used for charcoal, the tops and branches burned. With changing economic conditions, the habit gradually disappeared, and the last crop of rye grown on burned forest land was har-

vested in 1918. In the meantime, the demands of the important iron industry upon wood for charcoal greatly increased from 1830 to 1885; but, with the introduction of coke, it declined, and "in a few years the role of charcoal in the Swedish steel industry will be very insignificant" (Arpi, 1953, p. 27).

On the forest map of Europe today, the coniferous belt stands out strikingly (Heske and Torunsky, 1951——), and the demands of the twentieth century for lumber and for pulpwood have given it a new importance. The great extent of standing wood does not imply a lack of human interference. Much, perhaps most, of it has been logged over at least once, and forest fires have wrought havoc (Streyffert, 1934, p. 4). Much, too, has come under the care of forestry services. Not as dramatically as elsewhere in Europe, but quite unmistakably, the northern forest bears witness to the transforming hand of man.

REFERENCES

ALBION, R. G.
1926 *Forests and Sea-power.* Cambridge, Mass.: Harvard University Press. 485 pp.

ANDREWS, G. H.
1853 *Modern Husbandry: A Practical and Scientific Treatise on Agriculture.* London: Nathaniel Cooke. 404 pp.

ARPI, G.
1953 "The Supply with Charcoal of the Swedish Iron Industry from 1830 to 1950," *Geografiska Annaler,* XXXV, 11–27.

ARQUÉ, P.
1948 "La Conquête du sol en Périgord méridional," pp. 13–26 in *France méridionale et pays ibériques: Mélanges géographiques offerts en hommage à M. Daniel Faucher.* 2 vols. Toulouse: Éditions Toulousaines de l'Ingénieur. 685 pp.

AUBIN, H.
1941 "The Lands East of the Elbe and German Colonisation Eastwards," pp. 361–97 in CLAPHAM, J. H., and

POWER, E. (eds.), *The Cambridge Economic History of Europe,* Vol. I. Cambridge: Cambridge University Press. 650 pp.

BANFIELD, T. C.
1846–48 *Industry of the Rhine.* 2 vols. London: Charles Knight & Co. 244 + 252 pp.

BENNETT, H. S.
1937 *Life on the English Manor.* Cambridge: Cambridge University Press. 364 pp. (Reprinted 1938, 1948.)

BLACHE, J.
1923 "L'Essartage, ancienne pratique culturale dans les Alpes dauphinoises," *Revue de géographie alpine,* XI, 553–75.

BLOCH, MARC
1931 *Les Caractères originaux de l'histoire rurale française.* Oslo. 261 pp. (Reprinted 1952. Paris: Armand Colin.)

BOISSONNADE, P.
1927 *Life and Work in Medieval Eu-*

rope. London: Kegan Paul, Trench, Trubner & Co. 395 pp.

BROWN, J. C.
1884 *Forests and Forestry of Northern Russia and the Lands Beyond.* Edinburgh: Oliver & Boyd. 279 pp.

BRUNHES, J., and DEFFONTAINES, P.
1926 "Arbres et forêts: Types et sites d'activités humaines liées à la forêt," pp. 337–62 (chap. xxvi) in *Géographie humaine de la France,* Vol. II. Paris: Société de l'Histoire National. 652 pp.

BUFFAULT, P.
1937a "Les Forêts de l'Europe pendant le moyen âge," *Revue des eaux et forêts,* LXXIV, 140–50.
1937b "Le Déboisement: Ses causes, ses consequences," *ibid.,* pp. 432–41, 506–18.

CAGGESE, R.
1907–8 *Classi e comuni rurali nel medio evo italiano.* 2 vols. Florence: Tipografia Galileiana. 405 + 392 pp.

CAMPAGNE, A. J. P.
1912 *Les Forêts pyrénéenes: Évolution à travers les âges. État et rendement actuels. Avenir économique.* Paris: Laveur. 190 pp.

CÁNOVAS DEL CASTILLO, A.
1910 *Historia de la decadencia de España.* Madrid: Liberia Gutenberg de José Ruiz. 761 pp.

CAVAILLÈS, H.
1905 "La Question forestière en Espagne," *Annales de géographie,* V, 318–31.

CHILDE, V. GORDON
1931 "The Forest Cultures of Northern Europe: A Study in Evolution and Diffusion," *Journal of the Royal Anthropological Institute of Great Britain and Ireland,* LXI, 325–48.

CLARK, J. G. D.
1944 "Man and Nature in Prehistory, with Special Reference to Neolithic Settlement in Northern Europe," *University of London Institute of Archaeology, Occasional Paper,* No. 6, pp. 20–28.
1945 "Farmers and Forests in Neolithic Europe," *Antiquity,* XIX, 57–71.

1947 "Forest Clearance and Prehistoric Clearing," *Economic History Review,* XVII, 45–51.
1952 "Farming: Clearance and Cultivation," pp. 91–107 (chap. iv) in *Prehistoric Europe: The Economic Basis.* Cambridge: Cambridge University Press. 349 pp.

CLARKE, R. R.; MACDONALD, J.; and WATT, A. S.
1938 "The Breckland," pp. 208–29 (chap. xv) in DARBY, H. C. (ed.), *The Cambridge Region.* Cambridge: Cambridge University Press. 234 pp.

DARBY, H. C.
1936 "Colonisation," pp. 178–89 in DARBY, H. C. (ed.), *An Historical Geography of England before A.D. 1800.* Cambridge: Cambridge University Press. 566 pp. (Reprinted 1948, 1951.)
1950 "Domesday Woodland," *Economic History Review,* 2d ser., III, 21–43.
1951 "The Clearing of the English Woodlands," *Geography,* XXXVI, 71–83.
1952 *The Domesday Geography of Eastern England.* Cambridge: Cambridge University Press. 400 pp.

DARBY, H. C., and TERRETT, I. B. (eds.)
1954 *The Domesday Geography of Midland England.* Cambridge: Cambridge University Press. 482 pp.

DAVIES, R. W.
1952 "Russia in the Early Middle Ages," *Economic History Review,* 2d ser., V, 116–27.

DEBIEN, G.
1952 *En Haut-Poitou: Défricheurs au travail, XVe–XVIIIe siècles.* Paris: Armand Colin. 93 pp.

DEFFONTAINES, P.
1932 *La Vie forestière en Slovaquie.* Paris: Travaux Publiés par l'Institut d'Études Slaves. 94 pp.
1933 *L'Homme et la forêt.* Paris: Gallimard. 188 pp.

DES MAREZ, G.
1926 *Le Problème de la colonisation franque et du régime agraire en Belgique.* Brussels: Académie Royale de Belgique. 191 pp.

DIETRICH, B. F. A.
1928   "European Forests and Their Utilization," *Economic Geography*, IV, 140–58.

DION, R.
1938   "Usines et forêts: Conséquences de l'ancien emploi du bois comme combustible industriel," *Revue des eaux et forêts*, LXXVI, 771–82.

DOPSCH, A.
1937   *The Economic and Social Foundations of European Civilization.* London: Kegan Paul, Trench, Trubner & Co. 404 pp.

DUVIVIER, C.
1859   *"Hospites:* Défrichements en Europe et spécialement dans nos contrées aux XIe, XIIe et XIIIe siècles," *Revue d'histoire et d'archéologie*, I, 74–90, 131–75.

ECK, A.
1933   *Le Moyen Âge russe.* Paris: Maison du Livre Étranger. 574 pp.

ERMOLOV, A. S.
1893   "Systems of Agriculture and Field Rotation," pp. 62–73 (chap. iv) in CRAWFORD, J. M. (ed.), *The Industries of Russia*, Vol. III. St. Petersburg: Department of Agriculture, Ministry of Crown Domains. 488 pp.

FERNOW, B. E.
1911   *A Brief History of Forestry: In Europe, the United States and Other Countries.* Toronto: University of Toronto Press. 506 pp.

FICKELER, P.
1954   "Das Siegerland," *Erdkunde*, VIII, 15–81.

FLACH, J.
1893   "Les Villages créés dans les forêts et sur les terres désertes," pp. 139–57 (chap. xii) in *Les Origines de l'ancienne France*, Vol. II. Paris: Librairie du Recueil Général des Lois et des Arrêts. 584 pp.

FOX, SIR CYRIL
1923   *The Archaeology of the Cambridge Region.* Cambridge: Cambridge University Press. 360 pp. (2d ed., 1949.)

GARNETT, A.
1945   "The Loess Regions of Central Europe in Prehistoric Times," *Geographical Journal*, CVI, 132–43.

GEORGE, P.
1933   "Anciennes et nouvelles forêts en région méditerranéenne," *Les Etudes Rhodaniennes*, IX, 85–120.

GOBLET, F. (COUNT D'ALVIELLA)
1927   *Histoire des bois et forêts de Belgique. ... Des Origines à la fin du régime autrichen.* 3 vols. Paris: Paul Lechevaliers; Brussels: Maurice Lamertin. 491 + 351 + 140 pp.

GODWIN, H.
1934   "Pollen Analysis: An Outline of the Problems and Potentialities of the Method," *New Phytologist*, XXXIII, 278–305, 325–58.
1944a   "Neolithic Forest Clearance," *Nature*, CLIII, 511.
1944b   "Age and Origin of the 'Breckland' Heaths of East Anglia," *ibid.*, CLIV, 6.

GOVER, J. E. B.; MAWER, A.; and STENTON, F. M.
1942   *The Place-Names of Middlesex.* Cambridge: Cambridge University Press. 237 pp.

GRADMANN, ROBERT
1898   *Das Pflanzenleben der schwäbischen Alb.* Tübingen: Schnürlen. 376 pp. (2d ed., 1900; 3d ed., 1936; 4th ed., 1952.)
1901   "Das mitteleuropäische Landschaftsbild nach seiner geschichtlichen Entwicklung," *Geographische Zeitschrift*, VII, 361–77, 435–47.
1906   "Beziehungen zwischen Pflanzengeographie und Siedlungsgeschichte," *ibid.*, XII, 305–25.
1931   *Süddeutschland.* 2 vols. Stuttgart: J. Engelhorns Nachf. 215 + 553 pp.

GRENIER, ALBERT
1930   "Aux origines de l'économie rurale: La conquête du sol français," *Annales d'histoire économique et sociale*, Deuxième année, pp. 26–47.

HESKE, FRANZ, and TORUNSKY, RICHARD (eds.)
1951——   *Weltforstatlas; World Forestry Atlas; Atlas des forêts du monde; Atlas forestal del mundo.* Hamburg and Reinbeck: Zentralinstitut für Forst-

und Holzwirtschaft. (In course of publication.)

HOOPS, J.
1905   *Waldbäume und Kulturpflanzen im germanischen Altertum.* Strasbourg: Verlag von Karl J. Trübner. 689 pp.

HORNSTEIN, FELIX VON
1951   *Wald und Mensch: Waldgeschichte des Alpenvorlandes Deutschlands Österreichs und der Schweiz.* Ravensburg: Otto Maier Verlag. 282 pp.

IVERSEN, J.
1941   *Landnam i Danmarks Stenalder* ("Land Occupation in Denmark's Stone Age"). ("Danmarks geologiske Undersøgelse," Series II, No. 66.) Copenhagen. 68 pp. (For a review see Godwin, 1944a.)
1949   *The Influence of Prehistoric Man on Vegetation.* ("Danmarks geologiske Undersøgelse," Series IV, Vol. III, No. 6.) Copenhagen. 25 pp.

JÄGER, H.
1951   *Die Entwicklung der Kulturlandschaft im Kreise Hofgeismar.* ("Göttinger geographische Abhandlungen," No. 8.) Göttingen. 114 pp.
1954   "Zur Entstehung der heutigen grossen Forsten in Deutschland," *Berichte zur deutschen Landeskunde,* XIII, 156–71.

JULLIAN, C.
1920   *Histoire de la Gaule,* Vol. V: *La Civilisation gallo-romaine.* Paris: Librairie Hachette. 381 pp.

KELLER, B. A.
1927   "Distribution of Vegetation on the Plains of European Russia," *Journal of Ecology,* XV, 189–233.

KLEIN, J.
1920   *The Mesta: A Study in Spanish Economic History, 1273–1836.* Cambridge, Mass.: Harvard University Press. 444 pp.

KLUCHEVSKY, V. O.
1911–31   *A History of Russia.* 5 vols. London: J. M. Dent & Sons. 373 + 326 + 380 + 382 + 338 pp.

KNÜLL, B.
1903   *Historische Geographie Deutsch-*

lands im Mittelalter. Breslau: Ferdinand Hirt. 240 pp.

KOEBNER, R.
1941   "The Settlement and Colonisation of Europe," pp. 1–88 (chap. i) in CLAPHAM, J. H., and POWER, E. (eds.), *The Cambridge Economic History of Europe,* Vol. I. Cambridge: Cambridge University Press. 650 pp.

KÖTZSCHKE, R., and EBERT, W.
1937   *Geschichte der ostdeutschen Kolonisation.* Leipzig: Bibliographisches Institut. 251 pp.

KRETSCHMER, K.
1904   *Historische Geographie von Mitteleuropa.* Munich: R. Oldenbourg. 650 pp.

LAMPRECHT, K.
1893   *Deutsche Geschichte,* Vol. III. Berlin: R. Gaertners Verlagsbuchhandlung. 488 pp.

LANE, F. C.
1934   "The Timber Supplies," pp. 217–33 (chap. xii) in *Venetian Ships and Shipbuilders of the Renaissance.* Baltimore: Johns Hopkins Press. 285 pp.

LARROQUETTE, A.
1924   *Les Landes de Gascogne et la forêt landaise: Aperçu physique et étude de transformation économique.* Mont-de-Marsan: Imprimerie Dupeyron. 404 pp.

LEIMBACH, W.
1948   "Zur Waldsteppenfrage in der Sowjetunion," *Erdkunde,* II, 238–56.

LOUVILLE, E.
1897   "Les Taillis des Ardennes," *Revue des eaux et forêts,* XXXVI, 257–67.

LODIJENSKY, N.
1901   "The Forests of Russia," pp. 316–24 (chap. xxv) in LODIJENSKY, J. N. (ed.), *Russia: Its Industries and Trade.* Glasgow: Hay Nisbet & Co. 324 pp.

LORENZI, A.
1918–19   "L'Uomo e le foreste," *Rivista geografica italiana,* XXV, 141–65, 213–42; XXVI, 47–57.

MAGER, F.
1930   *Entwicklungsgeschichte der Kulturlandschaft des Herzogtums Schles-*

wig in historischer Zeit. Breslau: Ferdinand Hirt. 523 pp.

MANNINEN, I.
1932 *Die finnisch-ugrischen Völker*. Leipzig: Otto Harrassowitz. 384 pp.

MARSH, G. P.
1864 "The Woods," pp. 128–329 (chap. iii) in *Man and Nature: Or, Physical Geography as Modified by Human Action*. London: Sampson Low, Son & Marston. 560 pp.
1874 "The Woods," pp. 148–397 (chap. iii) in *The Earth as Modified by Human Action* (new ed. of *Man and Nature*). New York: Scribner, Armstrong & Co. 656 pp.

MARTONNE, E. DE
1931 *Géographie universelle: Europe centrale*. 2 vols. Paris: Armand Colin. 845 pp.

MAURY, L. F. A.
1850 *Histoire des grandes forêts de la Gaule et de l'ancienne France*. Paris: A. Leleux. 328 pp.
1866 *Les Forêts de la France dans l'antiquité et au moyen âge*. Paris: Imprimerie Impériale. 270 pp.
1867 *Les Forêts de la Gaule et de l'ancienne France*. Paris: Ladrange. 501 pp.

MAZOYER, L.
1932 "Exploitation forestière et conflits sociaux en Franche-Comté, à la fin de l'ancien régime," *Annales d'histoire économique et sociale*, Quatrième année, pp. 339–58.

MEAD, W. R.
1953 *Farming in Finland*. London: Athlone Press. 248 pp.

MINNS, E. H.
1913 *Scythians and Greeks*. Cambridge: Cambridge University Press. 720 pp.

MONKHOUSE, F. J.
1949 *The Belgian Kempenland*. Liverpool: University of Liverpool Press. 252 pp.

MONTELIUS, S.
1953 "The Burning of Forest Land for the Cultivation of Crops," *Geografiska Annaler*, XXXV, 41–54.

MORTENSEN, H.
1951 "Neue Beobachtungen über Wüstungs-Bandfluren und ihre Bedeutung für die mittelalterliche deutsche Kulturlandschaft," *Berichte zur deutschen Landeskunde*, X, 341–61.

MORTENSEN, H., and SCHARLAÜ, K.
1949 "Der siedlungskundliche Wert der Kartierung von Wüstungsfluren," *Nachrichten der Akademie der Wissenschaften in Göttingen, Philosophisch-historische Klasse, 1949*, pp. 303–31.

MUTTON, A. F. M.
1938 "Place-Names and the History of Settlement in South-west Germany," *Geography*, XXIII, 113–19.

NEF, J. U.
1952 "Mining and Metallurgy in Medieval Civilisation," pp. 429–92 (chap. vii) in POSTAN, M., and RICH, E. (eds.), *The Cambridge Economic History of Europe*, Vol. II. Cambridge: Cambridge University Press. 604 pp.

NEUMANN, K.
1855 *Die Hellenen im Skythenlande*. Berlin: Verlag Georg Reimer. 578 pp.

NIEMEIER, G.
1949 "Frühformen der Waldhufen," *Petermanns geographische Mitteilungen*, XCIII, 14–27.

NIETSCH, H.
1939 *Wald und Siedlung im vorgeschichtlichen Mitteleuropa*. Leipzig: Mannus-Bücherei. 254 pp.

OURLIAC, P.
1949 "Les Villages de la région Toulousaine au XIIe siècle," *Annales: Économies, sociétés, civilisations*, Quatrième année, pp. 268–77.

PARAIN, C.
1936 *La Méditerranée: Les hommes et leurs travaux*. Paris: Gallimard. 225 pp.

PASZKIEWICZ, H.
1954 *The Origin of Russia*. London: Allen & Unwin. 556 pp.

PATSCH, C.
1922 *Historische Wanderungen im Karst und an der Adria*. Vienna: Verlag des Forschungsinstitutes für Osten und Orient. 170 pp.

PENCK, ALBRECHT
1887 "Das deutsche Reich," pp. 115–596 in KIRCHOFF, A. (ed.), *Länder-*

kunde des Erdteils Europa, Vol. II: *Unser Wissen von der Erde*, Part I. Vienna: F. Tempsky.

POHLENDT, H.
1950 *Die Verbreitung der mittelalterlichen Wüstungen in Deutschland.* ("Göttinger geographische Abhandlungen," No. 3.) Göttingen. 86 pp.

POSTAN, M.
1952 "The Trade of Medieval Europe: The North," pp. 119–256 (chap. iv) in POSTAN, M., and RICH, E. (eds.), *The Cambridge Economic History of Europe*, Vol. II. Cambridge: Cambridge University Press. 604 pp.

POWER, E.
1932 "Peasant Life and Rural Conditions (*c.* 1100 to *c.* 1500)," pp. 716–50 in TANNER, J. R., *et al.*, *The Cambridge Medieval History*, Vol. VII. Cambridge: Cambridge University Press. 1073 pp.

RABOT, C.
1905 "Le Déboisement dans la vallée d'Aspe et son influence sur le régime des cours d'eau," *La Géographie*, XI, 207–8.

ROUDSKI, A. F., and SHAFRANOV, N. I.
1893 "Forestry," pp. 311–52 (chap. xv) in CRAWFORD, J. M. (ed.), *The Industries of Russia*, Vol. III. St. Petersburg: Department of Agriculture, Ministry of Crown Domains. 488 pp.

RUNGALDIER, R.
1943 *Natur- und Kulturlandschaft zwischen Donau und Theiss.* ("Abhandlungen der Geographischen Gesellschaft in Wien," Vol. XIV, No. 4.) 127 pp.

SCHLÜTER, O.
1920 "Wald, Sumpf und Siedelungsland in Altpreussen vor der Ordenszeit," *Geographischer Anzeiger*, XXI, 245–49.
1952 *Die Siedlungsräume Mitteleuropas in frühgeschichtlicher Zeit*, Part I. ("Forschungen zur Deutschen Landeskunde," Vol. LXIII.) Hamburg. 47 pp.

SCHMITTHENNER, H.
1923 "Die Reutbergwirtschaft in Deutschland," *Geographische Zeitschrift*, XXIX, 115–27.

SCHOTT, CARL
1935 "Urlandschaft und Rodung: Vergleichende Betrachtungen aus Europa und Kanada," *Zeitschrift der Gesellschaft für Erdkunde zur Berlin*, pp. 81–102.
1952 "Das Heideproblem in Schleswig-Holstein," *Verhandlungen des Deutschen Geographentages*, XXVIII, 259–68.

SCLAFERT, T.
1926 *Le Haut-Dauphiné au moyen âge.* Paris: Société anonyme du recueil Sirey. 765 pp.
1933 "A propos du déboisement des Alpes du Sud," *Annales de géographie*, XLII, 266–77, 350–60.
1934 "A propos du déboisement des Alpes du Sud: Le Rôle des troupeaux," *ibid.*, XLIII, 126–45.

SEMENOV, D. P.
1893 "Cultivation of the Soil," pp. 74–92 (chap. v) in CRAWFORD, J. M. (ed.), *The Industries of Russia*, Vol. III. St. Petersburg: Department of Agriculture, Ministry of Crown Domains. 488 pp.

SEMPLE, E. C.
1931 "Ancient Mediterranean Forests and the Lumber Trade," pp. 261–96 (chap. xi) in *The Geography of the Mediterranean Region: Its Relation to Ancient History*. New York: Henry Holt & Co. 737 pp.

SCÓ, R. DE
1929 "Die Vegetation und die Entstehung der ungarischen Puszta," *Journal of Ecology*, XVII, 329–50.

STENTON, F. M.; BUTLER, H. E.; HONEYBOURNE, M. B.; and DAVIS, E. JEFFRIES
1934 *Norman London: An Essay.* ("Historical Association Leaflets," Nos. 93–94.) London. 40 pp.

STRAKER, E.
1931 *Wealden Iron.* London: G. Bell & Sons. 487 pp.

STREYFFERT, T.
1934 "Softwood Resources of Europe," *Economic Geography*, X, 1–13.

THOMPSON, J. W.
1928a *An Economic and Social History*

of the Middle Ages (300–1300). New York: Century Co. 900 pp.

1928*b* *Feudal Germany*. Chicago: University of Chicago Press. 710 pp.

TRAUTMANN, R.

1948–49 *Die Elb- und Ostseeslavischen Ortsnamen*. 2 vols. ("Abhandlungen der Deutschen Akademie der Wissenschaften zu Berlin, Philosophisch-historische Klasse, 1947," Nos. 4 and 7.) Berlin. 187 and 119 pp.

TÜXEN, R.

1931 "Die Grundlagen der Urlandschaftsforschung: Ein Beitrag zur Erforschung der Geschichte der anthropogenen Beeinflussung der Vegetation Mitteleuropas," *Nachrichten aus Niedersachsens Urgeschichte*, No. 5, pp. 59–105.

TURRILL, W. B.

1929 "The Influence of Man on the Flora and Vegetation," pp. 189–239 (chap. x) in *The Plant-Life of the Balkan Peninsula*. Oxford: Clarendon Press. 490 pp.

VILLARI, L.

1904 *The Republic of Ragusa*. London: J. M. Dent & Co. 424 pp.

WADDINGTON, C. H.

1930 "Note sur la dépopulation des campagnes gâtinaises pendant la guerre de cent ans et leur reconstruction économique," *Annales de la Société Historique et Archéologique du Gâtinais*, XXXIX, 164–78.

WILCOX, H. A.

1933 *The Woodlands and Marshlands of England*. Liverpool: University of Liverpool Press. 55 pp.

WILHELMY, H.

1950 "Das Alter der Schwarzerde und der Steppen Mittel- und Osteuropas," *Erdkunde*, IV, 5–34.

ZON, R.

1920 "Forests and Human Progress," *Geographical Review*, X, 139–66.

ZON, R., and SPARHAWK, W. N.

1923 "The Forest Situation in Europe," pp. 72–349 (chap. ii) in *Forest Resources of the World*. 2 vols. New York: McGraw-Hill Book Co. 997 pp.

The Ecology of Peasant Life in Western Europe

E. ESTYN EVANS[*]

In 1944 there appeared a remarkable monograph on *Cereals in Great Britain and Ireland in Prehistoric and Early Historic Times* by two Danish scientists, Knud Jessen and Hans Helbaek. It is important as an original work on an obscure subject, but what makes it remarkable is the fact that it was published in Copenhagen, in English, during the Nazi occupation of Denmark. The maintenance of a modernized peasantry and the correlated enlightened outlook on education surely stand vindicated in the outstanding contributions made by Danish archeologists and paleobotanists to our knowledge of the evolution of European agriculture. It is no accident that Scandinavian scholars have pioneered in the study of agrarian history. Brøgger indeed has claimed that, to approach any understanding of early cultures, it is necessary to work back from the present, "to know something of life along the coast and at sea, in the forests and amid the mountains, on the land, the fields, the pastures, the hinterland and the mountain farms"

* Dr. Evans is Professor of Geography and Head of the department and former Dean of the Faculty of Arts in Queen's University, Belfast. He was Tallman Visiting Professor of Geography and Anthropology at Bowdoin College, Brunswick, Maine, in 1948–49. He has conducted many excavations on prehistoric sites in Ireland. His publications include: *Irish Heritage*, 1942; *Mourne Country*, 1951; and *Lyles Hill: A Late Neolithic Site in County Antrim*, 1953.

(1940, p. 166). Equally it may be asserted that a full understanding of peasant societies, as they have survived until yesterday, is impossible without a knowledge of their origins and of their painful but fateful adaptation to the difficult western European environments of forests, mountains, moorlands, clouds, and seas.

The roots of our folk life strike deep into the past, and the conventional documentary tools of the historian cannot reach down to them. But a Marc Bloch can read the runes of old field boundaries carved on the landscape as archeological documents and can glimpse the truth that, when the Middle Ages began, "l'agriculture était déjà, sur notre sol, chose millénaire" (Bloch, 1931, p. 1). Rural prehistory, says Bloch, dominates rural history. In Britain, as in Scandinavia, a great deal of research on prehistoric geography and archeology is in progress, and the co-operation of workers in several related sciences is proving fruitful. There are many gaps in the evidence—dark ages in time and dark areas in space—but in the course of some three decades much new light has been thrown on the origins of the peasantries of Western Europe. We have had, too, illuminating statistical studies of their present-day economies, but the ordinary laws of economics do not apply to traditional subsistence farming, and statistics cannot measure the values of rural living. They have come down to us from the past. I am therefore concerned with the patterns of rural life and landscape as they came to take shape and with their mutual relationships.

For our purpose Western Europe is taken to be the insular and peninsular ends of the Continent, north of the Mediterranean lands of summer drought and south of the cold coniferous forest, which lie open to the climatic influences of the Atlantic Ocean and to the impact of sea-borne cultures. Our region makes easy contact with the head of the Adriatic Sea by way of the Alpine passes leading from the upper Danube Basin. The transition to northeastern Europe is defined by a cultural watershed which runs approximately along the fourteenth east meridian and leaves western Sweden, with most of Norway, on the Atlantic cultural slope. Erixon has summarized the evidence (1938*a*) for these western European connections in Scandinavia, which is derived from such diverse material as archeology, peasant furnishings, house types, oaten bread, the two-wheeled cart, back baskets, and wooden shoes.

In middle Europe, between the Baltic Sea and the eastern Alps, the interpenetration of East and West—of upland and plain, of oceanic and continental climates, with their counterparts in the archeological record and in the historic conflicts of German and Slav—makes the definition of a frontier an insoluble problem for geographer and statesman alike. But our eastern limit lies somewhere within the transition zone of Mackinder (1944), between his "Marginal Lands" and "Heartland"; and we have chosen a line from Stettin to Trieste, which is effectively the present political divide between East and West (Fig. 66). It will be seen from the map that our line runs parallel to the January isotherm of 0° C., which defines the North Atlantic Gulf of winter warmth and marks the divide between areas having on the average at least one month of the year frozen, and those on the west, where January is normally a green month. In the extreme west the farthest peninsulas and islands of Ireland, southern England, and France lie on the warm side of the January isotherm of 6° C., the approximate zero of plant growth; and these favored evergreen ends of Western Europe are the homes of such milky breeds of cattle as the Kerry, the Jersey, and the Guernsey. Western Europe knows neither prolonged summer drought nor, as a rule, lengthy winter frost; in this equable climate soil erosion, save on steep slopes, is not a serious problem, and farming life has been continuous through the centuries. Rather it is the accumulation of waterlogged peats that has upset the ecologic balance of farming communities along the Atlantic seaboard.

Western Europe as thus defined, facing the Atlantic along thousands of miles of drowned coasts from Trondheim Fjord to the mouth of the Douro, belongs in the main to a single ecological zone, that of the temperate deciduous forest, broken only by the Scandinavian fjeld and its fringe of boreal forest and by the mountain islands of the High Alps and Pyrenees. If to these inhospitable regions we add the broken Caledonian and Hercynian uplands and certain areas of high precipitation or impoverished soils, we can distinguish two major types of environment within Western Europe, which we may term, following Fleure (1919), "regions of difficulty" and "regions of effort." They are marked on Figure 66, together with patches of fertile loessic soil which offered a relatively favorable habitat for early farming and which, linking with more extensive deposits in the middle Danube Basin and southeastern Europe, served repeatedly as avenues along which colonists and adventurers invaded the west. Our map marks also

Legend:
- Regions of difficulty
- Lowlands with light rainfall
- Loess and Limon

Jan. O°C.

OAK (quercus robur)

BEECH (fagus silvaticus)

60°

50°

40°

-N-

0   100   200   300
MILES

FIG. 66.—Some environmental factors in the rural life of Western Europe. Continental and Mediterranean regions are hatched. The map distinguishes between regions of difficulty having high relief and/or high rainfall and lowland areas. It also shows the distribution of loessic soils. The continuous line is the January isotherm of 0° C Broken lines show the historic limits of the oak and the beech.

the historic limits of the beech tree, which flourishes with summer rains on well-drained soils and provides us with an index of the most favorable conditions for early agriculture. Its eastern limit runs from about Danzig to the Balkan Mountains, and it is not native to the far northwest. It should be noticed, however, that the beech tree did not flourish in Denmark until the Dark and Middle Ages.

Not only are the regions of difficulty generally ill suited by topography, soils, and climate to large-scale cereal cultivation but they also tend to be refuge areas, conserving old layers of culture and resisting change. It is in these cloudy pastoral corners of Europe that old ways of life and linguistic minorities have persisted: Basque in the western Pyrenees, old Romance dialects in remote Alpine valleys, and Celtic tongues in Brittany, Wales, western Scotland, and western Ireland. The distinction is strikingly illustrated in Britain, where upland and lowland have preserved their cultural differences and where the English language, which has conquered continents, has failed to dislodge the Celtic tongue from the neighboring Welsh hills. Here it seems that an ecologic balance was struck in the Celtic Iron Age, some two thousand years ago, following the adoption of a new crop (oats), of a new technology (iron), and of a system of cattle transhumance which permitted permanent settlement and gave the pastoral uplands remarkable powers of resistance. Sir Cyril Fox has developed the thesis of the highland zone of absorption and the lowland zone of replacement in his study, *The Personality of Britain* (1947). But, before we resume the question of origins and regional differentiation, we must ask ourselves what we mean by a peasantry.

WHAT IS A PEASANTRY?

We may find peasant values persisting among farmers who would resent the term "peasantry," but it is doubtful that the name can be applied, for example, to the family farmers of England with their 100–300-acre holdings. On the other hand, we feel justified in speaking of a modernized peasantry in Denmark. The word has always carried an implication of rustic inferiority, and we tend to apply it to countries other than our own. Thus we readily use it for the cultivators of India and China. Yet the word implies a permanent link with the soil—the *paysan* with his *pays* —so that we hesitate to apply it to the shifting cultivators of tropical Africa. In Western Europe we cannot nowadays insist on a large measure of economic self-sufficiency as a criterion, but, where there is much mechanization and specialization, peasant values are undermined. For our purpose I take the peasant to be the self-employed farmer (as distinct from the non-operating landowner) who is largely dependent on the labor of his family; and we may expect the contribution of this labor to be more important than the contribution of capital.

Peasant proprietorship is not involved, for in many Western European countries it is a product of the nineteenth century, and landownership is no part of the immemorial peasant tradition. In fact, it has weakened it, because the old peasantries were attached to co-operative schemes of land use, and private ownership of the soil as we understand it was not found. Moreover, peasant proprietorship has brought with it as many problems as it has solved. It has meant money payments and capital investments which have left the owners at the mercy of moneylenders; it has led to inflated land values and acute land hunger where, as in Ireland, it is impossible to rent land save for short periods; and it has in some cases left the peasants without leaders.

The significant fact is that in most regions of Western Europe, in upland

and lowland, it is the small family farm of from 5 to 50 acres that predominates. More than half the Danish farms, for example, are under 25 acres. A considerable but decreasing number of holdings is less than 2½ acres (1 hectare) in size, and these derive as a rule from successive subdivisions among joint heirs, a process which, though now discouraged or prohibited in most countries, has left as a legacy not only diminutive properties but also the serious problem of fragmentation or *parcellement*. Some Swiss holdings of under a hectare are split into over fifty scattered pieces, and there are worse cases on record from pre-famine Ireland. It has happened in Brittany, even recently, that minute fragments of a square yard or so, too small and too remote to be worth cultivating and growing only thistles, are yet prized and jealously guarded. Moreover, a high proportion of good land is wasted in balks or fences, and a farmer may walk hundreds of miles each year merely in moving from one field to another. Fragmentation is one of the pathological problems of peasant farming which has been or is being solved in most parts of Western Europe but which is still the norm in southern Asia. Behind it we see the passion for equal shares of the precious soil as something to be handed down from one generation to another. It is this attachment to the land that gives a peasantry its strength and continuity—an attachment deepened by the devotion of daily work and seasonal festival and by the traditional use of home-grown foods and of local materials for tools, crafts, clothing, and housing. The quality of peasant craftsmanship resides in its ecological fitness, in the use of local products for local needs. The peasant, in continuous touch with the whole cycle of production, can sense the wholeness of life and derive therefrom satisfaction and self-confidence.

Reacting from the specialization and artificial values of urban life, many writers have idealized the untutored folkways of the peasant. We have become accustomed to uncritical eulogies from intellectuals who have never endured the toil of the fields and see only the gay festivals which mark its periodic breaks. More sinister is the political exploitation of peasant attitudes: of large families encouraged to supply the armed forces and of holdings recklessly multiplied to provide votes from "forty-shilling freeholders" in eighteenth-century Ireland. We have witnessed in our own day the consequences of a political philosophy in which peasant worship was prominent, and we recall Hitler's phrase, "Germany must be a peasant people" (Yates, 1940, p. 449). Under the mystical Nazi conception of "blood and soil," the peasant farm was to become "the cradle of the race," a symbol of supposed racial purity. But it also became the means of achieving strategic self-sufficiency in essential foods. Rural festivals were prostituted for political ends, and the peasant urge for progeny was exploited to increase the German birth rate. Nationalistic fervor was bolstered by extravagant claims for the Nordic center as an originator of prehistoric cultures. Since this Nordic center involves Danish territory, it is refreshing to recall the contemporary interest of Danish scientists in the Western European heritage.

There are, as I hope to show, significant differences in peasant values between our regions of difficulty and of effort, as well as between different countries with their varying experiences, but we may conclude this section by considering some attitudes and customs which were, until recently, universal. A very widespread feature is the extensive part played by women in the care of animals, especially cattle and their milk products, and in some field operations. Presumably the earliest cultivators, using the digging stick or stone hoe, were women. In the west of Ireland, potatoes grown in ridges are planted by women and children with a kind of digging stick—a dibble—and on the margin of our region, in Norrland, it is the housewife who has charge of the sowing of crops (Erixon, 1938*b*, p. 288).

Since sons and daughters are helpers from an early age, there is an economic urge for children, especially for sons, to inherit the land; and it must be remembered that, according to one calculation, it was necessary down to the eighteenth century for the average rural wife to bear six children in order to maintain the population. However much the position has changed in some countries, through delayed marriage or family limitation, it remains true that, immemorially, peasant families were large. There are many hints that the fertility of the family was magically connected with the fertility of the soil —that a birth each spring was lucky, an encouragement to the crops and animals to produce a like increase. Devotion to symbols of fertility was a powerful motive force, and its transference, in part, to the worship of the Virgin Mary was a source of inspiration to the medieval world.

Moreover, the peasant festivals which rounded off the seasons of the year have been more or less taken over by Christianity. In Celtic tradition the first day of each quarter, February, May, August, and November, is of great significance. The first of May and the first of November are, in rural Ireland, for example, family festivals, half-pagan, half-Christian; and even in towns they have become the gale days, the times when rents are paid. Traditionally they mark the completion of sowing and harvest and also the beginning and end of the season when the cattle were away on the hill pastures. Behind many of the May Day and Halloween customs there lies the idea of sympathetic magic per-

formed to insure good luck for another season. But they were also times when taboos were lifted and a good deal of license was permitted, serving as emotional outlets to ease the strain of periods of intense activity. Similarly, the festivals of midsummer and midwinter were both breaks in routine and occasions for the practice of magic associated with water (cf. Midsummer Day, the Feast of St. John the Baptist, June 24) and with fires, intended perhaps to assist the sun in its turning.

The ceremonies of the last sheaf, whether or not we accept the animistic theories of Mannhardt and Frazer and see in them fertility cults, came to be associated with the fear of being last and acted as a means of insuring the due completion of necessary tasks. Many of the rites of spring are looked on as omens and linked in the peasant mind with the necessity of beginning a new phase of work propitiously. The start of plowing and sowing and the gatherings for sheep-shearing and for the movements of livestock have also been times of ceremony, celebrated by feasting, singing, and dancing. In this way a wonderful wealth of folk tunes and folk songs has been bequeathed to us, handed down from one generation to another. The unlettered peasant often has an amazing memory and remarkable faculties of speech and rhetoric, and these qualities tend to be most marked in regions of difficulty. Poverty, indeed, may be a safeguard of quality in other ways; for example, our most highly prized cheeses come from the poor districts. Where there is little meat to spare, soups and stews have somehow to be made tasty, and, if a certain amount of dirt is involved, may there not be virtue in trace elements and wisdom in the Irish saying that "clean meat never fattened a pig"?

Folklore, proverbs, riddles, children's games, songs, dances, and an astonishingly rich oral literature are the heritage of Europe's peasantries, linking them with the cultivators of other parts of the Old World. Craft knowledge was similarly handed down from father to son, and its secrets cannot be found in books. (Handicrafts, however, are less developed in Western than in Eastern Europe, where towns are fewer and where winter cold limits outdoor work.) The extreme diffusionist view, that peasantries originate nothing, cannot be sustained, yet it is clear that they owe a great deal to ideas filtering down from other social classes. The self-contained community must always have been rare, and from early times no peasantry was entirely independent of external control. Periodic and annual fairs are a very old feature associated with pagan sites and seasons and later with religious centers and saints' days. They were a factor in the growth of towns, which became centers of government and administration as well as of exchange, and, as towns grew, their demand for an agricultural surplus affected in various ways the life of the countryside. The parallel growth of urban industries also profoundly affected rural life, both by flooding the countryside with machine-made goods and by depriving it of the craftsmen who brought to it a healthy variety of work and experience. "The drift from the land" is both a cause and a symptom of rising material civilization (Ashby, 1939). Yet there is general agreement that the rural tradition is an indispensable element in society, a source of vitality and continuity, conserving social values which urbanism tends to destroy. The problem is to preserve these values while increasing the efficiency of farming and the standards of rural living. Our views will be more hopeful if we realize the immemorial antiquity of peasant life.

PREHISTORIC ORIGINS

Farming communities had already reached the southern and eastern approaches to Western Europe before the end of the third millennium B.C. Danubians from the east seem to have been the first to enter the region, but the earliest farmers to reach Britain (about 2000 B.C.) were colonists from western Mediterranean lands who by that time had also pushed eastward from France into Switzerland and Lombardy and crossed the Rhine into the Elbe and Bavaria, where they settled in the fertile loessic areas previously occupied by farmers from the east (Childe, 1950, p. 88). There is evidence that from the beginning the westerners were more concerned with stock-raising than were the Danubians, and mixed farming was to become, as it still remains, the cornerstone of western European agriculture. Their western Neolithic pottery is characterized by its burnished, round-bottomed forms, significantly imitative of leather vessels. Already in the early centuries of the second millennium well-defined regional cultures were taking shape, distinguished by such traits as their pottery styles (Cortaillod, Michelsberg, Windmill Hill, etc.; see Fig. 67); and they occupy geographical areas which have had well-marked personalities in historic times. The differentiation of Western Europe into human regions is thus a fact of great antiquity, and the environmental conditions which colored the original Neolithic occupation of each region call for careful study if we are to comprehend the sources of regional consciousness and the persistent patterns of regional culture. We must also take into account the acculturation of local Mesolithic communities with their immensely old traditions. An inheritance from these deeper layers seems to be the survival of a pre-instrumental pentatonic scale in the haunting folk tunes of northwestern Europe, from Ireland to Finland. As we peer into the prehistoric twilight, we become aware of powerful forces which have shaped peasant life and persist in some

Fig. 67.—Late Neolithic culture areas in Western Europe (2000–1500 B.C.). The somewhat earlier First Danubian culture is marked in short bars; note its association with areas of loess. The distribution of megalithic tombs betrays coastwise diffusion. Arrows indicate directions of movement.

measure to this day, for the immobile peasantries provide the only unbroken human link with the past, maintaining social and religious as well as physical and economic ties with the soil. We begin to see the megaliths of the outer coast lands (Fig. 67) not as mute memorials of a forgotten civilization but as an integral part of the heritage of Western Europe. We need not be surprised at Sydow's claim (1948, p. 242) to have found folk tales "at least four thousand years old" in areas of megalithic culture. The natural and cultivated environment and the tools of early farmers took on a spiritual significance which is echoed in the folk practices of Ireland and Brittany, for example, to this day.

The polished stone ax has long been recognized as the index of Neolithic culture; we now see it as the hallmark of forest farmers, much as the steel ax was the symbol of the North American pioneers. Petrological studies have revealed the care with which Neolithic farmers sought the most suitable lithic materials and the extensive trade that took place in stone axes. For instance, certain bluestone axes found throughout the British Isles came from a small exposure of porcellanite on Tievebulliagh, County Antrim—so small, indeed, that it escaped the notice of the Geological Survey of Ireland and has only recently been rediscovered by archeological detection (Jope, 1952). Forest clearance was necessary almost everywhere, for the only considerable breaks in the forest were areas of bare rock or of soils so poor that they would not have supported the earliest cereal crops, wheat and barley.

The speed with which colonists spread through Western Europe, avoiding only the marshes, heavy clays, and barren mountains, is explained by their migratory slash-and-burn economy (*Brandwirtschaft*). The subboreal climate of the Neolithic and Bronze ages is believed to have been drier and more favorable to clearance by fire than the earlier Atlantic or the later Sub-Atlantic phases. We need not suppose that all the timber was felled; ring-barking would have sufficed for the larger trees. In Denmark layers of oak charcoal have been observed in some of the bogs, occupying horizons poor in tree pollens —indicating forest clearance—but rich in the pollens of grasses, cereals, and weeds, especially the telltale ribwort plantain (*Plantago lanceolata*). Regeneration of the forest in the form of scrub is attested by the predominance of birch, alder, and hazel pollens in the succeeding layer of peat (Iversen, 1949, p. 12). In Ireland, too, hazel, birch, thorn, and other forest weeds increase at about the same time as the first herbaceous and cereal pollens appear in the bogs, and on the same horizon there is a marked decline in the amount of elm pollen (Mitchell, 1953). It has been suggested that the reduction of the elm, relative to the oak—a reduction which has been observed in Neolithic horizons throughout northwestern Europe—may be explained by the use of the bark and branches of the elm as cattle fodder. The oak, on the other hand, would have been treasured for its hog-fattening mast. We know that, apart from the dog, cattle and swine were the earliest domesticated animals in Europe; and Sauer (1952, p. 37), developing Menghin's views, has postulated a pre-Indo-European pig cult which spread north from the western Mediterranean. The virtual absence of the pig from the Neolithic village of Skara Brae, Orkney (Childe, 1931, p. 203), may be correlated with the northern limit of the oak forest (Fig. 66) and with the surviving traces of an ancient pig taboo in the Scottish Highlands.

While livestock was clearly of great economic importance, nomadic herding societies could have found no place in Neolithic Europe. Forested country, poor in grasses and encumbered with dead branches, would have provided little grazing. Clark has shown (1952, p. 117) that sheep, which require extensive grazing grounds, become important only as the Bronze Age passes into the early Iron Age. The evidence points to small co-operating communities of farmers, presumably kin groups occupying clusters of from ten to twenty houses, who cleared successive patches of forest over a fairly extensive area round about and sent out daughter-colonies to repeat the process. Their well-built houses and finely finished pottery certainly imply fixed if temporary settlement; and the enormous quantities of ritually broken pots offered at megaliths—yielding to the excavator tens of thousands of sherds on some sites—show that occupation must have continued for a generation or two at least. With pottery, we note in passing, came the stockpot and the first stews, broths, and soups, which have remained a part of peasant diet; there is always something in the pot, even if only—in Highland Britain—stewed tea. Note also the good quality of Neolithic pottery, inherited from Mediterranean cultures, and the progressive deterioration of the potter's art through the Bronze Age—in Ireland until the end of the Middle Ages—which is partly to be explained by an increasing dependence on livestock as pastures and bogs replaced forests.

We must not assume that dramatic environmental change is proof of a change of climate. In Ireland the growth of heather and the initiation of blanket bog in upland areas cleared and farmed by Neolithic settlers followed land use which was intensive enough to bring about the podzolization of the soil. Scores of megaliths now buried in the Irish bogs testify to a deterioration of the environment, which has been too readily attributed solely to climatic change (Fig. 68a). Recent investigations suggest that far more weight should be given to ecologic factors, to the disturbances brought about by forest clearance, by leaching of the exposed soil, rapid runoff, blocked drainage, and the redistribution of surface water (Mitchell, 1953). But the clearing of forest also let in the winds. I doubt that cereals could be successfully harvested in many areas without the assistance of the wind: the equinoctial gales are the very life of corn harvest in the west.

PLOWS AND FIELDS

It has been claimed that the light plow, the *ard*, had reached the western Baltic from the Mediterranean region before the end of the Neolithic period (Erixon, 1938a, p. 137), and marks of furrows have been observed underneath barrows of the Bronze Age in Jutland and Holland (Clark, 1952, p. 99). The oldest identified field systems in Western Europe, however, date from the late Bronze Age, after 1000 B.C.; but, since they tend to survive only in marginal areas of poor soil where they have not been obliterated by later fields, it is possible that permanent settlement and true peasantries go back to the second millennium. The plots are squarish, as in the Celtic field system brought to southern Britain by invading urn-field peoples (Fig. 68b), and they were presumably cross-plowed with the *ard* in Mediterranean fashion. Danish fields of the "Celtic Iron Age" have been investigated by Hatt, who finds evidence to suggest (1939, p. 11) that there were both single farms individually owned and clustered hamlets with fields subdivided by inheritance. He thinks that, from the irregular sizes of the plots, they did not change hands periodically, though we know that this was traditional in many open-field schemes, especially in regions of difficulty. Nor do we know whether the single farms imply social distinctions, as is suggested by

a

b

FIG. 68.—Archeological evidence

a) In Ireland and elsewhere in northwestern Europe peat-cutting has revealed many ancient sites under the bogs. This air photograph shows a complex of megalithic circles and alignments after archeological excavation had been undertaken following the removal of up to 6 feet of peat for fuel. The site is at Beaghmore, County Tyrone, Northern Ireland, on a plateau of pre-Cambrian rocks at a height of 600 feet. The leached sandy soil under the peat shows white inside the circles. Stone walls and causeways, probably associated with prehistoric fields, pass under and are older than some of the megalithic structures. The basal peats contain the pollens of weeds such as ribwort plantain (*Plantago lanceolata*) and dock (*Rubex*) and among tree pollens a high proportion of hazel. The upper peats show a complete dominance of heather pollens.

Old lazy beds visible at top left betray recent outfield cultivation—after an interval of some thirty-five hundred years—on land from which the peat had previously been removed. They probably date from the nineteenth century. Heather is again invading the cultivated land.

b) Circular settlement site (*top center*) and associated "Celtic fields" near Grassington, Yorkshire, underlying the present-day field pattern.

field evidence and by the Irish Law Texts for Dark Age Ireland. Certainly, for most of Western Europe, the archeological evidence points to a concentration of economic and political power, by the early Iron Age, in the hands of conquering herders; already in the Hallstatt phase splendid horse trappings and long cavalry swords tell of mounted leaders who foreshadow the military aristocrats of the Middle Ages. And the introduction of urbanism under Rome was preceded by an approximation to city life and specialized professions in the La Tène culture, developed in the region north of the Alps under the stimulus of Mediterranean contacts after 500 B.C. In the last centuries B.C., La Tène war chariots carried the Celtic conquerors over nearly all parts of Western Europe (Childe, 1950, p. 230).

The improved plow, with colter and moldboard to cut and turn the furrow slice, is also the product of the pre-Roman Iron Age and was designed for the cultivation of the deep heavy soils now being cleared of their mixed-oak forests with axes of iron. With it came a new type of cultivated landscape and a new order of rural living and social stratification evolving in time into the feudal system and the historic kingdoms of Western Europe. The heavy plow, sooner or later fitted with wheels, had reached southern England in pre-Roman times, and it was to spread to most of the lowland areas of Western Europe (Fig. 66, p. 219), leaving the light plow and the older order to the upland regions of difficulty, whose thin, stony soils and uneven terrain were unsuited to the new plow. We may accept the view that the cumbersome moldboard plow pulled by large teams of oxen brought with it not only the long furrow (furlong) and the acre strip but also co-aration and an increasing measure of co-operation and fixed routine in field operations. It helped to stabilize settlement by the accumulation of

heavy gear and by its association with the system of open-field strip farming in (normally) three great fields, whose fertility was maintained by regular fallows and by stubble grazing and manuring. Moreover, while the light plow brought from the south had been adequate for Mediterranean soils, which tend to have their minerals concentrated at the surface by evaporation, the heavy plow was needed to renew the fertility of the leached soils of Atlantic Europe by bringing the plant nutrients from deeper layers to the surface. Archeological and botanical research in Ireland has thrown a suggestive light on this question. At Lagore, in County Meath—in the favored metropolitan lowland adjacent to the east coast—land previously cultivated by the light plow and overgrown with heather shows a marked reduction of heath vegetation after the introduction of the heavy plow about the seventh century A.D. (Mitchell, 1951, p. 201).

Once the accumulated fertility of the deep forest soils of the lowlands had been opened up to permanent settlement, the uplands, which had shown a precocious development in the Neolithic and Bronze ages, suffered a relative decline. They were faced with a crisis. Not only was there less demand for tools made of their hard stone and of their copper and tin but they were affected by a rapid growth of blanket bog about the time when the Bronze Age was passing into the early Iron Age. We have seen that the bogs were initiated in some areas by podzolization of the soil following cultivation, and theories of a general Sub-Atlantic climatic deterioration, though apparently well established for Scandinavia, need reconsideration. In Ireland the field evidence points to an increase in pastoral activities, above all in cattle and dairying; and upland areas which had been inhabited in earlier times came to be utilized by lowland settlers as summer grazing grounds under a system of transhumance. Wooden utensils, carved, turned, or stave-built, replace the abundant pottery of the Neolithic and Bronze ages. In Norway haymaking and barn-building seem to have become established practices with the early Iron Age. Records and traditions of the Celtic fringe tell of inclosures—even if temporary—from early times, and we can correlate this both with the need to protect the growing crops from grazing animals and with the folding of stock to enrich limited patches of land.

The three-field system was ill adapted to these regions of difficulty. Instead, there was evolved a scheme better fitted to the extensive rough grazing and the limited areas of fairly good soil on deltaic fans and fluvial or marine terraces. It relied on the old practice of shifting cultivation for the outlying areas of rough grazing, and supplemented this with more or less permanent cultivation of the carefully selected home fields (the infield of Scotland and Ireland; *terres chaudes* of Brittany) enriched by manure accumulated each winter in single-roomed long houses which were both homes and byres. To it the name "infield-outfield" is given; in Scotland, where its recent survivals have been most fully studied, it is also known as runrig (Handley, 1953). The field plots were small and resembled in shape those of the Bronze Age, and they were cultivated either with the plow or, for the tough-skinned outfield, with the foot plow, breast plow, or spade. We shall see that the social system that went with it was familistic, based on the kin group, which is perhaps the oldest form of human society.

Outfield cultivation is not entirely a thing of the past (Fig. 69a); it survives among the marginal mountains of Ireland and Switzerland, and in parts of Sweden the Neolithic method of clearing forest by fire persists to this day.

"Paring and burning" or *denshiring* (from "Devonshire") was a widespread practice in Highland Britain in the eighteenth century, and it was largely by this method of breaking in rough hill pastures that the rapidly expanding population of western Ireland was supported on the potato in the century preceding the Great Famine of 1845. Monoculture brought a terrible revenge. In France the outfield system was characteristic of the interior of Brittany, the Ardennes, the Vosges, Lorraine, the Jura, the Alps, the Pyrenees, and the Central Plateau (Bloch, 1931, p. 28). We find traces of it also in the Asturias and in Galicia. Most of the land thus broken in piece by piece to temporary cultivation before relapsing to rough grazing was coarse pasture, heather, or scrub (in Brittany chiefly gorse, which was harvested as a crop), but in the High Vosges it was forest country. Outfield farming is also known to have been customary in some of the less fertile parts of the Western European lowlands.

Infield cultivation was more restricted in distribution and characterized especially the Atlantic coast lands (rundale or changedale in Ireland, *rhandiroedd* [share lands] in Wales, *aarkast* [annual change] in Norway). As the names imply, the infield was an open field whose plots—on soils of varying quality —were periodically redistributed. They were held by joint tenants who were members of a co-operating kin group living in a more or less clustered settlement of small farmhouses situated, as a rule, on the uphill side of the open field (Fig. 69b). The Irish clachan was often placed at the infertile apex of a deltaic fan, the slope facilitating the washing and carrying-down of the accumulated manure, human as well as animal. (It is an interesting detail that for this purpose the women went with the cows, the men with the horses.) The peasants not only shared the infield and the out-

S. T. Carleton   *a*

V. B. Proudfoot   *b*

FIG. 69.—Infield and outfield in Ireland

a) Spade-dug lazy beds in outfield, Achill Island, now reverting to heather and encroaching peat. The ridges run downslope and may be beveled toward the sun, as in center of the picture. They probably date from the nineteenth century.

b) Ashleam, Achill Island. The linear hamlet, strung out between infield (*below*) and outfield (*above*), is typical of many areas along the Atlantic coasts. It goes with a modified form of rundale, without periodic redistribution. The infield has here been "striped" to give each farm its own land, but subdivision has persisted so that small plots and scattered holdings are reappearing. The outfield is now used for rough grazing only.

field but enjoyed rights of common grazing and peat-cutting, for peat bogs, instead of the forests which they replaced, came to supply fuel. Along the Atlantic coasts sea wrack and shellsand have traditionally been utilized, in complicated systems and rituals of distribution, to supplement supplies of animal fertilizers (Evans, 1951, chap. xv). This scheme seems to have taken its historic shape after the introduction of oats, which have a short growing season and take less out of the soil than wheat. Not only are they food for cattle but they became the vehicle of "an ovenless, thin-bread, open-hearth complex" which is part of the peasant culture of Celtic Europe. Free of winter crops, the infield could be grazed and manured by livestock for half the year (traditionally, from the end of October to the end of April; for the other half of the year they were away in the hills), and it grew crops of oats, varied occasionally with barley, beans, flax, or rye, more or less without rest. It is possible that this scheme was taking shape before the adoption of oats; it has been claimed that, in Denmark, wheat was spring-sown from Neolithic times onward, down to the thirteenth century A.D. (Steensberg, 1952, p. 302).

The pattern of life in areas of infield-outfield cultivation was pastoral and patriarchal, familistic and flexible, relatively independent but linked with a "tribal" or clan system. It stands in contrast both to the three-field scheme of the richer lowlands with its heavy, ordered routine and to the classical Mediterranean two-field system of southern France. Historians have generally assumed that the single farms with their inclosed fields are original forms of settlement and land use in Celtic lands, but it is necessary to add that prejudices against "primitive communism" have colored some statements. The truth seems to be that single farms are the mark of conquerors who were

more literary and have left written records, while the history of the peasants is traced only in the archeological record. It seems that both open fields and single farms have existed side by side in historic times, and we know from nineteenth-century records that a single farm might become a complex joint holding in two or three generations (Fig. 70). But I think that the co-operating kin group must be of high antiquity. The Welsh evidence strongly suggests that the open fields and clustered settlements originated in prehistoric times among mixed-arable farmers who later became the bondmen of pastoral overlords (Jones, 1953). These, in early medieval times, lived as large households under one roof. The Irish homesteads (the raths or forts), of which the remains of over thirty thousand can still be seen among the Irish fields, would be the Gaelic equivalent, the houses of the better classes of freemen. The bondmen would be the descendants of the prehistoric pioneers. Together they all fell victims to later landlords, but in the end they have won their freedom as the peasant proprietors of modern Ireland. Folklore and ethnology support this view, but we find very little evidence concerning the underdogs in the Irish Law Texts, since they relate to the upper classes. Documentary evidence by itself is thus misleading. What has archeology to say?

The techniques of archeological field work have made such rapid progress in recent years that we may expect much new light on field systems and methods of prehistoric cultivation, but we cannot yet say when settlements became permanent. I believe that the adoption of ridge cultivation was an important advance. The narrow ridges on which Irish potatoes are traditionally planted (Fig. 69a) were adapted from the wider ridges on which oats were sown. Their preparation required much

West Torr Townland, Co. Antrim   1782

-N-

a

1832

b

935   862   ESCORT 460   201·   214

1935

c

0   200   400   600 YDS

Fig. 70.—Part of the townland of West Torr, County Antrim, Northern Ireland, showing settlement in the eighteenth, nineteenth, and twentieth centuries.

a) Carrivegarive quarterland (West Torr Townland) from an estate map, *ca.* 1782. If this map is to be trusted, there were at most three farms in the quarterland at that time, presumably established in the outfield of the "town" (cluster) of Torr which is marked on William Petty's map (The Down Survey, *ca.* 1655).

b) The first Ordnance Survey map (1832) shows a cluster with its open field round about, the result of joint inheritance. Heights in feet.

c) Ordnance Survey map, 1935. The townland is now one of scattered farms and inclosed fields which have taken in much of the old outfield.

hard labor and "mannering" with spade, rake, and shovel and usually meant co-operation. As made in the outfield, the ridges depended on efficient sod-cutting implements and are therefore not likely to predate the early Iron Age. Similarly, I think that the great expansion of cultivation and population in the Irish "potato age" depended on the steel-edged spade, which is still hand-forged in hundreds of shapes to suit local conditions and techniques and which gave the Irish peasant his strong back and his reputation as a navvy. Even today spades are sometimes employed on old grassland which is said to be "too tough for the plow."

Ridge cultivation was the answer to the problem of the rapid loss of fertility involved in the shallow tillage of the pioneer farmers, and I suggest it was a factor in that new ecological adjustment in regions of difficulty—the Celtic synthesis—to which I have referred. The Irish "lazy bed" will illustrate one variety of spade ridge. It is so called because the sod under the ridge is left intact, and the layer of decaying grasses on which the potato sets are placed not only provides humus in the right place but prevents the plant nutrients in the covering manure and soil from being washed down. Moreover, the sods and earth pared and dug from the intervening furrows raise the bed above the water table, while the furrows themselves act as open drains and are also dug deep enough to break the iron pan and thus give improved soil drainage. Old ridges are to be seen almost everywhere in Ireland and Scotland, and there are traces of spade ridges in many other parts of Highland Britain, in Norway, and in Switzerland. The high-backed plow ridges of many lowland areas of open-field cultivation, typically in the clay lands, served a similar purpose.

CROPS AND ANIMALS

To the primary Neolithic crops and animals—wheat and barley, cattle and pigs—others were added in later prehistoric times. The subject has been so recently treated (Clark, 1952; Helbaek, 1953; Zeuner, 1954) that we may confine ourselves to some ecologic aspects. The fact that wheat thrived in northwestern Europe in the second millennium B.C. in areas where it will hardly ripen today has been adduced as evidence of the dry subboreal climate. Yet, in Ireland, bogs and alder were spreading during some phases of the period. The abundant remains of domesticated plants and animals recovered during the last century from the Swiss lake dwellings, which included in one case piles of manure with layers of litter and droppings of cows, sheep, pigs, and goats, have since been supplemented by evidence obtained from many sources. The dominant Neolithic cereal was emmer (*Triticum dicoccum*), which is still grown in a few isolated corners of our region. Barley became far more important than wheat during the Bronze Age, after the disturbances which broke up the Neolithic cultures, and it has been suggested that it was beer which gave the migrant Beaker folk their characteristic drinking vessels and their spirituous ascendancy. Rye and oats, beginning their careers as weeds among the older cereals, became established as secondary cultivated plants, it is claimed, when the Sub-Atlantic climatic deterioration deprived the wetter regions of their wheat. This correlation is too simple to be true. Vital ecologic changes followed the destruction of forests, and, since many of the weeds which found congenial pioneer habitats in the clearings were boreal or tundra species such as the birch, their invasion of the lowlands might easily be interpreted as proving climatic change. At any rate, both oats and rye are first recorded in Britain in the early Iron

Age, and the former was to become in time the "corn" of the highland zone, food for man and beast. The adoption of oats confirmed the Atlantic coast lands in their pastoral ways. Rye took root in the old massifs of mid-Europe and on the sandy moraines of the Baltic lands. It was these same areas that welcomed the potato in the eighteenth century, with immense social consequences for Ireland and Germany in particular (Salaman, 1949). It may be surmised that oats and rye brought changes of a similar order in the life of the marginal lands of Western Europe in late prehistoric times.

VILLAGE AND HAMLET

Meitzen's monumental work (*Siedelung und Agrarwesen,* 1895) attempted to explain field and settlement patterns in Western Europe by reference to historically attested peoples. Regional studies and archeological research have shown that the facts are more complex, and, though much is confused, it is at least clear that no single theory will suffice to explain them. An ecological approach which considers the interrelations of cultures and environments seems to be necessary, but it must allow for the inheritance of traditions from earlier phases of adjustment. We need intensive studies, before it is too late, of the dialects and traditional dresses, the crafts, oral traditions, folklore, and folk music of our peasantries—work in which Swedish scholars have pioneered —but we also need systematic, anthropological surveys of peasant communities as functioning entities.

In the present-day rural landscapes of Western Europe the contrast between the villages of the plain with their strip fields and the scattered farms of the Atlantic coast lands with their hedged fields, even if rarely so sharp as that shown in the air photographs (Fig. 71), is nevertheless striking. And the attitudes of the folk who live and work in them are correspondingly different. The English village has lost many of its old functions and has changed its social structure, but there can be little doubt that it bred a disciplined tradition of self-government and a respect for law and order which, to the Irishman, appear to be the mark of simple minds. Its favorite game, a figure of fun to the Irish, is the flanneled ritual of cricket with "gentlemen and players" in friendly rivalry on village greens. It is a pleasant theory that the twenty-two yards of the cricket pitch owe their origin to the chain-wide furlong strips of the open fields.

In the pastoral uplands loyalties are to kin rather than to community. The Irishman's inherent lawlessness and independence spring from this attachment. The countryman likes to have personal relations with those who govern him, and the outside world should be capable of being manipulated on a personal basis. It is all-important to "know the right people." "Friendship" keeps its original meaning of blood relationship, and the claims of friendship may be stronger than the claims of abstract justice. Civic virtues are poorly developed; the country towns are small and for the most part no more than three or four centuries old. With the breakdown of the clan system and the substitution of a money economy and alien landlords, the pastoral peasantries lost their leaders; they have remained suspicious of the borrowed trappings of representative government.

Taking Western Europe as a whole, the villages of the plains, unless deliberately broken up, as happened in Denmark, have retained their form as nucleated settlements. The little hamlets of the uplands, however, have almost entirely given way to scattered farms since the late eighteenth century. Sometimes the change was made by agreement with the landlord, and sometimes it was enforced; but, on the

Aerofilms Limited

a

British Crown Copyright. Published by permission of the Air Ministry

b

Fig. 71.—Contrasting patterns of land use and settlement in the European plain and the highland zone.

a) The village of Uetterath, Münster, Westphalia, showing open-strip cultivation and limited *parcellement*. It was estimated in 1943 that between a quarter and a third of the arable land of Western Europe was still held in scattered parcels. The landscape is loessic.

b) Inclosed landscape with hedged fields and scattered farms, County Tyrone, Northern Ireland. Glacial drumlin topography. Near the center is the site of a Dark Age rath on top of a drumlin, surrounded on one side by traces of concentric inclosures. A modern farm lies alongside the original homestead site. The average field size is about two acres.

whole, save for instances of pathologically complex *parcellement,* it was a peaceful process which left little trace in records or acts of Parliament. The hamlets were merely clusters of farms, with no public buildings, no church, shops, or other attractions; and, once the advantages of permanent inclosure were seen, the little houses were abandoned. For a pastoral people there are obvious advantages to living in the midst of the fields, with the animals close at hand; and the compact farm, either squarish or ladder-like in plan, according to the terrain, has become the standard holding of upland Britain and Ireland. The fields are small, and, while most are laid down to grass—for hay is the main crop—the plow is "taken round the farm" periodically. Thus the outfield method, improved by the sowing of grass and clover mixtures and by the laying of drains, evolved into the system of fairly long leys which is well adapted to humid climates where overcultivation leads to leaching and souring of the soil. We know from records of Cistercian granges in eastern Scotland that grass parks for alternate husbandry were inclosed as early as the fifteenth century, but the system did not become general until after the adoption of root crops. In the transformation of an open countryside with clustered houses into an inclosed land with scattered farms, the improved iron swing plow (i.e., without wheels), introduced into Scotland about the year 1765 by James Small, played an important part. It was pulled by two horses in place of the large ox teams required for the crude wooden plow, and it was well adapted to the small fields of the uplands, much as the *ard* had been to the little Celtic fields whose shapes they reproduce. Small's plow was speedily adopted throughout northwestern Europe from Norway to Ireland.

THE PAST IN THE PEASANT

I have drawn many of my examples and illustrations from that part of Western Europe with which I am most familiar, and if I now confine myself to Ireland it is because, in addition, this peripheral island provides abundant material for the study of archaic survivals among a peasant people (Arensberg and Kimball, 1940; Evans, 1942; Mogey, 1947). Despite the industrialization of the northeast and the drive toward economic self-sufficiency in the Republic, well over half the population remains rural, dwelling for the most part on farms averaging 25–30 acres. The lowing of kine and the bellowing of bulls echo through the folklore and legendary histories of the Celtic world. True to tradition in this land of grass, oats, and cattle, the consumption of milk and dairy products per head of population is the highest in the world: 1,439 pounds in 1953 (if we are to believe the astonishing statistics issued by the United States Department of Agriculure). For the Irishman, "meat" means beef. The pig, "the gentleman" that once paid the rent, is also a gentleman in his lineage, and he thrives on the by-products of the dairy.

To this day in isolated spots the breeding of cattle and the making of butter are hedged around with taboos and lucky omens which have to do with flowers and shrubs. It is noteworthy that they are the plants which followed in the footsteps of the pioneer farmers —the shrubs of forest clearings, the flowers of the fields, and the weeds of cultivation. There is great virtue in the golden "Mayflowers," in the hazel twig, the rowan branch, and, above all, in the flowering May tree—the hawthorn—to which offerings of milk were once made. Summer is welcomed on May Eve by ceremonies of decking with flowers the house, byres, middens, and springs which are thus linked in a golden chain of fertility, for the flowers chosen—

marigolds, primroses, and gorse—are golden-yellow, the color of fresh butter. Clearly there is in this an element of sympathetic magic. Thus the dandelion, which is blessed with both a golden head and a milky stem, is "the plant of Bride," associated with the favorite Irish saint who was a milkmaid, protector of cows, and successor of a pagan goddess. Birch twigs and green rushes fashioned into crosses are used in rites celebrating St. Bridget's Day on the first of February, the beginning of spring. The solitary thorn tree (the fairy or gentry thorn) is regarded with such superstitious reverence that I have seen a tractor plow carefully avoiding its roots, and there are parts of the country where the only trees left are fairy thorns, whose creamy white blossoms are both a sign that damaging frosts are over and a bounteous promise of a full flow of milk. I see in the strength of these beliefs a measure of the intimate associations between early man and his immediate surroundings, but do they not also reflect his efforts to ward off the evils of diminishing returns which followed the use of Mediterranean tools and crops in an Atlantic environment? Like the bogs which grew over many of the first farmlands, the timeless peasant mind holds the past in its depths.

The complex mosaic of peasant beliefs is also colored by lingering fertility rites associated with the great stone monuments which remain as visible reminders of man's early efforts. There are traces of an old belief that the fairies are the spirits of the dead waiting to be reborn, haunting old burial places. In the early nineteenth century it was written of County Clare: "If a woman proves barren, a visit with her husband to one of the megaliths certainly cures her." Some of the games formerly played at wakes for the dead were frankly pagan, involving, for example, symbolism derived from boat-building, which recalls the rock carvings of sacred vessels (associated with fertility cults) found on Bronze Age sites along the coast of Norway. One might refer to many other examples of survivals, such as the process of match-making and the fixing of the dowry, involving negotiations which clearly reveal the values of rural life. There is little room for romantic love or divorce—the luxuries of a landless society—in a community which measures wealth in terms of land and livestock.

Surveying the present cultural landscape, we see a countryside parceled out into isolated farms which have won their freedom but have lost their self-sufficiency and their local leaders. When farming began, the land was forested from coast to coast; in ecological terms it is the peasantry which now forms a closed association over the face of the land. The craftsmen, the petty kings, and the landlords have gone. It is an egalitarian society, and its most prized virtue is "modesty." It is difficult not to conform in a naked countryside where one's neighbors are always watchful. The drive for increased output and mechanization means that fewer people are required on the land. Families are dying out or moving out of the marginal areas, and it is those with initiative who move first. But a peasantry which has endured for so long and survived so many vicissitudes and technological changes will, I believe, still preserve some of the values it has kept through the centuries.

REFERENCES

Arensberg, C. M., and Kimball, S. T.
  1940 *Family and Community in Ireland.* Cambridge, Mass.: Harvard University Press. 322 pp.

Ashby, A. W.
  1939 "The Effects of Urban Growth on the Countryside," *Sociological Review,* XXXI, No. 4, 345–69.

BLOCH, MARC
1931   *Les Caractères originaux de l'his-toire rurale française.* ("Institutt for sammenlignende Kulturforşkning," Series B, Vol. XIX [Oslo, 1928].) Paris: Société d'Édition les Belles-Lettres. 261 pp.

BRØGGER, A. W.
1940   "From the Stone Age to the Motor Age," *Antiquity,* XIV, No. 54 (June), 163–81.

CHILDE, V. GORDON
1931   *Skara Brae: A Pictish Village in Orkney.* London: Kegan Paul. 208 pp.
1947   *The Dawn of European Civiliza-tion,* 4th ed. (1st ed. 1925.) London: Kegan Paul. 362 pp.
1950   *Prehistoric Migrations in Europe.* ("Institutt for sammenlignende Kul-turforskning," Series A, Vol. XX.) Oslo. 248 pp.

CLARK, J. G. D.
1945   "Farmers and Forests in Neo-lithic Europe," *Antiquity,* XIX, No. 74 (June), 57–71.
1947   "Forest Clearance and Prehistoric Farming," *Economic History Review,* XVII, 45–51.
1952.   *Prehistoric Europe: The Eco-nomic Basis.* London: Methuen & Co. 349 pp.

COLLIER, A.
1953   *The Crofting Problem.* Cam-bridge: Cambridge University Press. 191 pp.

DUIGNAN, M.
1944   "Irish Agriculture in Early His-toric Times," *Journal of the Royal Society of Antiquaries of Ireland,* LXXIV, No. 3, 124–45. Dublin.

ERIXON, SIGURD
1938a   "West European Connections and Culture Relations," *Folk-Liv,* II, 137–72. Stockholm.
1938b   "Regional European Ethnolo-gy," *ibid.,* III, 263–94. Stockholm.

EVANS, E. ESTYN
1940   "Transhumance in Europe," *Ge-ography,* XXV, No. 4, 172–80.
1942   *Irish Heritage.* Dundalk, Ireland: Dundalgan Press. 190 pp.
1951   *Mourne Country: Landscape and Life in South Down.* Dundalk, Ire-land: Dundalgan Press. 226 pp.

FLEURE, H. J.
1919   "Human Regions," *Scottish Geo-graphical Magazine,* XXXV, No. 3, 94–105.
1937   "What Is a Peasantry?" *Bulletin of the John Rylands Library,* XXI, No. 2, 1–19. Manchester.
1943   "Peasants in Europe," *Geography,* XXVIII, No. 2, 55–61.
1948   "Land Use and Liberty," *ibid.,* XXXIII, No. 4, 167–75.

FOX, SIR CYRIL
1947   *The Personality of Britain.* 4th ed. Cardiff: National Museum of Wales. 74 pp.

GODWIN, H.
1940   "Pollen Analysis and Forest His-tory of England and Wales," *New Phytologist,* XXXIX, 370–400. Cam-bridge.

HANDLEY, J. E.
1953   *Scottish Farming in the Eight-eenth Century.* London: Faber & Fa-ber. 314 pp.

HATT, GUDMUND
1939   "The Ownership of Cultivated Land," *Det Kongelige Danske Videns-kabernes Selskab: Historiske-filologiske Meddelelser,* XXVI, No. 6, 1–22. Co-penhagen.

HELBAEK, H.
1953   "Archaeology and Agricultural Botany," *University of London, Insti-tute of Archaeology, Ninth Annual Report,* pp. 44–59.

IVERSEN, J.
1949   *The Influence of Prehistoric Man on Vegetation.* ("Danmarks geo-logiske Undersøgelse," Series IV, Vol. III, No. 6.) Copenhagen. 29 pp.

JESSEN, KNUD, and HELBAEK, HANS
1944   *Cereals in Great Britain and Ire-land in Prehistoric and Early His-toric Times.* ("Det Kongelige Danske Videnskabernes Selskab: Biologiske Skrifter," Vol. III, No. 2.) Copen-hagen. 68 pp.

JONES, G. R. J.
1953   "Some Mediaeval Rural Settle-ments in North Wales," *Institute of British Geographers, Transactions and Papers,* No. 19, pp. 51–72.

JOPE, E. M.
1952   "The Porcellanite Axes of the

North of Ireland: Tievebulliagh and Rathlin," *Ulster Journal of Archaeology*, XV, 31–60. Belfast.

MACKINDER, H. J.
1944   *Democratic Ideals and Reality.* 4th ed. (1st ed. 1919.) West Drayton, Middlesex: Penguin Books. 155 pp.

MEDICI, SENATOR G., *et al.*
1950   "Diagnosis and Pathology of Peasant Farming," pp. 18–63 in MAXTON, J. P. (ed.), *Proceedings of the Seventh International Conference of Agricultural Economists.* London: Oxford University Press. 372 pp.

MITCHELL, G. F.
1951   "Studies in Irish Quaternary Deposits, No. 7," *Proceedings of the Royal Irish Academy*, LIII, B II, 113–206. Dublin.
1953 . "Vegetational Environmental Studies," *Advancement of Science*, IX, No. 36, 430–32. London.

MOGEY, J. M.
1947   *Rural Life in Northern Ireland.* London: Oxford University Press. 240 pp.

ORWIN, C. S. and C. S.
1938   *The Open Fields.* Oxford: Clarendon Press. 332 pp.

PIGGOTT, STUART
1954   *The Neolithic Cultures of the British Isles.* Cambridge: Cambridge University Press. 420 pp.

REES, ALWYN D.
1950   *Life in a Welsh Countryside.* Cardiff: University of Wales Press. 188 pp.

SALAMAN, R. N.
1949   *The History and Social Influence of the Potato.* Cambridge: Cambridge University Press. 685 pp.

SAUER, CARL O.
1952   *Agricultural Origins and Dispersals.* (Bowman Memorial Lectures, Series Two.) New York: American Geographical Society. 110 pp.

SINGER, C.; HOLMYARD, E. J.; and HALL, A. R. (eds.)
1954   *A History of Technology*, Vol. I: *From Early Times to Fall of Ancient Empires.* Oxford: Clarendon Press. 827 pp.

STEENBERG, A.
1952   *Bondehuse og Vandmøller: Farms and Watermills in Denmark through Two Thousand Years.* ("The National Museum's Third Department: Researches into Village Archaeology," Vol. I.) Copenhagen: National Museum. 325 pp.

SYDOW, C. W. VON
1948   *Selected Papers in Folklore.* Copenhagen: Rosenkilde & Bagger. 257 pp.

YATES, P. L.
1940   *Food Production in Western Europe.* London: Longmans & Co. 572 pp.

ZEUNER, F. E.
1954   "Cultivation of Plants," pp. 353–75 in SINGER, C., *et al.* (eds.), *A History of Technology*, Vol. I: *From Early Times to Fall of Ancient Empires.* Oxford: Clarendon Press. 827 pp.

The Quality of Peasant Living in Central Europe

GOTTFRIED PFEIFER[*]

INTRODUCTION

To pose the "quality of peasant living" as a problem related to man's role in changing the face of the earth presupposes that a special "man-made landscape" originated in Central Europe, produced not merely by agricultural activities but by the prolonged action of peasant living upon the soil. The proposed theme emphasizes the "quale" of such peasant living and not solely the peasant landscape. Discussion is weighted toward this factor, with its historical, social, and economic implications, which created certain forms and features on the face of the earth. Nature, as the more passive partner in the evolutionary drama, has had to be passed over briefly.

It is in the nature of peasantry that it has its own history, only slightly touched by strife and warfare among major political powers. Only cata-

* Dr. Pfeifer is Professor and Head of the Department of Geography, University of Heidelberg, Germany. In 1950 he traveled with Professor Waibel as a guest of the Conselho Nacional de Geografia, Rio de Janeiro, Brazil. He has been a visiting professor at the University of Georgia, Athens (1952), and at the University of Minnesota, Minneapolis (1953). His works include: *Das Siedlungsbild der Landschaft Angeln*, 1928; *Die räumliche Gliederung der Landwirtschaft im nördlichen Kalifornien*, 1936; "Sonora und Sinaloa, Beiträge zur Kulturgeographie des N.W. Mexico," 1939; "Die Ernährungswirtschaft der Erde," 1948; and "Die kulturgeographische Stellung Brasilien in des Neuen Welt (I)," 1952.

strophic movements that uproot all fundaments, like the French Revolution or the wars and revolutions of our times, which devastate not only the lands but also the peoples and their social structures, annihilate historical peasantries. On the other hand, the molding of influences working in the social and economic spheres to alter the quale of peasant living may not heed political frontiers. Thus, for our discussion of questions pertaining to cultural geography, political boundaries—past or present—may appear as factors but do not serve as boundaries of the first order.

Central Europe, in our definition, overlaps with the eastern fringe of Western Europe (cf. Evans, Fig. 66, p. 219). I include the drainage area of the Rhine in the west and the upper reaches of the Danube in the south. The eastern boundaries are less easily defined, owing to wide spacing of natural gradation and a complex history (Sinnhuber, 1954). Our discussion is here confined to the area where the peasants speak a German dialect and have a common history.

Between 48° and 52° N., the climate of Central Europe is moderate, of the northern, cooler variety. The growing season is in the summer, while the ground in winter is left dormant. The range of crops adaptable to the climate is limited but includes small grains and certain root crops, among the latter notably the Andean potato.[1] Between the oceanic and mild Western Europe and the great expanse of continental eastern Europe, the zones of climatic gradation follow from the northwest to the southeast. Topographic relief is moderate in most parts with respect to altitude and inclination of slope, but topography interacts with climate sufficiently to bring about decided regional variations.

Soil fertility is moderate, generally speaking. Sandy parent-materials are liable to podzolization in the northwest. In lee positions of the middle upland and mountain belt, and in basins with warmer climate, soils of substeppe-like quality occur, notably on loesses and limestones. The soils in the central upland belt and the escarpment landscape of southern Germany are conditioned more by great petrographic variety of parent-material than by climatic gradation.

Tilling of the soil in Central Europe (though not so old as early high civilizations) dates back to at least Neolithic times (cf. Evans, pp. 223 ff.), yet in the course of more than five thousand years and considerable historic turbulence the peasantry has maintained continuous productivity of the land. Although the expanse of agriculturally used territory changed considerably in historic times, emphasis has been placed upon increased productivity and intensification of use. At the same time one of the most surprising features of the Central European landscape is that forests have been preserved to such an extent. They still cover more than 25 per cent of the total surface, and the watersheds are still suf-

ficiently protected. The pleasing mixture of forests and open, cultivated land has led geographers to speak of a "harmonious landscape" (Gradmann, 1924, p. 30), which contrasts with some parts of western and southern European scenery. In spite of shifts in area between wilderness and cultivated land, the impression is of stability rather than of catastrophic change.

Although the mild nature of Central Europe threatens the peasant with fewer climatic hazards than those which occur in many other parts of the world, nevertheless peasant management of the land and peasant attitudes and institutions have to be credited for such stability through many centuries. Central Europe exhibits no extensive areas of soil erosion, nor have sizable areas completely passed out of production. We know that the land of European peasantry has not entirely been spared of various forms of land misuse, but recuperative powers have outbalanced the detrimental processes. In Central Europe, as in many parts of the world, the peasant areas of quality are not the ones where the conservationist is most needed.

The economic results of Central European peasant agriculture bespeak surprising adaptability, which has maintained a high degree of self-sufficiency of the population (for Germany, conventionally rated at 80 per cent). The harvest yields have increased—though they have not attained the very highest returns in a statistical average—and Central European agriculture has led that of other countries for nearly all crops grown. Yet it must not be overlooked that, for many decades, Central European farmers have enjoyed tariffs which, unlike some of the smaller countries, protected them from the full force of impact of the free world market.

Central European peasant society bears many affinities and similarities with that of Western Europe, but the

1. Grapes thrive and produce wine of commercial quality in the more favored parts, and the *"Weingärtner"* is decidedly an important subtype of the Central European peasant. The American will miss the soybean, which it has been impossible as yet to add to the Central European range of crops. Maize also is of minor, though increasing, importance.

distribution of sizes of holdings is somewhat different, and tenantry is far less important. This will be easily recognized by comparing Figures 72 and 73. Most conspicuous is the contrast in Central Europe between an area of very small farms, on the average, in the southwest, and an area of formerly large estates in the northeast. Tiny holdings and true latifundia occur, yet neither characterizes Central Europe as a whole. Like Western Europe, true peasant sizes of holdings prevail. Property structure points toward ownership of the soil (Fig. 73), in contrast with wide areas of Western Europe. Nine-tenths of the total utilized surface is in the hands of owners; one-tenth is held by tenants, though local variations are important.

Today, the Central European peasantry, like the rest of the world, feels the changes wrought by industrialization and urbanization. Rural depopulation, scarcity of labor, mechanization, traditional methods, and unfavorable price relations, as well as changes in modes of life and living standards, affect the countryside. The old peasant structures are shaken with uneasiness and a sense of approaching revolutionary alterations. It is our task to save what has been best in historic peasantry, lest we lose a fundamental basis of our society as it has grown through time.

CHARACTERISTICS OF PEASANTS AND PEASANT SOCIETY

Social Traditions

Who are peasants and why do we speak of a special "peasant" way of living? The English and German languages conform, in so far as the term denotes in both more than just a person occupied in agriculture (cf. Evans, p. 220). To be a peasant is to have a definite estate, in the historical sense of the term—to belong to the "*Bauernstand*" (Riehl, 1851, pp. 33 ff.). One

does not choose to be a peasant. One is born into peasantry. Peasantry does not derive its quality alone from the character of its economy but refers to the mode of life of a social group of traditional standing. After the great melting of medieval society in the fire of the French Revolution, peasantry and nobility retained longest the medieval quality of an estate and declined to become a class. Riehl (*ibid.*) characterized both nobility and peasantry as the forces for stability (*Kräfte der Beharrung*), contrasted to the forces for mobility (*Kräfte der Bewegung*) of the third and fourth estates (*Bürgertum* and *Arbeitertum*). Nobility, just as peasantry, has retained its rooting in the soil in Central Europe more than in many other parts of Europe. The fate of peasantry has been tied up with nobility for better or worse over a long period. We cannot understand the landscape unless we also recognize the influences of tradition and social institutions created by man, for these influences became the means by which the patterns of land distribution were established.

The peasant was born on the land inherited from ancestors as the son of a peasant. Birth determined one's status not only in a scale of wealth but frequently also in a rural hierarchy of graded rights and social status. The fully righted peasant—the "*Vollerbe*," as he was called in northwestern Germany—was born as such, just as was the lower man, the "*Kätner*," "*Seldner*," or whatever his particular character may have been. The accident of being a second son might spell non-participation in inheritance and even descent to lower social status, for the desire to keep the family landholding together led to majorates or minorates (*Anerbenrecht, geschlossene Hofübergabe*). The custom of dividing land among sons into equal parts (*Realerbteilung*), prevalent today notably in southwest-

Fig. 72.—Distribution of sizes of land in agricultural enterprises in Western Europe and parts of Central Europe. (After Abel, 1955.)

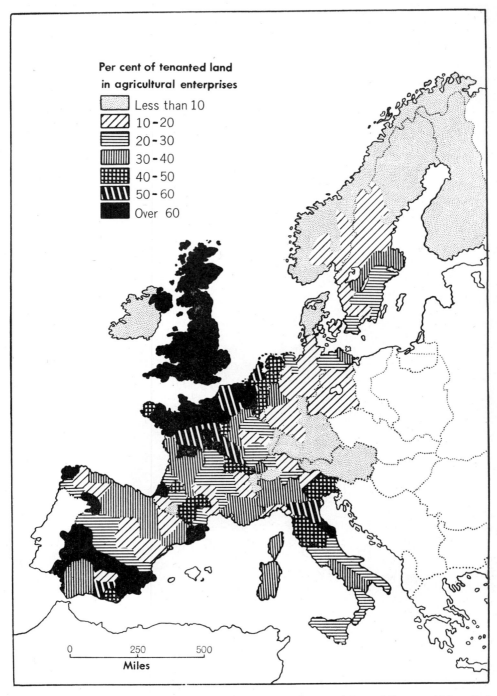

Fig. 73.—Distribution of tenantry in Western Europe and parts of Central Europe. (After Abel, 1955, and Huppertz, 1935.)

ern Germany, seems to be of more recent origin, developed under the influence of urban practices and the reception of Roman law. There, the peasant holdings tend to suffer *parcellement;* the older social orders dwindle; families rise and sink with the change of generations; the mobility of real estate increases; and something of the aboriginal quality of peasant life is lost.

The traditional customs of antecedents and neighbors determined behavior very rigidly. Food habits, modes of clothing, wooing and mating, worship and burial, material and ideal scales of values, even religious convictions, conformed to one's neighbors. Whether the settlement structure consisted of single farmsteads, hamlets, or villages, the peasant always found himself deeply rooted in communal bondage that was older than he himself. Family, neighborhood (*Nachbarschaften*), manorial relationships (*grundherrschaftliche Bindungen*), the single farmstead rural communities (*Bauernschaft*), or the modern forms of community (*Gemeinde*), and even political units made up of several estates (*Gutsbezirk*), framed his individual and social existence. Within such narrow but meaningful spheres, he carried on his contribution to public life. In spite of manor, serfdom, or other forms of bondage, the peasant exerted some kind of self-administration, by traditional and carefully watched laws and customs. Such laws and customs were set down in written texts as so-called "*Weistümer,*" "*Dorfwillküren,*" and "*Dorfbeliebungen.*" Peasantry arose hesitantly and with difficulty, from thinking in the realm of family and community, to acknowledge the modern state. The peasant wars (*Bauernkriege*) of the fifteenth and sixteenth centuries were caused largely by resentment to the rising state authority that tried to penetrate the countryside with new laws and regulations.

It is of extreme geographic importance to take cognizance of the fact that the rural scene is broken into small, areal units which are not merely expressions of natural sites, patterns, or artificial groupings for administrative or statistical purposes. The peasant way of living expresses itself on the land by the impress of groups acting on their respective areas. The home of the peasant is part of a traditional settlement structure; his fields are parts of a communal area, and frequently he participates in rights of usufruct on land held in common. "*Dorf,*" "*Flur,*" "*Allmende,*" "*Gemarkung,*" and "*Gemeinde,*" to use some German terms, are social and spatial institutions by which peasantry stamps its activity on the face of the earth.

The good peasant takes honor and pride in his work. To work and to live are still identical, the idea of limited hours of working being alien to his thinking. He feels a responsibility toward the land, as part of the duties bestowed upon him by the Lord. His economic spirit (*Wirtschaftsgeist*) is largely directed by considerations about the farmstead (*Hof*) rather than toward profit-making in a monetary sense; to think in terms of the market has not been foreign to him, dating to medieval times. But we should not glorify him as altruistic; avarice is one of his vices. Abel (1935) has endeavored to exemplify how business cycles have exerted strong influences upon rural life. Riehl (1859, pp. 233, 237–39) has given a vivid description of the cattle-raising peasant in the marshes, who bears himself like a "baron," and of the grain peasant in the fertile plain (*Börde*), who frequents the casino. However, truly conservative and frequently archaic refuges of traditional peasant life still may be found—on a lonely farmstead in the Low German heath, in a mountain hamlet, or even in villages not touched by strong currents of trade and communications, although the influences of the modern age tend to dissolve more and more of such islands.

Structure of Rural Society[2]

The basis of an individual peasant enterprise is the family. The family-size farm is the peasant holding par excellence. This definition does not prohibit the employment of hired hands (*Gesinde*), for such traditionally belonged to the family. They stemmed from the neighborhood, usually the same village, if not from the same family tree. The hired hand might have been born into his status, just as his peasant employer inherited status and property from his ancestors. The earliest Germanic societies of historical record were composed not solely of free peasants of equal rights and of a few leading families; a substratum of lesser order, varying in status from true slavery to bonded freedom (*Hintersassen*) and attached to individual peasants or the whole community, also inhabited the countryside. We may scarcely conceive of the peasant landscape of Central Europe having been created without such lower ranks in the rural society, who were usually shut off from usufruct of the common lands (*Allmende*). The breakup of such graded hierarchies of rural social structure, accompanying the downfall of medieval order, has been one of the major achievements of the last two centuries. The lower orders were personally freed

(like peasants of bondage) and given some land, which frequently was taken from the common lands, a process which increased the number of smallest holdings. Their homes filled the open spaces in the villages or were scattered along the borders of the communal territory.[3]

During the eighteenth century, governments endeavored to better the conditions of the lower rural orders by attempting to furnish the lower ranks with sufficient land to bring them close to family self-sufficiency—to bring them into *Ackernahrung*. In the *Ackernahrung*, denoting the smallest unit of family subsistence farming, was the man who was forced to seek additional work to make a living for his family and who did not properly belong to the full category of peasant. He belonged to the rural society, which had always been stratified, but he may have been classed as "*Tagelöhner*," "*Heuerling*," rural "*Handwerker*," or, under modern conditions, "*Arbeiter-Bauer*" and "*Pendler*," according to occupation or local term.

Family size, enterprise, and self-sufficiency have always been stressed as essential characteristics of peasantry. But production for the market and specialization of production by no means destroyed peasant quality. In fact, for as far back as we are able to trace rural economy historically, we must infer that peasants produced surpluses which went either into channels of the manorial system or, later, to urban populations. The *capitulare de villis* of Charles the Great embodied provisions concerning the grain trade. Livestock-raising, grape-growing, dye-weed production, etc., provided an early basis for specialization. It must be admitted, though, that such commercial specialization tended to prepare inroads for city ways not akin to, and not developed out of, primeval peasant life. Subtypes of peasantry evolved, but the up-

2. See the excellent article "Agrarverfassung" in *Handwörterbuch des Grenz- und Auslanddeutschtum,* edited by C. Petersen, O. Scheel, P. H. Ruth, and H. Schwalm (Breslau: F. Hirt, 1933), I, 23–70, especially the parts written by R. Kötzschke, K. Weimann, and S. Ipsen, pp. 23–52. The English reader may resort to the *Encyclopaedia of the Social Sciences,* edited by E. R. A. Seligman and A. Johnson (New York: Macmillan Co.), especially the articles, "Manorial System" by R. Kötzschke, IX, 97–102, and "Peasantry" by C. V. Dietze, XI–XII, 48–52, and related articles quoted there.

3. See Pfeifer, 1928, Part V, pp. 95–107.

per limit of rural structure was the estate (*Gut*). *Gut* is a large, rural enterprise where management and field work are carried out by different persons. Socially, the owner does not belong to the peasant estate.

Just as there was a lower order, there was also an upper stratum of landed aristocracy in rural society. The growth of the manorial system (*Grundherrschaft*), recognizable since Merovingian times, created the typical structure of medieval rural society. Extensive, but usually widely scattered, holdings and rights over peasants in bondage came into the hands of lords (*Grundherren*), either worldly or ecclesiastical. The manorial court (*curia;* Ger.: *Salhof*) was the center of the organization, and the *villicus* attended to the production on the manorial land (*Salland, demesne*) and of the dependent peasants (*Grundholden*). The *Grundherrschaft* has come to be reckoned more and more as the most important institution in medieval rural society and economy. Manorial ties (*Grundherrschaftliche Bindungen*) strongly controlled the development of settlement patterns, property order in the fields (*Flurverfassung*), the rights in the common lands (*Allmende* and *Markungen*), the laws of inheritance, the spreading and colonizing of new lands, and the fate of the forests. The decline of the manorial system was of equal importance and went in two directions: conversion of rights and delivery of work (*Frondienste*) and produce into cash income (*Rentengrundherrschaft*); or to consolidation for production in large enterprises (*Gutswirtschaft*) worked by peasants held in serfdom (*Gutsuntertanigkeit, Leibeigenschaft*). The former course was taken largely in the German southwest; the latter, in the northeast.

In the estate economy (*Gutswirtschaft*) the owner does not work the soil with his own hands. He supervises the enterprise or intrusts it to a manager, and it is connected with considerably larger holdings (Figs. 72 and 74). The separation of ownership and management does not always imply the development of true absentee ownership. It is characteristic for the larger areas of the *Gutswirtschaft* in Central Europe that a land-seated aristocracy remained and strikingly influenced the composition of the rural society. Other, more modern, capitalistic forms of *Gutswirtschaften* that developed later during the nineteenth and twentieth centuries were connected with the investment of urban and industrial capital in real estate. Absentee owners developed large-scale production, especially in strongly commercialized forms of agriculture like the sugar-beet production in the *Börden* of central Germany. In such areas manager-operated farms and tenantry attain greater proportions.

Regional Variety in Sizes of Property Holdings

The simple term "peasantry" will not be sufficient to cover the variability of the rural landscape. Maps of the distributions of property size (Figs. 72 and 74) serve for a first orientation. Several characteristic major areas are easily discernible. The one major area—now historic—where large-scale property with *Gutswirtschaften* has predominated is northeastern Germany, where the majority of holdings are larger than those typically held by peasants. In western and southern Germany such large holdings are infrequent. Along the North Sea coast more than 50 per cent of the surface is in large peasant holdings, the regions of the large farms or estates (*Hof-Bauer* or *Gutsbauer*). Medium-sized peasant holdings (5–20 hectares) prevail in southwestern Germany, in the Black Forest, in eastern Württemberg, Bavaria, Franconia, in the Kölner Bucht, Westphalia without

Münsterland, and southwestern Hannover and Saxony.

The larger part of southwestern Germany, notably the loess-covered *Gäulandschaften*, large areas in the *Rheinische Schiefergebirge*, in Hesse and Thuringia, is dominated by small holdings of less than 5 hectares. Conse-

is penetrated by industrial communities (*Gewerblichen Gemeinden*), workers' dormitory settlements (*Arbeiterwohngemeinden*), mixed workers, part-time farmers, and peasants (*Arbeiter-Bauerngemeinden*) (Hesse, 1949). Even more mottled would be a map showing the *parcellement* of property with re-

FIG. 74.—Distribution of sizes of rural holdings in parts of Central Europe (Germany within the boundaries of 1939). (After Huppertz, 1935.)

quently, the whole range of the peasant order is different. For example, the limit for owner-managed land (*Gutsbetriebe*) is low, commonly set at merely 75 hectares; and in the Kreis Ettlingen, in Baden, more than 92 per cent of all holdings are parceled out in tiny holdings below the limit of true peasant holdings (Fig. 75). A social map of southwestern Germany presents a very mottled aspect. The whole countryside

spect to the distribution of tiny plots over the *Flur.* Weingarten in Baden, a typical example, is a village of 6,000–7,000 inhabitants, with 1,700 hectares of field and some 100 hectares of woodland atomized into 14,000 parcels! This certainly is a morbid structure. It is here that consolidation of the holdings and rearrangement of the pattern of rural settlement are most urgently needed but meet almost insurmountable difficulties. It has been estimated that 7,000,000 hectares still wait for the process of rearrangement of the land (*Flurbereinigung*) in Germany (Bundesrepublik)!

PLOW AGRICULTURE IN CENTRAL EUROPE

Central European peasant agriculture is a branch of the larger Old World cul-

The Role of Animal Husbandry

The essential feature of plow agriculture, in contrast to other forms of cultivating the soil (planting stick, hoe, and Eastern Asiatic agriculture), is the integration of animal husbandry with plant production. It involves not merely a juxtaposition of both types of production (as in some parts of Africa, for instance); it is a genuine wedding, where-

Fig. 75.—Social types of rural communities, northern Württemberg-Baden, Germany. (After Hesse, 1949.)

ture complex of plow agriculture (in the sense of Hahn, 1909, 1914), which is the parent-form of modern agriculture. For some aspects of its prehistoric development see Evans (pp. 223 ff.). Our purpose is to analyze some of its traits with regard to the way in which Central European peasantry took roots on the surface of the earth.

by one branch supports the other. The animals are not only an object *of* production but also an important factor *in* production; the cultivated land serves not only for direct human use but also for the maintenance of livestock. Ask the peasant why he keeps so many animals, and he may answer, "Because I have so much land of such-and-such quality." Ask him why he plants his fields in a particular system, and he may reply, "For I have so many animals." The animals of importance are cattle, horses, and swine. They are used for food (meat and milk), for raw materials (hides, wool, leather), for work (drawing, carrying, and riding), and—very important—for manure to maintain the stability of soil fertility. For our purpose it is most important that (1) the domesticated animal was introduced into the working process and (2) that both types of land utilization are intricately combined and mutually support each other. This is the standard type of European peasant economy as it developed before medieval times. It is significant that this productive interlocking begins to loosen with the end of peasantry: in colonial agriculture the two productive lines frequently part, and, with the introduction of machinery and artificial fertilizers, the necessity of inner coherence of both branches is questioned.

The consequence of making the work animal a factor in production permitted cultivation of an expanded area. In this, the work animal proved to be the genuine forefather of modern machinery. In fact, plow agriculture contained a germ for further technology, in that the harnessed power of the animal was to be applied, in time, to other implements for sowing and harvesting. The consequence was always that larger areas might be conquered. The method was particularly adapted to the small grains, which are sown broadcast, but less to root crops, which must be planted and cultivated during the growing season.

The introduction of root crops—one of the major improvements of European agriculture during later medieval times —had far-reaching consequences. The animal and the plow brought the man out to the field as the chief agricultural worker and released the women, so prominent in hoe agriculture, for home-work. However, that the women historically served as a labor reserve was proved when root crops appeared in the plow system. The planting of root crops and the cultivation with the hoe during the summer are jobs for women. Men will never beat women in digging roots and potatoes in harvest time![4]

The use of animal and plow in breaking the ground called for a clean surface. The planting stick and hoe may successfully work among the litter of a clearing where the trunks of fallen trees still obstruct the ground and the slash has been reduced by burning, but the plow achieves optimum results on permanently cleared ground. This, of course, refers to the plow in its final development. Lighter, animal-drawn implements, like the *"Hakenpflug,"* or the *"Zoche,"* served in slash-and-burn economy.[5] But the exception will confirm the rule. The permanently cleared fields, to a considerable extent dependent in size on the capacity of man, work animal, and plow, appeared as the determining entities around which the agricultural system was organized, as distinguished from garden beds or the plots of planting-stick and hoe cultivation. Many important features of European peasant life, such as the plow team and field patterns (long strip, etc.), have been related to the development of plow types and working animals (oxen, cows, or horses).

Fallowing and the Danger of Erosion

The capacity to cultivate larger fields enabled the plowman to break more ground than used annually for production. Fallowing, in the true sense of the

4. The whole subject of women in Central European agriculture as a reserve labor force is worthy of study. It has been estimated that they perform about 50 per cent of the work.

5. For such forest-field rotation connected with burning, various terms are used, e.g., *Nordischer Brandrodungsbau, Reutbergwirtschaft,* or *Haubergwirtschaft.*

agriculturist, made its appearance. Fallowing, as opposed to shifting cultivation, is a feature of high importance, for it allows the land to rest and recover some of its spent fertility without reverting to wilderness. Fallow lands are ready for planting early in spring of the next year and are a great help where climate shortens the seasons (*jachère climatique, Höhenbrache, Brache in hohen Breiten*). Cultivated fallow land will absorb precipitation without giving it back by plant transpiration when handled by dry-farming methods (*jachère de secheresse*). Such climatic fallowing greatly favored the spread of the plow complex to otherwise unsuited climatic areas. The summer fallow, where fenced in, served as additional pasture, especially for the smaller animals.

Fallowing practices were equally important from the economic point of view. They provided another subject for common counsel (*Flurzwang*) and folkways among the peasants. They were the means for adapting the field system to the economic situation. With increasing distances from markets, fallowing was advocated as a labor-saving device. Regular fallowing determined the order of the most important early field systems: the two-field and the three-field systems. But fallow land also introduced a cleaned and cultivated reserve field, upon which new crops entered the system with growing intensity. Black fallowing changed to green fallowing. Root crops and potatoes covered the former fallow land in the improved three-field system. The loss in meager pasture was outweighed by the gain in fodder production of forage crops.

But clean fallow points to some dangers implicit in plowing. The plow breaks the total area, and all protective plant cover is removed. A clean surface lies bare to the erosive action of strong rainfall or sweeping, dry winds. The early sprouting of a dense carpet of winter-sown small grains may alleviate the danger of soil erosion, but where plow agriculture is applied in more dangerous climatic regions to crops taken over from hoe agriculture, as happened so widely with maize or cotton in the New World, dangerous soil erosion ensues.

The plow is inferior to the hoe or the planting stick on steep slopes. Plowed, inclined slopes are also endangered by soil erosion, especially when the furrows run down the slope. But peasant agriculturists early found remedies. The slopes were preferred, for reason of fresher soil and better natural drainage. By handling the plow skilfully along the contour lines, the peasant succeeded in building up low terraces, which, in time, were fastened by hedges or stones. The arrangement of property plots along isohypses anticipated, in effect, modern scientific contour farming. Some of these terraces are supposed to date back to the Bronze Age. Contour plowing and strip cropping (promoted by the structure of property division on the *Flur*) are common and old traditional features of the peasant landscape. Furthermore, by plowing the furrows together, the peasant could build up ridged fields ("ridge and furrow" [*Hochäcker*]) where low, damp ground made drainage advisable.

Certain conservational and reclamation practices are of long standing and may account for the absence of serious features of soil erosion. But it has not been avoided altogether. In fact, archival evidence (Jäger, 1951), as well as field evidence (e.g., Hempel, 1954a, 1954b), reveals that soil erosion left considerable scars locally and at certain times on the surface. Some of the excessive alluvial sediments, which have raised the surface, for example, around an early medieval church (*Grünsfeldhausen*) by 3 meters, may correspond to soil erosion following new clearings. The bases of stone walls in the Kocher

Valley, running downhill, today stand a meter above the cultivated plots in between. The matter of historic denudation due to soil erosion may not yet be ready for quantitative and regional discussion, for the preservation of periglacial soil features has been proved over wide areas. At any rate, the peasant landscape of today may again be suffering locally from soil erosion, but, *in toto,* it is blissfully absent in comparison with other parts of Europe or overseas areas of plow and hoe agriculture. How much this is due to careful action by the peasants is not known quantitatively, though it is known that peasant folkways call for recovery of soil when washed downhill by rain, and the peasants in the steep, terraced vineyards carry the soil up the slopes in baskets on their backs even today.

The permanently cleared fields, perhaps improved by ridging or slope-terracing, made for stability in the spatial arrangement of the landscape and tended to fix fields and settlements to the spot. It is not yet well known what importance forms of slash-and-burn agriculture, perhaps with shifting of fields and villages, had in prehistoric agriculture. Where we find such methods of forest-field rotation with burning (*Hau-Bergwirtschaft*), as in Siegerland, in the Moselle area (Schmithüsen, 1934), or in parts of the Black Forest or of Bayrischen Wald, evidence points to development in medieval times rather than to preservation from prehistoric times.

The Role of the Pasture

Pastures and meadows were important special areas that served to maintain the staple types of land utilization supplementary to or alternatively to crop production.

The pasture in historic peasant agriculture has changed through time from primarily natural pasture (woodland, degenerated woodland with grass and shrubbery, heath, "*Hutungen*") to predominantly artificial pasture (permanent, or alternating with field use, "*Feldgraswirtschaft,*" "*Koppelwirtschaft*"). From pastures held in common (*Allmende, Markungen*), the trend was to pastures as individual property. The pasture added to the plowed field a unit of land utilization highly adaptable to varying natural, economic, and social situations. Like fallowing, it helped to maintain peasant agriculture when field crops were restricted or had failed. Shifting emphasis on plant and livestock production made possible the triumph of plow agriculture.

It has been increasingly apparent that utilization of forests for pasturing promoted and guided the early penetration of forested Central Europe (Nietsch, 1939). Contrary to earlier concepts that the forest was inimical to the primitive Neolithic settler, it is now held that certain types of forest (notably more open, mixed, deciduous types, bearing fruit and suitable for fattening swine) had been indispensable. The rough, high-mountain uplands were opened for pasture in medieval times. In the poor heath countries of northwestern Germany a wide circle of semi-wildland pasture spread around the small, oldest permanent fields (*Esche*), which were fertilized by heath-bedding enriched by the manure from winter stables.[6] In-field and outfield systems were developed in the varied forms of field grass, where crops alternated with grassland. Maritime areas, not well suited to grain production, were developed highly by means of intensive pasturing. It is beyond our purpose to discuss the relationship of pasturing to changing economic conditions. The meadow as the land for hay production

6. *Eschland* was manured with *Plaggen,* i.e., clumps of heath that had been used as bedding in sheep stables. A special soil type resulted, the *Plaggenboden* (Niemeier and Taschenmacher, 1939).

opened the low-lying, damp bottoms along the brooks and rivers and thus added a new ecologic type to the system of land utilization in the plow economy.

Combined System of Plant Production and Animal Husbandry

The alternation of cropland and fallow, pasture and meadow, spatially in adaptation to ecological or economic situations or rotationally in varying proportions and time sequences, gives a high degree of flexibility to plow agriculture as practiced by Central European peasantry. This, in turn, leads to a wide range of regional variations in peasant life and economy.

The value of hoe and planting-stick agriculture rests with the care devoted to the individual plant and the possibility of raising many varieties in combination on one plot (see Sauer, p. 57). The achievements of plow agriculture come with intricate systems of land utilization, combinations, and rotational systems of plant production and animal husbandry. Several mixed plants on one field are not unknown (mixed grains for fodder), though this is the exception. The deductive schemes of von Thünen (Figs. 76a and 76b) and Aereboe (Fig. 77) serve as examples of the flexibility of plow agriculture in relation to changing market and climatic conditions.[7]

Equally important was the internal improvement of production based upon the plant-animal combination. The animals furnished manure to fertilize the fields as soon as stables for animals increased in importance. As the manure pile proverbially is a matter of pride to the good peasant, it also was the mainstay of traditional plow agriculture in Central Europe.[8]

The extension of fields at the expense of common pasture land and the closing of the forests for pasturing promoted the stabling of the animals. It is extremely important that the necessity to turn attention to forage crops to make up for loss of open-air pasture proved beneficial for field crops as well. The increase of hoe and forage crops, notably leguminous plants, led to new, improved rotations (e.g., the "Norfolk" system). "Green manuring" appeared as a practice that steadily improved up to present times. Such improved field practices seem to have originated first in Flanders and the lower Rhine area, as well as in Italy. Attempts at scientific field rotation aspire to proper alternation of crops with regard to both high economic yield and maintenance of soil fertility. The introduction of artificial fertilizers has somewhat lessened the emphasis on manuring. Today, advisers advocate bringing cattle out into the open air. New paddocks (*Koppeln*), sometimes held in common, make their appearance around settlements or outer fringes of fields.

It is not our aim to exhaust the lore of land management and field practices. Our endeavor has been to outline some characteristic qualities of plow agriculture as developed among Central European peasantry and to point out its high degree of flexibility and adaptability that may account for its surprising stability. How such agricultural systems have been realized within the social patterns of the peasant landscape remains to be outlined.

STRUCTURE OF THE PEASANT ECONOMIC LANDSCAPE

Two basic factors determine the structure of the peasant economic land-

---

7. Cf. Brinkmann, 1913; Beschorner, 1923; Waibel, 1933; Krzymowski, 1914; Otremba, 1953; Müller-Wille, 1936, 1938a, 1941, 1952, 1955.

8. The development of manuring practices and intensity is worth studying. In the eighteenth century many regions in Europe did not practice manuring in a satisfactory way. The early great agricultural scientists of the eighteenth and nineteenth centuries greatly helped to bring the lore of manuring to perfection and to spread knowledge of its use gradually over the countryside.

scape: (1) the individual family holding is the smallest unit and (2) many such holdings unite to form a community within an area.

The Family Holdings

The home of the peasant family and the center of activity is the *Bauernhaus* or, in its larger and functionally compound form, the *Bauernhof*. The construction of the house and the layout of the farm (*Hof*) determine more than anything else the regional aspect of the settlements. The distribution of such house forms is frequently independent of settlement patterns.[9]

9. For various explanations of development of the structure of the peasant economic landscape see Pessler, 1907–8; Schier, 1932; Schilli, 1953; and Ellenberg, 1937, 1941.

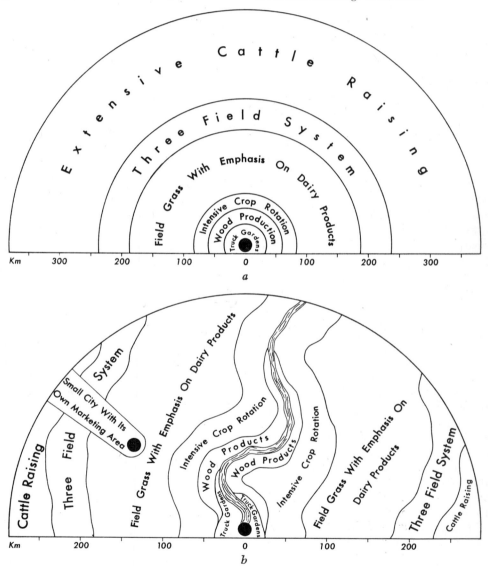

Fig. 76.—Arrangement of agricultural systems based upon the plow. (After von Thünen, 1826; the scale in kilometers has been added by Waibel, 1933.) *a*, the rings of an isolated state; *b*, the above as modified by a navigable river.

The historic term for the peasant holding belonging to the *Bauernhaus* or *Bauernhof* is the "*Hufe.*"[10] The *Hufe* (Lat.: *mansus*), as the basis of existence, combined individual property (*Sondereigentum*) with rights of usufruct in common holdings and social standing. All attempts to discover standard quantitative measures have come to naught, for the size of the *Hufe* varied in time and region. The *Hufe* is the peculiar form by which the principle of

10. *Hufe* (Lat.: *mansus;* Ger.: *hova, hoba, huoba,* etc.) denotes in most general meaning the basis for peasant existence, i.e., land and all material and juridical belongings. *Hufe* was

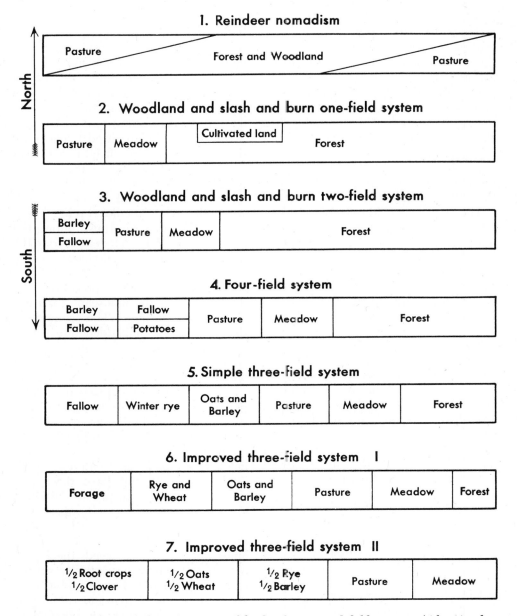

Fig. 77.—Influence of climate on types of land utilization and field systems. (After Aereboe, 1920.)

individual property was integrated into co-operative communal life and, beyond this, into the whole network of medieval social pattern. The *Hufe* encompassed *Hof* fields and participation in use of the common lands. The origin of the *Hufe* dates back to the times of first occupation, which occurred by families and in groups. It remained the accepted practice of land allotment and rural social unit at the time of developing medieval social and political order. The process of forest clearing and colonization in the east proceeded by assigning *Hufen*. The later colonial *Hufen* have a recognizable basis of measure: the "*Königshufen*" included more than 40 hectares; the Franconian "*hoba*" of free peasants, 24 hectares; the Flemish *Hufe*, 16.8 hectares, while in the west the *Hufe* usually did not contain more than 10–12 hectares.

The *Hufe* was held together and persevered where the right of undivided inheritance (*Anerbenrechte*) prevailed, and the early social order of the countryside remained intact. This has been the case in most of northern and northeastern Germany (Figs. 74, p. 248, and 78). The west and south divided early.

The Communal Holdings

The *Hufe* cannot be well understood without reference to the free-mark associations (*Marken* in lower Germany and *Allmenden* in upper Germany). These were grounds occupied by the communities but not yet subdivided into private property. Such communal holdings occurred in the village as well as on the outer fringes toward the

---

the constituent element of the medieval agrarian social structure and remained so well into the modern age. In late medieval times the term "*Hufe*" included the peasant's total belongings in land, buildings, and all rights of usufruct. The *Hufe* in Carolingian time was the basis for the allotment of public revenue and the basis of the military organization. *Hufe* also was the unit within the manorial system, the basis for all burdens, tithes, work, etc.

great woods. Around the administration of the *Marken* and *Allmenden* developed a good deal of peasant self-government and jurisdiction. The rights and terms of utilization were determined by peasant regulations concerning pasture, wood and timber supply, gathering of litter for stable-bedding, bee pastures, hunting, etc. The *Marken* served as the reserve land out of which individuals might reclaim new land for settling (*Bifänge*) or found whole new villages. With decreasing areas of forest, however, the remaining *Markungen* became the area of conflict between territorial overlords and those desiring to enter the remaining reserve lands.

But it must be admitted that closing the forests had a beneficial effect upon their preservation. Riehl (1854, p. 26) called the forests the "aristocratic features" in the Central European landscape, the living "medieval relics." Like most of the other rural institutions, the *Marken* and *Allmenden* demonstrate the interrelationship of individualism, co-operation, and dependence within the rural sphere, for they prevented the despoliation of the landscape for ruthless, egoistic purposes. The economy of the peasant was imbedded into superimposed structures of a social whole comprising his equals as well as those of superior rank and rights, who, in many ways, took the place of a later public authority. The individual was counterbalanced by the group. The ensuing pattern of land utilization according to distribution of its elements— fields, roads, pastures, meadows, woodland, etc.—could not have developed merely in response to private initiative as exerted within surveyed property but was dependent upon the whole community structure and its place in the landscape. This preserved the openness, the common accessibility of the German peasant landscape, and its construction by larger than individual patterns, which still make it possible to

0   100   200
MILES

FIG. 78.—Types of legal inheritance in Central Europe, *Anerbenrechte* and *Realerbteilung*. (After Huppertz, 1935.)

ramble over fields and forests without being constantly impeded by fencing and danger of trespassing.

Regional Variety in Settlement Patterns

Haus or *Hof, Hufe,* and *Allmende* or *Markungen* fitted into patterns of settlement that comprised the forms of the villages, hamlets, etc., as well as the pertaining *Fluren* (Table 1).

ment of private property and the distribution of the kinds of cultivation (*Kulturarten*). Fields, meadows, woodland, etc., were carved out of the whole of the ecological complex appropriated during the land seizure (*Landnahme*) of the group or—in later times—assigned to a group by the colonizing authorities. The major units of land utilization therefore followed as nature suggested: the meadowland along the brooks; the

TABLE 1*

SCHEMATIC ORDER OF SETTLEMENT AND *Flur* PATTERNS

I. SETTLEMENT PATTERNS

Number of Houses	1	2, 4, 8	16,	32, 64< (no fixed upper limit)

Irregular
  Without formal
  order
	Single farmstead
	(*Einzelhof*)
		Hamlet
		(*Weiler*)
		(*Drubbel*)
			Small village
			(*Dorf*)
				Large closed village
				(*Haufendorf*)

Regular
  With rational
  order
	Line villages
	Forest villages
	Marsh villages
		Small villages
		  with greens
		(*Rundling*)
				Colonial villages
				(*Strassendorf*)
				(*Angerdorf*, etc.)

II. *Flur* PATTERNS

Irregular
  Without formal
  order
	Compact, contiguous pattern
	(*Einödflur*)
		Aggregate of
		  blocks
		(*Blockgemengeflur*)
			Aggregate of strips
			(*Streifengemengeflur*)

Regular
  With rational
  order
	Wald-,
	Marsh-,
	Hufenflur
			Gewannfluren

* Source: Hömberg, 1935.

Older concepts have correlated settlement patterns with ethnic or tribal distributions in the time of early settlement (Meitzen, 1882). While Meitzen saw old primary differentiations, it is now agreed that changes in subsequent economic and social history are of far greater importance.[11]

The historical order of the Central European *Flur* determined the arrange-

11. Steinbach, 1927, 1937; Hömberg, 1935; Mortensen, 1945, 1946–47, 1955; and many others.

fields to the drier, easily plowable soils; the woodlands to the steeper parts of the terrain or to the farther fringes of the communal area. The pattern of distribution of individual property was subordinated to such larger groupings.

The pattern on the plowable land is of greatest interest. In northwestern Germany we find small, ecologically conditioned localities that rise slightly above the ground. These were used as the oldest plots of plowable land and have apparently determined the location of settlements since prehistoric times (Niemeier, 1938, 1944*a*, 1944*b*). They were called *"Esch"* and were owned only by peasants in possession of the full rights of their estate. These fully righted peasants (*Erben*) joined for working the *Esch* into so-called *"Eschgenossenschaften,"* from which the social substratum was excluded. In its most extreme form, the *Esch* was

During earlier medieval times new settlements of fully righted peasants developed on either single farmsteads (*Einzelhöfe*) or in small, loosely textured groupings (*Drubbels*). Later, those cottagers (*Kötter*) without the full rights of the peasant were furnished plots from the *Markungen*. Suitable land also was individually appropriated in blocklike fashion, as the so-called

Turnips, potatoes and other root crops

Wheat, winter corn

Oats

Potatoes, turnips

Rye, winter corn

Clover

Clover and forage oats

Mixed cultivation

Meadows

Village with gardens and fruit

FIG. 79.—The economic utilization of a *Flur* in the Odenwald. (After F. Tichy, 1954; part of unpublished field map.)

A seven-field system is practiced in a common rotation, proceeding in seven *Zelgen:* I–VII. Crops rotate in sequence from one to seven. Lands not in seven-year rotation are newly cleared and managed independently.

managed in a one-field system, which, year after year, served for the production of rye (Müller-Wille, 1939, 1942, 1944*a*, 1944*b*). This *Esch* pattern was surrounded by extensive areas of low-lying lands, heath, or bogs (*Markungen*), where pasturing was the normal activity (Fig. 79). In the outfield small plots for minor crops might alternate with long years of heath or bogs. Burning was practiced on the bogs before the land was put under cultivation.

"Kämpe," in which the upper and lower strata of the society participated. In the eighteenth and nineteenth centuries the *Merkungen* were divided as a result of an era of reform.

The arrangement differed in southern and western Germany. In the older settled areas—the basins, the loesslands, or corresponding landscapes—the closed village (*Haufendorf*) prevailed. The area of the fields increased early at the expense of the outer circle of woodland area (*Allmende*) by additions of plots of land called "*Gewanne*." In the fully developed arrangement the *Gewanne* determined the distribution of the single, small strips into which individual peasant holdings were subdivided. These small strips of the *Hufe* appeared parceled out over the entire plowed area and also over the meadowland, giving rise to the famous, frequently described "*Gewannflur*" (like virgates in the English open-field pattern). Few lanes branch off from the village and run out into the field grouped into *Gewanne*. It is obviously impossible directly to reach each single plot. A common order is necessary to work the fields, and this probably appeared along with the three-field system. The *Gewanne* were grouped into "*Zelgen*" (sometimes called "*Ösche*" and equivalent to the open-field pattern in England), which served as field units for summer grain, winter grain, and fallow (Fig. 80). The rights of trespassing and the dates for plowing, fencing, harvesting, or opening of stubble fields for pasturing were subject to common regulation and supervised by village officials. This is the pattern of community-regulated cultivation (*Flurzwang*) that prevailed on the fields of many *Gewann* villages well into the nineteenth century. Open-field practices (*zelgengebundene Bewirtschaftung*) may still be observed in many parts of western Germany (Figs. 81 and 83 [p. 269]). This system conditioned the historic complex of the peasant landscape in the regions of earliest occupation in southern and western Germany.

EVOLUTION OF PEASANT INSTITUTIONS AND PEASANT LANDSCAPE

Full appreciation and understanding of Central European peasant institutions and peasant landscape call for brief reference to the evolutionary stages. Northern Germany preserved old patterns, owing to less intensive cul-

tural historic movements and its peculiar social and ecological structure. Southern Germany underwent a succession of important changes. The catchwords denoting the trends are: increase of population; increase of plowed land in distributed individual plots at the expense of common land (*Allmende*); early, almost universal, spreading of the manorial system (*Grundherrschaft*); and surplus grain production. The results were crowded villages and complicated field patterns (*Vergewannung*). The earlier, smaller settlements grew into the typical large *Haufendörfer*.

The process of change continued and increased in late medieval times with the rapid development of urban life. Southern and western Germany became densely dotted with towns and cities, the mere presence of which affected the countryside. Market conditions improved, making specialization possible. A money economy began to replace the former autarchical situation, as well as methods of exchange or taxations in kind, in the countryside. Numerous small towns grew crowded, notably in the important wine-growing sections and along the routes of trade. These were also the areas of earliest agricultural specialization. These changes brought city ways to the country—market dependence, free mobility of real estate, declining conservatism—to create in the extreme what Riehl (1869, pp. 181–216) has aptly called "*Bauernland mit Bürgerrechten*." The growth of towns and cities also affected the settlement pattern of the countryside by attracting labor. Many a village with accompanying fields was embodied into urban areas, and the peasants became burghers, frequently quite willingly, to improve their legal status (*Stadtluft macht frei*, "town air does away with bondage"), while in the countryside (*Luft macht eigen*, "Country air puts into bondage") bondage often pre-

	Summer grain		Rape, turnip, cabbage, etc.
	Winter grain		Clover
	Hops		Meadows		Fir woods

FIG. 80.—Field pattern and economic organization of a small, closed hamlet in Lower Bavaria. (After Fuchs, in Otremba, 1953.)

The field is imperfectly distributed among the peasants in relation to contiguity of area. Three *Zelgen* are still recognizable, although frequent exceptions occur along the fringes in connection with the field lanes. Hops, being a crop that keeps the ground more permanently, does not fit into three-field rotation. Plots with hops, therefore, are not included in the *Zelgen* system. All hop lands are directly accessible from field lanes.

vailed. In many fertile areas, notably the basins and the *Börden,* the contraction of smaller groups into larger villages has repeatedly resulted in the formation of larger but structurally more complex field patterns (*Flurformen*).

In the regions of medieval forest clearing and colonization, peasantry developed under conditions formally and institutionally different. Such movement had already begun by the final settling after the migration of peoples and

scarcely stopped until it reached a climax at the end of the fourteenth century. At first the open spaces between the oldest settlements were filled by new villages, distinguishable usually by name suffixes, which sprang up on the outer fringes of the *Markungen.* By the end of the Merovingian and through Carolingian times, however, such areas had been filled, the stream of settlement turned toward the uplands, and the period of clearing began. Forest clearing and settling reached its height in

FIG. 81.—A typical eastern colonial village and its *Flur.* (After Krenzlin, 1954.)

The type represented is a somewhat narrow *Angerdorf.* The individual holdings are distributed in long, very narrow strips. The whole *Flur* is divided into three major blocks and several minor ones. This corresponds to the simplified *Gewannflur* type in the colonial east. The three larger *Gewanne* seem to coincide with the three *Zelgen* of the three-field system.

the twelfth to thirteenth centuries. Then suddenly the stream dried up, and, within a few decades, a reversal took place. Many settlements that had been founded a generation before were abandoned, and the forest recovered ground. The reasons for, and quantitative importance of, this period of sudden desertion of the settlements (*Wüstungen*) are even yet not fully understood (cf. Darby, pp. 198–99).[12]

Because of differences in time and geographical habitat, these later peasant settlements began under differing circumstances; their divergence widened with further evolution. The tilling of the settled land had begun under the changed historical milieu of the Merovingian and Carolingian world. In the Germania Romana, in what was later eastern France including the Basin of Paris, a process of culture contact had brought important amalgamations of Nordic Germanic and Mediterranean culture inheritance. The birth of the medieval *Grundherrschaft* and intense political and jurisdictional reorganization took place at that time. The free, open spaces had disappeared, having been either settled or taken over by legal claims of the king and the lords of the *Grundherrschaften*. Squatting did not entirely vanish, but the typical forest clearing was done upon ground pertaining to the king's domain or to some big *Grundherrschaft*. The forms that developed differed as well, as may be taken from Figures 82 and 83 (p. 269). Most important was the development of formally regulated patterns.

In the Black Forest, in the Odenwald, in the eastern *Mittelgebirge,* as well as in the forests of the northern lowlands, forest-line villages (*Waldhufendörfer*) appeared. Each settler re-

ceived a *Hufe* in an elongated strip running from the valley bottom to the top of the ridge. This pattern combined important features of single farmstead settlement with village community coherence.

Distance from the old regions of a few kilometers meant a great deal in later evolution. Such new forest lands were cherished ground for ambitious aristocracy to carve out territory by settling. The interlacing of manorial holdings and jurisdictional rights within one village were less than in the old areas. Under stronger manorial influence, the *Hof* structure remained more intact. Some of the parts of the central Black Forest are still today an island of undivided inherited right (*Anerbenrecht, Höferecht*) within the southwestern realm of equally divided inheritance rights (*Realerbteilung*). The influence of the new town integration into the former rural pattern of the old land was less felt. Market relations were impeded by distance and terrain. The higher altitude prevented the growing of grain, with its accompanying three-field system and subdivision (*Vergetreidung*). Rotation of grassland alternating with plowed land (*Feldgraswirtschaft*) and emphasis on livestock determined the agricultural system. Work in the forests or mines and on handicrafts (textiles, glassmaking, mechanical crafts) supplemented life when the soil and climate failed to support the population. Though late in origin, the peasantry of the forest clearing was the preserver of folklore, costumes, and old-fashioned peasant qualities and habits. Such regions have proved very attractive for tourism as well as for authors of peasant novels.

The neat regional juxtaposition to the older areas is characteristic for southern and some parts of central Germany, with its nicely configured landscape, though not so much so in northern Germany. The Saxon territory is

---

12. Recently there has been a revival of interest by geographers and agricultural historians. Field research (by Mortensen, Scharlau, Jäger, and others), as well as work in archives (by Jäger) and on the complex of economic history (by Abel), is in progress.

very old *Volksland,* having been occupied centuries earlier, before Franks and Alemannic tribes founded their new areas following conquest from the Romans. Medieval settlements arose in the intervening spaces between the old Saxon nuclei. The *Grundherrschaft* arrived later but maintained itself in older forms. Urban life was less densely intercalated than in the south and west. The maritime climate allowed emphasis on the growing of grain (*Vergetreidung*)

only along the inner continental fringes. The boundary of the three-field system with *Gewannflur* and *Flurzwang* followed decidedly a climatically and edaphically conditioned line to the north and northwest, where other systems with stronger emphasis upon livestock and green land were combined with the very old *Esch* type, one-field system, or very extensive ways of utilizing heath and bogs (Müller-Wille, 1938*a*, 1941; Pfeifer and Schüttler,

Single farms
Loosely connected villages
Hamlets
Compact villages
Round villages
Line villages along the coastal marshes and woods
Street and green villages of the east
Town-like villages
Large estates
--- Territorial boundaries
— Linguistic boundary

Miles
0   100

FIG. 82.—Distribution of types of settlement forms in Central Europe. (After Huppertz, 1935.)

Two major regions stand out rather clearly: western Germany, settled since the migrations of people, and eastern Germany, settled since the medieval colonial movement. Western Germany breaks down into the loosely grouped, smaller settlements of the northwest; planned patterns along the North Sea coastal marshes; irregular, compact patterns in the west and southwest. Eastern Germany contains large estates along the coastal regions; compact, planned villages farther inland; planned patterns in the mountain uplands and along reclaimed alluvial bottom lands.

1941). Only in certain areas did *Hagen-hufendörfer* develop, practically identical with forest-line villages (*Wald-hufendörfer*); they also were allocated upon manorial territory.

The zone of North Sea marshes, with Frisian and Saxon population, produced many forms of settlement. Reclamation and diking occurred during the phase of medieval colonization. It was brought to the eastern section by skilful people from Flanders and the Low Countries (A.D. 1106, near Bremen), along with a marsh village (*Marsch-hufendorf*) resembling closely the *Waldhufendorf*. The isolated marshes for a long time sustained a high degree of peasant independence. Proximity to the sea early brought commerce to the countryside; Frisian traders were among the earliest reported. Sheep-raising suggested early wool trade. Later, coastal shipping brought contact with the rising markets in the crowded Western countries. Grain, butter, and meat were exported by peasants who were shipowners as well. This type of economy fostered a lively spirit of trade and commerce among the people. The very even qualities of the soil suggested its commercial use as well. Quite in contrast to the upland (*Geest*), equally divided inheritance (*Realerbteilung*) is found today in many parts of the marshes.

A third region of peasant development is the east. Bavarian peasantry settled in the Tirols, Carinthia, and Styria and laid the foundations for the Austrian march between the eighth and tenth centuries. The great period of eastern colonization began in the tenth century, when the area east of the Elbe was added to the old German *Volksland* in the Old German Empire (*Altreich*). It was a mass movement of people into new lands contiguous to the homeland, in which peasants and nobility from most of the older sections participated. Warlike and peaceful diplomatic relations with the Slavs opened the way for the settlers, who were guided and directed by the nobility. "*Locatores*" spotted the places for new settlements and recruited people from back home. Not until the settling of the American continent was there a peasant movement of similar proportions.

The patterns of settlement were truly colonial. They were derived from traditional forms in the west but were adjusted to practices and experiences in the new environment. The unit of allotment remained the *Hufe*, but in its later concept as a measurable quantity of individual property. *Locatores*, functionaries of lower jurisdiction, and nobility received larger allotments (from 2 to 4 *Hufen*). The closed form of village settlement furnished the normal standard. The *Höfe* were regularly arranged on both sides of rectangular or almond-shaped "greens" (Fig. 81, p. 262). Special types were the *Rundlinge* and the *Wald-* or *Hagenhufendörfer*.

The *Flur* was normally laid out in the three-field system, which was the leading field system of the time. The *Hufen* property was subdivided in a few long strips, in numbers accordant with the larger subdivisions of the *Flur*. In a generalized way it may be said that the *Gewanne* and *Zelgen* coincided here more closely than in the west (Fig. 81, p. 262). The allotment of *Markungen* and *Allmenden* was insignificant in comparison with the old land.

The relations of colonial settlement patterns lately have been carefully investigated with regard to ethnical, ecological, and economic facts (Krenzlin, 1952). The variety is greater than is usually supposed, and—as in the west—the factors of change and succeeding development had greater importance. Changing field systems had considerable influence on the further evolution of the *Flur*. The east attracted the western peasants, not only in their quest for new soil, but also because it offered improved social conditions. Rights were improved, and the drive to new social conditions suggests comparison with the American West. Terms of tenantry were better defined, and the manorial burdens were less. The political aspect was decidedly of larger scale. The *Grundherrschaften* also were closed, compact holdings, in which manorial and jurisdictional rights could be more efficiently applied.

The truly colonial character of the movement subsided when the stream of peasants from the west dwindled by the fourteenth century. The great period of desertion (*Wüstungen*) touched the east as well. Wars and epidemics (the Black Death) decimated the population; even re-migration to the west may have taken place, at least locally. The nobility felt the loss of income when *Hufen* lay deserted. A good deal of former peasant land changed over into the hands of aristocracy as abandoned homes (*Heimfall*). Thus began a tendency to larger agricultural enterprises among the nobility, a factor of greatest importance for the peasantry in the east.

By the fifteenth and sixteenth centuries, with the growing markets in Western Europe and the development of shipping from the Hanseatic cities along the Baltic coast, a real opportunity opened for large-scale grain production. A similar market development in England also greatly influenced the countryside there. Nobility began actively to enlarge the land around the court. *Hufen* without heirs reverted to the *Grundherrschaft;* epidemics, feuds, and wars helped to reclaim peasant land; and obstinate peasants were evicted. But, contrary to similar actions by the English nobility, who went in for grazing, the eastern German barons turned to grain-growing; they needed the hands and consequently bound the evicted peasants to the ground as serfs to secure the necessary labor force. The large estate (*demesne*) enterprises (*Gutswirtschaft*) on latifundias were born and were followed by systems of bondage (*Leibeigenschaft*) and serfdom under jurisdictional authority of the feudal overlord (*Gutsuntertänigkeit*). It was the abuse of medieval manorial rights, which included also jurisdictional rights, that in time made conditions so vicious. While peasant villages degenerated until only little hamlets (*Gutsweiler*) remained, estates and subsidiary farms (*Gutshof* and *Vorwerke*) for outlying fields grew.

The fate of the peasantry largely depended upon the relations between nobility and *Landesherrschaft*. The stronger monarchies, like Prussia, earlier had tendencies to protect the peasant against the inroads of nobility (in Prussia, edict of 1709). But in Mecklenburg and Swedish Pomerania, which were strongly dominated by aristocracy, the process of peasant eviction (*Bauernlegen*) had greatest consequences. By the end of the eighteenth century, nearly two-thirds of the whole country was in latifundia.

Tragically enough, the so-called "reform movements" of the eighteenth and nineteenth centuries brought the greatest amount of peasant land into the hands of the nobility. In Prussia, peasants enjoyed a certain protection after 1709, and the domainal peasants were free. By the famous edict promulgated by the Freiherrn von Stein in 1807 all peasants were made free, and hereditary serfdom (*Erbuntertänigkeit*) was abolished. In 1811 all material and personal obligations of the peasants were theoretically removed. But, during 1808–10, the application of proclamations for reforms had largely canceled the earlier intentions. The large owners received emoluments for the liberation of their peasants amounting to one-third of the peasant land and, in some cases, even one-half. In this way, the nobility received 1,200,000 hectares in Prussia.

The old order had given a certain

protection, in a patriarchal way, for weak peasants. Such was no longer the case; consequently, many, if not most, of the smaller people were forced off the land or degenerated into landless day workers (*Tagelöhner*) near the lowest minimum of existence. The situation was most extreme in Mecklenburg. *Leibeigenschaft* was lifted here in 1820, but, with it, all rights of the people on the land. Nobility acquired, consequently, as much as 80–90 per cent of the total area (Fig. 74, p. 248). By the time the revolutionary movements of the middle of the nineteenth century stimulated legislation to improve conditions, it was too late. Industry attracted the poorer rural population and offered new occupations, and the large estates began to feel the scarcity of hands. The way out—to import Polish harvesters (*polnische Schnitter*)—did not improve social conditions in the countryside. Protective tariffs helped maintain this unhappy structure until the end of World War II.

The revolutionary change in eastern German land reform after 1945 may be gathered from a few figures (Abel, 1951, p. 178) on changes in property structure in the eastern German Democratic Republic (1939, 1946) as compared to West Germany (1949). In size of holdings the east has become similar to the west, as the accompanying tabulation

	EAST GERMANY (PER CENT)		WEST GERMANY (PER CENT)
HECTARES	1939	1946	1949
0–5	9.1	9.7	20.5
5–20	31.7	53.4	43.6
20–50	22.5	24.0	23.4
50–100	8.4	7.7	6.3
100 and over	28.3	5.2	5.8

shows, but the unfortunate circumstances of the reform and the continuing pressure with "plans" and productive quotas (*Solls*) has not allowed the growth of happy conditions.

But such conditions did not characterize the whole east until 1945. Healthy peasant structures had survived in many parts of eastern Prussia (notably within the old diocese Ermeland), Pomerania (back from the coast), Brandenburg (notably the lands reclaimed by Frederick the Great along the Oder and Warta), Silesia (outside the truly latifundia sections), and Saxony. In the east the right of undivided inheritance (*Anerbenrecht*) predominated, and the property structure was better preserved. *Parcellement* never attained such vicious consequences as in the southwest. The influence of the towns on the countryside was less than in the west. In fact, many small towns had a strong rustic flavor. Eastern peasantry retained a more truly traditional, rural character. If there is a peasantry in the world in which something of the pioneer qualities of the nineteenth century is still alive, it is in the eastern peasantry.

CONCLUSIONS

The problems of peasantry have been only touched upon but by no means covered. What I have endeavored to demonstrate is that peasantry in Central Europe developed in time and differentiated itself in area. Changing historic situations have left stratifications which vary from region to region. Peasantry is old as an estate (*Stand*), but many of its institutions are of recent origin. It is necessary to discriminate carefully between conditions that are truly old and those that have evolved during a long, sometimes complicated, history.

There remains to add a few remarks about some of the historical developments which I have not been able to cover. The great crisis in medieval development is the period of abandonment of villages (*Wüstungen*), which led to a settlement structure which was the basis for developments in the new era after 1500. The importance of this period with regard to the distribution of open land and forests has been evaluated in the "*Göttinger Schule*" (Mortensen, 1951; Scharlau, 1938, 1943; Jäger, 1951).

But later forces continued to shape the fate of peasantry. In the fifteenth and sixteenth centuries the modern state began to appear; its influences at first were frequently resented by the peasantry. The supervision of the forests was enforced, and the state gradually became the great forest proprietor. The developing state administration requested numerous innovations in law and taxation, which were felt especially in the many small territories of the southwest, where the personal bondage of the newly forming political dependencies (*Untertänigkeits-Verhältnisse*) was rather rigid. Here unrest prevailed, and finally the peasant wars of 1524–25 flared up.

On the other hand, it must be agreed that the *Landesherren* placed a protecting arm over the peasants against inroads from the nobility. Rising ideas of mercantilism brought new interest in the productiveness of the land and in an increase of population. The growing market economy also affected the countryside and stimulated the tendency toward specialization.

The sixteenth century, but even more the seventeenth and eighteenth centuries, saw great changes in some sections with respect to the pattern of settlement. In the Algäu and somewhat later in Schleswig-Holstein, movements began among the peasants, and were favored by the *Landesherren,* to separate the *Allmenden* and to establish properties. In the Algäu and later in northern Schleswig, villages disbanded, and single farmsteads replaced the former agglomerations.

The reforms affected the whole traditional way of peasant living and social order. With the *Gemarkungen* and *Allmenden,* the old social order of the countryside dwindled. It was no longer possible to maintain divisions of social rank and right among the rural classes. The eighteenth century also saw the start of liberation and modernization of the peasant society, which, in a way, led to a certain atomization. Where, formerly, almost indelible material bonds had supported the older order, now individual rights and properties dominated the scene. But the forces of tradition remained valid in strongly profiled areas, such as Lower Saxony.

The movement of separation or inclosure (*Verkoppelung*) spread over the greater part of the nineteenth century. In Hannover, an order of King George III in 1786 remained without much success. Later ordinances followed in lower Germany in 1802, 1824–25, and 1842. In southern Germany there were laws of land rearrangement (*Flurbereinigung*) in 1856 and 1862; in the Rhineland, not until 1888. But in many sections *Flurbereinigung* has not yet made such progress. With the nineteenth century, agriculture already was a subject for historic retrospective—partly for mere scientific interest, partly as the aboriginal image of national social character.

Today peasantry in Germany is again confronted with most severe problems. The industrialization of Germany has definitely diminished the importance of agriculture from the state's point of view. Autarchic interests, with a view to conditions in time of war, have supported protective tariff policies that gave an artificial climate to peasant economy. But the growing discrepancies between rural living conditions and urban industrial standards, as well as between rural wages and industrial wages, have created a latent labor crisis, especially felt under boom conditions as of today. The grotesque situation has arisen that the importation has been planned of seven thousand Italian agricultural workers into southern Germany —into areas of the smallest average peasant holdings, where part-time farming not connected with latifundia but with undersized rural property is abundant!

during the last few years; it is a sight to see the young peasant, with a companion on the rear seat who may carry a scythe, fly up the rough field lanes on a motorbike!

Figure 83 summarizes the most important facts and portrays the distribution of the major social regions of peas-

FIG. 83.—The areal differentiation of peasantry in Central Europe, according to size of holding and age of settlement. (After Otremba, 1942.)

The growing labor scarcity hastens the pace of mechanization. But many technical problems—let alone those of education and knowledge—await solution before we may say that adaptation of the tractor to the small-scale farm has been an all-round success. The increase of motorization has been amazing

antry, period of settling and size of property determining the construction of the map (Otremba, 1942). We can easily recognize the regions repeatedly distinguished in this paper: the northwest, the southwest, and the east beyond the line separating old land and colonial area.

REFERENCES

ABEL, W.
1935   *Agrarkrisen und Agrarkonjunktur in Mitteleuropa vom 13. bis zum 19. Jahrhundert.* Berlin: Paul Parey. 179 pp.
1943   *Die Wüstungen des ausgehenden Mittelalters: Ein Beitrag zur Siedlungs- und Agrargeschichte Deutschlands.* ("Quellen und Forschungen zur Agrargeschichte," Band I, ed. FRANZ GÜNTHER and FRIEDRICH LÜTGE. Jena: Gustav Fischer. 165 pp.
1951   *Agrarpolitik.* Göttingen: Vandenboeck & Ruprecht. 419 pp.
1955   "Schichten und Zonen europäischer Agrarverfassung," *Zeitschrift für Agrargeschichte und Agrarsoziologie,* III, No. 1, 1–18.

AEREBOE, FR.
1920   *Allgemeine landwirtschaftliche Betriebslehre.* 5th ed. Berlin: Paul Parey. 697 pp.

ANONYMOUS
1941–55   *Berichte zur Deutschen Landeskunde,* Vols. I–XIV. (Zentralarchiv für Landeskunde von Deutschland.) Ed. BUNDESANSTALT FÜR LANDESKUNDE. (A comprehensive periodical of current publications.)

BESCHOMER, F.
1923   "Zur Geographie der haupsächlichsten landwirtschaftlichen Betriebssysteme." Dissertation, University of Bonn.

BOBEK, H.
1952   *Südwestdeutsche Studien.* ("Forschungen zur deutschen Bundesanstalt für Landeskunde," Vol. LXII.) Remagen. 67 pp.

BRINKMANN, TH.
1913   "Über landwirtschaftliche Betriebssysteme," *Fühlings landwirtschaftliche Zeitung,* LXII, 184–214.

CREDNER, W.
1938   "Über Kartierung landwirtschaftlicher Nutzflächen," *Zeitschrift für Erdkunde,* VI, 229–36.
1943   "Die deutsche Agrarlandschaft im Kartenbild," *Sitzungsberichte europäischer Geographen,* pp. 177–201. Leipzig.

DÖRRIES, H.
1940   "Siedlungs- und Bevölkerungsgeographie (1908–1938)," *Geographisches Jahrbuch,* LV, No. 1, 3–380.

EBERT, W.
1937   "Ländliche Siedelformen im deutschen Osten," in KÖTZSCHKE, R. VON (ed.), *Auftrage des landesgeschichtlichen Instituts.* Berlin: E. S. Mittler & Sohn.

EHEMANN, K.
1953   *Das Bauernhaus in der Wetterau und im SW. Vogelsberg.* ("Forschungen zur deutschen Bundesanstalt für Landeskunde," Vol. LXI.) Remagen. 150 pp. (Contains comprehensive bibliography.)

ELLENBERG, H.
1937   "Über bäuerliche Wohn- und Siedlungsweise in Nordwestdeutschland in ihrer Beziehung zur Landschaft insbesondere zur Pflanzendecke," *Mitteilungen der floristisch-soziologischen Arbeitsgemeinschaft in Niedersachsen,* No. 3. Hannover.
1941   "Deutsche Bauernhauslandschaften als Ausdruck von Natur, Wirtschaft und Volkstum," *Geographische Zeitschrift,* XLVII, 72–85.
1954   "Steppenheide und Waldweide," *Erdkunde (Archiv für wissenschaftliche Geographie),* VIII, 188–94.

ENGEL, F.
1934   "Deutsche und slawische Züge in der Dobbertiner Kulturlandschaft." Dissertation, University of Kiel.
1949   *Das Rodungsrecht der Hagensiedlungen: Quellen zur Entwicklungsgeschichte der spätmittelalterlichen Kolonisationsbewegung.* ("Quellenhefte zur Niedersächsischen Geschichte," No. 3.) Hildesheim.

ERNST, V.
1926   *Die Entstehung des deutschen Grundeigentums.* Stuttgart: W. Kohlhammer. 146 pp.

FICKELER, P.
1954   "Das Siegerland als Beispiel wirtschaftsgeschichtlicher und wirtschaftsgeographischer Harmonie," *Erdkunde (Archiv für wissenschaftliche Geographie),* VIII, 15–51. (Contains illustrations of *Haubergwirtschaft.*)

FIRBAS, FR.

1949 *Spät- und nacheiszeitliche Wald-geschichte Mitteleuropas nördlich der Alpen,* Vol. I: *Allgemeine Waldgeschichte.* Jena: Gustav Fischer. 480 pp. (Modern synthesis, balanced appraisal of the controversial views of Gradmann and Nietsch in the light of postglacial vegetational development.)

GRADMANN, R.

1901 "Das mitteleuropäische Landschaftsbild nach seiner geschichtlichen Entwicklung," *Geographische Zeitschrift,* VII, Nos. 3–4, 361–77, 435–47.

1906 "Beziehungen zwischen Pflanzengeographie und Siedlungsgeschichte," *ibid.,* XII, 305–25.

1924 *Das harmonische Landschaftsbild.* (Zeitschrift der Gesellschaft für Erdkunde Berlin.) 130 pp.

1928 "Die Arbeitsweise der Siedlungsgeographie in ihrer Anwendung auf das Frankenland," *Zeitschrift für Bayerische Landesgeschichte,* I, 316–57.

1931 *Süddeutschland.* 2 vols. Stuttgart: J. Engelhorns. 215+553 pp.

1933 "Die Steppenheide-theorie," *Geographische Zeitschrift,* XXXIX, No. 5, 265–78.

1936 "Vorgeschichtliche Landwirtschaft und Besiedlung," *ibid.,* XLII, Nos. 9–10, 378–86.

1942 "Hackbau und Kulturpflanzen," *Deutsches Archiv für Landes und Volksforschung,* VI, 107–13.

1943 "Siedlungsformen als Geschichtsquelle und als historisches Problem," *Zeitschrift für Württembergische Landesgeschichte,* VII, 25–56.

HAHN, E.

1909 *Die Entstehung der Pflugkultur.* Heidelberg: Carl Winter. 192 pp.

1914 *Von der Hacke zum Pflug.* ("Wissenschaft und Bildung," Vol. CXXVII.) Leipzig: Quelle & Meyer. 121 pp. (2d ed., 1919.)

HANSSEN, G.

1861 *Die Aufhebung der Leibeigenschaft und die Umgestaltung des gutsherrlich-bäuerlichen Verhältnisses überhaupt in den Herzogtümern Schleswig-Holstein.* St. Petersburg: Eggers. 195 pp.

1875 "Zur Geschichte der norddeutschen Gutswirtschaft, seit dem Ende des 16. Jahrhundert," *Journal für Landwirtschaft.* Göttingen.

HARTKE, W., and WESTERMANN, E.

1940 "Zur Geographie der Vererbung der bäuerlichen Liegenschaften in Deutschland bis zum Erlass des Reichserbhofgesetzes," *Petermanns geographische Mitteilungen,* LXXXVI, No. 1, 16–19.

HAUSRATH, H.

1911 *Pflanzengeographische Wandlungen der Deutschen Landschaft.* ("Wissenschaft und Hypothese," Vol. XIII.) Leipzig and Berlin: B. G. Teubner. 274 pp.

HELBOK, A.

1925 "Der germanische Ursprung des oberdeutschen Bauernhauses," pp. 273–92 in *Ottenthal Festschrift Shlernschriften.* Innsbruck and Munich: Wagner.

1929 "Die Formenlandschaft des deutschen Bauernhauses," *Württembergische Monatschrift.*

1932 "Über vorzeitliche und heutige Haustypenlandschaften," *Zeitschrift für Volkskunde* (N.S.), II, 223–34. Berlin and Leipzig.

1937–38 *Grundlagen der Volksgeschichte Deutschlands und Frankreichs.* 2 vols. Berlin: Walter de Gruyter & Co. 564+565 pp.

1938 *Deutsche Siedlung: Wesen, Ausbreitung, Sinn.* Halle: Niemeyer. 228 pp.

HEMPEL, L.

1954a "Beispiele von Bodenerosionskarten im niedersächsischen Bergland sowie Bemerkungen über Berücksichtigung der Erosionsschäden bei der Bodenschätzung," *Neues Archiv für Niedersachsen,* pp. 140–43.

1954b "Die Entstehung einiger anthropogenbedingter Oberflächenformen und ihre Ähnlichkeit mit natürlichen Formen," pp. 119–26 in *Ergebnisse und Probleme moderner geographischer Forschungen, Hans Mortensen zu seinem 60. Geburtstage.* ("Abhandlungen der Akademie für Raumforschung und Landesplanung,"

Vol. XXVIII.) Bremen-Horn: W. Dorn. 332 pp.

HESSE, P.

1949   *Grundprobleme der Agrarverfassung: dargestellt am Beispiel der Gemeindetypen und Produktionszonen von Württemberg-Hohenzollern und Baden.* Stuttgart: W. Kohlhammer. 284 pp.

HÖMBERG, A.

1935   *Die Entstehung der westdeutschen Flurformen: Blockgemengflur, Streifenflur, Gewannflur.* With a Foreword by WALTHER VOGEL. Berlin. 64 pp.

1938   *Grundfragen der deutschen Siedlungsforschung.* ("Veröffentlichungen aus dem Seminar für Staatenkunde und historische Geographie an der Universität Berlin," Vol. VI.) Berlin.

HUPPERTZ, B.

1939   *Räume und Schichten bäuerl'cher Kulturformen in Deutschland.* Bonn: L. Röhrscheid. 315 pp.

HUTTENLOCHER, F.

1937   "Zusammenhänge zwischen ländlichen Siedlungsarten und geschichtlichen Wirtschaftsweisen im südwestdeutschen Raum," *Zeitschrift für Landesgeschichte,* I, 88–121. Württemberg.

JÄGER, H.

1951   *Die Entwicklung der Kulturlandschaft im Kreise Hofgeismar.* ("Göttingen geographische Abhandlungen," No. 8.) Göttingen: Hans Mortensen. 114 pp.

JESSEN, J.

1922   "Die Entstehung und Entwicklung der Gutswirtschaft bis zum Beginn der Agrarreformen," *Zeitschrift der Gesellschaft für Schleswig-Holsteinische Geschichte,* XLI, 1–206.

KÄUBLER, R.

1938   "Junggeschichtliche Veränderungen des Landschaftsbildes im mittelsächsischen Lössgebiet," *Wissenschaftliche Veröffentlichungen des Deutschen Museums für Landerkunde* (N.S.), V, 71–91.

KNAPP, G. F.

1887   *Die Bauernbefreiung und der Ursprung der Landarbeiter in den*

älteren Teilen Preussens, Vols. I and II. Leipzig: Duncker & Humblot. 352 +473 pp.

KÖTZSCHKE, R.

1942   "Die Siedelformen des deutschen Nordosten und Sudosten in volks- und sozialgeschichtlicher Bedeutung," *Deutsche Ostforschung,* I, 362–90. Leipzig.

1953   *Ländliche Siedlung und Agrarwesen in Sachsen.* ("Forschungen zur deutschen Bundesanstalt für Landeskunde," Vol. LXXVII.) 236 pp. Remagen.

KOTHE, H.

1953   "Völkerkundliches zur Frage der neolithischen Anbauformen in Europa," pp. 28–74 in KOTHE, H., and OTTO, K. H. (eds.), *Ethnographisch-archäologische Forschungen.* Berlin: Deutscher Verlag der Wissenschaften. 126 pp.

KREBS, N.

1937   *Atlas des deutschen Lebensraumes in Mitteleuropa.* ("Auftrage der Preussischen Akademie der Wissenschaften.") Leipzig: Bibliographisches Institut. (Not completed. The most detailed set of maps on the physical basis and some of the related historical and economic facts.)

KRENZLIN, A.

1940   "Probleme der neueren nord-ostdeutschen und ostmitteldeutschen Flurformenforschung," *Deutsches Archiv für Landes- und Volksforschung,* IV, 547–69.

1952   *Dorf, Feld und Wirtschaft im Gebiet der grossen Täler: und Platten östlich der Elbe.* ("Forschungen zur deutschen Landeskunde," Vol. LXX.) Remagen: Verlag des Amtes für Landeskunde. 144 pp.

KRZYMOWSKI, R.

1914   *Die landwirtschaftlichen Wirtschaftsysteme Elsass Lothringens.* Gebweiler. 477 pp.

1951   *Geschichte der deutschen Landwirtschaft (bis zum Ausbruch des zweiten Weltkrieges 1939) under besonderer Berücksichtigung der technischen Entwicklung der Landwirtschaft.* 2d ed. Stuttgart: E. Ulmer. 372 pp.

KUHN, W.
1953 *Hecken, Terrassen und Boden-zerstörung im hohen Vogelsberg.* ("Rhein-Mainische Forschungen," Vol. XXXIX.) 54 pp.

KURON, H.
1941 "Die Bodenerosion und ihre Bekampfung in Deutschland," *Der Kulturtechniker*, Vol. XLIV.

LEISTER, I.
1952 *Rittersitz und adliges Gut in Holstein und Schleswig.* ("Schriften des Geographischen Instituts der Universität Kiel," Vol. XIV, No. 2.) 157 pp.

LÖW, K.
1940 "Ackerterrassen im Vogelsberg," *Zeitschrift für Erdkunde*, VIII, 488–90.

LÜTGE, FR.
1937 *Die Agrarverfassung des frühen Mittelalters in Mitteldeutschen Raum, vornehmlich in der Karolinger Zeit.* Jena: Gustav Fischer. 570 pp.
1949 *Die Bayrische Grundherrschaft, Untersuchungen über die Agrarverfassung Altbayerns im 16–18. Jahrhundert.* Stuttgart: Piscator Verlag. 187 pp.

MAGER, F.
1937 *Entwicklungsgeschichte der Kulturlandschaft des Herzogtums Schleswig in historischer Zeit.* 2 vols. Breslau: F. Hirt (Vol. I); Kiel: Verlag Heimat & Erde (Vol. II).
1955 *Geschichte des Bauerntums und der Bodenkultur im Lande Mecklenburg.* ("Veröffentlichungen der Historischen Kommission," Vol. I.) Deutsche Akademie der Wissenschaften Berlin: Berlin Akademie Verlag. 580 pp. (Mager published many books and articles on the historical development of landscapes.)

MARTINY, R.
1926 *Hof und Dorf in Altwestfalen: Das westfälische Streusiedlungsproblem.* ("Forschungen zur deutschen Landes- und Volkskunde," Vol. XXIV, No. 5.) 66 pp.

MEITZEN, A.
1895 *Siedlung und Agrarwesen der Westgermanen und Ostgermanen, der Kelten, Römer, Finnen und Slaven.* 3 vols. and atlas. Berlin: W. Hertz.

MEYNEN, E. (ed.)
1949 "Bibliographien und Handbücher zur deutschen Landeskunde (1920–1945)," *Geographisches Taschenbuch (Bearbeitet im Amt für Landeskunde)*, pp. 98–105.

MORGEN, H., and SIEVERS, A.
1941 "Die natürlichen Grundlagen der ländlichen Besitzverfassung," *Berichte zur Raumforschung und Raumordnung*, V, No. 8, 368–77.

MORTENSEN, H.
1945 "Beiträge der Ostforschung zur nordwestdeutschen Siedlungs- und Flurforschung," *Nachrichten der Akademie der Wissenschaften in Göttingen, Philosophisch-historische Klasse*, pp. 12–14.
1946–47a "Fragen der nordwestdeutschen Siedlungs- und Flurforschung im Licht der Ostforschung," *Nachrichten der Akademie der Wissenschaften in Göttingen, Philosophisch-historische Klasse*, pp. 37–59.
1946–47b "Zur Entstehung der deutschen Dorfformen, insbesondere des Waldhufendorfes," *Nachrichten der Akademie der Wissenschaften in Göttingen, Philosophisch-historische Klasse*, pp. 76–80.
1951 "Neuere Beobachtungen über Wüstungs-Bandfluren und ihre Bedeutung für die mittelalterliche deutsche Kulturlandschaft," *Berichte zur deutschen Landeskunde*, X, 341–61.
1955 "Zur Entstehung der Gewannflur," *Zeitschrift für Agrargeschichte und Agrarsoziologie*, VII, No. 1, 30–48.

MÜLLER-WILLE, W.
1936 *Die Ackerfluren im Landesteil Birkenfeld und ihre Wandlungen seit dem 17. und 18. Jahrhundert.* (Beiträge zur Landeskunde der Rheinlande.) 2d ser. Bonn: L. Röhrscheid. 129 pp.
1938a "Der Feldbau in Westfalen im 19. Jahrhundert," *Westfälische Forschungen*, I, No. 3, 302–25.
1938b "Der Niederwald im rheinischen Schiefergebirge," *ibid.*, pp. 51–86.
1939 "Haus- und Gehöftformen im

Mitteleuropa," *Geographische Zeit-schrift,* XLII, 121–38.

1941 "Zu Systematik der Feldsysteme in Norddeutschland," *Zeitschrift für Erdkunde,* IX, Nos. 1–2, 40–43.

1942 "Das rheinische Schiefergebirge und seine kulturgeographische Stellung: Besiedlung, Siedelformen, Haus und Hofanlagen," *Deutsches Archiv für Landes- und Volksforschung,* VI, 537–91.

1944a "Langstreifenflur und Drubbel: Ein Beitrag zur Siedlungsgeographie Westgermaniens," *ibid.,* VIII, 9–44.

1944b "Die Hagenhufendörfer in Schaumburg-Lippe," *Petermanns geographische Mitteilungen,* IX, Nos. 9–10, 245–47.

1952 *Westfalen: Landschaftliche Ordnung und Bindung eines Landes.* Münster: Aschendorff. 384 pp.

1955 "Agrarbäuerliche Landschaftstypen in Nordwestdeutschland," *Deutscher Geographentag,* XXIX, 179–86. Wiesbaden.

MUNZINGER, H.

1936 "Die Flurbereinigung in Süddeutschland, ihre Geschichte und ihr Stand am 1. Januar. 1935," *Berichte über Landwirtschaft* (N.S.), Vol. CXXIII. Berlin.

NIEHAUS, H.

1933 "Agricultural Conditions and Regions in Germany," *Geographical Review,* XXIII, No. 1, 23–47.

NIEMEIER, G.

1938a "Eschprobleme in Nordwestdeutschland und den östlichen Niederlanden," pp. 27–40 in *Travaux de la Section V, Paysage géographique, Comptes-rendus du Congrès International de Géographie,* Vol. II. Leiden: E. J. Brill. 615 pp.

1938b "Bäuerliche Wohnweise in ihrer Beziehung zur Landschaft und Volkstum," *Geographische Zeitschrift,* XLIV, No. 4, 139–46.

1939 "Die Altersbestimmung der Plaggenböden als kulturgeographisches Problem," *Geographische Anzeiger,* XL, Nos. 9–10, 237–45.

1944 "Gewannfluren," *Petermanns geographische Mitteilungen,* XC, Nos. 3–4, 57–74.

1949 "Frühformen der Waldhufen," *ibid.,* XCIII, 14–27.

NIEMEIER, G., and TASCHENMACHER, W.

1939 "Plaggenböden: Beiträge zur Genetik und Typologie," *Westfälische Forschungen,* II, 29–64.

NIETSCH, H.

1927 "Mitteleuropäischer Urwald," *Zeitschrift der Gesellschaft für Erdkunde Berlin,* pp. 1–16.

1935 *Steppenheide oder Eichenwald: Eine urlandschaftskundliche Untersuchung zum Verständnis der vorgeschichtlichen Siedlung in Mitteleuropa.* Weimar. 81 pp.

1939 *Wald und Siedlung im vorgeschichtlichen Mitteleuropa,* Vol. LXIV. Leipzig: Mannus Bücherei. 254 pp.

OBST, E., and SPREITZER, H.

1939 "Wege und Ergebnisse der Flurforschung im Gebiet der grossen Haufendörfer, *Petermanns geographische Mitteilungen,* LXXXV, No. 1, 1–19.

OTREMBA, E.

1938 *Das Problem der Ackernahrung, untersucht an ausgewählten Beispielen des nördlichen Rhein-Maingebietes.* ("Rhein- Mainische Forschungen," No. 19.) Frankfurt on the Main: H. L. Brönner. 116 pp.

1942 "Die Gliederung der ländlichen Kulturlandschaft in Deutschland," *Zeitschrift für Erdkunde,* X, 513–30.

1951 "Die Entwicklungsgeschichte der Flurformen im oberdeutschen Altsiedellande," *Berichte zur deutschen Landeskunde,* IX, No. 2, 363–82.

1953 *Allgemeine Agrar- und Industriegeographie.* Stuttgart: Frank'sche Verlagsbuchhandlung. 341 pp.

PESSLER, W.

1908 "Die Haustypengebiete im Deutschen Reich," *Deutsche Erde,* VII, 14–22, 45–52.

PFEIFER, G.

1928 *Das Siedlungsbild der Landschaft Angeln.* ("Veröffentlichungen der Schleswig-Holsteinischen Universitätsgesellschaft," No. 17.) Breslau: F. Hirt. 167 pp.

1939–46 "Wirtschaftsgeographie," pp. 175–204 in WISSMANN, H. VON, *Naturforschung und Medizin in Deutsch-*

land, Vol. XLIV: *Geographie,* Part IV. Wiesbaden: Dieterich'sche Verlagsbuchhandlung. 220 pp.

PFEIFER, G., and SCHÜTTLER, A.
1941 "Die kleinräumige Kartierung landwirtschaftlicher Nutzflächen und ihre kulturgeographische Bedeutung," *Petermanns geographische Mitteilungen,* LXXXVII, No. 5, 153–67.

RIEHL, W. H.
1851 "Die bürgerliche Gesellschaft," in *Die Naturgeschichte des Volkes als Grundlage einer deutschen Sozial-Politik,* Vol. II. Stuttgart: J. G. Cotta. 486 pp.
1854 "Land und Leute," in *Die Naturgeschichte des Volkes als Grundlage einer deutschen Sozial-Politik,* Vol. I. Stuttgart and Augsburg: J. G. Cotta. 329 pp.
1857 *Die Pfälzer: Ein rheinisches Volksbild.* Stuttgart and Augsburg: J. G. Cotta. 315 pp. (1st ed., 1857; 3d ed., 1907.)
1859 *Culturstudien aus drei Jahrhunderten.* Stuttgart: J. G. Cotta'feher Verlag. 407 pp.
1869 *Wanderbuch.* Stuttgart: J. G. Cotta. 379 pp.

RIEPENHAUSEN, H.
1938 *Die bäuerliche Siedlung des Ravensberger Landes bis 1770.* ("Arbeiten der geographischen Kommission, Provinzial Institut für Westfälische Landes- und Volkskunde," No. 1.) Münster. 144 pp.

ROSHOP, U.
1932 *Die Entwicklung der ländlichen Siedlungs- und Flurbildes der Grafschaft Diepholz: Eine siedlungsgeographische Studie.* ("Quellen und Darstellungen zur Geschichte Niedersachsens," Vol. XXXIX.) Hildesheim and Leipzig. 104 pp.

SCHARLAU, K.
1933 *Beiträge zur geographischen Betrachtung der Wüstungen* ("Badische geographische Abhandlungen," Vol. X.) Freiburg in Breslau and Heidelberg: Selbstverlag Geographische Institut. 46 pp.
1938 "Zu Frage des Begriffs Wüstung," *Geographischer Anzeiger,* XXXIX, No. 11, 247–52.

1941 *Siedlung und Landschaft im Knüllgebiet: Ein Beitrag zu den kulturgeographischen Problemen Hessens.* ("Forschungen zur deutschen Landeskunde," Vol. XXXVII.) Leipzig: S. Hirzel. 335 pp.
1943 "Die Wüstungen des ausgehenden Mittelalters," *Petermanns geographische Mitteilungen,* LXXXIX, Nos. 9–10, 271–74.
1954 "Die Bedeutung der Pollenanalyse für das Freiland-Wald problem unter besonderer Berücksichtigung der Altlandschaften im hessischen Bergland," *Berichte zur deutschen Landeskunde,* XIII, No. 1, 10–32.

SCHIER, B.
1932 *Hauslandschaften und Kulturbewegungen im östlichen Mitteleuropa.* Reichenberg: F. Kraus. 456 pp.

SCHILLI, H.
1953 *Das Schwarzwaldhaus.* Stuttgart: W. Kohlhammer. 302 pp. (Contains comprehensive bibliography.)

SCHLENGER, H.
1951 "Forschungsprobleme der modernen Siedlungskunde," *Blätter für deutsche Landesgeschichte,* LXXXVIII, 41–72.

SCHLÜTER, O.
1911–13 "Deutsches Siedlungswesen," *Reallexikon der germanischen Altertumskunde,* I, 402–39. Straszburg.
1952 *Die Siedlungsräume Mitteleuropas in frühgeschichtlicher Zeit,* Vol. I: *Einführung in die Methodik der Altlandsforschung.* ("Forschungen zur deutschen Landeskunde," Vol. LXIII.) Hamburg: Atlantik Verlag; Remagen: Paulist und Verlag des Amtes für Landeskunde. 47 pp.
1953 *Die Siedlungsräume Mitteleuropas in frühgeschichtlicher Zeit,* Vol. II: *Erklarung und Begrundung der Darstellung,* Part I: *Das südliche und nordwestliche Mitteleuropa.* ("Forschungen zur deutschen Landeskunde," Vol. LXXIV.) Remagen: Verlag der Bundesanstalt für Landeskunde. 240 pp. (The latest and most comprehensive discussion of pertinent questions by the master of historic geography in Germany. Well-balanced résumé of divergent opinions. Map and bibliography.)

SCHMITHÜSEN, J.
1934 *Der Niederwald des linksrhei-nischen Schiefergebirges.* ("Beiträge zur Landeskunde der Rheinlande," Series II, No. 4.) Bonn: L. Röhrscheid. 106 pp.
1940 *Das luxemburger Land: Landes-natur, Volkstum und bäuerliche Wirtschaft.* ("Forschungen zur deutschen Landeskunde," Vol. XXXIV.) Leipzig: S. Hirzel. 431 pp.

SCHMITT, O.
1952 *Grundlagen und Verbreitung der Bodenzerstörung im Rhein-Mainge-biet mit einer Untersuchung über Bo-denzerstörung durch Starkregen im Vorspessart.* ("Rhein-Mainische Forschungen," No. 33.) Frankfurt on the Main: M. W. Kramer. 130 pp.

SCHMITTHENNER, H.
1923 "Die Reutbergwirtschaft in Deutschland," *Geographische Zeitschrift,* XXIX, 115–27.

SCHREPFER, H.
1938 "Zur Geographie des ländlichen Hausbaus in Süddeutschland," *Zeitschrift für Erdkunde,* VI, No. 1, 236–46.

SCHRÖDER, K. H.
1941 *Die Flurformen in Württemberg und Hohenzollern.* Tübingen: F. Rau. 71 pp.

SCHÜTTLER, A.
1939 *Die Kulturgeographie der mittel-devonischen Eifelkaklgebiete,* Series III, No. 4. Bonn: L. Röhrscheid. 197 pp.

SCHULTZE, J. H.
1951–52 "Über das Verhältnis von De-nudation und Bodenerosion," *Die Erde,* III, 220–33.
1952 *Die Bodenerosion in Thüringen: Wesen, Stärke und Abwehrmöglich-keiten.* ("Petermanns geographische Mitteilungen, Ergänzungs," No. 247.) Gotha: Justus Perthes. 186 pp.

SERING, M.
1908 *Erbrecht und Agrarverfassung in Schleswig-Holstein auf geschichtlicher Grundlage.* ("Die Vererbung des ländlichen Grundbesitzes im Königreich Preussen," Vol. II, No. 2.) Berlin: E. S. Mitler & Sohn. 588 pp.
1934 *Deutsche Agrarpolitik auf ge-schichtlicher und landeskundlicher*

Grundlage. Leipzig: H. Buske. 194 pp.

SICK, W. D.
1951–52 "Die Vereinödung im nörd-lichen Bodenseegebiet," *Württem-bergische Jahrbücher für Statistik und Landeskunde.*

SIEVERS, A.
1942 "Zu Geographie der landwirt-schaftlichen Betriebsgrössen. I. Eine vergleichende Betrachtung nordost-deutscher Diluviallandschaft," *Berich-te zur Raumforschung und Raumord-nung,* VI, Nos. 4–5, 114–26. Heidel-berg and Berlin.
1944 "Schrifttum zur Landwirtschafts-geographie: Ein Überblick über das letzte Jahrzehnt," *ibid.,* XI, 1–63. Leipzig.

SINNHUBER, K.
1954 "Central Europe, Mitteleuropa, Europe Centrale: An Analysis of a Geographical Term," *Transactions and Papers of the Institute of British Geographers,* Publication No. 20, pp. 15–39.

STEINBACH, FR.
1926 *Studien zur westdeutschen Stammes- und Volksgeschichte.* ("Schriften des Instituts für Grenz- und Auslandsdeutschtum, Marburg," Vol. V.) Jena. 180 pp.
1927 "Gewanndorf und Einzelhof," pp. 44–61 in *Historische Aufsätze: Festschrift für A. Schulte.* Düsseldorf: L. Schwann.
1931 "Das Bauernhaus der westdeut-schen Grenzlande," *Rheinische Vier-teljahrsblätter,* I, 26–47.
1937 "Geschichtliche Siedlungsformen in der Rheinprovinz: Aufgaben der Siedlungsgeschichte in der Rhein-provinz," *Zeitschrift des Rheinische Vereins für Denkmalspflege und Heimatkunde,* XXX, 19 ff.

THÜNEN, J. H. VON
1826 *Der isolierte Staat in Beziehung auf Landwirtschaft und National-ökonomie.* Rostock. (Vol. I, 1842, 391 pp.; Vol. II, No. 1, 1850, 285 pp.; Vol. II, No. 2, 1863, 444 pp.)

TRIER, J.
1938 "Das Gefüge des bäuerlichen Hauses im deutschen Nordwesten," *Westfälische Forschungen,* Vol. I.

TÜXEN, R.

1931 "Die Grundlagen der Urlandschaftsforschung: Ein Beitrag zur Erforschung der Geschichte der anthropogenen Beeinflussung der Vegetation Mitteleuropas," *Nachrichten aus Niedersachsens Urgeschichte*, No. 5, pp. 59–105. (With Nietsch and Schott, criticized the classical Gradmann theory and initiated a new phase in the discussion.)

WAIBEL, L.

1933 *Probleme der Landwirtschaftsgeographie*. Breslau: F. Hirt. 94 pp.

WERTH, E.

1954 *Grabstock, Hacke, Pflug*. Ludwigsburg: E. Ulmer. 435 pp.

WITTICH, W.

1896 *Die Grundherrschaft im nordwestlichen Deutschland*. 2 vols. Leipzig: Duncker & Humblot. 461+143 pp.

WÜHRER, K.

1935 *Beiträge zur ältesten Agrargeschichte des germanischen Norden*. Jena: Gustav Fischer. 152 pp.

On the Role of Nature and Man in Changing the Face of the Dry Belt of Asia

HERMANN von WISSMANN*

In Collaboration with H. POECH,† G. SMOLLA,‡ and F. KUSSMAUL§

Three subcontinents, green with forest, are divided from one another by the vast desert belt of the Old World: Africa south of the Sahara, Monsoon Asia, and Europe, including Siberia and the Mediterranean lands. The desert barrier as well as the frost line, the utmost limit of frost, which is (in more continental regions) the margin of the tropics (Wissmann, 1948; Coon, 1953), have probably been responsible for dividing humanity during parts of the Quaternary age, so that racial units could develop to some extent in isolation. Did this take place in one, perhaps in the long penultimate interglacial period?

CHANGES OF CLIMATE AND VEGETATION

According to its atmospheric circulation, the Dry Belt can be divided into a trade-wind section from the Atlantic coast to Arabia and a continental or "central" section from southern Russia and Iran to Mongolia. If we follow the thesis of Büdel (1952, 1953), the aridity of the trade-wind section probably was less intense during the last Ice Age, especially on the polar, but also on the equatorial, side. According to him, the steppe vegetation then replaced the semidesert vegetation of today.[1] So the Sahara and the desert of Arabia would have been not quite so effective barriers against human migrations during cold (glacial) periods as they are at present and were during parts of interglacial periods (compare below).

It is different in the continental section of the Dry Belt, that is, in Inner Asia. In this belt, as a whole, humidity

* Dr. von Wissmann is Professor of Geography and head of the department at the University of Tübingen, Germany. He is a corresponding member of the Akademie der Wissenschaften und Literatur in Mainz, the Akademie der Wissenschaften in Vienna, and the Akademie für Naturforscher (Leopoldina) in Halle. Of the latter he is recipient of the Carus Medal. He is recipient of the Carl Ritter Medal of the Gesellschaft für Erdkunde zu Berlin. He was professor of geography of the National Central University of China in Nanking from 1931 to 1937 and was on the staff of the Academia Sinica. He has made expeditions to different parts of China, especially Yunnan, as well as to southern Arabia (1927, 1931, 1939).

† Dr. Hella Poech is an anthropologist of the school of R. Poech, Vienna, at present living in Sumbawa, Indonesia.

‡ Dr. G. Smolla is Dozent and the scientific assistant in the Department of Prehistory, University of Tübingen.

§ Dr. F. Kussmaul is a curator of the Linden-Museum of Ethnology in Stuttgart.

1. The thesis maintained by Penck (1913), Klute (1930), Wissmann (1952), Willett (1953), and others, that during the last Ice Age the humid tropics were narrower in the west of the continents and the dry trade-wind belts shifted toward the equator, seems to be wrong. Flohn's considerations (1952, 1953) on atmospheric circulation during the last Ice Age should be compared here. They support Büdel's thesis in the trade-wind zone (1949, 1952, 1953).

was not much different from that of to-day.[2] It was somewhat lower in Central Europe and Hungary (Poser, 1948; Büdel, 1949; Wilhelmy, 1950; Frenzel and Troll, 1952), as well as in China (Wissmann, 1938). In both cases this lower humidity certainly depended on the eustatic regression of the seas (the North Sea, the seas round the British Isles, the Adriatic Sea, the Yellow Sea, and the East and the South China seas). By this regression the land masses became rounded off and more extensive than they are now. Thus Europe and China became more continental. Bobek (1953–54) supposes that even Turan was a little more arid than today, in spite of its terminal lakes being enlarged. According to his experience in Iran, he concludes that, in this country, precipitation was equal or even less than at present, so that, owing to lower temperatures, humidity was but slightly higher. Therefore, while vegetation was much the same as today (not taking the lowering of timber line into consideration), the runoff was stronger, and the terminal lakes showed higher levels, owing to reduced evaporation. The climate was more fluvial but not more pluvial (*ibid.*). Louis (1938, 1939) came to similar conclusions for the interior of Asia Minor, as did Picard (1938) for Syria.[3] According to Zeuner (1953), India had drier periods but no moister ones in the Upper Pleistocene and showed about the same distribution of humidity during the last glaciation as it does today.

In Figure 84 a synopsis is given of the vegetation in northern Eurasia during the last glaciation. This figure is based on Büdel's map (1949; Hack, 1953) for Europe, on my map (Wissmann, 1938)

for China, and on Frenzel and Troll's map (1952) for the U.S.S.R. area. The latter utilizes extensive Russian literature. Figure 84 differs strongly from that of Frenzel and Troll as regards the extent of glaciation in northeastern and central Asia, following the results of my studies on the snow line of Asia at present and in the Ice Ages (1956, MS). For Syria the map is based on Gradmann (1934, 1943) and Picard (1938); for Asia Minor, on Louis (1939); and for Persia and its surroundings, on Bobek (1951, 1952, 1953–54). The source material is of unequal value; the map represents a preliminary attempt. However, when compared with a map of the present climate or vegetation, it shows clearly that the boundaries of the thermal zones, especially the timber line, were displaced over much greater distances than the boundaries of the humidity zones, for example, the border of arable steppe and desert steppe, or the transition between forest and wooded steppe. After all, it is evident that the last Ice Age area of the Dry Belt of Inner Asia and its contours were much like those of the present day, while the area of the tundra and the northern timber line underwent a very striking change. The present large coniferous forest belt of Europe and western Siberia was more or less removed. It nearly disappeared by the swift advance of the tundra toward the wooded steppe margin, which remained almost in its original position. In the west of the continent, forest was reduced to the

2. Because of the reduction in temperature, evaporation was reduced and, by this, precipitation. Humidity is precipitation minus evaporation (evapotranspiration). In the continental Dry Belt precipitation, as well as evaporation, must have been much lower than at present (Klute, 1951).

3. However, Wright (1951) concludes, from geomorphologic reasons (accelerated stream deposition associated with eustatic low sea level), that there was a moister period at the time of the Paleolithic (last Ice Age) site of Ksar 'Akil on the slope of Lebanon toward the Mediterranean Sea. Yet, accelerated stream deposition here may better be explained by the fact that solifluction was spread in the higher slopes. According to Bobek (1953–54), the lower line of extension of solifluction was depressed 700 meters (2,300 feet) in Iran in this period.

Legend:

- Glaciated area
- Frost-debris, tundra and alpine zone
- Loess-tundra (Europe, E.Tibet)
- Desert, semi-desert
- Steppe
- Wooded tundra and wooded steppe mixed.
- Steppe with patches of boreal forest
- Boreal forest, mainly coniferous
- Cool temperate mixed forest
- Subtropical forest
- Gallery forest
- Tropical forest
- Ice age coasts and shores

Fig. 84.—The vegetation of Eurasia, except its south, during the last Ice Age. (After Frenzel, Troll, Bobek, and Wissmann.)

Mediterranean belt. In Monsoon Asia, however, its area did not become much smaller than it is now, except in the utmost northeast and around the fog-bound Sea of Okhotsk.[4]

The snow line was lowered about 1,200 meters in western Europe and the northwestern Alps as well as in monsoonal eastern and southeastern Tibet, and about 1,000 meters on the western front of the Pamirs. But it was lowered only 300 meters[5] and even less in central Tibet; so glaciation was not much more extensive there than today, in contrast with the Himalayas, which were strongly glaciated, with the glaciers of the main valleys coming down into the forest.[6]

Perennially frozen subsoil now covering Siberia east of the Yenisei, the U.S.S.R. Far East, and northeastern Mongolia, and strong inversions of winter (and night) temperatures in the lowlands and basins, which are now found in those regions (Flohn, 1947), were then spread as far as western Germany, Hungary (Poser, 1947; Weischet, 1954), and probably to large parts of central Asia.[7]

Temperatures seem to have been about 5°– 7° C. lower than at present as a global mean during the culmination of the last Ice Age (correspondence with Flohn; cf. Bobek, 1953–54). But in postglacial periods they were about 2° C. higher during the "Thermal Maximum," about 5500–2500 B.C., which is the middle phase of a period, which was warmer than before and after

("Postglaziale Wärmezeit") and extended from about 6800 B.C. to about 800 B.C. (Firbas, 1949; Smolla, 1953). For the climate of this warm period in northern Eurasia, three recent papers, including maps, are of importance: Neistadt on Russia (1953), Frenzel on northern Eurasia (1955), and Bobek on Iran (1953–54). The position of the northern timber line was shifted approximately 200–500 kilometers northward of this line today, so that mostly there was but a narrow rim of tundra, including wooded tundra, on the peninsular parts of the Arctic coasts of northern Russia and of the Far East of the U.S.S.R. In the mountains of Central Europe, especially in the Alps, as well as in the Karakoram Mountains (Visser, 1935), the timber line was located at least 400 meters higher than it is today.

In comparison with the temperature curve of climate, the fluctuations of humidity seem to have been comparatively small also in postglacial periods, and, therefore, they are much more difficult to establish. They often seem to run inversely in two zones adjacent to each other. It seems that the Thermal Maximum was a global phenomenon, just as was the last Ice Age and its last culmination, which has to be dated about 13000–9000 B.C. For the Thermal Maximum (5000–2500 B.C.), Bobek's considerations (1953–54) come to the conclusion that the climate of Iran and the Fertile Crescent was somewhat more arid than it is now. This, however, does

---

4. The area lost to the steppe in China and Manchuria was balanced by the area gained because of the eustatic regression of the Yellow Sea and the East and the South China seas.

5. These values for the snow-line depression are the differences between the last Ice Age snow line and the present one.

6. It seems that the southern rim of the High Himalayas has been lifted several hundred meters by tilting and probably overthrusting since the last Ice Age.

7. It probably is not accurate to speak of the culmination of the last Ice Age, for this long period had different culminating points. As in the United States (Flint, 1953), where the frontal moraines of the last Ice Age belong to an earlier substage in the more continental region west of the Mississippi than in the more oceanic East, new investigations of Graul (1956) show that, along the northern front of the Alps, the more one proceeds from the continental east to the oceanic west, the more the frontal moraines belong to younger substages.

not mean that precipitation must have been necessarily lower at that time.[8]

When reconstructing a previous climate, one has always to take into consideration that the effects of precipitation, evapotranspiration, and the duration of annual humid and arid periods are bound to be proportionally different for the discharge of rivers, for the rising and sinking of levels of terminal lakes, for river load, river-grading, and pediment slope than they are for the boundaries of the different graduations of vegetation and soil between forest and desert. We should also remember that a higher amount of precipitation is needed to obtain the same index of humidity in a warm climate than is needed in a cool climate. Pollen diagrams and a careful study of fossil soils are of decisive importance for a reconstruction of former climatic and vegetational conditions.

It has been our concern to show that the shifting of temperature belts between the culmination of the last Ice Age and the Thermal Maximum stretched over much greater distances than the shifting of humidity zones and that the fluctuations of humidity were relatively small, at least in the continental part of the Dry Belt. Thin populations of hunters and even those of steppe farmers, who were more livestock-breeders than agriculturalists (cf. below), could easily adapt themselves by means of migrations over short distances to such a small shifting of humidity zones. A crowded population engaged in rain agriculture without much irrigation, as, for example, in northwestern China, is always the worst off. A change of humidity (aridity) in Inner Asia, in the amounts known, cannot be made solely responsible for such migrations as are known in history, which ranged over enormous distances and even crossed the continent.

Pollen diagrams may mislead. In the subtropical and temperate belt the shaded slopes have a vegetation of the adjacent moister zone; a pollen diagram here may represent this "aclimatical"

---

8. The period of the Thermal Maximum (between *ca.* 5500 and 2500 B.C.) seems to have been somewhat more humid than today in the east of the United States and in Western and Central Europe, but also in Egypt (Deevey, 1953; Huzayyin, 1941, and the next chapter; Firbas, 1949). It seems, however, to have been somewhat more arid in Turan (Tolstow, 1953), with southern winds prevailing then, and in Iran (Bobek, 1953–54), including the borders of Mesopotamia. Bobek gives a list of the sites of this period and their present approximate precipitation. Wright gives a sketch map and description (1952) of the agricultural site of Jarmo of the fifth millennium in the foothills of northeastern Mesopotamia, excavated by Braidwood. Wright suggests that there was a period drier than before and after then. His argument applies the geomorphological hypothesis of Bryan (1941). The period of the site was one of dissection. But the dependence of river-grading upon climate is a very complex problem (Bobek, 1953–54). It is questionable whether Bryan's hypothesis is appropriate here. Wright estimates the present annual rainfall of Jarmo at about 16 inches (400 mm.), i.e., about 3 inches (80 mm.) more than on the marginal line of potential rain agriculture (Bobek's estimate is 500 mm.). The location of the Jarmo site shows that it could not have had irrigation. As the temperatures in that period must have been about 2° C. warmer, and, therefore, evaporation stronger, it seems that precipitation was not less than today. The same amount of precipitation in a warmer climate, however, would mean a lower degree of humidity.

Tolstow (1953) states that in the middle phase of the third millennium, the climate of the Amu Darya Delta into Lake Aral became cooler and moister. Until that time, he states, southern winds had prevailed, while northern winds have prevailed since.

The sudden "deterioration" of climate in Central and northern Europe about 800 B.C., with decrease of temperature and increase of rainfall, was most probably contemporary with a decrease of rainfall in the Mediterranean area, including Hungary (cf. Smolla, 1953).

In southern Russia the climate of the first stage of the warm period ("boreal," *ca.* 6500–5000 B.C.) was probably about as arid as in the last Ice Age and somewhat more arid than at present. It became more humid after the beginning of the Thermal Maximum (Gerasimov, 1946; Neistadt, 1953; Frenzel, 1955).

vegetation. Besides, pollen is spread over far distances. On the other hand, forest vegetation with a dry season, as well as a wooded steppe vegetation, will often be transformed into grassland by fire, especially in a period of more advanced hunters and of planters, farmers, and cattle-breeders (Sauer, 1952, pp. 15, 100).

HERDING STEPPE FARMERS AND IRRIGATING FARMERS CONQUER THE DRY BELT

In his book *Agricultural Origins and Dispersals* (1952) Sauer comes to the conclusion that in all probability the seat of the origin of planting (not of sowing) and of the domestic animals belonging to the human settlements, especially the dog, pig, and fowl (not herd animals), was situated in the moist tropics, on the riverbanks and coasts of southern Asia around the Bay of Bengal. Sauer looked for the progenitors in an unspecialized, sedentary fishing folk, with water communications, who, in addition, hunted and collected waterside plants. Werth arrives at similar results (1954) by a different method. My concise attempt (1946) to interpret the changes of significance for man of the subcontinental geographical units of the Old World, while not entirely free of misjudgments, arrived at similar conclusions.

It is a lucky coincidence that two scholars of the younger generation who have been engaged in research at Tübingen furnished me with extremely valuable contributions to the present theme. G. Smolla, a prehistorian, dealt (1955) in a cautious, judicious, and responsible way with the beginning of several important Neolithic traits of culture in the Old World. He included an examination of the questions concerning the beginning of the cultivation of plants and the domestication of animals. F. Kussmaul, a historical ethnologist, gave (1953) enlightening contributions

to our knowledge of the early history of the Inner Asiatic nomadic horsemen.

Smolla placed at my disposal some provisional results of his comprehensive research as follows:

The importance which C. Sauer attached to coastal fishermen and mussel-collectors for the origin and spread of planting gains even more in probability when considered in combination with archeological, climatological, and ethnological phenomena. Shell mounds (kitchen middens), with their world-wide distribution, seem to have been in many places destroyed either by the surf during the eustatic drowning of coasts of the postglacial age of increasing temperatures or by the tectonic sinking of coastal areas. The result is that those areas of shell mounds remaining must represent only a fraction of their former extent and distribution. At a time when only hunters and food-gatherers lived in the hinterland of the coast, these coastal peoples enjoyed a certain cultural ascendancy, since an assured supply of the basic foodstuffs allowed them fixed residence and relatively high population density.[9]

This old stratum of fishermen and mussel-collectors was important not only for the origin of planting but also, to a large extent, for the swift spread of several culture traits (from what can be gathered from prehistorical research), such as household animals (cf. Sauer), e.g., the dog and, to a lesser extent, the pig, but, above all, of ground stone axes and, later on, pottery.

The region of origin of tuber-planting in humid southern Asia, postulated by Sauer and others, cannot yet be proved archeologically. There has hardly, of course, been any intensive research in this direction, and

9. However, since the time when there were tribes in the hinterland with a productive food economy, the coastal inhabitants were mostly culturally amalgamated with the inland tribes. These later specialized fishing peoples may not, therefore, be lumped together with the fishermen and mussel-gatherers of the earlier period. Only at a few places, where the hinterland was unfavorable for a productive type of farming, could some rather poor survivals of this older stratum maintain themselves. This fact explains why they have scarcely been considered by ethnologists.

the remains of such cultivation would have to be searched for mostly under later delta deposits of rivers, in so far as they have not completely disappeared due to eustatic rising of the sea level. If there were not quite extraordinary conditions for their preservation—which are, in fact, difficult to imagine in tropical forest areas—the only survival of the culture of such planters was their stone industry, which probably was of a very primitive kind. The lack of archeological proof for these earliest planter tribes does not, therefore, speak against their former existence. Ethnographers, anthropologists and human geographers, botanists, and zoölogists should attempt to examine this question anew. The archeologist can maintain only that no discoveries are against such an argument and that, by using it, several phenomena become understandable which before were inexplicable.

The beginnings of this early science of planting may then be assumed to have been approximately at the time of the last culmination of the last glacial period, parallel to the western European Magdalenian (*ca.* 13000–9000 B.C.). The spread of these cultural phenomena, which developed from this region over vast areas, must, therefore, have taken place shortly before and during the postglacial Thermal Maximum, above all, in the seventh to fifth millenniums B.C. This spread must have been particularly swift among the coastal fishermen and mussel-gatherers. The further extension of planting into faraway zones lasted, of course, many thousands of years more.

The fact that the coastal belt from India, over southern Arabia, to East Africa, with its dry climate, and thence along the banks of the Nile must have been an early road for migration, not merely a passage along which new cultural "inventions" and goods were disseminated, results from the new anthropological research by Poech (MS), evaluating, among other materials, that of our expeditions in southern Arabia. She recognizes that two races, the Gondid and the Aethiopid, which both belong to the large family of "Europid" races, are to be found in India as well

as in southern Arabia and in parts of East and North Africa.

Especially of importance here is the distribution of the Gondid race. It is dominant and numerous in parts of central India. But people of the Gondid race are also frequent in southern Arabia, Nubia (Barabra), and Egypt (cf. Fig. 85). On the Nubian Nile (Korosho), a population of this race can be traced back as far as the Old Empire. Among the Egyptian sculptures of this period, we find clerks and officials of the Gondid race. Even the Berbers of northwestern Africa include elements of it. In all regions of their distributions

H. Poech

FIG. 85.—Three women of the Gondid race. *From left to right:* Tunisia, Yemen Highland, central India.

the people of the Gondid race belong to a busy agricultural population.[10]

It has to be emphasized that the above-mentioned races are only two out

10. As this race was not distinctly defined by von Eickstedt (1931–32), we give a description by Poech:
"According to south Arabian material, the people of the Gondid race show markedly Europid forms, with a total lack of prognathy. They have a slender and strong body with smooth and rounded forms. Their skin is of a light brown color. Their eyes are dark brown. The rich and wavy hair is black. Men have their hair floating down to the shoulder. The outline of the face, which is more or less broad, is oval. Their cheeks are full and rounded. Noses are narrow, straight, high, and of medium length. Their tips are pointed. The integumental upper lip is concave, and the mouth is not very big. The lips are rather thick. The vertical height of the lower jaw is short. The contours of the lower jaw converge in a more or less acute angle. In profile, the chin protrudes, softly rounded. The smooth features of the Gondid face may be of a gentle beauty."

of a rather great number of races sorted out by Poech in southern Arabia. As a matter of fact, most of the other races of this country are also found in other parts of the Middle East and Europe.

We go on to follow the exposition of Smolla:

The domestication of sheep and goats and the cultivation of grain were probably begun in the wooded steppe and steppe areas of northwestern India and the adjoining western Asiatic mountain regions during the sixth millennium B.C. at the very latest. For several reasons it is probable that the impulse which stimulated the transition to these new forms of production came from tuber-planting. Naturally enough, this cannot at the moment be proved archeologically. It is, however, possible that the cultivation of several small-seeded cereals, which we comprehend under the term "millet," forms the point of transition between tuber-planting and cereal-crop farming. Perhaps the round-butted ax (*Walzenbeil*), which serves as a connecting link between India and northern China, belonged originally to such a period of early millet farming in the wooded steppe regions of northern and western China.[11]

Forms of cereal farming combined with the herding of sheep and goats, and then of cattle, which seem to have been domesticated somewhat later, spread quickly over parts of the Old World. Beside rainfall agriculture, elementary types of irrigation and oasis economy were known at a very early period from Iran to Syria. This can be deduced from the fact that Jericho and other early agricultural sites show a

11. "Another question arises: Was it the case, perhaps, that in this early period a stream of culture proceeded westward from China through the natural oases of what later became the silk road, finally arriving as far as Central Europe, spreading the round-butted ax, and perhaps also *Panicum miliaceum* (proso millet), *Fagopyrum* (buckwheat), and *Setaria italica* (foxtail millet)? (For later movements from east to west of a fishing and hunting population through the northern belt of wooded steppe and through the taiga forest belt at the beginning of the second millennium B.C. see Jettmar, 1954*b*)."

marked desert climate and certainly cannot have had any rain agriculture as shown by their early excavated periods.

The ancient civilizations of the Near East—western Iran, northern Mesopotamia, Syria, Palestine, and Egypt—derived from this farming and herding culture. About 3000 B.C., with the invention of writing, they were completely developed. Among the first Sumerian characters we find a portrayal of the plow, the first known document of this tool. Since the townlike settlements, temple buildings, etc., began at an earlier date, the beginning of civilization (*Hochkultur*) will have to be dated back to the start of the fourth millennium B.C. In Jericho an early stratum has been discovered in which pottery was still unknown, yet which had already developed into a large type of settlement, surrounded by a town wall. Therefore, the lower strata of the southwestern Asiatic tells already represent early forms of the beginning of a civilization which led to the invention of the plow and of highly developed systems of irrigation.

This earliest phase of civilization obviously exerted its influence over a wide area, for it would be difficult to understand a large part of the development of the Neolithic on the Balkan Peninsula and in Central Europe, were we not to consider influences from this phase.

Geographically, this rise, spread, and development of cultures, which invented ways to put plants and animals into their service, may be hypothetically summarized approximately as follows.

In large parts of the Old World there was an early sedentary unspecialized fishing folk with varied occupations and a hinterland of roaming collectors and hunters. It spread along coasts and riverbanks, partly by means of primitive vessels. In the regions inhabited by such a fishing population, in humid tropical southern Asia, the planting of tubers and the domestication of dogs and pigs originated during the period of approximately 13000–9000 B.C. This unspecialized fishing population living along the widespread ribbons of coasts and river-banks passed on the spark of the new "inventions" of planting and domestication. At first, the monsoonal forests of southeastern Asia were penetrated. In areas which were seasonally inundated, taro root was planted and, at a later stage, rice. Then, in transitional areas between these monsoonal forests and the wooded steppes of India, of Burma, and of western and northern China, the sowing and cropping of small-seeded grains of the wooded steppe (i.e., of the so-called "millets") seem to have begun. This meant a penetration of a food-producing culture and economy into drier regions, into wooded and other arable steppes, and, by this, an increasing density of population in these regions. Then, somewhere among hunters of the Indo-Iranian border ranges, the breeding of sheep and goats was "invented." It is an open question whether an impulse came from those early food-producing and domesticating populations of the riverside, tropical forest, and steppe with which we just have dealt. But it is plausible that there really was some stimulus from this source.

Then, among tribes growing millets and herding sheep and goats, somewhere between Turan and Syria, grasses with larger seeds were cultivated for the first time, with grains which it was possible to store (i.e., wheat and barley). Yet, the high mountains of eastern and western Iran, which are surrounded by tillable steppes, are divided from one another by a broad zone with almost no land fit for rain agriculture, even in the mountains, which are lower than those to the east and west. But this intermediate zone was rich in natural oases along the foot of its mountains. Therefore, it is probable that a primitive kind of irrigation (which enabled storage) was already carried out at the time when wheat and barley were first sown. For in a period which was drier than today (Bobek, 1953–54) rain agriculture with-

out irrigation could not have easily crossed this dry zone. The same population may also have begun to domesticate wild cattle, not in the driest regions, as cattle are not suited to the desert steppe, but in wooded land around the forest margin of the mountains. Thus Iran and its surroundings fostered a farming, herding, and hunting people, for which a light pedocal soil, easily prepared, is convenient. Such types of soil can be found in open country of steppe and wooded steppe, or in light forest, as well as in natural oases of the desert, where irrigation may easily be carried out.

Two main ways of living could branch off from this stage of culture. One, based on irrigation and the storage of grains, led to larger settlements with brick buildings and, further, to the founding of the earliest form of civilization (cf. Wittfogel, p. 152 above). In the other mode of life, herding was, besides hunting, at least as important as grain-growing. Between the light forest and the margin of arable steppe, especially in the wooded steppes, this way of life of a herding farmer or farming herdsman spread far over large parts of the Dry Belt and its surroundings of light forest, becoming more pastoral here, more agricultural there, according to the vegetational circumstances. In most cases, it seems, there was no sharp tribal separation between agriculturalist and herdsman. Cain and Abel were brothers. We may call this a "steppe-farming" culture and economy. Besides these two branches of farming, a herding nomadism with sheep (and goats) not only may have branched off from steppe farming but also seems to have spread independently from its earliest source (cf. Jettmar, 1954b; Kussmaul, 1952–53).

Along the coasts from India westward and along the Mediterranean coasts as far as the Atlantic Ocean, all of which are drier than those of monsoonal southern Asia, the old culture of fishing peoples, impregnated with the cultural achievements of the tuber-planters and breeders of household animals, was combined in various ways with the other "producing," no longer "collecting," cultures developed in the Dry Belt, which we mentioned above. In tropical Africa a new selecting and molding of these elements took place under climatic, vegetational, racial, and spatial circumstances different from those in Asia. Yemen and Abyssinia be-

(black in Fig. 86). This middle belt stretches from Morocco and Spain to northern China. It is in this belt—from desert to semihumid climate—that natural oases and irrigation became, and still are, of the greatest importance, especially along the foot of mountain chains (cf. Gradmann, 1934). Toward the east this belt becomes ever narrower. In Kansu there is only one chain of oases. But, at its eastern end, it bulges out, forming the wooded steppes of northern China. In the west it is in-

⌐x˟x⌐ Highland Desert	⌐ ⌐ Desert, Semi-desert	⌐:::⌐ Forest	– – – Mountain Chain
⌐▨⌐ Oasis, Steppe Wooded Steppe	⌐▨⌐ Oasis, Cool summer, Steppe cold winter	⌐■⌐ Oasis, Long, hot Steppe summer	⌐⊞⌐ Oasis, Tropical, Steppe no frost

H. von Wissmann

Fig. 86.—Oases and steppe regions of the Dry Belt of the Old World, classified according to their thermal conditions.

came a secondary nucleus, where cultivation and domestication began of new plants and animals, such as the donkey and probably the tall tropical millets (perhaps sorghum, most probably *Pennisetum*).

The Dry Belt of the Old World, over which farming and herding spread, can be divided into three temperature belts (Fig. 86).

The region between southern Turan and Syria, in which the growing of large-grained cereals and the breeding of herd animals took its origin, lies in the center of the *middle belt,* a region of long, hot summers and short winters

dented, in a lucky way, as we may say, with the Mediterranean coasts and light forests.

West of Yemen and Abyssinia the *southern belt* of tropical steppe of the Sudan has conditions of its own kind but not dissimilar to those of peninsular India.

The *northern belt* of steppes (cf. Fig. 86) runs from Manchuria and northern Mongolia to Kazakhstan, southern Russia, and Rumania. In Hungary and Central Europe it ebbs away in dispersed islands of wooded steppe surrounded by oak and hornbeam forest. Like the other two belts, this belt must have made excellent hunting ground too. Yet, for primitive agricultural people used to winter crops, the climate of this northern belt becomes more severe from west to east. In this direction winters become harder and longer, and the snow cover gets thinner and scarcer, until finally the belt ends in the region of perennially frozen subsoil. In the whole of this northern belt, summers are too cool in the west and too short in the east to yield good, or several, crops sufficient to make intensive and laborious irrigation worthwhile. The milder winters of the westernmost wooded steppes of this belt, however, as well as the light oak forest on the loessal soil of Central Europe, which is easily tilled, favored the spreading there of winter cereals from southwestern Asia. The

"Danubian" culture (*Bandkeramiker*), in which agriculture was important or even predominant, seems to have already reached Germany in the fourth millennium B.C., when the temperature was about 2° C. warmer than it is today.

As to the question of the spreading of herding and agriculture into the steppes of the northern belt, from the middle of the third millennium to about 2000 B.C., Russian archeology has collected much material by excavation, which has been dealt with carefully by Jettmar (1945b, 1954c; cf. Fig. 89, p. 298).

In the Amur region the short summers are hot and must have been even somewhat hotter in those periods. Therefore, one might suppose that proso

| | forest | | wooded steppe (prairie), good for pasture and agriculture | | dry steppe, good pasture, rain-agriculture endangered | – – – | margin of possible rain-agriculture | | semi-desert meager pasture |

FIG. 87.—The zones of vegetation and

millet and buckwheat as summer crops came to the Amur area from the south before herding came in. But up to now no evidence of that kind has been discovered.

Figure 87 shows the zones of vegetation of the continental part of the Dry Belt running from southern Russia to Manchuria. Between dense forest vegetation and full desert there are three zones to be distinguished: (1) the wooded steppe, which is good for agriculture and pasture; (2) the open steppe, which is good pasture and is still arable (where, however, rain agriculture is endangered by dry years); and (3) the desert steppe or semidesert with meager pasture. It is probable that, in regions where the third of these zones is broad, an independent shepherd nomadism was preserved or branched off from the steppe-farming economy (with sheep and goats in the southern and central belts [Fig. 86, p. 287], and with sheep only in the northern belt). But it appears that such a nomadic shepherd folk always lived an impoverished life compared with the farming and herding tribes of the moister zones or of regions interspersed with oases.[12] Good pasture is found in the Tien Shan, in the Pamirs, and especially in eastern and southern Tibet above the cereal line. But it must be remembered that this line was several hundred meters, perhaps 400 meters, higher than today. (Painted pottery was

12. Such tribes may be only partly nomadic, a part of the tribes being agricultural, a part ranging as shepherds ("Teil-Nomadismus").

the oases of the Dry Belt of Inner Asia

desert   oasis   former oasis   above timber-line (rock, desert, ice).   pasture above timber line

found near the Ch'ing-hai [Kuku Nor].)
Nevertheless, a shepherd culture can
be clearly distinguished at the beginning of the northeastern Tibetan culture (Hermanns, 1949; Kussmaul, 1953).

Figures 84, 86, and 87 show clearly
that China north of the Hwai River is
the easternmost outpost of the middle
steppe belt with long hot summers.
These long summers mean that two
crops can be grown in one year on the
same field if water is sufficiently available. In Manchuria the summers are too
short for this. Southern China, with its
moist subtropical forest and its net of
navigable rivers, is broadly connected
with the forests of southern Asia, the
cradle of planting and of the breeding
of household animals, according to
Sauer. Descriptions of southern China
during the Chou and Han dynasties
demonstrate that the dog and pig had
a central position in the religious beliefs of many tribes, and fishing and
navigation were important for many of
them (Eberhard, 1942a, 1942c). Ssŭ-
ma Ch'ien, the Chinese Herodotus, in
the second century B.C. wrote as follows
about the forested south: "People eat
rice and make a soup of fish. They till
the field after burning, or cultivate by
flood-irrigation(?). Thanks to the fruits
of trees and plants and to snails and
mussels they have sufficient to live on
without depending on merchants." In
contrast to this, he states that China
proper, which at that time was still restricted to northern China with its
steppe climate, was densely populated,
that grain was grown and stored there,
but that the land was often harassed by
floods and droughts.

Even in the primitive culture of the
Suchen, who lived in the forests of eastern Manchuria, that is, north of the region where taro and yams can be grown,
the dog and pig were important elements in the economy and religion, during early Chinese history, and navigation was developed (Eberhard, 1942a;

Kussmaul, 1953). All this supports the
thesis of Sauer—that food-producing and
domesticating of household animals had
its origin in the monsoonal forests of
southern Asia. Jettmar, using recent
Russian and Swedish literature, shows
(1954a) that at the beginning of the
second millennium B.C. there must have
already been a kind of traffic carried
on by a fishing and hunting population, connecting Manchuria with the
river net of the forests of Siberia and
Russia even as far as Gotland in the
Baltic Sea.

Our hypothesis has been already
mentioned that, as in India, so in northern China, the growing of "millets" allowed the food-producing economy to
leave the forests and enter the wooded
steppes (proso, foxtail, and barnyard
millet and buckwheat). This must have
made possible a comparatively dense
population in the loess country. Otherwise, the invasions from the west, mainly by way of the narrow chain of oases,
which later became the "silk road,"
would have led to the formation of a
prevailingly Inner Asian people, language, and race in China, which, of
course, did *not* happen. The Chinese
of the Chou and Han dynasties would,
for instance, have drunk milk. It is not
surprising that, up to the present day,
no archeological traces have been detected of such a millet-growing people
without pottery and cattle.

A shepherd culture seems to have
been spread by an early migration from
the west to northwestern China. For
later periods, traits of such a culture
are mainly recognizable in northeastern
Tibet, especially in its grasslands above
the timber line (Kussmaul, 1953; Hermanns, 1949). Then, perhaps about
2300 B.C., a painted pottery appeared in
northwestern China ("Panshan-Yangshao"), and about 2000 B.C. or later, a
type of black and gray pottery made on
a wheel was brought to northeastern
China ("Lungshan"). The latter was

still contemporary with late phases of the painted pottery of more westerly parts of northern China.[13] The appearance of both these types of pottery must represent at least two invasions along the narrow chain of oases in Sinkiang and Kansu. The invading populations derived their culture from much earlier periods in Iran and its surroundings. The first probably brought cattle, wheat, and irrigation, as well as certain lunar and chthonic beliefs to northern China (Kussmaul, 1953). All this was superimposed upon the culture of the old millet-growing population, who were related to the peoples of the forest in race, language, habits, and belief.

In my opinion the work of Kussmaul (1953) has strongly confirmed the interpretation that the beginning of the Shang Dynasty, about 1500 B.C., signifies an invasion of a people of Aryo-Iranian culture through the narrow central Asian chain of oases. Kussmaul can prove this statement mainly by a new arrangement of the extensive and important ethnological material in old Chinese literature compiled by Eberhard (1942a, 1942b, 1942c). Though Eberhard formerly opposed this interpretation, which had been a supposition of many scholars before (cf. Bishop, 1932), he has informed us that he now shares Kussmaul's opinion. In the cultural complex brought by the Shang to China, the horse, the war chariot, and bronze were of special importance, as well as the belief in the Indo-Aryan god of sun and heaven. This and the old chthonic belief united to form a dualistic creed. Mythology and tradition show this distinctly. The Chou, who appeared in northwestern China

13. The date of "Panshan" given here is intermediate between that of Jettmar (1954a, 1954b, 1954c) and that of Loehr (1952). The dates of Jettmar are adapted to a new chronological arrangement of A. P. Okladnikov, who at present is the best expert of the archeology of Siberia.

about 1200 B.C., in the west of the Shang empire, and replaced the Shang about 1050 B.C., augmented and intensified the Aryo-Iranian cultural elements in Chinese civilization.

Although it would fit into the framework of our general thesis, we cannot, in this paper, follow the spread in many directions of the Indo-Europeans ("Aryans") and of the war-chariot tradition, out of the western part of the Inner Asiatic Dry Belt (Childe, 1926). But we must state that these Indo-Europeans, as far as they had not become oasis farmers, were what we have called steppe farmers above. As these were herdsmen, hunters, and farmers at the same time (though they may have included groups which led only one of these ways of life), they probably displayed more "nomadic" traits during their migrations and invasions. Nevertheless, it is most misleading to call them nomads. It is clearly recognizable, for instance, that the Aryans entering India and probably destroying the Harappa civilization were steppe farmers.

Excavations in the Shang capital in China have revealed that a fully developed pictographic script was used as early as 1300 B.C. In addition, the Shang empire shows many other civilizational elements which must have been stimulated from the early town civilizations of southwestern Asia or northwestern India (e.g., its priest kingdom). However, although the culture of the Shang was mainly Indo-Iranian, it cannot have been a steppe-farming culture. The Tarim Basin and its approaches to China, which were the only way of access to China from the west, are so dry that they cannot and could not support a steppe-farming population. Yet oases could be developed there because of the rivers coming from the high surrounding mountains. So the Shang, as well as the "Lungshan" and "Panshan-Yangshao" people, must have been irrigating oasis farmers when intruding into China. We do not know which of them brought the stimuli of script, priest kingdom, and other attributes of civilization.[14]

At the beginning of the Chou Dynasty the southern frontier of the feudal empire ran almost exactly along the margin between wooded steppe and forest (Wissmann, 1940).

EQUESTRIAN NOMADIZATION[15]

The herding and hunting culture of the northern steppe belt in the second millennium B.C. was, even in its eastern section, not without agricultural elements. At first the share of agriculture may have been but a small one, difficult to evaluate. But by and by it must have become quite essential. At least since the middle third of the second millennium B.C., we may call the whole wooded-steppe zone of this belt a zone of steppe farmers (Kussmaul, 1953). The farther east we go, the more this status holds true, as we shall see. We learn from Kussmaul that such steppe farming, with large herds on a vast area, offers the best conditions for a social gradation, of kinships, warlike nobility, and dynastic leadership, just as we find among the war-chariot people and most Indo-Europeans. Hančar (1951, 1954) has reconstructed some of the essential mental, spiritual, and economic characteristics of these steppe-farming communities of western Inner Asia.

The first peoples to find out that horse-riding was of great advantage in wartime and the first who developed the art of fighting on horseback were probably not the herding farmers of the open steppe but tribes of mountain basins, especially of Transcaucasia and of northwestern Iran (Jettmar, 1954c). In such mountainous countries, partly

covered with forests, the war chariot must have been of little use, but fighting on horseback must have been an excellent way of defense. These peoples cannot be called nomads, since they did not abandon farming and sedentary life.[16]

The first peoples of the steppe and wooded steppe to become horse-riding nomads seem to have been the "North Iranians" (e.g., the Scythians) and their neighbors (Rostowzew, 1931; Hančar, 1951). It seems that they lived between the rivers Volga and Irtysh. Until that time they had been leading the life of steppe farmers. Some hunting tribes, living farther north, also were included in the new movement. Once aware of the great superiority of fighting on horseback over the older ways of fighting, especially by war chariots, they gave up sedentary life entirely and specialized in the breeding of herd animals, especially horses. They became the first horse-riding nomads and the first to break into the neighboring countries, disseminating terror and panic among all sedentary populations. When we use the word "nomad," we usually think of this equestrian type.[17]

The distinct social and economic gradation of the steppe farmers of the rough northern wooded steppe was favorable to the formation of leaders of high political and military ability. This

14. Heine-Geldern assumes (1950) that writing arrived in China with the "Lungshan" culture (*ca.* 2000 B.C.).

15. Cf. Figs. 87 and 88.

16. The Medes and Persians of about 1000 B.C. probably have to be included here. Even in later times they did not abandon their three main knightly ideals: horse-riding, archery, and love of truth.

17. It has not been very long that equestrian nomadization has been clearly recognized and described. Jettmar and Kussmaul arrived at the same conclusion more or less at the same time, Jettmar, by making full use of recent Russian excavations, Kussmaul, mainly by utilizing the rich ethnological material of old Chinese literature, especially its compilation by Eberhard (1942a, 1942b, 1942c). Kussmaul arranged the characteristic attributes of the tribal cultures, as they had been described by the Chinese, into genetic groups according to modern ethnological methods.

was of essential importance during the period of nomadization. When a strong nomadic horde had been established, the warmer climate and the oasis civilization of the south, known to some of the men by mercenary services, as well as the milder climate of the open plains of the west, attracted their invasions. (That the climate became rather suddenly colder in the eighth century B.C. perhaps was a stimulus too.) Eastward, along the foot of the Altai Mountains and through the gap of Dzungaria, nomadization worked like a chain reaction of explosions. The poorer farmers and hunters probably were forced to join the "aristocracy" of horse-breeders, so that a new nomadic horde organization was brought about which grew by raiding, sacking, killing, and enslaving other populations, especially other hordes of horsemen, and by winning over vassals by disseminating fear.

Kussmaul shows in his work and map (1953, our Fig. 88) that the spread of equestrian nomadization began with the North Iranians, especially the Scythians, and was followed by the Wusun, whose home seems to have been central and eastern Tien Shan. We may suppose that during that period herdsmen, hunters, and farmers of the open steppes surrounding Mongolia were forced to take up nomadic life. It is possible that the pressure of the Wusun against the population of the oasis chain of present western Kansu caused the last invasion of farmers into China, especially the "Jung," which led to the breakdown of the dynasty of the western Chou (770 B.C.).

The first nomadization to be traced in Chinese reports is that of the Hsiung-nu. The Huns, as they were called later on in Europe, were neither Iranians nor "Proto-Turks." (According to Ligeti [1950–51], the Hsiung-nu language seems to stand isolated or to be related to that of the Yenisei Ostyaks.) In their habitat between ancient China and the Mongolian Desert, the Hsiung-nu took over en bloc a considerable group of elements of the culture of the nomadic North Iranians. During centuries of fierce wars, in which the Chinese defended themselves against the Hsiung-nu and built the Great Wall, the Chinese again took over a part of these elements, for example, iron, cavalry, trousers, and the concept of heaven as a tent. Other traits of the life of the Hsiung-nu, however, prove not only their former dependence on China but also their cultural relation to the non-nomadic primitive tribes of eastern Manchuria.

Figure 88 does not deal with the growth of more or less short-lived nomadic empires and with their conquests in the Dry Belt. It does not deal with their pressure on agrarian and urban China, which sometimes became vassal or even partly subdued (and even marginally transformed into pasture). Nevertheless, China was growing, during long periods of defense, retreat, and counterattack, although it was, in its north, a land of wooded-steppe climate, attractive for nomads. Into the forests of the south it was growing mainly by its civilizational superiority. Furthermore, Figure 88 does not deal with those tremendous migrations and invasions into the west, during which the Dry Belt served as a corridor through which the invaders broke into the countries of old oasis civilization in southwestern Asia or into the beginnings of forest civilization in medieval Central and Western Europe (Grousset, 1948, 1954; Spuler, 1950).

All these movements destroyed what had been left of steppe farming in the plains of the steppe. The hilly and mountainous countries surrounding Mongolia, however, with a pattern or mosaic of steppe, meadow, and forest (and sometimes of pasture above the timber line), and the marginal parts of the forest belt became areas of retreat and regeneration of a population which made its living by hunting, cattle-breeding, and farming (Lattimore, 1938). That the population of farmers must have been quite numerous and dense before the period of nomadization in some areas of the wooded steppe is shown, for instance, by the ruins of a wall of defense 650 kilometers long. This wall cuts off the northeastern corner of the steppes of Mongolia, running from west to east near the Gan River Valley (Plaetschke, 1939, pp. 132 ff.). The Gan River is an eastern tributary of the Argun.

We can see from Figure 88 how, again and again in such hilly and mountainous border regions of the eastern part of the great Dry Belt, new nuclei sprang up among hunting, herding, and farming groups, who led a simple life under hard conditions. In these we find some able man, endowed with the gifts of leadership, who organized a complex horde by raiding, robbing, and winning vassals. Here the name of a tribe or kinship, more or less unknown before, became the name of a growing power and sometimes even that of a vast empire. By some lucky chance, a "Secret History of the Mongols" has been preserved (Haenisch, 1948): a story of the life of Genghis Khan, of the origin of his kinship, and of how he founded the Mongol empire. It was written by a Mongol in A.D. 1240 as a plain, firsthand report. In the time of Genghis Khan's forefathers his semisedentary clan in the Kentei Mountains did not own many horses, cattle, and sheep. There

⅄⅄ ꝯ ꝯ *Margin of forest toward wooded steppe* |ı'ı'ı'ı'ı| *Pasture above timber-line*

F. Kussmaul

FIG. 88.—The spreading of explosive outsets of horse-riding nomadism, with feudal state-building. The previous population had a food-producing economy of farming, was little agriculture. Wild vegetables were collected. Hunting on horseback was very important. The neighbors in the open steppes outside the mountains, however, were true horse-riding nomads with large herds. Many of these had become saturated by raiding and addicted to the luxuries with which they had become familiar during their raids. From hiding places in the valleys and forests of the Kentei Mountains, the incipient clan of Genghis Khan began a life of robbery among the rich nomads of the plains. Their booty consisted of horses, cattle and sheep, women, children, and servants. Thus the clan turned entirely nomadic, steadily growing by the acquisition of new vassals, many of them of foreign blood, an association taking its name from the leader's kin-

ship, growing in strength according to the looting ability of the leader. Finally, well-known tribes and peoples of Mongolia lost their independence as well as their name and merged with the new great "Mongol" unit.

Kussmaul (1953, n.d.) shows that such a region on the margin of the Dry Belt of Mongolia hardly ever repeated the formation of a new and powerful nomadic aggregation if it had once before been the cradle of such a fast nomadization. The whole procedure, as we see it in Figure 88, worked like a chain reaction of explosions running from west to east and from south to north, rooting out steppe farming and continually regenerating equestrian nomadism, that terrible scourge of rural and urban communities of Eurasia,

_ ._ ._ ._ Margin of arable steppe toward semi-desert   🌿🌿 Oasis regions

herding, and hunting, mainly in the wooded steppes. The Roman numerals show the succession of these outsets. The dates are approximate.

which in itself was a cul-de-sac phenomenon.

We cannot say whether the destruction the mounted nomads carried into the countries in and around the Dry Belt, especially into the original cradle of civilization in southwestern Asia, is balanced by the contribution of nomadic states to the interchange of materials and ideas between these surrounding countries. All we see is that the empty spaces of the Dry Belt were terribly enlarged by the plague of nomadic migrations, which annihilated steppe-farming communities and reduced and weakened oasis civilization (Gradmann, 1943). We do not know to what extent suffering is necessary to save from degeneration and decay that which is sound and good in man's mind and how far it contributes toward opening man's eyes so that he can understand the import of wars.

The development of philosophical and religious thought toward a higher stage of consciousness, the appearance of the Greek philosophers, of the Jewish prophets, of Zoroaster, of Mahāvīra and Gautama Buddha, and of Lao-tzu and Confucius, in the short period between the eighth and the fifth centuries B.C.,[18] took place prior to the nomadic inroads into most of the countries contributing to this miracle of a growing and deepening of the "logos" in the human mind.

BEDOUIN NOMADIZATION

Albright supposes that the Semitic neighbors of the Sumerians were, above all, pastoral tribes when the Sumerians, at the outset of civilization, began to irrigate Lower Mesopotamia. Toward the end of the fourth millennium the Semites began to press upon the growing sedentary oasis states and to extend their territory into the steppes of northern Mesopotamia, before Semites became rulers in the oasis countries. Then, toward the end of the third millennium, there was a strong pressure of pastoral tribes on the whole Fertile Crescent, and the sedentary population decreased and lost much of its territory (climatic influence?). But by 1900 B.C. a reversal had set in. The Amoritic "nomads" (compare the migration of Abraham) possessed neither horses nor camels. But they had donkeys to carry loads. Hunting and robbing the harvest were important. They had to travel and attack on foot. This made complete crossings of the desert (except in spring) and rapid expeditions impossible. In summer they had either to depend on oases or other settled areas or to live in tillable regions of the Fertile Crescent. Albright shows that the inroad of camel-riding Midianites into Palestine, about or after 1100 B.C., is the first known appearance of mounted nomads in Arabia (Judges, chaps. 6–8; Walz, 1951).[19]

In the tenth century B.C. the story of the Queen of Sheba shows that, in addition to camel-riding, a busy traffic of camel caravans had been fully developed in competition with traffic by sea, with Saba (Sheba) in southern Arabia as its center. From the Assyrian reports (eighth and seventh centuries) on tributes of Arabian queens and princes, we can also conclude that there was a strong traffic with camel caravans crossing Arabia (e.g., from southwest to northeast). Even Indian and African wares, together with incense, were transported and exchanged from southern Arabia. Springs and wells of Arabia Deserta became of importance, first as resting places, then as commercial centers. Since the nomads were breeding the camels needed for these caravans, they were interested in the profits from the traffic. An Inner Arabian kingdom of that period therefore

18. Cf. Menghin (1937, p. 612), Wissmann (1946), and especially Jaspers (1949).

19. We cannot deal here with the late introduction of camel-riding and of mounted nomadism into Africa.

cannot be compared with a nomadic state of Inner Asia. Commercial oases or town centers played an important role. Taima, for instance, had its own script. The nomadic clans lived separately and, probably, rather independently, having their own rules of revenge and blood feud. Caskel (1953) demonstrates that a Bedouin nomadism comparable with the equestrian nomadism of Inner Asia is first found in the steppes and deserts between Syria and Mesopotamia and that it began to spread to the south in the second and third centuries A.D. The constant wars between Rome and Persia, the decay of the feudalized southern Arabian kingdoms and of their caravan trade, and the decline of overland traffic gave rise to great insecurity, which spread in Arabia from north to south (cf. Wissmann, 1953, Wissmann and Höfner, 1952). The nomads now form tribal organizations. The heads of these are *primi inter pares*. Their position depends on their wealth in good riding camels and their ability to raid and loot and to persuade their comrades and allies. This resembles what has been related above about the Mongols.

Yet it differs in some points of view (Bobek, 1943, 1948). Although the famous dam which watered the oasis of Marib (Saba) broke down, there still remained in Arabia a framework of impoverished oases, with townsmen, and peasants living in bondage. And there were still the qabā'il, the highland farmers in their fortified dwellings in Yemen and Oman, where feudalism led to an extreme dissipation of power and even to anarchy, as well as to tribal organizations similar to those of the barbarized camel-nomads, the Bedouins. These *bedu* we all know from the excellent descriptions of Doughty (1936) and Oppenheim (1939–52).

Mecca at first was a place of Bedouin religion and trade. Without the *bedu* and the *qabîlî*, as well as the townsman

and the fellah, the rise *and* the stability of the Islamic empire cannot be imagined.

THE SPREADING OF CULTURES IN EURASIA: A SUMMARY

In order to summarize and visualize our view of the spreading of planting and animal-breeding cultures in Eurasia, I drew Figure 89, which in parts is to a high degree hypothetical. Seen as a whole, the most ingenious line of development seems to run from the moist tropical forest around the Bay of Bengal (tuber-planting, pig- and dog-breeding) to the steppes of northwestern India (millets?) and the mountains and their foothills of eastern Iran (goats, sheep, large-grain cereals), then to the dry girdle of central Iran (oasis irrigation), the highlands of western Iran (cattle, steppe farming), and the river oases of Mesopotamia (rising of civilization, of *Hochkultur*). The later development of human genius spread into the forest again, in Europe, as well as in China and India. Greece, Shantung, and Magadha lie on the margins of the forest.

Each of these steps of development sends out a wave of spreading, which often combines with other waves or is overtaken by later ones. For the progression of these waves, the coasts, the vegetational belts, and the chains of natural oases are of (unequal) importance. The spreading of tuber-planting and pig- and dog-breeding, closely connected with fishing, were unhindered along the coasts of Indonesia and the coasts and rivers of eastern Asia. North of Korea the tubers had to be left behind because of the cool climate. Branches merged into the taiga boreal forest along the northern Asiatic rivers. On the dry coasts of the Arabian Sea the spreading of this oldest producing culture had to join with later waves on its way by southern Iran and southern

A   Region of earliest tuber planting and breeding of dog, pig and fowl
→   Spreading of this culture in close connection with fishing
--→   Spreading of this culture in close connection with fishing without tuber
       planting in colder regions
B   Millet as first seed plant in wooded steppe
C   Beginning of sowing large-grain cereals and of breeding sheep and goats
D   Beginning of oasis irrigation
E   Beginning of cattle breeding and steppe farming

······   Spreading of early complex cultures in close connection with fishing
→   Spreading of oasis irrigation
⟹   Spreading of steppe farming
F   Beginning of civilization
⟹   Spreading of civilization
〰〰   Wooded steppe and desert
☐   Forest

Fig. 89.—The development of food-producing man and his conquest of Asia (partly hypothetical)

Arabia to Africa. Early cultures based on fishing and shipping also reached the Mediterranean coasts (by the Nile and perhaps the Euphrates) and thence even the Atlantic Ocean and the North Sea. Chains of natural oases led irrigating agriculture to Turan and the Tarim Basin and finally to northern China. This wave was perhaps caught up on its way by traits of full civilization. Steppe farming found its way very early to Asia Minor and southeastern Europe. Then it adjusted itself to the forests which surround the islands of steppe in Central Europe. From Rumania, as well as from the Tien Shan Mountains, steppe farming conquered the northern belt of the steppes.

REFERENCES

ALBRIGHT, W. F.
  1946a *Archaeology and the Religion of Israel.* Baltimore: Johns Hopkins Press. 238 pp.
  1946b *From the Stone Age to Christianity.* 2d ed. Baltimore: Johns Hopkins Press. 495 pp.
  1949–50 "Zur Zähmung des Kamels," *Zeitschrift für die alttestamentliche Wissenschaft,* LXII, 315. Berlin.

ALTHEIM, F.
  1947–48 *Weltgeschichte Asiens im griechischen Zeitalter.* 2 vols. Halle an der Saale: Niemeyer. 412 + 262 pp.

BISHOP, C. W.
  1932 "The Rise of Civilization in China with Reference to Its Geographical Aspects," *Geographical Review,* XXII, 617–31. (Cf. XII [1922], 19–41.)

BOBEK, H.
  1943 "Der Orient als sozialer Lebensraum." MS. 101 pp.
  1948 "Stellung und Bedeutung der Sozialgeographie," *Erdkunde,* II, 118–25.
  1951 *Die natürlichen Wälder und Gehölzfluren Irans.* ("Bonner Geographische Abhandlungen," No. 8.) Bonn: Geographisches Institut der Universität. 62 pp.
  1952 "Beiträge zur klima-ökologischen Gliederung Irans," *Erdkunde,* VI, 65–84.
  1953–54 "Klima und Landschaft Irans in vor- und frühgeschichtlicher Zeit," *Geographischer Jahresbericht aus Österreich,* XXV, 1–42.

BRAIDWOOD, R. J.
  1952 *The Near East and the Foundations of Civilization.* (Condon Lectures, No. 5.) Eugene, Ore.: Oregon State System of Higher Education. 43 pp.

BRYAN, K.
  1941 "Pre-Columbian Agriculture in the Southwest as Conditioned by Periods of Alluviation," *Annals of the Association of American Geographers,* XXXI, 219–42.

BÜDEL, J.
  1949 "Die räumliche und zeitliche Gliederung des Eiszeitalters," *Die Naturwissenschaften,* XXXVI, 105–12, 133–39.
  1952 "Bericht über klima-morphologische und Eiszeit-Forschungen in Nieder-Afrika," *Erdkunde,* VI, 104–32.
  1953 "Die 'periglazial'-morphologischen Wirkungen des Eiszeitklimas auf der ganzen Erde," *ibid.,* VII, 249–66.

CASKEL, W.
  1953 *Die Bedeutung der Beduinen in der Geschichte der Araber.* ("Arbeitsgemeinschaft für Forschung des Landes Nordrhein-Westfalen, Geisteswissenschaften," No. 8.) Cologne and Opladen: Westdeutscher Verlag. 35 pp.

CHILDE, V. G.
  1926 *The Aryans: A Study of Indo-European Origins.* London: Kegan Paul, Trench, Trubner & Co.; New York: Alfred A. Knopf. 221 pp.

COON, C. S.
  1953 "Climate and Race," pp. 13–34 in SHAPLEY, H. (ed.), *Climatic Change.* Cambridge, Mass.: Harvard University Press. 318 pp.

DEEVEY, E. S.
  1949 "Biogeography of the Pleisto-

cene. Part I. Europe and North America," *Bulletin of the Geological Society of America,* LX, 1315–1416.
1953 "Paleolimnology and Climate," pp. 273–318 in SHAPLEY, H. (ed.), *Climatic Change.* Cambridge, Mass.: Harvard University Press. 318 pp. (Rich in references.)

DOUGHTY, C. M.
1936 *Travels in Arabia Deserta.* New ed. London: Jonathan Cape. 612 pp.

EBERHARD, W.
1942a *Kultur und Siedlung der Randvölker Chinas.* (Supplement to *T'oung Pao,* Vol. XXXVI.) Leiden: Brill. 506 pp.
1942b *Lokalkulturen im Alten China, Part I: Die Lokalkulturen des Nordens und Westens.* (Supplement to *T'oung Pao,* Vol. XXXVII.) Leiden: Brill. 447 pp.
1942c *Lokalkulturen im Alten China, Part II: Die Lokalkulturen des Südens und Ostens.* ("Monumenta Serica," Monograph III.) Peking: Catholic University; Leiden: Brill. 588 pp.

EICKSTEDT, E. VON
1931–32 "Der Zentral-Dekkan und die Rassengliederung Indiens," *Anthropologischer Anzeiger,* VIII, 89–103. Stuttgart.

FIRBAS, F.
1949 *Spät- und nacheiszeitliche Waldgeschichte Mitteleuropas nördlich der Alpen,* Vol. I: *Allgemeine Waldgeschichte.* Jena: Fischer. 480 pp.

FLINT, R. F.
1953 "Evidence from Glacial Geology as to Climatic Variations," pp. 165–78 in SHAPLEY, H. (ed.), *Climatic Change.* Cambridge, Mass.: Harvard University Press. 318 pp.

FLOHN, H.
1947 "Zum Klima der freien Atmosphäre über Sibirien. II. Die regionale winterliche Inversion," *Meteorologische Rundschau,* I, 75–79.
1952 "Allgemeine atmosphärische Zirkulation und Paläoklimatologie," *Geologische Rundschau,* XL, 153–78.
1953 "Studien über die atmosphärische Zirkulation in der letzten Eiszeit," *Erdkunde,* VII, 266–75.

FRANKE, O.
1930 *Geschichte des chinesischen Reiches,* Vol. I. Berlin and Leipzig: De Gruyter. 431 pp.

FRENZEL, B.
1955 "Die Vegetationszonen Nordeurasiens während der postglazialen Wärmezeit," *Erdkunde,* IX, 40–53.

FRENZEL, B., and TROLL, C.
1952 "Die Vegetationszonen des nördlichen Eurasiens während der letzten Eiszeit," *Eiszeitalter und Gegenwart,* II, 154–67 (with map).

GERASIMOV, I. P.
1946 "Ancient Soil and Eluvial Formations and Their Significance for the Paleogeography of the Quaternary Period," *Surveys of the Geographical Institute of the Academy of Science of USSR,* Vol. XXXVII. Moscow and Leningrad. (In Russian.)

GRADMANN, R.
1934 *Die Steppen des Morgenlandes in ihrer Bedeutung für die Geschichte der menschlichen Gesittung.* ("Geographische Abhandlungen," Series III, No. 6.) Stuttgart: Engelhorn's Nachf. 66 pp.
1943 "Blüte und Niedergang des Orients in geographischer Betrachtung." MS. Tübingen.

GRAUL, H.
1956 "Sind die äusseren Jungendmoränen im Alpenvorland gleich alt?" *Eiszeitalter und Gegenwart,* Vol. VII. Öhringen, Württemberg: F. Rau. (In press.)

GROUSSET, R.
1948 *L'Empire des steppes.* 2d ed. Paris: Payot. 639 pp.
1954 "Die Steppenreiche," pp. 359–90 in RANDA, A. (ed.), *Handbuch der Weltgeschichte,* Vol. I. Olten and Freiburg im Breisgau: O. Walter. 1,159 pp.

HACK, J. T.
1953 "Geologic Evidence of Late Pleistocene Climates," pp. 179–88 in SHAPLEY, H. (ed.), *Climatic Change,* Cambridge, Mass.: Harvard University Press. 318 pp.

HAENISCH, R.
1948 *Die geheime Geschichte der*

Mongolen. 2d ed. Leipzig: Otto Harrassowitz. 190 pp.

HANČAR, F.
1951 "Probleme und Ergebnisse der neuen russischen Urgeschichtsforschung," *33. Bericht der Römisch-Germanischen Kommission, 1943–50,* pp. 25–60. Berlin.
1954 "Der eurasische Raum: Das Steppenneolithikum," pp. 146–53 in RANDA, A. (ed.), *Handbuch der Weltgeschichte,* Vol. I. Olten and Freiburg im Breisgau: O. Walter. 1,159 pp.

HEINE-GELDERN, R. VON
1950 "China, die Ostkaspische Kultur und die Herkunft der Schrift," *Paideuma,* IV, 51–92.

HERMANNS, M.
1949 *Die Nomaden von Tibet.* Vienna: Herold. 325 pp.

HERRMANN, A.
1935 *Historical and Commercial Atlas of China.* ("Harvard-Yenching Institute Monographic Series," Vol. I.) Cambridge, Mass.: Harvard University Press. 112 pp.

HUZAYYIN, S. A.
1941 *The Place of Egypt in Prehistory.* ("Mémoires Présentés à l'Institut d'Égypte," Vol. XLIII.) Cairo: L'Institut Français d'Archéologie. 474 pp.

JASPERS, K.
1949 *Vom Ursprung und Ziel der Geschichte.* Munich: R. Piper & Co. 349 pp.

JETTMAR, K.
1954*a* "Mongolide Schädel in der Frühbronzezeit Mittel- und Nordeuropas?" *Archiv für Völkerkunde,* IX, 8–20.
1954*b* "Les plus anciennes civilisations d'éleveurs des steppes d'Asie centrale," *Cahier d'histoire mondiale,* I, No. 4 (April), 760–83.
1954*c* "Urgeschichte: China; Entstehung des Reiternomadentums," pp. 342–48 in RANDA, A. (ed.), *Handbuch der Weltgeschichte,* Vol. I. Olten and Freiburg im Breisgau: O. Walter. 1,159 pp.

KLUTE, F.
1930 "Die Verschiebung der Klimagürtel der letzten Eiszeit," *Petermanns geographische Mitteilungen,*

Supplement, CCIX, 166–82. Gotha. (*Hermann Wagner Gedächtnisschrift.*)
1951 "Das Klima Europas während der Würmeiszeit und die Änderung bis zur Jetztzeit," *Erdkunde,* V, 273–83.

KUSSMAUL, F.
1952–53 "Frühe Nomadenkultur in Innerasien," *Tribus: Jahrbuch des Linden-Museums, Stuttgart, 1952 und 1953,* pp. 305–60.
1953 "Zur Frühgeschichte des innerasiatischen Reiternomadentums." Dissertation. Tübingen. (Typewritten.)
N.d. "Einige Bemerkungen zur geheimen Geschichte der Mongolen." MS. 22 pp.

LATTIMORE, O.
1938 "The Geographical Factor in Mongol History," *Geographical Journal,* XCI, 1–20.

LAWRENCE, T. E.
1935 *Seven Pillars of Wisdom.* Garden City, N.Y.: Doubleday, Doran & Co. 672 pp.

LIGETI, L.
1950–51 "Mots de civilisation de Haute Asie en transcription chinoise," *Acta Orientalia Academiae Scientiarum Hungaricae,* I, 141–88. Budapest: Magyar Tudomanyos Academia.

LOEHR, M.
1952 "Zur Ur- und Vorgeschichte Chinas," *Saeculum,* III, 15–55. Freiburg im Breisgau and Munich.

LOUIS, H.
1938 "Eiszeitliche Seen in Anatolien," *Zeitschrift der Gesellschaft für Erdkunde zu Berlin,* pp. 267–85.
1939 *Das natürliche Pflanzenkleid Anatoliens.* ("Geographische Abhandlungen," Series III, No. 12.) Stuttgart: Engelhorn's Nachf. 132 pp.

LUNDHOLM, B.
1947 *Abstammung und Domestikation des Hauspferdes.* ("Zoologiska Bidrag från Uppsala," Vol. XXVII.) Uppsala: Almquist & Wiksells Boktryckeri AB. 287 pp.

MENGHIN, O.
1937 *Weltgeschichte der Steinzeit.* Vienna: Anton Schroll & Co. 648 pp.

NARR, K. J.
1952 "Das höhere Jägertum: Jüngere Jagd- und Sammelstufe," pp. 502–24 in VALJAVEC, F. (ed.), *Historia mundi*, Vol. I. Munich: L. Lehner. 560 pp.

NEISTADT, M. I.
1953 "Palaeogeography of the Natural Zones of the European Part of USSR in Postglacial Time," *Records of the Academy of Sciences, USSR, Geographical Series*, I, 32–48. (In Russian.)

OPPENHEIM, MAX VON
1939–52 *Die Beduinen*, in collaboration with ERICH BRAUNLICH and WERNER CASKEL. 3 vols. Leipzig and Wiesbaden: Otto Harrassowitz. 447 + 447 + 495 pp.

PENCK, A.
1913 "Die Formen der Landoberfläche und Verschiebungen der Klimagürtel," *Sitzungsberichte der Königlich Preussischen Akademie der Wissenschaften*, pp. 77–97. Berlin.

PICARD, L.
1938 "Über Fauna, Flora und Klima des Pleistozäns Palästina-Syriens," pp. 287–91 in GÖTZINGER, G. (ed.), *Verhandlungen der III. Internationalen Quartär–Konferenz, 1936*. Vienna: Geologische Landesanstalt. 393 pp.

PLAETSCHKE, B.
1939 "Landschaftliche Wesenszüge der östlichen Gobi," *Wissenschaftliche Veröffentlichungen des Deutschen Museums für Länderkunde Leipzig* (N.S.), VII, 103–48.

POSER, H.
1947 "Dauerfrostboden und Temperaturverhältnisse während der Würmeiszeit im nicht vereisten Mittel- und Westeuropa," *Die Naturwissenschaften*, XXXIV, 1 ff.
1948 "Boden- und Klimaverhältnisse in Mitteleuropa während der Würmeiszeit," *Erdkunde*, II, 43–68.

ROSTOWZEW, M.
1931 *Scythien und der Bosporus*, Vol. I. Berlin: Hans Schoetz & Co. 651 pp.

SAUER, CARL O.
1952 *Agricultural Origins and Dispersals*. (Bowman Memorial Lectures, Series Two.) New York: American Geographical Society. 110 pp.

SMOLLA, G.
1953 "Der Klimasturz um 800 v. Chr. und seine Bedeutung für die Kulturentwicklung in Südwestdeutschland," pp. 168–86 in KIMMIG, W. (ed.), *Festschrift für P. Goessler*. Stuttgart: W. Kohlhammer. 221 pp.
1955 "Bemerkungen zur Frage nach der Herausbildung neolithischer Kulturerscheinungen." MS. 334 pp.

SPULER, B.
1950 "Geschichte Mittelasiens," pp. 309–60 in WALDSCHMIDT, E. (ed.), *Geschichte Asiens*. Munich: Bruckmann. 767 pp.

TOLSTOW, S. P.
1953 *Auf den Spuren der altchoresmischen Kultur*. (14. Beiheft zur "Sowjetwissenschaft.") Berlin: Kultur & Fortschritt. 362 pp.

VISSER, C. and J.
1935–38 *Wissenschaftliche Ergebnisse der Niederländischen Expedition in den Karakorum und die angrenzenden Gebiete in den Jahren 1922, 1925, und 1929/30*. 2 vols. Leiden: Brill. 499 + 216 pp. (with maps).

VLADIMIRTSOV, G.
1948 *Le Régime social des Mongols: Le féodalisme nomade*, trans. M. CARSOV. ("Bibliothèque d'Études," Vol. LII.) Paris: Publications du Musée Quimet. 291 pp.

WALZ, R.
1951–54 "Zum Problem des Zeitpunktes der Domestikation der altweltlichen Cameliden," *Zeitschrift der Deutschen Morgenländischen Gesellschaft*, CI, 29–51; CIV, 45–87.

WEISCHET, W.
1954 "Die gegenwärtige Kenntnis vom Klima in Mitteleuropa beim Maximum der letzten Vereisung," *Mitteilungen der Geographischen Gesellschaft in München*, XXXIX, 95–116.

WERTH, E.
1954 *Grabstock, Hacke und Pflug*. Ludwigsburg: Eugen Ulmer. 434 pp.

WILHELMY, H.
1950 "Das Alter der Schwarzerde und die Steppen Mittel- und Osteuropas," *Erdkunde*, IV, 5–34.

WILLETT, H. C.
1953 "Atmospheric and Oceanic Circulation as Factors in Glacial-Interglacial Changes of Climate," pp. 51–71 in SHAPLEY, H. (ed.), *Climatic Change*. Cambridge, Mass.: Harvard University Press. 318 pp.

WISSMANN, H. VON
1938 "Über Lössbildung und Würmeiszeit in China," *Geographische Zeitschrift*, XLIV, 202–20.
1939 "Die Klima- und Vegetationsgebiete Eurasiens," *Zeitschrift der Gesellschaft für Erdkunde zu Berlin*, pp. 1–14, and map.
1940 "Südwest-Kiangsu, der Wuhu-Taihu-Kanal und das Problem des Yangdse-Deltas," *Wissenschaftliche Veröffentlichung des Deutschen Museums für Länderkunde Leipzig* (N.S.), No. 8, pp. 61–131.
1942 "Stellung und Bedeutungswandel des Orients in den Lebensräumen der Alten Welt," *Zeitschrift der Gesellschaft für Erdkunde zu Berlin*, pp. 353–68.
1946 "Die Entwicklungsräume des Menschen," *Universitas*, I, 313–31 (I), 445–64 (II).
1948 "Pflanzenklimatische Grenzen der warmen Tropen," *Erdkunde*, II, 81–92 (with 2 maps).
1952 "Discussion on the Climate of the Dry Belt of Eurasia in the Last Ice Age after H. Wilhelmy's Paper on 'Die eiszeitliche Verschiebung der Klima- und Vegetationszonen in Südamerika,' " *Tagungsbericht und wissenschaftliche Abhandlungen zum Deutschen Geographentag Frankfurt a.M. 1951*, XXVIII, 305 ff. Remagen.
1953 "Geographische Grundlagen und Frühzeit der Geschichte Südarabiens," *Saeculum*, IV, 61–114. Freiburg im Breisgau and Munich.
1956 "Die Vergletscherung und Schneegrenze von Hochasien. I. Die heutige Vergletscherung und Schneegrenze," *Akademie der Wissenschaften und Literatur, Abhandlung der Naturwissenschaftlichen Klasse*. Mainz. (In press.)

WISSMANN, H. VON, and HÖFNER, M.
1952 *Beiträge zur historischen Geographie des vorislamischen Südarabien*. ("Akademie der Wissenschaften und Literatur, Abhandlung der Geistes- und Sozialwissenschaftlichen Klasse," No. 4.) Mainz. 165 pp., 12 pl., map. (Also published in *Jahrgang, 1952*, pp. 221–385.)

WRIGHT, H. E., JR.
1951 "Geologic Setting of Ksar 'Akil, a Palaeolithic Site in Lebanon," *Journal of Near Eastern Studies*, X, 112–22.
1952 "The Geological Setting of Four Prehistoric Sites in Northeastern Iraq," *Bulletin of the American Schools of Oriental Research*, CXXVIII, 11–24.

ZEUNER, F. E.
1953 "Das Problem der Pluvialzeiten," *Geologische Rundschau*, XLI, 242–53.

Changes in Climate, Vegetation, and Human Adjustment in the Saharo-Arabian Belt with Special Reference to Africa

SOLIMAN HUZAYYIN[*]

THE SAHARO-ARABIAN BELT: DEFI-
NITION, SPACE RELATIONS, AND
SCOPE OF STUDY

The Saharo-Arabian belt of desert and semidesert has played a crucial part in the story of man on the earth. Perhaps in no other major belt was the interaction of *man* and *milieu* more oscillating in nature, and yet uniform in pattern, than in this area. The story of human activity in these deserts and semisteppes is characterized by its immense length. It goes back into the remote past of prehistory and paleogeography. Indeed, the intricacies of human adjustment and changes in nature in this area cannot be properly understood or deeply appreciated in the light of a study limited to the present-day geography. We must go back deep into paleogeographical stages at least to the beginnings of the so-called "Pluvial Period," when man was still in his early stages of exploiting natural resources and roaming over this wide belt. In such a study of paleogeography and paleoclimatology it is necessary to cover the whole area of the Saharo-Arabian belt as a geographical unit. The great rift of the Red Sea represented no real divide in the strict geographical sense. Conditions along each of its banks were practically the same, both in the past and in the present. Also, human intercourse and drifts of population were possible across both ends of the Red Sea. The Isthmus of Suez was a natural corridor for migrations and contacts in both directions. Movements of population, as well as drifts of culture and thought, were possible both along valleys dissecting the high mountains of southern Sinai and along the northern coastal plain. This latter has always received adequate Mediterranean rainfall and was also fitted with natural water reservoirs in the form of sand dunes from whose cores underground water seeped to intervening wells and waterholes. The Bab el Mandeb never represented a barrier between the highlands and semiarid plateaus along both its sides. Natural conditions on both sides of the Red Sea were so identical in southwestern Asia and northeastern Africa that, for all practical purposes, human life and human activity in exploiting nature were almost the same. For this reason we shall find it necessary, when dealing with vegetation and

---

* Dr. Huzayyin is Professor of Geography at the University of Cairo, Egypt. After graduation from Cairo in 1929, he did postgraduate work in England, France, and Austria in 1930–35. He then carried out field work in southwestern Arabia in 1936 and in the Nile Valley and the Egyptian deserts since 1937. His publications include: *Some Contributions of the Arabs to Geography,* 1932; *The Place of Egypt in Prehistory,* 1941; *Arabia and the Far East,* 1942; and "Physiographic History of the River Nile," 1953.

surface changes, whether due to natural or to human agencies, to keep in mind the very close connection and correlation between the two sides of the Red Sea or, rather, between the desert of the Sahara and Libya, on the one hand, and Arabia, on the other. We shall in this short treatise, however, concentrate chiefly on the African side of this belt.

The importance of the Saharo-Arabian belt may be attributed to more than one geographical factor. There is, perhaps first and foremost, the unique geographical situation between different zones and lands. It lies between the Mediterranean and western European climatic zones on the north, and the Sudanese and semimonsoonal zones on the south. But it may be noted that the dividing line between the Saharo-Arabian belt and the zones flanking it on both sides was never clearly demarcated, either in climate or in vegetation. This is true not only of the present day but also of the past climates and vegetation. The case, however, was not one of regular and fixed transition but rather one of oscillating and vibrating relation. There was always an encroachment either of the desert on its bordering lands or vice versa. This oscillation, which started with climatic conditions and changes in vegetation and surface, was finally reflected in, and in some cases affected by, human life and human adjustments. In this process it will be found difficult to separate data from the Saharo-Arabian belt and from its adjoining areas. But the importance of the geographical situation of this belt is manifold. To the northwest of it lay western Europe, connected with Africa through the Iberian Peninsula and across Gibraltar. Human migrations in this direction go deep into Paleolithic times and were affected both by climatic oscillations and by changes in vegetational and animal life. Migrations were in both directions, and, in turn, they had their effect upon the natural milieu in northwestern Africa and in Iberia. The Mediterranean represented no real barrier between its African and its European coasts. It has become abundantly clear, however, that no land bridge ever existed between the two continents during human times. The straits of Gibraltar and of Sicily have always been covered with water, at least since late Pliocene times. Evidence is being accumulated that the eastern Mediterranean was connected with the Atlantic and that the Mediterranean never really formed one or two lakes within the Pleistocene. It is true that some of its islands such as Malta, or some of the Cyclades, were connected with the European mainland; but the Mediterranean was never completely bridged over. Not only do we find high raised beaches practically all around the Mediterranean but we also find molluscans and water fauna migrating both from Lusitania and the Senegal coast into the Mediterranean. Human connections during Paleolithic times, however, were maintained either across Gibraltar or through Asia Minor and over Caucasia and the Balkans.

To the east, land connections were maintained between the Saharo-Arabian belt and the Iranian Plateau and east into innermost Asia. This connection had its effect upon the early migration of fauna and flora as well as that of man. In the domain of culture the land connections with the east fanned out in different directions—toward Caucasia and the Russian mainland, Turkestan and beyond, as well as toward the Indian peninsula. To the southeast of the Saharo-Arabian belt, connections were maintained over the waters of the Arabian Sea and the Indian Ocean. It is to be noted that, singularly enough, the southern seas of the tropics extend two arms toward the Mediterranean, namely, the Persian Gulf and the Red Sea. Various areas along the coasts of Arabia and northeastern Africa served as bases for sea connections. Natural conditions along the coasts of southern Arabia and northeastern Africa affected human activity and human expansion by sea toward the east. In some parts, arid or subarid conditions forced men to depend more on the sea and sea trade for their livelihood. In other parts, vegetational wealth was of such a kind as to provide a basis for a special type of trade, such as that of incense from the ancient coastal plateau of Hadhramaut. In other cases, the existence of semimonsoonal plateaus fringed by desert coastal plains gave a special pattern of life and activity, as in the case of the ancient lands of Punt, which covered Abyssinia, Somaliland, and Yemen. Human connections and human expansion in this part of the fringe area of the Saharo-Arabian belt, however, were not limited to its own population which spread actively toward southern Asia and eastern Africa. Both Indian and African elements spread northward and occupied parts of the coasts of southern Arabia. We have here, therefore, another example of the difficulty of demarcating the limits of the Saharo-Arabian belt either on natural or on human and historical grounds.

To the south of the Saharan belt, in the direction of Sudanese and subequatorial Africa, the border is even more loosely demarcated. We can never focus on a line which limits the desert in this direction either in the past or in the present. The shift was constant and was marked not only by major oscillations, owing to principal and radical climatic changes, but also by microchanges in climate and vegetation during short cycles or from year to year. The border area was also traversed in certain parts by high ridges which had their effect upon local rainfall and vegetation and led to curves and interlocking in vegetational zones. This is clear in the highlands of Urdi, Ennedi, Tibesti, and Hoggar in the central and western Sahara and in the highlands on both sides of

the Red Sea. The border area is also complicated by the existence of two types of river valleys, the one represented in streams running in an east-west direction, such as the Senegal and other rivers of the western Sudan, and the other represented in the great river Nile, which runs persistently from south to north. It is remarkable indeed that the Nile, whose headwaters lie a few hundred kilometers from both the Indian Ocean and the Red Sea, persists on heading northward for more than 6,000 kilometers to reach the Mediterranean across the great desert. Strictly speaking, this is not what one would have expected under regular and normal conditions of river drainage. But the Nile had such a complicated story of physiographic evolution that it had no alternative but to collect the waters of the equatorial and the Abyssinian plateaus and drain them northward across the plains of the Sudan and the Libyan Desert toward the Mediterranean. In doing so, it acquired the somewhat paradoxical achievement of running parallel to one of the arms of the Indian Ocean (the Red Sea), separated from it by the tilted edge of the so-called "Red Sea ranges." In doing so, it also complicated the story of vegetational distribution as well as that of human adjustment and human life. Not only did it represent the cradleland of settled life along its course in Egypt and the Sudan, but it also represented the highway of expanding tribal elements which fanned out, once they were able to cross the desert belt, into the savanna plains of the Sudan. This was particularly true of the Arab expansion in the Sudan during the Islamic phase. The effects of human movement, in one direction or the other during various phases of human history along the Nile Valley and across the desert belt, upon vegetational and animal life in the borders of the desert belt are still very little known. But we shall attempt to review some of them at a later stage in this treatise.

We may well see from this general review of the geographical situation of the Saharo-Arabian belt in the Old World that the story of its space relationships in different directions is a complicated one. It derives its complexity from both natural conditions in the belt and the instability of its climate and vegetation through the ages. This is perhaps why we find it essential, in order to have a proper perspective and a proper retrospect of man's tenure of this part of the earth through the corridors of time, to go into some of the details of the past climates and vegetation of the Saharo-Arabian belt.

A PALEOGEOGRAPHIC RETROSPECT: PAST CLIMATE, VEGETATION, AND HUMAN ACTIVITY

The study of prehistoric activity of man over a region like the Saharo-Arabian area can best be approached through a geographical treatment which brings in climatic changes (in the past) and their relation to plant, animal, and human life. Such a study would aim at treating the culture complexes of the past in their proper geographical setting. In trying to reconstruct the geographical stage of human activity in past times, however, we are usually forced to employ biogeographical observations for inferring changes of climate. But, unfortunately, data relating to past climates and drawn from various sources are not always compatible with each other; and the methods of their interpretation by experts are again less coherent. There is also the constant danger of generalizations and of drawing the same conclusions from sets of data which may be comparable only in appearance. For example, the existence of sandstones and similar formations and that of salts and gypsum may not necessarily all correspond to the existence of desert conditions in the climatic sense. This is why it is not always easy

to draw a picture of the climatic conditions as may be inferred from formations of the past. Yet we have to depend very largely upon physiographic data in order to infer the climates of the past in this desert region. These data may be represented either in the formations themselves, their nature and their kind, or in the shape which they take. Formations existing in these desert areas may be indicative either of dry conditions by the presence of sand dunes and sand seas or of wet ones, represented by wadi terraces, lacustrine beds, or travertines and tufas. The shape which these formations may take can also shed light upon past climatic features. The orientation of a fossil dune chain may indicate direction of prevailing wind different from that of the present day. Also, the length and extension of dry wadis now dissecting the surface of the desert, such as Wadi Tefezzezat in the western Sahara or Wadi Tilemsi north of the Niger or such as the many *wādis bi'lama* (waterless wadis) in the deserts of Egypt and Arabia, should give a picture of rainfall and vegetation entirely different from that of the present day. There are also wind-excavated depressions in the desert, such as those of Biskra and Faiyûm, whose extension and shape may be useful as indications of the character and strength of the wind which excavated them, or at least was partly responsible for their present outline and shape. But, apart from these physiographic data of paleoclimatology, we have to depend, in the study of past geographical conditions in the Sahara and Arabia, upon biogeographical evidence—namely, flora and fauna. The evidence from flora may be either fossil or of the present day. Fossil plants or seeds have been collected from various formations and beds in many different parts of the Sahara and its fringes. It will suffice for our present purpose to give a few examples in order to show the problems they may raise for the investigator. In the Oasis of Khârga, for example, some plant remains were discovered in the second part of the past century and were identified as belonging to the evergreen oak (*Quercus ilex*), now living in the northern Mediterranean. It was then inferred that the Oasis of Khârga must have received rainfall equivalent to that of the habitat of the evergreen oak. New discoveries and more recent identifications of these plant remains of the Pleistocene of Khârga, however, have shown them to belong to three varieties of *Ficus*, which need much less rainfall. Another plant discovered in Khârga is a seed of a variety of date (*Phoenix*) now living in tropical Africa between the Senegal and Kenya. Of course one has to allow for the migration of this variety across what is now forbidding desert. But evidence from flora is not limited to fossil species. The study of present-day vegetation also offers immense possibilities as well as problems for the research worker. Let us take but one example. The high mountains of Hoggar in the western Sahara are covered with vegetation of mixed origin. There are a few subequatorial or equatorial types, a larger number of Sudano-Ethiopian varieties, and a number of Algerian and Mediterranean plants. The slopes of these mountains may be divided into three zones:

1. *The* so-called *"subequatorial" zone.* —Up to 1,700–1,800 meters, with no permanent vegetation except in the bottom of the valleys and on alluvial fans. The flora is chiefly Sudano-Ethiopian, with some subequatorial types. There are also some Saharan species with Mediterranean affinities.

2. *The lower Mediterranean zone.*— Between 1,700–1,800 and 2,300–2,400 meters, with only a few Sudano-Ethiopian types and an increasing number of species from the Mediterranean, or having Mediterranean affinities.

3. *The high Mediterranean zone.*— From 2,300 to 2,400 meters to the summits (3,000 meters), with no Sudano-Ethiopian types, and having a number

of typically Mediterranean plants. This zone also has a permanent vegetation of steppe (outside the watered areas) similar to that on some of the Algerian plateaus.

All this indicates that the interior of the Sahara must have had a higher precipitation at some recent geological period. It was this precipitation which made possible the migration of species of plants both from the Mediterranean southward and from the subequatorial belt northward. But we must remember that the migration of northern types would need a relative lowering of the temperature, while that of the southern ones would need temperatures either similar to those of the present day or at least less fluctuating. In other words, the researcher in past climates is here faced with a problem which touches not only upon the past rainfall in this now desert area but also upon past temperatures—their degree and their range of variation.

Faunal evidences from the Sahara and Arabia are perhaps somewhat more complex in nature and more diversified in the problems which they set before the research worker. There are not only land and fresh-water molluscans but also fishes and land animals. The molluscans may be much disputed, but their evidence, as it stands, is very helpful. They not only indicate differences in climatic conditions but they also throw light upon possibilities of wide migrations across what are now desert stretches. It is true that some of them may have migrated through somewhat special agencies (such as birds), but most of them must have needed a certain amount of rainfall and vegetation in order to spread over the desert. Evidence from truly aquatic species is somewhat more conclusive. The study of these species in North Africa and in many oasis areas has brought forth interesting results. They show the wide spread of distinctly palearctic types. At the same time, however, these molluscans were capable of survival in certain favored spots, like oases, in spite of oscillations in water supply. Thus, from a study of them, we cannot get sufficient detailed evidence of violent extinctions or migrations during the successive phases of the Pleistocene. This, however, may not represent more than a negative piece of evidence. In other words, phases of such extinctions may have existed, though they are difficult for us to trace. Indeed, the study of other types of faunal evidence makes it imperative to assume the existence of such phases of extinction or migration. In this respect, mammalian and other fauna offer interesting and valuable evidence.

Animal remains from the so-called "Pluvial Period" (Upper Pliocene and Pleistocene) point to definitely better climatic conditions. Although the abundance of ostrich eggs would indicate the extension of grasslands, the appearance of the elephant, the waterbuck, and the hippopotamus must have coincided with the existence of running streams and fresh-water pools. This is also corroborated by the wide migration of various types of fishes and crocodiles, some of which survived during long periods and even to the present day. The migration of all these fauna across the desert must have been made possible only through better conditions of rainfall and running water. The fossil fauna of North Africa and the Sahara, however, are particularly mixed. There are both Eurasiatic and Ethiopian types. The research worker must therefore assume that migrations of animals into the Sahara, either from Eurasia via Palestine and Sinai or from Sudanese and subequatorial Africa, must have taken place during varying conditions of climate, especially in temperature. It is also noted that in North Africa certain types are found in formations belonging to two different stages of the Pleistocene, but not in those belonging to an intervening stage. For example, a

number of animals requiring a fairly abundant supply of rainfall, and which appear earlier in the Pleistocene, skip over the Upper Paleolithic phase (Uppermost Pleistocene) and reappear in the Neolithic, to disappear again in the post-Neolithic and historical phase. These include the serval panther, hippopotamus, buffalo, and reedbuck. But the history of fauna in North Africa is still far from being completely known. Complementary evidence has been forthcoming from Palestine, especially from caves. But the evidence of Palestine is again limited chiefly to the Upper Pleistocene; and identifications have shown that the fauna of this part of southwestern Asia were less diversified than those of northwestern Africa and the Sahara. The interior of Arabia is still almost a blank for us in its faunal history during Pleistocene and recent times. Also, the Nile Valley, which could have been expected to give us valuable data in this respect, has been proving singularly poor in well-preserved faunal remains. It is thought that calcification of the formations and beds may have been responsible for the destruction of such remains and of their evidence. Only from the Faiyûm depression do we have valuable material; but even in this area most of the evidence relates to the Uppermost Pleistocene and later phases.

The gist of evidence from faunal remains from different parts of the Saharo-Arabian belt indicates the very great and real need that exists for the co-ordination and correlation of data to be drawn from fauna, flora, and physiographic evidence. This means that we are still in great need of teams of workers collaborating with one another and trying to check and cross-check evidence.

But there is still another type of evidence with which the paleogeographer of this area has to deal, namely, that of human stone industries and antiquities. During various stages of the Stone Age the Saharo-Arabian belt played a particularly important role in the development of early human civilization. The remains left by man over practically all the desert are a clear indication to this effect. During the Stone Age, man was not only affected by the prevailing geographical conditions but he also worked as a positive agency in transforming certain aspects of his milieu. He roamed in groups, in what was at that time open and relatively poor grasslands, hunting animals and collecting plants. During phases of aridity his existence must have helped toward the extinction of other species of fauna as well as the cutting-down and burning of scrubs and scattered trees for fire. During such phases of aridity he also had to limit his activity to relatively small areas around springs or pools of water. During other phases of greater rainfall he must have expanded and spread in scattering groups. Later, when he knew how to cultivate plants and to tame animals, he was able to settle in oases and riverine areas and to contribute through his civilized and constructive actions toward the transformation of certain spots on the face of the desert.

But the study of human relics in desert areas during the Stone Age is important not only for the tracing of the story of human civilization and its development or for the study of man's destructive or constructive activity on the face of the earth but also for the study of climatic oscillations during the Pleistocene and later times. The very fact that we find stone implements in areas where there is now no possibility of livelihood for man indicates different climatic and vegetational conditions from those of the present day. The flourishing of stone industry during one phase of the Paleolithic and the degeneration of that industry during a following phase may well be taken as an indication of the deterioration of living conditions as a whole. Also, the wide spread of a certain industry over large areas of the desert indicates the facility of movement which could be afforded only under favorable conditions of rainfall and vegetation, while the concentration of stone industries around segregated favorable spots may well be taken as an indication in the opposite direction. A comparative study of successive human cultures over the Saharo-Arabian area may therefore represent a particularly useful source of information for anyone who desires to follow the history of changes and transformations in the face of this part of the earth as a living stage for man. In this respect, the desert represents an area of study much richer and more remunerative in results than perhaps any other type of environment.

Let us, for example, compare the Saharan belt, on the one hand, with the plateau of Kenya and eastern Africa, on the other. The Sahara was so situated as to represent an area of effective oscillation and fluctuation in rainfall during the whole of the Pluvial period. It lay between the northern latitudes and the Mediterranean, affected by the westerlies and their winter rainfall, on the one hand, and the Sudan and subequatorial latitudes, affected by the summer winds and the rainy semimonsoons, on the other. The Pluvial period coincided with the Ice Age, during which there were shifts in climatic zones. These shifts were most marked and effective along the Saharan belt. The zone of the northern latitudes, for example, was either expanded southward or contracted toward the north. The subequatorial and Sudanese zone was either expanded at the expense of the desert belt or compressed between this latter and the truly equatorial zone. But the desert belt was invaded and affected on both sides by different agencies of climate and different types of flora and fauna. The question does not seem to have been simply one of expansion or contraction of the desert belt, but rather one of penetration of either

Mediterranean or Sudanese and sub-equatorial conditions. We may recall in this respect that the prevailing winds at present are the dry northerly winds. In the western Sahara they shut off the southwest semimonsoons coming from the Atlantic and prevent them from taking rainfall beyond the Sudanese belt. The south fringes of the desert represent an area of contest between the dry northerlies and the wet winds penetrating from the south and southwest. It is possible to visualize conditions during pluvial phases of the Pleistocene. During such phases the depressions of the Mediterranean moving from west to east must have been more frequent and must have traveled along a more southerly course than they do at present. Their more frequent passage along the southern border of the Mediterranean and the northern edges of the desert belt must have cut the dry trade winds from their roots in the center of high pressure over inner Eurasia. The resulting weakening of the dry northerlies of the Sahara would lead to an increase in the penetrating power of the southerly semimonsoons, which could, in that case, reach the central massifs of the Sahara more frequently and more effectively than they do today. At the same time one must assume that the temperature of the northerly winds of the Saharan belt during glacial episodes must have been lower than that of the present day. This would make them carry cold air masses, which, on confronting the warm and moist masses of the southerly semimonsoons, would help promote condensation and precipitation over the southern parts of the desert belt. Thus we may well imagine that during pluvial phases the desert belt was invaded by moisture and rainfall from both sides.

This double climatic invasion and encroachment were followed by a similar double penetration of fauna, flora, and man from both directions. It is true that the invasion was never an excessive one and that the increase in precipitation and the enrichment of vegetation and animal life were always moderate in extent. However, the fact that this was a truly desert belt made any slight change in precipitation and vegetation a particularly effective one. The increase in rainfall in a spot like that of the Oasis of Khârga in the Libyan Desert of Egypt may not have exceeded 20 or 25 centimeters per year, but this was enough to alter the face of the desert and change the geographical milieu to make it possible for man to live and act as a positive agency. On the other hand, the change from wet to dry conditions could very easily be brought about by any small change in rainfall toward aridity. A drop in precipitation of 10 or 15 centimeters per year would have disastrous and far-reaching effects upon vegetation and animal life and would thus lead to large-scale migrations of human groups. In certain cases when it would not lead to such migrations, it would certainly lead either to degeneration of culture or to the concentration of human societies in small and more favorable spots such as near-by streams or springs.

Such changes and fluctuations in the geographical milieu during the Pluvial period in the Saharo-Arabian belt led to constantly changing conditions for man. Phases of prosperity and rainfall would make the desert an open paradise for man, where he could roam and develop his stone industries and widen his contacts. Migrating elements from the north could mix freely with migrating elements from the south. The desert became like a great sponge, seeping peoples and cultures from north and from south. Later on, when dry conditions began to prevail and the vegetational cover of the desert began to be destroyed by nature as well as by animals and man, the desert became powerless to support its peoples. They either degenerated or tried desperately to adapt themselves to the new conditions. Some of their communities relapsed into degeneration or were eaten away by hunger and deficiency of resources; but some of them would succeed through adaptations and innovations to meet varying and unfavorable conditions. This would finally lead to technological developments in stone industries, which would mean the appearance of a new phase in technological sequence. Other groups from the desert would perhaps prefer to disperse and migrate to adjoining areas such as Iberia and western Europe in the north, the Sudan, Eritrea, and eastern Africa in the south, or the more favorable riverine spots like the Nile Valley or the plains of Iraq in the east. There they would mix with older communities and would promote culture and civilization through the new contacts. Thus, we may well see how the changing geographical conditions in the Saharo-Arabian belt, even during the remote Pluvial period, gave a valuable impetus for change and development in the human occupation of the face of the earth.

This was quite different from conditions prevailing in an area like the high plateau of Kenya and eastern Africa. This latter area was a high one and was so situated as to receive a more constant and regular supply of rainfall. It is true that in eastern Africa the study of Pleistocene climatology has revealed the existence of a Pluvial period with more than one maximum of rainfall. That Pluvial period was divided into two pluvial phases with a dry interval in between. Each of the two pluvial phases had an oscillating crest of maximum rainfall. The Pluvial period as a whole was followed by increasingly dry conditions, which were interrupted by a wetter phase during Neolithic times. But, in spite of all these oscillations, there can be no doubt that the fluctuations were never so great as to affect vegetational, animal, and human life to the same extent as they did along the desert belt. During phases of relative aridity, plants, animals, and men could easily take refuge and find protection and means of survival in the many favorable spots, such as the tops of mountain blocks or the borders of wide lakes and water surfaces. Thus the change of geographical pattern on the plateau of eastern Africa as a whole was never deep enough to lead to far-reaching change in human life and industries. This is perhaps why the technological evolution of stone industries during all that phase was more regular in eastern Africa perhaps than in any other part of the world. The desert, on the other hand, was the land of constant change and constant need for adaptation.

IMPLICATIONS OF THE CHANGES IN MILIEU FOR THE RESEARCH WORKER

The implications for the research worker of these changes in the Saharo-Arabian area are even more complicated than may appear at firsthand. The complex sequence of culture and stone industries is but a reflection of the complex nature of changes in geographical environment. There is, therefore, the constant need for correlation of changes in climate, in vegetation, in physiography, and in human adaptations. No one specialist can claim on his own to be able to grasp mastery of all these different fields of study. The desert belt, therefore, is an arena where teams of workers and specialists must co-operate if the story of human life on the changing face of the desert is to be clearly discerned. Such a co-operation needs not only training in the field but also the special gift on the part of each worker to appreciate the value of evidence which others can afford. A sense of wide judgment and of balance would have to be promoted if any group of workers were to achieve any coherent results. There have, so far, been certain results achieved by co-operation of small groups of workers in missions sent to different parts of the desert belt. But the need is still very great for such missions to explore not only the fringes of the desert but also remote parts in its heart. Two types of research work are needed in this area. There is first the field work to be carried out by missions sent to still-unexplored areas. Then there is the need for studies of correlation with material obtained from areas already better known, such as the European latitudes or even parts of the tropics. In the first type of research a number of missions have already carried out most useful work in parts of Little Africa, Egyptian oases, and the Nile Valley. But the remainder of the Sahara is still very little known. What is really needed are not those quick-moving expeditions which carry out general exploration work, collect stone implements, or make tracings and photographs of rock drawings in remote areas. Rather do we need more of that kind of expedition which would include specialists in Pleistocene geology, physiography, paleontology, prehistoric archeology, and such studies as may contribute to the emergence of a coherent picture of past human activity in this area. These expeditions should settle down in limited areas and carry out intensive, systematic work. Only through such a method can we obtain that type of reliable and comparable data that would help discern the story of man, his activities, and his civilizations. As for research in correlation with other areas to the north and to the south, we shall have to depend mostly on theoretical studies. It is true that, in certain cases, one may be able to carry out practical field work in correlation. This may be possible, for instance, in the Nile Valley, where one could follow events of climatic oscillations in Ethiopia or in eastern Africa and link them directly with physiographic events in the lower Nile Valley. But this is a very special case, in which research work has started, though it remains incomplete. It was found that at one time the river Nile was made up of three distinct and independent river systems—one in Nubia and Egypt, the second in Ethiopia, and the third in the Equatorial Plateau. The linking-up of these three systems and the formation of the river Nile in its present shape, however, do not seem to go further than the Middle Pleistocene. Thus the possibility of a direct link in events is limited chiefly to the latter part of the Pluvial period. For any correlation covering the whole of the period of human occupation of the Saharan belt with events in northern and equatorial latitudes, one would have to depend almost entirely on theoretical studies and comparisons. Some effort has already been made in this respect, and it may be useful to make a brief review of the conclusions already reached. This would help bring out the lacunae in our knowledge and the gaps still to be filled by future research.

CORRELATIONS OF CHANGES IN CLIMATE, VEGETATION, AND SURFACE IN HUMAN TIMES

If we compare evidences drawn from physiographic data, flora, fauna, and archeological material, we can draw the following picture of climatic oscillations in the Saharo-Arabian belt during human times. The Pluvial period started in the Upper Pliocene and continued to the end of the Pleistocene. It was divided into two major pluvial phases. The First Pluvial was a very long one, marked chiefly with the cutting of large wadis in the rocks of the surface of the deserts, followed in places by the sedimentation of huge river terraces. In these latter, some early, Lower Paleolithic implements were discovered *in situ*. The details of this First Pluvial are not known, though it is almost certain that it must have had more than one submaximum. During part of it the climate was marked with a rise in temperature as well as in precipitation.

This First Pluvial continued to the end of the Lower Pleistocene and was followed by a phase of aridity, marked also by crustal movements. The interpluvial was a short one, but it was very effective, not only in extinctions and emigrations of plants, animals, and human groups, but also in the remodeling of large areas of the surface of the desert. Wind activity and sand abrasion became very strong and effective. Also, thermal weathering helped in the same direction. As a result, many of the former features of desert physiognomy became obliterated. Evidence has been increasingly forthcoming that many of the features in the present-day physiognomy of the Saharan deserts may have had their origin during this interval. We believe, for example, that such depressions as that of Faiyûm (and perhaps that of Biskra) may not have acquired their final shape until this dry interval, during which further excavation and widening of such depressions seem to have taken place. But this is still one of the main points in which complementary research is needed. There even may be a possibility of comparing the sequence of events in some of the desert depressions in Africa with that of similar depressions in other continents.

After the interpluvial came the Second Pluvial phase, which corresponded to the Upper Pleistocene. It also coincided with both Middle and Upper Paleolithic cultures. The Second Pluvial was much less intensive in precipitation than the First. It was also much shorter but had at least two, or perhaps three, submaxima. It was also characterized chiefly by a relative drop in temperature, and during this phase there was a clear immigration of Asiatic fauna through the Isthmus of Suez. It is also very likely that it was during this Second Pluvial that Mediterranean flora penetrated furthermost into the Sahara.

The Second Pluvial was followed by progressive aridity at the close of the Pleistocene. This aridity was also marked by a continuation of the relatively low temperature which characterized the previous phase. The condition of aridity, however, was interrupted during what we call the "wet phase" of Neolithic and later times. But the story of this latter phase is of special interest, and we shall come back to it a little later.

Thus we may see that the sequence of climatic oscillations and of vegetational changes connected with it in the Saharo-Arabian belt is a fairly simple one. To compare it, however, with the more complex story that we know from western Europe is not at all an easy task. In the northern latitudes, where the Ice Age existed and coincided with the Pluvial period, we know that there have been three or four glacial phases—namely, those of Günz, Mindel, Riss, and Würm in the Alps. They were separated from one another by interglacial phases, of which the one between Mindel and Riss was very long and was characterized by warm conditions. There have been various attempts to draw up correlations between the glacial episodes in Europe and the pluvial ones in Africa. Difficulties arose from the fact that the number of glacials is larger than that of pluvials. There is good reason at present, however, to correlate the First Pluvial with most of the glacial period until the end of the Riss phase. If this be accepted, the Second Pluvial would correspond to Würm, which, in Europe, also had two submaxima followed by further oscillations during the melting of the icecaps. This correlation is based on the fact that a glacial phase in Europe should lead to a southward shift of the climatic zones and consequently to pluvial conditions in North Africa and the Sahara. On the other hand, an interglacial in Europe could coincide with either pluvial or dry conditions in middle latitudes. If the interglacial is marked with a rise in temperature, this would increase evaporation from the seas, would accelerate wind circulation and activity, would foster the formation of storms due to excess of latent heat in the air, and then would lead generally to an increase of precipitation in all climatic zones. We know that the Mindel-Riss interglacial was marked by a rise in temperature, not only in the air, but also in the waters of the Atlantic and Mediterranean. This would mean that such an interglacial could well have coincided with pluvial conditions in the Saharo-Arabian belt. On the other hand, the Riss-Würm interglacial was marked, at least in its middle part, with cool conditions during which there was less evaporation, a relaxation in air circulation, and a general drop in precipitation. As for the earliest interglacial, that which separated Günz from Mindel, there was little evidence available, though on the whole it may have been relatively warm. The last interglacial (Mindel-Riss) is therefore the only one likely to have coincided with a dry interpluvial in the Saharo-Arabian belt. But the whole of the question of correlation of past climates still remains a primarily theoretical one; and added research is still to be looked for.

POST-PLEISTOCENE CHANGES IN GEO-GRAPHICAL ENVIRONMENT AND HUMAN ADAPTATIONS

If we may now pass on from the Pleistocene phase in the Saharo-Arabian belt to the Recent geological phase, we find the story of changes in geographical environment and human adaptations largely preserving the same character that we have been trying to trace in the Pleistocene. The desert belt remained as the scene of intense changes and wide repercussions in the relation of man to his milieu. As usual, changes al-ways started with the climatic cycle, had their direct effect in the general physiognomy and vegetational cover of the desert, and finished in human adjustments to the new conditions. In some cases, however, man was instrumental in the change. He destroyed vegetation and was, in turn, responsible for the onset of denudation and aridity. Until recent years it was generally assumed that the Neolithic stage in human civilization was marked by desiccation and aridity. It was assumed that this desiccation forced both animals and men to migrate from the open desert to settle down in riverine plains and oases. This led to a *rapprochement* between man and animal, which finally ended in the domestication of the relatively tame types of animals. It is also suggested that, when man was forced to concentrate upon and settle down in the well-watered spots, he gradually learned how to plant cereals. In other words, this gave rise to agriculture. More recent research, however, threw increasing doubt upon this relatively simple sequence of events. Evidence has been forthcoming that the dry interval which followed upon the Upper Paleolithic at the close of the Pluvial period was interrupted by the renewal of relatively wet conditions in the very early Neolithic. In other words, it was the Mesolithic stage which was characterized by aridity and degeneration in the stone industry. The pre-Neolithic and the Neolithic were characterized, on the other hand, not by the onset of the crisis, but rather by its relaxation and the renewal of relatively wet, though not truly pluvial, conditions.

Traces of the Neolithic occupation by man of many widely dispersed areas and spots in the Saharo-Arabian belt have been forthcoming during the last thirty years or more. By the sides of rivers and around springs and water-spots in oases, man cultivated the land, raised the domesticated animals, and settled down in small groups of huts and, in some cases, in villages proper. The date of such occupation may be difficult to fix, though in Egypt, for example, it has been fixed at about 5200 B.C. or a little after. The changes in environment as a result of this occupation were far-reaching, especially in areas where cultivation depended mostly on irrigation. The increase in precipitation was enough for cultivation only in limited areas, such as the slopes of mountains or favorably located areas, either near the coast of the Mediterranean or on the borders of Ethiopia and Sudanese Africa. More than one theory has been put forward as to how and where cultivation started. It would be superfluous to go into the details of these theories, though it may be useful to mention a few points about the lower Nile Valley, on the one hand, and the slopes of Ethiopia and Mount Hermon in Syria, on the other. We know that man cultivated both barley and wheat in Egypt as early as the close of the sixth millennium B.C. The variety of barley cultivated at that time was not much different from that of the present day. This may indicate that it was probably growing in the wild state in northeastern Africa, where it had been already domesticated for some time, and under similar conditions. It may, indeed, be inferred that man may have started domesticating barley even earlier than the 5200 B.C. date suggested above. As to wheat, it was probably introduced from without, most likely from southwestern Asia.

The question of how cultivation became known in the lower Nile Valley is also interesting to discuss. Some of the ideas put forward seem fantastic. It is very likely, however, that cultivation became known in this valley in a very normal and gradual way. We know that the Nile flood reaches Egypt in late summer and early autumn. It covers the flood plain and enriches it with silt, pro-

pitious for the cultivation of winter plants. The waters of the Nile subside exactly at the time suitable for the planting and growth of winter plants such as barley and wheat, and we may imagine that seeds could easily have been blown by wind from the adjoining plateau—at that time receiving slightly higher winter rainfall. All sorts of vegetable growth would cover the edges of the valley and delta immediately after the subsidence of the floods, and fishing and hunting groups may have marked and guarded them until the reaping season. This was admittedly not cultivation in the strict sense; but it represented a spontaneous and evolutionary progress toward cultivation proper. Such a suggestion would appeal more to reason because it averts the necessity of a sudden "invention" of agriculture as may be assumed by most current theories on the subject of how cultivation was first known. We may add that nature itself was very propitious for the growth of winter plants in the lower Nile Valley. After the subsidence of the floods the season of winter rainfall begins, which at that time was enough to foster the growth and maturing of both barley and wheat. Both these plants reach maturity with the close of spring, when the winter rainfall begins to cease. The role of man during the early stages of the development of agriculture may have been rather to take a complementary part in the natural process of wild growth, especially by guarding the maturing plant against wild game and birds. Gradually, through the observation of nature, man learned that he could take a more positive part in this process. In the same way we prefer to think that most of the domesticated animals may have been first kept in captivity before the idea of domestication proper was evolved. Gradually man became the tamer, in this desert area and its borders in Asia and Africa, of such animals as cattle, sheep, and asses.

Ethiopia and the horn of eastern Africa together with the borders of the Sudan may have been another area of easy cultivation and domestication. We have mentioned already that barley may have originally been a northeastern African plant; but we may also add that certain varieties of millet must have been first domesticated and cultivated either in Sudanese Africa or on the borders of Ethiopia. It is possible also that the zebu variety of cattle may have first been domesticated in eastern Africa. All these points, however, still require further research.

As for the cultivation of wheat, it is very likely that it first started in western Asia. The plateau extending from Anatolia to Afghanistan must have been the scene of selection of wild wheat plants from which man made his first domestications. The region of Mount Hermon and its vicinity must have played a particularly important role in the development of early cultivation. In these parts of Syria there are areas where soil derived from disintegrating volcanic material, such as in the region of Hauran, was particularly propitious for the growth of wheat. This soil keeps the moisture derived from winter rains and feeds the wheat grasses right through their season of growth. But the story of early cultivation in the Middle East is too wide for us to deal with in any detail.

In the African Sahara a relatively wet phase relieved the crisis of aridity which marked the Mesolithic stage of culture. The so-called "Neolithic wet phase" started about the middle of the sixth millennium B.C. and continued for about three thousand years before it gave way to gradual desiccation during the historic phase. Rainfall over the Saharan belt was certainly not consistent, but there were more frequent storms to provide vegetational life enough for roaming animals and migrating groups of men. Traces of Neolithic culture have been found in scattered spots in the Sudanese Sahara, on the borders of the deserts of Morocco and Algeria, in some spots on the tops of the high mountains of the central Sahara, as well as even in certain spots and oases of the relatively dry Libyan deserts of Egypt. The pattern of the desert Neolithic culture was relatively poor and less coherent than we find in the Nile Valley itself But there is sufficient evidence to show that the desert was not a forbidding area for cultural contacts to take place. We even have evidence of such contacts between the desert borders of the western Sudan and some of the oases of Egypt. These relations were partly coincident with early Chalcolithic cultures in Egypt.

One aspect which would be interesting for us to trace, and which would throw light upon the changes that took place in the fauna and flora of the desert during this phase of human occupation is represented in the rock drawings and paintings of the desert. These have been discovered in a large number of localities, mostly rock shelters in the central Sahara, the Uweinat massif, and other blocks in both the Saharan and the Egyptian deserts. Unfortunately, the question of dating these drawings is not easy to settle, as they have never been found in undoubted association with stone implements or other remains that may help to date them. Apart, however, from the historic drawings, the fauna include a wide variety of elephant, rhinoceros, lion, panther, giraffe, antelope, African cattle, African ram, ostrich, etc. In certain cases there are signs either of domestication or of semidomestication, which give indication of the Neolithic or even post-Neolithic date of these rock drawings. Accurate dating still needs further research, but it may be rightly inferred from the wide distribution of this culture and the variety of animal groups it represents that the desert must have enjoyed at that time a richer covering of vegetation. It was this which made it possible for human groups to roam about the deserts extending between the hills of the Red Sea and the slopes of the Atlas and to draw pictures of animals which they hunted or attempted to domesticate. The vegetational growth must have continued through the early historic phase, because we know that, later on, pharaonic influences seem to have become marked in some of the drawings of the Algerian Sahara—an indication of continued movements and contacts across what were still unforbidding tracts of desert. The Neolithic and early historic phase, therefore, was a period of relatively wet conditions and renewal in the vegetation and fauna of the Saharan belt. There are indirect evidences from Egypt that this phase was also marked in its earlier parts by a relative rise in temperature. In a limited way, therefore, it reminds us of what happened during the warm interglacial which took place between the Mindel and the Riss glacial phases. The small rise in temperature increased evaporation, fostered storm activity due to more latent heat in the air, and also accelerated air circulation on the whole. The desert belt, therefore, may have received more moisture and torrential storms (though varying in intensity from one place to another). It is interesting to note that this so-called "Neolithic wet phase" had its equivalent in Abyssinia and East Africa, where it is called the "Makalian wet phase." During this phase the Nile was characterized by exceptionally high floods which took place immediately before the beginning of the Neolithic and continued for some time, though subsiding gradually during the predynastic phase. It is very likely that this warm-wet phase may have coincided with the so-called "climatic optimum phase" of northwestern Europe. But the story of the so-called "Neolithic wet phase" of the Saharan belt, starting from about the middle of the sixth millennium B.C. and continuing for some time, is still one of the interesting subjects for students of paleoclimatology and ancient fauna and flora of the deserts. The changes which took place in the vegetational cover of the deserts, first due to the rather sudden onset of this wet phase, and later due to its gradual and oscillating ending, should be of particular interest to paleogeographers. They affected not only the aspect of the natural environment but also the activity of man during this very interesting phase of the human cultural development.

CHANGES DURING HISTORICAL TIMES

Mention must be made of the changes in climate and vegetation and their effect upon human activity in the Saharo-Arabian belt during historical times. Evidence has been forthcoming that the onset of aridity after the so-called "Neolithic wet phase" was a very gradual one. This is manifested by the presence and activity of man in many parts of desert areas during early historic times. The general tendency among students of past historical climates is to assume that aridity in its present form and extent does not go much beyond the early centuries of the Christian Era. It is even thought that the desert belt in Africa and Asia did not reach its present-day aridity until about the third or even the sixth century A.D. The question of climatic desiccation in historic times, however, remains still a very vexing one. The dispute between the two schools of changeability and non-changeability of climate during historic times becomes more complicated when we think of the fact that, even if we admit the gradual desiccation, it is always necessary to assume the existence of oscillations leading to more and more dry conditions. Also, such changes must have been very minute in their extent; and evidence relating directly to a decrease and oscillation in rainfall was often perplexed by evidence of migrations of tribal elements due to purely political reasons. Furthermore, we must remember that in certain areas like northern Arabia or the mountain blocks of the interior Sahara, the cutting of woodlands and the destruction of vegetational cover must have been in itself an important factor in promoting aridity and aggravating its aftereffect. There is always the danger, however, of running into a vicious circle by considering the gradual disappearance of the vegetational cover and of many of the wild animals in Arabia and the Sahara as an indication of the onset of drier conditions while at the same time attributing the aggravation of aridity to deforestation by cutting woodlands and scrubs for fuel and other purposes.

In dealing with this still unsettled question of relatively recent climatic changes, archeological evidence may be of particular value. Roman cisterns found on the Mediterranean coast of Egypt west of Alexandria and in several places on the edge of the Syrian Desert are not fully examined or even properly known. Their abundance and the large capacity of some of them may be taken as a sign of greater precipitation of rainfall at that time. In the desert east of the Jordan there is some evidence that the underground water level, which is ultimately affected by the supply of rainfall, has fallen by 2 meters since Roman times. Other and perhaps more conclusive evidence comes from such remote parts of Arabia as the highlands of Yemen. There we know that the earlier historic civilizations were established on the lower step of the table land, that of the Yemen Jauf, lying at about 1,000 meters elevation. Gradually, the ancient Minaeans and Sabaeans shifted their capitals to the higher slopes of Yemen until, finally, the capital was transferred to San'a at some 2,200 meters. Also, if we trace the an-

cient cisterns of the Sabaeans and Himyarites in Yemen, we find that invariably they were situated on the crests of hills rather than in collecting basins, where we find the present-day cisterns. At present, the ancient cisterns are never more than partly filled with water, while the low-lying new ones are usually filled to the rim. It is evident, however, that precipitation and runoff on the crests of hills must have at one time been enough to fill these Sabaean and Himyarite cisterns (*ca.* 1000 B.C.– A.D. 500) with water. In North Africa and the interior of the Sahara archeological evidence is still lacking, but the abundance of remains in many of the desolate areas may be taken as an indication of the somewhat more favorable climate lasting until Roman times. There is still, however, a very clear need for research on those ruins of the western Sahara as well as on traces of early and undated habitations on the Sudanese border of the western Sahara.

The story of climatic oscillations is still of some interest even in the study of present-day conditions. Certain studies have been carried out in the desert border of Nigeria, where it is thought that there is an encroachment of the desert upon the scrubland. Such an encroachment has also been studied in the case of oases, where cultivated areas have been either abandoned or covered by sand. In the region of Lake Mariut in Egypt, statistical data within the last sixty or eighty years has shown an oscillation of rainfall with what may perhaps give a slight indication of progressive aridity. Such studies, however, remain very inconclusive, and it is difficult to say whether this very recent aridity represents a steady factor or whether it is but an ebb in the oscillation of rainfall, to be followed by a new increase. The frequent annual changes shown by the records from Mariut make it difficult to draw any definite conclusions from them. As for inland oases, it has been found that the digging of new wells often leads to the seeping of water from the old wells to the new ones. Thus, with the increase of wells in the same oasis, old wells may even dry up, and the fields around them would be abandoned. This has been noted not only in Egypt but also in parts of southern Algeria. The question of present-day progressive aridity, therefore, cannot be easily settled. The likelihood is that the desert borders in the north and in the south are exposed to oscillating encroachment of truly desert conditions due to cyclic and temporary oscillations in rainfall. The nature of these cycles remains to be studied in the future.

CONCLUDING REMARKS

From this broad study of the changes in climate, vegetation, surface, and human adjustments in the Saharo-Arabian belt, with special reference to Africa, the following broad conclusions may be drawn.

1. The Saharo-Arabian belt of desert and semidesert represents an area of very special value for the students of past changes in climate, vegetation, and human activity and adjustment. Perhaps in no other area of the world have such changes been so violent, far-reaching, or effective. The amount of change in actual precipitation during the so-called "Pluvial Period" and down to the present day was not very great. But the fact that this region is a desert makes any perceptible change in precipitation most effective upon both vegetation and animal life.

2. The reflection of this change upon the story of man in this area was a very pronounced one. We must imagine that, even during the phases of maxima of rainfall, climatic conditions in this area must always have been unstable in character. In other words, micro-oscillations in pluviosity must have had their ef-

fects upon the milieu in which man lived and acted. The need was constant, therefore, for changes in human adjustment to the ever changing scene of human activity. Consequently, the Saharo-Arabian belt was never the scene for any stagnant industry or civilization during the whole of the Stone Age. If we remember that this latter covered by far the greatest portion of human history upon the earth, we would easily realize and appreciate the role of this Saharan belt in the evolution of human civilization. This was the scene of constant change and development.

3. The story of man in this belt was always closely connected with his story in the bordering margins. During the whole of Pleistocene times, the Saharan belt was like a big sponge, which during phases of rainfall attracted groups of migrating people both from Eurasia and from Sudanese and eastern Africa. During phases of aridity the big sponge squeezed its population out in both directions.

4. The question of space relationships between the desert belt and its bordering areas to the north, to the east, and to the south should also be a particularly interesting one to students of paleogeography. It is true that evidence is no longer tenable of the existence of land bridges across Gibraltar or the strait of Sicily since late Pliocene times; but water was no real obstacle in the face of expanding men, especially across Gibraltar. The Isthmus of Suez was fitted with natural conditions which made migrations easy between Asia and Africa. Bab el Mandeb was never really an effective obstacle. The borders of the Sahara to the south were open ones. Thus space relationships on all sides fostered interaction and contacts. Co-operation must, therefore, be complete between research workers studying the desert core and those working upon changes and adjustments in bordering areas.

REFERENCES

ADAMETZ, L.
1920 "Herkfunt und Wanderungen der Hamiten erschlossen aus ihren Haustierrassen," *Osten und Orient*, 1st ser., II, 7–10. Vienna.

ALIMEN, H.
1955 *Préhistoire de l'Afrique*. Paris: Éditions Boubée. 578 pp.

ANGSTROM, A.
1936 "Teleconnections of Climatic Changes in Present Time," *Geografiska Annaler*, XVII, 242–58.

ANTEVS, E.
1928 *The Last Glaciation: With Special Reference to the Ice Retreat in Northeast North America*. ("American Geographical Society Research Series," No. 17; Shaler Memorial Series.) New York: American Geographical Society. 292 pp.

ARKELL, A. J.
1948 *Early Khartoum*. London: Oxford University Press. 145 pp.

AUFRÈRE, L.
1932 "Morphologie dunaire et météorologie saharienne," *Extrait du Bulletin Association Géographes Français*, No. 56 (February), pp. 34–48.

BAGNOLD, R. A.; MYERS, O. H.; PEEL, R. F.; and WINKLER, H. A.
1939 "An Expedition to the Gilf Kebir and Uweinat," *Geographical Journal*, XCIII, 281–312.

BALL, J.
1939 *Contributions to the Geography of Egypt*. (Survey and Mines Department.) Cairo: Government Press. 308 pp.

BARTHOUX, J.
1925 "Paléogéographie de l'Égypte," *Comptes-rendus Congrès International de Géographie, Le Caire, 1925*, III, 68–100.

BEADNELL, H. J. L.
1905 *The Topography and Geology of the Fayum Province of Egypt*. (Survey Department.) Cairo: National Printing Department. 101 pp.

BERMANN, R. A.
1934 "Historic Problems of the Libyan Desert," *Geographical Journal*, LXXXIII, No. 6, 456–70.

BLANCKENHORN, M.
1921 "Aegypten," *Handbuch der regionalen Geologie*, VII, Abstract 9, 1–244. Heidelberg: Carl Winter.

BOURCART, J.
1937 "Géologie et archéologie quaternaires du Maroc: Extrait d'une conférence," *L'Anthropologie*, XLVII, Nos. 3–4, 437–39.

BREUIL, H.
1930 "L'Afrique préhistorique (extrait)," *Cahiers d'art*, Nos. 8–9, pp. 61–122, 440–500. Paris.

1934 "Peintures rupestres préhistoriques du Harar (Abyssinie)," *L'Anthropologie*, XLIV, Nos. 5–6, 473–83.

BROOKS, C. E. P.
1932 "Le Climat du Sahara et de l'Arabie," pp. 25–105 in *Le Sahara*, Vol. I. (Published under the Direction of MASAUJI HASCHISUKA.) Paris: Société des Editions Géographiques, Maritimes et Coloniales. 167 pp.

CATON-THOMPSON, G.
1946 "The Aterian Industry: Its Place and Significance in the Palaeolithic World," *Journal of the Royal Anthropological Institute of Great Britain and Ireland*, LXXVI, Part II (Huxley Memorial Lecture), 87–130.

1952 *Kharga Oasis in Prehistory*. With a Physiographic Introduction by E. W. GARDNER. London: University of London (The Athlone Press). 213 pp.

CATON-THOMPSON, G., and GARDNER, E. W.
1934 *The Desert Fayum*. 2 vols. London: Royal Anthropological Institute of Great Britain and Ireland.

CHUDEAU, R.
1931 "L'Hydrographie ancienne du Sahara," *Revue scientifique*, April 23, p. 194.

DALLONI, M.
1935 *Mission au Tibesti (1930–31)*, dirigée par M. Dalloni, Vol. II. (Mémoires de l'Académie des Sciences de l'Institut de France," Vol. LXII.) Paris. 449 pp.

DALLONI, M., and MONOD, TH.
1948 *Missions scientifiques au Fezzan*,

géologie et préhistoire. ("Institut de Recherches Sahariennes," Vol. VI.) Université d'Alger. 156 pp. and 49 pls.

DESIO, A.
1932 "Osservazioni geografiche e geologiche compiute dalla Spedizione della Reale Academia d'Italia nel Deserto Libico e nel Fezzan orientale (1931) (estratto)," *Memorìe geologiche e geografiche di Giotto Dainelli,* III, 111–49. Florence.

FLEURE, H. J.
1928 *The Races of Mankind: The Races of England and Wales.* 2d ed. London: Benn Bros.; Garden City, N.Y.: Doubleday, Doran & Co. 78 pp.
1937 "Racial Evolution and Archaeology," *Journal of the Royal Anthropological Institute of Great Britain and Ireland,* LXVII, 205–29.

GARDNER, E. W.
1932 "Some Problems of the Pleistocene Hydrography of the Kharga Oasis, Egypt," *Geological Magazine,* LXIX, No. 819 (September), 386–421.

GARROD, D. A. E., and BATE, D. A. M.
1937 *The Stone Age of Mount Carmel,* Vol. I: *Excavations at the Wady el-Mughara.* Oxford: Clarendon Press. 240 pp.

GAUTHIER, E. F.
1923 *Le Sahara.* Paris: Payot. 174 pp.

GRAZIOZI, P.
1941 *L'Arte rupestre della Libia.* 2 vols. Naples: Edizioni della Mostra d'Oltremare. 322 pp.

HELLESTROM, B.
1940 "The Subterranean Water in the Libyan Desert," *Geografiska Annaler,* XXII, Nos. 3–4, 206–39.

HUME, W. F.
1925 *Geology of Egypt,* Vol. I: *The Surface Features of Egypt, Their Determining Causes and Relation to Geological Structure.* Cairo: Government Press. 408 pp.

HUNTINGTON, E., and VISHER, S. S.
1922 *Climatic Changes, Their Nature and Causes.* New Haven, Conn.: Yale University Press. 329 pp.

HUZAYYIN, S. A.
1935 "Changement historique du cli-mat et du paysage de l'Arabie du Sud," *Bulletin of the Faculty of Arts, Cairo University,* III, Part II, 19–23.
1936 "Glacial and Pluvial Episodes of the Diluvium of the Old World: A Review and Tentative Correlation," *Man,* XXXVI, No. 20 (February), 19–22 (and correction in No. 115 [May], p. 88).
1941 *The Place of Egypt in Prehistory.* ("Mémoires de l'Institut d'Égypte," Vol. XLIII.) Cairo. 474 pp.
1942 *Arabia and the Far East.* Cairo: Geographical Society of Egypt. 319 pp.
1953 "Physiographic History of the River Nile" (in Arabic), *Risalat-al-Ilm,* IV, 184–202. Cairo.

LEAKEY, L. S. B.
1931 *The Stone Age Cultures of Kenya Colony.* Cambridge: Cambridge University Press. 287 pp.

McBURNEY, C. B. M.
1947 "The Stone Age of the Libyan Littoral," *Proceedings of the Prehistoric Society of East Anglia* (N.S.), XIII, 56–84.

MAIRE, R.
1928 "La Végétation et la flore du Hoggar," *Comptes-rendus de l'Académie des Sciences,* CLXXXVI, 1680–82. Paris.

NILSSON, E.
1931 "Quaternary Glaciations and Pluvial Lakes in British East Africa," *Geografiska Annaler,* XIII, No. 4, 249–349.
1935 *Traces of Ancient Changes of Climate in East Africa.* ("Meddelanden fran Stockholms Högskolas Geologiska Institut," No. 36; Särtryck ur *Geografiska Annaler,* Nos. 1–2.) 21 pp.
1938 "Pluvial Lakes in East Africa," *Geologiska Foreningens i Stockholm Forhandlingar,* LX, No. 3, 423–33.
1953 "Contributions to the History of the Blue Nile," *Bulletin de la Société de Géographie d'Égypte,* XXV, 29–47.

PEAKE, H.
1928 *The Origins of Agriculture.* London: E. Benn, Ltd. 78 pp.

PEDRALS, D. P. DE
1950 *Archeologie de l'Afrique noire.* Paris: Payot. 233 pp.

PICARD, L.
1937 "Inferences on the Problem of the Pleistocene Climate of Palestine and Syria Drawn from Flora, Fauna and Stratigraphy," *Proceedings of the Prehistoric Society of East Anglia* (N.S.), III, Part I, No. 5, 58–70.

ROMER, A. S.
1928 "Pleistocene Mammals of Algeria: Fauna of the Paleolithic Station of Mechta-el-Arbi," in "A Contribution to the Study of Prehistoric Man in Algeria, North Africa," *Beloit College Bulletin,* XXIX, No. 5, 79–163.

RUHLMANN, A.
1938 *Les Recherches préhistoriques dans l'Extrème-Sud-Marocain.* ("Publications du Service des Antiquités du Marocain," No. 5.) Rabat. 107 pp.

SANDFORD, K. S.
1934 *Prehistoric Survey of Egypt and Western Asia,* Vol. III: *Paleolithic Man and the Nile Valley in Upper and Middle Egypt.* ("Oriental Institute Publications," Vol. XVIII.) Chicago: University of Chicago Press. 152 pp.

SANDFORD, K. S., and ARKELL, W. J.
1939 *Prehistoric Survey of Egypt and Western Asia,* Vol. IV: *Paleolithic Man and the Nile Valley in Lower Egypt with Some Notes upon a Part of the Red Sea Littoral.* ("Oriental Institute Publications," Vol. XLVI.) Chicago: University of Chicago Press. 124 pp.

TOTHILL, J. D. (ed.)
1948 *Agriculture in the Sudan.* London: Oxford University Press. 974 pp.

URVOY, Y.
1933 "Les Formes dunaires à l'ouest du Tchad," *Annales de géographie,* XLII, No. 239 (September 15), 506–15.

VAUFREY, R.
1929 "La Question des isthmes mediterranéens Pleistocenes" (extrait), *Revue de géographie physique et de géologie dynamique,* II, No. 4, 325–42. Paris.
1939 *L'Art rupestre nord-africain.* ("Archives de l'Institut de Paléontologie Humaine," Mémoire 20.) Paris. 127 pp.

WALTHER, J.
1924 *Das Gesetz der Wünstenbildung in Gegenwart und Vorzeit.* Leipzig: Verlag von Quelle & Meyer. 421 pp.

WAYLAND, E. J.
1934 "Rifts, Rivers, Rains and Early Man in Uganda," *Journal of the Royal Anthropological Institute of Great Britain and Ireland,* LXIV, 333–52.

WINKLER, H.
1938–39 *Rock Drawings of Southern Upper Egypt, Sir Robert Mond Desert Expedition.* 2 vols. London: Humphrey Milford.

WOLDSTEDT, P.
1929 *Das Eiszeitalter: Grundlinien einer Geologie des Diluviums.* Stuttgart: Ferdinand Enke. 406 pp.

WRIGHT, W. B.
1937 *The Quaternary Ice Age.* 2d ed. London: Macmillan & Co. 478 pp.

ZEUNER, F.
1945 *The Pleistocene Period.* London: B. Quaritch, Ltd. 322 pp.

Introduction to the Subsistence Economy of India

E. K. JANAKI AMMAL*

THE INDIAN SUBCONTINENT

To examine the subsistence economy of India, it is first necessary to know the background history of the peoples who constitute the population of India and the relationship of these peoples with one another and with their environment. To do this, let us recall the physical aspect of India.

The subcontinent of India is composed of three well-defined regions: Peninsular India, the Himalayas, and the Indo-Gangetic Plain.

Peninsular India is geologically a very old land, being, perhaps, a pla-

teau fragment of the ancient continent of Gondwana, the breaking-up of which may have given rise to Australia, South America, and Africa. This disintegration having occurred after flowering plants had evolved on the earth, the flora of India has many genera in common with Africa, South America, and, to a lesser extent, Australia. Among common plants of economic value may be mentioned rice, cotton, sorghum, amaranthus, yams, and many species of the smaller millets. In this breaking-up of a mighty continent, fissures were formed through which series of lava flows reached thicknesses of up to 10,-000 feet and covered an area of over 200,000 square miles. The region in which this occurred, known as the Deccan trap, covers Kathiawar, Cutch, Madhya Bharat, Gujarat, and Hyderabad. It is characterized by its fertile, black, cotton soil, rich in calcium, magnesium carbonates, potash, and phosphates.

The Himalayas arose from the bed of the great Mesozoic sea Tethys, which once separated Gondwana from Eurasia and through which the warm currents of the Indian Ocean had found their way to western Europe. Along the shores of Tethys the palm *Nipa* grew at a period when species of *Magnolia, Artocarpus,* and *Cinnamomum* were flourishing in Greenland and Spitzbergen.

The Himalayan thrust, from north to south, resulted in the formation of a

* Dr. Janaki Ammal is Director of the Central Botanical Laboratory of the Government of India, at present located in Lucknow. After graduating in Honors at the University of Madras, she continued her postgraduate studies at the University of Michigan and received the Doctor of Science degree in 1931. On returning to India, she was appointed a professor of botany at the University of Madras. Her career has been devoted to genetical studies. She was the sugar-cane geneticist of the Central Agricultural Department of India and contributed to the understanding of the breeding behavior of sugar cane. Later she extended her work on the origin and evolution of cultivated plants. The *Chromosome Atlas of Cultivated Plants,* which she co-authored with Dr. C. D. Darlington, has become one of the great sources for cytological work on the economic plants of the world. She is a Fellow of the Linnaean Society of London, the Royal Geographical Society, the Asiatic Society of Bengal and London, and the Indian Academy of Sciences. An honorary *Legum Doctoris* was bestowed on her in 1955 by the University of Michigan.

trough 15,000 feet deep, in which the alluvium of the great rivers has been accumulating. From this has developed the third major landform region of India, the Indo-Gangetic Plain, comprising 300,000 square miles of fertile land into which have poured from the north and northwest, in spite of the barrier of the lofty Himalayas, wave upon wave of human migrations. It is difficult to say what the original flora of the Gangetic Plain was like. Quite probably it never supported a dense forest flora but grew from swamp and grasslands which could support both pastoral and agricultural economies. The flora of the Gangetic Plain today is mainly composed of plants that have been introduced from surrounding areas. The plain has been the seat of human activity for such a long time that it is impossible today to see any vestige of virgin vegetation.

From this brief description we can see that India became part of Asia as a result of the Himalayan uplift. Like Arabia, it was an annexation to Asia. It is possible that the evolution of man will be found to be very closely linked with this annexation. The close affinity between the flora and fauna of Sind and that of Africa and Arabia, the continuation of the Sahara into India as the Great Rajputana Desert, and the movement of this desert from west to east are factors that have to be taken into consideration when studying the movement of primitive man into India and within India.

The Ice Age of Europe and northern Asia has been studied very exhaustively in its relation to the evolution of man. In India the changes between interglacial and glacial periods have not been well examined. It is known that, while the ice was confined to the glaciers of the high mountains, Peninsular India was undergoing several pluvial periods corresponding to the advance and receding of ice in the north. The presence of temperate Himalayan plants on isolated hill ranges of southern India is indicative of their migration during periods when the climate of southern India was cooler and wetter than it is today. A most remarkable feature was noted by Blanford (1879) —"the occurrence on the Nilgiris and Anamalai ranges of a wild goat, *Capra Hypocrius,* belonging to a subgenus of which the only known species, *Capra Jeemlaica,* inhabits temperate regions of the Himalayas from Kashmir to Bhutan." *Viburnum* and *Rhododendrons* species of the Nilgiris examined by me are identical with those of the Himalayas (Janaki Ammal, 1952).

MAN IN INDIA

Man, being a naked animal, must have arisen in a tropical or subtropical country. It is impossible to say when men first appeared on the subcontinent of India.

Northwestern India was a great breeding place of anthropoid apes during the Tertiary period, judging from the great numbers of fossils reported from the Siwalik formation. According to Wadia (1953), at least fifteen genera have been found.

Australoids are found today in the Andamans, Madagascar, Indochina, Formosa, Philippines, and Ceylon. They are also found scattered over Peninsular India, where, as food-gatherers, they derive their subsistence by hunting and by the digging of roots. According to Majumdar (1947), Paleolithic people occupied Peninsular India first and then drifted north to the Schan Valley of the Punjab.

The proto-Dravidians must have evolved in India as segregates from the Australoid type. This southern element is to be found not only in India but also as far west as Baluchistan and southern Arabia (Coon, 1939).

The megalithic culture of India is very similar to that of the Mediterranean. The Indus civilization of the third millennium, typified in Mohenjo-Daro culture, is probably pure Dravidian. After the Indus culture came the Aryan invasion, believed to have originated from southern Russia, perhaps from a temporary invasion center near Lake Aral, beginning between 1500 and 1400 B.C. The Bronze Age Aryans brought with them their dairy and cattle culture, which gradually fused with the mainly agricultural culture of pre-Aryan India.

The ancient Aryans, who were practically patriarchal, met the strongly matriarchal Dravidian peoples of India somewhere in the Punjab, and intermingling of the two peoples resulted in the present hybrid Aryo-Dravidian population of the Indo-Gangetic Valley. This process of fusion is still in progress farther south, where the vedic Nambudiri Brahman, supposedly of Aryan stock, takes a Dravidian wife from the matriarchal people of Malabar. The children born from such a union belong to the matriarchal family of the mother. A pure line of Nambudiris is maintained by the eldest son's marrying a Nambudiri woman.

The highly developed Dravidian culture, together with its gods, Shiva and Vishnu, and the cult of the mother-goddess, was assimilated into the simple nature and clan cults of the Aryans to result in what is known as Hindu culture. This is a synthesis of all types of thought which have originated or have been introduced since man existed in India.

The main social feature of Hinduism is its acceptance of caste, or color (*varna*). Caste was at first a genetic classification by the Aryans of the hybrid progeny of Aryans and Dravidians. The Aryans before their invasion had only three castes which were functional—the Priests, the Fighters, and the Artisans. The Sudras, or Dasyus, who formed the fourth class in Aryan nomenclature,

were generally the Dravidian people.

In India today, caste is neither functional nor genetic. It essentially defines a mating and eating group, chiefly the latter. Having been a fluid institution, it became rigid during the British occupation. The tendency during the last century has been toward multiplication of caste divisions, so much so that anyone who disbelieved in caste created a new caste. Except the peoples of northwestern India and the vedic Nambudiris of Malabar, who have rigidly kept to their mating systems, there are no pure Indo-Aryans in India today: the bulk of the population of northern India is Aryo-Dravidian; Mongoloid types are found in Bengal, Assam, and Bihar; and Dravidians, proto-Dravidians, and Asio-Australoids form the bulk of the population of Peninsular India. The latter is the best region for analysis of the subsistence economy of the many primitive tribes of India, for Paleolithic and Neolithic cultures still are to be found there.

GENESIS OF TRIBAL ECONOMIES

Of India's total population of 360,-000,000, tribal people number about 25,000,000 (see Fig. 90). Many of them inhabit the fringe of civilized areas and are now being gradually assimilated into the populations of Hindu culture.

Tribal peoples must have formed a considerable part of the population of India during ancient and medieval times, yet the jungle tribes now found scattered over southern India can never have been very numerous, and it was only the first efforts of food production that paved the way to a settled life and resulted in gradual increase of population.

Qualities of Primitives

Primitive man must have devoted more time and expended more energy in securing a food supply than does civilized man. To understand the economics of primitive people, we must understand that, in their minds, all aspects of life are harmonized into a whole. This is due to the long mutual adaptation of mental and institutional life. Primitive economy is nearly static and remains so unless it comes into contact with a different culture, whereupon there first is conflict, then disintegration or assimilation. For the aborigine, every natural process is a manifestation of magical power. He tries to insure success through the exercise of certain ritual acts by which this magical power is evoked. Magic is thus a way of organizing intensive economic results; it is a way of concentration. For example, in Malabar, the man who sows seed has to remain celibate during the period of sowing. Most religious fasts among Hindus have a similar agricultural motivation.

Just as the origin of new forms in plants and animals is brought about by hybridization, resulting in new combinations of parental characters (as

FIG. 90.—India: tribal distribution

well as by isolation in which mutational changes may occur), so also different peoples and cultures arise out of the old by contact and fusion. For example, cattle-keeping evolved from hunting. In North America, whole communities used to follow a particular herd of buffalo upon which they owed their dependence and with which they felt themselves mystically united (Thurnwald, 1932). Once a measure of control over the herd is secured, the herd gradually becomes domesticated. The union between man and cattle then becomes even more intimate, as is seen among the Todas of the Nilgiri Hills, whose culture is bound up with their buffalo herds. The size of a Toda community formerly was determined by the herd that could support it, and female infanticide commonly was practiced, since, among the Todas, women were not of much use in herding.

The inordinate reverence paid to cows in India, especially on the Gangetic Plain, is undoubtedly a relic of this mystic relationship of an earlier pastoral people with their herds of cattle. So strong is this primitive tie between man and cow in India that in the *Code of Manu* killing a cow was considered more heinous than killing a Brahman. Today, cow protection is a political issue in India. It is highly probable that the antagonism of the Hindus to beef-eaters is based chiefly on this ancient mystic link with the cow. Where this complex did not penetrate, people are today more tolerant of people who eat beef. This is so in northern Malabar, where the descendants of Arabs and of Hindus live side by side in matriarchal amity.

Agriculture and Sex

Some institutions in early primitive life were associated with members of only one sex. Food-gathering, for example, was chiefly the duty of women. When food-growing later developed, this was also done by women. Where women regularly provided food, descent is mainly matrilineal, as among the Khasis of Assam, while in pastoral communities, where the herds are tended and kept by men and woman's part is secondary, descent is patrilineal, as with the Todas. In understanding economic patterns this has to be taken into account.

TYPES OF PRIMITIVE AGRICULTURE

Different stages in the development of agriculture have to be studied before the tribes who practice them can be classified in terms of their economies. The earliest type of subsistence economy was that of the food-gatherers, who used the digging stick. This tool first was made of wood, as among the Paniyars of Wyanaad, then tipped with iron, as with the Kadars of the Anamalai Hills. The hoe, probably at first a stone attached to a stick, followed the digging stick. The next stage was the simple plow, at first drawn by women. The use of oxen for plowing indicates a synthesis of a cattle-keeping tribe with one having an agricultural economy. The ox-drawn plow was a great landmark in the history of agriculture and human culture, for it made possible the production of a greater quantity of food than was necessary for mere subsistence.

In India, tribal peoples still practice all these stages in the development of agriculture. The digging stick of the Kadars has been mentioned. The matriarchal Khasis of Assam are still in the stage of hoe cultivation and do not use the plow. In Malabar the people of the plains generally use the plow, while those of the hills are still hoe cultivators. The Gonds of central India seem to have differentiated into two types (Singh, 1944). The more primitive hill Gonds, who are trappers and hunters, practice shifting cultivation by setting fire to the forest and scattering seeds in the ashes, while the Gonds of the plains are agriculturists who have mixed with Hindus and learned to use the ox-drawn plow. It is said that, when rain fails, the latter "harness nude girls to the plough that they draw bleeding under the spur of the goad" (Mukerjee, 1944). Such a reversion during times of stress to an ancient practice identifies the fertility of the soil with the fertility of women. Today, for example, the Khasis transfer women's fertility to the fields by a slow-moving dance (*Norgkrem*) by young girls who perform annually in the open fields. The sanctity of the cow among plow agriculturists derives from its replacing women as drawers of the plow; in India the cow is still designated as "Mother." By extension, cattle are considered holy in India among both pastoral and agricultural peoples.

Increase of population can make one tribe impinge on another's reserve and can thus lead to conflict and disaster. The upland migration of the fast-multiplying and aggressive Syrian Christians of Travancore and Cochin into Wyanaad has had a profound effect on the tribal people there. The Paniyars find their jungles under the plow of new settlers, and a tribe that once was independent in its habitat has now become "depressed," and its whole economy has been changed. The Kadars of Cochin, who once roamed the forests in search of honey, yams, and roots, are now under the care of the Forest Department and are paid in rice for collecting minor forest products. Their women, who were once food-hunters, have ceased to dig for roots, have taken to a life of idleness, and are fast becoming degenerate. Thus the "noble savage" in contact with civilization generally finds himself in an awkward state.

The changing subsistence economies of tribes have been well described by one of India's leading anthropologists, Dr D. N. Majumdar (1950), with reference to the Hos:

Primitive social groups are aptly called food groups, for the size of the groups depends to a large extent on the mode of food supply. Each stage of culture has its peculiar solution of the problem of numbers in relation to food supply, the mode of subsistence determining the social organisation of the group. Any increase in numbers must keep pace with the improvements in the technique of food production, as otherwise, there is every chance of destroying the social stability which is the pivot of economic progress. There has been a tremendous change in the economic environment of primitive tribes in India. Hunting tribes have given up hunting. The semi-nomadic tribes who lived on fruits and roots and occasional jhuming of their forest clad environment, have become permanent cultivators. Some have no land and are eking out their miserable existence as labourers in the village, and in the neighbouring industrial centres. Consequently many of the customs and practises that were necessary at an earlier stage have become useless, and therefore meaningless to their cultural life. With the restriction of the large areas of forest, over which the Hos were used to roam, and the resulting diminution in the supply of food, a change in diet among the Hos was called for. But they have yet failed to respond to the needs of the hour, as we shall find below.

The gradual increase in number among the Hos without any corresponding increase in the food resources, or improvement in the technique of food production, has lowered the standard of comfort, and many of their present troubles are traceable to this deficiency. Their vitality and the splendid co-operative organisation for exploiting the natural resources of their physical environment (to which competent authorities have given unstinted testimony) have suffered much.

There are many factors that restrict the life of primitive peoples. Since wild products collected by women do not provide suitable food for children, the time of nursing is prolonged, and the interval between births is thus greater in India among primitive people than among urban dwellers. One of the chief causes for the great rise in India's population is the urbanization of its rural population. The effects of a nomadic life, the hunting of dangerous animals, and fishing in the ocean also are great checks on the growth of tribal population.

AGRICULTURE IN RELATION
TO CLIMATE

India is part of the monsoon region of the world, and its vegetation is very much influenced by the amount and seasonal distribution of rainfall received. These factors again are reflected in the type of agricultural economies of the peoples occupying the region. The vegetative climax of India is the dense and tall tropical evergreen forest, found on the Western Ghats and in Assam, where the total annual rainfall averages well over 100 inches. Semi-evergreen forests, adjacent to the evergreen forests, are of lesser density, and there man has had a better chance of subduing the vegetation. Food-gatherers are found living in little groups in open places. Here, also, primitive agriculture in the tropics must have evolved. *Jhuming*, or shifting cultivation, by burning and by scattering seeds in the ash, is the only type of agriculture practiced in the region.

The most highly evolved type of *jhuming* is seen in Assam, where a regular rotation of forest clearing takes place once every eight years, so that sufficient time elapses for regeneration of the forest. It is apparent that this continual cutting has its effect, for the flora that come up after clearance are not always the same as those previously destroyed.

The practice of declaring part of the forests sacred has done a great deal to keep the vegetation unchanged. The sacred forests belong to local chiefs or tribal village communities and represent what may be called nature's primeval forests. People do not dare to cut the trees for fear of disturbing spirits. Hence these forests comprise rich stores of botanical specimens which have become extinct in other parts of Assam. Sacred forests are also a feature of Malabar, where they are known as *kavus*. They serve as sanctuaries for snakes and wild life and often become the nuclei of sylvan temples.

Shifting cultivation is generally practiced in hilly tracts where the rainfall is fairly high. As man becomes more sedentary, he reaches an equilibrium with his environment. This is best seen in Malabar, where mixed plantings (*paramba*) follow *jhuming*. Clearing is only partial, and useful trees are preserved either for timber or firewood or for the growing of pepper and other vines. Among trees kept uncut are species of *Artocarpus* and the wild mango, nutmeg, *Strychnos*, and *Cycas*. Ginger, turmeric, yams, bananas, and tapioca are grown between trees which are pruned annually. Around the houses garden vegetables are also grown. Lowlands are set aside for rice cultivation. This *paramba* form of cultivation is characteristic of the west coast of India. It does not upset the ecological balance of the natural vegetation, and a variety of useful plants is grown simultaneously the year round. Each *paramba* is a self-contained economic unit.

In the Gangetic Valley the type of agriculture varies with the annual rains. This area is the great grain belt of India, where rice, wheat, and barley are grown (Figs. 91–93). Wheat and barley are confined to the northern part, while rice is intensively grown chiefly in Bengal, Assam, Bihar, and on the deltas of Peninsular India. There are two well-marked cropping seasons known as *kharif*, or summer-rain season, and *rabi*, or winter-rain season. *Kharif* crops, sown at the commencement of the southwest, or summer, monsoon and harvested in autumn, are rice, maize, millets, cotton, hemp, sugar cane, tobacco, groundnuts, jute, castor seed, and sesamum. The principal *rabi* crops are wheat, barley, grams, peas, beans, potatoes, linseed, and mustard; they are sown in autumn and harvested in spring. Together these form the cash crops of India. As more and more land is being given to these crops, the subsistence economy of the inhabitants changes.

Low productivity has been the most serious deficiency in India's agricultural practices. One of the chief causes of low production is the uncertainty of rainfall. A weak monsoon results in famine; a too heavy one, in flood. The control of river waters for irrigation and the storage of excess water in tanks have been features of agriculture in India from ancient times. Though the acreage under crops is great, the yield per acre is very low. With an expanding population, more and more land yielding less and less comes under the

FIG. 91.—Important crops of India: wheat, maize, pearl millet, rice

plow. Independent India is making great strides to increase productivity of land already under cultivation; the first five-year plan made India self-sufficient in food supply.

PLANTS AND MAN IN INDIA

The region including India, Pakistan, and the surrounding countries of Afghanistan and Iran has been the center of origin of many cultivated plants (Vavilov, 1935). Among these, the following are classed as typically of Indian origin: *Oryza sativa*, rice; *Cajanus cajan*, dhall; *Phaseolus aconitifolius*, moth bean; *Phaseolus calcaratus*, rice bean; *Dolichos biflorus*, horse gram; *Vigna sinensis*, asparagus bean; *Amaranthus paniculatus*, amaranth; *Solanum melongena*, eggplant; *Raphanus caudatus*, rat-tailed radish; *Colocasia antiquorum*, taro yam; *Cucumis sativus*, cucumber; *Mangifera indica*, mango; *Gossypium arboreum*, tree cotton; *Corchorus olitorius*, jute; *Cannabis indica*, hemp; *Piper nigrum*, pepper; *Acacia arabica*, gum

FIG. 92.—Important crops of India: barley, sugar cane, sorghum, tobacco

arabic; *Indigofera tinctoria*, indigo (Darlington and Janaki Ammal, 1945). Many economic plants, like banana and rice, were domesticated simultaneously at various places in Southeast Asia, where many species are recorded. The wild banana with its stony fruit must have attracted, as it still attracts, primitive tribes. Evolution of the wild banana into cultivated forms has been been through the chance development of sterile forms produced either by hybridity or by triploidy. The occurrence of sterile and consequently stoneless forms is immediately noted by wild tribes which collect and grow them near their huts. In Assam it is possible to see the gradation from seed to seedless varieties in the local wild form.

Cultivation of the world's food crops has centered around the great cereals— wheat, rice, and maize. Combining with one or more of these are plants of great local or regional importance. For example, the coconut is the predominant tree along the west coast of India,

FIG. 93.—Important crops of India: jute, cotton, coffee–tea, oilseeds

and all parts of the tree are used by man as food or for domestic uses and rituals.

Primitive tribes make considerable use of the *Caryota* palm, found scattered in the forests; they use the leaves for thatching and the starch in the pith as food. The digging sticks of the Paniyars in Wyanaad are made of the outer hard rind of *Caryota urens.* Two other palms, *Borassus* and the wild date *Phoenix sylvestris,* also play an important part in the subsistence economy of tribal peoples. Sugar is made from the sap of both palms, while the leaves are used for thatching and for basketmaking. A plant of great significance to the tribals of Peninsular India is the mahua tree, *Madhuca latifoba,* the flowers of which are collected by Gonds, Hos, and other Munda tribes and eaten dried or fermented into a liquor. The seeds contain oil which is used for lamps. The fruit of *Cycas circinalis,* which is rich in starch, is eaten by both the tribal and the peasant population of Malabar. Its leaves are used for thatching and as an evergreen decoration during festive occasions.

REFERENCES

ANDERSON, J. D.
1913   *The Peoples of India.* Cambridge: Cambridge University Press. 118 pp.

BLANFORD, W. T.
1879   *Geology of India.* 4 vols. Calcutta: Geological Survey Office.

BOAS, FRANZ
1938   *The Mind of Primitive Man.* New York: Macmillan Co. 285 pp.

BODENHEIMER, F. S.
1951   *Insects as Human Food.* The Hague: W. Junk. 352 pp.

BRODERICK, ALAN HOUGHTON
1947   *Early Man: A Survey of Human Origins.* ("Hutchinson's Scientific and Technical Publications.") London: Hutchinson. 288 pp.

CHILDE, V. GORDON
1952   *New Light on the Most Ancient East.* London: Routledge & Kegan Paul. 255 pp.

COON, C. S.
1939   *The Races of Europe.* New York: Macmillan Co. 399 pp.

DARLINGTON, C. D., and JANAKI AMMAL, E. K.
1945   *Chromosome Atlas of Cultivated Plants.* London: George Allen & Unwin. 397 pp.

DUBE, S. C.
1951   *The Kamar.* Lucknow: Universal Publishers. 216 pp.

FIRTH, RAYMOND
1938   *Human Types.* London: Thomas Nelson & Sons. 211 pp.

GOLDENWEISER, ALEXANDER
1937   *Anthropology: An Introduction to Primitive Culture.* New York: Appleton-Century-Crofts. 550 pp.

GOPALASWAMI, R. A.
1953   *Census of India, 1951,* Vol. I. Delhi: Government of India Press. 234 pp.

HADDON, A. C.
1927   *The Wanderings of Peoples.* Cambridge: Cambridge University Press. 124 pp.

HERSKOVITS, MELVILLE J.
1952   *Economic Anthropology.* New York: Alfred A. Knopf. 547 pp.

HUTTON, J. H.
1951   *Caste in India: Its Nature, Function and Origins.* London: Oxford University Press. 315 pp.

JANAKI AMMAL, E. K.
1952   "The Race History of Magnolias," *Indian Journal of Genetics and Plant Breeding,* XII, 82–92. New Delhi.

KANJILAL and DAS
1954   *Flora of Assam,* Vol. I. Shillong: Government of Assam. 182 pp.

KEITH, ARTHUR
1948   *A New Theory of Human Evolution.* London: Watts & Co. 451 pp.

LOWIE, ROBERT H.
1949   *Primitive Society.* London: Routledge & Kegan Paul. 453 pp.

MAJUMDAR, D. N.
1947   *The Matrix of Indian Culture.*

Lucknow: Universal Publishers. 242 pp.

1950   *The Affairs of a Tribe.* Lucknow: Universal Publishers. 362 pp.

MASANI, MINOC

1945   *Picture of a Plan.* London: Oxford University Press. 63 pp.

MINISTRY OF INFORMATION AND BROADCASTING

1952   *First Five Year Plan.* Delhi: Publication Division, Ministry of Information and Broadcasting, Government of India. 263 pp.

MUKERJEE, RADHAKAMAL

1944   Foreword (pp. i–iv) in SINGH, INDRAJIT, *The Gondwana and the Gonds.* Lucknow: Universal Publishers. 200 pp.

SINGH, INDRAJIT

1944   *The Gondwana and the Gonds.* Lucknow: Universal Publishers. 200 pp.

THURNWALD, RICHARD

1932   *Economics in Primitive Communities.* London: Oxford University Press. 314 pp.

VAN LOON, HENDRIK WILLEM

1933   *The Home of Mankind.* London: George G. Harrap & Co. 506 pp.

VAVILOV, N. I. (ed.)

1935   *Theoretical Bases of Plant Breeding.* (The Lenin Academy of Agricultural Sciences, Institute of Plant Industry.) Moscow and Leningrad: State Agricultural Publishing House. (In Russian.) (See also English translation of selected writings of N. I. VAVILOV by CHESTER, K. STARR: *The Origin, Variation, Immunity and Breeding of Cultivated Plants.* [*Chronica botanica*, Vol. XIII, Nos. 1–6.] Waltham, Mass.: Chronica Botanica Co. 364 pp. Volume XIII bears the date 1949–50, but it was issued in spring, 1951.)

WADIA, D. N.

1953   *Geology of India.* 3d ed. London: Macmillan & Co. 531 pp.

The Quality of Land Use of Tropical Cultivators

PIERRE GOUROU[*]

* Dr. Gourou is Professor of Tropical Geography in the Collège de France, Paris, and Director of the Institute of Geography of the University of Brussels, Belgium. He has conducted extensive field work in Indochina, central Africa, Madagascar, and Brazil. His principal publications include: *Les Paysans du Delta tonkinois*, 1936; *L'Utilisation du sol en Indochine française*, 1940; *Les Pays tropicaux*, 1947; and *L'Asie*, 1953.

INTRODUCTION

What are the limits of our domain, the warm and rainy tropics? The average of the coldest month does not descend below 18° C.; the yearly total of rainfall is greater than 750 millimeters; agriculture is possible without irrigation. These limits are quite controversial, and we are not disposed to insist that they are the best. They seem reasonably good and differ little from other limits that could be proposed.

The continental area within the above limits is about 38,000,000 square kilometers—a notable portion of the emerged continents and an even more notable portion of the valuable area of these continents if we think of how much is cold desert and dry. The tropical rainy world covers a little more than one-third of the non-desert areas of the emerged earth. At first sight, it seems that the rainy tropical world is poorly utilized and that the intensity of tropical land use is below the world average. It seems that the rainy tropical world offers great possibilities of agricultural expansion and that minds disturbed by the quick increase of the world's population may therefore rest easy (Gourou, 1947b).

There are many approaches to the quality of land use of tropical cultivators: the extent of cultivated areas in the tropical world, physical conditions of tropical agriculture, outputs of the tropical fields, productivity of the individual tropical cultivator, density of the agricultural population in the total area, density of the agricultural population in the effectively cultivated area, various agricultural techniques, and length of fallowing. One approach, however, must be forbidden: to explain tropical agriculture (or tropical agricultures) by a simple determinism, in defiance of the results of observation.

The agricultural potentiality of an area whose climate is not hostile to agriculture stems only in part from the physical conditions of this area; it depends, too, and most importantly, on the techniques used, the number of inhabitants, the level of consumption, the duration of the soil's occupancy, and the nearness and the accessibility of markets. Unavoidably, there are many different kinds of tropical agriculture.

Is it useful to present general views on agriculture in the tropical world as a whole? Tropical Asia counts 8,000,000 square kilometers and 650,000,000 people. The remainder of the tropical world, however, has only 190,000,000 inhabitants for 30,000,000 square kilometers. It is clear that populations of such different densities cannot receive the same treatment. Within tropical Africa there is a remarkable unevenness of density. Large areas of the Sudan, the Congo Basin, and the Congo-Zambezi plateaus have from 2 to 3 inhabitants per square kilometer. On the other hand, dense concentrations of population appear in Hausaland, in Mossiland, in Iboland, in Ruanda-Urundi (and most generally in the area between the lakes Tanganyika, Albert, and Victoria), and on the southern slopes of Mount Kilimanjaro. It is impossible to explain this unevenness by hasty reference to the "soil's fertility" or to the "altitude's healthfulness"; for example, the Ibo of Nigeria live in a lowland not especially fertile. The same observations apply to the Mossi and the Hausa. A deeper explanation gives first importance to production techniques (especially to the agricultural techniques) and to the systems of organization of space (social and political organization) making possible control of long duration over large and expanding areas. The human geography of the tropical world is not simple even in Africa!

SMALLNESS OF THE CULTIVATED AREAS AND HEAVINESS OF THE AGRICULTURAL DENSITIES

One fact is striking: the areas actually under cultivation are small in the tropical world. By "areas actually under cultivation," we mean those which bear cultivated plants in the course of the year; fallows are excluded. Official statistics may be employed, though they are difficult to use. Brazil has 188,000 square kilometers actually cultivated out of a total area of 8,500,000 square kilometers; that is, 2 per cent of the total area. The agricultural density of Brazil (total number of inhabitants, urban and rural, reported for the cultivated area) is 250 inhabitants on a cultivated square kilometer. The Belgian Congo has an actually cultivated area

of 25,000 square kilometers (1 per cent of its total area); the agricultural density is about 400 persons on a cultivated square kilometer (Gourou, 1951). India has an actually cultivated area of 930,000 square kilometers (30 per cent of its total area); the agricultural density is 360 (Gourou, 1953a, pp. 392–403).

These few examples, which we could easily multiply, teach some important facts. Large differences exist in the percentages of cultivation of the total areas, yet in a country as highly populated as India the actually cultivated area rises only to the modest limit of 30 per cent of the total area—a very low percentage for a country evidently affected by a hunger for cultivated fields. Three things require explanation: the unevenness of the percentages of cultivation, the general smallness of the cultivation percentages, and the heaviness of the agricultural densities. Since, in the three countries examined, rural population is predominant, heaviness of agricultural density is a heaviness of peasant density on the area actually cultivated.

The general smallness of the percentages of cultivation is explained partly by physical conditions. For example, we may assume that in India 30 per cent of the total area is a maximum for the total cultivable area; in a country of ancient history, high civilization, and high density of population (general, agricultural, peasant densities), it is probable that all the cultivable land is actually under plow. Present efforts of Indian authorities are oriented not toward a large extension of the cultivated area but toward an intensification of agricultural processes (first by the transformation of dry fields into irrigated fields). But why this low cultivation of 30 per cent? The answer lies not with a respect on the part of Indian peasants for forests or in the necessity of great pastures for large herds (in fact, Indian oxen and buffaloes are pastured only on the strictly unarable areas). The answer is a physical one: Indian agriculture has reached the maximum of cultivated area. Seventy per cent of India is uncultivable because of the dryness of climate, the steepness of slopes, and the outcropping of rocks or laterite.

But what a difference among the actually cultivated areas in India (30 per cent), Brazil (2 per cent), and the Belgian Congo (1 per cent)! True, natural conditions partially explain this difference. Recent alluvial plains cover a far larger part of the total area in India than in Brazil or in the Belgian Congo. But the natural advantages of India are not large enough to account for the whole difference. We must consider the general densities of population: 6 inhabitants on a square kilometer of total area in Brazil, 5 in the Belgian Congo, and 130 in India. Inequalities in general densities of population mean differences in agricultural techniques, in the organization of space, and in history. India for a long time has been a country of high civilization; the agricultural techniques, especially that of inundating rice fields, and the social and political organization allowed an increase in population (and the capitalization of the increases) and an extension of the permanently cultivated area (and the consolidation of the expansion in cultivated areas).

Heaviness of agricultural densities (250 per square kilometer in Brazil, 400 in the Belgian Congo, and 360 in India) and heaviness of peasant density mean a low individual productivity and low levels of consumption for the peasant population. These facts result from human factors and express the economic value of the agricultural techniques. Hence we understand why the differences among the general densities in Brazil, the Belgian Congo, and India are bound not to substantial differences in the agricultural (and peasant) densi-ties but to differences in the percentages of the actually cultivated areas.

THE "LADANG"

In Africa, America, and New Guinea, shifting cultivation (*ladang*) is the primary source of vegetal foods; agriculturalists clear a portion of forest or savanna, burn the dried vegetation, make holes with a stick and put in various grains, weed or do not weed, protect the cultivated plants from wild animals, and reap. The cleared field may be abandoned after a single harvest or after two or three. Then it is permitted to lie fallow long enough for vegetation to increase so as to restore the soil's humus content and to produce a good quantity of ashes. A fallow of fifteen to twenty-five years appears rational. The *ladang* gives only a weak basis to human societies; such agriculture precludes a high density of population, since only a small part of the arable area is productive at any one time. An increasing population necessitates an extension of the cultivated area, a shortening of the fallow period, then the progressive ruin of the soils, and, after some delay, the inability of the population to continue to subsist in its ancestral home. Without technical innovations (manuring, irrigation, etc.), fields will not be able to support the increase of population; disasters surely will occur. It is often supposed that some process of this sort would explain some of the migrations and the decay of Mayan civilization. The Maya, endowed with the attributes of a superior civilization in respect to intellectual and political matters, had no agricultural technique other than the "milpa," that is to say, *ladang*. Such an agriculture in the end could not support the increasing population correlative with remarkable social and political institutions.

Are physical conditions responsible for the *ladang*, so widely practiced throughout the tropical world? More precisely, does the poverty of tropical soils (or of a very great percentage of tropical soils), owing to their weak resistance to leaching and erosion, favor *ladang* more than other agricultural systems?

In order to understand this problem, we propose to give examples which prove that there is nothing that requires *ladang* to be *the* agricultural technique in the tropical world. As with all agricultural techniques, *ladang* is the expression of a civilizational level and not the result of any inescapable physical constraint. Our first example concerns the Lala of Northern Rhodesia (Peeters, 1950). This tribe practices a particular system of *ladang*, the *chitemene* system, which for the Lala is even more elementary than the same practice of the neighboring Bemba (Richards, 1939). The Northern Rhodesian plateau has a very poor sandy soil, which bears a light forest of sparse and low trees. A Lala family clears each year about 7 hectares of this forest; the trees are chopped down, and then all the vegetal material is piled up in round heaps and the whole is burned. The area covered by the ashes is 50 ares (of the 7 hectares cleared). Eleusine, the cereal comprising the essential part of the food supply, is sown exclusively on these 50 ares. Since the eleusine harvested is able to feed 6.7 persons during one year; since the total area utilized under the *chitemene* system is only 60 per cent of the total area of the country (40 per cent being too steep, of rocky outcrops, or of fluvial beds); since the field cleared is cultivated only one year; and, since the fallow lasts twenty-two years, the agricultural system of the Lala is able to support, durably, some 2.6 persons per square kilometer.

Here is a well-linked whole, it seems: (1) very poor tropical soils, compelling the gathering onto a small part of the cleared area of the woody products of the entire clearing; (2) an elementary agricultural technique, which utilizes no tool except the ax; (3) very low density of population; and (4) a low level of consumption. However, nothing in this harmony is inevitable. The *chitemene* system utilizes only the soils of the plateau, which are very poor and often suffer from dryness. The swampy depressions, which have richer soils and are better supplied with water, are unused or very weakly used. The Lala do not possess agricultural techniques permitting them to benefit from these *dambo*, probably the best parts of their land, and the most valuable as the basis of a permanent and intensive agriculture. The *dambo* comprise 5 per cent of the total area and would assure a cultivated area more extensive than the minute fields of the *chitemene* system.

MADAGASCAR

A part of the population of Madagascar still practices *ladang*, here termed *tavy* (pronounced "tav"). The cultivators clear secondary vegetation (*savoka*, pronounced "savouk"), harvest once or twice, then allow the field to return to secondary vegetation. The *tavy* system has destroyed nearly all the forests of the island. *Tavy* supports only a scattered population, unstable, of low economic level. In contrast, other inhabitants of Madagascar make inundated rice fields. Why so large a difference in agricultural techniques? To answer this question, we shall rapidly describe the Merina and Betsileo lands. These are the most densely inhabited parts of Madagascar; population densities vary between 30 and 100 inhabitants per square kilometer, while the general average of Madagascar is only 6.5 per square kilometer.

Do the Merina and Betsileo regions have exceptionally beneficial natural conditions? Not at all. A visit there and an examination of the excellent maps available, covering a large part of the Merina and Betsileo homelands,[1] show that roughly 90–95 per cent is occupied by hills and plateaus bearing a very poor lateritic clay. On this clay grows a sparse steppe of scattered tufts of *Aristida,* which fire ravishes annually. Agriculture is impossible on the poor soils of the steppe—very poor lands, it would seem at first glance. However, these regions contain the most numerous populations of Madagascar. Merina and Betsileo peasants make inundated rice fields, evidently of Asiatic inspiration (but of *ancient* Asiatic inspiration, since until the twentieth century they ignored the plow and tilled the rice fields only by hoeing and by the stamping of oxen). The surface able to support inundated rice fields is very minute; on several maps[2] it is shown not to exceed 3 or 4 per cent of the total area. The crystalline pre-Cambrian rocks which constitute the high plateaus of Madagascar are dissected by a network of narrow valleys with flat bottoms. The waters filtering through the thick weathered soils covering the crystalline rocks reappear in the valley bottoms and cause the formation of narrow ribbons of swamps, sometimes not exceeding 20 meters in width. If the peat developed in the swamps is destroyed by drainage and fire, the valley bottoms are favorable to the creation of inundated rice fields. The bright green of the young plants in the narrow strips of inundated rice fields contrasts with the

1. Service Géographique de Madagascar publishes excellent maps on the scale of 1:100,000 with precise indications of the human occupation.

2. E.g., Map No. R.43 (Amparafaravola) shows only 1 per cent of the area effectively under inundated rice fields and 1.4 per cent cultivable (but non-utilized) by inundated rice fields. The same values for Map No. O.51 (Ambositra) are 2.2 and 1.4 per cent; for Map No. P.47 (Tananarive), 13 and 10 per cent.

mournful solitude of the steppes. In addition, peasants sometimes cut watered rice terraces on the lowest slopes. Since the peasant density is at least 4 persons per hectare of inundated riceland, it suffices that 4 per cent of a square kilometer (i.e., 4 hectares) be cultivated in inundated rice to give to this square kilometer a peasant density of 16 inhabitants per square kilometer. If the area of the rice field, in exceptional topographical conditions, reaches 10 per cent of the square kilometer, the peasant density rises to 40.

Thus, although the crystalline plateaus of Madagascar bear soils as poor as the soils of Lala country in Northern Rhodesia, the inundated rice-field technique feeds in Madagascar a much more numerous population. From the same point of view, Mysore, India, shows, on some parts of its ancient crystalline plateaus, populations which exceed 100 inhabitants per square kilometer of total area. Large rice fields are inundated from a remarkable network of artificial tanks or reservoirs.

THE LAND OF BELÉM

The land of Belém is situated in Brazil, to the east of the Pará River and to the north of the Guama River (Gourou, 1949). This area of 21,000 square kilometers is notable for its relatively high density of population. The average density was 14.4 inhabitants per square kilometer in 1940, excluding the town of Belém do Pará. The average density of both the remainder of the state of Pará and all the state of Amazonas was 0.28 inhabitant per square kilometer. In Amazonia one may find many areas of several thousand square kilometers each altogether without inhabitants.

On the low terraces which occupy the largest part of the land of Belém, the rural population practices an agriculture of a traditional kind which finds its origin in the Indian past. But today this agriculture is not only a subsistence agriculture but also a commercial agriculture, producing all the products necessary to the market of the city of Belém. The cassava (Portuguese *mandioca*), which is the basis for *farinha*, the principal food, is cultivated under the *roça* system, the same technique as *ladang*. Since the rural population is relatively large, and since it has to supply the great market of the city of Belém (with *farinha* and also with charcoal), the land of Belém has been entirely cleared of its primary forest, and all the vegetation is secondary. Frequently the fallow is not prolonged beyond five years. Moreover, Portuguese colonization began in the seventeenth century, taking on a more intensive rhythm in the eighteenth century (with immigration of Azorians). Then in the nineteenth century the rubber boom and catastrophic droughts in northeastern Brazil resulted in a heavy colonization by Cearenses.

Under such conditions, and without fertilizer, soils rapidly wear out. It is conceivable that the output of cassava will be so reduced within a few decades that the food supply of town and country will present a problem. However, the remedy lies near at hand. Experiments by the Instituto Agronomico do Norte in the vicinity of the city of Belém reveal that the flooded areas of the *igarapé* (valleys with flat bottoms, dissecting the terraces of the land of Belém) of the experimental station produce without manure, on 1 hectare, 4,000 kilograms of paddy, or 1,500 kilograms of jute fibers. The future of the land of Belém resides in the soils now being flooded by the tides (which, on the southern shore, move only fresh waters). The necessary condition of progress lies in the shifting of fields from the valley-top terraces to the bottom of the valleys and in the adoption of hydraulic techniques and collective works allowing for the utilization of the best soils, neglected until now. The higher soils will not be useless; they will have a commercial value as tree plantations producing rubber, cacao, oil palm, and so on.

It is interesting to compare the land of Belém and the island of Marajó, which is to the west of the Pará River. Marajó, largely similar to the land of Belém, is not an expansion of modern deltaic alluvium. It has large terraces of leached soils. Today these terraces are utilized as pastures for cattle. The density of population on Marajó Island is 3 inhabitants per square kilometer. Archeological evidence reveals that before European discovery Marajó Island was as notable for its relatively high level of civilization as for its large number of inhabitants. Great mounds give evidence of large public works and of an elaborate social and political organization. Fine pieces of pottery indicate that the Marajó people were socially stratified. It is logical (though hypothetical) to imagine that the Marajó people were too numerous for their agricultural technique; practicing only shifting cultivation, the Marajó people were unable to insure a permanent food production for the long run. Deterioration of the people and of their civilization was the end of the disharmony among the political, demographic, and artistic aspects and the agricultural technique of the Marajó civilization. Such decline was not an unavoidable result of poor soils. With inundated cultivation and with manuring, the Marajó people would not have been the victims of soil exhaustion (if such a cause was responsible for the decadence of the Marajó people).

RUANDA-URUNDI

Ruanda-Urundi, with agricultural techniques less refined than those of Asia, has a demographic evolution that generates problems similar to those in India or Java. A surface of 21,000 square kilometers has an average density of 135 inhabitants per square kilometer, and in the "Territoire" of Ruhengeri, for example, the general density reaches 166 inhabitants per square kilometer of total area. The agricultural density is 393 inhabitants per cultivated square kilometer (Gourou, 1953*b*). Of the total area, 42 per cent is effectively cultivated. This percentage is remarkably high, given the greatly incised relief of the country, where differences of 1,000 meters frequently occur between summits and valley floors. Several *collines* ("hills")—as the townships are called—have a general density higher than 400 inhabitants per square kilometer. The high general density has been possible by extension of the cultivated area. The agricultural techniques are, unfortunately, only a little better than *ladang*. The production per hectare and per cultivator is very low, though men and women devote a great deal of work to the fields. The high density of population of Ruanda-Urundi is consequently not the result of advanced techniques; it results from local political circumstances and from history. From the sixteenth or seventeenth century, the Ruanda and the Urundi had a strong system of government; hereditary monarchies with relatively efficient administrations gave to Ruanda-Urundi a protection against external dangers and the possibility of capitalizing on the annual increase of population.

The situation suggests a population stage intermediate between the human geographies of Negro Africa and tropical Asia. Such a development is full of dangers, as we saw for the land of Belém. One possible partial remedy would be inundated rice fields, as in Madagascar. Such a technique is not unthinkable in the Ruanda-Urundi, where so many valley bottoms are swampy. However, it is evident that the area of possible rice fields is not enough for the increasing demand of a growing population (birth rate, 52 per thousand; death rate, 27).

ASIAN TROPICAL CULTIVATORS

In many parts of tropical Asia the valuable area is totally utilized. In the case of the delta of Tonkin (Gourou, 1936, 1940*a*, 1940*b*), the entire alluvial plain—15,000 square kilometers—is effectively cultivated every year (with the exception of roads, rivers, houses, graveyards), and one-half of the cultivated area yields two harvests a year. Such intensive agriculture is the result of fertile alluvial soils, of dikes and irrigation canals assuring protection against river floods and against dryness, and of a skilful agriculture paying a great deal of attention to the manure problem. The peasant population averages 500 persons per square kilometer of total area and 600 persons per square kilometer of cultivated area (areas harvested twice in a year are taken only for their topographical, cartographical value).

The agriculture of the Tonkinese Delta is highly expensive in terms of human labor. One harvest of paddy requires up to 200 days of work for 1 hectare, so that, if this harvest produces 2,000 kilograms of paddy, a day's work has produced only 10 kilograms of paddy; a field with two annual harvests requires as much as 400 man-days of work per year. It is certainly feasible to reduce the quantity of agricultural work without reduction of the output; the problem is to find employment for the unemployed agriculturalists in a country with an annual surplus of births over deaths not lower than 25 per thousand. The annual increase of the peasant population of the delta must be on the order of 150,000 persons, already a large group to be added each year to the people employed in industrial and tertiary activities. Yet the reduction of agricultural work (with the corollary increased productivity) would certainly induce a great exodus from the country-side. If the expenditure of human agricultural labor be only a quarter of the present expenditure, if a rice field twice harvested requires only 100 days of work instead of 400, will it be possible to find employment for the three-quarters of the peasantry deprived of work? Is it not possible to say that intensive agricultural techniques (and vegetarian food habits) have led the Tonkinese peasants into a blind alley? The same situation is found in all countries with high peasant-population densities per cultivated area. It is not too disturbing when the cultivated area is only a modest percentage of the total area, but it becomes terribly disturbing if the cultivated area extends to the entire valuable part of the total area.

To repeat, natural conditions do play a role in such an evolution but not in a decisive fashion. For example, the island of Madura, with a total area of 5,971 square kilometers, had in 1940 an average density of 313 inhabitants per square kilometer. Yet Madura does not benefit from volcanic soils (too often held to be determinant of the high densities of some parts of Indonesia), and only 740 square kilometers of the 4,460 cultivated are irrigated.[3] Madura, with its low hills and its soils of medium grade at best, has a remarkably high percentage of the total area in permanent fields, or *tegalan*. The peasants of Madura have set off elaborate techniques of permanent dry agriculture—artificial terracing, rotation, manuring, etc.—which demand much work but which every year produce remunerative crops (remunerative, that is, relative to the economy of the peasant of Madura). The quality of land use in the Asiatic tropics is not fundamentally different from that in the Asiatic temperate plains; it derives from a civiliza-

3. Gourou, 1953a, pp. 350–52; some observations on the relations between density of population and soils in Indonesia.

tional complex and not particularly from tropical conditions.

PROSPECTS

In the largest part of the tropical world (keeping in mind that the majority of tropical cultivators are concentrated in a small part of the tropical world), the peasants practice extensive techniques as poor when measured by output (harvest per hectare) as when measured by productivity (harvest per day of work). The quality of land use is very low; such a situation is primarily the result of techniques (and of the civilizations in a broader sense) and not the direct result of unfavorable physical conditions. Surely large areas of tropical soils are very poor. But, except in Asia and in some other places like Madagascar, tropical cultivators have not employed the techniques which would allow them to make the best of the richest soils, of the soils well watered. Thus tropical cultivators, circumscribed by their techniques, have limited themselves to the use of poor soils (selecting, from the large category of poor tropical soils, the less poor and the physically arable soils). The *ladang* permits one harvest on very bad soils, the extreme example being the Lala of Northern Rhodesia, who sow only on the patches of ashes and neglect the remainder of the cleared area. Numerous tropical cultivators, knowing only extensive techniques, have cultivated just the areas best adapted to these techniques—areas with light soils on the terraces and the plateaus. They have neglected the swampy and heavy soils of the valley bottoms, which are endowed with the greater agricultural potentialities but are less easily utilizable by means of *ladang*. On the contrary, the cultivators of the Asiatic tropics have applied their intensive techniques on the lowest soils. To the various "levels" of the agricultural techniques correspond various topographic levels of application of these techniques. The simplest techniques apply to the lighter soils, whose clearing is rather easy. The intensive techniques apply to heavy soils, whose clearing is less easy. Human choices have been influenced much more by the level of techniques than by physical conditions.

A true "inversion" of the cultivated areas is necessary if tropical agriculture is to become more intensive, more productive, and able to support increasing populations. Given the conditions of soil fertility and the need for water for the plants, the tropical agriculturalist has to concentrate his efforts on the lowest topographic levels, generally the richest and the wettest. Mastery over water is the first necessary condition of agricultural progress in the tropical world, particularly in the dry fields of food plants. By descending the slopes, abandoning the fallows, and limiting itself to the most fertile areas, tropical agriculture will increase the output per hectare, the productivity per man-hour, and the total mass of food delivered to a mankind expanding in numbers. Tropical agriculture has a bright and considerable future if it concentrates on the very soils able to reward intensive techniques and if it is not reluctant to improve dry and poor soils.

The confining of tropical agriculture on the best soils would ease the introduction of motorized implements and, incidentally, increase the productivity of the cultivators. Let us keep in mind that one hour of work of a tropical peasant produces no more than 4 or 5 kilograms of grain (De Schlippe, 1948). Among the obstacles to mechanical tropical agriculture, first place must be given to the present necessity for fallowing; the careful and expensive work required for perfect mechanical clearing is justified if the clearing is definitive, but it is less justified (and less re-warded) if a new clearing must be made after a long fallow. Mechanized clearing must be associated with intensive and permanent agriculture. Another obstacle to clearing by machines is the extreme hardness of the plateau soils in dry seasons. Because of this hardness, the land is cleared only in the rainy season, and this delay in beginning the planting means that the period of cultivation is dangerously short and that the employment of mechanical implements is correlatively expensive. These various inconveniences have been underlined by the "groundnut scheme" of Tanganyika (Wood, 1950).[4]

In tropical agriculture intensive production of food products must replace extensive production; the more favorable situation for intensive production of food products is in the bottom of the valleys; and the slopes and the plateaus must be utilized for tree plantations (*Hevea, Elaeis,* etc.) and for scientific silviculture. I do think that tropical cultivators will have a brilliant economic future with a balanced agriculture: irrigated and inundated fields in the valley bottoms, animal husbandry (not by extensive pasture but by cultivation of food for animals on fields intensively cultivated), and tree plantations.

I must say that other views have been published. In an interesting paper (Vine, 1955) a specialist on Nigeria says that the soils on the Nigerian low plateaus are able to support for an in-

4. This interesting experiment, made between 1947 and 1952 in three parts of Tanganyika Territory—Kongwa, Urambo, and Nachingwea—was intended to produce enormous quantities of groundnuts (peanuts). It was abandoned, after an expenditure of £36,000,000, because of the scarceness of the yields. The failure was explained as due to uniform clearing of very different soils and to very expensive methods of clearing. It was found very difficult to clear the soils of all the woody roots, which were obstacles against the use of mechanical implements.

definite time native agriculture with short fallows (three to four years) and that prospects of integrating modern techniques into the native agriculture of the plateaus (green manure, chemical manuring, selection, etc.) are good. The soils of Nigeria are very different from one field to the next; it is incautious to generalize about them.

It is easier to talk about means of improvement than to carry them out. The first step must be acceptance by tropical cultivators of the necessity for a re-evaluation of their techniques. Will the new methods give the peasants a greater productivity? Within a framework of premechanical techniques, the passage from *ladang* to intensively cultivated, permanent fields does not necessarily carry with it an increase of productivity—not if the available arable area is so spacious as to permit suitable fallows and thus evade the risk of soil exhaustion. Tropical cultivators are aware of this. Thus, the peoples of some mountains of West Africa (Atacora Mountains, Bauchi Plateau, Mandara Mountains, Adamawa, etc.) learned relatively intensive agricultural techniques, such as artificial terracing and manuring, in response to a crisis: they had retreated into the mountains primarily for defense against external dangers, particularly against the raids of slavers. The establishment of peace and the suppression of slavery allowed these peoples to abandon their mountains and to clear the surrounding plains where arable areas were plentiful. In the new environment they are forgetting these techniques and returning to *ladang*, in which they find a greater productivity. In the same way, all the efforts made between 1920 and 1940 to lead the Moi Rhade (Annamite Cordillera of Indochina) to utilize the plow and to till inundated rice fields have been wasted. Since administrative pressure has been relaxed in keeping

with political events affecting eastern Indochina, the Rhade have returned to *ladang*. They have rediscovered cherished habits (we must not underestimate the strength of custom), and they obey also the lessons of experience; they have observed that permanent rice fields, without manure, gave a lesser output per day of work than *ladang*. To be sure, this point applies only with reference to a rather sparse population, *ladang* on unexhausted soils, suitable fallows, and annual rice fields without manure. In the same way, the Mnong Rlam of Darlac, Indochina, forced by the authorities to use the plow and to replant rice, have reverted to stamping by buffaloes and to direct sowing. Still worse, the Vietnamese colonists of Ban Methuot, Darlac, have turned for the first time to *ladang* and have abandoned the ancestral plow.

The passage from extensive to intensive techniques does not appear to the tropical peasant to be necessarily advantageous. Such an evolution is likely to be realized only where the following conditions prevail: exhaustion of the soils because of short fallows, reasonably high intellectual level of the population, introduction of techniques enhancing the productivity of intensive agriculture (motorization, manure, etc.), opening of markets, and development of commercial agriculture.

CONCLUSIONS

I have intended to explain by some examples the quality of land use by tropical cultivators; I have made some comments about the renovation of tropical agriculture. It seems certain to me that the tropical world is able to produce larger and larger quantities of agricultural products and to give the cultivators a higher level of consumption. Good roads and railways to destroy the isolation and enlarge the markets and the rational use of water, manure, and machines will allow immense progress. The comparison of cultivated areas in diverse tropical countries underlines the magnitude of the possible progress.

However, nothing very valuable will be realized if all the elements of the present situation are not clearly understood. It is not less indispensable to study the relations between the elements of a part of the earth's surface than to analyze each of those elements.

Perhaps it will be useful to indicate that such an intellectual position is exactly the position of human geography. Human geography is a synthetic discipline, aiming at the description and explanation of the relations between man and his environment. But what is the "natural environment"? The geographer would be wrong if he considered the natural environment as independent from man. The natural environment in two ways depends on man: first, man has transformed profoundly the environment (savanna substituted for forest, fields substituted for forest, secondary forest substituted for primary forest, etc.); second, man has interpreted the environment in terms of his techniques. The same natural environment will result in different human landscapes when interpreted (and transformed) by traditional European peasant civilization, by Chinese civilization, and by modern American civilization. The Merina of Madagascar and the Bemba of Rhodesia have created very different human landscapes in similar physical environments.

Density of population is a good basis for the study of human geography. A detailed map of the density of the population asks many questions: Why so few inhabitants here? Why so many there? Answers may be given by climate, physiography, soils, diseases, history, or techniques (of production and of spatial organization). Each particular question may be the field of specialists. But the weight of a population over a particular area is not explained by the juxtaposition of specialized studies; it must be explained by geographical appreciation of the interdependence of multiple factors.

No progress in the understanding of the human aspects of the landscape is possible if these aspects are simply considered to react to the physical elements of the landscape. The relations between the two are not direct; they are obliged to cross the prism of a civilization. Explanation does not progress if the human groups are considered to be compelled by the natural environment to adopt such-and-such techniques. Nor does the explanation make better progress if we consider that a human group examines a natural environment, evaluates the "possibilities," and chooses the more attractive. "Determinism" (physical determinism) and "possibilism" are unable to give a total explanation. The "possibilities" are in man much more than in nature; they are given to man by the civilization. Civilization is not a product of the physical environment, nor is it a product of a choice oriented by a finality. If a human group selected a certain type of exploitation of some resources, the choice was undetermined. Man has made himself, without knowing where he was willing to go. He has made himself by the making of himself. There was no physical determination, finalistic predestination, or conscious decision; there was a necessity for an undetermined choice and, consequently, a departure into a future. This geographical interpretation of the position of man on earth and in history is full of hope. The future, good or bad, will be the work of man and not the result of physical constraints.

REFERENCES

ADRIAENS, E. L.
1951 "Recherches sur l'alimentation des populations au Kwango," *Bulletin agricole du Congo belge*, XLII, No. 2, 227–69, 473–550.

ALLOUARD, P.
1936 "Pratique de la lutte contre les feux de brousse," *Bulletin économique de l'Indochine*, XXXIX, 991–1009.

ANONYMOUS
1954–55 *Comptes-rendus de la 2ᵉ Conférence interafricaine des sols, Leopoldville.* 2 vols. Brussels: Ministère des Colonies.

AUBRÉVILLE, A.
1949 *Climats, forêts et desertification de l'Afrique tropicale.* Paris: Société d'Editions Géographique, Maritime et Coloniale. 352 pp.

BEARD, J. S.
1946 *The Natural Vegetation of Trinidad.* ("Oxford Forestry Memoirs," No. 20.) Oxford: Clarendon Press. 152 pp.

BECKETT, W. H.
1943 *Akokoazo: A Survey of a Gold Coast Village.* ("London School of Economics Monographs on Social Anthropology," No. 10.) 96 pp.

BENNETT, H. H.
1928 "Some Geographic Aspects of Cuban Soils," *Geographical Review*, XVIII, No. 1, 62–82.

BRIGGS, G. W. G.
1941 "Soil Deterioration in the Southern District of the Tiv Division, Benue Province," *Farm and Forest*, June, pp. 8–12. Ibadan.

BROWN, W. H.
1919 *Vegetation of Philippine Mountains.* Manila: Bureau of Printing. 434 pp.

CHEVALIER, A.
1935 "Les Îles du Cap-Vert," *Revue de botanique appliquée et d'agriculture tropicale*, XV, Nos. 170–71, 734–1090.

COOK, O. F.
1921 "Milpa Agriculture," *Annual Report of the Smithsonian Institution for 1919*, pp. 307–26. Washington, D.C.: Government Printing Office.

CRAENE, A. DE
1955 "La Fertilité des latosols du nord-est du Congo belge et des relations avec la morphologie des profils pédologiques: La Latérisation," pp. 309–29 in *Comptes-rendus de la 2ᵉ Conférence interafricaine des sols, Leopoldville.* 2 vols. Brussels: Ministère des Colonies.

CRIST, R. W.
1935 "Le Llanero," *Revue de géographie alpine*, XXIII, No. 1, 97–114. Grenoble.
1944 "Cultural Crosscurrents in the Valley of the Rio São Francisco," *Geographical Review*, XXXIV, No. 4, 587–612.

FALKNER, F. R.
1938 "Die Trockengrense des Regenfeldbaus in Afrika," *Petermanns geographische Mitteilungen*, LXXXIV, Nos. 7–8, 210–14.

FARMER, B. H.
1954 "Problems of Land Use in the Dry Zone of Ceylon," *Geographical Journal*, CXX, 21–33.

FORDE, C. DARYLL
1937 "Land and Labour in a Cross River Village," *Geographical Journal*, LXXXIX, No. 1, 24–51.

FÜRER-HAIMENDORF, C. VON
1943 *The Aboriginal Tribes of Hyderabad, Vol. I: The Chenchus.* London: Macmillan & Co. 391 pp.

GOUROU, PIERRE
1936 *Les Paysans du Delta tonkinois.* ("Publications de l'École Française d'Extrême-Orient," Vol. XXVI.) Paris: L'Éditions d'Art et d'Histoire. 666 pp.
1940a *L'Utilisation du sol en Indochine française.* Paris: Centre d'Études de Politique Étrangère. 466 pp.
1940b *La Terre et l'homme en Extrême-Orient.* Paris: Librairie Armand Colin. 224 pp.
1947a "Geographie du peuplement en Nigérie méridionale," *Bulletin de la*

Société Belge d'Études Géographiques, XVII, Nos. 1–2, 58–64. (After C. DARYLL FORDE and C. SCOTT, *The Native Economies of Nigeria*. London, 1946.)

1947*b* *Les Pays tropicaux*. Paris: Presses Universitaires. 196 pp. (Translated into English as: *The Tropical World: Its Social and Economic Conditions and Its Future Status*. London, 1953. 156 pp.)

1948 "Problèmes du monde tropical," *Les Cahiers d'Outre-Mer*, I, No. 1, 4–13. Bordeaux.

1949 "Le Pays de Belém," *Bulletin de la Société Belge d'Études Géographiques*, XVIII, No. 1, 19–36.

1951 "Carte de la densité de la population au Congo belge et au Ruanda-Urundi," *Atlas général du Congo*. Brussels: Académie Royale des Sciences Colonials. (Seven-page separate for *Atlas* in course of publication.)

1953*a* *L'Asie*. Paris: Hachette. 542 pp.

1953*b* *La Densité de la population au Ruanda-Urundi; esquisse d'une étude géographique*. ("Institut Royal Colonial Belge, Section des Sciences Naturelles et Médicales," Vol. XXI, No. 6.) Brussels. 239 pp.

1955 *La Densité de la population rurale au Congo belge*. ("Académie Royale des Sciences Coloniales, Classe des Sciences Naturelles et Médicales" [N.S.], Vol. I, No. 2.) Brussels. 168 pp.

HARDY, F.
1939 "Soils and Soil Erosion in St. Vincent," *Tropical Agriculturist*, XVI, No. 3, 58–65.

JONES, G. L.
1943 "The Human Factor in Land Planning," *Farm and Forest*, December, pp. 161–66.

KEESING, F. M.
1938 "Population and Land Utilization among the Lepanto," pp. 458–64 in *Comptes-rendus du Congrès International de Géographie, Amsterdam*, Vol. II. Leiden: E. J. Brill. 615 pp.

KOPP, A.
1932 "La Vanille dans l'assolement de la canne à sucre à La Réunion," *Revue de botanique appliquée et d'agri-culture tropicale*, XII, No. 125, 32–47.

KUHNHOLTZ-LORDAT, G.
1939 *La Terre incendiée: Essai d'agronomie comparée*. Nîmes: Éditions de la Maison Carrée. 362 pp.

LAL, R. B., and SEAL, S. C.
1949 *General Health Survey, Lingur Health Center, 1944*. Calcutta: All India Institute of Hygiene and Public Health. 323 pp.

LAMAL, R. P. F.
1949 *Essai d'étude demographique d'une population du Kwango: Les Basuku du territoire de Feshi*. ("Institut Royal Colonial Belge, Section des Sciences Morales et Politiques," Vol. XV, No. 4.) Brussels. 189 pp.

LEHMANN, H.
1938 "Die Bevölkerung der Insel Sumatra," *Petermanns geographische Mitteilungen*, LXXXIV, No. 1, 3–15.

LÉVI-STRAUSS, C.
1948 "La Vie familiale et sociale des Indiens Nambikwars," *Journal de la Société des Americanistes* (N.S.), XXXVII, 1–132.

McBRIDE, G. M. and M. A.
1942 "Highland Guatemala and Its Maya Communities," *Geographical Review*, XXXII, No. 2, 252–68.

MAURAND, P.
1938 "L'Indochine forestière," *Bulletin économique de l'Indochine*, XLI, No. 4, 801–29.

MAURICE, A., and PROUX, G. M.
1954 "L'Âme du Riz," *Bulletin de la Société des Études Indochinois*, XXIX, Nos. 2–3, 125–258.

MENDES DA SILVEIRA, RENATO
1948 "Paisagens culturais da Baixada Fluminense." Doctoral dissertation, Faculdade de Filosofia, Ciencias e Letras, Universidade de São Paulo.

MURPHY, R. C.
1939 "The Littoral of Pacific Colombia and Ecuador," *Geographical Review*, XXXII, No. 1, 1–33.

NICOLAÏ, H., and JACQUES, J.
1954 *La Transformation des paysages congolais par le chemin de fer: L'Exemple du B.C.K.* ("Institut Royal Colonial Belge, Section des Sciences Na-

turelles et Médicales," Vol. XXIV,
No. 1.) Brussels. 208 pp.

PEETERS, D. U.
1950 *Land Usage in Serenje District.*
("Rhodes-Livingstone Institute Paper," No. 19.) London: Oxford University Press. 100 pp.

PELZER, K. J.
1945 *Pioneer Settlement in the Asiatic
Tropics.* (Special Publication No. 29.)
New York: American Geographical
Society. 290 pp.

PENDLETON, R. L.
1941 "Laterite and Its Structural Uses
in Thailand and Cambodia," *Geographical Review*, XXXI, No. 2, 177–
202.
1942 "Land Utilization and Agriculture in Mindanao," *ibid.*, XXXII, No.
2, 180–210.

PITTIER, H.
1936 "Consideraciones acerca de la
destrucción de los bosques y del incendio de las sabanas," *Boletín Sociedad Venezolana de Ciencias Naturales*, III, No. 26, 1–12.

RICHARDS, A. I.
1939 *Land, Labour and Diet in Northern Rhodesia.* London: Oxford University Press. 423 pp.

RODHAIN, J.
1950 "Documents pour servir à l'histoire de la maladie du sommeil au
Congo belge: La Trypanosomiase humaine au Katanga," *Institut Royal
Colonial Belge, Bulletin des Séances*,
XXI, No. 3, 692–707. Brussels.

SCAETTA, H.
1936 "Les Pâturages de haute montagne en Afrique centrale," *Bulletin
agricole du Congo belge*, XXVII, No.
3, 323–78.

SCHLIPPE, G. P. DE
1948 "Sous-station d'essai de l'INEAC
à Kurukureta: extraits du premier
rapport annuel," *Bulletin agricole du
Congo belge*, XXXIX, No. 2, 361–
402.

SHAH, V. and S.
1949 *Bhuvel: Socio-economic Survey
of a Village.* Bombay: Indian Society
of Agricultural Economics. 154 pp.

SPURR, A. M. M.
1955 "A Basis of Classification of the
Soils of Areas of Composite Topography in Central Africa, with Special
Reference to the Soils of the Southern Highlands of Tanganyika," pp.
175–90 in *Comptes-rendus 2e Conférence interafricaine des sols, Leopoldville.* 2 vols. Brussels: Ministère
des Colonies.

STAMP, L. DUDLEY
1938 "Land Utilization and Soil Erosion in Nigeria," *Geographical Review*, XXVIII, No. 1, 32–45.

TOTHILL, J. D.
1940 *Agriculture in Uganda.* London:
Oxford University Press. 551 pp.

VINE, H.
1955 "Is the Lack of Fertility of Tropical African Soils Exaggerated?" pp.
389–406 in *Comptes-rendus 2e Conférence interafricaine des sols, Leopoldville.* 2 vols. Brussels: Ministère
des Colonies.

WAIBEL, L.
1948 "Vegetation and Land Use in
the Planalto Central of Brazil," *Geographical Review*, XXXVIII, No. 4,
529–54.

WHITE, S.
1941 "Notes on Mixed Farming as
Practised by Some Shuwa Arabs in
Parts of Dikwa Emirate," *Farm and
Forest*, June, pp. 24–25.
1944 "Agricultural Economy of the
Hill Pagans of Dikwa Emirate, Cameroons (British Mandate)," *ibid.*, September, pp. 130–34.

WISER, W. H. and C. V.
1946 *Behind Mud Walls.* New York:
Friendship Press. 180 pp.

WOOD, A.
1950 *The Groundnut Affair.* London:
Bodley Head. 264 pp.

The Grassland of North America: Its Occupance and the Challenge of Continuous Reappraisals

JAMES C. MALIN[*]

THE PROBLEM OF DEFINITION

Any attempt at regional definition of a portion of earth space involves time as one of the determining criteria. Also, in view of the fact that the term "grassland" has been designated as the term descriptive of the region proposed for study, that selection implies that the definition is in terms of vegetational cover. As plant growth varies with total prevailing conditions, both temporary and long term, every vegetational map has to be dated. For some areas conditions have been so decisive that over long periods of time no major variation has occurred. In transition zones between such relatively stabilized nuclear areas, the vegetational cover has fluctuated to a greater or lesser degree with the prevailing variability of environment. Extremes of moisture and temperature operated differently upon each type of vegetation as well as upon particular species. As between trees and grass, trees may expand their coverage over a period favorable to their growth

* Dr. Malin has been in the Department of History at the University of Kansas since 1921. He was president of the Agricultural History Society in 1943–44. His books include: *Winter Wheat in the Golden Belt of Kansas*, 1944; *The Grassland of North America: Prolegomena to Its History*, 1947; *The Nebraska Question*, 1954; and *The Contriving Brain and the Skillful Hand in the United States*, 1955.

and then suffer a severe setback, or even destruction, by an extreme of drought and heat or extreme cold; such weakened woody growth as may have survived may be finished off by disease or insect enemies. In addition, we know that destruction from fire caused by lightning took its toll.[1] Added to these

1. Two examples of reported lightning-ignited prairie fires in the High Plains are cited. The location was Cheyenne County, Kansas, near the intersection of 40° north latitude and 102° west longitude at an altitude of nearly 4,000 feet. The number of such examples might be multiplied indefinitely. In using newspaper sources as evidence, not all references to lightning as a cause of fires would be acceptable. These particular instances possess characteristics that contribute to credibility: the specific location is given; the community turned out to fight the fire; the area burned was specified; and the record was printed within the week. The point to be emphasized is that such discriminative details would seem to differentiate these reports from the rumor category and, in making the record specific, would justify the use of these cases and many other similar ones that might be cited in the High Plains newspapers and would constitute proof of lightning as a cause of prairie fires.

St. Francis (Kan.) *Herald*, July 13, 1911, Bird City Department: "Not every year will the prairie grass burn in July, but such is the case now. During one of our electrical storms last week lightning struck a little ways southwest of W. D. Kyle's place burning over quite a territory before the flames were extinguished."

St. Francis (Kan.) *Herald*, August 3, 1911: "Last Thursday a bad prairie fire destroyed the winter range of Henry Weaver. Sunday hazards were those introduced by man, primitive and modern, particularly the use of fire. The factor of fire has been little understood and has been subject to much exaggeration as well as lack of discrimination. Generalization is always dangerous and nowhere more so than on the matter of fire and vegetation. The variables are too numerous: time and method of using fire, hot or cold, variations in response to fire of different types of vegetation, the several species of grasses and of woody growth.

These matters are not merely theoretical, although they strike at the very foundations of the ecologists' concepts of succession and climax. They raise an honest doubt as to whether the idea of climax vegetation is even legitimate or of practical value. At any rate, the idea needs restatement based upon fresh thinking. Possibly the term "steady state" recently introduced into soil-science literature might be open to less objection because it is not yet freighted with so many unwarranted overtones, implications, and inferences.

Gilpin (1860) compared the European and the North American continents to a bowl: Europe, a bowl turned upside down, therefore high in the middle and sloping to the sea in all directions; North America, a bowl turned right side up, a rim around the outside and great valleys in the interior, closed off from free atmospheric circulation from the seas. North America had in fact a double rim on the west and on the south of 49° north latitude. This double rim encompassed the Great Basin area, mostly moist desert; at the north the Palouse prairie, in the middle the sagebrush desert, and at the south the Larrea Desert. The moist desert permitted some grasses, and this, therefore, in a limited sense made it a grassland.

The Rocky Mountains continental divide, however, was the major physical feature of the interior. It formed a barrier separating all west of it from the great interior valleys whose rivers emptied northward into the Arctic waters, eastward into the Atlantic through the St. Lawrence gap in the eastern rim, and southward into the Gulf of Mexico. The high point of the three watersheds was the nearly level plain of the Dakotas and Minnesota, modified by the glaciation of the Pleistocene.

Geologically speaking, all this was the work of comparatively recent time. The Appalachian Revolution formed the mountains of that name, the eastern rim of the American bowl, during Permian time. The Rocky Mountains were formed by the Laramide Revolution of late and post-Cretaceous time, but the Cascadian Revolution of Pleistocene time completed the Pacific coastal rim. The Mississippi Valley proper was largely Pennsylvanian (Later Carboniferous); parts of east-central Kansas, much of Oklahoma, and northern Texas were Permian; and the northwest of these areas were Cretaceous and Tertiary formations. However, much of the entire surface was reworked during the Pleistocene by glaciation, combined with winds and water.[2] Cut off from ocean moisture on the west by the double rim of mountains, the moisture of this area east of the continental divide is derived from warm, moist air masses moving northward from the Gulf of Mexico to meet cold, dry air masses

---

another big fire raged off southwest of Asa Cress's place. It burned a place 2½ miles long and 1½ miles wide. It was set by lightning and required the most heroic efforts on the part of the settlers to extinguish it and save some winter pasture. This year when feed is scarce the loss of the grass will be sorely felt."

2. Any clear realization of the role of glaciation dates from slightly more than a century ago. An intensive investigation of Pleistocene times, especially accompanied by a realization of the interplay of geological processes and primitive man, dates particularly from the Folsom discoveries of the second quarter of the twentieth century.

from the Canadian plain; the whole moves eastward. Thus, close to the mountain barrier the annual rainfall is scanty, increasing somewhat to the eastward, but highly variable within the unique continental interior (Borchert, 1950).

The geologists who dealt with the rocks of later geological time represented in the central part of this grassland commented upon their relative softness, which meant that, where exposed, they were subject to rapid erosion; most of them were covered by unconsolidated Pleistocene deposits. Few of the streams but were turbid. Hayden recorded that water in the several tributaries of the Missouri River began to clear only above the meridian of the mouth of the Musselshell (1863, chap. xii). The high country received an annual average rainfall of 10–25 inches. A rhetorical question that may be worth pondering is what would happen in the way of erosion if the Great Plains area should be visited with an annual average rainfall of 40–50 inches. The fact is that the scanty rainfall of the area constitutes its major value to the occupying human culture.

The "natural" properties of the vegetation of the Mississippi Valley east of the river itself were long a subject of disagreement mixed with a degree of mystery (Adams, 1902*a*, 1902*b*; Transeau, 1935). Shaler (1889, 1891) considered the prairie condition of much of the country to be the consequence of fire used after about A.D. 1000. Interested particularly in Kentucky history, he suggested that, if European intervention had been delayed another five hundred years, the prairie might have extended as far east as the Appalachian Mountains. He had been impressed particularly by the excavations he had made around the salt springs at Big Bone Lick, Boone County, Kentucky, which revealed a succession of deposits from glacial times to the date of his

work. In Mississippi, Hilgard (1860, pp. 349, 361–62) contrasted the vegetational status of parts of that area as the white man had received it from the hands of the Indians with its condition in 1860: a well-grassed, longleaf-pine savanna versus a country denuded of both trees and grass.

In the northern Ozark country west of the Mississippi River, Beilman and Brenner (1951) emphasized "the recent intrusion of forests in the Ozarks" during historic time. The invasion of trees dated from the time that the use of fire by the natives was curtailed and virtually eliminated. The rapid spread of woody growth in eastern Kansas and Nebraska during the first decade under white settlement was the subject of particular comment in 1867 by Bayard Taylor. So far as he described what he saw of the spread of woody growth at the expense of grass, his account was a significant document. A syllogistic conclusion from these last two examples is to be avoided, however. Only in some of the terrain most favorable to trees could timber have grown to maturity for marketable lumber, especially in eastern Kansas and Nebraska. Even in the stream bottoms, the oak-hickory-walnut combination disappeared west of 97° west longitude (Fort Riley and Council Grove), or at about the western boundary of the tall-grass country.

In the mid-latitudes west of the hundredth meridian the short grasses, the buffalo (*Buchloë dactyloides*) and the blue gramma (*Bouteloua gracilis*), were characteristic. Between 97° and 100° west longitude in this area the vegetation was conspicuously mixed and represented species from both the tall-grass and the short-grass areas. There was wide variation in accord with topography and soil. Two strips of sandy outcrops in Oklahoma and northern Texas produced the Cross Timbers which ran generally north and south. Sand-dune country along the Cimarron, south of the Arkansas and north of the Platte rivers, grew bunch grasses. At the extreme north the needle grasses (*Stipa*) predominated, and at the south the mesquite grasses (*Hilaria*) were characteristic. Variety was more conspicuous than were the uniformities emphasized by some of the plant ecologists

The soils formed in the tall-grass area were mostly on the acid side, while those west of about 97° or 98° west longitude were alkaline, a characteristic of so-called "arid soils" first explained by Hilgard (1892). The scanty rainfall and the absence of leaching, which accounted for alkalinity, also contributed to the explanation of the phenomenal fertility of these grassland and desert soils.

ON THE NATURE OF GRASSLAND INSTABILITY: PROBLEM OF CONCEPTUAL ORIENTATION

Whenever and wherever a discussion is proposed of man-earth relations, or of man-food relations, certain fundamental conceptual barriers usually tend to block a free and effectual meeting of minds about even the nature of the problem. One of these is the assumption, tacit or explicit, that, as differentiated from plants and other animals, man's relations with the earth and all its properties are always destructive. A second barrier, which is really a corollary of the first, is that the imperative responsibility of any student of these matters is to provide the bases for restoring what man, especially "civilized" man, has supposedly destroyed. The overtones, if not the explicit assumption, are those of urgency of decision and of action to forestall disaster. The time scale of the geologist and the anthropologist is essential to maintain perspective on the area in question which has been "destroyed" repeatedly, both before and since the appearance of man, and is now the abode of man. The grassland of North America is conspicuously the product of destruction, and, as applied to this problem, destruction and creation are merely different aspects of the same thing. All areas of the earth's surface present a similar process to challenge the curiosity and understanding of men, but possibly a grassland reveals to the observation of contemporary men a more direct opportunity to study certain of the forces actively at work than do some other areas.

As the first draft of this paper was being written, March 11, 1955, a thermonuclear bomb had just been exploded in the Nevada desert. Afterward, red dust, falling over Baltimore, Maryland, some 2,200 miles eastward, aroused fear of radioactive fall-out from the explosion. In undertaking to allay that alarm by assuring the public that the red particles were nothing more dangerous than red dust blown from the Texas range country, the Weather Bureau inadvertently created another alarm about the destruction of the Great Plains by dust storms, supposedly caused by overgrazing and by plowing up the grass for wheat, cotton, and sorghum. Man is not happy unless he is worrying about something.

The Great Plains dust storms are a case in point that illustrate the problem and its overtones—the immediate push-button reaction in terms of a supposed solution to dust storms—to restore the Great Plains to their "original" grassland equilibrium as supposedly enjoyed in the state of nature. According to this stereotype, aboriginal man was a superior being, endowed with the wisdom of nature and of nature's God of the so-called "Enlightenment" of the eighteenth century—only civilized man was evil. Of course, not everyone reacted to the Weather Bureau's explanation in this manner, but this generalized response was more inclusive than it should have been, even among people in possession of some specialized knowledge about the subject.

The red dust that fell over Baltimore had its determinable origin in Permian time, hot and dry, during which beds of gypsum and salt were deposited, along with the materials from which the red soils of northern Texas and western Oklahoma were derived. The restoration philosophy does not propose to restore Permian conditions or those more favorable to prolific growth of vegetation which laid down the Pennsylvanian, Cretaceous, or Tertiary coal fields. There is no intent here merely to be facetious. If some past condition must be restored, why not choose that most favorable to present desires? Is it any more possible to restore less remote than more remote time conditions? Are not all such changes in space and time irreversible? Each space-time situation is the product of a unique combination of factors which never can be brought together again.

Early interpretations of the geological history of Pleistocene time as applied to the area east of the Rocky Mountains were oversimplified generalizations. Johnson's monograph (1901, 1902) was the most influential and, from the standpoint of geological history, represented the Great Plains as having been formed from debris washed out from the Rocky Mountains and thereafter undisturbed, except as it was eroded on either side and cut through from west to east at its northern end by such rivers as the Platte, the Republican, the Arkansas, the Canadian, and the Red. But that oversimplified view of the stability of the area has been disproved conclusively by Pleistocene research and archeological excavation, separately and in co-operation, during the second quarter of the present century. Instead of having been cut once, it was found that a large part of the Great Plains had been eroded and redeposited several times. Aboriginal village sites were excavated which revealed a succession of occupations of

identical spots, separated by varying thicknesses of wind-blown material. Also, even on the high ridges of eastern Kansas south of the glaciated area, a large portion of the current soils are derived from loessal materials.

The stereotyped formula for soil formation pictured by Marbut, in the Department of Agriculture's *Atlas of American Agriculture* (1935), divided the soil body into four horizons: A, B, C, and D—the D horizon being unweathered rock. A stabilized, soil-forming process was represented as being found in the weathering of rock at the bottom as fast as erosion removed top soil. Thus, soil was supposedly formed normally from the bottom up. Whatever the degree of validity of that formula as a generalization, it has comparatively little applicability to the grassland, where the soils are derived so extensively from material transported by wind, water, and glacier. The soil material is added at the top as well as being eroded from the top. More often than is realized, the additions are in excess of the subtractions. The red dust that worried Baltimore in March, 1955, was only a demonstration of the continuance of Pleistocene geological and soil-forming processes actively at work in unbroken sequence. Mature soils in the sense of Marbut's soil stereotype can scarcely be expected. The same observations apply to the plant ecologists' stereotype of plant succession and climax. They are constructs of the mind, not realities, and never have been realities.

A further emphasis upon the absence of a stabilized condition in the grassland must be focused upon the period of about three centuries between the first arrival of Europeans into the interior of America and the middle of the nineteenth century, when the actual displacement of the Indians by white men began. Two changes of conditions occurred during that interval that were revolutionary in their effects upon Indian culture: the introduction of the horse and the change of location of many tribes. The Sioux, in part at least a forest people, were pushed southwestward into the northern grassland, the last stage in that process being completed after the New Ulm, Minnesota, massacre of 1862. Both of these revolutionary changes in the cultural pattern of what are usually called "Plains" Indians were too recent and too sudden to represent a stabilized culture in equilibrium with environment.

The question does not appear to occur to historians that the Indian culture might have been headed for a major crisis, possibly disaster, even if displacement by white culture had not intervened to give disaster a different form as well as to provide the Indian with a good alibi. In fact, there is reason to assert that these Indian cultures were already off-balance and were running into trouble prior to any definite "pressure" being placed upon them by the actual invasion of the area and their displacement by white men. Proof of such an assertion would be difficult, and, in a strict sense, possibly it is not subject to proof. But at the same time the opposite, which is the orthodox assumption upon which most history has been written, presents even greater difficulties. A mere unquestioned acceptance of an unproved assumption does not constitute proof, regardless of the penalties imposed upon those who refuse to conform to the requirements of orthodoxy. In any case, the conditions prevailing in the grassland interior during the century from 1750 to 1850 were anything but the eighteenth-century ideal "state of nature."

Proof is yet forthcoming that imitation of the Indian culture would have been a safe course. But under no circumstances could such a course have

prevented dust storms in this grassland. No more vivid description of a dust storm has been recorded than that of Isaac McCoy, written on the spot in what is now north-central Kansas during the fall of 1830 (not 1930),[3] when

8. "Had a little rain last night—the country is exceedingly parched with drought. When we got on to the prairies, the ashes from the recently burned prairies, and the dust and sand raised so by the wind that it annoyed us much, the wind raising, I found that the dust was so scattered that it became impossible to perceive the trail of the surveyors, who had gone a few hours ahead of the horses. While conversing with Calvin about the course we should go, we discovered the atmosphere ahead darkening, and as it had become cloudy, we fancied that a misting rain was coming upon us, and made some inquiry respecting the security of our packs. A few minutes taught us that what we had fancied to be rain, was an increase of the rising dust, sand, and ashes of the burnt grass, rising so much and so generally that the air was much darkened, and it appeared on the open prairies as though the clouds had united with the earth. Our eyes were so distressed that we could scarcely see to proceed. . . . The wind blew incessantly and excessively severe. . . . Was about to select a camping ground, when we met a man whom the Doctor [sent] to inform me that he could not proceed with his work, and that they waited for us in a wood a mile ahead. It being very difficult for me to look at my pocket compass I told the soldier . . . to lead us back. He set off with great confidence that he could find his way back and in a few minutes was leading us north instead of west. . . . On finding the surveyors, we encamped for the residue of the day. Even in this wood, and after the wind had somewhat abated, the black ashes fell on us considerably." (Barnes, 1936, p. 365).

Wind and dust accompanied the expedition farther west, and on October 26 the Republican Valley was reached: "Wind very high, scarcely allowing us to pass" (*ibid.*, p. 368). October 27: ". . . Today we reached the Republican, . . . and to our great disappointment we found it more destitute of grass than any place we had seen where wood was to be found. The river runs over a bed of sand —the banks low, and all the bottom lands are a bed of sand white and fine, and now as dry as powder ought to be. I never saw a river along which we might not find some rich alluvial moist bottoms, on which, at this the so-called "native Plains Indians" were still in full possession. And dust storms in Kansas (1850–1900) have been described from contemporary records by the present writer. No more brazen falsehood was ever perpetrated upon a gullible public than the allegation that the dust storms of the 1930's were *caused* by "the plow that broke the Plains."

RAILROADS AND LAND-MASS POWER

The United States completed legal possession of the mid-latitude grassland

----

season of the year, could not be found green grass. But here there is in a manner none.

"We examined along the river for grass until satisfied that none could be found and then turned back to a creek we had passed five miles back. . . . The scarcity of wood on the river and the sandiness and poverty of the bottoms, greatly discourage me as to the country—While the great scarcity of food for our horses made us fear that we should not be able to proceed much further" (*ibid.,* pp. 368–69).

The entry of November 5 represents the country about the ninety-eighth meridian and reads: "Completed the line of the outlet to 150 miles, and stopped. For some days we have discovered that our horses were failing so fast, that we must soon return, or lose them all. . . . We are beyond all Indian villages, and 50 miles, or more, into the country of Buffaloes. . . .

"After we completed our survey, we turned on to a creek, and were looking for an encampment—the day calm and fair—when suddenly the atmosphere became darkened by a cloud of dust and ashes from the recently burnt Prairies occasioned by a sudden wind from the north! It was not three minutes after I had discovered its approach, before the sun was concealed, and the darkness so great, that I could not distinguish objects more than three or four times the length of my horse. The dust, sand, and ashes, were so dense than one appeared in danger of suffocation. The wind driving into one's eyes seemed like destroying them. . . .

"The storm commenced, sun three quarters of an hour high in the evening, and blew tremendously all night. It had abated a little by morning. The dust was most annoying at the commencement. There was no clouds over us" (*ibid.,* pp. 371–72).

of North America (between the forty-ninth parallel and the Rio Grande) during the late 1840's. This made of the United States a two-front nation, facing both the Atlantic and the Pacific oceans, and laid the basis for a claim of right to a voice in the affairs of both the Atlantic and the Pacific systems. At that particular time in modern history the possession of the mid-latitude portion of the land mass of North America was fraught with a peculiar significance and one that has not been adequately interpreted. The power lent to this geographical position, and to the United States as its possessor, was for a duration of but one hundred years, since which the whole situation has changed. The greater part of that century was the century of world peace (1814–1914) and a century in which steam railroads virtually monopolized the communication systems of land-mass interiors.

The new series of world wars since 1914, air communication, and atomic bombs have changed basic relationships. The point is stressed here that the power vested in geographical position is held only on temporary loan and is not inherent in geographical position per se. The power wielded by a geographical site changes with the cultural technology that uses it. It is not the purpose of this paper to explore the ramifications of these facts from the standpoint of world history, but what is said here about the grassland of North America must be envisioned in such a world perspective in order to have any particular meaning (Malin, 1955*b*).

Down through the centuries, when the Western world faced the Mediterranean Sea and, after 1492, the North Atlantic Ocean, power was wielded through water communications. So long as land communications were dependent upon the muscle power of men and animals, costs of interior transport of heavy commodities were prohibitive. Economies of water transport did not extend to upstream navigation of the great rivers that drained continental interiors. The steam locomotive operating on iron railroads changed all this, because even the steamboat operating against the current of great rivers could reach only limited interior parts.

Prior to the steam railroad, penetration of the interior of the North American continent had followed water-communication systems. Penetration of the interior country from any water-based point was limited by the prohibitive costs of muscle power. The exceptions only tend to highlight the rule. Large areas not served by water were bypassed in the settlement process. Conspicuously, there was no connected frontier line in the Turner tradition. instead, scattered water-based diffusion centers served the land-mass interior areas. This applied particularly to the country east of the Mississippi River. West of that stream the diminished rainfall and the number and navigability of streams rendered water-based penetration of the grassland relatively unimportant for the area as a whole. By the early 1850's, in the state of Missouri, the argument was made that the available land accessible by water was already virtually taken up. To occupy and to develop the remainder of Missouri, railroads would have to be built. In Kansas, where there were no navigable rivers, and which was organized and opened to settlement in 1854, the issue was explained explicitly by Robinson (1859). Without railroads, corn at Lawrence, thirty to forty miles from the Missouri River, was worth nothing for sale on the Missouri River markets, because the cost of carriage by animal power equaled the normal market price. The steam railroad not only made the grassland a grain-growing area but also provided a structure for its livestock economy. It made possible also the marketing of the Pacific Coast fruits of California and the Northwest at the population centers of the East. So much for the grassland and its occupance in its own right. Comparatively, however, during the period of nearly a century of steam-railroad dominance of communication in continental interiors, by coincidence, the United States was the only great land-mass state that was in a position to capitalize fully upon this unique advantage (Malin, 1947, chap. xii; 1954a, pp. 56–71, 320–27, 408–16, 446–48; 1955a, 1955b).

COMMERCIAL ECONOMIES

In approaching the study of the history of the commercial economies of the grassland, certain prerequisites are imperative. Because the grassland possessed environmental peculiarities quite unlike the conditions of the forest, European-American culture with its forest background approached it with an unconscious ecological outlook quite foreign to the requirements of life under the strange conditions that had produced a grassland. Regardless of what the origin of the grassland may have been, the fact remained that conditions had produced grass there and not forest. Again, regardless of origins, occupance must be effected in terms of grass, not of forest. Still again, regardless of origins, the potential capacities of the grassland had to be tested by the new occupants to determine what they were. There were no precedents for European-American culture, which was derived predominantly from the British Isles and northern Europe. The first obligation of the historian in studying this particular stage of occupance is to determine the total body of knowledge and the ecological outlook these people possessed at the outset of the invasion of the grassland, regardless of whether it be called "science" or "folk thought." Next on this theme of knowledge and attitudes must be traced the growth and accumulation of the total fund of information and the transformation of attitudes. The record is not in the nature of a straight-line growth but is one of highly irregular pattern, if pattern there be, and of many false starts and by-paths. Only in large perspective can it appear to represent anything like a consistent and reasoned structure of thought about man and the earth. Too often the tendency appeared to insist upon simple answers and to create stereotypes, and nowhere more conspicuously than in the sciences, theoretical and applied; and stereotypes interfere with understanding.

An approach to the grassland from the standpoint of the history of agricultural economies must necessarily emphasize the range-livestock industry and field-crop production. The tall-grass area to the eastward presented relatively little difficulty to the westward extension of traditional forest man's livestock and crops: cattle, hogs, sheep, corn, oats, and soft wheats. West of the strictly tall-grass area the issues were increasingly challenging. Westward toward the Rocky Mountains, rainfall diminished and elevation increased. Also, the north-south latitudinal range was greater and imposed wider variability in temperature and photoperiodicity. Domesticated livestock and field crops introduced into the area could scarcely be expected to possess equally the capacity to exhibit their full potentials, or even to survive, in all parts of so extended a geographical space. Livestock presented lesser difficulties in these matters than field crops, but, with more extensive and sounder scientific information, greater emphasis was being placed upon specialized breeds of livestock for each area and purpose.

The history of the livestock industry in the North American grassland has never been told in a comprehensive manner or with objectivity and perspective. Besides the bias of a particular frame of reference which vitiates the standard accounts, the basic research

for much, if not most, of a comprehensive history is yet to be done. The past of the livestock industry in all its aspects needs to be written as a whole without pretense of telling the whole of the past.

The particular frame of reference which distorts the history of the range-livestock industry is the result of undue emphasis upon the Texas influence and upon cattle. Of course, Texas has never been noted for modesty. According to United States history, the United States annexed Texas, but, according to Texas history, Texas annexed the United States. That is the Texas contribution to the generalized theory of relativity.

When Texas "brags," of course it is done facetiously, and each "brag," bigger than its predecessor, is expected to bring a hearty laugh. Nevertheless, there is a serious side to the Texas exaggeration that has left an indelible impress upon the writing of the history of the whole western area of the United States and especially upon the history of the livestock industry and upon land-utilization policies. Webb's *The Great Plains* (1931) brought those elements together within the covers of one book in such a form as to give them a wide currency, if not influence. It incorporated the Johnson geological interpretations of the High Plains (see pp. 10–17, 419–22) with the combined views of the Powell report on arid lands and the Johnson High Plains report on land utilization. All this fitted neatly into the "big cattleman's" view of the type of society that should monopolize the area and keep it in grass. The erroneous view of Johnson on Pleistocene geological history of the Plains is no longer a matter of doubt. Unfortunately for accurate thinking, the social philosophies of both Powell and Johnson, especially the former, have gained an acceptance that is remarkably uncritical of geographical determinism and its consequential regimentation of society.

Among the merits of the Powell report on arid lands was the fact that he did recognize that the limited area with which he dealt possessed a unique character that justified a special treatment. Yet, in spite of the fact that he was both a geologist and an ethnologist, his social philosophy for the area was essentially a prescription of social statics. Landholding in large lots, except for limited irrigation communities, would have afforded opportunity for only a favored few; and this view committed him to a social structure so rigid and static as to be without capacity to absorb even a normal population increase. At the same time, by creating a powerful vested interest, the plan would not necessarily have insured constructive, long-term utilization policies. Quite certainly it could not have prevented either the physical or the economic disasters of the 1930's.

Powell was notably blind to soil science and was in no sense abreast of the status of the subject even in his own day and in the environment for which his system was designed. At the time of the arid lands report in 1878, Hilgard had not yet published much of his basic ideas leading to a new soil science; but, as those contributions were issued, Powell failed to understand their significance. He never realized what the soil problem was that needed to be understood.

This emphasis upon Powell, Johnson, and Webb is not intended to leave the impression that the Powell plan was adopted as the policy for the original occupation of the arid region for which it was designed. But it did have some bearing upon more recent policies and still possesses an unfortunate propaganda influence.

Besides cattle from Texas, the northern ranges were stocked from the Pacific Coast (Oliphant, 1932, 1933, 1946, 1948) as well as from the farms of the eastern states. The most important influence of all, however, for reconstruction of the history of the cattle industry as a whole has been the contribution of pure-bred animals from Great Britain, the European continent, and India and the creation of new hybrid breeds (Malin, 1947; Hazelton, 1939; Rhoad, 1949). The story of sheep likewise is in the process of being reconstructed on a more meaningful basis (Wentworth, 1942, 1948, 1954).

The first English colonists to settle in what is now the United States brought with them the seed for traditional English crops: wheat, oats, barley, rye, etc., and the tillage methods of the homeland. For various reasons, their labor achieved no great success. The Indians taught them the culture and uses of the maize, the Indian staple. One of the most remarkable aspects of European adaptation to America was the manner in which corn (Indian maize), especially the dent type, became an integral part of American culture. When Americans reached the western extent of the tall-grass prairie where corn could not be depended upon because of the hazards of climate, they stubbornly persisted in growing corn because they could not, or would not, adjust to an agricultural system without it. A large part of the excessive hardships in the grass country of the late nineteenth century was the result of this failure in adjustment. The soft wheats, spring and winter types, according to latitude, were likewise subject to a high casualty rate. The belated introduction to and reluctant schooling in the uses of hard wheat provided a remarkably reliable grain crop for bread. After the opening of the twentieth century came durum, a spring wheat suitable for macaroni flour. The hard spring wheats dominate the northern grassland and the hard winter wheats the central portion (Malin, 1942; 1947, pp. 327–30; Ball, 1930; Clark *et al.*, 1923).

For the central part of the grassland

the sorghums became a major crop, affording a reliable substitute for corn. Introduced first, after the middle of the nineteenth century, were the saccharine varieties, used for syrup, but which became more widely grown as a forage substitute for corn. Kaffir and milo, etc., were introduced near the end of the century. In their mid-twentieth-century forms, as developed by plant-breeders, the grain sorghums afford a reliable feed for livestock as a substitute for corn and thus have become an integral part of the range-livestock economy where corn could not be grown. This facet of the whole situation must be stressed as one of several which demonstrate that the range-livestock industry could not survive on grass alone.

Fibers, both cotton and wool, were produced extensively. Texas and Oklahoma were the leading short-staple cotton states but were challenged after World War II by California, which developed the growth of irrigated, long-staple cotton under a highly mechanized regime. Historically, the range-sheep industry was identified almost exclusively with wool production, using the fine-wool breeds, especially the Merino. The shift to the dual-purpose English breeds for meat and wool came late. The interregional aspects of lamb production will be noted later.

REGIONAL INTERRELATIONS

No summary of commercial economies of the grassland, however sketchy, can forego reference to the mineral resources of the region and their peculiar relation to the necessities of such an area. Without forests, the grassland was dependent largely upon outside areas for the building materials and fuel traditional to American culture. The search for substitutes for wood was persistent and not immediately or fully successful. This introduces one of the most conspicuous aspects of the occupance of the grassland—regional interdepend-

ence. Not only the steam railroad but industrialization in all its aspects contributed what were essentials to the grassland economy. Capital and consumption goods furnished by the industrialized regions had to be paid for in money derived from cash crops. A degree of subsistence economy, such as had been the resort of the pioneer in the forest, was virtually impossible on natural grounds, and this imperative demand for money emphasized the necessity of specialized cash crops. Railroads made possible the import of sawed lumber, which was put together with machine-made nails. The grassland was characteristically a "sawed house," not a "sod house," country and still remains so (Malin, 1944, 1950, 1954*b*, 1954*c*). Coal for fuel was shipped in largely to supplement the lower-grade bituminous or lignite coals produced in some parts of the region (Malin, 1944, pp. 102–4; 1950*a*, chaps. i–iv, xvi, xix). The opening of the mid-continent oil and gas fields on a large scale after the beginning of the twentieth century afforded for the first time an efficient fuel, not only for use in the grassland, but eventually for large-scale export to other regions. The industrial minerals existed only in the mountain areas, but the accent on uranium during the last decade opened unknown possibilities.

Regional interdependency of another sort evolved out of the Texas cattle drives of song and story. First driven northward to market, the animals were found to fatten on the way, or were held on northern range to fatten on grass, before shipment by rail to Corn Belt feed lots or to market for slaughter. In 1887 the Santa Fe Railroad built southward into the Texas range country, and others followed. Soon afterward the controls for Texas fever were worked out. On the basis of these developments a stabilized procedure evolved to ship southwestern cattle to the Kansas-Oklahoma bluestem pastures to be grass-fattened for slaughter or to be fattened and matured for Corn Belt feed lots. Out of these practices a favorable rail-rate structure emerged: billing, with pasture stopover privileges, and standard pasture contracts from April 1 to October 1. According to the estimates of the United States Department of Agriculture's Agricultural Marketing Service, an annual average of 360,000 head of cattle was received in these pastures over the period 1943–52. Not only was this a larger number of animals but it represented a far larger potential of high-quality beef than was ever marketed from the southwestern range during the most fabulous days of the notorious Texas cattle drives, when grass, cattle, and Texans were supposed to be close to a "state of nature." This simple statement of facts suggests many more challenging questions about grass, soil, conservation, and cattle than can be considered here (Malin, 1942).

The chain of established services just described, that is, breeding on the range, maturing, and grass-fattening in transit on the bluestem pastures, full-feed finishing in the Corn Belt feed lots, and slaughter at the packing centers of Kansas City, St. Louis, and Chicago, represented, among other things, the pull of the great population centers of northeastern United States and Europe. It was an intricately woven pattern stretching diagonally across the United States, virtually from one corner to the other, and was the product of a complex of forces operating through a century of time. Like Topsy, it "just growed" and was not planned, although, after it had taken shape, interested parties at various points and times did consciously perfect details. In the sheep industry, although on a less permanent basis and in less volume, a somewhat comparable procedure also operated to move Idaho and Arizona lambs to feed lots near the major packing centers for finishing or to the winter-wheat pastures of the hard winter-wheat belt for maturing and fattening.

The first challenge to these systems came from the Pacific Coast, especially from southern California, which was sustaining a phenomenal population growth (Buechel, 1933). The bid of the Pacific Coast for food supplies became conspicuous during the depression decade of the 1930's and mounted to all but revolutionary proportions during and after the World War II boom. The economic continental divide had been located some distance west of the physical continental divide. Before the end of World War II the economic divide had moved eastward to such an extent as to draw much business to the southern Pacific Coast from western Nebraska, Kansas, Oklahoma, and a large part of Texas (Haystead, 1945; Malin, 1947, pp. 318–22). Thus far, the Pacific Northwest has not generated a comparable drawing power from the northern end of the grassland (Freeman and Martin, 1942). Great oil and gas developments and hydroelectric power may operate similarly in that area, but on the eve of atomic industrial power the historian must refrain from prophecy.

The interrelationships that have become effective between or among regions have not been the consequence of any preconceived plan, but that does not mean that no planning was undertaken. During the winter of 1876–77, and while the controversy was pending over the outcome of the disputed presidential election of 1876, a conciliation program was proposed. According to this plan, a through railroad was to be assembled and/or constructed from Philadelphia through the southern states to connect with the Texas and Pacific Railroad and southern California (Woodward, 1951). Had this over-all project been executed together with a favorable rate structure, the effects upon the Old South and upon the southern grassland would have been momentous.

Possibly the Texas–Kansas–bluestem pasture–Corn Belt–Chicago system previously described might not have emerged.

At the outbreak of World War II a similar plan was before the Interstate Commerce Commission, with a view of making Richmond, Virginia, a packing center and of diverting southwestern livestock through the Gulf states to be fed on their way east. World War II blocked the plan, but it was fought by all the interests in the Texas–Kansas–Corn Belt–Chicago system already in being, as well as by southern California, just then drawing heavily upon the same source for supplies of meat. One observation at least about the proposed Richmond plan is in order. Like much social planning of such magnitude, there was little, if anything, that was positive in the system for the country as a whole; its conspicuous characteristic was a proposal to benefit one region at the expense of others without any certainty of benefiting anybody on a long-term basis.

STRATEGIC STATUS

The regional interdependence just described was the product of railroads, supplemented by internal combustion engines on land wheels, whether tractors, trucks, or automobiles. New forces of air communications were at work on a reorientation and a redistribution of power. Already the fact has been pointed out that, for the first time in history, the potential of land-mass power had been implemented by steam railroads, dating from the mid-nineteenth century. The internal combustion engine in its several applications to surface movement in space supplemented and extended what steam railroads had begun. The effect of air power was not

necessarily to withdraw the loan of power from geographical positions intrusted with power under the rail regime. But the strategic significance of every site underwent a re-evaluation in terms of air power. Significantly, in a north circumpolar system, the North American grassland interior again rated a new loan of power, but subject to a substantial reassessment of relationships —among them a north-south orientation in addition to, rather than instead of, the exclusive east-west orientation of surface communication systems. Besides being called upon to provide bread, meat, fibers, coal, oil, gas, and uranium, the North American grassland served other functions at the mid-point of the twentieth century.

At the center of the North American continental land mass, this grassland contained the nerve centers of the military communication systems that defend or strike in its behalf. In such a perspective would anyone be so naïve as to insist that the problem of the grassland could be solved by turning it back to the Indian or to the cattleman? Instead of a return to the simplicity of a grazing country, the challenges of atomic power indicate a further incorporation into the complex network of areal and cultural interdependence. Much more, indeed, has become involved than the exclusive interests of the United States as an individual nation. This grassland region of North America, the interior of the United States and Canada, occupies one of the key geographical positions in the north circumpolar system of political power actually in being. Intrusted with such a loan of power, a heavy responsibility rests upon its holders for the use that is made of the opportunities committed to its charge.

REFERENCES

Something of the extent of the present writer's deviation from orthodoxy in the writing of history may be gathered by comparison of the essay offered here with an article by

Earl Pomeroy, "Toward a Reorientation of Western History: Continuity and Environment," *Mississippi Valley Historical Review*, XVI (1930), 579–600. Books that also represent conventional treatments are Eillington, Briggs, Caughey, Richardson and Rister, and Winther. Thus far, little has been done toward a synthesis of the newer point of view presented here. Such an over-all revision awaits research representative of a wider range of areas and topics, together with fresh interpretations of old and of new facts. Regions are not superior, inferior, or equal to one another. Each region is unique as well as are all the parts of which it is composed. The historian's emphasis is upon uniqueness; the social scientist's emphasis is upon likenesses subject to classification.

ADAMS, C. C.
  1902a "Postglacial Origin and Migrations of the Life of the Northeastern United States," *Journal of Geography*, I, 303–10, 352–57.
  1902b "The Southeastern United States as a Center of Geographical Distribution of Flora and Fauna," *Biological Bulletin*, III, 115–31.
BALL, CARLETON R.
  1930 "A History of American Wheat Improvement," *Agricultural History*, IV, 48–71.
BARNES, LELA (ed.)
  1936 "Journal of Isaac McCoy for the Exploring Expedition of 1830," *Kansas Historical Quarterly*, V, 339–77.
BEILMAN, A. P., and BRENNER, L. G.
  1951 "The Recent Intrusion of Forests in the Ozarks," *Annals of the Missouri Botanical Gardens*, XXXVIII, 261–82.
BILLINGTON, RAY A.
  1949 *Westward Expansion: A History of the American Frontier.* New York: Macmillan Co. 873 pp.
BORCHERT, JOHN R.
  1950 "The Climate of the Central North American Grassland," *Annals of the Association of American Geographers*, XL, 1–39.
  1953 "Regional Differences in the World Atmospheric Circulation," *ibid.*, XLIII, 14–26.
BRIGGS, HAROLD E.
  1940 *Frontiers of the Northwest: A History of the Upper Missouri Valley.* New York: D. Appleton–Century Co. 629 pp.
BRYAN, KIRK
  1940 "Erosion in the Valleys of the Southwest," *New Mexico Quarterly*, X, 227–32.
  1941 "Pre-Columbian Agriculture in the Southwest, as Conditioned by Periods of Alluviation," *Annals of the Association of American Geographers*, XXXI, 219–42.
BUECHEL, F. A.
  1933 *Eight Years of Livestock Shipments in Texas, 1924–1932, Part I: Cattle and Calves. . . .* (Bureau of Business Research Monograph No. 10.) Austin: University of Texas. 131 pp.
BYRON, LEONARD A., and FRYE, JOHN C.
  1954 "Ecological Conditions Accompanying Loess Deposition in the Great Plains Region of the United States," *Journal of Geology*, LXII, 399–404.
CAUGHEY, JOHN W.
  1938 *History of the Pacific Coast of North America.* New York: Prentice-Hall, Inc. 429 pp.
CLARK, JACOB A., et al.
  1923 *Classification of American Wheat Varieties.* (U.S. Department of Agriculture Bulletin No. 1074.) Washington, D.C.: Government Printing Office. 238 pp.
CLEMENTS, F. E., and SHELFORD, V. E.
  1933 *Bio-ecology.* New York: John Wiley & Sons. 425 pp.
COLBERT, EDWIN H. (ed.)
  1948 "Pleistocene of the Great Plains (A Symposium)," *Bulletin of the Geological Society of America*, LIX, 541–630.
CONDRA, G. E., and REED, E. C.
  1943 *The Geological Section of Nebraska.* (Nebraska Geological Survey Bulletin No. 14.) 2d ed. Lincoln, Neb. 82 pp.
  1948 *Correlation of the Pleistocene Deposits of Nebraska.* (Nebraska Geological Survey Bulletin No. 15.) Lincoln, Neb. 73 pp.
EGLER, FRANK E.
  1951 "A Commentary on American Plant Ecology, Based on the Textbooks of 1947–1949," *Ecology*, XXXII, 673–

94. (This is a must for anyone dealing with ecology in the United States.)

ELIAS, M. K. (ed.)
1945 "Symposium on Loess," *American Journal of Science*. CCXLIII, 225–303.

FLINT, RICHARD F.
1947 *Glacial Geology and the Pleistocene Epoch.* New York: John Wiley & Sons. 589 pp.

FLINT, RICHARD F., *et al.*
1949 "Pleistocene Research: A Review by the Members of the Committee on Interrelations of Pleistocene Research, National Research Council," *Bulletin of the Geological Society of America*, LX, 1305–1525.

FREEMAN, O. W., and MARTIN, H. W. (eds.)
1942 *The Pacific Northwest.* New York: John Wiley & Sons. 542 pp.

FRYE, JOHN C.
1945 "Problems of Pleistocene Stratigraphy in Central and Western Kansas," *Journal of Geology*, LIII, 73–93.
1946a "Review of Studies of Pleistocene Deposits in Kansas," *American Journal of Science*, CCXLIV, 403–516.
1946b "The High Plains Surface in Kansas," *Transactions of the Kansas Academy of Science*, XLIX, 71–86.
1951 "Soil Forming Intervals Evidenced in Kansas Pleistocene," *Soil Science*, LXXI, 403–8.
1955 "Erosion History of the Flint Hills," *Transactions of the Kansas Academy of Science*, LVIII, 79–86.

FRYE, JOHN C., and BYRON, LEONARD A.
1951 "Stratigraphy of the Late Pleistocene Loesses in Kansas," *Journal of Geology*, LIX, 287–305.
1952 *Pleistocene Geology of Kansas.* (State Geological Survey of Kansas Bulletin No. 99.) Lawrence, Kan. 230 pp.

GILPIN, WILLIAM
1860 *The Central Gold Region: The Grain, Pastoral and Gold Region of North America.* Philadelphia: Somer, Barnes & Co. 194 pp.

GLEASON, H. A.
1926 "The Individualistic Concept of the Plant Association," *Bulletin of the Torrey Botanical Club*, LIII, 7–26.

1939 "The Individualistic Concept of the Plant Association," pp. 92–108 in JUST, THEODORE (ed.), *Plant and Animal Communities.* Notre Dame: Notre Dame University. 255 pp.

HAYDEN, F. V.
1863 "On the Geological and Natural History of the Upper Missouri [Expedition of 1857]," *Transactions of the American Philosophical Society* (N.S.), Vol. XII, chap. xii: "Quaternary Deposits."

HAYSTEAD, LADD
1945 *If the Prospect Pleases: The West the Guide Books Never Mention.* Norman: Oklahoma University Press. 208 pp.

HAZELTON, JOHN M.
1939 *A History of Linebred Anxiety 4th Herefords of Straight Gudgell & Simpson Breeding.* Kansas City: Missouri Associated Breeders of Anxiety 4th Herefords. 569 pp.

HILGARD, E. W.
1860 *Report on the Geology and Agriculture of the State of Mississippi.* Jackson: Mississippi State Printer. 391 pp.
1892 *A Report on the Relations of Soil and Climate.* (U.S. Department of Agriculture, Weather Bureau Bulletin No. 3.) Washington, D.C.: Government Printing Office. 59 pp.

JOHNSON, W. D.
1901 "The High Plains and Their Utilization," pp. 601–768 in *Twenty-first Annual Report, United States Geological Survey*, Part IV: *Hydrology.* Washington, D.C.: Government Printing Office. 768 pp.
1902 "The High Plains and Their Utilization," pp. 631–69 in *Twenty-second Annual Report, United States Geological Survey*, Part IV: *Hydrology.* Washington, D.C.: Government Printing Office. 671 pp.

KOLLMORGEN, WALTER M., and JENKS, GEORGE F.
1951–52 "A Geographic Study of Population and Settlement Changes in Sherman County, Kansas," *Transactions of the Kansas Academy of Science*, LIV, 449–94; LV, 1–37.

LAUTENSACH, HERMANN
1953 *Das Mormonenland als Beispiel sozialgeographischen Raumes.* ("Bonner Geographische Abhandlungen," No. 11.) Bonn: The Author and the Geographischen Instituts der Universität. Bonn. 46 pp.

MALIN, JAMES C.
1935 "The Turnover of Farm Population in Kansas," *Kansas Historical Quarterly,* IV, 339–72.
1942 "An Introduction to the History of the Bluestem Pastures," *ibid.,* XI, 3–28.
1944 *Winter Wheat in the Golden Belt of Kansas.* Lawrence: University of Kansas Press. 290 pp.
1946a "Dust Storms, 1850–1900," *Kansas Historical Quarterly,* XIV, 129–44, 265–96, 391–413.
1946b *Essays on Historiography.* Lawrence, Kan.: The Author. 188 pp.
1947 *The Grassland of North America: Prolegomena to Its History.* Lawrence, Kan.: The Author. 398 pp. (Contains an extensive bibliography.)
1950a *Grassland Historical Studies: Natural Resources Utilization in a Background of Science and Technology,* Vol. I: *Geology and Geography.* Lawrence, Kan.: The Author. 377 pp.
1950b "Ecology and History," *Scientific Monthly,* LXX, 295–98.
1952 "Man, the State of Nature, and Climax: As Illustrated by Some Problems of the North American Grassland," *ibid.,* LXXIV, 29–37.
1953 "Soil, Animal, and Plant Relations of the Grassland, Historically Reconsidered," *ibid.,* LXXVI, 207–20.
1954a *The Nebraska Question, 1852–1854.* Lawrence, Kan.: The Author. 455 pp.
1954b "Emergency Housing at Lawrence, 1854," *Kansas Historical Quarterly,* XXI, 34–49.
1954c "Housing Experiments in the Lawrence Community," *ibid.,* pp. 95–121.
1954d Review of SAUER, CARL O., *Agricultural Origins and Dispersals,* in *Agricultural History,* XXVIII, 34–35.
1955a "Notes on the Writing of General Histories of Kansas, Part Three: The Historical and Philosophical Societies; Repositories of the Material of History and of Science," *Kansas Historical Quarterly,* XXI, 331–78.
1955b *The Contriving Brain and the Skillful Hand in the United States: Something about History and Philosophy of History.* Lawrence, Kan.: The Author. 436 pp. (This book undertakes to deal with the issues raised in the third section of the present paper, "Railroads and Land-Mass Power," but in a much larger setting, with special reference to the nineteenth century and to cultural technology.)

MARBUT, C. F.
1935 *Soils of the United States,* Part III: *Atlas of American Agriculture.* Washington, D.C.: Government Printing Office. 98 pp.

MARTIN, PAUL S., et al.
1947 *Indians before Columbus: Twenty Thousand Years of North American History Revealed in Archeology.* Chicago: University of Chicago Press. 582 pp.

OLIPHANT, J. ORIN
1932 "The Cattle Trade from the Far Northwest to Montana," *Agricultural History,* VI, 69–83.
1933 "The Cattle Trade of Puget Sound, 1858–1890," *ibid.,* VII, 129–49.
1946 "The Eastward Movement of Cattle from the Oregon Country," *ibid.,* XX, 19–43.
1948 "History of the Livestock Industry in the Pacific Northwest," *Oregon Historical Quarterly,* XLIX, 1–29.

PHILLIPS, RALPH W.
1944 "The Cattle of India," *Journal of Heredity,* XXXV, 273–88.

POWELL, J. W.
1878 *Report on the Lands of the Arid Region of the United States, with a More Detailed Account of the Lands of Utah.* (House Executive Document No. 73; 45th Cong., 2d sess.) Washington, D.C.: Government Printing Office. 208 pp.

PRICE, EDWARD T.
1955 "Values and Concepts in Conservation," *Annals of the Association of American Geographers,* XLV, 64–84.

RHOAD, A. O.
1949   "The Santa Gertrudis Breed," *Journal of Heredity*, XL, 115–26.

RICHARDSON, RUPERT N., and RISTER, CARL C.
1935   *The Greater Southwest.* Glendale, Calif.: Arthur H. Clark Co. 506 pp.

ROBINSON, CHARLES
1859   "Letter to the Editor," *Lawrence (Kan.) Herald of Freedom*, May 7.

SAUER, CARL O.
1952   *Agricultural Origins and Dispersals.* (Bowman Memorial Lectures, Series Two.) New York: American Geographical Society. 110 pp.

SCHOEWE, WALTER H.
1948–53   "The Geography of Kansas," Part I: "Political Geography"; Part II: "Physical Geography"; Part III: "Hydrogeography," *Transactions of the Kansas Academy of Science*, LI, 253–88; LII, 261–333; LIV, 263–329; LVI, 131–90.

SHALER, N. S.
1889   *Aspects of the Earth.* New York: Charles Scribner's. 344 pp.
1891   *Nature and Man in America.* New York: Charles Scribner's. 290 pp.

SHANNON, FRED A.
1940   *Critiques of Research in the Social Sciences. III. An Appraisal of Walter Prescott Webb's "The Great Plains: A Study in Institutions and Environments."* (With a panel discussion.) New York: Social Science Research Council. 254 pp.

TAYLOR, BAYARD
1867   *Colorado, a Summer Trip.* New York: G. P. Putnam's. 185 pp.

THORP, JAMES, *et al.*
1950   "Some Post-Pliocene Buried Soils of Central United States," *Journal of Soil Science*, Vol. II, Part I.

TRANSEAU, E. N.
1935   "The Prairie Peninsula," *Ecology*, XVI, 423–37.

WEATHERWAX, PAUL
1954   *Indian Corn in Old America.* New York: Macmillan Co. 253 pp.

WEAVER, JOHN E.
1954   *The North American Prairie.* Lincoln, Neb.: Johnsen Publishing Co. 384 pp.

WEAVER, J. E., and CLEMENTS, F. E.
1938   *Plant Ecology.* 2d ed. New York: McGraw-Hill Book Co. 601 pp.

WEBB, W. P.
1931   *The Great Plains.* Boston: Ginn & Co. 525 pp.

WENTWORTH, EDWARD N.
1942   "Eastward Sheep Drives from California and Oregon," *Mississippi Valley Historical Review*, XXVIII, 507–38.
1948   *America's Sheep Trails.* Ames, Iowa: Iowa State College Press. 667 pp.
1954   "Trailing Sheep from California to Idaho in 1865: The Journal of Gorham Gates Kimball," *Agricultural History*, XXVIII, 49–83.

WILLHAM, OLIVER S.
1937   "A Genetic History of Hereford Cattle in the United States," *Journal of Heredity*, XXVIII, 283–94.

WINTHER, OSCAR O.
1947   *The Great Northwest: A History.* New York: A. A. Knopf. 383 pp.

WOODWARD, C. VANN
1951   *Reunion and Reaction: The Compromise of 1877 and the End of Reconstruction.* Boston: Little, Brown & Co. 263 pp.

The Age of Fossil Fuels

EUGENE AYRES[*]

Significant changes in man's way of life have often come about with almost inconceivable slowness. The characteristics of an age do not dawn suddenly upon our consciousness but are likely to be fully realized only when we have gone so far upon the long new path that the end of the path is almost in sight. Is the so-called "atomic age" an exception? I do not think so. The very readiness with which we have accepted nuclear energy and have woven intricate scientific fancies about it seems to strike a false historical note. Almost the only thing we can say with assurance about the future is that it will bear little resemblance to preconceptions of it.

REMOTE BEGINNINGS

No one can say when the age of fossil fuels began. We might set the date before 6000 B.C., when the forests in the Garden of Eden had almost disappeared and when the fertile valleys had become desert. Or when the Babylonians began to use pools of native asphalt. Or when ancient Persian kings (according to Aristotle) had their food cooked in caves where seepages of natural gas were continuously aflame. Or when the Chinese, about two thousand years ago, were mining coal and using it in considerable volume. Or perhaps a little later when the Chinese drilled laborious wells through solid rock to tap great reservoirs of natural gas. Or when the Burmese, beginning before the tenth century, similarly drilled wells to tap, abundantly, the reservoirs of liquid oil.

The real beginning of the fossil fuel age may be more properly regarded, I believe, not as a matter of production but as a matter of effective utilization, and this came much later.

An understanding of the present age requires that we see how it came into being. As Becker (1932, p. 19) has said, "We can identify a thing only by pointing to what it was before it became the thing that it will presently cease to be."

By the thirteenth century, England's forests had been seriously depleted and people were cold. King Henry III gave his grudging consent to the inhabitants of Newcastle to mine coal. This was about a thousand years after the Roman invaders had burned coal in England and more than a thousand years after the beginning of Chinese coal production, but Henry's act made an official beginning in England. Henry's son, Ed-

* Mr. Ayres is consultant to the Gulf Research & Development Company, Pittsburgh, Pennsylvania. In 1934 he became associated with this company to undertake the organization and direction of research concerned with the refining of petroleum and refined petroleum products, later becoming Technical Assistant to the Executive Vice-President of the Gulf Laboratories. During the past few years, Mr. Ayres has devoted most of his time to the study of national and international energy resources—production, use, and economy—and is consultant to several government agencies and petroleum industry organizations. Holder of more than fifty patents on a wide variety of inventions, he also is the author of numerous articles in various technical fields and is co-author, with C. A. Scarlott, of *Energy Sources: The Wealth of the World*, 1952.

ward I, found it necessary to propitiate the barons, and he signed a decree prescribing the death penalty for the burning of coal in London while Parliament was in session, "lest the health of the Knights of the Shire should suffer during their residence in London." At least one man was executed for this crime. Later, Queen Elizabeth I also signed a decree against the use of coal. France in earlier centuries had legislated against the use of coal, but in 1600 Henry IV of France exempted coal from the ground rent of the one-tenth due the sovereign by virtue of his royal right and prerogative. The French had already perceived the utility of encouraging the production and use of fossil fuels. Unfortunately, this perception was to become dull in later years, and France, like England, was to become prematurely deprived of its magnificent forests.

By the fifteenth century the forests of Scotland were already largely a thing of the past. Pope Pius II, whose writings are said to have influenced Christopher Columbus, told how he had seen at the doors of churches in Scotland mendicants in rags who "received for alms pieces of black stone with which they went away contented. This species of stone they burn in place of wood of which their country is destitute" (Taylor, 1845, p. 211).

SEVENTEENTH CENTURY

In the early part of the seventeenth century a Franciscan missionary traveled through what is now Upper New York State and reported "some very good oil" there issuing from the ground. The item aroused no particular interest. Petroleum was already well known but was of no importance anywhere. In particular, America was a vast wooded wilderness, and no one knew or cared about the stores of coal, oil, and gas beneath the forest floor.

By 1650 a fair start had been made at coal utilization in England, Scotland, Belgium, and France. Two sailing vessels were constantly employed in carrying coal from Newcastle to London, and England's export trade in coal was under way. Most of the coal then burned in Paris was from Newcastle. The price of coal on board ship at Newcastle was about a dollar a ton (10s. for a chaldron of 53 cwt.). But Oliver Cromwell's Parliament was petitioned by the people of London against two nuisances—hops and coal—because "they spoyle the taste of drinck and endanger the people" (*ibid.*, p. 320). Gas at this time was described by the Chinese as being applied very advantageously to economic uses. These uses were not understood by contemporary European reporters—in no sense technologists—who said, in effect: "We have wells of water in Europe, but the Chinese have wells of fire. Beneath the surface of the earth are mines of sulfur which are already lighted. They have only to make a small opening whence issues heat enough to cook whatever they wish." We know now that the Chinese at this time were carrying out certain industrial operations with the heat of burning natural gas. About a century later the Western world learned some of the details—how gas was being distributed in bamboo pipe lines with clay terminals to homes and industrial establishments. Streets of some towns and many homes were lighted with gas, and gas was being used to heat buildings and to evaporate brine. Central heating with gas and coal had been widely practiced for many centuries, although not continuously. Such arts were used for a few generations, lost because of some economic or military cataclysm, and then rediscovered. (One period of rediscovery of central heating in China came about A.D. 900.)

Coal was common in China. The mountains west of Peiping contained "coal in such abundance that a space of half a league cannot be traversed without meeting with rich strata." Coal in Peiping was abundant and was sold at a moderate price. The provinces of Shansi and Chihli were supplying large quantities of coal. Many boats were being used continuously for transportation of anthracite from Liaotung to Tientsin. Both anthracite and bituminous coal were in the Nanking and other Chinese markets—also coal briquettes for the fires of the poor. Coal brought into Canton was high in sulfur and ash and was used for the manufacture of green vitriol. Iron ore was being smelted with anthracite. This was in the seventeenth century, when the utilization of coal in England was much more primitive and when coal in America was still unknown.

The earliest notice of the presence of coal in America came in 1665, when a French missionary marked "houille" on a map of the country then occupied by Indians at Pimitoui (now Peoria, Illinois). This was almost a century before coal was known to exist in Pennsylvania. Purchases of land from the Indians by William Penn and his family, and later by the proprietaries, did not include any portion of the coal land of Pennsylvania until 1749. In that year the 3,750 square miles embracing the whole anthracite region were acquired for £500 ($2,000)! And acquisition of bituminous coal lands came even later.

Before 1700, European technologists were finding new things to do with coal. British patent No. 214 was for distillation of coal to obtain coal tar. J. J. Becher, a German "chemist" who had been trying to transmute Danubian sand into gold, published a report on coal gas. An English patent was granted for "a way to extract and make great quantities of pitch, tar, and oil out of a sort of stone." This stone was oil shale. The idea was to be used on a limited scale in England about a century and a half later. Its general use is still in the future.

EIGHTEENTH CENTURY

The use of coal in England grew rapidly. By 1700 about six hundred sailing vessels were engaged in the London coal trade, and coal was selling in London for the equivalent of about four dollars a ton. Some unknown English inventor tried the smelting of iron ore with coke instead of wood charcoal, but this use of coke (from bituminous coal) was not to become general in England for a century, and an additional half-century was to pass before coke superseded charcoal in America. In both places the Chinese process of anthracite smelting was rediscovered and used before coke.

In 1715 France began commercial mining of coal (Anzin); England started, in a small way, to smelt iron ore with coke (Colebrookdale); and the first blast furnace was erected in America (eastern Virginia)—but here charcoal was the fuel, for it was not until 1735 that coal-mining started in America. Local wood near Richmond, Virginia, had, at last, become scarce, and transportation of wood was impractical. By this time steam-engine pumps were in quite general use in England to drain water from deep mines, and now this operation began in France. This was the small beginning of the conversion of heat to power.

In the 1750's Samuel Johnson completed his famous *Dictionary of the English Language*. "Coal" was well defined, and so was "petroleum," but a "mill" was "in general an engine in which any operation is performed by means of wind or water; sometimes it is used of engines turned by hand, or by animal force." No mention was made of steam as a motive force. It was also about this time that the presence of petroleum in northwestern Pennsylvania was noted on a map of the "Middle

British Colonies in America." The word "petroleum" was printed close to the present site of Titusville and Oil City —the very area that was to have the first wild American oil boom a century later. Thus the occurrence of oil in Pennsylvania was recorded several years before the occurrence of coal there was reported. But petroleum at this time was already being produced on a small scale in Rumania, and production was now started also in Galicia.

By 1760 a few tons of bituminous may have been dug up and used locally in western Pennsylvania. But this is by no means certain, for Pennsylvania coal was not known east of the Alleghenies for about a half-century, and up to this time there was probably not a white man living within the limits of the present Allegheny County.

In 1766 anthracite coal was reported in eastern Pennsylvania, and a few tons were consumed in a local blacksmith's forge. At this time the proprietaries made their last purchase of land from the Indians. This purchase embraced the whole great area of bituminous land in Pennsylvania, and the purchase price was about $10,000. The land was valued, of course, not for its coal but for its vast resource of timber. At this time petroleum was also in the news. Since moderate importation of Burmese petroleum for a century was beginning to pique the curiosity of London, the governor-general of India sent Major Michael Symes of the British army as ambassador to the Burmese king. Symes reported that the annual petroleum production of Burma was about 400,000 hogsheads. He counted 520 oil wells in a small area bordering Petroleum Creek, a tributary of the Irrawaddy. Somehow Britain was unimpressed. The British waited until a half-century later to make a more detailed report of the phenomenon.

The indifference of Western nations is odd, considering the fact that the suitability of petroleum as a fuel was then well known in Europe. And David Zeisberger, famous Moravian missionary to the Indians, reported in 1769 that the oil being collected in Forest County, Pennsylvania, "can be used in lamps" (Egle, 1877, p. 613). But America had no real need at this time for any fuel except wood. This was pointed up when the Provincial Convention held in Philadelphia in 1775 adopted a lengthy and detailed resolution covering all the items of agriculture and manufacture that the authors considered important to the defense of the Colonies. Fuel was not mentioned.

Immediately after the American Revolution the first American coal-mining company was organized at Pottsville, Pennsylvania. The first few tons of coal (anthracite) were sent down the Susquehanna River from Wilkes-Barre to the armory at Carlisle, Pennsylvania, probably for use in blacksmith forges. This was the tiny beginning of the great coal production in America. On the other side of the earth, in India, 73 tons of coal were sent down from Burdwan to the armory at Calcutta. Burdwan coal was to become of minor importance later on, but Indian production has not even yet fulfilled its potentialities.

At long last coal was recognized in America as a resource of consequence. The first sale of land purchased because of its coal was recorded in 1785 at Clearfield, Pennsylvania, but the first load of coal from this land was not shipped for nineteen years! In the meantime Russia was employing English miners to dig coal along the Donets River. At this time France produced about 213,000 tons of coal and imported much more than this amount from England. The United States imported 3,850 tons of coal and produced almost none. The price of coal in London had risen to $10.00 a ton. American petroleum was selling for $16.00 a gallon, but as a medicine rather than as a fuel.

The discovery of coal in the Lehigh Valley came in 1791. A sample of the hard anthracite was taken to Philadelphia, where a group of adventurous men thought that something profitable could be done with it. So they formed the Lehigh Coal Mine Company. Their hopes were doomed, for nobody would buy or use such coal at this time. The company was succeeded some years later by the Lehigh Coal and Lehigh Navigation Companies, which prospered mightily.

1800 TO 1850

The story of the battle to win acceptance for coal in America is interesting. In 1800 the only American concern with coal of any sort was on the Atlantic Seaboard, where a little bituminous was being imported from England. Commercial use of coke for ironmaking was still far in the future for America but was in some use in Europe (e.g., in Upper Silesia), and coal tar was in commercial production in England. More than 99 per cent of the heat produced in America was from the burning of wood.

In 1804 the first coal of any sort reached the interior villages of the American East. A little bituminous was floated down the Susquehanna River to Columbia. This was a great surprise to the inhabitants of Lancaster County, Pennsylvania, who had never seen coal before.

In 1808, for the first time in America, a grate was constructed for the use of anthracite for domestic heat. The grate was made for Judge Jesse Fell of Wilkes-Barre, Pennsylvania, who wrote: "Made the experiment of burning the common stone coal of the valley in a grate, in a fireplace in my house, and found it will answer the purpose of a fuel, making a cleaner and better fire at

less expense than burning wood in the common way" (*ibid.*, p. 876).

News of this sensational discovery spread over the countryside, and people came to witness the phenomenon that had been so familiar to the Chinese about two millenniums earlier. Soon, similar grates had been constructed by Judge Fell's neighbors. In the same year, John and Obigah Smith loaded two arks with anthracite in Ronson's Creek and floated them down the Susquehanna to Columbia. The people of Columbia had seen bituminous a few years before, but never anthracite, and no one could be induced to buy. The "black stones" had to be left behind in a dump heap. Not discouraged, the Smith brothers took two more arks of coal down the river the next year, but this time they took along one of Judge Fell's grates. The practicability of using the "black stones" as domestic fuel was convincingly demonstrated, and the coal was sold. Thereafter the market was grudgingly assured.

While this first primitive appreciation of coal was being developed in the United States, coal-gas lighting was spreading in London. Street lighting with gas did not start until 1810 in London. World street lighting was limited to a few whale-oil lamps in London and to a few petroleum-distillate lamps in Genoa and Parma. The distillate was obtained from petroleum flowing from a well in Modena, Italy. Added to this were lamps in India supplied with oil from Burma—but this had been going on for many centuries. Because the demand was so meager, the cost of petroleum in America dropped to $1.50 a gallon.

The periods from 1780 to 1820 in America and from 1800 to 1820 in England saw intensive development of power uses for the steam engine, but this had no effect on fossil fuel consumption, for wood was used almost entirely as fuel for steam-raising, and wood charcoal was the preferred fuel for iron manufacture. The impetus toward large-scale substitution of heat power for animate power was beginning to be felt in the Western world, but it was not to become really important until the twentieth century, when generation of electric power (from coal) and the internal combustion engine (for petroleum) were well launched.

During the first decade of the nineteenth century the Chinese are said to have had about ten thousand wells at the foot of the high mountains of the Tibetan chains (Taylor, 1845, p. 402). Many individual Chinese personally owned hundreds of wells producing brine and natural gas and averaging about twelve barrels a day of oil. The wells were through rock, with walls as polished as glass. In general, they were almost 2,000 feet deep (sometimes 3,000) and 5 or 6 inches in diameter. They had been drilled without power machinery, but so was the famous Drake well that came forty-seven years later.

While anthracite had been used in China for centuries, it was having a rough time not only in America but in England. Bakewell, in the first edition of his *Geology* (1813, p. 47), remarked: "It is true that a considerable part of the coal in South Wales is of an inferior quality [anthracite] and is not at present burned for domestic use; but in proportion as coal becomes scarce, improved methods of burning it will assuredly be discovered."

By 1815 bituminous coal was being used in Pittsburgh to operate steam engines for generation of about 150 horsepower. This meant that industrial consumption of coal in Pittsburgh was about 700 tons a year, and this was probably not far from the total United States industrial consumption of domestic coal. Industrial use of anthracite was about nil. Tried at the Philadelphia

Water Works, it was rejected because it "put the fire out." One of the principal manufacturers in Philadelphia, a Mr. Wetherill, buried the coal that had been consigned to him. Others crushed the coal and used it like gravel. Intensive sales effort was employed, including the printing of directions for burning, provision of certificates of approval from blacksmiths, and even bribery of foremen. A handicap to development was the relatively high price ($14.00 a ton) because of cost of transportation. But the price of English coal in New York was about $17.00 a ton (duty was $2.75). Wood and wood charcoal were soon to become even more costly. France, in 1815, produced 870,000 tons of coal and imported 230,000 tons from England. No figures were yet available on English production.

By 1820 the first consignment of coal from Wilkes-Barre reached Philadelphia. The total production of anthracite in the United States was estimated by Taylor (1845, p. 217) as not over 365 tons.[1] But the use of anthracite was to grow very rapidly, for, six years later, Philadelphia brought in 16,000 tons. A writer expressed his opinion that anthracite would some day become the principal fuel not only of Philadelphia but of some other cities. He was talking about domestic use, for even in 1830 almost no anthracite was being used industrially. And even for domestic heat, coal was of minor consequence. France was in about the same stage as America except that its records were much more precise. Charcoal was used all over the world, except in China and Wales, for the smelting of iron ore.

The first use of anthracite in America to raise steam for operating a steam engine came in 1830 in Pottsville, Pennsylvania. Abraham Pott used special grate bars that could resist the high heat of combustion. Thus, iron, made

1. I believe that some recent estimates of about ten times this amount are in error.

with wood charcoal, in turn made possible the burning of coal to provide steam for an engine used to saw wood.

In the 1830's wood was still king, but coal was growing. Annual consumption of domestic fuel in New York City was valued at $616,000 for wood, $100,000 for wood charcoal, and $613,000 for coal. Most of the coal was anthracite, but some was bituminous from Virginia. Philadelphia spent $740,000 for wood and $404,000 for coal (all anthracite). These figures do not include imported fuel. Vienna, with a much larger population than New York City, spent the equivalent of $300,000 for wood, $100,000 for wood charcoal, and only $30,000 for coal.

During the 1830's oil wells were beginning to appear in the United States. One, in Burksville, Kentucky, gushed oil 12 feet into the air before subsiding to a more moderate flow. We were doing what the Chinese had been doing for many centuries—drilling wells for brine and often finding oil or gas instead. And people began to notice oil seepages all over the world. In western Iran, where so much oil is being produced today, exudant liquid bitumen was being collected in the way described by Herodotus about twenty-four hundred years ago. Productive springs of naphtha were in operation on the borders of the Persian Gulf. Oil from the provinces of Fars and Azerbaijan was being used in lamps and to coat the bottoms of vessels on the Tigris and Euphrates rivers. In fact, oil was noted in the majority of places where modern production has been successful—Baku, Venezuela, California, Mexico, Texas. Men began to wonder what the eventual importance of oil might be. Someone said: "It surely was not placed there in vain" (Taylor, 1845, p. 213).

In 1840 an official attempt was made through the Census Act to determine the production of bituminous coal in the United States, but the attempt was

a failure. It was thought by many that "this species of investigation savors too much of scrutiny into the private affairs of men, and is unsuited to the spirit of republican institutions." The statisticians of the period concluded that the extent of the bituminous coal fields was so large that "it seems futile to hazard even the roughest calculation." This uncertainty was to continue for a decade, but it was assumed that production of bituminous was somewhat less than production of anthracite, the amount of which could be estimated with reasonable accuracy because so much of it was shipped by common carrier.

A guess was made in 1840 that about a million tons of bituminous were produced in Pennsylvania and perhaps an additional half-million tons in West Virginia and Kentucky. These figures do not agree with actual census returns for the year, but, in my opinion, they are probably more accurate. France kept good records: its production of coal was nearly three million tons. But in spite of the fact that Britain was the oldest coal-producing nation, its records were as indefinite as ours. Not even a good guess could be made of Britain's production in 1840 except that it was probably larger than that of France and the United States combined. Belgium was in second place. Any statistics prior to 1850 (except for France) must be regarded with suspicion.

An increasing proportion of the iron of the world was being produced with coal, but in the United States all blast furnaces except six were still using charcoal.

Much of the coal in the middle of the nineteenth century was being mined by actual, or virtual, slaves. But laws were being passed in France, the Netherlands, Belgium, and the United States for the regulation of mining. Britain was the last to establish a system of humane, judicial interference. In spite of laws, miners were being poorly treated everywhere. In the United States the wage in Pennsylvania was 87.5 cents a day. In England and Scotland thousands of females were being used as beasts of burden to carry coal from the mines, the ordinary load for a woman being 230 pounds. The report of the Midland Commission was characterized by sickening and almost incredible details of such coal-mining practices in Britain. Long after the Civil War had freed our Negro slaves, England was still regarding its white mining force as a part of capital investment. Denmark was using convict labor.

Contemporary estimates of the life of coal reserves of the United States and the world are interesting today, because they were so fearfully wrong. It was thought then that Pennsylvania had as much coal as we now believe can be produced ultimately by the entire nation. United States coal was expected to be adequate for a great many thousand years. This fallacious conception lasted a full century. We believe now that our peak of coal production (all grades) will come within a hundred years if some of the higher coal-consumption estimates can be relied upon. United States anthracite reached its peak of production in 1915. The peak of production of "cheap coal"—coal that can be mined at anything like present costs—is likely to be around 1975. It was thought that coal fields in Britain could produce 116 billion tons, "or more than 5,500 years of supply for consumption and exportation." But Britain's coal production has already passed its peak. The coal future belongs not to Britain but to the rest of the world.

1850 TO 1900

Figures for 1850 are the first that can be relied upon. Total coal production of the world was about 50 million tons, with Britain supplying 62 per cent. Belgium, the United States, and France each supplied about 11 per cent. We had 540 blast furnaces, of which only 43 were not using wood charcoal. These 43 were using anthracite coal, but anthracite was to be promptly supplanted by coke from bituminous coal—already common in England.

Transportation of bituminous was a problem. This is highlighted by the fact that, while Pittsburgh was consuming three-quarters of a million tons, only 40,000 tons were finding their way east of the Allegheny Mountains. The railroad systems were soon to take care of this.

By 1850 the great deposits of sub-bituminous coal and lignite on the eastern flank of the Rocky Mountains had been roughly located. This coal area had been described (Taylor, 1845, p. 575) as exceeding "all others on the present surface of our planet." More than a century later we are looking forward to extensive use of this store of energy.

The 1850's saw the awakening of world-wide interest of Western nations in liquid fuel. James Young, in England, took out his patent for obtaining oil by distillation of cannel coal and oil shale. Two Boston chemists started to make lubricating oil from coal tar. A Canadian geologist developed a process for making oil from coal and founded the New York Kerosene Oil Company. Large plants were built in Boston and Portland for making liquid fuel from coal and oil shale, and some fifty smaller plants appeared at various inland points. Oil wells were not uncommon. At least a dozen men owned wells with moderate production, and oil was having a ready sale. But synthetic oil from coal was being produced twenty times as fast as natural petroleum. Smart men of the time thought that we were entering upon a synthetic-oil period, but they were wrong.

The famous Drake well, drilled in 1859, was not the first well for petroleum and by no means the largest. The well was drilled in about the same way that the Chinese and Burmese had drilled their wells a thousand years earlier. But, for some strange reason, the Drake well aroused the imagination of speculators. People with a little money flocked to the wilderness of Pennsylvania to try their luck without benefit of technology. Some made fortunes, while others became bankrupt. The net result of eight years of violent confusion was proof that petroleum and natural gas could be produced in the United States in abundance, as it had been produced in Burma in abundance for many centuries. We had been ranging the seven seas for whale oil, and our whale oil "take" for 1859 was two hundred times our oil production, but it seemed to occur to no one to import Burmese petroleum. Perhaps this is because such importation would have involved so much less physical danger and hardship than whaling or, indeed, than oil production in Pennsylvania in those initial years. Until recently, Americans have been a romantic and speculative people.

At the end of eight years of violent turmoil, the oil boom subsided in Pennsylvania. The drop of oil production in those early wells to a mere trickle had a sobering effect. Drunken audiences no longer threw five-hundred-dollar bills on the stage in appreciation of cheap shows. Men no longer threw fireballs into oil tanks. Locomotives no longer fixed chains about oil pipe lines to uproot them. Personal degradation, dishonesty, and murder were no longer accepted as normal. The oil business was about to mature.

Smart people (John D. Rockefeller, for example) thought we were entering a period when petroleum was to light the lamps of the world. There was no other known use for petroleum at that time. But, of course, these people were wrong. Electric lighting had already appeared above the horizon and was destined soon to supplant kerosene. Unsuspected by petroleum pioneers, the internal combustion engine was ready to take the load of production in the twentieth century, after smart people (in Wall Street, for example) thought we were entering a period of steam motorcars and, later, electric motorcars. They, too, were wrong. When the internal combustion engine was established, smart people (Henry Ford, for example) thought that we were entering a period of expensive cars for the few. Later, Ford and others discovered that the trend was toward relatively inexpensive cars for the many.

Literally no one has foreseen the present universality of American motorcar use. Now that the highways are almost saturated with gasoline-burning vehicles, we call this a motorcar age, but recorded predictions make incredible reading. They came from automotive companies, oil companies, investment bankers, and economists. They were all wrong—even predictions as recent as 1950. This is no reflection on their intelligence. But I believe it is a reflection on present intelligence when we presume to know what the next age will be like.

But we are ahead of our story.

By 1870, when both coal and petroleum had been launched in the world, no country was yet mechanized with mobile power except for the locomotive. We had more than half the railroad mileage of the world, and steam locomotives had finally supplanted horses and mules; but railroads had all been built without benefit of tractors, bulldozers, or power equipment of any sort. Our system, and all other systems, had been built by the sweat of men and horses—as the ancient pyramids had been built by the sweat of the Egyptians. Smart people thought that railroads were the most conservative of all investments, but they were wrong. By the time power equipment was available (in the twentieth century), railway systems had reached their peak and were thereafter to decline, because power equipment has been used to build competitive highway systems for cars, busses, and trucks.

Steamships were common, but they still all had sails. Sails were beginning to be considered auxiliary to steam power instead of the other way around. But England had only two naval steamers. The rest depended entirely upon sails. McCormick reapers were multiplying on the farms, but they were all horse-operated. Most mining was still done with wood as fuel, and many thousands of acres of woodland were being denuded to supply fuel for steam boilers.

But the foundations for power equipment had been laid. Everywhere wood was becoming scarce and expensive, and coal and oil were becoming plentiful and cheap. The small high-pressure steam engine was in production, and the steam turbine was just around the corner. Men had made workable mobile vehicles (as early as 1800). Generation of electric power had been developed, and various forms of electric lighting had been demonstrated. The telegraph was in operation, and the telephone was about to come. (The Western Union Telegraph Company mistakenly thought we were entering a period of telegraphic communication and turned down Bell's offer to sell them the rights to the telephone for $100,000.) Wireless communication and the motion picture were in embryo. The stage was all set for the rapid industrial development that has taken place within the last fifty years.

TWENTIETH CENTURY

All industrial operations require power (and fuel), but the two outstanding circumstances that have sky-rocketed fuel demand during the last fifty years have been electric power and the internal combustion engine. Each one has advanced more rapidly than had been thought possible. The drain on the world's finite supply of fossil fuels is becoming fantastic and shows every sign of continuing acceleration. Today, day in and day out, we are consuming in the United States over a quarter of a million barrels of petroleum, nearly 45,000 tons of coal, and a billion cubic feet of natural gas *every hour*. No wonder we think of this as the fossil fuel age. But these overwhelming rates of depletion of finite resources have come only recently. In 1900 the petroleum production of the world was about 400,000 barrels a day, and more than half of this was in Russia. Thus, our daily production in 1900 was much less than our hourly consumption is now. The rest of the world is moving forward nearly four times as rapidly as the United States. The reasons for more rapid increase in consumption abroad are (1) that we already have our tens of millions of motorcars, while automotive development in many other nations is just beginning, and (2) that the rest of the world has about ten times as much potential oil land as we have. We have developed our oil production energetically and effectively, while other nations have not. Most of the oil production outside the United States has been accomplished with American technology and American money. We have drilled about 150,000 wells in this country, and current rate of drilling is about 10,000 wells a year. We are spending several billion dollars a year for exploration and drilling. Other countries have not been able to afford such rapid dissipation of fossil fuel resources. So the petroleum future naturally belongs not to the United States but to the rest of the world.

What can be said about the petroleum future? Smart prophets have been consistently wrong in the past. It would be presumptuous to assume any supe-

Fig. 94a.—Coal-crushing plant by river and railroad. Modern coal-crushing plants are not so unsightly as two decades ago.

Fig. 94b.—Strip mining for coal. For strip mining of coal, power shovels are many times as large as those used for digging the Panama Canal.

FIG. 95a.—Early oil derricks. In 1925, oil wells were closely spaced above oil pools. Today this wasteful practice has been largely eliminated. Now, modern steel derricks are widely spaced.

FIG. 95b.—Modern oil refinery and storage tanks. Modern oil refineries are largely automatic with huge capacity and few operators.

rior clairvoyance today. But certain conditional statements are quite safe to make. If we have a 100-gallon tank of water and start to drain the tank at the rate of 1 gallon an hour, it is safe to say that the tank will be empty in 100 hours if the rate of outgo remains constant. Economists have applied this simple reasoning to petroleum with absurd results. The hypothetical 100-gallon supply has had the awkward habit of growing to 500 or 1,000 gallons by discovery of more oil. The rate of outflow has not remained constant but has increased rapidly. Under these complicating conditions it is not possible to determine how long it will take to empty the tank. In the case of oil the tank is not likely to be empty for several thousand years, because much of the oil will not be *found* for a long, long time. But it *is* possible to draw a curve of production rates for the future, and the curve is not a prediction. It is a definite thing *if* the assumptions upon which it is based are correct. The assumptions are (1) that geologists are reasonably correct in their present estimates of the total remaining oil to be discovered and (2) that demand for oil will keep on rising for a few years. Both of these assumptions may be wrong.

Studies along this line have been made for United States and world petroleum and for natural gas and coal in the United States. According to these studies, we are likely to reach the peak of petroleum production in the United States about 1965, the peak of world petroleum production about 1985, the peak of United States gas production about 1965, and the peak of United States production of coal of all grades about 2025. After these dates production will decline. Some technologists believe that the dates are too early, because they have little faith in the order of magnitude of estimates of ultimate reserves. Some others believe that the dates are too early, because they expect

future demand for energy to be less lively. Some others believe that the dates are too early, because it will not be practical to increase production during the next few decades at the predicated rates. These men may all be right, but if ample allowances are made—if present estimates of recoverable reserves prove to be only half of what they should be, if the demand curves rise only half as steeply as they have in the past, if we are destined to put only half as much effort in exploration and drilling and mining as demands would justify—the cold mathematics of the problem shows only moderate postponement of peaks of production: perhaps 1970 for United States oil production, 1975 for gas, 2000 for world petroleum, and 2050 for United States coal.

The United States and the world have other fossil fuels to fall back upon —oil shale and tar sands. Oil shale is undoubtedly abundant in the United States. Ample supplies of shale oil can be obtained at an indeterminate average cost, and an undetermined amount can be obtained at moderate cost. These are about the only safe statements that can be made at this time. Most of the oil shale is in Colorado, Utah, and Wyoming, where water for processing is scarce. The consensus of technologists is that we may expect not more than seven billion barrels of shale-oil production during the first twenty years of operation. Since we are consuming more than two billion barrels of petroleum a year, the shale-oil figures are not impressive. But, to produce even this amount, we would need a mining force five times as large as that employed by the entire United States iron-ore-mining industry, extensive intermountain water-storage reservoirs would have to be created, and seven billion dollars would have to be invested. Any increase in shale-oil production would depend upon the rates at which labor, money, and water can be provided and, of course, upon the location and quality of oil shale. Oil shale will provide another chapter in the fossil fuel story, but it will be a small one unless present technical studies of underground retorting of oil shale should lead to a practicable process.

As far as the United States is concerned, tar sands will provide not a chapter but a sentence, for our reserves of tar sands are small. Canadian reserves are great but are not economically accessible. A little oil will be produced there in the course of time.

Petroleum, natural gas, coal, oil shale, and tar sands are believed to be continually forming in the earth, but they are of no use to us as fuels until they accumulate in massive deposits from which they may be produced. When they are gone, we shall have to wait for hundreds of millions of years and for unpredictable geologic shifts in the earth's crust before the present fossil fuel age could be repeated. In a practi-

cal sense, fossil fuels, after this century, will cease to exist except as raw materials for chemical synthesis.

If one might hazard a guess, the next age might well be one in which power is obtained from chemical and nuclear reactions without the intermediate generation of heat with attendant losses. This would be in contrast with the present age, in which nearly all power is obtained from heat. But this will require inventions of high order, and few are even thinking about the problem now.

Only now that we can see what has been called the "climactic approach to exhaustion" are we fully conscious of the importance of the fossil fuel age. We cannot name the next age before it has even begun. Technology has not failed us in the past, and I am confident that it will not fail us in the future. But what its solutions will be to the world's energy problem lies in Thomas Carlyle's "continents of darkness."

REFERENCES

ANONYMOUS
  1935–54 *Drilling and Production Practice, 1934–1953.* New York: American Petroleum Institute, Division of Production. (Annual.)
  1949 *Petroleum: The Story of an American Industry.* New York: American Petroleum Institute. 95 pp.
  1952 *Bituminous Coal Annual, 1952.* Washington, D.C.: Bituminous Coal Institute. 176 pp.
  1953a *Gasification and Liquefaction of Coal.* New York: American Institute of Mining and Metallurgical Engineers. 621 pp.
  1953b *Oil for Today—and for Tomorrow.* Oklahoma City: Interstate Oil Compact Commission. 83 pp.
  1954 *Technology of Lignitic Coals,* Parts I and II. (Bureau of Mines Information Circulars Nos. 7691 and 7692.) Washington, D.C.: U.S. Department of the Interior. 142 and 120 pp.

ASHTON, T. S., and SYKES, JOSEPH
  1929 *Coal Industry of the Eighteenth Century.* Manchester: Manchester University Press. 268 pp.
AYRES, EUGENE
  1953 "U.S. Oil Outlook: How Coal Fits In," *Coal Age,* LVIII, No. 8, 70–73.
  1954 "Raw Materials for Organic Chemicals," *Chemical and Engineering News,* XXXII, No. 29, 2876–82.
AYRES, EUGENE, and SCARLOTT, C. A.
  1952 *Energy Sources: The Wealth of the World.* New York: McGraw-Hill Book Co. 344 pp.
BAKEWELL, GEORGE
  1813 *Geology of the Earth.* London. 212 pp.
BALL, M. W.
  1950 "Oil and Human Welfare," *Quarterly of the Colorado School of Mines,* XLV, No. 1A, 29–37.
BECKER, CARL
  1932 *The Heavenly City of the Eight-*

eenth-Century Philosophers. New Haven, Conn.: Yale University Press. 168 pp.

CHARLES, J. M.
1950 "Coal and Its Future," *Quarterly of the Colorado School of Mines*, XLV, No. 2B, 67–75.

DONATH, E. E.
1954 "Fuels and Chemicals from Coal Hydrogenation," *Industrial and Engineering Chemistry*, XLVI, No. 10, 2032–35.

DUNSTAN, A. E., *et al.* (eds.)
1938–53 *The Science of Petroleum*, Vols. I–VI. New York: Oxford University Press.

EAVENSON, H. N.
1939 *Coal through the Ages*. New York: American Institute of Mining and Metallurgical Engineers. 123 pp.
1942 *First Century and a Quarter of American Coal Industry*. Pittsburgh, Pa.: The Author. 701 pp.

EGLE, W. H.
1877 *An Illustrated History of the Commonwealth of Pennsylvania*. Harrisburg, Pa.: De Witt C. Goodrich. 1,204 pp.

ELLIS, CARLETON
1934–37 *Chemistry of Petroleum Derivatives*, Vols. I–II. New York: Reinhold Publishing Corp. 1,464 pp.

FANNING, L. M.
1948 *Rise of American Oil*. Rev. ed. New York: Harper & Bros. 178 pp.

LOWRY, H. H. (ed.)
1945 *Chemistry of Coal Utilization*, Vols. I–II. New York: John Wiley & Sons. 1,868 pp.

POPE, P. C. (ed.)
1953 *Coal: Production, Distribution, Utilization*. New York: Anglobooks. 236 pp.

SACHANEN, A. N.
1948 *Conversion of Petroleum*. 2d ed. New York: Reinhold Publishing Corp. 602 pp.

SALL, G. W.
1954 "Short History of Coal Mining," *Mining Congress Journal*, XL, No. 4, 36–39.

STRUTH, H. J. (ed.)
1954 *World Petroleum Statistical Yearbook*. New York: Mona Palmer. 454 pp.

TAYLOR, R. C.
1845 *Statistics on Coal*. Philadelphia: J. W. Moore. 754 pp.

WHITESHOT, C. A.
1905 *The Oil-Well Driller: History of the Oil Industry of the World*. Mannington, W.Va.: The Author. 895 pp.

WILSON, P. J., and WELLS, J. H.
1950 *Coal, Coke and Coal Chemicals*. New York: McGraw-Hill Book Co. 509 pp.

The Natural History of Urbanization

LEWIS MUMFORD[*]

* Mr. Mumford since 1952 has been Professor of City Planning at the University of Pennsylvania, Philadelphia. He is a fellow of the American Academy of Arts and Sciences, a member of the American Philosophical Society, an honorary associate of the Royal Institute of British Architects, and an honorary fellow of Stanford University. His publications include: *Technics and Civilization,* 1934; *The Culture of Cities,* 1938; and *The Conduct of Life,* 1951.

THE EMERGENCE OF THE CITY

The natural history of urbanization has not yet been written, for only a small part of the preliminary work has been done. The literature of the city itself, until a half-century ago, was barren to the point of nonexistence; and even now the ecologists of the city, dealing too largely with a late and limited aspect of urbanism, have hardly staked out the ground that is to be covered. Our present purpose, accordingly, is to make use of such studies as have so far been made in order to ask more pointed questions and so, incidentally, to indicate further fields of profitable study.

Whether one looks at the city morphologically or functionally, one cannot understand its development without taking in its relationship to earlier forms of cohabitation that go back to non-human species. One must remember not only the obvious homologies of the anthill and the beehive but also the nature of fixed seasonal habitations in protected sites, like the breeding grounds of many species of birds.

Though permanent villages date only from Neolithic times, the habit of resorting to caves for the collective performance of magical ceremonies seems to date back to an earlier period; and whole communities, living in caves and hollowed-out walls of rock, have survived in widely scattered areas down to the present. The outline of the city as both an outward form and an inward pattern of life might be found in such ancient assemblages. Whatever the aboriginal impetus, the tendency toward formal cohabitation and fixed residence gave rise, in Neolithic times, to the ancestral form of the city: the village, a collective utility brought forth by the new agricultural economy. Lacking the size and complexity of the city, the village nevertheless exhibits its essential features: the encircling mound or palisade, setting it off from the fields; permanent shelters; storage pits and bins, with refuse dumps and burial grounds recording silently past time and spent energy. At this early stage, at least, Mark Jefferson's observation (1931) holds true: urban and rural, city and country, are one thing, not two things.

Though the number of families per acre in a village is greater than the number per square mile under a pastoral economy, such settlements bring with them no serious disturbance in the natural environment; indeed, the relation may even be favorable for building up the soil and increasing its natural productivity. Archeological explorers in Alaska have been able to detect early settlements by noting the greenness of the vegetation around the otherwise submerged village sites, probably due to the enrichment of the soil from the nitrogenous human and animal waste accumulated near by. Early cities, as we find them in Mesopotamia and Egypt, maintain the symbiotic relation with agriculture that we find in the village. In countries like China, still governed by the principles of village economy, even contemporary cities with high population density, such as Keyes describes (1951), exhibit the same reciprocal relations: "The most concentrated highly developed agriculture is just outside the walls of cities." King estimated (1927) that each million city dwellers in China account for more than 13,000 pounds of nitrogen, 2,700 pounds of phosphorous, and almost 4,500 pounds of potassium in the daily night soil returned to the land. Brunhes' description (1920) of cities under "unproductive occupation of the soil" does not altogether hold for the earliest types or, as I shall show, for the latest types of city.

The emergence of the city from the village was made possible by the improvements in plant cultivation and stock-breeding that came with Neolithic culture; in particular, the cultivation of the hard grains that could be produced in abundance and kept over from year to year without spoiling. This new form of food not merely offered insurance against starvation in the lean years, as was recorded in the famous story of Joseph in Egypt, but likewise made it possible to breed and support a bigger population not committed to food-raising. From the standpoint of their basic nutrition, one may speak of wheat cities, rye cities, rice cities, and maize cities, to characterize their chief source of energy; and it should be remembered that no other source was so important until the coal

seams of Saxony and England were opened. With the surplus of manpower available as Neolithic man escaped from a subsistence economy, it was possible to draw a larger number of people into other forms of work and service: administration, the mechanical arts, warfare, systematic thought, and religion. So the once-scattered population of Neolithic times, dwelling in hamlets of from ten to fifty houses (Childe, 1954), was concentrated into "cities," ruled and regimented on a different plan. These early cities bore many marks of their village origins, for they were still in essence agricultural towns: the main source of their food supply was in the land around them; and, until the means of transport had greatly improved and a system of centralized control had developed, they could not grow beyond the limit of their local water supply and their local food sources.

This early association of urban growth with food production governed the relation of the city to its neighboring land far longer than many observers now realize. Though grains were transported long distances (even as special food accessories like salt had circulated in earlier times), cities like Rome, which drew mainly on the distant granaries of Africa and the Near East—to say nothing of the oyster beds of Colchester in England—were exceptions down to the nineteenth century. As late as fifty years ago large portions of the fruits and vegetables consumed in New York and Paris came from nearby market gardens, sometimes on soils greatly enriched, if not almost manufactured, with urban refuse, as Kropotkin pointed out in *Fields, Factories, and Workshops* (1899). This means that one of the chief determinants of large-scale urbanization has been nearness to fertile agricultural land; yet, paradoxically, the growth of most cities has been achieved by covering over and removing from cultivation the very land—often, indeed, the richest alluvial soils—whose existence at the beginning made their growth possible. The tendency of cities to grow along rivers or near accessible harbors was furthered not alone by the need for easy transportation but by the need to draw on aquatic sources of food to supplement those produced by the soil. This rich and varied diet may itself have contributed to the vital energy of city dwellers as contrasted with the more sluggish ways of hinterlanders and perhaps may also have partly offset the bad effect of close quarters in spreading communicable diseases. While modern means of transport have equalized these advantages, they have not yet hastened the migration of urban populations to upland sites on poorer soils, though often these present more salubrious climates and better living conditions.

The village and the small country town are historic constants. One of the outstanding facts about urbanization is that, while the urban population of the globe in 1930 numbered around 415,-000,000 souls, or about a fifth of the total population, the remaining four-fifths still lived under conditions approximating that of the Neolithic economy (Sorre, 1952). In countries as densely peopled as India, as late as 1939, according to the *Statesman's Yearbook*, less than 10 per cent of the total population lived in cities. These "Neolithic" conditions include the utilization of organic sources of energy, vegetable and animal, the use of a local supply of drinking water, the continuous cultivation of land within walking distance of the village, the partial use of human dung along with that of animals for fertilizer, a low concentration of inorganic refuse, like glass and metals, and an absence of air pollution. In many parts of the world, village settlements, far from encroaching on ara-

ble land, occupy barren hill sites of little use for agriculture; the stony outcrop of an Italian hill town involves only a slightly more symmetrical arrangement of the original rock strata. The chief weakness of these settlements, particularly in parts of the world long cultivated, notably in Spain, Greece, or China, is due to the peasant's begrudging the land needed for forest cover; he thus tends, by overtillage, to promote erosion and to create a further imbalance among the bird, insect, and plant populations. But, just as the early village economy was indebted to the astronomical calendar produced in the temple cities for the timely planting of their crops, so the present development of ecological knowledge, which has led to increasing concern and care for the woodland preserves in highly urbanized countries, may in time counteract the otherwise destructive effects of earlier stages in urban settlement.

URBAN SYMBIOSIS AND DOMINANCE

With the first growth of urban populations in ancient Mesopotamia, the symbiotic relations that originally held between village and land were not greatly altered. "The city," as Childe (1942, p. 94) describes its earliest manifestations, "is girt with a brick wall and a fosse, within the shelter of which man found for the first time a world of his own, relatively secure from the immediate pressure of raw, external nature. It stands out in an artificial landscape of gardens, fields, and pastures, created out of reed swamp and desert by the collective activity of preceding generations in building dykes and digging canals." Though these cities represented "a new magnitude in human settlement," the populations of Lagash, Umma, and Khafaje are "reliably estimated to have been 19,000, 16,000, and 12,000 respectively during the third millennium." The Levitical cities described in the Bible, confirmed by modern excavations of Gezer, had a town area of about 22 acres, with pasture land, permanently reserved, amounting to about 300 acres (Osborn, 1946). More than four thousand years later, as late as the sixteenth century, the characteristic size of the city in western Europe ranged from 2,000 to 20,000 people; it was only in the seventeenth century that cities of more than 100,000 began to multiply. In both the Near East in ancient times and in western Europe in the Middle Ages, cities prudently retained some portion of the land within their walls for gardens and the harboring of animals for food in case of military siege. Even the vast domains of Babylon must not mislead us into looking upon it as comparable in density to modern London. A map drawn in 1895 by Arthur Schneider, and republished by Hassert (1907), shows that Babylon covered an area big enough to contain Rome, Tarentum, Syracuse, Athens, Ephesus, Thebes, Jerusalem, Carthage, Sparta, Alexandria, and Tyre, together with almost as much open space between these cities as they occupied in their own right. Even in Herodotus' time, Babylon had many of the aspects of an overgrown village.

The Neolithic economy appears to have been a co-operative one. The concentration upon plant cultivation in small neighborly communities, never with a sufficient surplus of food or power to promote too much arrogance in man's relation with other men or with nature, established a natural balance between fields and settlements. In Europe, as Élisée Reclus long ago noted, country towns and villages tended to spread evenly, as far as topography allowed, about the space of a day's walk apart. With the introduction of metallurgy, during the succeeding period of urbanization, came technological specialization, caste differentiation, and heightened temptations to aggression; and with this began a dis-

regard for the welfare of the community as a whole and, in particular, a tendency to ignore the city's dependence upon its local resources. Excess of manpower abetted an excessive belief in the power of man—a belief deepened, no doubt, by the efficacy of the new edged weapons and armor in giving control to aggressive minorities who took the law into their own hands. With the development of long-distance trading, numerical calculation, and coinage, this urban civilization tended to throw off its original sense of limits and to regard all forms of wealth as purchasable by trade or procurable by a demonstration of military power. What could not be grown or produced in the local region could be, by theft or exchange, obtained elsewhere. In time this urban economy made the mistake of applying the pragmatic standards of the market place to the environment itself: the process began of building over the interior open spaces and building out over the surrounding land.

Until modern times the extension of a city's walls marked its growth as surely as does each additional ring of a tree. The wall had perhaps a formative role in the transformation of the village into the city; when made of heavy, permanent materials, surrounded by a moat, it gave the city a means of protection the little village could not afford. Not merely was it capable of military defense, but the city, through its surplus population, could muster enough manpower to hold against a large army of attackers. The earliest meaning of "town" is an inclosed or fortified place. The village that, because of its defensible site, offered protection against predators of all kinds would in times of peril attract families from more exposed areas and so, with a larger, mixed population, would turn into a city. Thus the temple citadel would add to its original population and, even after the danger had passed, would retain some of those who sought shelter and so become a city. In Greece, at least, the city comes into existence, historically, as such a synoecism.

But the morphological difference between the village and the city is not simply the result of the latter's superior site or of the fact that its geographic situation enables it to draw on a wider area for resources, foods, and men and in turn to export their products to a larger market, though both are facts conducive to population growth and economic expansion. What distinguish city from village are mainly two facts. The first of these is the presence of an organized social core, around which the whole structure of the community coheres. If this nucleation may begin in the village stage, as remains of temples seem to indicate, there is a general shift of household occupations and rituals into specialized collective institutions, part of the intensified social division of labor brought in with civilization itself. But, from the standpoint of the city's relation to the earth, the important point to notice is that, in this social core or nucleus, the sharpest departures from the daily habits and the physical structure of the village take place. Thus the temple, unlike the hut, will be built of permanent materials, with solid stone walls, often plated with precious stones or roofed with rare timber taken from a distant quarry or forest, all conceived on a colossal scale, while the majority of dwelling houses will still be built of clay and reed, or wattle and daub, on the old village pattern. While the temple area will be paved, the streets and alleys of the rest of the city will remain unpaved. As late as imperial Rome, pavement will be introduced first into the Forum, while most of the arteries remain uncovered, to become sloughs of mud in rainy weather. Here too, in the urban palace, as early as Akkad, such technological innovations as baths, toilets, and drains will appear—innovations that remain far beyond the reach of the urban populations-at-large until modern times.

Along with this bold aesthetic transformation of the outward environment, another tendency distinguishes the city from the village—a tendency to loosen the bonds that connect its inhabitants with nature and to transform, eliminate, or replace its earth-bound aspects, covering the natural site with an artificial environment that enhances the dominance of man and encourages an illusion of complete independence from nature. The first age of the "urban revolution," to use Childe's term, had little extrahuman power and few machines. Its technological heritage, once it had learned to smelt copper and iron, was in every sense a static one; and its major skills, weaving aside, were concentrated on fashioning utensils and utilities (pots, jars, vats, bins) and on building great collective works (dams, irrigation systems, buildings, roads, baths) and, finally, cities themselves. Having learned to employ fire of relatively high intensity to glaze and smelt ores, these early civilizations offset its danger by creating a fireproof environment. The importance of this fact, once papyrus and paper were in use, can hardly be overestimated. In this general transformation from the transient to the fixed, from fragile and temporary structures to durable buildings, proof against wind, weather, and fire, early man emancipated himself likewise from the fluctuations and irregularities of nature. Each of the utilities that characterized the new urban form—the wall, the durable shelter, the arcade, the paved way, the reservoir, the aqueduct, the sewer—lessened the impact of nature and increased the dominance of man. That fact was revealed in the very silhouette of the city, as the traveler beheld it from a distance. Standing out in the vegetation-clad landscape, the city became an inverted oasis of stone or clay. The paved road, a man-made desert that speeds traffic and makes it largely independent of the weather and the seasons; the irrigation ditch, a man-made river system that releases the farmer from irregularities of seasonal rainfall; the water main, an artificial brook that turns the parched environment of the city into an oasis; the pyramid, an artificial mountain that serves as symbolic reminder of man's desire for permanence and continuity—all these inventions record the displacement of natural conditions with a collective artifact of urban origin.

Physical security and social continuity were the two great contributions of the city. Under those conditions every kind of conflict and challenge became possible without disrupting the social order, and part of this new animus was directed into a struggle with the forces of nature. By serving as a secure base of operations, a seat of law and government, a repository of deeds and contracts, and a marshaling yard for manpower, the city was able to engage in long-distance activities. Operating through trade, taxation, mining, military assault, and road-building, which made it possible to organize and deploy thousands of men, the city proceeded to make large-scale transformations of the environment, impossible for groups of smaller size to achieve. Through its storage, canalization, and irrigation, the city, from its earliest emergence in the Near East, justified its existence, for it freed the community from the caprices and violences of nature—though no little part of that gift was nullified by the further effect of subjecting the community more abjectly to the caprices and violences of men.

URBAN DISPLACEMENT OF NATURE

Unfortunately, as the disintegration of one civilization after another reminds us, the displacement of nature in the city rested, in part, upon an illusion—or, indeed, a series of illusions—as to the nature of man and his institutions: the illusions of self-sufficiency and independence and of the possibility of physical continuity without conscious renewal. Under the protective mantle of the city, seemingly so permanent, these illusions encouraged habits of predation or parasitism that eventually undermined the whole social and economic structure, after having worked ruin in the surrounding landscape and even in far-distant regions. Many elements supplied by nature, necessary for both health and mental balance, were lacking in the city. Medicine, as practiced by the Hippocratic School in the great retreats, like that at Kos, concerned with airs, waters, and places, seems at an early age to have employed in therapy natural elements that were depleted or out of balance even in the relatively small Aegean cities of the fifth century B.C., though their ruling classes spent no small part of their leisure in the exercise of the body. Through the ages the standard prescription for most urban illnesses—and perhaps as effective as more specific remedies—is retreat to some little village by seacoast or mountain—that is, restoration to a pre-urban natural environment. In times of plague the retreat repeatedly has taken on the aspects of a rout. Though man has become the dominant species in every region where the city has taken hold, partly because of the knowledge and the system of public controls over both man and nature he exercises there, he has yet to safeguard that position by acknowledging his sustained and inescapable dependence upon all his biological partners. With the ecological implications of this fact, I shall deal later.

Probably no city in antiquity had a population of much more than a million inhabitants, not even Rome; and, except in China, there were no later Romes until the nineteenth century. But, long before a million population is reached, most cities come to a critical point in their development. That occurs when the city is no longer in symbiotic relationship with its surrounding land; when further growth overtaxes local resources, like water, and makes them precarious; when, in order to continue its growth, a city must reach beyond its immediate limits for water, for fuel, for building materials, and for raw materials used in manufacture; and, above all, when its internal birth rate becomes inadequate to provide enough manpower to replace, if not to augment, its population. This stage has been reached in different civilizations at different periods. Up to this point, when the city has come to the limits of sustenance in its own territory, growth takes place by colonization, as in a beehive. After this point, growth takes place, in defiance of natural limitations, by a more intensive occupation of the land and by encroachment into the surrounding areas, with the subjugation by law or naked force of rival growing cities bidding for the same resources.

Most of the characteristics of this second form of urban growth can be observed in the history of Rome. Here the facts are better documented than they are for most ancient cities; and the effects upon the landscape have remained so visible that they suggested to George Perkins Marsh (1864, 1874) the principal lines of his investigation of *The Earth as Modified by Human Action*. Rome of the Seven Hills is an acropolis type of city, formed by a cluster of villages united for defense; and the plain of the Tiber was the original seat of their agriculture. The surplus population of this region conquered first the neighboring territories of the Etruscans and then those of

more distant lands. By systematic expropriation, Rome brought wheat, olive oil, dried fish, and pottery back to the original site to sustain its growing population. To facilitate the movement of its legions and speed up the processes of administration, it carved roads through the landscape with triumphant disregard of the nature of the terrain. These roads and viaducts went hand in hand with similar works of engineering, the aqueducts and reservoirs necessary to bring water to Rome. By short-circuiting the flow of water from mountainside to sea, the city monopolized for its special uses a considerable amount of the runoff; and, to offset some of the effects of metropolitan overcrowding, it created a cult of the public bath that in turn imposed a heavy drain upon the fuel supplied by the near-by forest areas. The advance of technology, with central hot-air heating, characteristically hastened the process of deforestation, as was later to happen in the glass- and ironmaking and shipbuilding industries of northern Europe and to be repeated today in the heavy industrial demand for cellulose. Meanwhile, the sewers of Rome, connected to public toilets, polluted the Tiber without returning the precious mineral contents to the soil, though even in imperial Rome dung farmers still collected most of the night soil from the great tenements of the proletariat. At this stage the symbiotic relation turns into a parasitic one; the cycle of imbalance begins, and the mere massing of the demand in a single center results in denudations and desiccations elsewhere. The more complete the urbanization, the more definite is the release from natural limitations; the more highly the city seems developed as an independent entity, the more fatal are the consequences for the territory it dominates. This series of changes characterizes the growth of cities in every civilization: the transformation of eopolis into megalopolis. If the process wrought damage to the earth even in the ancient world, when cities as big as Rome, Carthage, and Alexandria were the exception rather than the rule, we have good reason to examine carefully the probable consequences of the present wave of urbanization.

MODERN FORCES OF EXPANSION

Let me sum up the observations so far made with respect to the natural history of cities. In the first stage of urbanization the number and size of cities varied with the amount and productivity of the agricultural land available. Cities were confined mainly to the valleys and flood plains, like the Nile, the Fertile Crescent, the Indus, and the Hwang Ho. Increase of population in any one city was therefore limited. The second stage of urbanization began with the development of large-scale river and sea transport and the introduction of roads for chariots and carts. In this new economy the village and the country town maintained the environmental balance of the first stage; but, with the production of grain and oil in surpluses that permitted export, a specialization in agriculture set in and, along with this, a specialization in trade and industry, supplementing the religious and political specialization that dominated the first stage. Both these forms of specialization enabled the city to expand in population beyond the limits of its agricultural hinterland; and, in certain cases, notably in the Greek city of Megalopolis, the population in smaller centers was deliberately removed to a single big center—a conscious reproduction of a process that was taking place less deliberately in other cities. At this stage the city grew by draining away its resources and manpower from the countryside without returning any equivalent goods. Along with this went a de-

structive use of natural resources for industrial purposes, with increased concentration on mining and smelting.

The third stage of urbanization does not make its appearance until the nineteenth century, and it is only now beginning to reach its full expansion, performance, and influence. If the first stage is one of urban balance and co-operation, and the second is one of partial urban dominance within a still mainly agricultural framework, behind both is an economy that was forced to address the largest part of its manpower toward cultivating the land and improving the whole landscape for human use. The actual amount of land dedicated to urban uses was limited, if only because the population was also limited. This entire situation has altered radically during the last three centuries by reason of a series of related changes. The first is that world population has been growing steadily since the seventeenth century, when the beginnings of reasonable statistical estimates, or at least tolerable guesses, can first be made. According to the Woytinskys (1953), the average rate of population increase appears to have gone up steadily: 2.7 per cent from 1650 to 1700; 3.2 per cent in the first half of the eighteenth century and 4.5 per cent in the second half; 5.3 per cent from 1800 to 1850; 6.5 per cent from 1850 to 1900; and 8.3 per cent from 1900 to 1950. As the Woytinskys themselves remark, these averages should not be taken too seriously; yet there is a high probability that an acceleration has taken place and hardly any doubt whatever that the world population has doubled during the last century, while the manpower needed to maintain agricultural productivity in mechanized countries has decreased.

By itself this expansion might mean no more than that the less populated parts of the earth would presently acquire densities comparable to those of

India and China, with a great part of the increase forced to undertake intensive cultivation of the land. But this increase did not take place by itself; it was accompanied by a series of profound technological changes which transformed the classic "age of utilities" into the present "age of the machine" and a predominantly agricultural civilization into an urban one—or possibly a suburban one. These two factors, technical improvement and population growth, have been interacting since at least the sixteenth century, for it was the improvement in the sailing ship and the art of navigation that opened up the almost virginal territory of the New World. The resulting increase of food supply, in terms of added tillage, was further augmented by New World crops like maize and the potato. Meanwhile, the increased production of energy foods—vegetable oils, animal fats, and sugar cane and sugar beet—not merely helped support a larger population but in turn, through the supply of fat, turned soap from a courtly luxury to a household necessity; and this major contribution to hygiene—public and personal—probably did more to lower the death rate than any other single factor. From the beginning of the nineteenth century the surplus population made it possible for old cities to expand and new cities to be founded. As Webber long ago pointed out (1899), the rate was even faster in Germany in the second half of the nineteenth century than it was in the United States.

This wave of urbanization was not, as is sometimes thought, chiefly dependent upon the steam engine or upon improvements in local transportation. The fact is that the number of cities above the 100,000 mark had increased in the seventeenth century, well before the steam engine or the power loom had been invented. London passed the million mark in population by 1810, before it had a mechanical means of transportation or the beginning of an adequate water supply (in parts of London piped water was turned on only twice a week). But a marked change, nevertheless, took place in urban growth during the nineteenth century.

At this moment the four natural limits on the growth of cities were thrown off: the nutritional limit of an adequate food and water supply; the military limit of protective walls and fortifications; the traffic limit set by slow-moving agents of reliable transportation like the canalboat; and the power limit to regular production imposed by the limited number of water-power sites and the feebleness of the other prime movers—horse and wind power. In the new industrial city these limits ceased to hold. While up to this time growth was confined to commercial cities favorably situated at the merging point of two or more diverse regions with complementary resources and skills, urban development now went on in places that had easy access to the coal measures, the iron-ore beds, and the limestone quarries. Pottery towns, cotton towns, woolen towns, and steel towns, no longer held down in size, flourished wherever the tracks for steam locomotives could be laid and the steam engine established as a source of power. The only limitation on the spread and multiplication of towns under this regime was the disability of the steam locomotive to operate efficiently on grades of more than 2 per cent. Whereas the water power and wind power of the eotechnic period had tended to distribute industry in the coastal cities of high winds or along fast-running upland streams, coal power tended to group industry in the valleys near the mine pits or along the railroad lines that constituted a continuation of the mine and the mining environment (Mumford, 1934). Industry, like agriculture, competes for the heavy lowland soils. As for the railroad itself, it is one of the greatest devourers of land and transformers of landscape. The marshaling yards of its great urban terminals put large areas out of urban or agricultural use.

GROWTH OF THE CONURBATION

Up to the middle of the nineteenth century, water-power sites, the seats of earlier industrial improvements, continued to attract industries into mill villages; but, with the coming of the railroad, industries grouped together in cities in order to take advantage of the surplus labor that accumulated there. From this time on, whole districts, such as Elberfeld-Barmen, Lille-Roubaix, the Black Country, and the Delaware Valley, become urbanized, and the limits of city growth are reached only when one city, by its conversion of farmland into building lots, coalesces with another city engaged in the same process. Growth of this kind, automatic and unregulated, a result of the railroad and the factory, had never been possible before; but now the agents of mechanization not merely created their own environment but set a new pattern for the growth of already existing great cities. Looking at Bartholomew's population map of Britain early in the present century, Patrick Geddes discovered (1915) that urbanization had taken a new form: urban areas, hitherto distinct, both as political units and as topographic features, had in fact flowed together and formed dense population masses on a scale far greater than any of the big cities of the past, forming a new configuration as different as the city itself was from its rural prototypes. He called this new kind of urban grouping the "conurbation." This new urban tissue was less differentiated than the old. It presented an impoverished institutional life; it showed fewer signs of social nucleation; and it tended to increase in size, block by block, avenue by avenue, "develop-

ment" by "development," without any individuality of form and, most remarkable of all, without any quantitative limits (West Midland Group, 1948).

This concentration of industry had marked effects upon the entire environment. The new source of power—coal; the new industrial processes, massed in the new steelworks and coke ovens; the new chemical plants for manufacturing chlorine, sulfuric acid, and hundreds of other potentially noxious compounds —all poured their waste products into the air and waters on a scale that made it impossible for the local environment to absorb them as it might have absorbed the effluvia of a village industry or the organic waste of a tannery or a slaughter-house. Streams hitherto well stocked with fish, salubrious for bathing, and even potable became poisonous sewers; while the fall of soot, chemical dust, silica, and steel particles choked vegetation in what open ground remained and left their deposits in human lungs. The effects of this pollution, and the possibility of more radical and irretrievable pollution to come through the use of atomic reactors, are dealt with in chapters that follow. Here the point to mark is that it was a natural penalty of overconcentration. The very ubiquity of the new type of city, coupled with its density, increases, for example, the threat of a lethal fog from chemicals normally in the air, such as wiped out over five thousand lives in a single week in London in 1952; a mass exodus by cars, at the low speed imposed by a heavy fog, would itself add to the deadly gases already in the air.

The extension of the industrial conurbation not merely brings with it the obliteration of the life-sustaining natural environment but actually creates, as substitute, a definitely antiorganic environment; and even where, in the interstices of this urban development, land remains unoccupied, it progressively ceases to be of use for either agriculture or recreation. The removal of the topsoil, or its effacement by buildings and slag piles, brings on no temporary denudation; it results in deserts that, even if every effort suggested by science were made, might take centuries to redeem for human occupancy, to say nothing of more organic forms of cultivation. Though the conurbation came into existence through the dense industrial occupation of a whole region rather than through the overgrowth of a single dominant city, the two types overlap. In England, Birmingham itself, though the center of congeries of smaller towns, has passed the million mark, to become the second city in Britain. By offering a big local market, the great conurbations, in addition to attracting the consumption trades and industries, have brought in petroleum refineries, chemical plants, and steelworks, which gravitate to the cheaper land on the edge of metropolitan areas. This tends to create industrial defilement at the point where Sir John Evelyn, in 1661 in his pamphlet *Fumifugium* (1933), proposed to create a protective green belt, filled with aromatic shrubs, to purify the already noisome air of London. This extension of the area of industrial pollution into the very land that the overgrown city needs for mass recreation—accessible to sunlight, to usable ocean, river front, and woodland—likewise lessens the advantage of the only form of temporary escape left: retreat to the suburb.

From the very nature of the city as a market, a workshop, and a place of civic assemblage, there is a direct relation between its growth and the growth of transportation systems, though, in the case of seaways and airways, the latter may be visible only in the increase of harbor facilities and storehouses. In general, one may say that, the heavier the urbanization, the heavier the transportation network, not merely within but without. From ancient Rome to recent times, the fifteen-foot roadway remained the outsize. But, with the eighteenth century, land transportation takes a new turn. In 1861, Wilhelm Heinrich Riehl noted it (1935) in the change from the rural highroads of the old town economy to the new *Landstrasse,* planned in more systematic fashion by the new bureaucracy—wider by three feet, more heavily paved, and often lined with trees, as in the beautiful highway lined with ancient lindens between Lübeck and Travemunde. With the coming of railroad transportation, the width of the new kind of permanent way again increased; the railroad made fresh demands for large areas of flat, low-lying land to serve as marshaling yards, adjacent to the city or even cutting a great wedge through it. The economy of the water-level route again turned to a non-agricultural use of precisely the land that was often the most fertile available and spoiled even its recreational value. With the introduction of the motorcar, even secondary roads demanded pavement, and arterial roads both widened and multiplied, with the result that around great metropolises six-, seven-, and eight-lane highways with two-hundred-foot rights of way have become increasingly common. They are further complicated by great traffic circles or clover-leaf patterns of overpass and underpass to permit the continuous flow of traffic at intersections, however wasteful of land these junctions may be. In the case of parkways planned to follow the ridges, like the Taconic State Parkway in New York State, the land given over to the road may be of minor value either for agricultural or for civic use; but where the highway engineer ignores the contours, follows the valleys, and cuts through hills to maintain his level, the motorway may be an active agent both in eroding the soil and in disrupting the habitat. The yielding of water navigation to land transport has aggravated this damage; and every further congestion of population leads to still more highway-building of a permanent and costly kind to accommodate the mass week-end exit of motorists. Thus the city, by its incontinent and uncontrolled growth, not merely sterilizes the land it immediately needs but vastly increases the total area of sterilization far beyond its boundaries.

THE SUBURBAN OVERSPILL

At this point we are confronted with two special phenomena known only in embryonic form in other urban cultures: the production of a new kind of urban tissue, in the open pattern of the suburb, and the further development of a mass transportation by means of self-propelled, individual vehicles, trucks, and motorcars. The first change, the result of seeking an environment free from noise, dirt, and overcrowding of the city, actually antedated the means that made it possible on a mass scale. In London this suburban movement began as early as Elizabethan times as a reaction against the overbuilding and overcrowding that had then taken place in the center of the city; and at the end of the eighteenth century a similar exodus occurred among merchants who could afford a private coach to take them into the city. With increased facilities of transportation offered by the public coach and the railroad, this suburban movement became more common through the nineteenth century, as witness the growth of St. John's Wood, Richmond, and Hampstead in London, of Chestnut Hill and Germantown in Philadelphia, and of the Hudson River suburbs in New York. But, up to 1920, it was mainly the upper-income groups that could afford the luxury of sunlight, fresh air, gardens, open spaces, and access to the open country. The new open-type plan, with houses set in gardens, at densities of from two houses to ten or twelve per acre, had long been characteristic of American country towns, most notably those of New England; indeed, this open pattern dominated west of the Alleghenies. But this standard now became universalized in the upper-class suburb, though its economic base lay outside the area the suburb occupied and from the beginning demanded a heavy sacrifice of man-hours in commuting to the distant metropolis. The low cost of suburban land and the possibility of economizing on local utilities like roads and sewers encouraged luxurious standards of space and gave those who could afford to escape a superior biological environment and perhaps, if Thorndyke is correct (1939), a superior social one. The initiative of a few farsighted industrialists, like Lever (Port Sunlight, 1887) and Cadbury (Bournville, 1895), proved that similar standards could be applied to building working-class quarters when land was sufficiently cheap.

Since 1920 the spread of private motor vehicles has completed the work of enlarging potential suburban territory, an expansion already well begun in the 1900's by interurban electric transit. The exodus to suburbia has taken in wave after wave of city dwellers, at lower and lower income levels, seeking to escape the congested and disordered environment of the big city. This removal from the city has not been accompanied by any equivalent decentralization of industry; rather it has served to sustain an antiquated pattern of concentration. The pattern of population distribution around great cities has been the product, not of social foresight for public ends, but mainly of private initiative for private profit, though it could not have taken place on its present scale in America without a vast public investment in highways, expressways, bridges, and tunnels. The result of this uncontrolled spread of the suburb has been to nullify the very purposes that brought the movement into existence.

But suburban agglomeration cannot be treated as a fact in itself; it carries with it, through the demands of the motorcar, both for private transportation and for the movement of goods, an enormous increase in paved roads, which eat into the surviving agricultural and wilderness areas and permanently sterilize ever larger quantities of land. The filling-up of marshes, the coverage of rich soils with buildings, the felling of woodlands, the clogging of local brooks and streams, and the abandonment of local springs and wells were all secondary disturbances of the early type of metropolis, even when it reached a population of a million people. When Rome was surrounded by the Aurelian wall in A.D. 274, it covered, according to Carcopino (1940), a little more than 5 square miles. The present area of Greater London is about a hundred and thirty times as great as this, while it is roughly six hundred and fifty times as great as the area, namely, 677 acres, surrounded by its wall in the Middle Ages. The metropolitan area of New York is even more widespread; it covers something like 2,514 square miles; and already a good case could be made out for treating a wide coastal strip from Boston to Washington as one continuous conurbation, geographically speaking (see Fig. 43, pp. 38–39). This difference in magnitude between every earlier type of urban development and that characterizing our own age is critical. What is more, as population increases, the percentage of the population in cities increases, too, and the ratio of those going into metropolitan areas is even higher. Even in England, though the amount of land occupied by cities, "built-over land," is low (2.2 per cent) in proportion to the entire land area of the British Isles, this is more than half the area of "first-class" land available for agriculture and is a tenth of the "good land" available, according to Sir L. Dudley Stamp's classification (1952). Since requirements for manufacture and urban development are for accessible, graded land, these demands conflict with the needs of the farmer; they compete for the same good soils, and only government intervention in England, since 1932, has saved this misuse of valuable agricultural land.

Under modern technical conditions the open pattern of the residential suburb is not confined to domestic needs alone. The demand for large land areas characterizes modern factory organization, with its horizontally ordered assembly lines, housed in spreading one-story structures, and, above all, airports for long-distance flights, whose demand for landing lanes and approaches on the order of miles has increased with the size and speed of planes. In addition, the noise of planes, especially jets, sterilizes even larger areas of land for residential use as both hazardous to life and dangerous to health. There are many urban regions, like that tapped by the main-line railroads from Newark, New Jersey, to Wilmington, Delaware, where urban tissue has either displaced the land or so completely modified its rural uses as to give the whole area the character of a semi-urban desert. Add to this, in every conurbation, the ever larger quantity of land needed for collective reservoir systems, sewage works, and garbage-disposal plants as dispersed local facilities fall out of use.

As a result of population increase and urban centralization, one further demand for land, unfortunately a cumulative one, must be noted: the expansion of urban cemeteries in all cultures that maintain, as most "Christian" nations do, the Paleolithic habit of earth burial. This has resulted in the migration of the burying ground from the center to the outskirts of metropolitan areas, where vast cemeteries serve, indeed, as temporary suburban parks, until they become a wilderness of stone monuments. Unless the custom of periodically emptying out these cemeteries, as was done in London and Paris with the bones in old churchyards, takes hold, or until cremation replaces burial, the demand for open spaces for the dead threatens to crowd the quarters of the living on a scale impossible to conceive in earlier urban cultures.

URBAN-RURAL BALANCE

Whereas the area of the biggest cities, before the nineteenth century, could be measured in hundreds of acres, the areas of our new conurbations must now be measured in thousands of square miles. This is a new fact in the history of human settlement. Within a century the economy of the Western world has shifted from a rural base, harboring a few big cities and thousands of villages and small towns, to a metropolitan base whose urban spread not merely has engulfed and assimilated the small units, once isolated and self-contained, as the amoeba engulfs its particles of food, but is fast absorbing the rural hinterland and threatening to wipe out many natural elements favorable to life which in earlier stages balanced off against depletions in the urban environment. From this, even more critical results follow. Already, New York and Philadelphia, which are fast coalescing into a single conurbation along the main-line railroads and the New Jersey Turnpike, find themselves competing for the same water supply, as Los Angeles competes with the whole state of Arizona. Thus, though modern technology has escaped from the limitations of a purely local supply of water, the massing of population makes demands that, even apart

from excessive costs (which rise steadily as distance increases), put a definable limit to the possibilities of further urbanization. Water shortages may indeed limit the present distribution long before food shortages bring population growth to an end.

This situation calls for a new approach to the whole problem of urban settlement. Having thrown off natural controls and limitations, modern man must replace them with an at least equally effective man-made pattern. Though alternative proposals may be left to that portion of this volume dealing with the future, one new approach has fifty years of experience behind it and may properly be dealt with under the head of history. In the last decade of the nineteenth century two projects came forth relating to the need, already visible by then, to achieve a different balance among cities, industries, and natural regions from that which had been created by either the old rural economy, the free town economy, or the new metropolitan economy. The first of these suggestions was the work of the geographer Peter Kropotkin. His book *Fields, Factories, and Workshops* (1899) dealt with the alteration in the scale of technically efficient enterprise made possible by the invention of the electric motor. The other book, *Tomorrow*, published in 1898 by Howard, embodied a proposal to counteract the centralization of the great metropolis by reintroducing the method of colonization to take care of its further growth. Howard proposed to build relatively self-contained, balanced communities, supported by their local industry, with a permanent population, of limited number and density, on land surrounded by a swath of open country dedicated to agriculture, recreation, and rural occupation. Howard's proposal recognized the biological and social grounds, along with the psychological pressures, that underlay the current movement to suburbia. It recognized the social needs that were causing an exodus from rural regions or drab, one-industry towns into the big city. Without disparaging such real advantages as the concentrated activities and institutions of the city offered, Howard proposed to bring about a marriage between town and country. The new kind of city he called the "garden city," not so much because of its internal open spaces, which would approach a sound suburban standard, but more because it was set in a permanent rural environment.

Besides invoking the Aristotelian ideas of balance and limits, Howard's greatest contribution in conceiving this new garden city was provision for making the surrounding agricultural area an integral part of the city's form. His invention of a horizontal retaining wall, or green belt, immune to urban building, was a public device for limiting lateral growth and maintaining the urban-rural balance. In the course of twenty years two such balanced communities, Letchworth (1903) and Welwyn (1919), were experimentally founded by private enterprise in England. The soundness of the garden-city principle was recognized in the Barlow report (1940) on the decentralization of industry. Thanks to World War II, the idea of building such towns on a great scale, to drain off population from the overcrowded urban centers, took hold. This resulted in the New Towns Act of 1947, which provided for the creation of a series of new towns, fourteen in all, in Britain. This open pattern of town-building, with the towns themselves dispersed through the countryside and surrounded by permanent rural reserves, does a minimum damage to the basic ecological fabric. To the extent that their low residential density, of twelve to fourteen houses per acre, gives individual small gardens to almost every family, these towns not merely maintain a balanced micro-environment but actually grow garden produce whose value is higher than that produced when the land was used for extensive farming or grazing (Block, 1954).

On the basis of the garden-city principle, Stein (1951) and others have put forth the possibility of establishing a new type of city by integrating a group of communities into an organized design that would have the facilities of a metropolis without its congestion and loss of form. The basis for this kind of grouping was laid down in the survey of the state of New York made by the Commission of Housing and Regional Planning, of which Stein was chairman, and was published with Henry Wright in 1926. Wright, the planning adviser, here pointed out that the area of settlement was no longer the crowded terminal metropolitan areas of the railroad period but that electric power and motor transportation had opened up a wide belt on each side of the railroad trunk lines, equally favorable for industry, agriculture, and urban settlement. The most fertile soil and the most valuable geological deposits were almost entirely in the areas below the thousand-foot level; and, in planning for new urban settlement, the reservation of forest areas for water catchment and recreation, for lumber, and for electric power was important. Instead of treating the city as an intrusive element in a landscape that would finally be defaced or obliterated by the city's growth, this new approach suggested the necessity of creating a permanent rural-urban balance. In the regional city, as Stein conceived it, organization would take the place of mere agglomeration and, in doing so, would create a reciprocal relation between city and country that would not be overthrown by further population growth (Mumford, 1925, 1938; MacKaye, 1928; Stein, 1951).

With this statement of the problems raised for us today by the natural history of urbanization, our survey comes to an end. The blind forces of urbanization, flowing along the lines of least resistance, show no aptitude for creating an urban and industrial pattern that will be stable, self-sustaining, and self-renewing. On the contrary, as congestion thickens and expansion widens, both the urban and the rural landscape undergo defacement and degradation, while unprofitable investments in the remedies for congestion, such as more superhighways and more distant reservoirs of water, increase the economic burden and serve only to promote more of the blight and disorder they seek to palliate. But however difficult it is to reverse unsound procedures that offer a temporary answer and immediate—

often excessive—financial rewards, we now have a prospect of concrete alternatives already in existence in England and partly established in a different fashion by the regional planning authority for the highly urbanized Ruhr Valley in Germany. With these examples before us, we have at least a hint of the future task of urbanization: the re-establishment, in a more complex unity, with a full use of the resources of modern science and techniques, of the ecological balance that originally prevailed between city and country in the primitive stages of urbanization. Neither the blotting-out of the landscape nor the disappearance of the city is the climax stage of urbanization. Rather, it is the farsighted and provident balancing of city populations and regional resources so as to maintain in a state of high development all the elements—social, economic, and agricultural—necessary for their common life.

REFERENCES

BARLOW, ANTHONY M.
  1940 *Royal Commission on Distribution of Industrial Population Report.* London: H.M. Stationery Office. 320 pp.
BLOCK, GEOFFREY D. M.
  1954 *The Spread of Towns.* London: Conservative Political Centre. 57 pp.
BRUNHES, JEAN
  1920 *Human Geography, an Attempt at a Positive Classification: Principles and Examples.* 2d ed. Chicago: Rand McNally & Co. 648 pp.
CARCOPINO, JEROME
  1940 *Daily Life in Ancient Rome: The People and the City at the Height of the Empire.* New Haven, Conn.: Yale University Press. 342 pp.
CHILDE, V. GORDON
  1942 *What Happened in History.* Harmondsworth: Penguin Books. 288 pp.
  1954 "Early Forms of Society," pp. 38–57 in SINGER, CHARLES; HOLMYARD, E. J.; and HALL, A. R. (eds.),

A History of Technology. Oxford: Clarendon Press. 827 pp.
EVELYN, JOHN
  1933 *Fumifugium: Or the Inconvenience of the Aer and Smoake of London Dissipated.* Reprint of 1661 pamphlet. London: Oxford University Press. 49 pp.
GEDDES, PATRICK
  1915 *Cities in Evolution: An Introduction to the Town Planning Movement and to the Study of Civics.* London: Williams & Norgate. 409 pp. (Rev. ed. by JAQUELINE TYRWHITT and ARTHUR GEDDES. London: Williams & Norgate, 1949. 241 pp.)
HASSERT, KURT
  1907 *Die Städte: Geographisch Betrachtet.* Leipzig: B. G. Teubner. 137 pp.
HOWARD, EBENEZER
  1898 *To-morrow: A Peaceful Path to Real Reform.* London: Swann, Sonnenschein & Co. 176 pp.

1902 *Garden Cities of To-morrow.* London: Swann, Sonnenschein & Co. 167 pp.

1945 *Garden Cities of To-morrow.* With a Preface by F. J. OSBORN and an Introduction by LEWIS MUMFORD. London: Faber & Faber. 168 pp.

JEFFERSON, MARK
1931 "Distribution of the World's City Folks: A Study in Comparative Civilization," *Geographical Review,* XXI, No. 3, 446–65.

KEYES, FENTON
1951 "Urbanism and Population Distribution in China," *American Journal of Sociology,* LVI, No. 6, 519–27.

KING, F. H.
1927 *Farmers of Forty Centuries.* New York: Harcourt, Brace & Co. 379 pp.

KROPOTKIN, PETER
1899 *Fields, Factories, and Workshops.* New York: G. P. Putnam & Sons. 477 pp.

MACKAYE, BENTON
1928 *The New Exploration: A Philosophy of Regional Planning.* New York: Harcourt, Brace & Co. 235 pp.

MARSH, GEORGE P.
1864 *Man and Nature.* London: Sampson, Low & Son. 577 pp.

1874 *The Earth as Modified by Human Action: A New Edition of "Man and Nature."* New York: Scribner, Armstrong & Co. 656 pp.

1885 *The Earth as Modified by Human Action: A Last Revision of "Man and Nature."* New York: Charles Scribner's Sons. 629 pp. (Note that in this last edition of *Man and Nature,* Marsh refers for the first time, in a long footnote [p. 473], under the heading "Inundations and Torrents," to the influence of large urban masses on climate, particularly heat and precipitation—an anticipation of present-day studies.) Last printing in 1907.

MUMFORD, LEWIS
1934 *Technics and Civilization.* New York: Harcourt, Brace & Co. 495 pp.

1938 *The Culture of Cities.* New York: Harcourt, Brace & Co. 586 pp.

MUMFORD, LEWIS (ed.)
1925 "Regional Planning Number," *Survey Graphic,* LIV, No. 3, 128–208.

OSBORN, F. J.
1946 *Green-Belt Cities: The British Contribution.* London: Faber & Faber. 191 pp.

RIEHL, WILHELM HEINRICH
1935 *Die Naturgeschichte des Deutschen Volkes.* Reprint of 1861 edition. Leipzig: Alfred Kröner Verlag. 407 pp.

SCHNEIDER, ARTHUR
1895 "Stadtumfänge in Altertum und Gegenwart," *Geographische Zeitschrift,* I, 676–79.

SORRE, MAX
1952 *Les Fondements de la géographie humaine.* 3 vols. Paris: Librairie Armand Colin.

STAMP, L. DUDLEY
1948 *The Land of Britain: Its Use and Misuse.* London: Longman's Green. 570 pp.

1952 *Land for Tomorrow.* New York: American Geographical Society; Bloomington, Ind.: Indiana University Press. 230 pp.

STEIN, CLARENCE S.
1951 *Toward New Towns for America.* Chicago: Public Administration Service. 245 pp.

STEIN, CLARENCE S., and WRIGHT, HENRY
1926 *Report of the Commission of Housing and Regional Planning to Governor Alfred E. Smith, May 7, 1926.* (New York State Document.) Albany. 82 pp.

THORNDYKE, EDWARD LEE
1939 *Your City.* New York: Harcourt, Brace & Co. 204 pp.

WEBBER, ADNA FERRIN
1899 *The Growth of Cities in the Nineteenth Century: A Study in Statistics.* New York: Macmillan Co. 495 pp.

WEST MIDLAND GROUP
1948 *Conurbation: A Planning Survey of Birmingham and the Black Country.* London: Architectural Press. 288 pp.

WOYTINSKY, W. S. and E. C.
1953 *World Population and Production.* New York: Twentieth Century Fund. 1,268 pp.

Symposium Discussion: Retrospect

Symposium Discussion: Retrospect

Man's Tenure of the Earth

The Impress of Primitives on Environment

The Classical Period—East and West

The Modern Era of Exchange Economy

Man's Attitudes toward Nature

Unstable Equilibrium and Constant Change

Dr. F. FRASER DARLING, who chaired the first of the discussion sessions, called attention in his introductory remarks to Sauer's expression, "Man's deformation of the pristine." If man is to civilize, he must *de*form; yet many are concerned at how man has de*formed* the pristine—and this is the central theme of the symposium.

As man reached consciousness and changed from the hunting and food-gathering state of existence, he began in some measure to dig into the accumulated organic and inorganic wealth of the world. The tapping of this wealth of resources provided man with the leisure and the time to think, to play, and to create.

Western civilization has been markedly influenced by the idea of man's dominion over the earth put to him in Genesis. Western man has tended to set himself apart from the rest of animate nature, while other and older civilizations and systems of religion have regarded man as being a part of nature. Though very different from the nineteenth-century approach, nevertheless there is today a very real movement in science toward resolution of this dualism through studies of the association of mankind with nature.

THE IMPRESS OF PRIMITIVES ON ENVIRONMENT

STEWART emphasized that man has influenced the face of the earth for a million years or so. Before agriculture and herding, there were the effects during the long reaches of prehistory of man's use of fire and tools. Setting fire to the landscape has been a universal cultural trait. All peoples apparently did it in all places, so that burning has been effective in producing the first landscape of which man has record. Early human activity influenced vegetation, and, in turn, vegetation has had a very great influence on changes in soil.

BANKS asked how small numbers of men associated in primitive tribes and having very short life-spans really could have been effective modifiers of the surface of the earth. What meaningful lessons are to be drawn from early times, when now we are facing times when few die young and many live to maturity—when there is a clear difference in scale of populations? SPOEHR, in reply, stressed the broad framework in space and time of man's activities. By at least 10000 B.C., if not by 20000 B.C., man had penetrated into every major land area of the world as we know it today; the

401

effects of small societies are not to be gauged by their size but rather through their wide and early distribution and the great time span of thousands of years through which they have acted.

SAUER cited examples from Lower California and the lower Mixteca area of Mexico. The southern end of the former, a quite arid area, contains peoples who are among the most primitive in skills that the New World knows. Yet, without fire, they have driven back palms and other useful vegetation. Primitive agriculture, too, has produced some very significant deteriorations of soils on slopes. The field studies of Sherburne Cook have shown that man's cultivation of slopes, even where the general system of agriculture was benign, has led to losses which culminated in catastrophes of considerable duration. The lower Mixteca today comprises hundreds of square miles of limestone hill country with apparently little else but palmetto growths. Yet all through the area there are remains of early settlement. The pottery fragments, for example, point to the period of Monte Albán I, but further studies are necessary combining knowledge of physiography, archeology, and plant composition. SEARS pointed out that Cook's work substantiates a guess made many years before by Vaillant that the pyramid-builders of Teotihuacán, who flourished from about 500 B.C. to A.D. 800, must have cleared the forests extensively for the burning of lime. Cook found evidence of very heavy erosion concomitant with the period of active occupation of Teotihuacán.

DAVIS described another example of the work of early man—the building of shell mounds or refuse heaps, of which some in Florida are as long as 3 miles, 30 feet in height, and about 150 yards wide. To build these obviously required a very long time or a considerable population.

NARR, in writing, called attention to the book of Kraft[1] as one of the most important works in the field of prehistory that has appeared in recent years.

WISSMANN, also in writing, summarized the point of his chapter that plants and animals were first domesticated by man in the moist tropics, then adapted to the margins of the steppes and oases of the deserts, where the first civilizations were formed, and then spread from the deserts and steppes into the forests. More recently, the European occupation of North America went from the moist east to the dry west.

THE CLASSICAL PERIOD—EAST AND WEST

In India, Southeast Asia, and central and southern China something distinctly different from the westward trend of civilization developed. WITTFOGEL pointed out that many civilizations were greatly concerned about water control for the sake of combating floods and creating a standardized, artificial environment in which standardized irrigated crops could be grown. With the emphasis placed on intensive agricultural production, there was not much space for labor animals. Man in horticulture-fashion and with the simplest tools did most of the work. By the time of Confucius, China worshiped three great culture heroes, Yao, Shu, and Yu, all of whom worked to regulate water. From the beginnings of settled life, man, in the North China plain, had to tame the rivers and dig irrigation canals. This effort has been perpetuated through the ages and has transformed the swampy North China plain into a man-made landscape.

Arab sources, too, provide useful indications of conditions of the past, though such sources, as HUZAYYIN pointed out, are not very well known,

1. Georg Kraft, *Der Urmensch als Schöpfer: Die geistige Welt des Eiszeitmenschen* (2d ed.; Tübingen: M. Matthiesen & Co., 1948).

since they exist mostly in manuscripts not fully studied. Masoudi, writing in the tenth century, mentioned changes in northern Arabia, especially in the southern part of the Syrian Desert. In about the sixth century there were wells and oases sufficient to enable a woman to travel alone across the desert, passing from one watering area to another in safety and with an abundance of water and of food along the way. Perhaps there is a tendency by writers of the East to glorify the past, yet the archeological evidence bears out this point. In late Roman times wells in the Syrian Desert region of Azraq had a level of water about 6 feet higher than at present.

Explanations of such phenomena are complex rather than simple: there were natural reasons, perhaps changes of climate, and there were human reasons, such as the cutting-down of vegetation, which had a secondary effect on water sources and the increase of evaporation. Also involved were indirect effects of human activities; for example, the development of the Arabian horse, a subject requiring further study. The horse was introduced into Arabia in lieu of the camel, which is rather a peaceful animal, not one for expansion or trouble. But the horse was different, and the Arabian species made expansion possible. The importance attached to the development of the particularly Arabian horse is reflected in pre-Islamic mythology: one of the most important intertribal wars was named after two mares—the War of Dahis and Ghabraa.

HEICHELHEIM cited the examples of French colonization measures in North Africa and the recent colonization in Israel as showing clearly that the potential fertility of the soil had not been destroyed to any measurable degree in the regions of Numidia, Mauretania, and Cyrenaica. He also pointed out that Plato, when speaking of Attica, is a second- or third-hand source, for he could not possibly have known about the deforestation of Attica in the seventh century B.C. or before, about which he wrote in his *Critias*. Referring to the recent monograph by Kahrstedt, HEICHELHEIM brought out that in Greece during Roman imperial times there were more forest estates than in classical times. Similarly, in Italy, air photos taken by the Royal Air Force during World War II, and studied by Bradford, revealed many ancient structures and farm estates from the prehistoric period to the early Middle Ages. In Italy it was only with the introduction of Spanish sheep-breeding and other more recent changes that destruction of fertility resulted.

Both GLACKEN and OSBORN questioned Heichelheim's views. GLACKEN made note that in his chapter he neither accepted nor rejected Plato's arguments but had cited his work as a landmark in the history of an idea. Plato had grasped the notion that man could change his environment, that a remnant of soil might be representative of a former fertile soil, and that a certain patch of forest might suggest a past condition. OSBORN referred to the works of Columella and others—contemporary Romans—which were filled with observations made by them during their lifetimes on what might be called the "degradation of the Italian peninsula"—that the capacity of the soil to grow wheat and other crops constantly declined. Also, Vladimir Simkhovitch, in an essay called "Hay and History," expounded the thesis that the causes for the decline of the Roman Empire were twofold: the falling-apart of family life and the inability of wheat production to support the population.[2]

DARLING agreed that we do need to

2. Vladimir Gregorievitch Simkhovitch, *Toward the Understanding of Jesus, and Two Additional Historical Studies: Rome's Fall Reconsidered; Hay and History* (New York: Macmillan Co., 1933).

examine the sources of the general historical view of latifundia. The large estate means some measure of conservation, and conservation goes when, under a money economy or an export-import situation, the estate is broken into small peasant holdings.

To DARWIN's query, "How did the cedars of Lebanon, of biblical record, survive longer than the forests of Italy?" HEICHELHEIM replied that the forests of Italy in Roman times were, over all, really not depleted, while in Lebanon there was a gradual decline, because the trees were extremely valuable.

In summarizing, at the end of the session, DARLING felt that Heichelheim spoke not as a biologist but primarily as a classicist, though with a certain chemical awareness. In considering that potential fertility in the Mediterranean lands and Arabia was not impaired, what perhaps had been lost sight of was the biologic complex, which makes use of the potential mineral wealth in the soil. With the loss of that biologic complex, only a desert results, though a satisfactory chemical analysis may remain.

DARBY introduced a concrete example from England to illustrate the effects upon the contemporary landscape of the works of a small number of people in ancient times. The Anglo-Saxons who invaded England during the fifth and sixth centuries were very small in total numbers. As small bands of practical-minded immigrant farmers, they experimented and finally settled at various places. But these settlements fixed for all later time the pattern of the geography of England. For instance, where men named "Redder" and "Wals" settled in the sixth century, there stand the towns of Reading and Walsingham today. While a great deal had gone on in the Roman and earlier periods, this relatively small group effected a "re-start" in the history of the landscape. Through all the later changes in techniques and methods and all the quickening and slowing of economic life, this pattern of settlement persisted until the industrial revolution. And even today the main network of population dates from the efforts of that small group of people in the fifth and sixth centuries. DARLING added the thought that the Anglo-Saxons, possibly more than any earlier people in Britain, used animals as a means of achieving their desired landscape—in this case, the use of swine to clear the forest floor, followed by sheep-grazing on the soil, which then grew grass.

THE MODERN ERA OF EXCHANGE ECONOMY

The idea of population growth is a very ancient one, GLACKEN commented —the notion that there is a niche for things and that these niches in the universe will gradually be filled up. This "principle of plenitude," though very deep in Western thinking, really did not emerge until the eighteenth and nineteenth centuries, when such writers as Süssmilch and, later, Malthus, expressed the notion of a gradual filling-up of the earth. And so in the modern era, as BANKS pointed out, we must take into account the changing age pattern and the changing numbers of the population, for we are facing a time when few die young and many live to maturity.

Adding to Banks's remarks, GREGG remembered that once in inland Brazil he had met a *caboclo*, a peasant, who said about his clearing: "When my sons were here and before they married, we had a good *roça*, but they wanted to have farms of their own; they left me, and soon came the 'green wave,' and I lost it all." This suggested that the capacity to fight the battle against the growing forest involved the use by a farmer of his sons. In the Connecticut River Valley of the United States a man who had plenty of sons could settle and manage the land; but, when families became smaller, the management of farms was lost to Italian immigrants, who took up the land again and made a go of it because they had sons to work cost-free to keep the thing going. A culture in which many children are born but in which many die early offers very different opportunities for the management of the land from one in which all the sons grow to maturity and in which the law of primogeniture, together with the increased span of life, means that a man will not turn over his farm to his son until his son is nearly forty years old or more. Nobody develops a wild enthusiasm for property by having to wait until he is over forty to get it.

JANAKI AMMAL introduced the problem of the population of India—four hundred million people being quite a large percentage of the world's population. In India the industrial revolution meant the clearing of land used chiefly for a subsistence economy of village farming, cattle-grazing, and hunting and the shifting to a money economy, using the land for the growing of cotton, oilseeds, and other export crops. The result has been that for the last one hundred and fifty years the Indians have lived hedged in, as it were, by an artificial environment, with all the necessary facilities of security and safety to increase their population. Any kind of medical aid only makes them live longer and increases demands on food supply; any method of curtailing population must deal with people who have not yet assimilated the scientific attitude.

GOUROU provided an example from India of the impact of a commercial economy. At the end of the sixteenth century, Goa was a great Portuguese city of three hundred thousand people, a considerable market for the consumption of produce. Transport was not well developed, and it was necessary to buy from the immediate surroundings. The result was destruction of the soil on the lateritic plateau of the interior, which today is without trees, fields, houses, or even much grass. In Travancore, to the south, the plateau soils have been used only since the beginning of the twentieth century. Fifty years ago there were no fields on the plateau; now the cassava produced there by poor, low-caste Christians is beginning to be of importance for the food supply of the growing population of Travancore.

The question was raised by KLIMM of whether there is going to be less communication in the future between parts of the world, and smaller markets, less exchange, and fewer people in an exchange economy, or whether the exchange economy is going to become more nearly universal, with more people entering into an exchange relationship. If the world market as a whole is going to increase, then we must not put too much emphasis on locally closed environments but must realize that man's habitat is actually the world and that pieces of the world compete with each other. However, if there are going to be fewer people in the world exchange economy, if regions like India and China are not going to become commercialized and compete for production and consumption, then we are able to take another view of man's relation to his habitat.

GUTKIND felt that there is already a settled answer to the question of whether the world will be more unified in the future than it is today. It will be one because it is one. If the world is one, we can get our food from anywhere; there is no fear that population increase will outrun food supply.

OSBORN brought out that at least three-fifths of all the people of the world are at a virtual minimum diet and below the standard of a desirable diet. Even if the United States were to, and could physically, export its entire surplus of food to one country only—India—it would but barely meet the minimum requirements of the objective of the Indian government's five-year plan. GUTKIND in reply suggested that the problem is one of proper distribution of settlements but that for the next two or three generations there is nothing else but to do what we can to develop natural resources.

In summarizing, DARLING expressed the thought that the replacement of subsistence economies by money economies is a central point in the effect of man on the planet. But, where there is export of produce, almost everywhere there is a very considerable deterioration of habitat. A subsistence economy maintains itself for a very long time and engenders its own conservation ethos, but an export economy spells deterioration. With an increasing and expanding economy, we may, indeed, without very great knowledge and without very great thought, be heading for disaster. This is not inevitable, but a much greater knowledge is required than we have at the moment.

JONES, in writing, questioned Darling's thesis that subsistence societies reach a harmony with their habitat in all cases, while an export economy leads to deterioration. A Pacific atoll, completely under subsistence in past times, *could* become overpopulated, unless a hurricane or other disaster took place, and bring about migration. An exchange economy *might* have made migration unnecessary.

MAN'S ATTITUDES TOWARD NATURE

The influence that environment has on a culture and the contrasting notion —much more difficult and confused—of man as a changer of the environment are both very old ideas, but, as GLACKEN pointed out, they are more notable for the frequency of observation than for systematic study. Related to them is the notion of the unity of nature and man's interrelationships with nature. The history of the idea of nature must include the history not only of biology but also of aesthetics, of religion, and of philosophy, because teleology must be taken into account: Is the earth designed for man; is the earth designed for use with man at the top of the scale; or is there another relationship of man to the earth? Many seventeenth-century scientists were very strongly concerned with looking into nature to see there the proofs of a living God. One of the most frequently quoted Psalms was the One Hundred and Fourth: "How wondrous are Thy works, O Lord! In wisdom hast Thou made them all." The concept of a balance or harmony in nature goes back fundamentally to the seventeenth-century idea of a sort of primordial harmony in the world with which man has interfered. The feeling we have in reading the background papers is not only that man was no passive instrument in the past but also that he not always quite knew what he was up to—a sort of clash between the conscious controls of science and the great unintended effects of man's activity.

SEARS provided several examples of man's attitude toward the landscape, what kind of thing he thinks it is, what it means to him in terms of his fundamental concepts—all of which determine how he treats it. In the valley of Mexico it was not simply that the Spaniards had found a use for timber and needed the space it occupied. Their action, according to contemporary testimony, was influenced by their values. They were homesick for the treeless plains of Castile. They preferred the type of landscape in which they had grown up and which had been produced by the activities of the Mesta, that great grazing syndicate that operated over the Spanish peninsula and effectively denuded it. In another example, communities have been observed that have practiced good land use over several generations, some for as much as two centuries. So far as known, these have been communities which have been united by some common religious bond, and it does not make too much difference what religion it was. Whether these communities are in Texas, eastern Pennsylvania, Ohio, or Iowa, their system of ethics is fundamental to the way they treat the land.

ANDERSON reported on the attitude toward nature which the botanist Bor observed during his collections in the forests of Upper Burma and of Assam. Since unrecorded time the peoples there have had a simple nature worship; although they had a *Brandwirtschaft*—they burned and moved on—their hilltops were not burned over. The hilltops were sacred; as places of worship, they were not cut over or pastured. Therefore, in this back country, in a place where man has been the longest in a state similar to what he must have been in the Stone Age, an attitude toward nature has preserved inviolate a very considerable proportion of the landscape.

SEIDENBERG, in writing, drew by analogy a moral from this primitive example. The recent "conquest" of Mount Everest, universally acclaimed as a triumph and culmination of mountain-climbing, was in fact a profane act which denuded man of the last symbol left on earth of unconquerable nature. The ascent of Everest, which represented a kind of psychological, if not spiritual, peak, resulted in what can only be termed a belittling of our world. It would have been singularly appropriate to have preserved it inviolate, if only as a universal symbol of man's place in the infinity of nature.

In his summary DARLING brought out another example of the importance of social behavior to land-use practices. In Scotland, rod-and-line fishing of salmon would never fish out a river, while

continued bag-netting at the coasts would certainly do so. But, especially in the highland areas of Scotland, where bag-netting is done, there is a strong Sabbatarian feeling, and the bag nets are taken up at six o'clock on Saturday evening and not put down again until six o'clock Monday morning. That piece of socioreligious behavior is quite sufficient to act as a conservation measure on the salmon stocks, since for 21 per cent of the time fish can go up the river unhindered.

For GALDSTON a crucial philosophical or cultural question was whether man looks upon himself as within or without nature. In science generally, but in the medical sciences in particular, man regards himself as quite without nature, in that he assumes he can manipulate nature freely and without suffering any untoward consequences. This is very clearly reflected in the history of medicine. There was a time when the microcosm and the macrocosm and the relationship of the two were deliberated on seriously, as, for example, by Hippocrates and later by Paracelsus. Today, except to a few ecologists, this is looked upon as a rather silly concern; and we have grandiose enterprises to "wipe out" infantile paralysis, tuberculosis, and a host of other diseases, based on the very serious assumption that, once they are wiped out, they stay wiped out and that there are no equilibration upsets.

DARLING disagreed with Galdston's contention that any definition of ecology takes its line of departure from some value system which is essentially homocentric. The ecologist is not concerned with what man considers desirable or not but rather with what is most fitting to any particular environment. In any habitat there is an ecological situation which is the most efficient in the circulation of energy. This situation, or particular association of plants and animals, for every environment in which there is life is termed "climax." It is that ideal situation that ecologists consider—what it is that a particular habitat can produce without the presence of man at all and what efficiency is lost in certain situations due to man's activities.

The concern of most preliterate peoples, at least philosophically, has not been so much with natural resources as with habitat. Philosophically, too, ancient man felt himself to be a part of nature; only in the last two or three centuries has man set himself apart from nature. For these reasons, SPOEHR felt that a consideration of "natural resources" could not be held at any time except the present, for it is a term which is culturally defined and which has grown out of our world-wide preoccupation with how the millions of people today are to live.

Darwin the naturalist had a sensitive insight, SPOEHR added, into the interrelationships within nature, a point of view that was represented by preliterate peoples, except that he was dealing with observed reality rather than with created reality. On the other hand, the achievements of the physical sciences and their practical applications have led us to a very practical concern with controlling nature. In SEARS's observation biologists, geologists, and geographers are all concerned with the question of natural resources. On the other hand, there are many who are intimately concerned with technology and its application and who tend to play down the concern about man's relation to natural resources. This very serious cleavage of opinion or attitude within the ranks of science is to be found in other groups of thought. For example, we frequently hear talk of an expanding economy as though it were the dream of the American people. Yet the term is used without qualification and without saying for how long the economy is to expand or by how much. It is

assumed to be the basic concept of our civilization.

UNSTABLE EQUILIBRIUM AND CONSTANT CHANGE

DARLING, in his introductory remarks, emphasized that Sears's paper has an important passage on "niche" and "role." The occupation of a niche and its maintenance thereafter mean, in our civilization, having a regard for, or obligation to, the environment in which our niche is located. Developing from that is the new ethic of conservation which ultimately may have a great deal more religious consequence than it has had up to the present. Respect for habitat is fundamental in some of the other past and present religions of the world, but in our own it has been foreign to our idea that we have dominion over the earth.

CLARK thought that one of the reasons why the world sometimes does not listen to conservationists as keenly as it ought is that different datum lines are assumed from which deformation may be said to begin; each person has his own "Garden of Eden," his own "Golden Age," and tends to measure what is going on in the world, or what is bad with what is going on, in terms of his own conception of what would be perfect. This is partly implied in any concept of niche: that plants, animals, and particular cultural groups have a special niche in the world and that, somehow or other, things must be fitted so that the niche is properly occupied. The difficulty is that niches are not stable but constantly changing. They have been appearing and disappearing for countless thousands of years. It is a prehistorical and historical viewpoint that provides the framework for the idea of a constantly changing world. If less were said about deformation and more thought given to living in a constantly changing world, then some of the difficulties continually brought out by those who seem opposed to the conservationists might be surmounted.

SEARS replied that, as a student of vegetation history, he thought himself to be sufficiently aware of the constancy of change. The main point with which the ecologist is concerned is that there is in the landscape a system of energy and material transformation whose trend—whether or not it is at climax—is very easily disrupted. Any landscape involves a multitude of organisms, all very closely integrated and interrelated, and each more or less helping to sustain the system. There is a tendency or a trend toward relatively efficient use of the energy which impinges and of the material which is present and toward minimizing the destructive action of the forces of climate and weather and toward regulation of the flow of water. It is this process that makes possible man's occupation of the earth and provides relatively efficient returns. And whether man maintains it or substitutes something else which performs the same function is immaterial.

JONES, in writing, suggested that, since ecologists are recognizing that the environment is not a constant but is unstable, for both natural and human reasons, a need is created for studies of "the topography of environmental instability," using "topography" in its classical sense.

Subsistence Economies

In his introductory statement Chairman ALEXANDER SPOEHR referred to the time scale of human history, during most of which subsistence economies have been dominant. This kind of life was general throughout the world before 5000 B.C. and common to considerable parts of the world almost to modern times. What have been the relations of such societies to the earth's surface?

THE TIME ASPECT

It seemed to BLUMENSTOCK that the climatic upheavals of the Pleistocene interposed a very important kind of semipermeable screen through which only certain kinds of things resulting from the influence of man could move. Ninety-nine per cent of human history lies within the pale of the archeologist. By ten to twenty thousand years ago man had pushed his way, except for a few islands, to the remote corners of the earth. HAURY felt that we need to ask ourselves what this long and widely based tenure has meant. The archeologist has not yet supplied adequate information of a sort that the ecologist and others perhaps want. The framework within which the archeologist operates has broad dimensions in space and time. Change comes as a response to continual adjustment to changing environmental conditions; out of the continual adjustments man has made, new things have emerged. From an early hunting condition in the Americas there was change to a gathering type of economy incident to the extinction of some of the large game animals. Correlated with that change were certain cultural losses and gains which then led to the nuclear developments in South America, Central America, Mexico, and, to a lesser degree, North America.

HUZAYYIN stressed the importance of having a true perspective of the time scale in the evolution of human culture. The Paleolithic represents by far the longest chapter in human activity compared with the Neolithic and later stages. In some areas, such as the mid-

410

latitude deserts, the importance of the Paleolithic unfortunately has been over-shadowed by stress on the Neolithic phase of human settlement. As com-pared to the historic phase with its doc-uments and descriptions left by man, our study of the tools and stone imple-ments of prehistoric man is not preju-diced. Among the Lower Paleolithic industries (Chellean-Acheulean com-plex, etc.) there was no significant dif-ference between one world area and another, except for South Africa and perhaps Southeast Asia. Not until the Upper Paleolithic was there a signif-icant change in human life: different kinds of stone industries localized in certain areas—Aurignacian, etc., in Eu-rope, Capsian in North Africa, Aterian in the Sahara, Badarian in Egypt, etc. This localization of industry for the first time in human history can be inter-preted as being due to a clearer adjust-ment of human activity to natural en-vironmental conditions. It was in the Upper Paleolithic, too, that art began as a result of sufficient leisure for de-velopment of spiritual aspects of hu-man life. Co-operative efforts of arche-ologists, paleogeographers, paleobot-anists, and paleoclimatologists are called for to shed light on this first phase of human settlement in which groups of men began to differentiate local patterns of culture.

FIRE

Omitting consideration of energy of the human body, the first chapter in a history of energy technology would treat of man's use of fire and of the un-anticipated side effects that occurred with its use, such as the role it played in creating new environments for hu-man habitation. SAUER's field work in Mexico was largely in the mountains during the warm season. The difficulty of obtaining landscape photographs ir-ritated him; it was annoying that good pictures could not be had until the rains

hit heavily. Gradually he realized that fire was the most important step that the people had for preparing land for cultivation or in improving pastures. Out of this experience came further thoughts on the universality and lon-gevity of man's use of fire.

NARR, though he did not attend the symposium, submitted the following written statement about the oldest evi-dence for the use of fire by man:

I think that the doubt which has persisted about the "hearths" discovered near Ips-wich cannot be diminished by the "rostro-carinates" and other pretended "artifacts" of the "crag series." As far as I see, S. H. Warren[1] in 1923 was the first who denied the artificial origin of those flints. Further arguments were brought forth by statistical inquiries of A. S. Barnes[2] in 1938. This op-position against the "artifacts" was shared by most participants at the International Geological Congress in 1948 (see *Man*, LXIX [1949], 58). Also, the abbé Breuil has modified his former views,[3] though he still regards "traces of fire" and "a certain number of flakes" as "possible," simultane-ously admitting that "their flaking angle is generally unfavorable." A 1954 study by K. P. Oakley on "Evidence of Fire in South African Cave Deposits" (*Nature*, CLXXIV, 261–64) shows that the vitreous material in question probably has been due to fires. But the cave deposits consist largely of bat guano, which could have easily been ignited at the cave entrance by a natural grass fire. The oldest evidence for the human use of fire thus seems to be the hearths of Peking man. Nevertheless, this cannot be taken as proof that man learned the use of fire only in the mid-Pleistocene. In my opinion the use of fire is, beneath language and manu-factured tools, a criterion which distin-guishes mankind from other primates.

1. "Sub-soil Pressure-flaking," *Proceedings of the Geological Association*, XXXIV, 153 ff., and "Sub-soil Flint-flaking Sites at Grays," *ibid.*, pp. 38 ff.
2. "Les Outils de l'homme tertiaire en An-gleterre: Étude critique," *Anthropologie*, LXVIII, 217 ff.
3. See H. Breuil and H. Lantier, 1951, p. 63 (cited by Sauer, p. 69 above).

Therefore, if there should turn up evidence that the "Australopithecinae" were true men (in the psychologic and philosophic sense), I shall not hesitate to ascribe to them the ability of having used fire, whether the latter can be proved or not.[4] I think that in this respect I am in full accord with Dr. Stewart.

Man is cutting into the wealth of ecological climaxes, but very few men (certainly not civilized men) lived in forests under climax conditions. DARLING commented that fire has been man's instrument for setting back succession in creating his habitats. There are extensive habitats in stages of succession well below climax which, through loss of organic natural wealth, must be considered as deteriorated by factors other than the occurrence of natural fire only.

In Ireland, and probably in much of northwestern Europe, EVANS observed, the use of fire as a major force in altering the environment would seem to have depended upon climatic change. Scandinavian students of the history of technology and agriculture claim that the extensive use of fire began with subsistence economy and could not have been effective under the old hunting economy. The sub-boreal climate which followed the Atlantic phase was a factor in the establishment of subsistence economies which have been fossilized to a certain extent ever since and whose last remnants in Europe are only now passing away.

It was the contention of STEWART that fire has always been an environmental factor in areas such as the Great Plains. On the other hand, where there is adequate moisture, a tremendous amount of burning will not produce a pure grassland. The best example is found in the southeastern United States, where the longleaf pine forest is the re-

4. See also Narr's short 1954 paper on "Australopithicinen und älteste Geröllindustrien," *Germania*, XXXII, 315–18.

sult of burning. Without fire the forest simply will not reproduce itself. A related question, difficult to answer, is the distinction between man's production of fire and fire produced from natural causes, such as lightning. Frequently, assertions are made that lightning has caused fires on the prairies, yet Stewart had found no record of lightning-ignited prairie fires.

DAVIS considered the southern longleaf pine (*Pinus palustris*) to have evolved over many hundreds of thousands of years, with fire sufficiently prevalent to produce the species. A fire every ten years is even better than one every other year. He saw no difficulty in postulating lightning as the origin for a fire every fifteen to twenty years in any forest in Florida without human beings necessarily ever having been there. EGLER granted that fire is of extraordinary importance, but he felt that we should be very careful in considering whether fire (of whatever origin) produced a species or a vegetation type. There is an important difference. Most weed species, like the red birch in the northeastern United States, undoubtedly existed for a long time, but as a community the red birch has come into existence with a different regime. In dealing with a system—a holistic unit—we cannot isolate fire as a causal factor and hold to that alone.

In all his personal experience in tropical grasslands (Indochina, central Africa, Madagascar), GOUROU, in writing, stated that he had never seen a fire produced by lightning, in spite of numerous thunderstorms. While personal experience is not a proof, it nevertheless explains his strong skepticism about lightning fires in grass or forest. Also, he cautioned against "observations." In some "protected parks" of tropical Africa, some fires officially attributed to lightning are perhaps man-made fires. In effect, cessation of fires produces a diminution of the land occupied by grasses and a progress of trees. The result is a diminution of herbivores (antelopes, zebras, etc.) and, in consequence, of lions. Yet, great herbivores and lions are the principal attraction and interest of these parks. Without fires the vegetation would return to forest. Fire is a means—perhaps the only means—of maintaining the vegetation in a static situation. Officially, the use of fire is not allowed, but it is providential that responsibility for fire may be attributed to lightning.

MALIN read into the record quotations from two newspaper articles, later inserted as footnotes (see pp. 350–51) to his chapter in this volume. His point was that considerable evidence of firsthand observations of lightning-set prairie fires may be obtained from county newspapers which report the week-by-week activities in a neighborhood. In Kansas, for example, the State Historical Society has a virtually complete file of every newspaper, weekly or daily, printed in the state since 1876 as well as earlier ones. The evidence that meets reasonable tests of accuracy and validity is there for the collecting in newspaper reports. Malin was stimulated to introduce this comment because Sauer, in 1944 (pp. 553–54 of "A Sketch of Early Man in America," *Geographical Review*, XXXIV, 529–73), and Stewart, in his present chapter (see p. 128), had stated that they knew of no documentation of lightning-set fires for the plains.

To BARTLETT, newspaper reports of the kindling of grass fires seemed entirely credible. In a United States National Park Service report on the Florida Everglades, Robertson (1955) states that lightning-started fires in that subtropical area actually have been seen by trained fire-prevention observers (see the full reference to Robertson, p. 718).

World wide, approximately ten thousand thunderstorms occur daily, with roughly a hundred thousand lightning strokes per day to the ground, LANDSBERG remarked. Lightning should not be underestimated as a source of fire. In Florida, for example, there are at least ninety days per year with thunderstorms. From the amount of lightning, there is no doubt whatsoever of its ability to start fires.

The large problem is not the effect of fire on grass, ANDERSON commented, but the effect of fire on vegetation. Grass is a special and dramatic example, but what of the subtler effects, where forest or savanna did not change to grass?

ALBRECHT thought it would be helpful to look at fire on the land in terms of soil. Fire is more detrimental for the survival of forests than for grasslands, because forest residues burn very handily, while grass is an annual which dies, with its roots adding organic matter to the soil where fire does not destroy it. Fire converts vegetation residues into the more soluble form of ash. The result of fire is equivalent to a fertilizer treatment to the soil. If the ratio of nutrient elements is suited to a particular physiological performance, then certain plants are given a boost toward species dominance. Species should be viewed in terms of physiological requirements from the soil rather than taxonomically.

TAX, in writing, thought that we should think of the influence of man as the extinguisher of fires as well as the maker of them.

In the wooded Northeast of the United States there were various patches of grasslands known as "plains." The White Plains in Westchester County, New York, gave their name to the modern city. MURPHY, in writing, pointed out that on Long Island the more extensive Hempstead Plains (250 square miles in area), as described by Daniel Denton (1670), were certainly sustained by fire set by Indians. It is likely that annual burning was carried out in late summer, so that the Indians might snare great numbers of Eskimo curlew and golden plover on their southward migration. At any rate, the Hempstead Plains remained grassland well toward the opening of the twentieth century. As recently as 1893, Long Island folklore held that trees would not grow on Hempstead Plains. About this date residential development began, and, within two decades, Garden City became a sylvan community. Today, the Hempstead Plains are a region of wood lot and copse. The reversion to forest was, in short, concomitant with the cessation of fire.

DOMESTICATION AND MIGRATION

SPOEHR, as Chairman, shifted the discussion from fire to plants and animals. Wherever man has gone he has been the center of a biotic assemblage of plants, both cultivated and wild, of insects and terrestrial arthropods, and of microörganisms, some of which are parasitic on man himself. In the time scale of human history these factors occurred early.

BATES called attention to the phenomenon of pre-adaptation with respect to plants and animals. When change is brought into a situation, many adaptations among the organisms for some other purpose will switch over and protect them against this new change. For example, many groups of insects, such as ants, have resisted the insecticide DDT. Other populations have rapidly shifted, so that certain elements within them which were resistant are able to take over as dominants. The same is true of resistance to fire. Certain plants, such as the pines, might have been extremely rare, but, because of their adaptation to fire, they became the ecological dominant under conditions where fire was an important element. The organisms associated with man perhaps belong in this category of organisms with very odd characteristics

which made them rather unsuited to the world before man started to mess it up but which enabled them to join in and reinforce man's activities in remolding the landscape. There is a general tendency for biologists, as natural scientists, to ignore man and his crop plants in their search for something in which man has not interfered, so that they can study "natural" processes. In so doing, they overlook the possibility of studying man as a part of nature; in studying human modifications, we are studying nature as well as man.

ANDERSON pointed out that there is mounting evidence that evolution proceeds very rapidly when there are new niches for things to flow into. Hybridization, for instance, may have been going on for a long time. It may not have been getting anywhere; but, when a new niche is formed into which the products of hybridization flow, something new is created very quickly. Therefore, it would be one thing to have the longleaf pines. But if there were an increased use of fire, so that longleaf pines and things like them which can withstand fire come together, a new association is formed. With new niches, there is a place for the product of hybridization which had been previously ignored by natural selection. There is a place for something new and something different. Therefore, as soon as early man created new associations —not new species—such as a longleaf pine forest, there was change from an occasional pine here and there among hardwoods to great stands of pine. This kind of thing must have happened in various ways throughout the world as soon as man arrived bringing fire with him. In this way a rapid evolution of new kinds of things followed in man's track.

NARR, in writing, contributed the following discussion on the origins of pastoralism and on the beginning of important sheep-breeding in Europe:

That domestication of sheep and goats began somewhere among tribes of the Indo-Iranian border ranges, probably stimulated from early plant-cultivating populations, is a view favored by Wissmann and his collaborators. However, an assumption that pastoralism had an independent origin somewhere farther north and thence (perhaps in the still primitive form of "companionship") spread to the south would require no severe modification of the other views expressed by Wissmann. If we admit, furthermore, that an early plant cultivation was already in existence between 13000 and 9000 B.C. or, more cautiously, before the beginning of the fifth millennium B.C., though it cannot be proved archeologically,[5] we wonder whether the same possibility also should not be conceded to pastoralism.

The theory that pastoralism rose independently is by no means contradictory to the assumption that plant cultivation originated rather early in southern Asia. It should be remembered in this respect that the very partisans of the theory of a separate origin of pastoralism, namely, the older generation of the ethnological school of Vienna and, among prehistorians in particular, O. Menghin (1931), also favored the view that agriculture began in southern Asia, probably as a kind of tuber-planting. Furthermore, that does not exclude the possibility that those early southern Asiatic plant-cultivators domesticated some animals, in particular, the pig. This domestication may have originated from "taming" (*Zähmen*) in the sense given that word by H. Pohlhausen (1954). "Taming" consists of accustoming animals to the neighbor-

hood of men, so that the beasts no longer shrink from them, remain close to human settlements, and accept additional food from men. Similar "taming" can be observed especially in southeastern Asia and Melanesia.[6] According to Pohlhausen, "taming" was developed by "territorially fixed hunters"; this statement is in agreement with the assumption that tuber-planting originated among sedentary hunter-fishers and food-gatherers. I think that it would be wise not to stress too much one specified theory about the origin of pastoralism, for it seems that on the evidence available today there is no possibility for a definite, objective, and really conclusive decision.

The material on sheep in prehistoric Europe, used by J. G. D. Clark (1952), comes from full Neolithic and from late Bronze Age and early Iron Age sites. The late Neolithic and, in particular, the early and middle Bronze Age are virtually unrepresented. Therefore, the statements of Clark cannot mean more than that sheep were unimportant in the economy of the full Neolithic of Europe, as far as this could be ascertained, whereas they were really of great importance in the closing Bronze Age and the early Iron Age. The regrettable lack of evidence from the early and middle Bronze Age leaves open the question whether and when sheep-breeding became more important during that time. But there is direct evidence from the late Neolithic Pontic, and similar inferences can be made for late Neolithic Middle Europe, that sheep-breeding had grown more important in this period and probably was introduced on a greater scale by a distinct culture group, namely, the Battle-ax civilization.

EVANS added this anecdote: With regard to the movement of plants with man, there is a delightful essay by Lord Acton, who must have been one of the first to look into this question with the eye of a historian and with an aesthetic sense. He has an essay in his studies in history on the commerce of thought, with a wonderful section about a sol-

---

5. On the unlikelihood of archeological evidence for nomadic pastoralism see in particular M. Hermanns, 1949, pp. 160, 180–81, as quoted by Narr and by Wissmann (pp. 148 and 301 above). Indeed, we may modify the statement of G. Smolla (quoted by Wissmann, p. 284 above) as follows: "The lack of archeological proof for these earliest planter tribes [pastoralists] does not, therefore, speak against their former existence. . . . The archeologist can maintain only that no discoveries are against such an argument [see Narr, 1953, pp. 69, 73] and that, by using it, several phenomena become understandable which before were inexplicable."

6. See also p. 754 of K. Jettmar, 1952, "Zu den Anfängen der Rentierzucht," *Anthropos*, XLVII, Nos. 5–6, 737–66, and Narr, 1953, p. 89.

dier in Vespasian's army invading England. The soldier's great tramping boot wore out, and, with it, the seed lodged in the dirt picked up in Gaul was discarded in Kent. From it, he says, "Next year England gained another wild flower." And he goes on in assessing, no doubt in a prescientific way, the long list of plants which the Romans brought; and he has, I remember, this very delightful phrase: "We owe to the Roman"—then he lists a succession of plants and adds—"green peas. God bless him."

DARLING pointed to the impoverishment of the flora of wild lands under the intentional pastoralism of domesticated stock. He put it as a fundamental that domestication cuts down the mobility of animals. Having got them where they are wanted when they are wanted, they are on the spot for a longer time than under natural conditions. Pastoralization puts wild land under pressure which, in general, it is unable to withstand for an indefinite period. The result is an impoverishment of the flora, which is, in turn, an impoverishment of the organic circulation within the particular habitat.

In the islands of the French West Indies the lowland plains and foothills differ from the hill lands in soil types and, in a way, in local climatic types. The vegetation type of the flatlands is all savanna—isolated thorny trees and grassland; that of the hills is scrub. Usually these vegetation differences are interpreted in terms of climate and soil, yet the real explanation, EGLER found, lay in the form of grazing. The key to it was located where fence lines ran no longer between slopes but up them. Goats, almost omnivorous and keeping to the higher rocky slopes, did not eat certain scrub plants; the result was croton thickets. Cattle ate almost anything except thorny leguminous trees and stayed mostly on the lowlands; the result was the savanna cattle country.

The marked division correlated with soil and climate differences but not in a cause-and-effect relationship.

DEFORESTATION

The clearing of woodlands was important in Europe and America and in various parts of Asia. WITTFOGEL spoke of the avoidance of woodland in early China. China's culture originated in the Yellow River Valley, whose loesslands were not densely wooded. The more heavily wooded areas of central and southern China were only gradually opened up to Chinese culture. Records of the Han dynasty (about the time of Christ) describe the Yangtze area as still backward agronomically. In the T'ang dynasty (A.D. 618–906) the great majority of the Chinese still lived in the north, only two million Chinese then residing south of the Yangtze. Thus, it took the Chinese a long time to conquer the woodlands and to create the artificial landscape of terraced paddy fields which characterizes central and southern China.

It was PFEIFER's impression that the 27 per cent of area in Germany preserved in forest is rather exceptional. In England, for example, only 3–4 per cent remains in forest cover. Riehl, the nineteenth-century sociologist, always spoke of the forests in Germany as the autocratic feature of the landscape: during revolutions, the peasantry, taking advantage of their freedom, reduced the forests by their cuttings. Thus are the changing relations of man and nature linked to social conditions of particular times.

SEARS reported that Enrico Martínez, an engineer who attempted the drainage of the valley of Mexico, wrote in 1609 that at the time of the conquest, which was less than a hundred years before his birth, the hills were densely forested. It was not until the Spaniards came and tackled the forests with steel tools and fire and turned what he called

"Christian cattle" loose on the hills that the erosion cycle once more was resumed. Martínez described very vividly the consequent flow of mud and water down into Mexico City. That is not conjecture but the testimony of a trained observer at the time.

The modern world, since the sixteenth century and especially since the mid-nineteenth century, has become alarmed over a shortage of suitable timber. DARBY mentioned that the woods, their destruction and its consequences, and the need for some policy of conservation were one of the main themes of George P. Marsh's *Man and Nature* in 1864. "The Woods" was the title of his very long third chapter.

The large surfaces still remaining in forest (about 20 per cent) in present-day France, GOUROU, in writing, accounted for by the facts that (1) large areas of forests are in state lands or *terres communales*, which are collective lands with special forest legislation; (2) on marginal lands forest is the best economic system; (3) a rural exodus has occurred (economically justified); and (4) sheep have regressed.

GRAHAM commented upon the relationship between clearing of land and subsistence economy as illustrated in northeastern North America. By the late eighteenth century much of the land in New England had been cleared. In north-central Massachusetts, which we know very well in terms of its land-use history, there was essentially a subsistence economy—not in a primitive sense but certainly in comparison with the present day. By 1850 the land which had been cleared and brought into cultivation was largely abandoned due to the opening of new lands in the prairie states, where it was economically much easier to produce food crops, or (as TUKEY pointed out) because of migration to the California gold fields. Today, that land in north-central Massachusetts is practically all

forest. Thus a reverse generalization is true here, for the disappearance of a subsistence economy has resulted in the rapid appearance of a heavy forest growth.

PLOW AGRICULTURE

Following the Paleolithic, special types of agriculture arose: digging-stick and hoe cultivation, the clearing of woodland, and the eventual development of plow agriculture. EVANS thought that an important topic to be looked into was the introduction of and various modifications of the plow. He asked for advice from technologists on the exact differences in purpose and function between the chill plow and the steel plow and between the left-handed and the right-handed plow. PFEIFER reiterated that in his chapter he emphasized the importance of plow agriculture as a stabilizing factor. Central Europe has been cultivated since the fourth century B.C. without very detrimental effects. There is hardly anything by way of soil erosion to compare with what happened in the New World under colonial European agriculture. It is possible that plow agriculture was adaptable to different conditions by the shift of emphasis between animal-raising and crop tillage.

FROM TECHNIQUES TO SOCIAL ORDERS

SPOEHR made reference to Gourou's statement, in his chapter on tropical agriculture, that human choices have been influenced much more by the level of techniques than by physical conditions alone.

SAUER suggested that Gourou's paper was interesting because it emphasized the significance of wet-land crops, of drainage, and of their possibilities. Wet-land plants made into crop plants apparently was an exclusively Old World set of techniques. The establishment of modern contacts was a means of invitation to admission of a large number of crops.

Brazil provided an example where modern man has reverted to more primitive types of agriculture. PFEIFER pointed out how German agricultural colonists in the state of Espíritu Santo took over *caboclo* ways, using fire and shifting fields in forest clearings. But the colonists could not move around fully like the *caboclo;* restricted to colonies of limited areas, the colonists had to rotate their fields so fast that there was incomplete recovery of vegetation and of soil productivity. EVANS, in his discussion of the Danish fields of the "Celtic Iron Age," mentioned that in many open-field systems, especially in regions of difficulty, plots changed hands periodically. This type of tenure in which land was periodically redistributed seemed to GLACKEN to be of great antiquity and to have existed in many parts of Eurasia. He first became acquainted with it in studying Ryukyuan history. In Okinawa, village lands were communally held by a village and were periodically redistributed. The system, which apparently existed in early China and Japan, was abolished by the Japanese around the turn of the century. At present it is found in the Near East, where it is known as *mashá;* here, pastoral lands are periodically redistributed. A criticism made of both types was that the system led to land deterioration because of neglect and carelessness in its use toward the end of the allotment period. Periodic redistributions also were characteristic of old Russian village communities. Ancient land-tenure systems, of which this periodic reallotment is an illustration, are of great importance in studying the mechanisms through which changes of the earth have occurred in the past.

Several speakers, among them PFEIFER and WITTFOGEL, directed attention toward the social and cultural circumstances which had to develop before certain techniques of land use could be employed on a wide scale.

In Central Europe the sociological structure of peasant society was of importance. State authority, directing settlement and political economy, developed at the end of the fifteenth century. Forests were to be preserved. Emphasis in housebuilding shifted to bricks; hedges and walls replaced movable fences to shut off pastures. Peasant wars of the early sixteenth century had the effect of canceling out the forest conservation acts of the government.

Before the modern industrial period, between 60 and 70 per cent of all mankind during the last three to four thousand years lived under conditions shaped by hydraulic civilizations. This cultural development, with its complex technological, economic, and governmental institutions, required large communities for its development.

In the retreat from the imperial Roman social organization, the cities of Western Europe shrank, and the countrysides became more populous. HEICHELHEIM suggested that there might be something of a law: that a subsistence economy populates the countryside, while market economies produce much more but empty the countryside. He posed the question: Was the retreat from urban centers of civilization to church monasteries, royal courts, aristocratic estates, and humble villages really a catastrophe? There is a good deal of evidence that in Egypt, in the eastern Mediterranean, and in the West the late Roman time was not a period of decline. For example, comparing the evidence of what the population of Helvetia knew of Roman order and civilization under Roman rule with what was known in Alemannic time, the Swiss actually knew considerably more Latin literature in the later period than they had known under Roman rule. In the south of France the Greco-Roman survival was even more marked. Thus, such a retreat, to something near a sub-sistence economy, does not necessarily destroy civilization.

At the time white men came to the northeastern United States there were very extensive stretches of white pine, EGLER explained. We know today that white pine is a one-generation type; it does not reproduce itself without dis-turbance, nor does it become a domi-nant type except after disturbance It would seem that a disturbance oc-curred—or an otherwise different situ-ation prevailed—about A.D. 1400, ap-proximately two hundred years before white men arrived. Did an epidemic possibly wipe out a very large Indian population, and did pines enter into areas that formerly had been grass-lands? With great changes in Indian populations, there were enormous changes in vegetation. White men ar-rived at a very unstable moment.

Archeology reveals that during the period from A.D. 1400 to 1500 there was a very marked change in Iroquois pop-ulation, or at least in Iroquois culture, SCHAEFER reported. About 1450 there was a gathering-together of small vil-lages into very large ones. Around 1500, these suddenly disappeared, to be fol-lowed by scattered, smaller villages.

A further coincidence concerning the 1450 period was pointed up by CURTIS, in writing. Extensive pine forests around the upper Great Lakes and the pine forests that preceded hemlock for-ests in Pennsylvania both date back to 1450. Though not the only possible ex-planation, this may be correlated with a temporary decrease in Indian pres-sure.

DARBY indicated that the great and fairly continuous expansive movement of the clearing of woodland did not continue uninterruptedly into modern times. Only recently has it been appre-ciated that a very great economic re-cession took place between A.D. 1300 and 1500. Causes are obscure—perhaps plague, perhaps warfare, perhaps a crisis resulting from something else. But abandoned holdings and deserted villages are dated from this period. In England alone, thirteen hundred de-serted villages date from the period 1400–1550, and the number is increas-ing with further discoveries. Over many of their cleared fields, the woods spread again. Jäger has recently shown that many tracts of woodland in Ger-many came into being during the fif-teenth century and have remained as woodland ever since.

BANKS drew attention to the obvious coincidence between the period of A.D. 1400 (mentioned by Egler, Darby, and others) and the Black Death, which was a world-wide pandemic in 1346. The death rate in Europe was one in two or one in four. The plague spread slowly from Asia to Europe, but how would it have gotten to the New World? MALIN pointed out that there was a Scandinavian connection with North America to about the mid-four-teenth century. Then there was a break, and connection between Scandinavia and North America was not resumed until the 1480's, before the time of Columbus. This gap in the record has never been satisfactorily explained.

DARBY then made the point that in Europe the Black Death must have been, and certainly was, a considerable factor, yet it is quite clear that the re-cession was well under way *before* the Black Death. While the matter is con-troversial, to pin the recession entirely on the Black Death would be a mis-take.

PFEIFER agreed that the Black Death, while a known phenomenon, must not be held fully responsible. What about climatic change? Floehn has pointed out that in the mid-fifteenth century there was a definite change for the worse in climate, which might have accounted for certain retreats in the less favorable uplands of central Germany. For this area an apparent climatic optimum in the thirteenth century coincided with the spread of colonization; the fifteenth century saw the retreat. Again this is too simple an explanation. The abandonment of land began much earlier—and in different sections. It was very early in the best areas of old settlement; there was a redistribution of population and a consolidation of smaller settlements into larger ones. Mortensen holds that the datum level for the modern development of the landscape is at just this point which marks the end of the medieval period.

HEICHELHEIM thought that behind the recession of about 1400 was an economic catastrophe in Islam, the leading economic center of the time, which led to an enormously high price for silver. The resultant upheaval in all medieval market economies was made good only by the discovery of America.

THE QUALITY OF PEASANT LIVING

With the thought that perhaps a clearer conception of how man's social order is related to his environment and to his quality of life ought to be striven for, Chairman SPOEHR turned to TAX for the session's closing comments.

TAX again posed the question: Is man conceived as a part of nature? Man certainly is a different kind of animal in nature. He mediates his relationship through a set of values which are thought of as basic to the culture, and he has what some think of as free will. In other words, man knows what he wants sometimes and goes out to get it, and in this respect he is different from other animals. Man must not be thought of as something which is only being used or is using. It is man and the human element that must be brought in when different kinds of cul-

tures are characterized. The peasant way of life is to be contrasted, on the one side, with the way of life of the tribe and, on the other side, with the commercial way of life, whether in the city or elsewhere.

The tribal way of life presumably was characteristic of that long, long Paleolithic period right into the Neolithic. A peasant way of life can be spoken of only in the Neolithic (food-producing, hydraulic civilizations, and all the rest), which, of course, is very recent. To speak of a commercial way of life or an urban way of life is to be concerned with only the most recent movement in world perspective.

The way of life in the innumerable "savage" tribes, to use the old evolutionary terminology, is a kind of web of meaning in which man achieves a satisfactory relationship to the universe, including the ecology around him, and which for a long time can slowly change, but change only within a limited area. By the end of the Paleolithic there were a great number of these tribes who achieved a level of culture where they could fairly well control the environment as they found it. They were confidently able to move into new environments, and culture change was very rapid before the period of the Neolithic. This was the period during which man explored and spread out over the world even more than before, for he rapidly invaded the New World in a relatively short space of time and adapted himself to the thousand different physical-biological environments that were there.

Tribal man, or whatever he is called, never is, or was, unchanging or unchangeable or conservative. The history of humanity would not be what it is if man had not adapted very quickly and adjusted to change wherever necessary.

What happened next was that, in numerous places, for numerous reasons in different places, and for some common reasons in all places, a group of small societies became one large society. This is what Childe called the "urban revolution," from which are derived civilizations. This second stage was based on agriculture and the domestication of animals wherever it occurred and on such things as irrigation. But then there exist side by side what Redfield terms both a large tradition, based on literature, held by an elite class, so to speak, and carried on by that class, and small peasant traditions. Always in this stage of human society there is the peasantry as well as towns and cities and commerce. We have to think of a peasant way of life as part of a large way of life—a civilization—including some commerce and some division of labor. The tribal way of life continues in some, but not all, respects.

Three ways in which peasants seem to differ from tribes are:

1. Landownership and inheritance become very important. With property comes the whole notion of savings and investment and the notion of "a rainy day." In other words, property—animals, plants, barns, houses, land, land boundaries, and all the rest—becomes a terribly important concern for man, and, consequently, so does the next generation.

2. Where there are domestic animals with full agriculture rather than simple tillage, time becomes terribly important, and a heavy sense of responsibility is felt. The animals have to be fed; man cannot leave them. He has to "make hay while the sun shines." The whole notion of time makes man not only a slave to property—this is the true story of the Garden of Eden—but a slave to time as well.

3. Individual motivation and competition begin. There arises a conflict of values between the individual's life-ambition and what he thinks of as saving for his children and his grandchil-

dren. The conflict between an individual's values and the values of society as a whole arises, generally, only within the peasant state of life. In the tribal state of life as it is lived at the present time among North American Indians, this conflict is not important. It is won by the community or society; individual competition just does not have a prominent place, and people are able to adjust to one another. The great value is the characteristic harmony in the society. Competition and individual initiative have to take second place to the notion of the harmonious whole. This is important, because the harmonious whole in the tribal society relates to nature as well. And this value of harmony is certainly not entirely lost by peasants. There is a feeling of the harmony of the universe and a proper relation with nature, with God, with one's fellow-men, and with the whole web of human culture which is important in tribal life, which remains important in peasant life, but which undoubtedly becomes lost in some degree with the development of commerce and of urbanization.

Neither is evolution inevitable nor must all people proceed through the same stages. An important historical or archeological point to be made is that differences persist. Peoples do have different ways of life on any level, and one of the ways in which they do tend to differ is in the basic value judgment of harmony versus competition. Did man ever universally give up the notion of the harmony of society as contrasted with what he could get for himself? Does it necessarily follow that man ever will in all places or that this will become widespread throughout the world?

This becomes exceedingly important, because many people believe that, in order to get economic development in the underdeveloped areas of the world, it is necessary to make people over into the kind of people that Europe developed at the time of the commercial and industrial revolutions. But, Tax asked, are there not many roads, not simply one, to development of better lives for different peoples in different cultures? Westerners take a very narrow view if they assume that their way of getting a better life is either transportable or should be transported to groups with very fundamentally different cultures and, with respect to many human values that are shared, better cultures than their own.

Commercial Economies

Forest Regions outside the Tropics

Grasslands

Arid Lands

Humid Tropics

Capital and Surplus

Dr. PAUL B. SEARS, as Chairman, began the session by putting on the blackboard the notation

$$\frac{R}{P} = f(C) \, ,$$

with R representing resources, environment, or land; P, human population; and C, culture. The sum total of resources and the population among which the resources have to be divided are a function of the pattern of culture.

There is a definite connection between the culture pattern and the resources which are considered useful. The flint ridges in northern Wyoming or in eastern Ohio which were tremendously important centers for the Indian are today negligible for us. The great deposits of coal, petroleum, and ore which lay under the surface near by meant nothing to the Indian but mean everything to our own way of life.

The pressure of population on resources also is a function of culture. Some populations maintain themselves by cultural means in fairly stable equilibrium with available resources. On the other hand, American culture is inclined to value continual expansion: some is good; more is better; more and more are both bigger and better. This is a cultural value which seems to be inherent in the system.

In considering the interrelationships among resources, population, and culture. we must remember that each is a complex of many factors. Much discussion of correlations or cause and effect seems beside the point because of the multiple impact of the great number of factors involved. The key factor may be conspicuous and overabundant or scarce and limiting.

The distinctions among subsistence economies, commercial economies, and technological civilizations seem flexible; we can expand or contract the distinctions in relation to others even at the present time. For example, during the depression of the 1930's many unemployed in the cities returned to simple hill farms such as those in the Ozarks. Such hill farmers made the quickest adjustment to the economic depression; they shot a few more squirrels, picked a few more blackberries, and got along very well. Though some of their tools were of metal, they had essentially a Neolithic culture which was cushioned against the impact of what was regarded as a great tragedy in most of the country.

Something of this flexible arrangement is reflected in our patterns of land use. In an area put under commercial pressure to obtain maximum revenue, a definite sequence often occurs. The three common types of land use in western Europe and eastern North America are forest, pasture, and cropland. Under pressure of a commercial economy, the tendency is to plow up everything that possibly can be plowed, to pasture everything that cannot be plowed, and, if there is anything left, to leave it in forest or other wild vegetation. The paradox is that to attempt maintenance of a permanent commercial economy destroys capital in the long run. Much of the conservation movement as it has evolved in the United States has been able to reverse this trend.

An economy partly commercial and partly subsistence which, after several hundred years, is still operating on a very solid basis is that of the Amish of eastern Pennsylvania. Hilltops remain forested; the pastures on the hillsides are grass-covered and cross-fenced, so that one part may rest while another is grazed; and the plowland or cropland is confined to the rich valley-floor alluvium. This prudent, permanent, successful pattern maintains the value of its capital in the midst of a commercial civilization.

Discussion turned to the presentation of case histories of specific instances of man's relation to his environment in connection with commercial economies and the effects of that relationship.

FOREST REGIONS OUTSIDE THE TROPICS

SEARS began the discussion by citing such a case history. The state of Ohio at the time of European invasion was 95 per cent forested. Its Indian population was between twelve and fifteen thousand; but, even if it had been twenty thousand, the average density would have been but one-half person per square mile. On a partly agricultural subsistence economy, though there were some exchange goods brought in from the outside, such as

copper, obsidian, and shells, the people, as far as we can tell, were crowded at the end of the fifteenth century. The Indian population in North America at the time of European discovery was in a condition of very delicate balance; the effect of the first encroachment of Europeans on the Atlantic coast was like the snipping of the outer connecting strands on a spider web. Repercussions which were felt across the continent brought on profound readjustments, so that true pre-Columbian conditions in the interior were never known to the whites except by inference. Some years ago the locations of Indian settlement were plotted on a map in correlation to the distribution of original vegetation. It was hoped that relationships could be found between Indian settlement and vegetation types. Instead, the result was that settlements were grouped along the rivers, regardless of the type of forest, because rivers were more important than vegetation differences.

New England in the 1830's was from 80 to 90 per cent in farms. Most of these clearings reverted to forest, for 60 per cent of modern New England is in forests, which produce less than 10 per cent of the rural income. The ancient fields now covered with forest were divided by stone walls. On the upper slopes the bases of these walls are exposed; at the bottoms of slopes these bases are buried under transported soil. Land abandonment was due not solely to the competition of cheap land to the west but was aided by a faulty relation of land use and management to the economic base—a faulty relation of culture to resources.

THORNTHWAITE was asked to speak of his experience at Seabrook Farms in disposing of waste water as an example of the difference between forest land and cropland. Seabrook Farms is a huge commercial agricultural enterprise devoted to raising vegetables and to harvesting, processing, freezing, storing, and distributing them. In preparing the vegetables for freezing, a large amount of water is used for washing, fluming, and other operations. Polluted with dirt and organic matter, this water, for lack of dissolved oxygen, cannot be discharged into near-by creeks without destroying the fish. In attempting to use the water for irrigation it was discovered that the plowed land had a very low infiltration rate, for, after receiving an inch of water, the soil became soupy. Then a woodland was sprayed with the waste water, and it seemed that there was no limit to the amount that could be applied. In preliminary experiments, 5 inches an hour for ten hours were absorbed, whereas, only 600 feet away, forest-cleared, cultivated land of the same soil type could not take over an inch. As a result of this astonishing experiment, ten million gallons of waste water have been disposed of daily in this forest since 1950. This is equivalent to 600 inches of water a year for the last five years. And weeds and other vegetation flourish.

In central southern New Jersey there is an empty area of some two million acres known as the "barrens" and considered to be essentially useless, except as an area for storage of water supplies for peripheral cities and towns. Apparently it was once heavily forested, but, owing to a sandy soil incapable of holding much water, it suffers tremendously from drought and in rain-deficient periods is very subject to fire. At present the area is covered with woody growth only a few feet in height, but, where fire has been kept out, trees are 20 feet or more high. From the experiments at Seabrook, it seems clear that what is wrong with the "barrens" is its lack of water. Water is there, only 10 feet beneath the surface. Here is an opportunity for a reclamation project

that would outstrip the controversial one on the Colorado River.

SEARS emphasized that the principle back of Thornthwaite's remarks is that a great deal of agricultural practice tends to lessen the capacity of the soil to absorb water. A commercial enterprise sometimes can be too smart for its own good; in the interest of increasing production, it can destroy an asset essential to its continuance. This principle is in the same category as urbanization, which has the effect of waterproofing the land surface while at the same time raising the per capita consumption of water. As THORNTHWAITE summarized: Here is one powerful way man has modified the earth. By clearing the forests and cultivating the soil, he has reduced the infiltration capacity of the soil by a phenomenal amount.

SMITH asked Thornthwaite whether the New Jersey "barrens" has a layer of hardpan under it, while EVANS, in writing, asked whether there is hardpan under the arable land which does not absorb water or if the lack of absorption is due to change of soil structure without leaching. Evans' question bears closely on the problem of waterlogging of early cultivated lands (forest-cleared) in northwestern Europe and the subsequent accumulation of peats. THORNTHWAITE replied that the area has no hardpan under it. In drilling ground-water observation wells throughout the "barrens" in Lebanon State Forest, no hardpan was found, only clean white sand: fine grains interspersed with coarse, from the surface down to 70 or 80 feet. Hardpan sometimes develops in areas where there is excessive water. At Seabrook Farms a battery of evapotranspirometers has been in operation for eight years. This is a series of identical tanks, about 7 feet in diameter and 3 feet deep, filled with soil in which crops are raised; for the last five or six years the crop has been grass. It is possible to irrigate the soil in the tanks by a pipe from beneath and to keep track of the amount of water used, so that the rate of evapotranspiration can be determined by the amount of water applied and the amount used. This was the purpose of the installation. Four years ago the method of applying water to three of the tanks was modified. While three were irrigated from below, as before, three others were supplied by water from the surface by sprinkling. On these latter three, slightly more water was put on in the morning than would be evaporated and transpired during the day. There would be a slight amount of percolation through the soil; this was caught and the amount subtracted from that applied; this gave the amount of evapotranspiration. In early June, 1955, efforts were made to determine the effect of the difference in watering on the permeability of the soil in the tanks to see how it compared with the soil permeability in the surrounding cultivated fields. On three tanks, water was poured on. Amazingly, the one that had been watered from above for four years took water at a rate more than five times as great as the irrigated tanks, which, themselves, took water at about twenty-five times the rate of the cultivated soil.

That the "barrens" had porous soil that did not hold water and that the plants suffered from drought indicated to THOMAS that such conditions were not true of the usual forest or grassland. Rather, such conditions are typical of the places for the best ground-water recharge, such as the mouth of the Lost River in Idaho or some of the beach gravels around Lake Bonneville. But these areas that contribute to prolific and perennial ground-water reservoirs comprise only a very small proportion of the earth's surface.

BLUMENSTOCK wondered whether if water were raised from beneath the "barrens" for agricultural purposes

there would be further underground invasion of salt water, which is now a problem at Atlantic City. THOMAS replied that with modern pumps it is certainly possible to bring on salt-water encroachment but that, being aware of the problem, it should be possible to maintain a balance and not overdraw by pumping to excess.

LEOPOLD thought the discussion was getting dangerously close to the conclusion that the way to control floods was merely to allow wasteland to revert to forest under as ideal conditions as civilization would allow. There are two complicating factors in flood control. First, one of the most important principles to emerge from study of the effects of different kinds of vegetation on floods has been contributed by the United States Forest Service. At Coweeta Experiment Station it was demonstrated that floods in that part of the Appalachian Mountains were formed by water, none of which had been surface flow. Water that had infiltrated into the forest soil reappeared in the stream channel from underflow. This is just a warning that reforestation will not necessarily be a primary means of controlling floods. Second, in most soils there is a tendency for infiltration rates to be reduced with increased application of water. The rate decreases with time, even under natural vegetative conditions. Floods generally occur during times when flood-producing rainfalls immediately follow a period of moisture sufficient to reduce the infiltration rate to a minimal value. That there have been floods throughout all time, long before the existence of civilization, must be recognized.

HEICHELHEIM asked whether libertarian administration of forests is especially difficult. Is it a matter of chance, or do forests to be administered well require organization collectively for the common interest. Even the otherwise most libertarian Hellenistic and Roman societies tended to be administered as large collective units in accord with a unified plan. Athens tried to administer collectively the forests of Macedonia for naval and peacetime needs. The Ptolemies established a monopoly for all forests in their territories. For Rome, forests at first were public property, then later were taken care of by large latifundia, and, finally, there were great imperial forest estates throughout the Empire. In the medieval period, forests were very often exclusively in the hands of the king.

The classic sequence of what happens to forest when commercial activities are introduced is that the land is cleared, leaving the forest only in a few relict areas, and that the forest does not return to the land unless something disastrous happens to the economy. KLIMM brought out that field study and aerial photo interpretation had revealed the opposite for the northeastern United States. With increasing commercial intensification of agriculture and competition with the western states, the tendency has been for crop acreage to shrink. Crops are produced only on the best land. There has been a shrinking downhill of the cropland, with increased abandonment of hill farms and an increase of forest. Competition has restricted agriculture to the better lands, the poorer lands have gone out of production, and the forests have come downhill. Every state in the Northeast, except Delaware, has had an increase in forest area and, correspondingly, a decrease in cropland. But the cropland, however, has increased in per acre yield. Most of the abandoned land was originally owned in farms. As it gets to the debit side of the tax rolls, the states buy it up for protected hunting land. One might argue that commercialization of agriculture is the way to bring about conservation of the landscape.

GRASSLANDS

Regardless of whether fire was started by man or by lightning, its prevention was of some consequence to the commercial range-cattle industry, MALIN remarked. In the early twentieth century, after pastures were fenced, conservation of grassland became even more important, because cattle owners could not move from place to place but had to depend upon what lay within their fenced land. Another point to be kept in mind when discussing the Great Plains was that dust storms have always been a regular part of the phenomena of the area. Archeologists have supplied evidence for repeated occupations of the same prehistoric site— the levels of successive occupation being separated by dust or other wind-blown material. Dust storms were present before commercial livestock ranged the prairies; they arose when winds blew over the plains after denudation of vegetation, whatever the cause. In an article in *Scientific Monthly*, early in 1953, Malin raised questions on the significance of dust storms not only to the areas from which dust was blown but also to the areas on which it fell. He pleaded for soil scientists to publish their views on whether the chernozem soils of the grasslands are maintained, at present, by dust-fall. And what effect would stoppage of dust storms have on all the eastern areas that regularly receive falling dust.

SEARS remarked that there are three sources of dust: the wide river valleys, perennially full of fine material; dried lake beds, full of fine silt; and the plowed fields. Resource men not only do not deny the importance of wind-transported source material for soil but recognize it as a very important factor. JONES, in writing, thought Malin's use of accounts in local newspapers as evidence for dust storms to be a good idea if the accounts were evaluated with care. The evidence, however, is likely to be qualitative rather than quantitative. For instance, we would learn of dust storms in the Great Plains prior to agriculture but not of how they compared, in quantity of soil removal, with the dust storms of the 1930's, for it would not be reported what land types (dry lakes or potentially arable land) were being eroded.

We attach a value to grassland, AL-BRECHT pointed out, because the vegetation cover is a forage for livestock. But this necessitates a soil that makes a forage worth a cow's time to eat. Much of our food has come out of the grasslands by a type of extensive agriculture that is more speculation than production, because we depend upon the cow to supply something capable of being fattened. The pressure for beef supply from the grasslands is very rapidly depleting the potential for protein. Where the plow went ahead of the cow, we have been able to measure the reduction in soil capabilities. The protein content of the wheat now grown on the eastern edge of the grassland area has been dropping decidedly. Where once it ranged from 19 to 11 per cent, it is now 14–9 per cent.

GRAHAM pointed out that the wheat yield in the Nile Delta is something like 30 bushels per acre, while the wheat yield in the United States under commercialized farming is only 17 bushels per acre. Commercial agriculture forces us to utilize a great deal of land which probably never should have been utilized for agricultural production and, as a result, forces an exploitation of our soil resources. KLIMM replied that economists and other social scientists for a long time have been critical of comparison of yields per acre as an index of the value or efficiency of agriculture. For the comparison depends on what is produced and what is conserved. Peasant agriculture in Egypt does manage to produce more bushels to the acre, but many more people are engaged in pro-

duction per unit area than in the United States. Are we interested in producing the most per acre or the most per man? If land "should not" have been plowed, what is it that so determines? That it will blow away or wash away? Is this a value superior to the backbreaking labor of peasant agriculture that produces so much more from so little land on very small per capita yields? The meeting of these two concepts is perhaps one of the better things that can arise from this symposium.

STEWART drew attention to an example of a complete change from grassland to virtual forest land by commercial overgrazing. In Texas millions of acres of prairie have been converted into mesquite jungle, a process accelerated by the cessation of burning. Under conditions of wild-game grazing and in the early years of open-range grazing, these Texas prairies were burned by Indians and later by the stockmen. But they were overgrazed, especially after fencing, so that not sufficient fuel remained to carry fire and burn off the mesquite seedlings that soon spread over the ground. Ancient prairie flora is still preserved in experimental plots along railroad rights of way that were fenced but also burned.

CLARK could not feel that those bits of prairie have the same ecological situation as in the days prior to the coming of the railroad or of commercial economy. In a discussion of "Retrospect" the contrast of precommercial and postcommercial economy has been missed. In writing, he asked whether we were not talking about processes of change before we have had any serious discussion of the kind and dimensions of change which have taken place? He could not speak about very extensive areas, but, with regard to the New World unplowed grasslands, he hoped his chapter had raised some doubts as to fairly widespread assumptions about change. This did not involve very much of the earth's surface or very many people; the point is that it is hopeless to talk about processes of change anywhere at any time unless the change itself can be established, at least as to probability, in its general outlines. The changes of nature involved in the establishment of hydraulic civilizations are in certain respects clear; in many others they deserve much more searching analysis if we are to know what the establishment of a great irrigation network really has meant in this or that place or time. Again, we recurrently lose our focus on man's role in changing the face of the earth if we talk too closely to the point of what commercial economies have done to primitive cultures and unless we compare more closely than we have the contrast of the two in changing vegetation and soils. But this, too, involves at least a reasonable guess at a "before and after" picture. We are concerned always with a changing and not a static picture, or, to express it perhaps more precisely, we are concerned with comparative rates of change. But we must, surely, first be reasonably definite as to what we are talking about.

ARID LANDS

In evaluating the historical importance of commerce in promoting and upsetting institutions and ways of life, WITTFOGEL desired to place on record some facts in connection with hydraulic societies operating in arid and semi-arid lands. The primitive and supposedly harmonious relation between man and nature had been disturbed long before professionalized trade became a major feature of civilization. A system of class distinctions, with one group controlling the mass of the population, existed long before the development of a merchant class. The records of pharaonic Egypt indicate no development of an important group of professional merchants before the beginning of the New

Kingdom. Scholars, such as Breasted and Kees, have shown that trade expeditions were carried on by the governments of the Old and Middle Kingdoms, but professional merchants played no role. Means and others claim that in the Inca Empire there were no professional merchants. The empire was operated essentially on a non-commercial basis. But it certainly was no classless society. A similar situation prevailed in China up to the middle of the Chou dynasty. There was a strong development of a ruling bureaucratic-military elite and a peasantry, but there were virtually no merchants. In all simpler Oriental ("hydraulic") civilizations, societal stratification occurred under conditions having nothing to do with commercial economies.

At the end of the first millennium B C., the Chinese system of village agriculture was destroyed; the peasants who had lived in regulated village communities became owners of land. A contemporary statement noted, in effect, that, whereas on the public fields the peasants showed no zeal, on their private land they worked "their heads off." China, by spreading private property, introduced more competition among peasants than did most other great hydraulic civilizations. For two thousand years China maintained a very intensive peasant agriculture, based on private landownership and tenancy. Until the end of the Chiang Kai-shek regime, peasants cultivated their land intensively. Yet today the government has to exhort the peasants to till their fields with care. Today the Chinese Communist newspapers *Jen Min Jih Pao* and *Ta Kung Pao* implore the peasants not to sell or slaughter their work animals, because they will be needed later. Today the peasant lands are being pooled (collectivized) throughout China. This is a development similar to the tragic experience in Russia in 1929 and 1930, when the peasants killed their work animals for food rather than pool them in collectives. Generally speaking, private ownership of land has been a great stimulus for the peasant economy.

HUZAYYIN brought in the significance of geographical situation for an area. The arid zone of northern Africa and southwestern Asia lies between the tropics and subtropics and the Mediterranean, where the seas do not meet. In this land interruption to the seas, man had the camel as a beast of burden suitable for caravan travel. A middle area developed for exchange of products between different zones. The spirit of an intermediary or middle man is reflected in the cultural thought and mental and spiritual attitudes of the people. Trading is almost a sacred profession. Commercial economies, however, are not necessarily based upon the production of surplus. The Arabs, for example, had no surplus except in a few oases, and their commercial activity was based not upon local subsistence economies but on surpluses from other regions.

There is at present an increasing pressure to make more intensive use of the arid lands of the world, SEARS remarked. But in practically all places, over millenniums, or at least for centuries, there have been going economies which would be jeopardized by further use. Engineers who have worked in the Near East report that, in trying to locate irrigation works, they can do no better than to relocate old systems in use during prehistoric times. Empirical experience over long periods has been very effective in the Old World. Any increased pressure on such arid-land regions is fraught with certain danger.

ALBRECHT added the point that arid-land economies are based upon the buying and selling of water. Crop plants are grown more by a kind of hydroponic procedure, with water being poured onto lithic deposits, rather than in true soils, because arid soils have not been able to break down into the fine clay particles required for their absorption and exchange of nutrients to plant roots.

Having been in the Middle East just prior to coming to the symposium, BANKS called attention to Iraq as an arid land to watch for future development under a commercial economy. In that country there are now five million people when once there were thirty million. It has the rivers and the ancient irrigation system but, in addition, now has an income of £70,000,000 from oil.

HUMID TROPICS

BARTLETT, characterizing himself as a "Neolithic" man, spoke of his experiences many years ago in the east coast of Sumatra, where he was concerned with establishing vast rubber plantations for the United States Rubber Company and became appalled at the contrast between the manner of European life on the plantations and that of the natives in the adjoining jungle and grassland. Going south from Medan through the great cultivated belt, one passes first through the Deli tobacco country. Then comes a much more sterile region covered with great fields of lalang, a tropical grass of very little usefulness to man except for the grazing of cattle or water buffalo on its very young shoots that appear after annual burning. Finally, one enters the country planted to rubber. In 1917, when Bartlett arrived, only one tiny patch of primary forest remained. All the rest of the great expanse of rain forest had been cut and burned, for it was easier to convert forest into rubber culture than to subdue the relatively useless grassland.

An almost Neolithic culture existed alongside of the most highly developed commercial agricultural enterprise in the East Indies. The two reacted upon one another in a most interesting way.

There is nothing more admirable, theoretically, for the utilization of tropical lands than the growing of rubber trees. Nothing is actually removed from the land except carbon, hydrogen, and oxygen, derived ultimately from air and water. There is no loss of combined nitrogen or fertilizer salts. The plantations had a population of twenty-five thousand, including laborers' families. The trees were all planted in beautiful rows on land cultivated absolutely clean by an army of workers who went forth each morning and, after the rubber had been tapped, scraped off every vestige of a weed.

At the edge of the plantation stood an abrupt wall of the old secondary forest in which the Pardembanan Batak lived. The agriculture of these people consisted of cutting down successive, small areas of forest, waiting until the debris had dried sufficiently to burn, and then burning as completely as possible. However, to plant at the right time, the large logs not yet entirely dry would be left helter-skelter, only the areas between being completely burned. The ash that coated the land represented a tremendously valuable asset, for it contained all of the useful soluble fertilizer salts that the trees had brought up from beneath the ground. Although the first season's cultivation did not completely exhaust this resource, it nearly did so. The burning which followed a season or two later consumed what remained of the fallen logs. Planting in these fields was based upon long experience; it had been learned which crops were shade-tolerant and which were not. In addition to upland rice, a mixture of crops was grown, so that a field was covered with different crops having a wide range of utility. Seemingly abandoned after two or three years to secondary growth, the former clearings still contained fruit trees and sugar palms. This manner of living was exceedingly important to those who practiced it.

The local forest dwellers refused to work for the plantations, for they did not want their way of life destroyed; instead, laborers had to be obtained from Java, a region of surplus population.

SMITH emphasized how plantation agriculture, by bringing in mid-latitude techniques of the plow, fallow, and clean cultivation, had contributed to soil erosion in the tropics. Most of present tropical plantation agriculture is in trees: coconuts, oil palm, rubber, tea, coffee, etc. Fertility is found not on the heavily leached lowlands but on the hillsides. It is on the hillslopes that the tropical farmer seeks a place to plant if he can. Can there be developed a hill tropical agriculture which will preserve the forest? We should be able to apply to the tropic hillside the idea of unplowed orchards as developed over the last thirty years by apple-growers in the eastern United States. The grass cover is mowed, the soil is fertilized, and the grass mat keeps the soil in place while the trees produce the crop. SMITH called for the creation of tropical experiment stations to pool information with existing research stations and to work out a tropical agriculture that would keep the forest cover on the valley floor and develop hill crops above it.

While Smith had just advocated tropical hillside tree crops, GLACKEN recalled that Gourou's chapter urged commercial agriculture of wet-land crops in swampy valley bottoms. A further comment originated from the thesis of Richards (*The Tropical Rain Forest*, 1954) that the tropical rain forest is a great gene reservoir for future plant evolution throughout the world but that it might very well be eradicated by commercial agriculture during the next century.

CAPITAL AND SURPLUS

BOULDING could not help feeling that the study of ecology did not fit one to speak about commercial economies. The significance of the rise of world-wide trade is that it makes man into a single organism, and hence the conclusions derived from study of small parts of man's habitat are not wholly relevant. He had the feeling that ecologists want us to go back to the Neolithic, but he was not going, for it was a very uncomfortable and disagreeable time to have lived. Why assume that soil should not be mined? We mine coal; then why not mine soil under certain circumstances, in certain places, at certain times? If it is assumed, implicitly, that nothing should be exported from any piece of land, does that mean every piece of land has a natural, moral right to be what it was, if it ever was? But we *are* going to mine certain soils; we *are* going to turn certain areas into deserts; we *are* going to have shifting populations. Because commercial economy makes man a single unity rather than a multitude of disparate self-supporting population groups, we can afford to do this. Is the population of Greece today larger or smaller than it was at the time of the flowering of classical civilization? Considerably larger—in spite of all the awful things man has done to the earth. He has been able to multiply practically everywhere over the last two thousand years because of a commercial economy. If man had not mined the soil and cut down the forests, he would still be in the Neolithic. This is not to deny the existence of real conservation problems.

GALDSTON asked to play the tail to this comet. He mentioned that in epidemiology there is a category known as *civilisations sociales,* which includes the miserable epidemic diseases known as tuberculosis, scarlet fever, diphtheria, cholera, typhoid, and sclerosis, which were in part produced by the concentration of man in the cities made possible by commercial agriculture. Whose ecology is being discussed? If man's, then these factors are to be included.

The thought expressed by Darling, that man gains his leisure and builds up his civilization by "breaking into the stored wealth of the . . . natural ecological climaxes," was considered rather pessimistic by GLIKSON, in writing. Though greatly true for our time, he asked whether this is the only way for man to develop higher activities. Are not biological as well as socioeconomic processes of production and reproduction ruled by a natural principle of surplus production which makes possible a peaceful development of higher activities and living conditions? Animal life in nature subsists on a surplus growth of vegetation apparently not needed for the survival and annual renewal of plants. Moreover, it is essential for the very existence of vegetation that its surpluses be consumed by other species. The same relation of mutual dependence exists with respect to the surplus in animal life on which predatory animals and man partly subsist. Somewhat similarly, economic and social organization and division of labor are possible when a well-balanced family farm can produce a quantity of foodstuffs sufficient to nourish an additional number of non-farm families. Such a surplus production, based upon the biologic capabilities of the land, represents a sufficiently reliable basis for the development of civilization. Industrial development has been possible by the forceful concentration, by combined technological and political means, of large surpluses of food and raw materials into specialized regions. If such concentrations of surpluses create scarcity and deterioration in the areas of their production, they are neither true surpluses nor reliable bases for civilzation. Surpluses are dynamic factors which initiate natural and social development. But man has often been misled to believe that there are no limits to nature's capability to produce a surplus. Only when he transgresses these limits does man begin to break into the "stored wealth" of the earth.

HEICHELHEIM added to Sears's notation with which the Chairman began this discussion session by stating that capital is the most important factor in commercial societies—even more important than resources or population.

In conclusion, SEARS expressed the thought that mankind's relation to environment *can* be analyzed in terms of accounting if so desired. The main problem is not to confuse two items in the accounting budget: (1) income and (2) depreciation. What is done to maintain the value of the capital structure is good; what is done that destroys it is bad. And that, it seems, is all we have been trying to say.

Industrial Revolution and Urban Dominance

The Rise of Cities

Influence of the City on Exploitation of the Earth

Is the Industrial World Community a Permanent Civilization?

Why Change?

Differences in Approach to Man and Environment

Dr. KENNETH BOULDING, as session Chairman, spent the first several minutes in developing an agenda for discussion. Additional topics suggested from the floor were added to an outline previously distributed by the Chairman. The final roster of topics was as follows:

1. What is the relative importance, in explaining the rise of cities, of the following?
   a) Agricultural techniques; fisheries
   b) Transportation techniques
   c) Industrial techniques (capital, trade, resources such as fossil fuels)
   d) Political techniques
   e) Demand for gregariousness; sociability; vanity and gossip; playfulness
   f) Ownership
   g) Cultural facilities
   h) Religion
   i) Protection (defense)
2. What part is played in cultural dynamics by the *contrast* between urban and rural cultures, and what is the significance of this contrast in modern society?

BOULDING suggested that the most important and inevitable consequence of the present urban revolution is the disappearance of differentiation between urban and rural life in the United States outside the South.

THE RISE OF CITIES

ANDERSON suggested that many people like cities because people like to get together. Man is an animal, and animals come together. Early man, when he could not afford to get together permanently, did so for temporary periods.

The biological basis for this togetherness is reproduction. The very sexual conjugation is a getting-togetherness. As DARLING pointed out, there could be no continuance in a bisexual species without a coming-together. It is a social need of the species. Cities come to be by allowing people to rest together in numbers which, in early hunting and food-gathering systems, they could not do in an environment of relatively poor yields. For example, the Indian settlement of Council Bluffs on the Missouri River was based upon this intense social desire to get together, although technologically the settlement was unable to maintain itself permanently. Even today the Eskimos get together in summer, which is not their busy hunting period, but their environment and technological development do not allow the social amenities to achieve permanence.

STEWART added that non-agricultural peoples gather together whenever the opportunity arises. Even the Australians or the natives of Lower California, when the food supply was sufficient, congregated to eat the surplus food and then dispersed again. The Kwakiutl of the Northwest Coast, merely by having enough salmon, were able to live together in towns.

HEICHELHEIM thought that the urge in man to congregate is not so much for reproduction as simply for the sake of congregating, which is a distinct characteristic of man. MUMFORD, on the other hand, characterized the city as primarily a protected human breeding place. The element of protection brings together a larger number of people within a small area and increases the opportunity for people from quite different biological stocks to intermingle and to produce more combinations than would be possible in a more widespread community.

But KNIGHT pointed out that the city is antibiological. He asked: How and in what stages of human history do cities universally fail to maintain themselves without recruitment from outside? BROWN wondered whether the failure to maintain itself is a phenomenon of the city or of the economy with which it is associated. In India, for example, age-specific birth rates of Calcutta and Bombay are equal to those of the smallest villages.

BATES cautioned that getting-togetherness underlies the whole phenomenon of human society; the discussion should strive to emerge from that into the particulars. EVANS, in writing, warned that it should not be forgotten that society is older than man, is inherited from prehuman ancestors, and is not a human invention. STEINBACH, in writing, considered the discussion of gregariousness on a biological basis to have confused two issues: (1) the basic tendency to aggregation, which is reversible, accounts for *initial* formation of groups and is a biological factor; and (2), once aggregation takes place in organisms or communities, the setting-in of *differentiation,* which is irreversible, applies to communities following the formation of groups and is a cultural factor.

HUZAYYIN preferred to start from space relations rather than from human activity to explain the rise of cities. The social need of man to come together may be perfectly true, but what of the natural forces which compel man to agglomerate? About 7500 B.C. there came a phase of aridity in the Middle East that forced man and animal to come together in small, limited watering areas. About 5500 B.C. more rainfall, a phase of relaxation, allowed space relationships to be established among these areas of concentration.

It seemed to MAYER that biological factors account for the village but not for the city and that a distinction between the city and the village was necessary. BROWN agreed and pointed out that plotting a frequency-distribution curve of sizes of living units gave a continuum, whether for India or for the United States.

GUTKIND did not feel that size meant anything. The big village towns of Hungary, which are miles apart and contain up to thirty thousand people, are not cities, because everyone in them, save a few artisans, is engaged in agriculture. He suggested the real distinction between city and country to be based on function. Another distinction is that in villages a person may have a close group of many relatives, while in a city he is freer to form elective affinities, which has led to an atomization of society.

Among those who could not accept the distinction between town and village based upon function was HUZAYYIN. As far back as we can go in Egypt and the Middle East, where villages and cities began, the two can never be distinguished in their functions. Villages are not always agricultural; some are based on industry, others on trade. Rather the criterion is space relations —the village limited to the surrounding subsistence area, the town having a wider hinterland and wider space relationships. GUTKIND replied that the very large village towns of Hungary have enormous areas around them, yet they remain villages, because everyone is engaged in agriculture. He could not see any possible distinction between town and village other than the functional activities of men living in either place.

GLIKSON found that the size of villages is ordinarily limited by the distance from the house of the farmer to the land on which he has to work. There is a certain maximum limit to this distance and a certain minimum size for the area of land on which the villager has to do his work. Exceptions to this occur, such as in Bavaria, Italy, and Hungary, for reasons of security; villagers concentrate in rural towns, but even today they suffer the handicap of the distance which must be traveled from home to fields.

The meaning of the terms "city" and "town" has fundamentally changed, WISSMANN added, in writing. Until the nineteenth century and in some parts of the world to a later time, a town in most countries was a *fortified* settlement, generally founded by the government and having governmental functions. This was especially true in China, in ancient and medieval Europe, and in the Near and Middle East. In all these regions the development of cities was different, but fortification, except perhaps in Egypt, and government centralization were present.

The classic area for the study of the industrial revolution is nineteenth-century Britain; but, despite a great deal of work on many aspects of the movement, little has been done to show how cities came into being. DARBY asked: What really happened when Manchester grew or Birmingham came about? What were the mechanics of the movement that produced these "million" cities by the end of the nineteenth century? Based upon census information that from about 1841 included data on

birthplaces, Arthur Redford, in a pioneer study published in 1926, showed that the movement to any growing center was essentially short term. People came into Manchester from the surrounding countryside, which, in turn, was replenished from the more remote countryside; that, in turn, was replenished from adjacent regions until the coast was reached. This was true of every growing center; the whole island was one mobile mass of population. Later in the century a long-term movement obviously became more important, but exactly how, when, and which areas were most closely affected are not known, because material about birthplaces has not been worked out. If we knew the how, perhaps we would be better equipped to answer the why.

It was suggested by LANDSBERG, in writing, that some valuable information could be gathered by studying the rebuilding of cities after catastrophes in a scientific, objective manner. There are many of these in all lands and all ages. A few come directly to mind from recent history: Chicago after the fire (1871); San Francisco after the earthquake and fire (1906); Messina after an earthquake (1908); the destruction wrought by Mount Pelée on Martinique (1902); the destruction of Tokyo and Yokohama by earthquake (1923), with a repeat performance for the former city by fire bombs (1945); the destruction of World Wars I and II, in particular during the last war in such different habitats as Coventry, Plymouth, London, Berlin, Hamburg, Frankfurt, Warsaw, Hiroshima, Nagasaki, Agaña, Manila, etc.

What patterns did reconstruction take? Why did people go back to the old places? What improvements were made? Did the people make "choices"? Were there notable differences in different nations? How do reconstruction practices differ with time? How does the further development of reconstructed cities compare with untouched towns in the same area? Answers to these and similar questions seem to contain "ecological" information comparable in value to that obtained for plants after prairie and forest fires.

JONES, in writing, referred to Boulding's list of factors of importance to explain the rise of cities and pointed out that we must differentiate among (1) the *requirements* for a city; (2) the *functions* of cities; and (3) the *developmental history* of specific cities or of cities in specific societies. Among the requirements for a city are means of subsistence, transportation, government (for reasonable internal order and protection), and site. The functions of cities are many, and the hierarchy is different in different cities. Washington, D.C., is governmental but has recreational functions. Atlantic City is recreational but, of course, has its government. And, as Darby properly stressed, there is need for developmental histories of cities, since the present city may be structurally and functionally different from what it was in earlier periods.

BOULDING proposed that cities are the products of agriculture and exploitation. That is, without agriculture there is no surplus to feed the cities, and without exploitation there is no way of gathering the surplus together.

It seemed to THOMPSON that there was a very marked change in the agriculture of Europe during the seventeenth century. The industrial revolution was preceded and accompanied by an agricultural revolution. This latter was not so obvious; it did not attract attention. The improvement in techniques effectively increased the productivity per hour of labor bestowed on a particular type of work. When the industrial revolution began, probably not more than 20 per cent of the people of any country lived in what would be called "cities," as characterized by differentiations in occupations of their inhabitants. With the growing efficiency in agriculture (introductions of new crops and improvements in animal breeding), the proportion of people who could be spared to live in communities and carry on non-agricultural occupations slowly increased. As the industrial revolution grew in its use of power and as more labor was needed, people moved from the country to the city. The modern growth of cities has been based fundamentally upon changes in agriculture. These changes have taken place gradually but continuously, so that in a country like the United States only about 13½ per cent of the population now resides on farms. Basically, the growth of modern cities has depended upon moving along *pari passu* with improvements in techniques and knowledge of agricultural production, though this does not altogether answer the question why. As agriculture became more efficient in modern times, other countries, such as Japan, were able to make the industrial transition much more quickly.

The influx of population to towns depended on the state of agriculture only to a certain degree, GUTKIND countered. There is an old saying in Germany that "town air sets people free." People came to towns desiring to escape the feudal powers which were then stronger in the countryside. The towns were not able to absorb them all, and, in consequence, a sort of unemployed proletariat arose in many European medieval towns.

GOUROU, in writing, observed that a diminution in density of rural population was possible in the United States and in Western Europe, because rural densities were not very high. In Japan, however, the rural density in 1868, before the industrial revolution, was 600 per square mile, and it has continued at that level until today. Growth of Japanese cities has not resulted in rural exodus but has been possible only by demographic excedents of rural population. When the rural population is very heavy at the onset of industrialization, the role of cities and industrialization is very different. Therein lies a great difference between East and West.

Again, in writing, GOUROU presented an obverse example. In central Africa the cities are in a somewhat difficult situation with regard to their food supply. For example, Leopoldville (300,000 Africans) finds difficulty in obtaining enough food. Yet the average density of population in the Belgian Congo is only 5 per square kilometer, and 85 per cent of the inhabitants are rural. The explanation is found in the disparity between the two civilizations. European civilization is responsible for the creation of the city; the traditional African civilization is responsible for the scarcity of salable foods. Today it is easier and cheaper to import wheat flour to make bread for consumption by Africans in Leopoldville than to find in the countryside sufficient quantities of *chikwangues* (cassava paste).

GALDSTON inquired whether the agricultural population under conditions of agricultural surplus automatically reduced itself through exodus in inverse proportion to the quantity produced. BOULDING then modified his original proposition that cities are the products of agriculture and exploitation. A surplus from agriculture is necessary but is not a sufficient condition to account for the formation of cities.

GOUROU, in writing, said that, for him, the discussion of the city had been most confused. Is it necessary to ask why there are cities and what are their characteristics? The only point that appeared to him important was whether the development of cities in modern civilization was dangerous, profitable, or indifferent for the future of humanity.

At this point in the discussion, BLU-MENSTOCK rose to voice his objection that the discussion had strayed too far from the theme and that consideration should be given to the influence of the industrial revolution on the ability of man to change the face of the earth. Cities do change the face of the earth, but, while a fascinating subject, their modes of origin do not.

INFLUENCE OF THE CITY ON EXPLOITATION OF THE EARTH

MUMFORD thought it must be realized that the cities of the nineteenth century and, very largely, the present day were successful in a commercial sense because they were parasitic on a subsistence economy. The assumption was that the farmer should not be able to make a normal commercial living from his work and the rent of his land; that he would not be a good bookkeeper and find out whether it was worthwhile to supply food to the city. As long as that condition prevailed and as long as a colonial population—an external or internal proletariat, to use Toynbee's terms—was available, cities were able to flourish at a great rate. Now, subsistence economies are in rebellion. In the United States the farmer, through the influence of education in agricultural colleges, keeps books and demands profits on his farm labor and farm investment comparable to those made on industrial investments. This becomes a limiting factor in the growth of cities. For example, cities are now obliged to offer subsidies to dairy farmers in order to obtain a sufficient amount of milk, and that is true of such other products as cotton and tobacco. We have reached the point where the fundamental relationship of the city to the land is being changed through the very success of the commercial economy in invading agriculture. This, in the long run, MUMFORD thought, is going to have very serious, and perhaps beneficial, results both on the spread of cities and on the exploitation of the land.

Harris objected to Mumford's use of the term "parasitic" for cities. Cities are no more parasitic on the land than farmers are parasitic on the cities. Who is paying the subsidies now, for example? Cities exist because they perform important economic functions. They are the most efficient areal technique yet devised by man for most types of production. For most of the things that people want, production can be organized more efficiently in urban agglomerations than by any other means. Cities also transform agriculture. That farmers have learned to do bookkeeping is part of the urban transformation of rural society. It has been said that only in the South is there still a genuine rural society. The commercially oriented farmer of the Middle West has become to a certain extent urbanized. His places of work are dispersed, but his attitudes are urban. The most atrocious waste of resources on earth today is rural underemployment. The technique of improving the utilization of this resource probably lies through industrialization and urbanization.

Far from ruining the countryside, cities are perhaps its salvation, Ullman suggested. Tractors made in the city have enabled individual men to handle more then they could before; agriculture thereby has made enormous strides in productivity.

Boulding asked whether cities today are not utterly different from those even of three hundred years ago. Though agricultural incomes are lower than industrial income—and this is doubtfully true in the Middle West—this is a temporary result of the difficulties caused by migration from agriculture. Actually, cities can produce enough to pay the agricultural population almost anything it wants—almost too much.

In the modern era a great change has taken place in the relation between town and village. Wittfogel suggested that the term "parasitic" was used perhaps with the thought that parasitism did not occur in the early days but came into existence with the development of commerce. Assuming that function is the basis for the rise of cities, two conditions have to exist, that is, surplus and the transport of surplus. What do people in cities have that people in the countryside do not? Thought of trade focuses upon the *things* that are exchanged. People of the cities, ever since the time of early Egypt have provided *services*. They kept peace and order, administered the regulation of the waterworks, and so on, albeit, Wittfogel added, he preferred the present service relationship with Washington, D.C., over that in existence at the time of the Pyramids. One of the great revolutions is the democratic revolution that in the United States involved considerable influence over the cities, enabling the farmers, although a minority, to wield considerable political power. A completely new city-village relationship has arisen.

There is a difference between the large nations and the small. Banks pointed out that the United States in the last decade had experienced the largest peacetime migration in the history of the world—ten million people moved to the West Coast. Such a phenomenon, little noticed and certainly not disruptive of internal affairs of a large country, is to some extent incomparable with conditions in small countries such as Israel, in which, as Glikson expressed it, the nearness and importance of what may be termed the biological-ecological equilibrium existence is felt very well. Hislop was reminded that England, too, is small, though it has a large population. At one time it could feed itself, but today it cannot, and so it has developed industrially. It has large cities and conurbations composed of cities and their gradually merging adjoining towns, for example, Tyneside. The Tyne, a little river toward the north of England near the Scottish border, had various towns along its banks, north and south as far as the coast, about ten miles distant. But now these towns are gradually approaching one another until there is almost a continuous city stretching from the coast to Newcastle and the west. These conurbations are necessary, because England must manufacture goods and export them to feed itself. It cannot carry on solely through inward and outward traffic between the cities and their adjacent rural countrysides.

MALIN, in writing, discussed the significance to the industrial revolution and to the English Midlands cities of the development of interior communications *within* the landmass during the second quarter of the nineteenth century. Historically, water transport had served to carry bulky commodities, but muscle power for that purpose was too expensive in energy expenditure. The rise of England's Midlands cities during the late eighteenth century had been based in large part upon canals which were designed to introduce economies of water transport into the interior of the landmass. They served remarkably well up to a certain point. But canals soon reached their maximum capacity to serve their purpose and gave way to a new order of magnitude in interior communication. Canals could be built only in a few places because of limitations of topography, water, etc. The steam railroad and locomotive were tested by Richard Trevithick in 1804 in the all-but-inaccessible country of southwestern England. The steam railroad introduced cheap interior communication into the landmass. Its great significance lay in opening up interiors hitherto unavailable, together with their mineral wealth. Thus the railroad enlarged the limits of natural resources. It also provided access to

new markets and enlarged existing ones, affording outlets for surpluses and inducements to enlarging production of surplus products. Furthermore, interiors could be supplied from the abundance of the outside world with commodities new to them or scarce. Socially, railroads spread intelligence and cultural amenities throughout England. The railroad as a mode of interior communication exerted a revolutionary influence upon international competition. In his book on railroads (1825, 1831), Nicholas Wood argued that the nation first to acquire this new technology would lead the world into a new era. The most remarkable aspect of this dictum was that Britain's leadership has been attributed usually to sea power. The implication of Wood's argument was that, even in a small country like England, landmass was critical to Britain's international position—even to Britain's sea power. The sea was equally available, theoretically, to all nations as a highway to states fronting on oceans. Landmass was different. It was unique to each state, and the effectiveness of its use was the responsibility of each state and its *opportunity* to wield this uniqueness as an advantage over rivals. During the nineteenth century England's industrial system capitalized upon that fact in a big way. Later, of course, large, continental, landmass countries were to challenge Britain, but Britain, as Wood had predicted, held the lead for quite some time. Railroads were the basis of the rise of Britain's rivals later in the nineteenth century, which partly neutralized Britain's sea power. Still later, air power, another new order of magnitude in communication, largely neutralized both sea power and landmass power per se.

Improvements in transportation were an obvious part of the industrial transformation, ULLMAN thought. The main effect was to enable areas to specialize in what they could do best. The scale of the earth's regions thus has been changed by the developments in transportation.

The last century or so, probably, was one of the first times in which man had almost unlimited choice as to what the configuration of a country should be as among big cities, small cities, and towns. On this point, MAYER introduced the subject of choice. Probably in established countries, but certainly in underdeveloped countries, no one questions organization, gregariousness, agriculture, and the other absolutely true things that have here been discussed. But are we choosing the kind of configuration that is most efficient? If we want to exercise choice, we can do so, because we now command the technology. Rural underemployment can be remedied. Certain areas of India are being developed in ways that do not involve huge cities; many consumer industries can be handled in very small cities. In discussing choice and the configuration to be chosen, we are confronted by certain problems. What is the effect on people of the size of the city in which they live? What kinds of relationship can or cannot exist in cities of different sizes? Are the cultural values in the very big cities outweighed by the passivity with regard to participation?

ULLMAN granted that technology now permits the choice of picking the size of the city desired, but who makes the choice? In our society is it not the factory-builder? And where does he build? For footloose industries, where he can get labor. Formerly this meant the cities; now, the favored spot is the satellite-suburb, where, by compromising, he can be close to labor and other urban aspects yet have a good site on cheaper land with access to good roads and better living conditions for his labor. Such are the growing places which have experienced the greatest shift in population over the last two decades

in the United States. But this does not mean a dispersed population in small towns scattered over the countryside. North Carolina, for example, is almost a truly dispersed industrial area, with a few large cities of about 100,000 and many tiny towns. Labor in the rural population was dispersed to begin with, and industry has dispersed to reach its labor supply. But the industries, such as textiles, pay relatively low wages, for skilled specialists are not found among dispersed populations. The dilemma of North Carolina is its low per capita income. Does man have the power for change? Is it real or only apparent?

SMITH spoke of recent changes in the Philadelphia suburbs. It depressed him to travel the ten miles from his home into the city. What was last year a field is now row after row of little houses, only a few feet apart, with nothing between, in front, or behind them but a slight touch of green and several little trees. These accursed rows of houses are the action of an individual who happens to own a farm or to buy a field and wants to jam as many houses as possible onto his pasture to sell at from $14,000 to $20,000. About sixty years ago an English shorthand reporter, Ebenezer Howard, wrote a little book with a plan called *Garden Cities of Tomorrow* (1903). Based on a concentric-circle concept, with two or three great circular streets, the plan included business buildings in the center, residences all around, and the fields beyond reserved as fields. Lots were big enough to have a little garden, and in the fields beyond a larger garden could be had by those who wanted it. Such cities have been brought into existence in England, as described in Mumford's chapter (pp. 395–96). Here has been a true revolution—a place for people to live, where they can dig, have fresh air, have more sunshine, and have a place to play and which will not be turned into a slum by the next real estate operation. MUMFORD added that fourteen garden cities are in existence, some just coming into completion. All are of limited size, none proposed numbers over 90,000, and all have green belts of varying amounts around them.

MAYER mentioned that something much more revolutionary had happened in England in the last several years. A new law permits big cities to buy land beyond their own limits to set up satellite towns. These subtowns are being built around certain existing small communities as nuclei. This is done by covenant with communities which are willing and ready to accept this planned expansion. For the first time in Western civilization over the last century, a city (London) has decided that it is too big and is going to resettle some of its population, not in a suburb a few miles away, but way beyond, in new settlements. BANKS added the comment that it has been recognized that, in making such a new town, there must be included a mixture of types of people with different interests—not all slum dwellers or all professional people. GUTKIND spoke of physical planning. These developments in Britain were achieved not by planning single towns or a single county but by planning on a regional or sometimes national scale. Ten satellite towns are being built around London, almost like the earlier garden cities. Most of these towns have mixed populations, but a problem that arises is that up to 60 or 70 per cent of the people have to work elsewhere. Thus it is also important to decentralize industry. A garden city was originally conceived as an independent, almost self-contained unit, but the final result of physical decentralization without cultural decentralization is that all these very nice cities, planned with the best intentions, will be new, stuffy small towns with small-town folk, because the cultural amenities, save the cinema and a few others, do not exist. BANKS did

not entirely agree that there would be lack of culture in the satellite towns. Television, radio, improved education, and transportation have opened new vistas, giving access to incredible beauty and knowledge to persons wherever they may live. As he put it, "When I buy my cigarettes every morning in Cambridge, I learn more archeology than I myself know from the lady who serves me who has witnessed Glyn Daniel the night before describing the beautiful things on television. She has seen things which I have not seen."

Most of the discussion had been spent on the additions that cities have made to the face of the earth and very little about the losses that have taken place, CLARK remarked. There are very important losses, culturally, of many satisfactory folkways. And there are also the tremendous losses in the organization of biological communities—in the soil and in vegetation. He was not at all sure that we are very much better off for having so many more people or for extending cities in such fashion. In an inventory of what cities have done to the face of the earth, it is peculiar that thought should have been given only to additions and not to subtractions in the long historical record.

ALBRECHT personally did not like the lining-up of city versus country, because both contribute to food production. The city man makes machines for the farmer to produce more food. It is not antithesis; everybody is hungry, and everybody must be fed if he is to survive. Man has done a good deal to populate the face of the earth in regions where he could not have survived if forced to depend on what was produced there. Transportation, industry, and politics have enabled people to reach back into "oasis" areas where surplus foods or tools are produced. The specializations of certain men have extended resources to other world areas. But biological man is a manifestation of certain forces; there must be energy behind him. The high level of energy in the United States has been based on the tremendous fertility of resources that could be mined, converted into food, and started flowing toward the oceans by means of sanitary sewage disposal. The energy stream of China and Japan does not run to the ocean; part of what goes to the cities is carried back. That reversal of the energy differential slows down the congestion of cities. The United States has been mining its resources; and now conservation is a kind of post mortem. The protein content of wheat is dropping; crops have been substituted that neglect protein, but they fill and fool and bring on degenerative diseases; and it has not yet been seen that cities are merely the concentration of "flies collecting around the honey jar." Soil fertility, the agricultural capital of food production, is not perpetuated in the United States. City values can be transformed into a common unit—the dollar —but the pounds of calcium, potassium, magnesium, copper, zinc, and cobalt in the soil cannot be so readily transformed. A farm is bought for its fertility capital, but it is assessed in terms of such utilities as highway frontage, not fertility, its real value. Commercial agriculture liquidates capital assets and calls it "taking a profit." Fertility capital has not yet been put into monetary values and reduced to the level with which other resources are viewed.

IS THE INDUSTRIAL WORLD COMMUNITY
A PERMANENT CIVILIZATION?

STEWART proposed that the industrial revolution be thought of in terms of villages. Almost every village in Switzerland has its factory. Is Switzerland one town—an urban center as a whole —or has industrialization so spread to the villages that the "industrial" city versus "rural" village distinction is not really proper? Industrial villages have

so developed in the United States that there is even the phenomenon of a watch-crystal factory being built on an Indian reservation.

Industrialization has erased the distinction between cities and non-cities, TAX suggested. Industrialized societies appear to be a kind of integrated whole to those from other societies. For example, the Indians of highland Guatemala are organized into villages each practicing agriculture but each, also, having economic specialization, such as pottery-making in one village, basketry in another. When Tax told them where he was from, he was told, "Well, if you're from the United States, then you know how to make an airplane." This naïveté is significant; the important difference between them and us is not geographical location but organization— economic, social, political. What the industrial revolution meant was not simply some technological advances but organizational changes.

It seemed to BOULDING that the present industrial civilization is completely unprecedented. If a map of the world could be drawn on which all distances were in proportion to cost of transport, then the oceans would disappear, and it would be clear that there is one world city—that all cities are suburbs of one another. All previous civilizations also have rested on the differentiation of rural and urban, whereas the industrial civilization does not. Both the Swiss villager and the Iowa farmer are signs of this. If past civilizations have been unstable because they were made in cities and overthrown in the country, the establishment of a modern rural-urban identity has profound implications for cultural dynamics. Human history has consisted of the long Paleolithic, then the Neolithic, followed by the rise and fall of civilizations based on agriculture and exploitation. Now, if we do not blow ourselves to pieces, there is a long chance that the next stage of man will be a permanent high-level civilization.

HEICHELHEIM accepted this as a plausible hypothesis. He submitted that the decisive factors behind all earlier urban developments were environment and a new organization of capital. Behind the industrial revolution were the religious changes in Protestantism, Catholicism, and Judaism to what is called a "capitalist mentality." As an illustration, the farmer no longer looked upon his cow as an animal to be loved, petted, or maltreated but as a piece of capital to be used as well as he could for the betterment of himself and of mankind. New money structures brought cities into stronger relationships to the countryside than they had had before. For example, active investment banking of the nineteenth century completely changed the agricultural-urban structure of the United States.

BROWN noticed that agricultural and transportation revolutions had been suggested as responsible agents for the industrial revolution, and an economist had just spoken of capital formation. A geologist would refer to coal fields, and a technologist would speak of Abraham Darby, who first linked coal with iron. BROWN preferred to look upon the industrial revolution as a mesh—to see it in the same way that one looks upon an ecological assemblage, in which everything interacts on everything else. The net result is that feedback is encountered, which enormously accelerates everything. The industrial revolution is not one thing but the interaction of a vast complex of things.

GRAHAM reminded everyone that in all interrelationships there is a limiting factor. For example, one of the limiting factors today in the location of many large industrial developments is water. Lacking this single factor, many find it impossible to settle where they wish to settle.

The reference to capital led to GLIKSON's recall of the analysis by G. T. Wrench in his 1946 volume, *Reconstruction by Way of the Soil,* which compared the capital of the farmer with that of the nomad. Man's attitudes to the environment and to life are expressed in his various ideas of capital. According to Wrench, land is the basic capital of the farmer. All care is given to maintenance of soil fertility as a preservation of capital not only for the present but also for future generations. Domestic animals are the capital of the nomad. As movable property, they can be transferred from one land area to another, exhausting a maximum of land fertility in a minimum of time, then moving on (with the wealth of the land stored in the animals) to another region for another period of exploitation. Though clashes between farmers and nomads today have become rare, the basic controversy in attitudes remains. The economic values prevailing among the majority of city populations (and often among modern farmers, too) are very close to the idea of the nomad: land and its products are valued in terms of money. In the past, nomad actions endangered and destroyed land as a permanent source of livelihood; with the development of techniques, transportation, and markets, the "nomadic" values today represent an even greater danger. On the other hand, the work by the Dutch of reclaiming agricultural land from the sea expresses the farmer's values: an increase of fertile land is an increase of the basic capital of the country.

This question of the measure of value, BOULDING felt, was critical for the symposium. There is a strong feeling that the dollar is not the perfect measure—that there are other values which are not conserved under a banking civilization. On the other hand, no simple physical measures are satisfactory—neither phosphorus nor protein.

There is no escape from the psychological nature of utility.

LEOPOLD took up the question of values. Continual development of the urban community during the industrial revolution has been directed presumably toward, we can say, more and better bathtubs. What will happen in the future depends on what people consider to be the values to be obtained or achieved. In California, for example, urbanization has continued to the point where cities have become so large that there has been a very surprising and rapid movement of people not only to the suburbs but actually to the desert. So great is the desire, apparently, for certain aesthetic and perhaps ethical values not obtainable in the city that people, in their movement to the desert, have built homes to which they actually haul water. What happens next to man will depend upon the rapidity and nature of change in values, influenced more and more by a desire for improved ethical and aesthetic standards beyond the limit of what can be achieved through industrialization and urbanization.

WHY CHANGE?

BOULDING was interested in the theoretical background of the dynamics of change. What is the model underlying the extraordinary phenomenon of development and change in society? He suggested the mutation-selection model and asked whether it could be applied to changes in technology and organization. If so: (*a*) What factors affect the rate of *mutation* (new "ideas")? (*b*) What is the relation between the rate of mutation and the over-all rate of "development," however measured? (*c*) Why is there such a strong relation between religious nonconformity and technical change? (*d*) What are the factors in society which *prevent* development? (*e*) The weakness of the mutation-selection model in explaining

technical development is that mutations in "ideas" are *not* random. How can this "un-randomness" be expressed in a theoretical model?

All evolution falls into periods of relative stability, which leave records, interspersed with periods of rapid development, of which very little is known. In the history of man there have been perhaps three periods of rapid development: (1) the development of *Homo sapiens* himself; (2) the great transition from the Paleolithic, with the invention of civilization (agriculture, cities); and (3) the present period—the second great transition. Can a mutation in society, in ideas, in institutions, be identified? Is there such a thing as a rate of mutation in social institutions? What is the relation of this to development? In a stable society all mutations are strangled at birth; in an equilibrium society selection cancels out all mutations, and the society reproduces itself. In the process of biological evolution partial isolation is important. Is it important in social change? Obviously, social change is not the same as biological change. What are the important differences that can be identified?

The great problem to BOULDING was why change occurred at all. There is something in human society which will not permit rest. If men are to understand change, let alone dream of controlling it, they must understand the processes of change. Almost the only theoretical scheme which has an account of change is that of biological evolution. This theory is certainly shaky and highly dubious, but it is the only theory that can offer any kind of explanation of the processes of change. There are what might be called "social species" in the shape of ideas, organizations, customs, types, and ways of doing things. Mutations occur occasionally—new ideas, new ways of doing things—and there is obviously a selective process of society which enables some mutations to survive and not others. The difficulty when studying the basic empirical problem is that things which do not survive are not there to study. We talk about survival of the fittest—not the fittest for what, but the fittest for survival. Evolution, then, is the survival of the surviving, but do we know what makes for survival?

GREGG suggested that man's inborn curiosity, when reasonably actively employed, is more nearly responsible for such changes as are known than many other factors. He thought also of age-group pressures. It is almost certain that, after a certain set of values persist for a reasonable time, the next generation will come along inclined to challenge it. "I always liked the account of Mussolini having a meeting in Bologna. The triumph of his speech was, 'The man to succeed me is not born.' And the next line in the newspaper was, 'At this moment the band struck up "Giovanezza, Giovanezza." '"

Innovators belong to a different class, suggested GALDSTON. How the biological sport arises among humans we do not know. He granted that the technologies of agriculture, fisheries, transport, and industry are the instruments by which certain end results are actually realized; only an idiot would deny the cardinal importance and historic potency of those factors. But what he wanted to know was: Who creates a Da Vinci? Who inspires a Darwin? Who gives us a Pasteur? A Wagner? Do we really pretend that by the study of technologic factors we can ever assess how they come into being? Can we ever gauge what such people have done in order to produce the instrumentalities that have led to cities and all?

Take, for example, three important things related to the industrial revolution—steam, internal combustion, and the electric motor. We have had copper; we knew about electricity—Volta long antedated Watt. But why was it,

GALDSTON wondered, that the electric motor and the dynamo were not created before the steam engine? Also, what of significance preceded the Renaissance? Long before inclosures were started, there were such things as the vulgar languages, the cult of the Virgin, the troubadours, and many cultural factors contributing to the rise of cities and of agriculture. Human beings have certain cultural and intellectual impulsions. And these must be included in any ecological assessment.

GLACKEN took the Chairman to task for importing a biological scheme to the neglect of human history. During the session various speakers had brought up important historical details very troublesome to makers of theoretical systems. Many European colleagues have a far greater sense of the tremendous value of the historical experience of mankind and the events that have determined it. To import biological analogies, no matter with how many qualifications, is to repeat a system which began with the Greeks and ended with the fanciful theories of nineteenth-century German political thought and sociology. GLACKEN, in writing, suggested, too, that the chapters dealing with the early history of man's modifications of the earth are an excellent corrective to the view—widely expressed in contemporary literature— that the greatest and most significant changes in the earth's surface have come as a consequence of the industrial revolution. These chapters show how extensive were the modifications by non-industrial peoples. Notable, too, was that a large part of Marsh's work dealt with changes brought about in ancient and medieval times and in the preindustrial era.

DIFFERENCES IN APPROACH TO
MAN AND ENVIRONMENT

BOULDING pointed up what seemed to him the fundamental issue which had arisen in the symposium and which probably would continue in all subsequent sessions. Quite obviously within the group present there was a sharp division between the "biological-ecological" point of view and the "socioeconomic" viewpoint.

The biological-ecological view is expressed in terms of equilibrium systems and of movements toward equilibrium, that is, systems in which there is circulation and conservation. The form of something is changed, but everything eventually returns, and the cycle is repeated. Biologists and conservationists feel that man has to find his place with-

EGLER felt extremely enlightened by at last being able to comprehend the extraordinary references to ecology that he had found in various parts of the literature on economics. But ecologists no longer think that, when white men came to America, everything was in a stable equilibrium or in a fixed balance of nature; that white men knocked it down; and that, if left alone, nature would rise up again to a certain productive point and stay there, moving along at a balance. To the contrary, the past was an extraordinary series of irregular upheavals, not little cycles. Present cultures produce additional

Stage of Life	Organisms	Communities
Aggregation	Cleavage of eggs, movement of slime-mold cells, etc.	Formation of original communities
Morphogenetic Movements (slowly reversible sluggish movements)	Cell orientations, etc.	Organization of technology and government
Differentiation (practically irreversible)	Tissue and organ formation (obligatory interaction)	Specialization of function, including obligatory interaction within community and environment
Variable Growth and/or Differentiation		
Adult?		
Senility and Death?		

in a cycle of this kind; if he violates it, he is heading for trouble.

On the other hand, all history, geological as well as human, is not the repetition of a cycle. It is an irreversible process of curiously decreasing entropy —that is, of increasing complexity of organization. This process of agricultural improvement, urbanization, and industrialization has just been discussed. The development of surplus from agriculture permits the establishment of towns. Also, the towns develop the skills and techniques of science and industry, and these feed back on the agricultural countryside. This is a cumulative process in which the critical element is not the conservation of materials or of energy but information.

imbalances through which they move on to new irregularities, not inscribed in the finite world of traditional ecology. Ecologists should not be blamed for what is no longer ecology. STEINBACH, in writing, supported Egler's contention that biologists do *not* assume equilibrium systems. He felt rather that the most relevant area of biology was *not* field ecology, which he considered largely sterile and archaic, but developmental biology. The "curious" non-additive, locally irreversible, entropy decrease is fundamental and destructive for biological (including sociological) existence. The accompanying diagram was presented.

SAUER asked the Chairman to expand his remarks on the deficiency of the biological group in its lack of knowledge of an antientropic system. BOULDING explained that organization was introduced into human evolution through man's consciousness, his learning capacity, and the development of such cultural factors as language, communication, and information transfer. Man is a problem-solving animal. Antientropy refers to the extraordinary process of rapid increase of organizational complexity. Culture builds up entropy instead of tearing it down, and this has to be taken into account in ecological systems. Biological systems are subsystems with which we should not rest. There must be taken into account the process of communication and information among human beings, which is antientropic. For example, a class when taught knows more, and the instructor does not know any less. This is the key to life, which is a process for diminishing entropy, and civilization is its extension.

DARWIN asked whether increasing organization and increasing complication are not themselves increasing the entropy of the world. He thought quite confidently that this had been very rapidly increased by all that has been going on in the last fifty years. Putnam, in his *The Future of Energy,* states that half the coal which has been burned in the whole history of the world has been burned in the United States in the last thirty years. In this sense, then, the United States in the last thirty years has done as much to increase the entropy of the world as the whole of the human race in the whole of the past. This is not a boast!

Part II
Process

Introductory

Introductory

Environmental Changes through Forces Independent of Man

RICHARD J. RUSSELL*

If the time that life has existed on earth—on the order of one thousand million years—be represented by a line 100 inches long, the terminal one-tenth inch suffices for the history of man. During his one million years man has experienced neither the typical distribution of climates over the earth's surface nor the normal tempo of geological activity of the earth's crust.

Man's appearance at an abnormal time, when Ice Age climates existed and the crust was particularly restless, was not a matter of chance. Similar interruptions in the tranquillity and monotony of geological events have occurred at other times—in the late

pre-Cambrian and during the Caledonian, Hercynian, Cordilleran, and other revolutions—and each was accompanied by an acceleration of evolutionary processes which brought profound changes in plant and animal life. By the end of the Tertiary the evolution of primates had reached the point where a large-brained, erect, short-toed, comparatively hairless, and in many respects primitive and helpless animal could rise to a dominant position.

In a conference on "Man's Role in Changing the Face of the Earth," a summary of environmental changes through forces independent of man appears to be an assignment to the voice of a loyal opposition. It seems important to recognize and hold in mind that a variety of natural processes are operative and have not ceased to operate simply because man made his appearance on the scene. Of his general dominance there can be no question, but man's control of his own destiny is actually far from complete. He stands passive in the face of forces which he is unable to harness, subdue, or even modify. His increased technical competence brings many changes, but man's tenure on earth is still subject to many ungovernable environmental controls. The more significant affect him gradually, as a rule, but some of the less important strike him with catastrophic impact. Before discussing such

* Dr. Russell is Professor of Geography and Dean of the Graduate School, Louisiana State University, Baton Rouge. In 1937 he received the first W. W. Atwood Award for studies in physical geography from the Association of American Geographers and in 1948 a C.R.B. Special Fellowship for field work in Belgium. He has served as distinguished lecturer, American Association of Petroleum Geologists, 1943; president, Association of American Geographers, 1948; and councilor, Geological Society of America, 1950–52; and is now Chairman of the Earth Sciences Division, National Research Council, and a member of the Advisory Panel in General Sciences to the Assistant Secretary of Defense for Research and Development. He is an honorary member of the Belgian Society of Geology, Paleontology, and Hydrology and of the Royal Dutch Geographical Society. His publications include: *Climates of California*, 1926; *Geomorphology of the Rhone Delta*, 1942; and (with F. B. Kniffen) *Culture Worlds*, 1951.

unpleasant topics it is well to examine the setting upon which man's earthly drama unfolds.

From the standpoint of landscapes the earth's crustal history may be divided into four main periods. First, between the dawn of geologic time, when the oldest rock was formed—some three thousand million years ago—and the appearance of the first land plants, the earth's surface stood naked and fully exposed to atmospheric forces that shattered rocks freely and moved the resultant debris about with an ease unknown during later time. Landscapes were dominated by forms resembling those of today's harshest environments, such as extreme desert or ice-free high arctic areas. Slopes remained steep during their denudation, and it is doubtful whether clay existed anywhere.

During the second period, between the Silurian and mid-Mesozoic, at least parts of the land were covered by low forms of plants. Rain beat less effectively against a surface partially armored with incipient soils, water rushed less vigorously down slopes, and hills started to assume rounded profiles. Depositional surfaces began to be covered with something more than discrete mineral or rock fragments, and biogenetic agencies capable of forming new clay minerals came into operation. Though primitive, some of the plants attained enormous sizes, and the amount of vegetable material incorporated into sedimentary deposits at times bulked large.

The appearance of woody trees and higher types of plants in the later Mesozoic brought a transition to the third period in landscape development. Soils became widely developed, and topographic profiles more closely resembled those we know today. But it was not until the Tertiary that modern grasses ushered in the fourth period by making possible the development of several of our most significant soil groups, with clearly differentiated profiles which include compact, tough, clayey subsoils.

The final period has two main subdivisions. During much of the Tertiary there was comparative freedom from extremes of orogeny, vulcanism, and the sharply differentiated climates which have characterized the Quaternary. Mountains were created here and there, huge volumes of basaltic lava spread over surfaces of the Columbia River plateaus, Peninsular India, and elsewhere, and there was some localized valley glaciation; but, on the whole, these evidences of crustal unrest were mild preludes to the tremendous changes that occurred during the Quaternary.

The world of early Pleistocene man was one in which continental elevations were being pushed up to abnormal heights, mountains were being created and maintained with extraordinary vigor, and icecaps were growing to continental proportions. The broader climatic belts of the Tertiary were being replaced by sharp zonation and complicated differentiation, with new extremes of aridity, frigidity, and storminess. But the drama was being played on a stage well prepared for its reception. A modern earth armed with tough soils and widespread vegetation has proved far less susceptible to change under the impacts of denudational forces than the earth of earlier geological history. Though debris is formed and deposition of continental sediments occurs rapidly in certain harsh environments today, natural denudational and degradational processes operate extremely slowly in most habitable areas. As a rule, nothing short of removing an area of subsoil breaks the armor sufficiently to permit a conspicuous acceleration of erosion. Even the most spectacular cases of gullying are sharply localized.

ICE, SEA, AND LAND

Pleistocene glaciation affected man profoundly, but changes came so gradually that nobody was aware of them. Expansions and contractions in volumes of continental ice slowly drove early man toward lower latitudes or permitted him to follow the forest as it crept poleward. Beyond the borders of the ice during glacial stages came more pluvial periods, with the appearance of lakes in what had been dry basins, the extension of streams beyond former lower limits in steppes and desert margins, and striking changes in distributional patterns of plants and animals. In at least the non-tropical parts of the Northern Hemisphere man was either forced into or afforded the opportunity of migrating widely during the several alternations between glacial and interglacial stages of the Pleistocene. In the vicinities of ice margins minor migrations were caused directly by fluctuations in ice-front positions. Even in places as remote as the East African lakes came ascent or descent of sites of habitation with shifting shore lines. Pleistocene climatic changes probably account for some major group displacements, such as the movement of Caucasoids to India and Arabia, where they interrupt the continuity of Negroids between southeastern Asia and Africa.

Man's preference for coastal lowlands undoubtedly concentrated populations of primitives along shores of lakes, seas, and oceans—in locations where the effects of glaciation and deglaciation were felt most sensitively. Five Pleistocene continental ice accumulations attained sufficient volume to lower universal sea level by as much as several hundred feet. Each of the low-level stages was sufficiently pro-longed to permit the deposition of broad belts of sedimentary materials that formed coastal plains. Man undoubtedly migrated seaward, as these attractive lowlands were created, to occupy extensive areas beyond and below the present limits of northwestern European, southeastern Asian, and other coasts of today.

There has been much ill-informed physiographic speculation concerning the origin of the submerged benches off continental shores. A base of effective erosional cutting by waves has been lowered hypothetically from a maximum of about 70 feet to 600 feet in order to support an erosional theory of the origin of the continental shelves. But abundant evidence confirms the early explanation advanced by Shaler (1895): the shelves are the deltaic coastal plains of low-level, glacial-stage Pleistocene seas. The artifacts of primitive man must lie concentrated along old shores which are now buried beneath later deposits.

Coastal populations are being driven inland and upward today at a pace which seems trivial in terms of the time span of several generations—about 1 foot per century. The average rate since the end of the Pleistocene has been on the order of twice that. This estimate accepts Reade's definition (1872) of Recent—that period of time during which sea level has made its last major rise—and evidence that the rise along the northern shore of the Gulf of Mexico has amounted to somewhat more than 400 feet, together with an allowance of some twenty thousand years as the duration of the Recent. The landward migration of the shore line in western Louisiana was on the order of 100 miles. The march is still in progress and affects all seacoasts.

If current rates of sea-level rise continue, it may take some two hundred centuries of ice-melting to bring the oceans to their maximum stand, according to Ahlmann's estimates (1953) of ice volume. Should the Ice Age thus terminate, new coastal plains will build seaward from about the level of today's 200-foot contours. Most of the world's existing population clusters will thereby be buried under terrigenous sediments, far from coasts.

It is possible that the Recent rise of sea level brought catastrophic results to early man; the Mediterranean Basin may have been flooded when Atlantic waters rose to the level of the sill at Gibraltar. Legends of a great flood, whether the Noachian Deluge or some other, may dimly reflect this event. There is evidence both for and against the possibility.

The saddle of the Gibraltar sill, well to the west of the Strait, now has a controlling depth of 1,056 feet—well below most estimates for the pre-Recent level of the Atlantic. This may not rule out the flood hypothesis. Bottom scour may have lowered the sill somewhat, but more likely is the possibility of lowering by faulting. The surrounding region is characterized by seismic activity, and the bottom topography appears to be tectonic in origin. Shoals rise to within 60 feet of the surface in the Strait, whereas the average depth is commonly stated as 1,200 feet. Broad shelves in the Adriatic, toward the head of the Gulf of Lions, and in other places suggest a low-level Mediterranean in early Recent time. Similarities in plants, animals, and human cultures are so striking on opposite shores of Gibraltar that biologists and archeologists tend to insist on the presence of a land bridge during some part of the late Quaternary. There is little likelihood that glacial-stage pluvial periods reached the Mediterranean Basin with effect sufficient to provide surplus water. The wadies of northern Africa, while longer during the last glacial stage, were distinctly the watercourses of an arid region throughout the Pleistocene, and the Libyan Desert bears no suggestion whatever of increased precipitation.

Each major increase or shrinkage in volume of Pleistocene continental ice was undoubtedly characterized by numerous and complicated minor fluctuations at less than glacial, or interglacial, proportions: times of reversal of general trends and stillstands. The complications of the latest major retreat are fairly well known.

To comparatively advanced man during the late Pleistocene and early Recent ages came experiences such as being driven higher in the Alps, to caves above thickening valley glaciers, or from dwellings in lakes which stood at levels lower than today's levels. Man has been forced, or has chosen, to migrate back and forth across territory marginal to desert and steppe. These experiences have related in part directly to fluctuations in ice volumes and in part to such secondary consequences as increases or decreases in rainfall and snowfall. With the arrival of historical time came an increasingly well-documented record of such minor migrations and changes in ways of life.

The Greenland voyages followed routes which would be impossible today, across seas now regularly blocked by ice. Warmer summers permitted raising crops that now will not mature in Greenland. All northern lands experienced increasing storminess during the thirteenth century, and the next century brought abnormal cold and snow in at least Iceland and Denmark. Meanwhile, Mexico was the scene of greatly augmented precipitation, and Aztecs were being driven upward from lakes that were rising well above today's levels. Alpine glaciers pushed their fronts down valleys well beyond positions occupied during Roman times, and similar "Little Ice Age" advances occurred in the United States. During the twentieth century, however, many of the glaciers of the western United States have disappeared, and ice volumes are diminishing everywhere.

While the association between volumes of continental ice and the stand of seas is positive and has affected man in many ways, there is no basis for predicting either a continuation of the trend toward higher seas or its reversal during the centuries immediately ahead. But man will make adjustments in either case. He may slowly withdraw from the shores of encroaching waters or gradually advance across newly exposed bottoms. He may occupy newly uncovered land in the wake of glacier retreat or be forced back by advancing ice fronts. What appears improbable is stability for any appreciable length of time—in ice volumes, in stand of the oceans, or in climatic trends.

WEATHER AND CLIMATE

Though the profound changes in environment that affect man most severely occur during intervals so prolonged that ordinarily he does not recognize their occurrence, he has long been keenly aware of vagaries in local weather conditions and of short-term climatic fluctuations. Dry world and Mediterranean peoples placed their gods in the sky and saw signs and omens in atmospheric or celestial settings. The regularity in daily and seasonal temperature marches emphasized the importance of the giver of light and heat. Solstice and equinox marked significant changes in the routine affairs of man, governed from on high. It was inevitable that a sun-god should rise to highest rank among deities. Sun worship may have been twenty centuries old when reorganized in Egypt by the pharaoh Amenhotep III before 1360 B.C. A moon-goddess or planetary deities commonly supplemented sun worship. The coming or prevention of rain, wind, thunder, or flood might be regulated by petition to the sky-gods.

Severe storms or unusual fluctuations in wind, temperature, or precipitation may change the value of a site of habitation appreciably within a short time. Every marginal agricultural belt has a history of alternations between times of prosperity, when rain is abundant, and of destitution, when water supply diminishes to normal or less. The mining of water—drawing upon accumulated supplies at rates exceeding those of replenishment—may serve as a palliative, but in the long run man must adjust his ways to resources at hand. Even technical advances such as large-scale distillation of sea water promise little relief to agriculture in arid regions.

Living organisms exhibit varying degrees of toughness and endurance in the face of adversity. Distributional ranges, whether natural or cultural, extend from areas characterized more or less by optimal conditions to limits determined by various factors at variance with the optima. As a rule, the mean experience in any factor has less meaning than the frequency with which adverse conditions occur. The probability that most of the citrus trees will be killed once in fifty years is not sufficient to prohibit the raising of oranges commercially near the mouth of the Mississippi River; but inland, where the frequency of disaster caused by killing frost may be as often as once in ten years, man appraises the risk as excessive.

The spread of natural vegetation toward limits set by heat, cold, dryness, or windiness may be quite independent of the appraisals of man but operates in a similar manner. If the limiting factor is a season too cold for the maturing of individual plants, for example, and such seasons occur commonly enough to prevent the establishment of a species beyond a given zone, the distributional range is as firmly controlled as if by man's judgment. The limits of a distributional range may be likened to a battle, in which individuals move forward during favorable seasons as seeds germinate successfully ahead of the general front. A succession of favorable seasons may result in a considerable advance along the front, but the occurrence of a single unfavorable season may not only destroy the vanguard but also drive the main line well back of its original position. Whether it be the most poleward trees of the taiga, the position of the cold or the dry timber line, or the boundary between tree-covered plains and adjacent steppe, the limits are set by endurance to adversity, and crucial tests depend on extreme, rather than average, climatic years. Man has succeeded in breeding a few domestic crops, such as rapidly maturing wheat or cotton, that cope successfully with limited degrees of climatic adversity, and his activities may extend grasslands beyond their original limits; but, on the whole, natural vegetation is distributed according to patterns determined by climates and relief features rather than by the desires of man.

The distribution of typical desert, steppe, or other significant type of climate is never precisely the same in successive years. Drought typical of the desert may extend broadly across the adjacent steppe one year, while precipitation characteristic of the outer, wetter margin of the steppe may reach some part of the desert the next year. A map of the climates of the continents based on occurrences of 1954 would not duplicate one based on records of 1953, even though all criteria of classification were identical. A satisfactory method of mapping climatic distribution employs median, rather than mean, values and median climatic year experience. But there may be better ways; for example, frequency of departure beyond quartile or other limits deserves careful study. The fictional value of mean rainfall, one of the most significant climatic elements, is illustrated by the fact that any given place is practically certain to receive less than its mean in more than half of all years. This is a natural consequence of variability between limiting values approaching zero in one direction and extraordinary values in the other, which distort the means upward.

Man ordinarily faces his climatic environment passively. He may air-condition his home, irrigate his fields, seed clouds, plant windbreaks, or in other ways alleviate some deficiency or other; but in the long run his endurance is likely to yield, so that he adjusts himself to the inevitable or plans in terms of calculated risks. He copes not only with direct effects, such as actual rainfall, but also with many secondary consequences. For example, if the disappearance of an advanced civilization from parts of Middle America was associated with increased precipitation, it was not the rain itself that caused the retreat or the inability to maintain old ways so much as the flourishing of rank vegetation, insect populations, or pathogenic organisms.

Now and then man acts promptly and decisively when afflicted by some catastrophic event, such as a terrific storm. Isle Derniere, which for many years was a favorite resort for residents of New Orleans, has remained unused since being ravished by a hurricane about a century ago. Breton Island to the east, a thriving community for many years, has remained unpopulated since being evacuated in advance of a hurricane in 1915. But such radical changes are ordinarily limited to places which had somewhat marginal value to begin with. The drowning of six thousand people by sea waves in 1900 failed to prevent Galveston from becoming a thriving city and surviving lesser catastrophes in later years. The inhabitants of Kyushu and many other places have learned to escape typhoons by building their structures in sheltered locations, high enough above shores to avoid the brunt of wind and wave. Bengal increases rapidly in population in spite of floods that killed seventy thousand in 1864, two hundred and fifteen thousand in 1875, and forty thousand in 1940.

The tornado of the central United States is a more violent cyclonic disturbance than the hurricane. During a single month in 1893 more than three thousand people were killed by a succession of these storms. In March, 1925, eight hundred were killed and thirteen thousand injured. The average year brings a hundred and fifty tornadoes, which cost well over two hundred lives and result in more than $14,000,000 property damage. Storms appear in the central part of the tornado belt with sufficient frequency to account for "cyclone cellars" and other means of protection. But few persons appear to have appraised the risk as sufficiently serious to warrant their leaving the region, though it may be probable that tornadoes have influenced many against settling there. It seems to be a human trait—and a fortunate one—to fear the other person's disaster, not one's own. Kansans at times express reluctance even to visit California, where they might risk the consequences of an earthquake, while Californians often wonder why Kansas is inhabited, when warm weather brings the possibility of the world's most destructive winds. As a rule, people are more inclined to remain and rebuild than leave a region subject to repeated disaster, whatever its origin. Man endeavors to be enduring and tough when confronted with adversity.

Winds of less than storm velocities are of utmost consequence to man. A sharp differentiation between windward and leeward landscapes is strikingly exhibited in trade-wind islands, and rainshadow effects exist in the lee of uplands in all latitudes. Even the less persistent mistral that blows down the Rhone Valley has caused the Guardians of the Camargue to evolve a curious type of house—more or less streamlined, with prowlike front toward, and flat face with outer door and windows away from, the wind. On the High Plains weather-stripping windows and doors diminishes the dust that accumulates within houses during "black northers," when mail carriers don goggles and many activities come to a standstill. Low temperatures associated with such winds create blizzards in the north and even as far away as coastal Texas prove fatal to hungry cattle in unprotected marshes, while bringing widespread destruction to less robust types of plants. The afternoon sea breeze shears trees, limits distributions of plants, and brings moist, saline air to corrode metals and increase depreciation costs of buildings and machines. Sea-moistened air also accounts for unusual vegetational assemblages in places such as West Coast deserts and benefits activities such as cotton-spinning in Lancashire and Bombay. The greatest beneficial effect of the wind, however, is the drifting of moisture from ocean toward continental interior, making possible the existence of life away from coasts.

From the standpoint of man, optimal climatic conditions closely approximate the averages experienced on the earth's surface. Atmospheric pressure characteristic of mean land elevation, precipitation of about 30 inches annually—quite evenly distributed seasonally or with a summer maximum—and absolute temperatures from about 253 to 313 degrees represent the ideal. This is not a matter of chance. Man was certain to be best adapted to the environmental conditions under which he evolved. He endures varying departures with some success, either on a temporary or on a permanent basis. Certain human groups have become thoroughly conditioned to life at elevations in excess of 15,000 feet, but the physiological makeup of most men is such that body functions falter under exposure to the low pressure at that level and fail completely in somewhat more rarefied air. The heat tolerance is really an insignificant fraction of the range between absolute zero and the temperature of the sun's surface. Death or other serious consequences result from prolonged exposure to either cold or heat approximating the limits of the acceptable range indicated. Unfavorable precipitation, storminess, windiness, or insolation are tolerated quite well but with greater difficulty as departures from the earth's averages increase.

FLOOD

Flood and drought rank foremost among earth tragedies. Some three hundred thousand persons perished during the Hwang Ho flood of 1642. It is estimated that a hundred thousand died during the Hwang Ho flood of 1887 and as many during the Yangtze flood of 1911. Food sufficient to sustain ten million people is destroyed by floods along the rivers of northern China during the average year, but in the same region it is also estimated that thirteen million died from hunger resulting from drought in the three years 1876–79. In 1939 ten million Chinese starved, drowned, or were left homeless as a consequence of flood. Though damage can be reduced, even the most advanced engineering works fail to eliminate flood dangers. Notwithstanding elaborate flood-control measures, floods claimed 732 lives in Ohio and Indiana in 1913, and some 250 drowned along the Allegheny, Ohio, and Mississippi rivers in 1939.

Many floods arrive from the sea. Slowly subsiding coastal plains are particularly vulnerable. The lowering and gradually disappearing Frisian Islands have experienced such catastrophes as the drowning of a hundred thousand people in 1228. The 1953 Netherlands flood covered 4.6 per cent of the country and 5.7 per cent of its cultivated land, drowned eighteen hundred persons, and caused a hundred thousand to evacuate their homes. Saint Elizabeth's flood of 1421 drowned ten thousand. Subsidence at a rate of about 1 foot per century expanded Lake Flevo of Caesar's time into the broad Zuider Zee, which man reclaims only with greatest difficulty and possibly only temporarily.

One of the curious things about floods is their destructiveness in arid regions. A popular misconception relates desert floods to cloudbursts, but a strict application of Humphreys' definition (1940)—rainfall at a rate of about 4 inches per hour or its equivalent—apparently denies any desert the experience of a cloudburst. It is well established that intensities of excessive precipitation vary closely with total amounts: the wettest places have the heaviest rains, and dry places are not subject to impressive downpours. But even the mild rains of the desert commonly result in violent floods. Slopes are steep, surfaces are barren, runoff is rapid, and water readily rises to flow with torrential swiftness along well-prepared channels or to spread across smoother slopes. Nogales, in arid southern Arizona, and Mitchell and Heppner, in the Oregon steppe, have experienced drownings occasioned by floods. One does well to scramble up the walls of a box canyon in southern Nevada when a heavy cloud appears. The Foreign Legion prohibits camping in the beds of wadies, however clear the sky. During the summer of 1952, I witnessed a sharply localized flood on the northern side of the western Sahara. Though it is improbable that the rainfall anywhere amounted to as much as one-tenth of an inch, a flash flood suddenly appeared in a wadi and in a few minutes completely destroyed a thick slab of concrete—a Moroccan version of an "Arizona bridge" or "dip."

When service is interrupted by floods along the direct railroad between New Orleans and Los Angeles, the cause is usually not the excessive rainfall of Louisiana, where hardly a year passes without many cloudbursts and where rains in excess of 20 inches per day are experienced at times, but ordinarily a result of tracks being washed away somewhere to the west of Texas—most commonly in the Colorado Desert of southern Arizona and southeastern California. Cloudbursts seldom occasion serious damage in Louisiana or other places where rainfall is torrential, for the reason that soils, slopes, and vegetation are thoroughly conditioned for them. But in semiarid southern California even a small rain may cause disaster, as in 1953, when twenty-one persons were killed and two thousand made homeless. There are many more miles of dikes protecting roads and railroads in the American Southwest than in the well-watered lower Mississippi Valley. In the Southwest it is considered prudent to construct "dips" across watercourses which, though dry most of the time, are capable of destroying practically any conventional bridge as a result of a single, modest rain.

Closely related to floods are damaging mudflows and other types of mass movement of wet or unstable debris. The Goldau debris slide of 1860 killed 457 persons, and in 1951 more than 200 fatalities resulted from avalanches in the Alps. Even the gradual slumping of unstable foundation materials or the slow subsidence under the weight of structures distorts buildings, disrupts traffic along roads, and results in other types of property damage, such as breaking water pipes or distorting hillside fences.

EXPLOSION AND MAGMA

If, as in most cases, man remains passive when facing the consequences of climatic or weather phenomena, he at least has the option of migrating to places where a more certain livelihood awaits him. But from the possibility of bombardment from space he has no protection whatever. Some twenty million meteorites reach the earth's atmosphere daily, and on the average of once in five days a solid visitor from space reaches the ground. While it is possible that several large craters are scars of meteoritic impacts, and while a number of narrow escapes are on record, such as a direct hit on an Alabama farmhouse in December, 1954, there seems to be no proof that anyone as yet has had the misfortune of being killed. Not without some probability, however, looms the specter of some huge mass of spatial material striking a city—with results as tragic as those which might accompany a man-devised thermonuclear reaction. And, eventually, life may be extinguished completely in this way rather than having to await more orderly, extremely slow refrigeration or incineration in keeping with normal astronomical processes.

Not negligible is the possibility of being blown to eternity for the inhabitants of craters and sides of dormant volcanoes. Neither Greek nor Roman preserved any tradition concerning the activity of Vesuvius, nor were the inhabitants of Pompeii, Herculaneum, or Stabiae aware that earthquakes starting in A.D. 63 presaged one of the most spectacular volcanic explosions of history. Sixteen years later some thirty thousand people were buried under volcanic debris. Vesuvius has remained intermittently active since A.D. 79, at times with tragic results, as in 1631, when eighteen thousand people were killed. Sicilian Etna bursts into activity every five years or so, but while lavas pour down its sides, at times to engulf villages, as in 1929, the loss of life is ordinarily negligible, and property damage is small in comparison with that caused by explosive volcanoes. In 1669, Etna lavas advanced 13 miles in twenty days—a rate of 162 feet per hour. Man escapes from paths of flowing lava, as a rule, but is less successful when debris falls from the air. Even peaceful Etna, however, is responsible for many tragedies. Earthquakes associated with its activity in 1693 killed some sixty thousand persons.

Mount Pelée, on the island of Martinique, after lying dormant since 1851, suddenly blew a vent through its side in 1902 and, after a number of violent explosions, discharged a cloud of superheated gas, dust, and rocks having an estimated temperature of 1,500° F. directly into the city of Saint Pierre. Traveling 3 miles in 2 minutes, this cloud instantly suffocated thirty thousand people. Mount Tambora, to the east of Java, blew some 30 or more cubic miles of rock and dust into the atmosphere in 1815—the equivalent of one hundred and eighty-five mountains the size of Vesuvius. Places near by experienced complete darkness for three days. Together with debris discharged from Mayon, Luzon, in 1814, the dust floated in the upper atmosphere and spread out on a globe-encircling basis to blanket the earth's surface from insolation so effectively that the year 1815 has gone down in history as lacking a summer. Coseguïna, Nicaragua, brought darkness to an area within 35 miles from its vent in 1835 and spread appreciable quantities of volcanic dust as far as Jamaica, 700 miles away. Glass shards which now accumulate on the beach near St. Augustine, Florida, may have left Coseguïna a hundred and twenty years ago.

One of the most spectacular volcanic explosions of historic time occurred in 1883, when Krakatau, an island in Sunda Strait, was about two-thirds blown away, leaving water 1,000 feet deep where formerly there had been land. The volcano had been dormant for a century and gave little warning of the impending eruption. A cubic mile of rock and enough dust to redden sunsets around the world for a year or two were blown into the air with a report strong enough to break windows 100 miles away and loud enough to be heard 2,200 miles away in Australia and 3,000 miles away at Rodriguez Island in the Indian Ocean. The accompanying sea wave attained an estimated height of 135 feet along the shores of near-by Java. Nearly forty thousand people were drowned, and over three hundred villages were demolished.

On several occasions man has witnessed the building of volcanic hills or islands within a matter of months or very few years. Parts of Monte Nuevo west of Naples, which rose to a height of 440 feet when created in 1538, are visible today. Less permanent was Graham Island, south of Sicily, which in 1831 built from a bottom 800 feet deep into an island 200 feet high, with a circumference of 3 miles—in less than a month. All that remains today is a Mediterranean shoal. Camiguin Island, north of Mindanao, added over 1,900 feet to its height in four years, starting in 1871.

Mexico offers several examples of the birth of volcanic cones, some of which have risen above cornfields. Jorullo, 1759; Pochutla, 1870; Ajusco, 1881; and Parícutin have all been created before the eyes of man. The latter, a satellite of inactive Tancitaro, rose 300 feet during the first five days following its creation in 1943. Within a year it attained a height of 1,410 feet. In 1952 activity ceased abruptly, and it is now thought that Parícutin is extinct. But there is little doubt that some place in the vicinity will experience a similar outburst before many decades have elapsed.

The disaster aspect of volcanoes excites the imagination, but of much greater significance are the beneficial results of igneous activity. Slow accumulation of the greatest mass of lava on earth created the Hawaiian Islands, which are densely populated in spite of the fact that they are still growing. Flows of lava have pushed downslope as far as 40 miles in the presence of eye-witnesses. Trees near by remained unscorched. Though some lavas and ejected materials remain sterile for centuries, others rapidly develop productive soils, and soils derived from older lavas are commonly valuable, as in the Regur region of India or the Columbia River plateaus of the United States. Some seventy thousand people farm the crater of Mount Aso, Kyushu, and the slopes of Etna have attracted the cultivator for many centuries.

To igneous activities man must gratefully acknowledge the accumulation of many valuable mineral resources. Some form rapidly, and at times within man's sight, as in the case of sulfur from vents or of residual salts from hot springs. But the most important depositional activities—those responsible for many of our most important metal deposits—accumulate slowly, as magmas and gases move at depth, below the surface.

EARTHQUAKE

It is estimated that a hundred and fifty thousand earthquakes occur annually. Of these, about a hundred may be destructive locally, one or two causing spectacular damage. A few earthquakes are associated with volcanic activity, but nearly all are the result of rock blocks on opposed sides of faults grinding past each other as the earth's crust seeks to attain a more perfect equilibrium through relief from gradually accumulating stresses. The causes of stress are matters of speculation.

The Assam earthquake of 1897 was felt over an area of 1,700,000 square miles and brought complete destruction to buildings within an epicentral district of 9,000 square miles. The Lisbon earthquake of 1755 was felt from Ireland to Morocco, over an area of 500,000 square miles. Other widely felt earthquakes include the Kansu, 1920, 600,000 square miles; San Francisco, 1906, 375,000; Kwanto, 1923, 160,000; and Mino-Owari, 1891, 120,000.

The Yakutat Bay, Alaska, earthquake of 1899 resulted in a vertical displacement of rock amounting to about 50 feet. This record "throw" is thought to approach the maximum offset possible during a single earthquake. The limiting value of frictional resistance of blocks pressed together along faults or of the initial strength of rock sets limits beyond which crust-distorting stresses cannot accumulate; when a critical point is reached, the blocks are offset, and an earthquake occurs. The Assam displacement was 33 feet. That during the Bavispe, Sonora, earthquake of 1887 was 26 feet. The San Francisco earthquake accompanied a horizontal displacement of 22 feet, and the Owens Valley, California, earthquake of 1872 not only added a slight increment to the general rising of the Sierra Nevada but also was associated with a horizontal offset of 18 feet. The rocks shear, the earth trembles, and disasters occur within brief intervals of time. In Japan it has been found that the average duration of an earthquake is 8 seconds. Some major earthquakes appear without warning, but as a rule they are preceded by minor tremors and followed by numerous aftershocks.

Nearly a hundred and fifty thousand people were killed as a result of the Kwanto earthquake, but, as in the case of similar disasters, the direct causes of tragedy were secondary results of the earth's geological activity. Fire and sea wave accounted for most of the deaths. Collapse of buildings was a minor cause, but, in spite of tales to the contrary, no case has been verified, either in Japan or elsewhere, of a person being swallowed by the ground or crushed in an earth fissure. Fire was responsible for 95 per cent of the property damage and a large proportion of the deaths in Tokyo. In one incident there thirty-six thousand out of thirty-eight thousand persons who were gathered on a large space of open ground perished because suddenly a whirlwind appeared which changed their position from one of shelter to one of lying directly in the path of flames. The two thousand who survived were standing close to the bank of a river and escaped by jumping into its water. A seismic sea wave rose to a height of 35 feet, submerging Yokohama and other coastal locations around Tokyo and Sagami bays.

The Kansu earthquake of 1920 killed about a hundred thousand persons, mainly for the reason that they occupied dwellings carved in loess. A severe earthquake seven years later did little harm, because cave dwellings surviving the 1920 shocks withstood those to follow. The Messina earthquake of 1908 reaped a similar toll for the reason that buildings which were poorly constructed originally had been weakened by lesser shocks in 1894, 1905, and 1907. The Lisbon earthquake of 1775 killed some sixty thousand, the chief causes of death being fire and sea wave, but collapse of buildings accounted for many deaths in Madeira and even as far away as Fès, Morocco. Many earthquakes fail to realize their potential destructiveness. The Bihar-Orissa-Nepal earthquake of 1934 killed 7,250 persons, but, had it occurred at night, when most of the population slept in the dwellings that actually collapsed, the total could well have reached a hundred thousand.

While it is true that alluvium commonly develops spectacular fissures, shakes longer, and at times localizes earthquake damage, unconsolidated sediments also have the effect of dampening shock waves. Alluvial sites close to bedrock are particularly dangerous, as in the case of man-made land in San Francisco, or valley fill under Santa Rosa, during the earthquake of 1906. But in the Long Beach earthquake of 1933 there was insignificant damage at Balboa and Newport Beach—towns built on a sand bar—while near-by Costa Mesa, with a more substantial foundation, suffered severely. Alluvial Louisiana is one of the least seismic parts of the United States, and in 1886 the alluvium of the lower Mississippi Valley sharply limited the area affected by the Charleston earthquake. A bad reputation, resulting from the destructiveness of the Assam earthquake and a number of poorly founded notions regarding the New Madrid earthquakes of 1811–12, is really undeserved by alluvial areas. In both these cases the intensities of shocks depended on the presence of near-by bedrock.

In an effort to avoid earthquake destruction man has gone to such lengths as moving cities. In 1642, Port Royal, Jamaica, had 75 per cent of its buildings destroyed. As its successor, Kingston arose some distance away, only to suffer 85 per cent destruction in 1907. The most effective protection against earthquake damage stems from learning how to live in a seismic region. After a disastrous earthquake in Tokyo in 1896, the Japanese carefully studied means of reducing loss of life and property damage. Comparative safety was achieved by adopting building codes which added some 10–15 per cent to costs of construction. False fronts, overhanging cornices, and designs involving the abutment of one type of construction against another should be prohibited in all seismic regions. Wooden structures, however safe from collapse, are serious hazards from the standpoint of fire. Personal behavior needs correction. Chimneys that fail at the roof line cause many fatalities among people who rush out of comparatively safe buildings in a state of panic. The most dangerous area in a city is a down-town sidewalk or street.

During the earthquake of 1939 in Anatolia, two-thirds of the people of Adapazari lost their lives because they occupied buildings covered by heavy tile roofs that crushed supporting frameworks when shaken. A death toll of a hundred thousand in northern Tur-key was for the most part unnecessary but will undoubtedly be repeated, for the reason that throughout this highly seismic belt people persist in roofing their houses with thick tiles or heavy slabs of stone. Italian earthquakes are ordinarily highly destructive, because structures are so commonly built of rounded stones which are bound to-gether by ineffective mortar. While man can prevent neither rocks from shear-ing nor volcanoes from exploding, he could go far toward reducing the tragic consequences of such events by reform-ing his ways.

Man can do little about tsunami oth-er than attempt escape. These seismic sea waves, generated at a time of earth-quake, resemble volcanic sea waves and other abrupt disturbances of sea level in bringing destruction and heavy loss of life along shores. An average of more than one occurs annually, and in 1918 there were five. The rise of level is slight in open ocean, but the velocity of the wave is astonishing, and its amplitude increases toward coasts, so that ships have been washed far ashore. The frigate "Swan" was thrust to an inland position during the Port Royal earthquake of 1692, and huge blocks of masonry were hurled against build-ings in Lisbon in 1755. Widespread flooding occurs at times, as in Chile in 1922, when the height of the tsunami reached 100 feet. The Kwanto wave was 35 feet high; the Messina wave, 30 feet. Tsunami spread widely and travel rapidly. The Chilean wave of 1922 was felt on all shores of the Pa-cific. A wave starting from Unimak, Alaska, in 1946, reached Honolulu in 4 hours, 34 minutes, progressing at an average rate of 490 miles per hour. The first warning of a tsunami is an ebb of water. In 1896 the fall went well be-low the limits of extreme low tide, and 40 minutes elapsed before a 100-foot wave appeared, to spread across low-lands toward Tokyo and drown more than twenty-seven thousand persons.

The tragic consequences of earth displacements affect man severely and abruptly, but of even greater conse-quence over long periods of time, such as a significant part of man's residence on earth, are the topographical changes of which they are manifestations. Now and then an escarpment formed during an earthquake may become a local an-noyance, but the cumulative effects of such crustal movements, each ranging from small fractions of an inch to sev-eral tens of feet, may create mountain ranges or deep depressions which bring marked modifications in climatic pat-terns and profound changes in habitat values. Matthes (1942) has attributed an important stage of local glaciation to uplift of the Sierra Nevada which occurred well within man's time on earth. Every high mountain range on earth today owes its elevation to the fact that it is actively growing.

GEOMORPHOGENY

The Davisian concept of the geo-graphical cycle confused many observ-ers who attempted to apply its theories to natural landscapes, because they were not aware of isostatic adjustments that affect all uplifted areas. The ini-tial rise of mountains is undoubtedly rapid, as Davis (1899) postulated, but during their degradation each reduc-tion in general elevation of 1 foot must involve a rise of the underlying rock column of some 9–11 feet. This isostatic compensation has the effect of prolonging the stage of maturity, so that sharp ridges and deep valleys characterize mountain ranges for enormous intervals of time. Periods on the order of the length of the Paleozoic era are required to reduce the general relief sufficiently to degrade a mountain range to near-flatness. By that time, all, or practically all, the original sedimentary rock section which comprised the initial mountains will have been removed, and parts of the rock column that originally lay many thousands of feet deep will have been exposed to atmospheric forces and eroded away. The trends and locations of ancient and extinct mountains are evident to geologists in terms of lineations, inactive faults, and elongations of belts of granitic and metamorphic rocks. The concept "peneplain" is useful only when applied to old shield areas which were once occupied by mountain ranges. Geological time as yet has been insufficiently long to permit the development of a widespread perfect peneplain.

Within man's million years many mountain ranges have increased notably in elevation and have become somewhat more rugged. But during that period there has been only insignificant reduction in the general relief of any large area. There have been spectacular small-scale anomalies, such as the disappearance of the spine of Mount Pelée, much of Krakatau, or of Bogoslof Island; but these involve rock types, agencies, and processes which are not characteristic of the normal Davisian cycle. If from the start man had possessed the mental faculty and material facilities which he enjoys today, he could have recorded an interesting history of local relief; but only in limited areas—generally where poorly consolidated rock exists—would he have recorded conspicuous examples of denudation or degradation.

Man's contact with the processes of alluvial morphology has been intimate. Encroaching sand has driven him from habitable sites. He has seen advances of alluvium which have incorporated islands into the mainland, as around the shores of San Francisco Bay during the last century, and the growth of deltas well past his own seaports, as in the case of Ephesus or Miletus. He has observed reservoirs of his own making filled by sediment in distressingly brief intervals of time.

Changes in river courses affect man severely and at times disastrously. When the Tarim River abruptly abandoned its course eastward toward Lop Nor in favor of diversion southeastward toward Arghan, in A.D. 330, the Old Silk Road had to be abandoned, oasis dwellers either perished or escaped in haste, and the city of Lou-lan was promptly evacuated. In 1921, when the Tarim as abruptly experienced a second great diversion, back into its older channel, there was similar disaster along the course leading toward Arghan.

It was unfortunate that scientific explorers interpreted ruins along the Lou-lan course of the Tarim as evidence of a climatic change. The imaginative appeal of a "dry heart of Asia" led to ready acceptance of a poorly founded thesis of migrations, based on controls of desiccation. In most marginal arid regions, populations shift according to minor fluctuations in precipitation, so that in places such as western Kansas, the Harney Basin of Oregon, or the steppes of Iran, cultural landscapes normally include many abandoned dwellings or even deserted towns. Estimates of former populations are likely to be exaggerated, because appraisals based on numbers of habitations are likely to assume contemporaneous occupance of more dwellings than actually occurred at any one time. But the reason for abandonment is not always climatic.

Faulting may have ended the water supply of a particular oasis, water may have been mined to a degree which rendered further habitation impracticable, or, as in the case of the Tarim Basin, a river may have shifted its course in obedience to some minor hydrographic control located far upstream. Of even greater consequence may have been the decisions of man himself. The orders of a ruler, the taboos of a religion, or the appearance of a plague have undoubtedly driven man as far afield as climatic fluctuations of intensities on up to glacial-interglacial magnitude.

Even in well-watered lands river diversions have dislocated human activities profoundly. The shifting of the Hwang Ho from an outlet north of Shantung to one south of the peninsula in 1192, the return to courses north of Shantung in 1852, and the natural diversion to the south in 1938 resulted not only in immediate tragedies of flood, famine, and pestilence but also in land abandonment and widespread rearrangements of population according to patterns determined by the availability of water. By the time of the last natural diversion the Chinese had acquired the ability to dispute the whims of hydrography so well that by 1947 the Hwang Ho was artificially returned to its northern course, leading to the Gulf of Po Hai.

Geologists commonly and erroneously have attributed river diversions to causes such as the extension of channels along gradients too flat to permit delta growth beyond some assumed limit of advance. As a matter of fact, conditions near the coast ordinarily have little or nothing to do with the abandonment of one river channel in favor of some other route to the sea. All major diversions of the Hwang Ho occurred some 250 miles inland. The threatened diversion of the lower Mississippi into the channel of the Atcha-falaya River involves a shift about that far from the Gulf of Mexico. A complicated history of delta advance near the head of the Adriatic Sea has resulted from diversions of the Po Valley channels well back from the coast and wholly independent of shore processes. The rise of Dordrecht, the creation of successive systems of natural levees that have become, in turn, the most favorable sites of habitation in Holland, the abandonment of large tracts of land along the Schelde in Belgium, and many similar developments caused by changes in lower Rhine or Maas courses have resulted from diversions occurring 100 or more miles inland. Though coastal subsidence has added to the complexities of recent river history of the Low Countries, the submergence of any localized coastal tract is never the determining factor in the origin of a new river outlet. Diversions depend on hydrographic circumstances at localized points which are commonly situated well upstream. On a grand scale the huge discharge of the Mississippi River could not be the result of subsidence along the Louisiana coast. That the Ohio, Missouri, and other large rivers are tributary to the Mississippi depends on very minor topographic conditions within the continental interior.

EVOLUTION

In their slowness and general freedom from the interference of man, evolutionary processes somewhat resemble those of geology. Man's environment has changed in accordance with ecological developments accompanying plant and animal evolution. Man, however, gradually learned that selective breeding might result in the increase or decrease in populations of specific plant and animal mutants. More recently, through an application of various forms of short-wave energy or of chemicals, he has learned to accelerate, or possibly distort, evolutionary processes with a result that, instead of depending on nature to supply new types of plants and animals, his own decisions are becoming a controlling factor.

Now that man has started to control evolution, his own development may proceed in various directions. Will he apply to himself his knowledge of genetics? Will his newly acquired mobility result in the disappearance of races? Will his physical deterioration at length destroy his ability to survive? Will his mental ability, coupled with physical decline, alter him toward "an ultimate colloid," a domineering brain which so completely controls environmental processes that its own physical requirements become negligible? Or will he charge the atmosphere with deadly particles, or pry into the atom one step too far, and bring about his own complete destruction?

The evolution of pathogenic organisms is possibly the most serious threat to man's survival. Whether locally evolved or introduced from elsewhere, it was presumably a new organism that wiped out one-third of the population of Ireland in 1202–4 or which brought the Black Death that halved the population of Great Britain during the fourteenth century. This latter tragedy was proportionately as severe as the famine caused by excessive precipitation in Ireland, which dropped the population from more than eight million to about four million between 1845 and 1850. London's plague of 1665 caused sixty-eight thousand deaths, and many other epidemics rank high among human disasters. The southeastern United States was almost depopulated between the time of De Soto and that of Marquette, presumably by disease. Infectious diseases caused one-third of all deaths in the United States in 1900. Although a reduction of about 40 per cent in the crude death rate during the last half-century has resulted mainly from con-

trol of such maladies, the trend has been interrupted at times by the appearance of epidemics. Whether improvements in sanitation, discoveries of drugs and antibiotics, and other advances will really combat successfully the development of new pathogenic organisms is one of the most fundamental questions faced by man. The next year could bring a new virus or amoeba against which we have no immunity and for which there is no known control. Examples affecting crops and animals have been common. A new blight, rust, or borer suddenly appears, to end successful production of a commercial crop or to wipe out endemic species of plants.

In a sense independent of man's control but yet a critical part of his total environment is man's own evolution—physical, mental, and intellectual. Mutation, or kindred processes, has developed racial differentiations which were accentuated so long as man was divided into relatively isolated groups. When one group came into contact with another, the effect was an environmental reaction at times more potent in changing ways of life than the disaster of earthquake or the slow effects of a pronounced climatic change. Assyrian, Roman, or Chinese invaded new lands, wiped out parts of existing populations, created new blends in racial stocks, or dominated the lives of others. Most striking of all have been the changes wrought by the New World revolution, which was born with the voyages of discovery and nurtured by the commercial revolution. European peoples and ways now reach widely over the earth at the expense of previously existing peoples and cultures, most positively where indigenous cultures were primitive. Proceeding with accelerated tempo in an age of science, the New World revolution threatens to end racial diversification and possibly to evolve techniques that will eliminate life from the globe. As a result of the drama in which man has briefly occu- pied the center of the stage, the earth may return to a more normal routine of events—one more in keeping with the record of its geological past.

REFERENCES

AHLMANN, H. W:SON
  1953 *Glacier Variations and Climatic Fluctuations.* (Bowman Memorial Lectures, Series Three.) New York: American Geographical Society. 51 pp.

BOWIE, WILLIAM
  1927 *Isostasy.* New York: E. P. Dutton & Co. 275 pp.

BROOKS, C. E. P.
  1949 *Climate through the Ages: A Study of Climatic Factors and Their Variations.* New York: McGraw-Hill Book Co. 395 pp.

DALY, REGINALD A.
  1934 *The Changing World of the Ice Age.* New Haven, Conn.: Yale University Press. 271 pp.

DAVIS, WILLIAM MORRIS
  1899 "The Geographical Cycle," *Geographical Journal,* XIV, 481–504.
  1902 "Base Level, Grade and Peneplain," *Journal of Geology,* X, 77–111. (Both of these articles were reprinted in *Geographical Essays* [1909], Boston: Ginn & Co., 777 pp., and [1954] New York: Dover Publications.)

GAUTIER, E.-F.
  1935 *Sahara: The Great Desert.* Trans. from the French by DOROTHY FORD MAYHEW. New York: Columbia University Press. 264 pp.

HECK, NICHOLAS H.
  1936 *Earthquakes.* Princeton, N.J.: Princeton University Press. 222 pp.

HEDIN, SVEN.
  1940 *The Wandering Lake.* Trans. from the Swedish by F. H. LYON. New York: E. P. Dutton & Co. 291 pp.

HENRY, A. J.
  1928 "The Distribution of Excessive Precipitation in the United States," *Monthly Weather Review,* LVI, 355–63.

HUMPHREYS, W. J.
  1940 *Physics of the Air.* 3d ed. New York: McGraw-Hill Book Co. 676 pp.

JAGGAR, T. A.
  1945 *Volcanoes Declare War: Logistics and Strategy of Pacific Volcano Science.* Honolulu, T.H.: Paradise of the Pacific. 166 pp.

LEET, L. DON
  1948 *Causes of Catastrophe: Earthquakes, Volcanoes, Tidal Waves, and Hurricanes.* New York: McGraw-Hill Book Co. 232 pp.

LEET, L. DON, and JUDSON, SHELDON
  1954 *Physical Geology.* New York: Prentice-Hall, Inc. 466 pp.

MATTHES, FRANÇOIS
  1942 "Report of Committee on Glaciers," *American Geophysical Union, Transactions,* pp. 374–92.

NANSEN, FRIDTJOF
  1911 *In Northern Mists: Arctic Exploration in Early Times.* Trans. from the Norwegian by ARTHUR G. CHATER. 2 vols. London: W. Heinemann. 318+415 pp.

RAYMOND, PERCY E.
  1939 *Prehistoric Life.* Cambridge, Mass.: Harvard University Press. 324 pp.

READE, T. MELLARD
  1872 "The Post-glacial Geology and Physiography of West Lancashire and the Mersey Estuary," *Geological Magazine,* IX, 111–19.

RUSSELL, RICHARD J.
  1934 "Climatic Years," *Geographical Review,* XXIV, 92–103.
  1936 "The Desert Rainfall Factor in Denudation," pp. 753–63 in *Report of XVI Geological Congress.* Washington, D.C., 1933.
  1941 "Climatic Change through the Ages," pp. 69–97 in HAMBIDGE, G., and DROWN, M. J. (eds.), *Climate and Man: Yearbook of Agriculture, 1941.* Washington, D.C.: Government Printing Office. 1,248 pp.

1948 "Coast of Louisiana," *Bulletin de la Société de Géologie, de Paléontologie et d'Hydrologie,* LVII, 380–94.

RUSSELL, RICHARD J., and KNIFFEN, F. B.
1951 *Culture Worlds.* New York: Macmillan Co. 620 pp.

SEWARD, A. C.
1931 *Plant Life through the Ages: A Geological and Botanical Retrospect.* Cambridge, England: Cambridge University Press. 601 pp.

SHALER, NATHANIEL SOUTHGATE
1895 "Evidences as to Changes in Level," *Bulletin of the Geological Society of America,* VI, 141–66.

SHARP, C. F. STEWART
1938 *Landslides and Related Phenomena.* New York: Columbia University Press. 137 pp.

WRIGHT, W. B.
1914 *The Quaternary Ice Age.* London: Macmillan & Co. 464 pp.

The Processes of Environmental Change by Man

PAUL B. SEARS[*]

MAN'S PLACE IN NATURE

To understand and measure the change which man has produced in his environment, it is first necessary to view his place in nature. His flexibility as an organism is often emphasized, sometimes being referred to as his "unspecialization." What is meant is his freedom from evolutionary characteristics that would sharply restrict his activities and choice of habitat. That he is highly evolved cannot be questioned. Often overlooked is the fact that he exists by virtue of an environment which is itself highly evolved and specialized, having become so in the course of more than two billion years of earth history.

The most obvious features of this specialized environment include the presence of an angiosperm flora—notably grasses and legumes—and a mammalian fauna dependent upon it. From these sources man is able to derive sustenance with an ease and efficiency that

would have been inconceivable had he been surrounded only by organisms of the remote geological past. Less obvious is the presence of a complex population of microörganisms and invertebrates which, among other functions, takes care of the breakdown of organic wastes and their return to chemical forms that can be reused to sustain life. Of major importance also is the persistence of numerous species of gymnosperms that, along with many kinds of woody angiosperms, furnish facilities without which man would have been severely handicapped throughout his existence. Indeed, that existence appears to have hinged upon trees, for his arboreal ancestors were obliged to develop the free shoulder articulation, grasping hands, and stereoscopic vision which serve him so well.

Least obvious, at any rate to modern urbanized man, is the effect of our present highly complex fauna and flora, organized as they are into communities, upon the environment itself. Through reaction upon habitat these communities not only insure an orderly cycle of material and energy transformations but also regulate the moisture economy, cushion the earth's surface against violent physiographic change, and make possible the formation of soil. In short, man is dependent upon other organisms both for the immediate means of survival and for maintaining habitat conditions under which survival is possible.

* Dr. Sears is Chairman of the Conservation Program and Professor of Botany at Yale University, New Haven, Connecticut, and for 1953–55 also Chairman of the Department of Plant Science. He has been president of the Nebraska Academy of Science, the Ohio Academy of Science, and the Ecological Society of America and is president for 1956–57 of the American Association for the Advancement of Science. His present research interests are on Pleistocene vegetation, pollen analysis, and applied ecology. His works include: *Deserts on the March*, 1935; *This Is Our World*, 1937; and *Charles Darwin: The Naturalist as a Cultural Force*, 1950.

Man is also dependent upon minerals, his consumption of the two used longest, water and stone, still ranking first by volume. His present economy rests chiefly upon the use of fossil fuels and metals, both irregularly distributed and present in finite amounts. The fossil fuels, once used, can be restored only by the slow organic and tectonic processes which formed them, while the use of metals results in the dissipation of the ore concentrations by which they have been made available to man. Their present convenient form, like the character of the organic world, is the result of prolonged earth history before the coming of man. Man is clearly the beneficiary of a very special environment which has been a great while in the making. This environment is more than an inert stockroom. It is an active system, a pattern, and a process as well. Its value can be threatened by disruption no less than by depletion.

Any species survives by virtue of its niche—the opportunity afforded it by environment. But in occupying its niche it also assumes a role in relation to its surroundings. For further survival it is necessary that the role at least not be a disruptive one. Thus one generally finds in nature that each component of a highly organized community serves a constructive, or at any rate a stabilizing, role. The habitat furnishes the niche, and, if any species breaks up the habitat, the niche goes with it. The guest who helps with the chores may prolong his stay, but the inconsiderate one may wreck the house. Systems or processes which involve organic activity resemble purely physical systems in being expressions of thermodynamic law, tending to approach a condition of minimum stress and unbalance. But, since living systems are active and dynamic, they tend to approximate what is known as a steady state rather than a condition of repose. That is, to persist, they must be able to utilize radiant energy not merely to perform work but to maintain the working system in reasonably good order. This requires the presence of organisms adjusted to the habitat and to each other, so organized as to make fullest use of the influent radiation and to conserve for use and re-use the materials which the system requires. The degree to which a living community meets these conditions is therefore a test of its efficiency and stability. This gives us a criterion by which the effects of environmental change can be judged.

While these principles have been shown to apply to what is generally called the world of nature, that is, the world apart from man, there is considerable resistance to the idea that they apply to him in any serious way. Much of this resistance is emotional, having its roots in that part of Judeo-Christian tradition which separates man from nature to a greater extent than perhaps was common in oriental and Mediterranean thought. Some of it certainly comes from those who resent, for whatever reasons, any warning sign along the road to a perpetually expanding economy. And surprisingly, perhaps, some resistance comes from scientists and technologists, especially those unacquainted with the general field that used to be called natural history. In defense of this last group it must be said that they are as aware of still unexploited reserves as the ecologist is of the existence of limiting factors. And, in view of the fabulous results they have produced, they are perhaps less concerned with the law of diminishing returns than their colleagues whose business it is to study the interrelationship of life and environment. As responsible scientists, both groups have an obligation to collaborate and to weigh scrupulously any pronouncements, whether these be cautions or promises. Mankind is not well served either by hysteria or by false visions.

It will be shown subsequently that the changes induced by man, whether by sheer destruction or indirectly by accelerating natural processes, are probably more serious to him than the so-called "natural changes" for which he is not responsible.

MAN AS AN AGENT OF CHANGE

Unfortunately, the situation is clouded by a widespread confidence that this impact of man upon environment can continue indefinitely. We are told that the greatest resource is human resourcefulness and that ways and means will be found, through the applications of science and technology, to meet all emergencies as they arise. The economy and the social and political policy of the United States are based upon this assumption of more and more, bigger and better. The phrase "an expanding economy" is frequently heard without any qualifying explanation.

It is true that we are far from the end of the rope. North of Mexico, America has great reserves of space and other essentials. Direct utilization of solar energy is a reasonable probability and with it the tapping of now unavailable mineral resources in igneous rocks. There is no call to sell applied science short. On the other hand, there is no justification for writing off the judgment of biologists, demographers, geologists, and anthropologists, all of whom have special competence with respect to the context of human activity—the broad but finite pattern within which man must operate.

The Problem

There are many interesting approaches to the problem of man and his environment, and all, save perhaps the technological, seem to lead to the same conclusions. With this possible exception, these various approaches indicate that humanity should strive toward a condition of equilibrium with its environment. This is the verdict of ethics, aesthetics, and natural science. And, despite the prevalence of the idea of a continually expanding economy, it is probably the verdict of that branch of economic analysis known as accounting.

Accounting seeks to identify certain entities—assets, liabilities, income, expense—and to construct therefrom its equations. It must be particularly careful to identify those changes in capital structure known as depreciation and not to confuse them with income. Assuming, therefore, that the physical environment represents the basis of humanity's capital assets, the question becomes: Does our levy upon it represent sustaining income in excess of expenditure, or has it been obtained through deterioration of the capital base, that is, through depreciation?

By Way of Background

An extensive literature upon man and his environment has appeared during the last twenty years, generally emphasizing the extent and seriousness of depreciation of the capital structure. Useful examples include Osborn's *The Limits of the Earth* (1953) and Brown's *The Challenge of Man's Future* (1954), the former written from the viewpoint of a biologist, the latter from that of a geochemist. So far as I know, the evidence of neither has been countered directly—that is, by demonstrating that humanity has not made serious inroads upon natural resources. The nearest exceptions to this have taken the form of statements that vast mineral resources remain to be discovered, though at increasing cost, and that the production of food and fiber can be greatly increased by better methods. Both assertions are probably true.

Rather has the rejoinder been indirect. Thus Hanson, in *New Worlds Emerging* (1949), stresses the vast potential of the tropics and the ocean, while De Castro, writing *The Geography of Hunger* (1952), advances the thesis (a curious one to biologists) that ample diet will slow down the birth rate and so relieve population pressure. Fortunately, our task is one of appraisal, not of passing on the merits of prophecy.

First, however, some comments on commercial economies are in order. Early commerce was probably on the basis of mutual plenty—tin for glass, wine for fish, wheat for lumber. But with the growth of empire and other forms of power a trend developed which can still be observed between nations and even within them. The flow is from the sources of raw materials and cheap labor toward the centers of power—military, political, or economic. And because of this drainage there is often left too little energy, capacity, or capital at the source for the exploited to safeguard their own interests. The process tends to become purely extractive, to the detriment of land capital. Interesting exceptions, not fully appreciated at both ends of the line, are certain of our extra-territorial agricultural corporations whose net effect upon the economy of the countries where they work is constructive (Sears, 1953*b*). Unfortunately, the beneficiaries of this system may say, "Es bueno, pero no es nuestro," and who can blame them? We all like the privilege of making our own mistakes.

In spite of the recurring abuses of power throughout history, commerce and industry were until the Reformation, in principle at least, subordinate to other cultural forces and restraints, notably religion. The extent to which they took the bit in their teeth after the industrial revolution is shown by the demand for an antitrust law at a time in our history when the most radical leaders were men who would now be considered sober conservatives. Today—

again in principle—no one seriously questions the social responsibility of those engaged in commerce. Little would be gained if he did!

Curiously, however, the very structure of our modern economy, based as it is on mass production, intensifies the problem that here concerns us. Everything is geared to the speedy conversion of raw materials into consumers' goods at a rate governed only—when it is governed—by the capacity of the public to buy. Presumably the public does not buy unless it needs, but there is sound, if sardonic, reason to believe that this is not always true.

Compared to the efforts at conversion of raw materials, the effort to conserve them is still relatively slight. But the growth of industrial enterprise is having a wholesome effect in some quarters. So much capital is being tied up that the larger concerns are beginning to think about their own permanence, and this in turn involves thinking about the continuing future supply of raw materials. Banks and public utilities, both dependent upon general prosperity, are taking an active interest in soil and water conservation. Some of the larger lumber companies have adopted excellent sustained-yield plans. And national associations representing various economic interests are paying at least lip service, often a good deal more than that, to the restoration and preservation of resource capital. The occasional sounding of a sour note is no cause for alarm, since it serves to keep vigilant those who are deeply concerned with the problem.

ENVIRONMENTAL CHANGES
PRODUCED BY MAN

The Increasing Intensity in Land Use

The effect of man upon vegetation before the origin of agriculture and pastoral life is not known. The incidence of fires, even during the hunting stage of economy, must certainly have increased. Man is known to have hunted Pleistocene mammals, for example, the mammoth and the bison. The mammoth, horse, and camel evidently became extinct in the Americas after man's arrival there.

Human influence on vegetation registers in many pollen profiles through the abrupt appearance of certain weeds, notably composites, amaranths, and chenopods. These multiply when the natural cover is destroyed and show up in prehuman pollen profiles following volcanic activity or erosion due to tectonic change. The chenopods are still used for food; thus they may be regarded as precursors of agriculture. Of especial interest is the recent evidence of their appearance during the second interglacial in association with artifacts of pre-Acheulean age.

Agriculture requires the removal of native vegetation, while pastoral life is sustained by such vegetation. Iversen's recent experiments (1949) demonstrate strikingly the effectiveness of stone tools and fire in clearing the drier types of forest. The practice of felling and burning trees and planting cleared ground until the yields decline, then abandoning it and moving on, is known in Latin America as the *milpa* system. It is not particularly harmful until the increasing pressure of population extends the system to the hills and shortens the cycle needed for the vegetation and soil to recuperate. Erosion then follows.

Similarly, so long as a pastoral economy has sufficient space to permit nomadic life, the grasses and other herbs which sustain it can recuperate between periods of heavy use. Moreover, the pastoral cultures tend to be somewhat more aggressive than the legend of Abel and other "gentle shepherds" would suggest. One cannot doubt that primitive herders knew good pasture when they saw it and took vigorous

measures to prevent undue trespassing. Even so, the growth of population brought steady pressure on the world's natural grasslands. Under such conditions the floral composition of these grasslands is modified, and less nutritious species come in as weeds. If the pressure continues, and particularly if it is extended to arid or hilly land, erosion by wind and water ensues. All these effects are intensified and extended to forest country when goats, valuable as they are to man otherwise, are present in great numbers. The goat is a thin-lipped, destructive grazer, as is the sheep; but, to a greater extent than sheep, it is a resourceful browser, damaging to woody vegetation.

With agriculture, urban life and the leisure arts and crafts became possible. Repeatedly in human history, this appears to have thrown the art of husbandry and the importance of good land use out of perspective. Except perhaps in China, the status of the man who worked the land was gradually demeaned as cities grew in size, power, and prestige. The effect of such change on the quality of rural techniques was probably bad, and the effect on the land itself, intensified by increasing food demands, was clearly so.

Two aspects of the growth of cities were particularly important. One was the expansion of irrigation works; the other, the harvesting of timber for fuel and structural purposes, thus clearing land not needed for, or suitable to, agriculture. Early irrigation in both hemispheres seems to have been well engineered, probably because the irrigators of arid lands had the stark choice of doing a proper job or being eliminated.

Where such irrigation depended upon wells, these afforded a positive check upon expansion, and an equilibrium of land use was reached which persisted in parts of the Near East for millenniums, only to be broken by the growing cone of depression of the water table incident to modern pumping for water used in oil refining.

Important irrigation works of great antiquity, notably in Mesopotamia, were based on the use of streams arising in forested uplands. Here, the clearance of forests, no doubt followed by heavy grazing, stimulated erosion. Vast amounts of silt were washed down, so that increasing labor had to be used for the clearance of the otherwise excellent system of irrigation ditches. While it is true that this interfluvial culture persisted long after the empires which it built—until its ditches were wrecked by Mongol invaders during the thirteenth century—the immense piles of silt alongside the ditches show that the system was well on the way toward being choked out before it was destroyed.

It is in the world of today, where industrialization and death control have produced an explosive growth of population, that land-use problems have become most acute and dramatic. Man has long competed with other forms of life for space. Increasingly he is his own competitor—a situation made worse by the diversity of his interests as they affect land use. Residence, business, industry, transport, waste disposal, water supply, agriculture, forestry, military needs, recreation—not to mention many intangibles—all have intensified their rival claims, frequently upon the same limited area. The effect has been confusing almost to the point of disaster, as can be seen in any metropolitan "urban fringe" area.

Allocation of space by planning and zoning, while not a new idea, has been outlined on a scientific basis by Geddes and his followers. It has been rather effectively developed in Great Britain by Stamp (1952) and others and in some parts of western Europe. But in Holland, where it is extremely advanced, it now faces the crisis of a saturated population. In the United States it faces grave political obstacles, made worse by the fact that we do still have a margin of safety and by the prevalence of our conviction that an economy can continue to expand without limits. This of course runs counter to the scientific experience that the factors in any process must ultimately work toward some kind of equilibrium. This principle, so widely applied in the purely physical sciences, seems to be as widely ignored—or disbelieved—when it comes to land use. A curious and dangerous phenomenon in a technological culture!

Soil Erosion

It would be misleading to say that man is the cause of erosion or that erosion per se is a bad thing. As frequently pointed out, it is a normal part of the natural process of base-leveling and has been the source of some of the richest alluvial terraces and plains on earth. But under natural conditions, and except in very arid mountainous regions, the rate of erosion is controlled by the presence of vegetative cover in the form of stable communities. Under these conditions erosion proceeds so slowly as not to interfere greatly with the normal process of soil formation, which, in turn, is a resultant of the interaction of living communities with the physical environment. It is when we remove this natural cover *without providing a substantial artificial equivalent* that the rate of erosion is accelerated to a dangerous degree.

Where this occurs, soil is removed from the uplands, and the rich alluvium of the lowlands is buried, first by upland soil, later by the sterile mineral materials which have underlain the upland soil. In either instance the productive capacity of former surfaces is greatly reduced even where, as in sheet erosion, the surface form is not much affected. But sheet erosion, if not checked, rapidly passes into gullying, which frequently renders the topography unsuitable for use.

Forest Regions

Because forest regions are usually well supplied with water and, at first, with fuel and building material, they often become heavily populated. But it is a characteristic of forest soils that the most fertile organic layer of the surface is shallow, thinly overlying a mineral layer from which the plant nutrients have been largely leached. This kind of soil profile under pressure of use rapidly loses its productivity; the result is likely to be extensive abandonment. This explains much of what happened in New England, which was under extensive cultivation in the early nineteenth century, later largely changed to pasture, and is today two-thirds in forest of such inferior quality that it yields less than 10 per cent of the total rural income.

The situation is less serious where, as in Ohio, the minerals in the deposits brought in by glaciation are rich in nutrients and fairly deep. Here it is possible, through the use of cover crops and improved pastures and wood lots, to stabilize the surface and tap the underlying minerals, thus restoring the fertility lost when the original top soil was removed. In western Europe, where relief is low, rainfall gentle, and economic pressure has enforced good husbandry, damage from removal of the original vegetation is relatively slight. Except for hunting preserves, the original forests of western Europe were largely destroyed during the Middle Ages in order to obtain not only building material but also charcoal for fuel and for the manufacture of steel. This is surprising in view of the fact that in the seventeenth century some 360 tons of steel more than met the annual needs of England—at least from the seller's point of view. Today, the art of

forestry has reached such levels that, from Denmark to Italy, one finds that good agricultural land can be used profitably for the production of wood. Moreover, the forests of France and the pasture lands of Britain fill admirably the role of natural vegetation as a stabilizer of the landscape.

Grasslands

Changes in forest cover are more obvious and better known than those in the grassland regions. Thus Ohio, once about 90 per cent forested, now is about 15 per cent in such cover. Farther west the proportion of native tall-grass prairie that has been destroyed is probably even greater. This is especially serious because of the remarkable resilience with which the rich prairie flora can adjust to the recurrent crises of climate—a property not shared by the plant cover which agriculture has substituted.

Where precipitation does not exceed the evaporating power of the atmosphere measured in inches of water, grassland, scrub, or desert occur. The subhumid grasslands of the world have developed a deep and fertile topsoil, well supplied with mineral nutrients and remarkably suited to the production of high yields of cereal protein. Because the thickness of the humus horizon varies from 3 to 5 feet, erosion goes largely unnoticed, and the use of artificial fertilizers can be postponed for decades. Yet there is evidence that in Iowa, for example, an average of perhaps one-third of the original A-horizon of the surface has been lost since settlement, while the depletion of mineral nutrients is now making necessary the use of chemical additives.

The semiarid grasslands sustain a growth of short grasses and other low-growing herbs which have served to bind the soil into a turf or sod. Here there is a marked excess of evaporative power over precipitation and a consequent upward movement of water, bringing nutrient minerals to the surface. The soil is inherently productive except for the lack of moisture. Under natural conditions good, though sparse, grazing was afforded by the native grasses, which not only held the surface in place but cured on the stalk, retaining their value as forage.

Outward pressure from the centers of population brought these lands under settlement, and techniques of dry farming were developed. The level land being well suited to mechanized farming, good yields of high-protein cereal at minimum cost were found to be possible. The concurrence of moist years with periods of high demand and good prices encouraged the extensive plowing-up of the original short-grass sod during World Wars I and II. But in both instances the moist years were followed by dry, and the autumn-planted wheat either failed to germinate or made such feeble growth that it could not stabilize the lighter types of soil against the strong dry winds of late winter and spring. Severe dust storms were produced by the resulting erosion. This phenomenon is all the more remarkable for having repeated itself in less than a quarter-century in a literate, highly technological culture that had made notable efforts to repair the effects of the first series of dust storms and was well informed of the consequences to be expected from repeating the mistakes which had led to them. However, the fault does not lie entirely with the more speculative and less responsible segments of the free-enterprise system. Influential spokesmen for scientific agriculture, more concerned with the latent fertility of arid soils than with the inevitable pattern of recurrent drought, did too little to discourage exploitation and in some cases encouraged it.

Some confusion is due to the clear evidence of periods of rapid erosion and gully formation in recent geological time but before the known advent of man. This is especially noticeable in our own Southwest and has led some scientists to minimize the effects of overgrazing as a cause of accelerated erosion today. Past erosion cycles were due to intervals of dry climate, and we have been in the beginning of such an interval since about 1700; so, runs the reasoning, why blame man for a natural phenomenon? The answer lies in comparing such overburdened ranges as those of the Navaho with others which have been subjected to reasonable use. It is possible to find hillsides on which a fence separates a field of gullies from one which is intact. That we are in a time of increased climatic hazard is certain. It would seem equally certain that a scientific culture therefore should exercise more rather than less caution in its pattern of land use.

The effect of destroying or damaging natural communities is not confined to increased erosion. Water, with wind, is the chief erosive agent. Besides stabilizing the land surface, natural vegetation is a major regulator of the hydrologic cycle—indeed, it is chiefly in this way that the surface is stabilized.

The Problem of Water

If the water cycle be roughly described as (1) evaporation from the seas, (2) transport over the land, (3) rainfall or snowfall, and (4) flow back to the sea, it is chiefly during stage (4) that water is available for the sustenance of life on land. By prolonging this stage, terrestrial life gets the maximum benefit from moisture. Whatever shortens the time that water is in or on the land decreases its utility to land life, including our own.

Continuous vegetative cover retards the flow of water. It also renders the ground more permeable, thus maintaining the water table. In one instance it has been shown (Mather, 1953) that, while pasture and cultivated land soon become saturated, forest absorbs the equivalent of nearly 500 inches of rainfall. It seems reasonable to suppose that the same relationship holds as between native prairie and average farmland derived from it. A number of factors, not the least of which is compaction due to increasing use of heavy farm machinery, are responsible for this reduction in permeability.

A closely related phenomenon is the rapid increase of virtually waterproofed surface areas represented by cities and highways. Except in isolated cases, notably parts of Texas, where highway drainage is channeled into storage ponds, the water falling on roofs, sidewalks, and roads is speeded on its way. If used at all, it is reclaimed from rivers and requires purification. At the same time the per capita demand for water in urban centers continues to rise for both domestic and industrial purposes. Our cities are almost wholly dependent upon water which falls in non-urban territory. Thus we have the phenomenon of a technological culture whose demand for water is steadily rising at the same time that its processes accelerate the return of water to the sea.

But the problem of water involves quality as well as quantity. In this respect, also, a curious picture is presented. No highly developed organism in nature carries massive effluent wastes and influent necessities in the same system of transport. No organized living community in nature is without components that transform waste materials back into harmless and usable form. Yet our streams are utilized as sources for domestic and industrial water supply and concurrently as convenient sewers for domestic and industrial waste—beyond the capacity of their normal process to purify.

To urban wastes is often added the silt from eroded surfaces. The net effect is not only to impair the quality of the water but seriously to affect it as a habitat for aquatic life, both in the stream bed and in the estuary into which it discharges. This has damaged recreation and sport as well as commercial fishing and shell fishing. Pearl Harbor is no longer hospitable to the mollusks which gave it its original name.

Commerce is affected also. Computations of the dredging costs due to erosional silt in Cleveland Harbor and at the mouth of the Brandywine show that these costs are equivalent to a tax of several hundred dollars on each ship that enters the two ports each year. Such are the hidden costs of man-made change, patent to the ecologist, yet largely ignored by the industrial and financial leaders of a great technological civilization, in which the art of accounting, or business analysis, has been carried to a high degree of perfection.

Any discussion of water involves not only shortage and quality but also the question of flood. It is difficult to say to what extent floods have been increased by man's activity, for certain catastrophic types of rainfall would almost certainly produce floods in any event. But buildings and other installations within the flood plain of a great river should be in the same category of calculated risks as vineyards on the sides of an active volcano. Though they are seldom so regarded, nevertheless it is man who is responsible for flood damages, if not for the floods which cause them.

On the other hand, there are at least local floods that can be traced to human disturbance. This applies to northeastern New Jersey, a country of ridges and folds, where clearing, building, and paving of the ridge tops for extensive suburban developments have left rainfall with only one course—that of running downhill and swamping the homes below. Similarly, burning of chaparral or forest clearance of mountain slopes above our western cities has been responsible for flash floods and mudflows of a serious character. On general principles we would expect denuded and exploited headwater regions to intensify the destructive character and frequency of floods. While this is assumed as a basic element in national forest policy, far greater funds are expended upon efforts to control flood *after* water has reached the river channels than are devoted to securing proper land use on the tributary uplands to retain the water where it falls. This is an interesting aspect of a technological culture whose emphasis is on engineering rather than on biological controls.

The impoundment of water for various reasons is rapidly increasing, owing to the substitution of powerful earth-moving machinery for hand labor. In some instances, most notably the Tennessee Valley Authority, there has been an attempt to relate such impoundments to the entire economy of a region, making them serve multiple purposes. Thus flood control, recreation, power, and water transport have been combined with measures to improve public health and land use in the Tennessee Valley. In numerous instances the approach has been on a narrower basis.

Small farm ponds are being used to compensate for the growing scarcity of suitable ground water. Great public works in arid and semiarid regions have made possible the extension of irrigation, generation of power, and augmented urban water supplies. Such irrigation has not been uniformly successful, as witnessed by the inability of the beneficiaries to carry out contract payments on schedule. In some instances the high rate of evaporation has resulted in the accumulation of salts which interfere with plant growth.

Problems arise from the necessity, in heavily industrial-residential areas, of excluding recreational activities from public water-supply watersheds in order to protect them from contamination, even though suitable recreation space is at a premium.

The Atmosphere

The atmosphere has become a medium of transport and the scene of experiments to modify the weather. On this latter problem scientific opinion is divided as to both feasibility and wisdom. Our failure thus far to adjust our economy in marginal climatic areas to what we know about their compulsive and recurrent hazards suggests that, even if we can modify climate, the operation at this stage is somewhat premature. Modern society is not yet organized to control the powers which science already has placed at its disposal.

Of perhaps more immediate concern is the growing volume of volatile and solid wastes which pollute the air of great urban centers across the United States. Hydrocarbons from refineries and automobiles, no less than by-products of chemical works, are particularly serious. Vegetation, not only in the vicinity of smelters, but in places like Pasadena, has been affected, and there have been instances of known damage to human beings. Pittsburgh has been greatly improved, and commissions are at work elsewhere; but the problem of protecting the quality of two basic resources, formerly regarded as free economic goods—water and air —remains urgent.

Mineral Resources

The per capita consumption of minerals, unlike that of renewable resources, has continued to rise steadily with the level of living. Re-use is growing but not sufficiently to offset the depletion of concentrated reserves. Once taken into the economic process, these minerals tend to become dissipated or, in the case of energy sources, altered beyond recovery except through the slow biological and geological changes which made them.

The measurement of reserves is difficult technically, and exploration is increasingly expensive. Strategic and business considerations may hinder us from finding out where we stand. As an official in the copper industry put it, no figures on reserves are given out, as a matter partially of protection to the American public!

However, a few figures will suffice to emphasize the situation. Department of Commerce figures for March, 1954, show that petroleum consumption within the United States is substantially in excess of domestic production. Again, the United States, with less than one-tenth of world population, is today consuming more than half of the world's mineral production. The fact that much of the wealth so created is being dispensed among other friendly nations is some compensation but no guaranty that this condition is either desirable or secure. And, finally, more than half of the many kinds of minerals used in the American economy must be imported, not being commercially available within our borders.

CHANGE AND ETHICS—A SUMMARY

Change in the ecosystem of which man is a part is inevitable, since this system is a process, and he is inevitably affected by such changes. On the whole, those changes which are natural (i.e., not due to his interference) take place on a scale and at a rate which is not disastrous to him. While some of his activities may regulate and utilize these changes to his benefit, more of them serve to accelerate the rate and widen the scope of natural changes in ways that lower the potential of the environment to sustain him. For such effects man is responsible, and where responsibility enters so do ethical problems.

Through science, man now has the means to be aware of change and its effects and the ways in which his cultural values and behavior should be modified to insure their own preservation. Whether we consider ethics to be enlightened self-interest, the greatest good for the greatest number, ultimate good rather than present benefit, or Schweitzer's reverence for life, man's obligation toward environment is equally clear.

REFERENCES

AHLMANN, H. W.
  1953 *Glacier Variations and Climatic Fluctuations.* (Bowman Memorial Lectures, Series Three.) New York: American Geographical Society. 51 pp.

ANDERSON, E.
  1952 *Plants, Man and Life.* Boston: Little, Brown & Co. 245 pp.

ANONYMOUS
  1953 *Desert Research: Proceedings of the International Symposium Held in Jerusalem, May 7–14, 1952, Sponsored by the Research Council of Israel and the United Nations Educa-* tional, Scientific, and Cultural Organization. Jerusalem: Research Council of Israel. 641 pp.
  1954 *Growing Food for a Growing World.* ("The Work of FAO, 1952–53.") Rome: United Nations Food and Agriculture Organization. 37 pp.
  1955 "Europe Issues Aired on Overpopulation." *Christian Science Monitor,* January 29, p. 2.

AVELEYRA, L., and MALDONADO-KOERDELL, M.
  1952 "Asociación de artefactos con mamut en el pleistoceno superior de la cuenca de México," *Revista mexi-*

cana de estudios antropológicos, XIII, 3–30.

AYRES, E., and SCARLOTT, C. A.
 1952   *Energy Sources: The Wealth of the World.* New York: McGraw-Hill Book Co. 344 pp.

BENCHETRIT, M.
 1954   "L'Erosion anthropogène: Couverture végétale et conséquences du mode d'exploitation du sol," *L'Information géographique,* XVIII, No. 3, 100–108.

BLIVEN, B.
 1953   *Preview for Tomorrow: The Unfinished Business of Science.* New York: Alfred A. Knopf. 347 pp.

BROWN, H.
 1954   *The Challenge of Man's Future.* New York: Viking Press. 290 pp.

CASTRO, JOSUÉ DE
 1952   *The Geography of Hunger.* Boston: Little, Brown & Co. 337 pp.

COLEMAN, E. A.
 1953   *Vegetation and Water-shed Management: An Appraisal of Vegetation Management in Relation to Water Supply, Flood Control, and Soil Erosion.* New York: Ronald Press Co. 412 pp.

CRAWFORD, M. D. C.
 1938   *The Conquest of Culture.* New York: Greenberg. 250 pp.

CURRY, L.
 1952   "Climate and Economic Life: A New Approach, with Examples from the United States," *Geographical Review,* XLII, No. 3, 367–83.

DARWIN, C. G.
 1953   *The Next Million Years.* Garden City, N.Y.: Doubleday & Co. 210 pp.

DIOLÉ, P.
 1954   *4,000 Years under the Sea.* New York: Julian Messner, Inc. 237 pp.

DOUGLASS, A. E.
 1935   *Dating Pueblo Bonito and Other Ruins of the Southwest.* ("Pueblo Bonito Series," No. 1.) Washington, D.C.: National Geographic Society. 74 pp.

ELLIS, C. B., *et al.*
 1954   *Fresh Water from the Ocean for Cities, Industry, and Irrigation.* New York: Ronald Press Co. 217 pp.

FOX, SIR C. S.
 1952   *Water: A Study of Its Properties —Its Constitution, Its Circulation on the Earth, and Its Utilization by Man.* New York: Philosophical Library. 148 pp.

FRIED, M. H.
 1952   "Land Tenure, Geography and Ecology in the Contact of Cultures," *American Journal of Economics and Sociology,* XI, No. 4, 391–412.

GOOD, R.
 1953   *The Geography of the Flowering Plants.* 2d ed. London: Longmans, Green & Co. 452 pp.

GOTTMAN, J., *et al.*
 1952   *L'Aménagement de l'espace: Planification régionale et géographie.* Paris: A. Colin. 140 pp.

GUTKIND, E. A.
 1953   *The Expanding Environment: The End of Cities, the Rise of Communities.* London: Freedom Press. 70 pp.

HADLOW, L.
 1953   *Climate, Vegetation and Man.* New York: Philosophical Library. 288 pp.

HANSON, E. P.
 1949   *New Worlds Emerging.* New York: Duell, Sloan & Pearce. 385 pp.

HATT, P. K. (ed.)
 1952   *World Population and Future Resources: The Proceedings of the Second Centennial Academic Conference of Northwestern University, Evanston, Illinois, March, 1951.* New York: American Book Co. 262 pp.

HORBERG, L.
 1952   "Interrelations of Geomorphology, Glacial Geology, and Pleistocene Geology," *Journal of Geology,* LX, No. 2, 187–90.

HOWELL, F. C.
 1952   "Pleistocene Glacial Ecology and the Evolution of 'Classic Neandertal' Man," *Southwestern Journal of Anthropology,* VIII, No. 4, 377–410.

HYMANS, E.
 1952   *Soil and Civilization.* London: Thames & Hudson. 312 pp.

IVERSEN, J.
 1949   "The Influence of Prehistoric Man on Vegetation," *Danmarks Geologiske Undersøgelse,* III, No. 6, 5–25.

JARRETT, H. (ed.)
1953 *The Nation Looks at Its Resources.* (Report of the Mid-century Conference on Resources for the Future.) Washington, D.C. 418 pp.

JENSEN, L. B.
1953 *Man's Foods: Nutrition and Environments in Food Gathering and Food Producing Times.* Champaign, Ill.: Garrard Press. 278 pp.

JUDSON, S.
1952 "Arroyos," *Scientific American,* CLXXXVII, No. 6, 71–76.

KENDALL, H. M., and GLENDINNING, R. M.
1952 *Introduction to Physical Geography.* New York: Harcourt, Brace & Co. 508 pp.

KRAEMER, J. H.
1952 *Wood Conservation Bibliography: A Selection of References in the Field of Production and Utilization of Lumber and Other Wood Products.* Washington, D.C.: U.S. Department of Commerce, Office of Industry and Commerce. 77 pp.

KRICK, I. P.
1954 "Weather Modification and Its Value to Agriculture and Water Supply," *Journal of the Royal Society of Arts,* CII, No. 4924, 447–68.

LA BARRE, W.
1954 *The Human Animal.* Chicago: University of Chicago Press. 371 pp.

LEET, L. D., and JUDSON, S.
1954 *Physical Geology.* New York: Prentice-Hall, Inc. 466 pp.

LEOPOLD, A.
1949 *A Sand County Almanac.* New York: Oxford University Press. 226 pp.

LEOPOLD, L. B., and MADDOCK, T., JR.
1954 *The Flood Control Controversy.* New York: Ronald Press Co. 278 pp.

LOWDERMILK, W. C.
1953 *Conquest of the Land through Seven Thousand Years.* (Agriculture Information Bulletin No. 99.) Washington, D.C.: U.S. Soil Conservation Service. 30 pp.

MALIN, J. C.
1953 "Soil, Animal, and Plant Relations of the Grassland, Historically Reconsidered," *Scientific Monthly,* LXXVI, No. 4, 207–20.

MANGELSDORF, P. C.
1952 *Plants and Human Affairs.* ("Niewland Lectures," Vol. V.) Notre Dame, Ind.: University of Notre Dame. 29 pp.

MARSH, G. P.
1885 *The Earth as Modified by Human Action.* New York: Charles Scribner's Sons. 629 pp.

MATHER, J. R.
1953 "The Disposal of Industrial Effluent by Woods Irrigation," *Transactions of the American Geophysical Union,* XXXIV, 227–39.

MEGGERS, B. J.
1954 "Environmental Limitation on the Development of Culture," *American Anthropologist,* LVI, No. 6, 801–24.

MINIKIN, R. R.
1952 *Coast Erosion and Protection: Studies in Causes and Remedies.* London: Chapman & Hall. 240 pp.

MONKHOUSE, F. J.
1954 *The Principles of Physical Geography.* London: University of London Press. 452 pp.

ODUM, E. P.
1954 *Fundamentals of Ecology.* Philadelphia: W. B. Saunders Co. 384 pp.

OJALA, E. M.
1952 *Agriculture and Economic Progress.* London: Oxford University Press. 220 pp.

ORDWAY, S. H., JR.
1953 *Resources and the American Dream.* New York: Ronald Press Co. 55 pp.

OSBORN, F.
1953 *The Limits of the Earth.* Boston: Little, Brown & Co. 238 pp.

PETERSON, E.
1954 *Big Dam Foolishness.* New York: Devin-Adair Co. 224 pp.

SAUER, C. O.
1952 *Agricultural Origins and Dispersals.* (Bowman Memorial Lectures, Series Two.) New York: American Geographical Society. 110 pp.

SEARS, P. B.
1935 *Deserts on the March.* Norman: Oklahoma University Press. 231 pp.
1949 "Integration at the Community Level," *American Scientist,* XXXVII, 235–42.

1953*a* "The Interdependence of Archeology and Ecology, with Examples from Middle America," *Transactions of the New York Academy of Sciences*, Series II, XV, 113–17.

1953*b* "An Ecological View of Land Use in Middle America," *CEIVA*, III, 157–65.

1954 "Human Ecology: A Problem in Synthesis," *Science*, CXX, 959–63.

1955 "Changing Man's Habitat: Physical and Biological Phenomena," pp. 31–46 in THOMAS, W. L., JR. (ed.), *Yearbook of Anthropology—1955*. New York: Wenner-Gren Foundation for Anthropological Research, Inc. 836 pp.

SHANTZ, H. L.
1954 "The Place of Grasslands in the Earth's Cover of Vegetation," *Ecology*, XXXV, No. 2, 143–51.

SHAPLEY, H. (ed.)
1953 *Climatic Change*. Cambridge, Mass.: Harvard University Press. 318 pp.

STAMP, L. D.
1952 *Land for Tomorrow: The Underdeveloped World*. Bloomington: Indiana University Press. 230 pp.

SUTTON, O. G.
1953 *Micrometeorology: A Study of Physical Processes in the Lowest Layers of the Earth's Atmosphere*. New York: McGraw-Hill Book Co. 333 pp.

THOMPSON, L. M.
1952 *Soils and Soil Fertility*. New York: McGraw-Hill Book Co. 339 pp.

THORNBURY, W. D.
1954 *Principles of Geomorphology*. New York: John Wiley & Sons. 618 pp.

THORNTHWAITE, C. W.
1953 "Topoclimatology." Seabrook, N.J.: Johns Hopkins University, Laboratory of Climatology. 13 pp. (Mimeographed.)

VERULAM, J. B. G.; ANGUS, J. H.; and CHAPLIN, S.
1952 "The Geography of Power: Its Sources and Transmission," *Geographical Journal*, CXVIII, Part 3, 251–66.

VEYRET, P.
1951 *Géographie de l'élevage*. Paris: Gallimard. 254 pp.

VIAL, A. E. L.
1952 *Alpine Glaciers*. London: Batchworth Press. 126 pp.

WEAVER, J. E.
1954 *North American Prairie*. Lincoln, Neb.: Johnsen Publishing Co. 348 pp.

WOYTINSKY, W. S. and E. S.
1953 *World Population and Production: Trends and Outlook*. New York: Twentieth Century Fund. 1,268 pp.

YERG, D. G., under direction of GRAY, D. E.
1951 *Annotated Bibliography on Snow, Ice, and Permafrost*. Wilmette, Ill.: U.S. Library of Congress, Science Division. 226 pp.

Man's Effects on the Seas and Waters of the Land

Man's Effects on the Seas and Waters of the Land

Harvests of the Seas

MICHAEL GRAHAM*

OCEANIC ECOLOGY

Taken altogether, the seas are enormous. They cover 70 per cent of the surface of the globe and are deep enough for the dry land to be submerged in them, 10,000 feet below the surface on the average (Murray, 1913, p. 30). Approximately three thousand million tons of salts, washed down in rivers, are added annually to the sea (*ibid.*, p. 47). This is as though three thousand tramp ships discharged a cargo of salt into the sea each day; and this process has been going on daily since early geological time. Every known natural element is found in sea water. About 10 per cent of the elements are combined as salts, the remainder being free ions, including a slight preponderance of the hydroxides, which make sea water slightly alkaline. The sea contains bacteria, plants, and animals, which require salts, warmth, and light, as on dry land, including minute but important quantities of nitrate and phosphate as well as some other as yet undiscovered trace elements. That some trace elements required are still undiscovered is known, because artificial sea water, however carefully made, will not support the growth of living things for long. One of the special requirements in the sea is silicate, which is used by some animals

* Mr. Graham is Director of Fishery Research in England and Wales. His publications include: *The Victoria Nyanza and Its Fisheries*, 1929; *Soil and Sense*, 1941; *The Fish Gate*, 1943; and *Human Needs*, 1951, 1955.

and by many of the microscopic plants to form shells.

There is no part of the sea water that is completely devoid of life, however deep and therefore dark it may be. It follows that somehow oxygen must reach the great depths, even down to 5,000 fathoms or more. Only in certain confined basins is the deep water devoid of oxygen, developing hydrogen sulfide and inhabited only by the suitable bacteria. That condition is found in the Black Sea and in certain fiords in which the deep water is confined by a shallow sill at the mouth of the fiord. Oxygen reaches the main areas of great depth by a circulation system. By the time warm water, which has been made more saline by evaporation in the tropics, is transported by the great current systems into the cold of high latitudes, it is already fairly well oxygenated through being stirred up with the atmosphere. With its fall of temperature in the subarctic regions, it absorbs more oxygen. As it becomes chilled, it becomes heavier than the relatively fresh water derived mainly from the melting of ice and therefore tends to sink, as, indeed, does also a quantity of mixed water, which is also well oxygenated from the component due to the melting of ice. This sunken water travels slowly toward the equatorial regions and, to oversimplify the complicated picture, rises to the surface to take the place of water driven away from the tropics by the trade winds. According to G. L. Clarke (1954, p. 250), some oceanographers think that the bottom current takes a thousand years to travel from the poles to the Equator, but that is not certainly so.

In this way life can continue at great depths—but only animal life, because plants need light (Fig. 96). Near the surface of the sea there is plenty of light, and, when other conditions are favorable, there is a growth of microscopic plants, sometimes strong enough to color the sea water green or to make

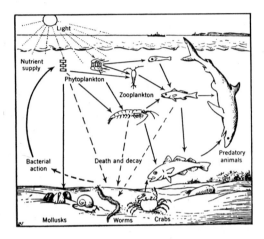

Fig. 96.—Clarke's diagram of marine ecology. A coastal type of system, which is typical of all marginal seas, is represented. In the open oceans it would be necessary to assume that the arrow bearing nutrient supply upward goes via some distant area of upwelling. It is also doubtful if any nourishment from the sea bed would reach predatory animals that also hunt near the surface, since surface-hunting animals might not care to dive to a sea bed some thousands of fathoms deep and characterized by darkness and great pressure. Murray and Hjort (1912, p. 782) cite a reputed dive of 400 fathoms by a sperm whale in distress. (From Clarke, 1954, p. 477.)

it feel slimy to the touch. As the plants grow and multiply, they make the water more opaque, and then light cannot penetrate so deeply. The layer occupied by plants varies in different areas according to how deep the light can penetrate. It is commonly some 20 meters deep in waters near the land and is not often more than 100 meters deep.

That, however, is a greater thickness of productive layer than is common on the land, where the productive layer may be not more than a few inches deep. It is, therefore, not surprising that the total "basic production" of living matter from inorganic matter is thought to be as great from the seas of the world as it is from the land (Sverdrup, cited and discussed in Graham and Kesteven, 1954).

Typically, some way below the center of gravity of the plants will be found the animals, the two groups together being termed "plankton." The animals extend to a considerable depth in some abundance. This is shown partly by the very great number of the progeny of some kinds of fish that have been found in the open ocean. In the tropics, in the "Michael Sars," Murray and Hjort (1912, p. 747) thus found the larvae of the saury pike (*Scombresox*) and horse mackerel (*Caranx*), and, in the "Dana," Tåning (1944, p. 91) similarly found an enormous number of the redfish, or ocean perch (*Sebastes*), in the more northerly latitudes of the Atlantic. The animals are continually excreting nutrients, such as phosphate, so it is not surprising that there is a vast reserve of these nutrients extending from 1,000 meters depth downward to the abysses. The concentration there is 150 milligrams or more per cubic meter, which is about four times as rich as seems to be necessary to nourish plankton in our shallow northern seas.

In and about in this whole system are the marine bacteria, class for class like those of the land, but adapted to life in sea water.

The more one learns of marine ecology, the less likely it seems that man would have any effect upon it.

Let us consider that valuable nutrient, phosphate. From G. L. Clarke (1954, pp. 302, 306) we may call the phosphate concentration below 1,000 meters depth 160 milligrams P_2O_5 per cubic meter of sea water, or 16 parts per 100 million. However, there are 118 million cubic English miles of water below 1,000 meters depth (Murray, 1913, p. 26), from which it can be calculated that the phosphate in that deep water amounts to 80,000 million tons.

Let us now suppose that there are in the world fifty million people whose water-borne sewage goes into the sea or into swiftly moving rivers and so to the sea without absorption of phosphate on the way. Each person may be taken to excrete about 3 grams of phosphate P_2O_5 per day. Let us further assume that, as water-borne sanitation spreads, so do recovery processes develop and that fifty million remains the number whose phosphate discharges into the sea. Their discharge of phosphate annually would amount to 55,000 tons. At that rate it would take 360,000 years to raise the oceanic phosphate by a quarter, which is the sort of magnitude that might be perceptible in spite of the usual spatial and temporal variations.

It might well be concluded that all man's activity can hardly alter the ocean as a whole. The issue is not, however, clear; even this vast cosmos of water is not secure. It has been established that during the present century the consumption of coal and other "fossil fuels" has been so great that the carbon dioxide content of the air has been raised by at least 10 per cent, of which the sea will slowly absorb the greater part. Whether the average concentration of carbon dioxide in the sea will be detectably higher, or whether there will in consequence be a detectable increase in production, remains to be seen. At any rate, enormous amounts of carbon dioxide stream into the sea, where it is combined, so that, in fact, the carbon is mainly held as bicarbonate (Buch, 1952, p. 44).

So much for the known effects of man on the sea as a whole—that is, considered as one uniform whole.

CONCENTRATIONS OF PRODUCTION

However, the sea is by no means one uniform whole. Although the surface water is, as we have seen, well oxygenated and although most of the lower layers are also well oxygenated, there is a middle between 200 and 800 meters in the North Atlantic where oxygen can be distinctly short (Brennecke, cited in Murray and Hjort, 1912, p. 256). Also, in summer the surface layers of water do not, in general, mix well with those below. Consequently, they tend to become exhausted of phosphate and other nutrients, owing to the growth of plants up to the limit. This surface shortage in summer probably takes place over a vast area comprising the majority of waters.[1] However, there are certain areas, such as off the west coast of America, off Alaska, in the Peru Current, and off the west coast of Africa (Benguela Current), where deep water rises at all times of the year, bearing its load of phosphate and other nutrients. In these places there is perpetually a rich plankton, with fish perpetually feeding upon it, and birds perpetually feeding on the fish and depositing their guano about the islands off the coast of Peru, making manure derived so conveniently, but unfortunately exceptionally, from the great deep store of nutrient material. Not all the nutrients in special upwelling regions are used up. Some are transported, used, and regenerated seasonally as the ocean currents carry the water from tropical to temperate and subarctic latitudes, on which in part the great fisheries in most areas with which we are familiar must make shift to sub-

1. My colleague D. H. Cushing, warns me, as indeed his predecessor, the late A. C. Gardiner, did, that it may be a considerable over-simplification to state that phytoplankton production is limited by nutrients.

sist. The other part of their nutrient supply comes from the runoff from the land. Trivial as this is on a world scale, its contribution to the marginal seas may be of the same order as that from the ocean supply. The nutrients from the two sources can, in the shallow areas, enter into local accumulation in the bed of the sea and be cyclically liberated into the overlying water, and in this way a concentration of living things occurs, forming with the upwelling areas a second source of concentrated crop for harvesting.

Thus, we have, in various favored parts of the ocean, concentrations of living things which man can use or abuse. The most spectacular example is in the story of the whales.

Early American Whaling

The organic world is arranged in pyramids, in that at each level the few at the top live by consuming the many below them. When an animal which is a higher member of the pyramid is suitable to be used by man—that is, there will be only some percentage of waste —then that animal is in danger. It has concentrated some of the greatly dispersed and thinly spread production of the seas and so is in peril (Clark, 1887, p. 6).

Had he not eaten for three days, even a conservation-minded naturalist would probably join in killing a Steller's sea cow for food, whether or not it was the last specimen on earth. At about the end of the nineteenth century this large animal, 20–30 feet long, which lived by browsing on the seaweeds of the shores of Bering Strait, became extinct (Beddard, 1902). It may be assumed that during the long watches of life in whaling and sealing ships, one or another of those engaged in the gradual reduction of the more vulnerable marine mammals realized what he was doing. But, he might argue, even if it were the last, he deserved to have it. He needed money, and, after the hardships that he

had endured in order to reach the prize, no scruple at the last stage would be strong enough to stay his hand. Whaling ships in those days were accustomed to go away for a matter of years: a year for the right-whale fishery and two years for the sperm-whale fishery, according to Howard Clark (1887, p. 6), quoting Starbuck, who wrote in 1880. Starbuck compared those prosperous days of the middle of the century with the time of writing, when ships could go away in the sperm-whaling for four or five years and return not yet fully laden with oil. Some authorities doubt this change, writing that voyages in the mid-century were just as long (Mackintosh, N. A., personal communication). The mentality that led men to endure such a life must surely have been partly akin to the hunger imagined for the conservation naturalist which would cause him to attack the last Steller's sea cow. For example, in the United States, whaling had developed in the seventeenth and eighteenth centuries on the coast of barren New England (Clark, 1887, p. 106) and in an intensity from Nantucket Island particularly that deserves enshrinement in legend rather than in sober history. We find this description of the Nantucket population (*English Annual Register*, 1775, p. 85, quoted in Clark, 1887, p. 118):

This extraordinary people, amounting to between five and six thousand in number, nine-tenths of whom are Quakers, inhabit a barren island fifteen miles long by three broad, the products of which are scarcely capable of maintaining twenty families. From the only harbour which this sterile island contains, without natural products of any sort, the inhabitants, by an astonishing industry, keep an 140 vessels in constant employment. Of these, eight were employed in the importation of provisions for the island and the rest in the whale fishery.

And as Burke said of them (*ibid.*, p. 119): "No sea but is vexed by their fisheries. No climate that is not a witness to their toils."

So important was the whaling to Nantucket that it became part of the culture pattern. It is even reported— admittedly in a work of fiction, *Miriam Coffin,* but quoted by Brown (1887, p. 220)—that the principal resolution of a secret society of young women who called themselves "freemasons" was to the effect that they would prefer a whale fisherman to any landsman and would deny any favor even to an islander until his harpoon had struck the body of a whale. This, whether myth or history, is reminiscent of customs in other parts of the world where peoples can survive only by brave actions. It is commonly said that among the Masai tribe in Kenya a young woman would not look seriously upon a man until he had bloodied his spear in a human being or in a lion.

Early European Whaling

In Europe the whale fishery seems to have developed first from the shores of the Bay of Biscay, being mentioned in privileges granted to San Sebastian in A.D. 1150 (according to Beddard, 1902, p. 360) but almost certainly belonging very much earlier in time. Whales of various kinds doubtless differ in temperament, but the testimony is clear that a right whale (Fig. 97) is a gentle, timid creature which would easily be driven ashore and killed by a sufficient number of people, whether on the Basque coast or in Charleston Harbor. Later the Dutch and others carried on fishery for a northern right whale to Spitsbergen and to other boreal and hyperboreal regions, and sperm-whaling developed in the warmer seas.

Nineteenth-Century Whaling

Clark's chart (1887, Pl. 183) shows that in the middle of the nineteenth century the seas between 80° north and 55° south latitudes were almost thickly marked with whaling grounds. A whaler finding himself unlucky on one ground would not, it seems, have had to sail for more than 1,200 miles to arrive on some other well-known ground. The variety of climate can be appreciated when some of the grounds are

Fig. 97.—Principal genera of large whales. During the last one hundred and fifty years the history of whaling has seen the transfer of attention from *Balaena* (*top*), now too scarce, to *Balaenoptera* (*bottom*), too active for the early boating. *From top to bottom:* right whale (*Balaena*), sperm whale (*Physeter*), humpback whale (*Megaptera*), rorqual or fin whale (*Balaenoptera*). (After Clark, 1887, who, in order to show the spouts, evidently drew them on reduced scale.)

named: Spitsbergen, Baffin Bay, Florida, Brazil, Kerguelen, China Sea, Bering Strait, Galápagos Islands, New Zealand. A sperm-whale ground extended all the way from California to Japan, another from Peru to the Gilbert Islands, and yet another from Chile to

Australia with hardly a break. The Arabian Sea, the waters off Ceylon, the China Sea—all contained fishable sperm whales.

According to Ayres (p. 375 of this volume), this sperm-whale fishery was quite unnecessary, equivalent products to those made from sperm oil and spermaceti being available from Burma since earliest times.

By 1880 the grounds that Clark could record as in use had, in most areas, shrunk as compared with 1850. The transpacific sperm-whale grounds were now reduced to relatively small areas in the Peru Current, with a few small spots in the Australian region. Similar shrinkage is found in the other regions mentioned in the preceding paragraph.

Arctic Whaling

On the other hand, there was also expansion—in the dangerous and arduous whale fishery for a northern right whale, the one that American whalemen called the "bowhead" and that Scoresby and the English called the "Greenland whale." That fishery was being prosecuted to beyond Point Barrow in the Beaufort Sea and in Lancaster Sound in the farthest north of Canada. On the Atlantic side there were the whalers from Europe, and on the Pacific side the American ships and officers with cosmopolitan crews.

What that arctic whaling was like can best be understood by a quotation from one of the many reports published by Howard Clark. This one is from a letter by Captain Pease, 1870 (quoted in Clark, 1887, p. 78). After being beset by ice in Bering Strait, he got his ship clear, and he writes thus:

Passed into the Arctic July, and found most of the fleet catching walrus; about a dozen ships (this one among the number) went cruising along the northern ice for bowheads. After prospecting from Icy Cape to near Herald Island, and seeing not a whale, I returned to the walrus fleet. The first ship I saw was the *Vine-*

yard, with one hundred and seventy five walrus; since then I have not seen or heard from her. This walrusing is quite a new business, and ships which had engaged in it the previous season and came up prepared were very successful. While at it, we drove business as hard as the best of them, but soon became convinced that the ship's company (taken collectively) were much inferior to many others; they could not endure the cold and exposure expected of them. I have seen boats' crews that were properly rigged, kill and strip a boat-load of walrus in the same length of time another (not rigged) would be in killing one and hauling him on the ice. We took some four hundred, making about 230 barrels. About August 2 all the ships went in pursuit of bowheads (most of them to Point Barrow). When off the Sea Horse Islands we saw a few whales working to the westward, just enough to detain us; we took two making 200 barrels; the weather cold and a gale all the time. In September I worked up about 70 miles from Point Barrow; saw quite a show of small whales in the sea; took four which made about 100 barrels. As that was a fair sample, and not having the right boys to whale in that ice, where the thermometer stood only 8 above zero, I went back to the westward. Ships that had from forty to fifty men (clad in skins) and officers accustomed to that particular kind of whaling, did well. In going back the fourth mate struck a whale which made about 70 barrels. From the 29th of September to the 4th of October we saw a good chance to get oil, had the weather been good, and a well, hardy crew. We could not cut and whale at the same time. We took four whales which would have made 500 barrels had we had good weather to boil them. On the 4th of October we put away for the straits, in company with the *Seneca, John Howland,* and *John Wells*—a gale from the northeast, and snowing. On the evening of the 7th it blew almost a hurricane; hove the ship to south of Point Hope, with maintopsail furled; lost starboard bow boat, with davits—ship covered with ice and oil. On the 10th entered the straits in a heavy gale; when about 8 miles south of the Diomedes, had to heave to under bare poles, blowing furiously, and the heaviest sea I ever saw; ship making bad weather of it; we had about 125 barrels of oil on deck, and all our fresh water; our blubber between decks in horse-pieces, and going from the forecastle to the mainmast every time she pitched, and impossible to stop it; ship covered with ice and oil; could only muster four men in a watch; decks flooded with water all the time; no fire to cook with or to warm by; made it the most anxious and miserable time I ever experienced in all my sea service. During the night shipped a heavy sea, which took off bow and waist boats, davits, slide-boards, and everything attached, staving about 20 barrels of oil. At daylight on the second day we found ourselves in 17 fathoms of water, and about 6 miles from the center cape of St. Lawrence Island. Fortunately the gale moderated a little, so that we got two close-reefed topsails and reefed courses on her, and by sundown were clear of the west end of the island. Had it not moderated as soon as it did, we should, by 10 A.M. have been shaking hands with our departed friends.

Sometimes the ships were caught by the winter ice, and the crews, including women and children whom they had taken with them, had to make their way over the ice to return as passengers in other ships, which had got clear and waited for them. There was also the hazard of losing the crew, and even the masters and officers, in San Francisco, when there was the rush for gold in California. Clark's quotations show that this offended against another feature of the culture pattern in pious New England, where the owners of the vessels were shocked that these men and officers could so abandon their trust. Indeed, I suppose that shipowners all over the world, and in all times, would agree with the writer from New England that the sailors had been put in charge of property whose value it was their duty to increase, not to render worthless. I suppose, too, that shipmen have accepted that obligation from time immemorial.

Changes in Stocks

The two kinds of whales of the classical fisheries occupy rather different positions in the pyramid of the animal world. Right whales live only on plankton, which they sieve out of the water with the much-prized whalebone, which is a horny growth in the place of teeth. Sperm whales, on the other hand, eat squids, including the giant squid, and, when struck by a harpoon, are said to dive deep, as if they normally frequent great depths.

Man has made a noticeable change in these particular forms of concentration of production—whales—a change on a truly cosmic scale. Sperm whales, it is true, have maintained their numbers wonderfully, in 1952 constituting no less than 11,526 out of 49,752 of all whales caught (Mackintosh, N. A., personal communication), and to the present day a local sperm-whale fishery is carried out from small boats by inhabitants of the Azores (Clarke, R. H., 1954). But right whales everywhere and humpbacks in some seas have become small remnants of once great populations. There is probably no change that man has made in the sea which compares in scale or importance with the reductions of the populations of right whales and humpbacks and, latterly, blue whales.

At the time when Howard Clark was drawing his chart on whaling, there was a considerable fishery for the humpback whale both in northern and in tropical seas. That fishery persisted into the present century, when it was carried especially by the Norwegians into the regions close to the antarctic ice (Hjort, 1933, p. 21).

In the Norwegian whaling from South Georgia during 1906–9, humpbacks were almost the only species taken. The catch reached its peak at over 6,000 annually in the season 1910–11, but by 1913 the catch of humpbacks was in the neighborhood for a few years or so of

500 only. From this low number it did recover, but from 1917 onward very few humpbacks were taken; instead, the fishery became dependent upon the finback whales proper. At the time Clark wrote (1880), only two whaling grounds at Iceland and to the north of Norway were marked as grounds for finback whales, that is, whales belonging to the rorqual group. In the present century the whaling industry has become almost entirely dependent upon the several species of this group, concentrating at first mainly on humpbacks, then on blue whales, and then on others of the genus *Balaenoptera*. With fast catchers and good harpoon guns, this is a powerful fishery, mainly Norwegian. From 1921 modern whaling took only six years to find, develop, and abandon the rorquals of Spain and Portugal (Hjort, 1933, p. 20), and it has dealt almost as swiftly with the humpbacks off the west coasts of Africa and of Australia (Ruud, 1952).

Sea Mammals and Eskimos

Probably the pioneer model for conservation efforts was the protection by the United States, in 1870, of the fur-seal rookeries in the Pribilof Islands. This species breeds by harems, and there are plenty of spare males pushed off the breeding plots and suitable for slaughter. Provided the slaughter is regulated, the species can be saved as a productive resource, as it has been. But, in varying degrees, populations of sea otter, white whale, narwhal, walrus, and sea elephant have been reduced by modern hunting methods.

The reduction of the populations of the arctic mammals has almost certainly had a corresponding effect on the number of Eskimos. This cannot be stated on historical evidence; but, if it is correct that certain groups of Eskimos relied on those animals for subsistence, it follows mathematically that the Eskimo population will have been reduced as the food population has been reduced. Such reduction may not have been proportional, but equally it may have been, or it may even have been more than proportional. Statistics, which have been kept only since commercial whaling developed, show an increase of population of Eskimo ancestry (Dunbar, M. E., personal communication), but that does not bear on the question of the effect of the Bering Sea whalers. Introduction of any new hunting method is liable to reduce a population of prey to equilibrium at a new lower level than before. Then the old method of hunting will no longer provide a living—in reward per day's work. Thus, I would suppose that in Europe, in early days, Neanderthal man with club and spear could have been starved out by *Homo sapiens* with bow and arrow. Reduction of Eskimos would, of course, be, by all accounts, a dead loss to the world, as the *paysan* at the North American arctic.

Modern Whaling

This history of whaling is in many respects a sad one, and it will be one of tragedy if it ends with these last resources being cut off altogether from commercial exploitation, owing to the level of the stock being too low to make the fishery worth engaging in. There is no doubt that in one way or another whale fishing has greatly benefited humanity, and, if the history proves to be a tragedy, it will have been a grand tragedy. There was the heroism of the early whaling from small shore boats hurriedly manned during the Middle Ages. Then the same hurried launching on the boundless surface of the empty ocean in the eighteenth and nineteenth centuries. Surely seamanship never rose to a greater height than in the small boats of the sailing whalers, spilled on to the sea from one thousand ships in the middle of the last century (Hjort, 1933, p. 19). And today there is the enormous commercial adventure of modern whaling, when a score of great factory ships with attendant whale-catchers, each enterprise worth a prince's ransom, set out for the antarctic and, by a narrow margin of profit, bring back in all over two million barrels of oil. This may, without offense perhaps, be compared with probably about a half-million barrels in the middle of the last century. The fishery today may be less romantic; it is certainly less cruel to men; it is certainly more productive.

Two attempts are being made to conserve this fishery to prevent a tragic ending. One is the International Whaling Commission, which deals mainly with the antarctic regions. It arose out of a conference of 1937 which met in London at the invitation of the British government. Fourteen countries adhered to the Washington Convention of 1946 and agreed to restrict the total capture to a certain number of whales, known as "blue-whale units." Provisions were also made on the opening and closing days of the season, on minimum size limits, and on protection of calves. These rules have not prevented the stock of whales from declining, as judged by the composition by species and by other signs (Ruud, 1952). Another attempt is the Santiago Agreement, concluded by Chile, Peru, and Ecuador and relating particularly to the stock of whales off the west coast of South America. It may be fortunate that these whales, mostly sperm whales, are to be protected, though it happens that the other conservation body does not think restriction of sperm-whaling justified. That confusion in whaling regulation is a comparatively simple example of the complications that arise when men try, as indeed they are trying in various fisheries in many parts of the world, to make some amends for the reckless exploitation that went with the

starvation mentality of the nineteenth century.

The history of whaling is an outstanding example of man's effect on the ocean; there is not another to match it. In no other way is the world-scale production of the ocean so concentrated as it is in the body of a whale. Nevertheless, there are changes of importance in more ordinary fisheries.

GENERAL CHANGES

It will be recalled that the layer of water where basic production takes place is usually not more than 100 meters thick. It extends all over the oceans, and below it, to an unlimited depth, it nourishes, by raining dead fragments for their consumption, various kinds of fish, cuttlefish, and other invertebrates. Where this productive layer touches the land, the bed of the sea is that much nearer and forms, as it were, a trap for the fish population, in which men can take them. That is putting it very crudely. In fact, the whole production is, as it were, trapped and made heterogeneous by the variety of conditions near the coast, so that the species of fish and other forms encountered near the land are not those characteristic of the waters of the open ocean. In consequence, all the arguments heretofore used about the vastness of the ocean cease to apply when one comes to consider the fisheries of historical importance, apart from whaling. Although it is not always easy to decide whether a stock of fish is being pressed too hard by human exploitation, there is very little doubt that fishing is, or has been, too heavy for one or two species in areas where the fish are particularly good (Fig. 98) or which are conveniently near to large markets.

Halibut

On the margins of the North Atlantic there exists the large and excellent fish, the halibut, and it is still present in small numbers from Greenland and Iceland to the North Sea and off the coasts of Norway. Numbers have been so reduced, however, that there is no longer any large and regular fishery for the halibut, although on a small scale occasional voyages are still made with halibut as a principle objective, and a carefully regulated fishery survives off Norway. The present state of the fishery seems sad to one who in his formative years heard fishermen talk proudly of their captures of these fish.

FIG. 98.—Statistical signs of overfishing. As a result of a natural expansion of the cod stock, fishing increased at Iceland, especially between 1925 and 1930 (*broken line*). The result for haddock (not on cod) was a new lower level of annual yield (*upper graph*) and of catch per unit effort (*lower graph*). (From Clarke, 1954, p. 492; his modification of Russell's version of Graham's figure!)

In the northern part of the Pacific, however, the story is very different, and this is due to the initiative and enterprise of Canada and the United States (Thompson, 1936). In the years from 1925 to 1930, North American scientists found what they considered unmistakable signs that their halibut fishery was heading in the direction that the other halibut fisheries had taken. The two governments therefore made a treaty and set up a commission, after which not only did the halibut fishery survive but the stocks on the grounds recovered and increased very greatly, so that the annual yield in recent years has been nearly 50 per cent above that when regulation was started in 1930. There is no doubt in the minds of most fishery scientists that this result is due to the self-denying regulations of the countries concerned, which ordained that fishing should stop when a prearranged quantity of halibut had been taken from each of two areas. The effect on the halibut has not, however, been to restore it exactly to what it was before large-scale fishing took place, for nearer banks are now harder fished, and so on. Man's effect has not been erased; instead, there has been restoration of a basis for a profitable fishery.

North Sea Fishes

In northern Europe the North Sea has been one of the classical fishing grounds, for more than a dozen nations, for a very long time. It is naturally a productive area, both for ground-living fish such as plaice, cod, and haddock and for "water-living" ("pelagic" is the technical term) fish such as the herring. But smack owners who had kept records could show how the annual catch *per smack* of the most valuable species fell during the period between 1860 and 1880. In the meanwhile fishing was being extended farther into the deep water, to the north, and less esteemed species such as the haddock were being brought into the market. Even for the valuable species, the *total* catch each year was not falling but was still rising somewhat. However, there can be no doubt that, even then, fishing was having an appreciable effect upon stocks of fish in the North Sea (Graham, 1943, p. 143.)

It seems rather remarkable that this should be so. In the North Sea the principal method of fishing is that of dragging a trawl along the bed of the sea, and, if one works out the number of days trawlers are absent in a year and the area that they can draw their nets over during this period, one finds that the North Sea is fished over but once during the course of a year. Evidently, the fish are highly localized, and evidently the fishermen know their grounds and routes. From about 1925 to 1938 and again since about 1950, but not quite so severely, the stocks have been so low that trawlers have operated on the basis of a minimum possible profit. The hard life of fishing is not, then, attractive. Hours are long, a hundred a week compared with the landsman's forty to fifty; separation from home is painful; and the physical conditions are hard. Now, the unprofitableness is self-created. This was demonstrated when during World Wars I and II the virtual cessation of fishing led to three- or four- or fivefold increases in weight density of stocks (Clark, 1948). That was due to greater survival in the absence of fishing and was shown partly in greater numbers and partly in greater average size of fish. The same story is more or less true for all regions neighboring the British Isles and for some stocks farther afield, including one or two—haddock and plaice—in such productive areas as Iceland (Fig. 98).

That history has been amply documented, as the references in Graham (1952) show. It has also been discussed at length for a half-century, and an attempt is being made to improve the situation by introduction of mesh regulations and size limits on fish. For that purpose an international permanent commission was established under the London Convention of 1946, and regulations were put into force in 1954. However, it is not easy to devise suitable remedies for the situation when a half-dozen valuable species overlap in distribution and are caught with a great variety of fishing gear by peoples of many nations. A similar convention between Great Britain and France in 1839, which faced some of the same difficulties, was a failure (Johnstone, 1905, pp. 7–8). But, with more nations involved, there is probably a stronger international will to succeed, and the fishing interests appear to look on the convention hopefully and as merely a beginning toward obtaining better fishing from these excellent stocks of fish.

In a few places in the world, then, man has altered the ecology of the sea sufficiently to cause himself considerable embarrassment and is struggling to reinstate productivity. For many other regions the condition is that, although the catch of fish per unit effort is falling, there is no sign that fishing is really too hard; the total yield is being maintained or rising. These two quantities do not go together all the way; indeed, the largest catch per unit effort is obtained when there is only one ship engaged in a fishery, and usually the largest total yield is obtained when there are so many ships at work that none of them can get a reasonable living.

Changes in Conditions for Species

Earlier in this chapter it was concluded that phosphate in the runoff from the land could not appreciably affect the deep reserve in the sea, considered as a whole. That is true. Nevertheless there can be local effects. It has been found in the sea outside the vast conurbation of London (nine million souls) that the phosphate is often higher than can be explained by contributions from deeper water coming from the north or from the west through the English Channel (Graham, 1938). There can be little doubt that this high phosphate is utilized by microscopic plants, one species in particular being found in that neighborhood. It is called the Chinese *Biddulphia*, because it came to Europe in the early part of the century, apparently carried on the bottoms of ships trading from the China

Seas. Early in 1955 *Biddulphia* was found in the stomachs of minute plaice larvae (Shelbourne, J. E., verbal communication), and, although it was not the commonest organism present, it may well be that it does contribute to the survival of the plaice, at a vital moment in its career, when its own yolk is almost used up and when it

useful way of using the nutrients in human sewage, although, indeed, it is a venerable and respectable method in ancient China.

Mention of *Biddulphia sinensis* is a reminder of a number of exotic marine species taken from one part of the ocean to another on ships' bottoms, or in ballast, or with transplanted shell-

Fig. 99.—Graham's manifesto on rational fishing. On the left the stock is held steady under a rate of fishing (instantaneous, or logarithmic, rate) three times that on the right and costing, therefore, something like three times as much to generate. But the right-hand state produces as great a weight of fish as the left, without counting the older survivors that extend off the page to the right. The fish are also a better run of sizes. Also, it is assumed, perhaps pessimistically, that when the stock is allowed to be more numerous, as on the right, only an equal number of recruits, twenty, is still found. (From Clarke, 1954, p. 347.)

must find some other suitable food to give it energy to grow and survive.

There must be other places in the world where sewage from cities has some effect of the same kind on the fisheries. However, we may hope that concentrations of people to set up such effects will not become more but less common, and the recovery as fish cannot be regarded as necessarily the most

fish. More interesting, perhaps, is the passage of species through the Suez Canal, including about twenty Red Sea species of fish, which have had the help of the current in the canal (Ben-Tuvia, 1953).

So much for some of the effects that man has had on the ocean in the past. Let us now consider what effects man could have in the future.

PROSPECT

Strange as it may seem, it is possible that the yield of whales could be increased by fishing for them rather less hard. There are no data showing such a possibility for whales, and indeed it may not be so. Nevertheless, it is possible, sometimes, to obtain a better crop of any living resource by a smaller rate of exploitation, as can be exemplified perhaps by considering fish rather than whales.

Rational Fishing

In the 1930's fishery naturalists became aware that the possibility had

let us consider that 20 fish represent a stock—which might really number 200 million—with young fish coming in and old ones dying or being caught, but the number yet remaining constant, just as, in even a swift stream, a pool can retain the same level. In this case, which is quite realistic for hard-fished stocks, we suppose that a rate of fishing of 0.80 holds the stock level, that is, the average annual catch is 80 per cent of the average stock. The resulting age census might be as in Table 2, which also shows average weights of fish. The catch would be 0.8 × 20 fish, of an average weight of 46/20 kilo-

TABLE 2

CENSUS OF FISH BY AGE, NUMBER, AND WEIGHT
(AVERAGE ANNUAL CATCH, 80 PER CENT)

	AGE							TOTAL
	I	II	III	IV	V	VI	VII	
No.	6	4	3	3	2	1	1	20
Average weight (in kilograms)	0.17	1	2	3	5	7	9	....
Weight of stock	1	4	6	9	10	7	9	46

arrived of controlling the yield of a fishery by controlling the rate of fishing (Fig. 99). Since then the theory has been worked out in great detail—indeed, transformed—by Beverton and Holt (1956). A childish example will serve to show the principle on which fishery management is now supposed to work, and undoubtedly does, to a first approximation at least.

It will be readily granted that, if one agent of death becomes able by its rate of fishing to claim more fish than die by all other agencies put together, then that agent has control of the average age of the stock of fish; and the "life-table" of the fish substantially is under that agent's control.

Having thus agreed that the rate of fishing could control the average age,

grams, which is 0.8 of 46 kilograms, or 36.8 kilograms.

Now, let us suppose that a rate of 0.70 would allow the census to alter to the steady level shown by age and number in Table 3. Then, using the same average weights, and one extra for the oldest fish, the weights of stock would be as shown as in Table 3, and the new catch would be 0.7 × 74, or 51.8 kilograms. That is a gain in yield and shows how fishing *less* can catch a *greater* weight.

If one looks closely at this comparison, one can see that the gain is not automatic. The lower of the fishing rates, which allows greater survival to form a heavier stock, also takes less of that stock, and the gain cannot increase indefinitely. For example, it is difficult to conceive of a 1 per cent rate of fishing giving a high annual catch; a 0 per cent rate certainly could not.

In order that the arithmetic in the example might be followed easily, I used convenient imaginary data. In Table 4, however, are the values for some North Sea species for a fishery using a trawl mesh 70 millimeters on the gauge.

gious number of seeds. Fish must lie somewhere in between on this debatable ground; many have an enormous number of eggs, some two to four million in the cod, for example, and for this species it must happen but rarely that a shortage of spawners is of great significance at the levels of stock that allow any fishery at all. In other species it may be that the hazards of larval

TABLE 3

CENSUS OF FISH BY AGE, NUMBER, AND WEIGHT
(AVERAGE ANNUAL CATCH, 70 PER CENT)

	AGE								TOTAL
	I	II	III	IV	V	VI	VII	VIII	
No.	6	5	4	4	3	2	1	1	26
Weight of stock	1	5	8	12	15	14	9	10	74

TABLE 4*

RELATIVE YIELDS OF PLAICE, HADDOCK, AND COD

FISH	RATE OF FISHING			
	0.70	0.50	0.30	0.20
Plaice	196	212	217	197
Haddock	134	137	125	112
Cod	1,030	1,440	2,100	2,450

* Source: Beverton and Holt, 1956.

It will be noticed that the hypothetical example used has allowed nothing for an increase in the rate of reproduction as the result of allowing the stock to become heavier. There were still only six of the youngest class of fish allowed to enter the fishery. For mammals and birds it is probable that the main burden of the conservationists should be to make sure that sufficient young are being born. By way of contrast, for many plants it is certainly unnecessary to worry greatly about the seeding rate, and this probably applies to a good many lowly organisms, some of which have a prodi-

life are so great that a heavy seeding is important.

Thus, one of the effects that man can have on the sea is to arrange that it is populated with fish rather younger than those naturally present but rather older than those left in an overfished stock. For mankind, this would mean a somewhat greater annual production of food and very considerable reduction in the effort expended to obtain it.

Latent Resources

1. There are certain areas even on the high seas where something even

more like animal husbandry could be cf value. In the middle of the North Sea there is an ancient island, now submerged to a depth of from 30 to 60 feet, called the Dogger Bank. It has an area of 6,214 square nautical miles; if it were a rectangle, it could be 113 statute miles long by 70 broad. That area is for the most part well furnished with razor clams and other small clam species, which afford first-class food for plaice. The main plaice nurseries on the continental coasts are, however, separated from the Dogger Bank by deeper water, which the young plaice do not seem very willing to cross. At any rate, the Dogger Bank remains under-stocked. When plaice of a suitable size are transplanted from the coast to the Dogger Bank, their growth rate in a linear dimension is doubled, which means that their rate of increase in weight is multiplied about eight times. Obviously it would not do to crowd the Dogger Bank with young fish; but it is usually thought that it would pay to plant the Dogger Bank with young plaice. There may be other areas of the high seas that are amenable to similar treatment. Certainly there are a number of estuaries and inshore areas where cultivation of fish or shellfish could greatly be increased.

2. There has been for several years a good deal of rather naïve speculation on the subject of making a mechanical whale, to filter out vast quantities of plankton and make them into human food or cattle food. This does not seem very sensible, compared with obtaining the free services of herrings, which eat plankton and therefore concentrate the product in a form in which man can obtain it more freely. Nor does it seem particularly promising to place nutrient salts in the sea in order to obtain greater growth of plankton and fish, although that has been done in salt-water lochs.

3. One enormous source of valuable substances that is hardly touched at present is the food of the lost Steller's sea cow, namely, the seaweeds. But using them more will not alter the ocean appreciably, confined as they are to coastal regions.

4. One attractive major project might conceivably become practicable. That is to use atomic or other energy to initiate an upwelling current from the deep basic store of phosphate in some of the tropical areas that are at present barren, compared with those fortunate places where there is naturally an upwelling cool water rich in nutrients (Cooper and Steven, cited by Finn, 1954, p. 492).

5. Alternatively, or in addition, it may be possible to fish some of the larger animals that do already, we believe, take advantage of the descent of organic matter to the depths and concentrate it. There is the vast population of redfish in the North Atlantic already referred to, and there may be enormous numbers of black scabbard fish in more southern latitudes; but the biggest numbers of all would surely be those of the squids, which formerly supported such a large population of sperm whales. Possibly, however, strict regulation of sperm-whaling might produce the same result more efficiently.

THE GREAT MATRIX

It seems that the effect of man on the ocean has been small, that there remain relatively untouched sources of wealth, and that, even if these are greatly exploited in the future, the ocean will remain much as it is and has been during the human epoch. It may be rash to put any limit on the mischief of which man is capable, but it would seem that those hundred and more million cubic miles of water, containing every natural chemical element and probably every group of bacteria, supporting every phylum of animals, moving on the surface from the Equator toward the poles, and returning below, stirred to many fathoms depth by the wind—it would, indeed, seem that here at the beginning and the end is the great matrix that man can hardly sully and cannot appreciably despoil.

ACKNOWLEDGMENT.—I wish to thank Dr. N. A. Mackintosh, of the National Institute of Oceanography (in England), for help with part of what I have written about whales; and also the editorial staff of the Wenner-Gren Foundation for many thoughtful and constructive suggestions on presentation, most of which have been embodied above.

REFERENCES

BEDDARD, F. E.
　1902 "Mammalia," pp. 269–385 in *The Cambridge Natural History,* Vol. X. London: Macmillan & Co., Ltd. 605 pp.

BEN-TUVIA, A.
　1953 *Mediterranean Fishes of Israel.* (Sea Fisheries Research Station, Bulletin No. 8.) Caesarea. 40 pp.

BEVERTON, R. J. H., and HOLT, S. J.
　1956 *On the Dynamics of Exploited Fish Populations.* ("Fishery Investigations," Series II, Vol. XIX.) (In press.)

BROWN, J. T.
　1887 "Vessels, Apparatus, and Methods of the [Whale] Fishery," pp. 218–93 in BROWN, GOODE, et al., *The Fisheries and Fishery Industries of the United States,* Sec. V, Vol. II, Part XV, No. 2. 2 vols. Washington, D.C.: U.S. Commission on Fish and Fisheries. 217 pp.

BUCH, K.
　1952 "The Cycle of Nutrient Salts and Marine Production," pp. 36–47 in *Conseil Permanent International pour l'Exploration de la Mer,* Rapport Jubilaire CXXXII, No. 3. Copenhagen: Andr. Fred. Høst & Fils. 85 pp.

CLARK, A. H.
　1887 "History and Present Condition of the Whale Fishery," No. 1 in BROWN, GOODE, et al., *The Fisheries and Fishery Industries of the United States,* Sec. V, Vol. II, Part XV. 2 vols. Washington, D.C.: U.S. Commission of Fish and Fisheries. 217 pp.

CLARK, R. S. (ed.)
　1948 "Effect of the War on the Stocks of Commercial Fishes," pp. 1–62 in *Conseil Permanent International pour l'Exploration de la Mer,* Rapport Ju-

bilaire CXXII, No. 3. Copenhagen: Andr. Fred. Høst & Fils. 85 pp.

CLARKE, G. L.
　1954 *Elements of Ecology.* New York: John Wiley & Sons; London: Chapman & Hall, Inc. 534 pp.

CLARKE, R. H.
　1954 "Open Boat Whaling in the Azores," *Discovery Reports,* XXVI, 281–355. Cambridge.

FINN, D. B.
　1954 "The Sea and World Food Supplies," *Nutrition Abstracts and Reviews,* XXIV, 487–96. Aberdeen.

GRAHAM, M.
　1938 *Distribution of Phosphate in 1934–1936.* ("Fishery Investigations," Series II, Vol. XVI, No. 3.) London. 30 pp.
　1943 *The Fish Gate.* London: Faber & Faber, Ltd. 196 pp.
　1952 "Overfishing and Optimum Fishing," pp. 72–78 in *Conseil Permanent International pour l'Exploration de la Mer, Rapport Jubilaire* CXXXII, No. 3. Copenhagen: Andr. Fred. Høst & Fils. 85 pp.

GRAHAM, M., and KESTEVEN, G. L.
　1954 "Biological Possibilities in World Fisheries," *Food and Agricultural Organization of the United Nations, Fisheries Bulletin,* VII, No. 1, 1–13. Rome.

HJORT, J.
　1933 "Whales and Whaling," *Hvalrådets Skrifter,* No. 7, pp. 7–29. Oslo.

JOHNSTONE, J.
　1905 *British Fisheries: Their Administration and Their Problems.* London: Williams & Norgate. 350 pp.

MURRAY, SIR JOHN
　1913 *The Ocean.* 2d ed. London: Williams & Norgate. 256 pp.

MURRAY, SIR JOHN, and HJORT, J.
  1912 *The Depths of the Ocean.* London: Macmillan & Co., Ltd. 821 pp.
RUUD, J. T.
  1952 "Modern Whaling and Its Prospects," *Food and Agriculture Organization of the United Nations, Fisheries Bulletin,* V, No. 5, 165–83. Rome.
TÅNING, A. V.
  1944 "On the Breeding Places and Abundance of the Red Fish *(Sebastes)* in the North Atlantic," *Conseil Permanent International pour l'Exploration de la Mer, Journal,* XVI, No. 1, 85–95. Copenhagen.
THOMPSON, W. F.
  1936 "Conservation of the Pacific Halibut," *Smithsonian Report for 1935,* pp. 361–82. Washington, D.C.: Government Printing Office.

Influences of Man upon Coast Lines

JOHN H. DAVIS[*]

Coastal regions are the most continually changing zones of the earth. In them many ceaseless and great forces and processes of nature are at play on a large scale, and man for all his efforts has had relatively little effect on them. He has, however, promoted some coastal modifications by indirect influences upon a number of natural processes and accomplished some direct modifications, of which the reclamation of land from the sea has been the most notable.

Many geologic processes are involved in the coastal conflict zone between the land and the sea, such as degradation and aggradation, diastrophic uplift and depression, faulting, slipping and thrusting, glaciation, vulcanism, and eustatic changes in sea level. Animals, such as corals and shellfish, and plants, such as mangrove-swamp forests and dune grasses and shrubs, take part in the struggle. The atmosphere joins in the fray by processes of slow weathering and the impact of violent storms that hurl the sea at the land. Many currents in the sea, tides that ebb and flow, and even the salinity and temperature of the water affect the coast. Rivers from the vast interiors of the continents bring down loads of sediments, glaciers gouge out shores, and many materials are dumped into the sea in great volume by these and other agents. Therefore, these tremendous forces and processes need review before considering the influences of man upon coast lines.

GEOLOGIC FEATURES AND PROCESSES

The term "coast line" as used here includes features of both the coast and the shore line. "Coast" usually designates wide zones involving both land and water, across which shifts the shore line, as the active narrow zone of contact between the land and the sea. "Coast" includes in its seaward part the tidal, littoral areas and some of the shallow, shoal-water areas and in its landward part the strand and some other parts of the coastal plain.

Many types of coasts have been distinguished and classified on the bases of their form and development. Some familiar ones are advancing coasts compared to retreating coasts; submerging coasts compared to emerging coasts; and drowned coasts compared to uplifted coasts. Processes of marine erosion or retrogradation contrast with processes of deposition, progradation, or aggradation. These are stressed in some classifications of types, such as by Cotton (1954), who proposed three main kinds: (1) retrograding; (2) prograding by alluviation; and (3) prograding by beach-building. Many cliff-type retreating coasts are good examples of the first type, delta coasts are examples of the second, and strand

* Dr. Davis is Professor of Botany at the University of Florida, Gainesville. He was research associate of the Florida Geological Survey, 1941–46; visiting professor, Auckland University College, New Zealand, 1950. His publications include: "The Ecology and Geologic Role of Mangroves in Florida," 1940; *The Natural Features of Southern Florida*, 1942; *The Peat Deposits of Florida*, 1946; and "Biotic Changes in New Zealand Science," 1954.

coasts with beaches and dunes are examples of the third. But any one of these types may change to one of the others, and cycles of change are the rule over long periods. In addition to these, there are compound coasts that combine the features of two or more of these three types, and there are coasts termed "neutral" that occur where very slow or no particular processes seem in progress.

In general, there is a geomorphic cycle of coastal development during which depositional and erosional forms develop through a sequence. Spits and bars are typical depositional features, and cliffs, some headlands, and many deep-water embayments are erosional features. The littoral and continental shelf sediments also shift about in cycles.

Some coasts have been classified (Price, 1954) as high-energy coasts, where the wave, tide, wind, and other factors are intense and processes of change are rapid. In contrast, other such coasts are classified as low-energy coasts, where forces are moderate or small. The high-energy type produces either a high relief retrograding coast or a dune-forming prograding coast. The low-energy type is generally of low relief with shallow lagoons and embayments.

There are also a few distinctive type coastal forms, such as coral-reef coasts, volcanic coasts, and glacial coasts. The coral-reef coasts are very extensive in the tropical regions; the glacial, in the polar regions. The retrograding and prograding features of any of these are very complex.

Other complexities of the coastal processes are the factors of uplift and of depression of the land. Both are usually due to active diastrophism that is very difficult to determine, especially when eustatic changes in sea level occur at the same time. The uplifting process is taking place in parts of north-

ern Europe and North America, where there is postglacial rebound due to the diminishing of glacial ice; and a downward depression of land is in progress in some regions, such as in parts of New Zealand.

Man has been associated with most of these coastal forms and processes, has modified a few forms, and has influenced a few processes. He has not been very effective along the high-energy coasts. In general, most of his effectiveness has been along the prograding, outbuilding coasts in regions of low coastal energy, where the changes have been slow and where he could cope with the other forces of nature. On some of the degrading, retrograding, and submerging coasts man has built strong structures, such as port and channel establishments, lighthouses, and forts, but only a few of these along high-energy coasts have withstood for long the ravages of the sea.

During the whole Pleistocene period there were four or five major glacio-eustatic oscillations in sea level, resulting particularly in rises during interglacial periods, which have been estimated by geologists and other scientists (Cooke, 1938; Russell, 1940). Paleolithic man was probably associated with one of these periods of sea-level change, and modern man has, since the last glacial period, encountered a slow but sure sea-level rise. This rise has not been continuous but has been interrupted by stillstands or slight recessions. At present the rate of rise seems relatively greater (Anonymous, 1952, p. 11) than at other postglacial times, probably owing to a recently accelerated increase in the melting of glaciers. This was the case, for instance, during the Peorian interglacial period of the "Pamlico Sea," when a rise of about 25 feet occurred.

Without being fully aware of it, man has been combating the eustatic rise of sea level in many areas. He also has encountered land uplift or depression in a number of regions. But, in general, such changes have been so slow that they would not have influenced his activities even if he had been aware of them. The recent period of rise of the sea and its very slow invasion of the land should, however, be taken into consideration when estimating the long-term effects of man upon coast-line changes in some regions; and it is possible that man may have actively to combat sea-level changes, if they become more rapid, in future land reclamations from the sea that he may undertake.

BIOLOGIC AND OTHER FEATURES AND PROCESSES

Life in the intertidal, littoral zone and over shoal-water areas is very abundant and varied, as is also life on the strand dunes, cliffs, and similar areas above the tides. All these organisms are of some effect in coastal processes, but some, such as the shellfish and corals of the shallow-sea areas and the plants of the strand dunes and salt marshes or mangrove swamps, are particularly important. The dune-forming and dune-holding plants play an important role over extensive areas of land, and the corals build enormous reefs and actively form new land areas. Even the algal growth, most significant as the initial part of the sea's food chain of productivity of organisms, is important in some regions in both coastal processes.

Man has used or influenced these organisms in many ways, especially the shellfish that have been a part of his food supply for ages. He has for various purposes changed the coastal marshes and mangrove swamps, reclaiming many of the former for agricultural purposes. He has used plants to stabilize dunes, and recently he has dumped waste and other polluting materials into the sea in such large quantities that these have had influences on the local fauna and flora.

The atmosphere has been influential mainly through violent storms that in a few short hours have undone the efforts of man over centuries. Winds, alternating cold and warm conditions creating ice and then its melting, and the slow weathering processes of the atmosphere have all been significant. These and other factors will not be enumerated further.

THE HUMAN FACTOR

Our present concern is the relatively small role of man as one of the biologic factors. Although insignificant as compared to much greater natural processes, man has been influential upon some coast-line areas and upon some processes which are in many instances very important to him. Man is also partly a product of the complex environment of coastal regions, along which he has engaged in many varied activities for thousands of years. In his relation to the coasts, sea, and land he may be classified into three ecological types, each of which in some way affects differently from the others the coast-line processes and forms, namely, (1) *maritime* men; (2) *coastal* men; and (3) *inland* men.

Maritime men are similar to pelagic animals because they are dependent mainly upon the open sea for their livelihood. Their use of coastal land areas has been mainly as domiciles and ports, and some of the structures of their great ports have persisted for centuries. In some cases their establishments have aided in the stabilization and enlargement of areas upon which they were built, especially the lighthouses and forts. These port, channel, and other structures erected by maritime men are discussed more fully by Klimm in the chapter that follows.

Coastal men are those who claim and use both the land near the sea and the shallow-water areas of the sea. Their commerce and fishing are usually near shore. They catch fish, gather shellfish, and build towns and villages on the strand and in small embayments. Their coastal activities have been so numerous and varied that their total effect has been significant. One of their most persistent activities has been the building of shell mounds, which are large piles chiefly of refuse resulting from various uses of shellfish. These mounds are so extensive on the Atlantic coast from Newfoundland to Florida and on the coast of the Gulf of Mexico that in some parts they occur along as much as 10 per cent of the shore line. They also occur in many other parts of the world. Many of these mounds have been instrumental both in holding the coast line against retrogression and in aiding progression. Coastal men also engage in some agriculture, particularly in conjunction with inland men crowded toward the sea by population pressure. These two have carried out some of the great projects of land reclamation from the sea.

Inland men have been afraid of the sea because it was strange to them, and the term "landlubber" suits them admirably. However, they have sought the sea or been forced toward it for a number of reasons—for pleasure, recreation, commerce, and agriculture. Their activities near or at the sea have grown in proportion with increases of population and with increased desire for recreation, made possible by rising standards of living. They have built cottages and fashionable hostelries along some coasts to avoid the heat of summer or the cold of winter, and such activities have become very extensive in areas such as Florida, California, and the Mediterranean. These structures often rest on dunes or on filled-in areas of the tidelands, and numerous groins, jetties, sea walls, and other devices have been constructed to protect this valuable property from the erosive forces of the sea (Fig. 100). The agricultural activities of inland men have impelled them to undertake some great land reclamations, especially in the Low Countries of Europe. For thousands of years they have taken advantage of good soils of delta regions and have influenced delta development at the mouths of many great rivers, such as the Tigris-Euphrates, Nile, Po, and Ganges.

DIRECT AND INDIRECT INFLUENCES

Many of the efforts by these three ecological types of men to improve their lot on the earth have had both direct and indirect influence on coast-line changes. Direct efforts have been made mainly toward harbors and channels, some agricultural reclamation developments, and the retardation of erosion along beach and dune areas. In these connections some of the progradational geologic processes that were present have been encouraged, but in most cases man has merely fought back the retrograding activities of the sea. Since the ancient past, maritime and coastal men have been most instrumental in these direct influences, but recently inland men have increased their direct efforts, especially in agriculture and in the prevention of beach and dune erosion.

In general, the indirect influences have been so well integrated with, or submerged in, the geologic and other processes of nature that they are very obscure and difficult to calculate quantitatively. They include some activities of inland men that occur far inland, such as deforestation, farming, and mining in the drainage basins of the rivers that enter the sea. Such activities result in soil erosion, which is reflected by increases in river sedimentation and the extension of coasts at the mouths of many rivers; but the amount of such increases is very difficult to estimate. Fishing activities, for both shellfish and swimming fish and including the culture of fish, have had mainly an indirect influence. Pollution of waters by urban and manufacturing developments has greatly increased since the industrial revolution, particularly in areas of Western civilization, and some effects are apparent in coastal changes. For example, perhaps the most indirect effects are seen in the few cases of radical upset of the biological balance in nature, such as disturbance of coastal shellfish and bird life.

Man, in fact, is part of the total of

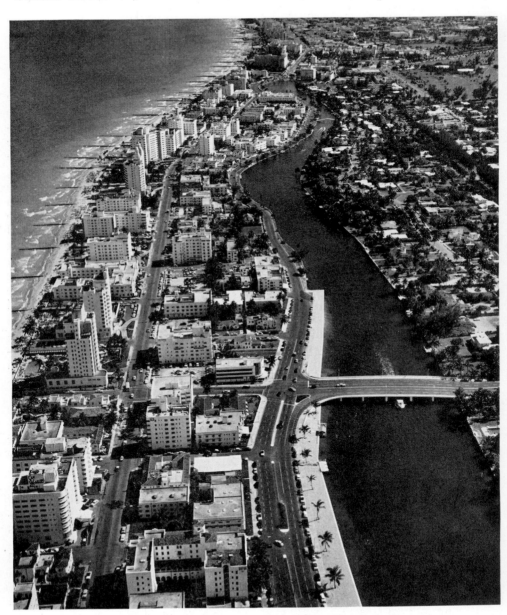

FIG. 100.—Miami Beach, Florida. To the left are numerous resort hotels on the dune-strand areas and the groins built to control beach erosion; to the right of the lagoon is the area of homes that are built on land reclaimed from littoral mangrove swamps.

natural forces, and he acts within a complexly integrated whole of natural processes. For this reason many of his activities indirectly affect numerous conditions along the coasts. Farming in the flood-plain and delta areas has had both direct and indirect effects, but how and how much is uncertain. We know little of the total or multiple effects of all these indirect activities, and it will be difficult to predict some of the future influences. We might expect that the large-scale use of atomic, fissionable materials would upset many of the biological balances in nature as well as have some direct topographic effect on such particular areas as those in the Pacific, where bomb tests have recently been made. The following descriptions exemplify types of human activities that have either directly or indirectly modified coast lines of particular areas.

SOME REGIONS OF PROLONGED CHANGES

Some of the oldest continuous civilizations have flourished along rivers where sediments in their valleys and at their deltas furnished alluvial materials useful for both agriculture and urban development. Some notable examples are the Mesopotamian region of the Tigris and Euphrates rivers, the Po River Delta region of Italy, the Nile Valley and Delta, the Ganges Valley and Delta, and the Hwang Ho, or Yellow River, Valley. The civilizations of the Volga, Danube, Rhone, and Rhine rivers in Europe and of the Mississippi in America have in some cases been of relatively short duration, but they also have affected sedimentation at the river mouths. Of these, the greatest continued changes probably have occurred in the Mesopotamian region, which involves the Persian Gulf as well as the

1. Many sources have been used for history and changes in Mesopotamia, among which are: Strabo (1917–50), Ritter (1843), Rawlinson (1854), Putzger (1931), Hogg (1910–11), and personal correspondence (1954) with Youseph al-Jebori of Baghdad.

two rivers and their valleys. Shorter-term changes are noticeable in northern Italy along the Adriatic Sea.

Mesopotamia and the Persian Gulf

Lowland areas that lie between and flank the Tigris and Euphrates rivers inland from the head of the Persian Gulf have been the home of a number of ancient and modern civilizations. The coast line in this region has changed during recorded history (Fig. 101), and

Fig. 101.—Changes in the mouths of the Tigris and Euphrates rivers and in the Persian Gulf area since the seventh century B.C. (After Putzger, 1931, and other atlases.)

the civilizations have had some effects on these changes.[1] The main human influences have been canal irrigation, drainage, and farming systems along and between these two rivers, which have affected the alluviation and other changes in the region and at the mouths of the rivers entering the Persian Gulf. This region has supported large populations that have done much construction and farming.

Geologic evidence shows that the Persian Gulf shore line, during an interglacial period, was probably above Ramadi at Hit on the Euphrates River and above Baghdad on the Tigris River. At this time human activity had little effect on it. However, during the Sumerian culture period, perhaps as early as 4000 B.C., the development of irrigation canals began, and records of the shore line of the Persian Gulf during the second and third millenniums B.C. indicate that the mouth of the Euphrates was located near Eridu and Lagash, probably before 3000 B.C. Pliny and other historians noted that the Euphrates had a separate mouth to the gulf until about the seventh century B.C. and that the men of Erech dammed this mouth. Ur is noted in some old descriptions as the chief seaport of the Sumerians.

The present, single river, the Shatt-al-Arab, that takes the waters of both the Tigris and the Euphrates to the Persian Gulf, is about 123 miles long, and the combined river flood plain and delta region from ancient Ur and Lagash to the present delta mouth covers more than 2,000 square miles. The Shatt-al-Arab Delta in modern times, between 1793 and 1833, extended itself near Fao at the rate of 53 feet per annum, according to Rawlinson (1854). Other estimates of Mesopotamian delta increase indicate a linear extension of nearly 180 miles from the ancient mouth of the Euphrates River to the present mouth of the Shatt-al-Arab during a period of about forty-five hundred years. The rate of the extension of the delta now seems to be about a mile per seventy years, which is slower than the older rate of change if 180 miles of land were added in forty-five hundred years.

Although all these distances, areas, and time intervals are but approximate estimates, nevertheless the total land area developed in the ancient embayment of the Persian Gulf has been great. Progressive delta and river deposition, mainly by alluviation, has been responsible for most of the great plain of Mesopotamia, covering some 35,000 square miles and with a gradient of only some 100 feet from Baghdad to the sea. This plain is below sea level over large areas that are now inland from the delta, and many marshes and lakes occur on it. The two rivers have shifted their courses over the plain, in some instances encouraged or made by man, such as the shift accomplished by King Rim-sin when he straightened a few miles of the Euphrates. The Tigris has changed less than the Euphrates. Both rivers almost converged just south of Baghdad when early irrigation by canals was begun, and the canals probably extended between the two rivers. The Euphrates has progressively shifted west and southwest since that time. It has the greater load of sediments and has built up the larger riverine deposits.

In addition to this ancient type of irrigation farming and city development, there were upland, inland activities that had their indirect effects. The hills and mountains of northern Iraq and Iran and adjacent countries were denuded of their forests, and grasslands deteriorated over many centuries of use and exploitation by numerous civilizations. Erosion over these uplands increased the sedimentary loads of the rivers, and this probably increased the alluviation in the plain of Mesopotamia, especially by floods, which at present occur between February and June, when melting snow and rains convey heavy loads of red mud to the rivers. There is some evidence that these annual floods formerly did not occur. In the old records and legends of Sumeria and Babylonia there are no references to floods, which suggests that floods probably followed the advent of intensive settlement and agriculture that led to eroded uplands.

Some effects of canals and irrigation in retarding sediment at the delta mouths of these rivers are shown for three periods in the history of Mesopotamia. From the beginning of the Christian Era to about the ninth century A.D. the canal systems were neglected; the few records of this period indicate a greater formation of delta than before the canal systems were extensively used. During the five-century period of the caliphate that followed, canals and cultivation were extensively developed; delta formation, together with coastal extension, decreased. The Mongol invasions abruptly ended this period with the destruction of most of the irrigation system; ever since, the rate of the coastal extension has been greater than during the caliphate period.

It seems, therefore, that a complex of many direct and indirect activities has affected the long-term development of Mesopotamian coastal extension. The direct effects have been very few, and, while some of the canal and other agricultural activities have indirectly retarded rather than accelerated the natural processes of progradation of land into the sea, inland devastation has accomplished an increase in this progradation.

The Italian–Adriatic Sea Coastal Region

The Italian coast from south of Ravenna north and eastward almost to Trieste has been extending itself into the Adriatic Sea for at least twenty centuries (Putzger, 1931). This region was described at about the time of Christ by the Greek geographer Strabo (1917–50, pp. 309, 313–15) as follows: "Now this whole country is filled with rivers and marshes. . . . Of the cities here, some are wholly island, while others are only partly surrounded by water." He noted about the ancient city of Ravenna that "at tides the city receives no small portion of the sea, so that, since the filth is all washed out by these . . . the city is relieved of foul air." Today this city is 6 miles inland, and most of the other ancient coastal cities, such as Adria and Aquileia, are also inland. Brown reports (1910–11) that the encroachment of land on the sea has been at the rate of about 3 miles in a thousand years,

which amounts to approximately 200 square miles of increase in land area along this coast since about 200 B.C.

As noted by Brown (*ibid.*, p. 995), "a strong current sets round the head of the Adriatic from east to west. This current catches the silt brought down by the rivers and projects it in long banks, or *lidi*, parallel with the shore. In process of time, as in the case of Venice, these banks raised themselves above the level of the water and became the true shoreline, with lagoons behind them."

Most of this Italian coastal extension has been by the action of this Adriatic Sea current on the sediments brought down by the rivers, particularly the Po, which has helped fill in the lagoons formed behind the barrier *lidi*—and has built deltas. The activities of man on the upland watersheds drained by these rivers have been long, and his intensive agriculture, causing denudation and increasing the sediments of the rivers, has promoted progradation. In this way man has indirectly aided in extending the Italian coast line.

Other Changes in Delta Regions

Many other delta regions in Asia and Europe have been affected, but reliable information about most of them is very fragmentary. There has probably been some extension of the Nile Delta: archeological evidence indicates that man has occupied it since before the dynasties, and cultivation in the delta has been intensive and of long duration. Since the building of the city of Alexandria, just prior to the Christian Era, all but two of the seven distributaries of the Nile over this delta have become filled or nearly filled, though no appreciable extension of the coast has been recorded recently.

The Mississippi River Delta has probably accelerated its extension since the advent of European man into the mid-continent areas of North America. Inland deforestation, soil erosion, straightening of the river channel, and pollution have been indirect causes of increased sedimentation at the delta mouths. The construction of levees and jetties in the delta has been a direct cause of land extension. But the extension so caused has been only a few miles at most.

DIRECT RECLAMATION

Most of the continuous, extensive, and direct reclamation has been in Eu-

type of reclamation, of which the fen-type marsh development in England is an example. Both of these will be described briefly. Both are the result mainly of the combined efforts of inland and coastal men driven to the necessity of developing land from the sea.

Low Countries Polder-Development Reclamation

The early, partly civilized peoples of the Low Countries built mounds in the moorland marsh and swamp areas for

Courtesy of Trio Printers

FIG. 102.—Zuider Zee Dam, The Netherlands. Twenty miles long, the dam separates the Wadden Sea, on the left, from the fresh-water lake, on the right. Polders, like those in the foreground, will be developed from this lake by drainage and pumping, as shown in Fig. 103. (From Van Veen, 1948.)

rope, especially in the Low Countries along the North Sea, where the deltas, estuaries, embayments of many kinds, and lagoon areas between the barrier islands and the mainland have been modified by many kinds of engineering and agricultural endeavors. The most extensive of these has been the building of a system of dikes and canals which inclose various drained areas known as "polders." Other lowland, coastal regions have experienced a less direct

probably a thousand years before their successors began building dikes about A.D. 900. Since that time dike-building and polder development by drainage, dredging, and pumping have increased until the total area claimed from the sea is probably a million acres of farm land, pastures, and sites for towns and cities.[2] Most of these areas are in Belgium and in the Netherlands (Figs. 102

2. Most of the information about reclamation in the Low Countries is derived from Van Veen, 1948.

and 103). Reclamation is now even more intensely pursued, and very extensive projects, such as the Zuider Zee development, will add over a million and a half acres to these regions by about 1980.

Part of this development is in a region where delta channels of the Rhine, Maas, and Scheldt rivers bring in fluvial rograding activities of the sea, including such violent storms as that of February, 1953, many of the reclaimed areas have been lost. Also, incorrect engineering in the building of dikes and the dredging of channels has caused the loss of some areas. The cumulative total of these losses has been estimated at nearly two-thirds of the total area

Courtesy of Trio Printers

FIG. 103.—Outer, or sleeper, dikes, The Netherlands. These dikes, built against the sea, protect the polders to the right. Strong stone groins protect the dikes against excessive marine erosion. (From Van Veen, 1948.)

clays and where marine deposits accumulate back of barrier islands. Organic materials, especially peats and mucks, also accumulate in the moor-type marshes. Fresh-water lakes, some natural and some artificial, are present. The whole region is being drowned both by the eustatic rise of sea level and by the downward movement and settling of deposits and soils. As a consequence of these geologic changes and of the ret- claimed from the sea. But now most of the former polders have been restored. These, together with new projects, such as the Zuider Zee and Wadden, will increase the total area far beyond that of all the former reclamations.

Construction of the outer or watcher dikes formerly was slow and accomplished mainly by the use of willow mats and clay. Now, many improvements have hastened construction and made the dikes stronger—stakes, fitted basalt blocks, bricks, and concrete—and with modern machinery much larger projects are being undertaken. Many of the dikes are massive and in some parts wide enough for villages and towns. The inclosures behind the dikes are subdivided by secondary dikes and canals and are drained by electrical and engine-type pumps that have replaced the old, picturesque windmills. Dredging has become more efficient and important; canals and rivers are kept deep enough to carry off flood waters better than formerly. Much of the recent reclamation has been attained by pumping dry the lakes formed behind the watcher dikes, and the watcher dikes are now better protected from erosion by a series of heavy groins.

The soils of the polders are usually drained, reflooded with fresh water, and variously tilled to lessen their salinity and make them suitable for many different crops. In some areas the calcium deficiency of the soils is overcome by using gypsum. Outer dike construction is the chief means of extending this reclamation farther and farther out into the sea.

This coastal reclamation has notably affected the ethnic group known as the Frisians, who for centuries were typical coastal men living along the sea front of nearly all the Low Countries. These people, refusing to become agriculturists, have moved away from many reclamation areas and now reside mainly on the northern border of the Netherlands and in Denmark.

Fen-Type Reclamation

Marshy vegetation areas are known in England and in a few other countries as fens. Some of them near coasts have been variously drained to transform their flooded, wet-land character for farming and industrial uses (Darby, 1940, 1952). In many other places this reclamation has been applied to inland areas, and no coastal areas have been directly influenced. But in one large fen area in the eastern part of England, adjoining the North Sea embayment known as the Wash, fen reclamation has been so extensive and of such long duration that some increase of land into the Wash has resulted.

This fen region of nearly 1,200,000 acres was not in any part reclaimed until work began in it about 1640. Some canals for draining small areas had been constructed during the Roman occupancy before the fifth century A.D., but these canals had fallen into disuse. Reclamation, after the seventeenth-century beginning, was slow and covered only small areas until the last century and a half, during which most of the fen drainage finally was accomplished. The main method of reclamation has been to convert the many small rivers of the region into canals by improving their banks and channels so that they drained the marshes more efficiently. Gravity drainage was first used; later, dikes, field drains, canals, and pumps were established.

The native, coastal-type people of these fens were fishermen, fowlers, and sod-gatherers, who led an almost amphibious life, and it was because of their resistance to the drainage projects that no well-co-ordinated development occurred until the king's government began some of the reclamation.

That there has been some extension of land area into the Wash embayment is due to increases in sedimentation at the mouths of the rivers used in the reclamation project. New land thus added to the Wash since the eighteenth century is computed at about 90,000 acres, principally in the areas between Welland and the Great Ouse. Most of this type of modification is due to indirect rather than to direct efforts.

Beaches, dunes inland from them, and the shallow foreshore areas to seaward are becoming increasingly important for recreation and for vacation homes. Some forest and pasture development also is occurring in some dune areas. Man's efforts are concerned mainly with protection of the strand from excessive erosion, the stabilization of the beaches and dunes, and, in some favorable places, the seaward extension of the strand areas. Mechanical means are employed in the foreshore waters and along the lower parts of the beaches, but both mechanical and vegetational means are used on the upper beaches and on the dunes or other inland parts of the strand.

Engineering Devices

Mechanical methods of protection and enlargement of the strand have not proved very successful, mainly because many of the projects were started after the onset of retrograding processes, and these processes have not been appreciably curbed. In fact, as stated in an engineering bulletin (Anonymous, 1952, p. 1), "Too many of the things men do to improve beach-fronting property merely increase these rates of erosion —valuable sea beaches have almost disappeared due to the harmful effect of certain unwise improvements." Man has thus changed the coast line by direct action but not in the manner that he planned.

Some of the engineering devices used for protection are heavy sea walls and light bulkheads located on or near the upper beach and the seaward face of the strand scarp, dune, or bluff. Revetments also are used to hold the upper or sloping faces of these structures and as surfacing over the dunes and bluffs near them. In some areas a number of foreshore, shallow-water structures, such

as groins, pilings, and jetties, are continuous with onshore structures.

Sea walls frequently cause a depletion of beach sands, because the high-wave action against them pulls the sands away from the base of the walls. This process and the enhanced pounding of violent storm waves often cause sea walls to be undermined or breached. The less heavily constructed bulkheads are usually used along coasts of low energy and are especially effective where mud sedimentation occurs. The methods of building and maintenance of these structures usually improve as the areas protected increase in value, and these practices are leading to better-managed erosion control, often resulting in some coastal extension.

Groins (Figs. 100, 103) and jetties are the two types of foreshore and onshore structures most used either alone or in conjunction with shore structures. Jetties are usually the more massive and ordinarily are employed along channels and harbors. Groins are extensively used to slow beach erosion and to build beaches. They are designed to take advantage of the longshore currents that drift the sediments along the beach, and they vary in height, length, materials used, and angle of set toward the beach. Groins usually are developed in a series, so that their spacing, length, and height form a tapering system. However, there is disagreement as to whether the direction of taper of the series should be toward or away from the currents—a disagreement which is caused by the dissimilarity of coastal situations. It is difficult also to predict the amount of beach drift so as to build the groins in anticipation of this drift. Consequently, these groins often fail to check erosion or to extend a beach. Some of the best-built, heavy groins are used in connection with the Low Countries system of dikes. The great value of the dikes they protect has warranted their extensive development.

Revetments of many types are used behind sea walls, dikes, and jetties, or on their tops, to prevent the erosion of their sloping faces or upper surfaces. Riprap, brush mats, clay, asphalt, and concrete are employed. As coastal protection becomes more and more necessary, the types of revetments are improved.

Dune and Upper-Beach Stabilization

Stabilization of the dunes and upper beaches is important because they are "the savings account of the beach, deposits made in time of surplus to be drawn out in time of need" (*ibid.*, p. 11). Mechanical methods, such as some retaining walls and revetments, are employed, but most effective have been the use of the natural vegetation and the development of plantings of herbs, shrubs, and trees. In addition the numerous buildings, such as homes, hotels, and motels, constructed mainly by inland men, have served as factors for stabilization.

The natural vegetation is improved mainly by promoting, in accordance with some of the principles of plant ecology (Kurz, 1942), the progress of plant-community succession on the dunes, so that the normal change toward a climax forest or scrub type of vegetation is more rapidly developed. Some conditions are also made better for the pioneer, dune-forming herbs and shrubs, so that they may begin dune stabilization more rapidly and intensely.

The planting method (Chapman, 1949; Van der Burgt and Bendegorn, 1949) is widely practiced from areas bordering the Baltic Sea to the Ninety-Mile Beach in New Zealand. Foreign species and favorable native species are both used, one of the most common choices being the marram grass, *Ammophila arenaria*. A hybrid *Spartina* grass, *S. townsendi*, is also employed in dune swales and over tidal areas.

Woody plants are extensively used, and in some cases useful forests are developed. Among the many species of conifers are *Pinus maritima, P. austriaca, P. nigra corsicana*, and *Picea falcata sitchensis;* among the hardwoods are species of *Betula, Quercus, Populus, Alnus*, and *Salix*, which are planted mainly in the damper, swale parts of the strand. Wattles, fences, stakes, and other mechanical means are used in conjunction with the plantings to stop some movement of sands, especially in Germany and Algeria.

Most of the plantings are either line or group plantings, the choice usually depending upon the mode of growth of the species used. Most of the grasses grow in lines or rows by rhizomes, and the lupines grow in groups. The systems of planting are also related to the topography, wind, and drift character of the sands. In some cases these plantings have actively promoted the extension of the dunes and the beaches outward into the sea.

As economic importance of the strand areas increases, these methods of dune and beach protection and stabilization are becoming extensively and intensively used to insure the maintenance of increasingly valuable property. Co-operative efforts of engineers, plant ecologists, agronomists, and foresters have been necessary, because the problem of dune management is complex. The utilization of dune areas for pasturage and forests probably will increase as better methods of handling the vegetation and plantings are developed. But the most intensive use of strand areas is in some recreational regions where the habitations and other real estate improvements have, in many cases, acted in favor of dune stabilization.

Habitations along Coast Lines

Extensive developments of coastal area property for recreation and vacation living have greatly increased recently, particularly along the Florida and California coasts. In Florida many hotels have been built near the beaches since 1946. The total development of coastal property in Florida is now over 150,000 acres of both the strand and the littoral areas. Some of these areas, such as part of Miami Beach, have been reclaimed from the littoral, mangrove swamps and salt-water marshes, but most of them are developments of strand dunes, such as those near the St. Augustine and Daytona beaches.

The houses, hotels, motels, and other constructions help hold the dunes by their presence, which aids in keeping the sands in place. The lawns, gardens, walks, and road-paving associated with these buildings also contribute to dune stabilization. Both the well-sodded lawns and the hard-surfaced roads are important factors, because they usually cover more area than do the buildings. In many instances the ornamental shrubs and trees used to landscape the property have proved even more effective than the original vegetation in holding the dunes or the filled littoral areas. In general, as real estate values increase, the newer beach property developments are better landscaped than the older ones, thus increasing their efficiency in dune protection.

SOME INLAND SEA AND LAKE CHANGES

Some of the inland seas and lakes have recently been the scene of extensive human activity which has had notable effects upon coast lines. Among these are the changes in the offshore areas and coasts of the Caspian and Aral seas owing to large-scale developments of dams for power and irrigation on the rivers supplying water to these seas (Taskin, 1954; Field, 1954).

The Caspian Sea is shrinking in volume, and the coasts are now extending into it much more rapidly than formerly because of engineering activi-

ties on the rivers entering it, particularly the Volga. An evidence for the effect of power dam and irrigation projects is that, soon after 1932, when these projects began, the water level in the Caspian Sea fell progressively each year. There had been fluctuations in this water level before 1932, but records show that these have been most intensive since that date. Very good evidence of the effects of the dams is the fact that lowering of the water level was definitely retarded during the period of World War II, when dam construction halted; since then a further increase in dam construction has caused the rate of lowering to increase.

A similar and potentially more extensive lowering of water level is beginning in the Aral Sea Basin with the development of irrigation projects on the Amu Darya and Syr Darya, which supply most of the water to this sea. It is the aim of these projects eventually to divert for irrigation most or all of the waters of the rivers from entering the sea. It has been calculated that within twenty-five years the water area of this sea will shrink to half the size that it was in 1940, when the irrigation projects began. This would bring about an increase of nearly 13,000 square miles of land area.

Other navigation, power, and irrigation projects on all continents have variously affected the coastal areas around lakes and inland seas. In many cases the bodies of water have been enlarged, and in some cases new bodies of water have been created. In the Great Lakes region of North America the main efforts have been to keep the water levels stable, with the result that coastal changes have been minor.

ADDITIONAL EXAMPLES OF
INFLUENCES

Fishing Activities

One of the general and long-term activities of coastal men has been the gathering of shellfish for food and other purposes. As a result of this, numerous shellfish mounds have been left along many coasts, and they have aided progradational processes in a number of instances. Some of them are large and have been effective in holding their areas against erosion, helping to form headlands or capes in some places. These and many smaller mounds are so numerous along parts of the Atlantic coast of North America that they occur over nearly 10 per cent of some areas, such as parts of the Florida coast, and, consequently, their total effect in stabilizing coasts and as progradational agents has been great. Many of them are old structures, dating back a few thousand years.

Recently shellfish have been cultivated as well as gathered, especially in the Orient. This activity has increased sedimentation in some littoral and shoal-water areas, such as Manila Bay, and in this way has promoted progradation of coast lines in a few places.

Only a few of the numerous methods of catching fish have in the past had any appreciable effect on coasts, but one of these, the construction of long stone weirs to trap fish in some Pacific areas, has influenced sedimentation. However, the cultivation of fish in tidal basins and other pools (McIntyre, 1954) has recently been increasing and is causing some coastal changes. This practice is common in the Philippines, China, and other parts of the Orient, where the growing populations have increased the demand for food. The fish are raised in built-up inclosed pools at or near the coast, and the construction and maintenance of these pools have locally influenced coastal extension.

Coastal Swamps and Marsh Changes

The tidal-zone mangrove forests and thickets along many low-energy, tropical coasts have been great progradation-al agents, causing appreciable extension of the coast line (Davis, 1940). Man has variously used these mangrove plants (Watson, 1928) for poles, lumber, charcoal, tannin materials, and firewood, and in some cases his exploitation of these forests has altered the rate of progradation, causing a decrease in coastal extension and even active erosion. Recently man has increased the drainage of a few mangrove swamps by digging ditches to reduce breeding areas for mosquitoes, and this activity has had a small effect on rates of progradation.

Tidal-zone salt and brackish-water marshes have been deliberately changed by many agricultural and other uses to which they have been put. The greatest alterations have been by direct reclamation, which has been described. But some such marshes have been drained or flooded for wildlife purposes, while others have been drained as health projects to reduce mosquito and other insect populations. These activities are now increasing and may become more important factors of coastal changes.

Biological and Pollution Changes

Coastal bird life has been disturbed in many ways, such as obtaining guano from areas where great rookeries of sea birds occur, and this activity has caused some local increases in erosion. Protection of bird life has in some instances influenced land changes. An example of this occurred in the Dry Tortugas island group west of Key West, Florida, where a common practice had been the seasonal collection of eggs and birds, which kept their numbers reduced. Conservation people prohibited this activity, and the bird population increased, causing overcrowding and a consequent loss of vegetation that held the island against erosion. The end result was a complete loss of one of the islands.

The collection of seaweeds, mainly

algae, in large quantity along some coasts has altered some processes slightly. Similarly, slight changes in coral-reef biota and in their activity as progradational agents have been effected, mainly by pollution or by increases in sedimentation onto reefs due to dredging and other harbor or channel improvements. The recent A- and H-bomb tests in the Pacific Ocean had direct effects on coral areas, and anyone may speculate as to how many more such violent changes will occur in the future.

In the Gulf of Mexico along the coast of Florida there has recently occurred a series of large "blooms" of microscopic sea organisms, causing what are known as "red tides" that kill many fish. The dead fish have washed up on some beaches and into marshes in large quantity, and their bodies have in a small way altered normal processes of land change. These blooms seem to be partly the result of recently increased washing of phosphate materials into the gulf, owing to mining operations in the interior; if this is the case, the red tides are caused by an inland human activity.

An example of a more definite effect of pollution is in Great South Bay on Long Island, New York (Lackey, 1952), where the bay waters and shellfish have been altered by excessive mineral and organic excreta from duck-farm areas that drain into this bay. The quality and quantity of the oysters have been changed, and the plankton has been increased, causing intense blooms of *Chlorella*. This biological alteration may have affected the sediments and size of the bay.

A number of other types of pollu-

tion are also probably instrumental in causing local coastal changes, especially the industrial wastes brought down by rivers. These will increase with increases in manufacturing and mining, but they are seldom very extensive.

SUMMARY

In terms of total effect on coast lines, the indirect influences of numerous activities of both inland and coastal men have probably been more important than the direct influences of man. Evidences of extensive and prolonged coast-line changes indicate that many agricultural and other soil-altering pursuits of both inland and coastal men have indirectly altered rates of progradation, especially in delta and lagoon regions.

Direct claiming of land from the sea is increasing, and improved methods are insuring more effectiveness in the future. But reclamation is dependent upon numerous fluctuating economic and population factors, such that prediction concerning it is difficult to make.

In some areas, such as Florida, rapidly increasing demand for various recreational establishments along coasts is promoting activities directly aimed at stabilizing and extending the coast line. Probably, with increased economic well-being of inland men, these activities will become more intensive and extensive.

Other generally less important human activities variously affect coast-line changes, some of which activities, such as pollution and agriculture in marsh areas, may become more influential in the future.

REFERENCES

ANONYMOUS
    1952 *Information on Beach Protection in Florida.* (Water Survey and Research Paper No. 8.) Tallahassee: State of Florida, Division of Water Survey and Research. 41 pp.

BROWN, H. F.
    1910–11 "Venice," *Encyclopaedia Bri-*

tannica (11th ed.), XXVII, 995–1007.

CHAPMAN, V. J.
  1949 "The Stabilization of Sand-Dunes by Vegetation," pp. 142–57 in *Proceedings of Conference on Biology and Civil Engineering*. London: Institute of Civil Engineers.

COOKE, C. W.
  1938 *Scenery of Florida*. (Florida Geological Survey Bulletin No. 17.) Tallahassee. 118 pp.

COTTON, C. A.
  1954 "Deductive Morphology and Genetic Classification of Coasts," *Scientific Monthly*, LXXXVIII, 163–81.

CRESSEY, G. B.
  1936 "The Fenghsien Landscape," *Geographical Review*, XXVI, No. 3, 396–413.

DALY, R. A.
  1934 *The Changing World of the Ice Age*. New Haven, Conn.: Yale University Press. 271 pp.

DARBY, H. C.
  1940 *The Medieval Fenland*. Cambridge: Cambridge University Press. 200 pp.
  1952 "Fens," *Encyclopaedia Britannica*, IX, 161–64.

DAVIS, J. H.
  1940 "The Ecology and Geologic Role of Mangroves in Florida," pp. 303–414 in *Papers from Tortugas Laboratory*, Vol. XXXII. (Carnegie Institution of Washington Publication No. 517.) Washington, D.C.

FIELD, N. C.
  1954 "The Amu Darya: A Study in Resource Geography," *Geographical Review*, XLIV, No. 4, 528–42.

HOGG, H. W.
  1910–11 "Mesopotamia," *Encyclopaedia Britannica* (11th ed.), XVIII, 179–87.

JOHNSON, D. W.
  1919 *Shore Processes and Shoreline Development*. New York: John Wiley & Sons. 584 pp.
  1938 "Offshore Bars and Eustatic Changes of Sea Level," *Journal of Geomorphology*, I, 273–74.

KURZ, H.
  1942 *Florida Dunes and Scrub, Vegetation and Geology*. (Florida Geological Survey Bulletin No. 23.) Tallahassee. 154 pp.

LACKEY, J. B.
  1952 "The Rehabilitation of Great South Bay." Gainesville: University of Florida. 27 pp. (Mimeographed.)

LOBECK, A. K.
  1939 *Geomorphology*. New York: McGraw-Hill Book Co. 731 pp.

McINTYRE, W. E.
  1954 "Philippine Fish Culture," *Scientific Monthly*, LXXVIII, No. 2, 86–93.

MARTENS, J. H. C.
  1931 "Beaches of Florida," pp. 19–119 in *Florida Geological Survey, 21st–22nd Annual Report*. Tallahassee.

PRICE, W. A.
  1954 "Shorelines and Coasts of the Gulf of Mexico," *Fishery Bulletin*, No. 89, pp. 39–65. Washington, D.C.: U.S. Department of Interior.

PUTZGER, F. W.
  1931 *Historischer Schul-Atlas*. 50th Anniversary Edition, ed. VELHAGEN and KLASING. Bielefeld and Leipzig: Max Pehle & Hans Silberboth.

RAWLINSON, SIR HENRY
  1854 *Notes on the Early History of Babylonia*. London: J. W. Parker. 45 pp.

RITTER, C.
  1843 "West Asien," *Die Erdkunde*, VII, 3–277.

RUSSELL, R. J.
  1940 "Quaternary History of Louisiana," *Bulletin of the Geological Society of America*, LI, 1199–1234.

STRABO
  1917–50 *The Geography of Strabo*, Vol. II, Book v. Greek text and trans. from the Greek by H. L. JONES. London: William Heinemann.

TASKIN, G. A.
  1954 "The Falling Level of the Caspian Sea in Relation to Soviet Economy," *Geographical Review*, XLIV, No. 4, 508–27.

UNITED STATES CONGRESS
  1948 *Palm Beach, Florida, Beach Erosion Study*. (80th Cong., 2d sess.

[House Document No. 77].) Washington, D.C.: Government Printing Office. 36 pp. (plus 9 maps).

VAN DER BURGT, J. H., and BENDEGORN L.
   1949   "The Use of Vegetation to Stabilize Sand-Dunes," pp. 158–70 in *Proceedings of Conference on Biology and Civil Engineering.* London: Institute of Civil Engineers.

VAN VEEN, J.
   1948   *Dredge Drain Reclaim: The Art of a Nation.* The Hague: Trio Printers. 165 pp.

WATSON, J. G.
   1928   *Mangrove Forests of the Malay Peninsula.* (Malayan Forest Records No. 6.) Singapore: Federated Malay States. 275 pp.

Man's Ports and Channels

LESTER E. KLIMM[*]

> But if we have no natural harbour suitable for protecting ships from a stormy sea, we must proceed as follows. . . .—VITRUVIUS (*ca.* 27 B.C.) *On Architecture* v. xii. 2.

When the Roman architect wrote this introduction to his chapter on harbors, he was already heir to at least two millenniums of man's experience in modifying shore lines and waterways to facilitate communication between them. Certain it is that, when the European and Asiatic civilizations began to write down their history and traditions, man had long since learned that persons and goods could be moved with less expenditure of labor on water than on land. He had developed boats and ships and encountered the problems involved in loading and unloading them.

THE PORT FUNCTION

Very soon after he launched his first craft, primitive man must have discovered the convenience of being able to float it alongside firm, dry land, so that he could step easily from one to the other. This is the function of the port, reduced to its simplest terms. Here land and water transport meet, and simple modifications of banks and channels greatly facilitate the exchange

between them. A few rocks dropped in line to form stepping stones out to depths sufficient to float a boat, or a log laid as a span to a steep-to off-lying rock, probably served the early boatman as a landing place, much as similar arrangements serve the modern summer camp as misnamed "docks"! By 2000 B.C. many Greek and Phoenician ports on the Mediterranean had crude piers and moles built into deep water (Lehman-Hartleben, 1923, pp. 6 ff.).

Or, if the banks were soft or marshy, it was relatively easy to dig a passageway penetrating the bank at a sharp angle to let boats come alongside firm ground (see Fig. 104, *e*, for such an arrangement at Bremen). If the sides of such a "slip" had a tendency to crumble, they could be lined with primitive piling or stone. These landings were called "hithes" or "hythes" by the Saxons and were common along the waterways of southeastern England (Ekwall, 1951, p. 231). The term survives in numerous place names. Rotherhithe in the Port of London was named after one of these landing places (it is now appropriately the site of the Commercial Docks), and *Bartholomew's Survey Gazetteer of the British Isles* (Bartholomew & Son, 1927, p. 361) lists five "Hythes" and numerous combinations, such as Hythe End, Small Hythe, and Hythe West.

---

[*] Dr. Klimm is Professor of Geography at the Wharton School of Finance and Commerce of the University of Pennsylvania, Philadelphia. His recent research has been concerned with an examination of the process of geographic generalization. His publications include: "The Relation between Field Patterns and Jointing in the Aran Islands," 1935; "The Rain Tanks of Aran," 1936; and "The Empty Areas of Northeastern United States," 1954.

HABANA
CUBA

A

TYPE A—COASTAL (NATURAL)

A coastal harbor sheltered from the wind and sea by virtue of its location within a natural coastal indentation or in the protective lee of an island, cape, reef or other natural barrier.

CHERBOURG
FRANCE

B

TYPE B—COASTAL (BREAKWATER)

A coastal harbor lying behind a man-made breakwater constructed to provide shelter, or supplement inadequate shelter already provided by natural sources.

BOMBAY
INDIA

C

TYPE C—COASTAL (TIDE GATES)

A coastal harbor, the waters of which are constrained by locks or other mechanical devices in order to provide sufficient water to float vessels at all stages of the tide.

JACKSONVILLE
U.S.A.

D

TYPE D—RIVER (NATURAL)

A harbor located on a river, the waters of which are not retained by any artificial means. The facilities may consist of quays or wharves parallel to the banks of the stream, or piers or jetties which extend into the stream.

EXAMPLES OF HARBOR TYPES

FIG. 104.—Examples of harbor types. (From United States Navy, 1953.)

TYPE E—RIVER (BASINS)

A river harbor in which slips for vessels have been excavated in the banks, obliquely or at right angles to the axis of the stream.

TYPE F—RIVER (TIDE GATES)

A river harbor, the waters of which are constrained by locks or other mechanical devices in order to provide sufficient water to float vessels at all stages of the tide.

TYPE G—CANAL OR LAKE

A harbor located in the interior portion of a canal or lake that is connected with the sea by a navigable waterway.

TYPE X—OPEN ROADSTEAD

A port which has no natural or artificial barrier to provide shelter from the wind, sea and swell

EXAMPLES OF HARBOR TYPES

FIG. 104—*cont.*—Examples of harbor types. (From United States Navy, 1953.)

From such simple beginnings the line of stones was improved and developed in masonry or concrete to become a "pier," or "mole," and the hithe became a "slip" or—equipped with gates to lock it against fluctuations of water level—a true "dock" (see Fig. 104, *c*, *f*, for such docks at Bombay or Bremerhaven). The bank of the waterway was lined with masonry, and craft could discharge at this "quay." On all these structures roads and railroads were laid, cranes of various kinds facilitated the lifting of goods in and out of the craft, and warehouses became available for storage.

For specialized cargoes special handling facilities were developed. Grain elevators (fixed or floating), ore piers, coal piers, car-float "bridges," oil terminals, and many others came into being. Many of these are perhaps more appropriately "devices" rather than strictly modifications of the environment, but they serve to illustrate the length to which man has gone to facilitate the transfer of people and goods between land and water.

HARBORS

Where man's transport by water was confined to rivers, canals, or small lakes, there was little need for concern about wind and wave; but, where he used his boats and ships on the large lakes or the seas, the performance of the port functions was largely limited to harbors.

When the *Odyssey* was being composed, between nine and seven hundred years before the Christian Era, men had already been sailing the seas in "hollow ships" for so long that Homer could describe a "fair haven"—the Laestrygonian harbor—in terms calculated to make glad the hearts of sailor men:

. . . whereabout on both sides goes one steep cliff unbroken, and jutting headlands over against each other stretch forth at the mouth of the harbour, and strait is the entrance. . . . Now the vessels were bound within the hollow harbour each hard by other, for no wave ever swelled within it, great or small, but there was a bright calm all around [Homer, 1948, trans. Butcher and Lang, Book x].

Here are the deep water, the narrow entrance for protection from sea and swell, and the surrounding hills to shelter from winds from all directions which are still the basic features of the ideal natural harbor. This might be a poet's description of Halifax, or Rio de Janeiro, or Havana (Fig. 104, *a*). Knowing only the practically tideless Mediterranean, Homer had no concern with tidal range. But good natural harbors are scarce, and often the routes of trade or the requirements of a fishing people call for ports where there is no harbor or a poor one. And then, truly, as Vitruvius says, "We must proceed as follows . . ."!

Shelter

Harbors in Egypt and Syria began to be improved or created through construction of breakwaters from about 2000 B.C. (Lehmann-Hartleben, 1923, pp. 5 ff.). In many cases the shelter was provided by connecting an offshore rock, or island, to the mainland by a breakwater of loose stones or rubble. Of this sort was the long breakwater at Eretria, which was 600–700 meters long and overcame depths of 30 meters (Fig. 105; cf. Lehmann-Hartleben, 1923, p. 51 and Plan II). At Alexandria, by the time of the Roman Empire, the harbor had been developed as shown in Figure 106.

At ancient Tyre two offshore islands were joined artificially by Hiram (*ca.* 1000 B.C.) to shelter a harbor, and the city grew up on these islands. The original settlement here may have been nearly a millennium old by Hiram's time, but a description of Hiram's Tyre survives (Josephus, quoted in Fleming, 1915, p. 4). Tyre is an especially interesting example of man's modification of his environment. Not only was the harbor created and land won from the sea but Alexander the Great built a cause-

FIG. 105.—Harbor works at Eretria, Greece, about 700–500 B.C. (After Lehmann-Hartleben, 1923, Plan II; United States Navy, 1952, p. 181, Chart 4123.)

way 200 feet wide to the island city as part of his siege operations in 332 B.C. This grew by accretion of sand to an isthmus at least a quarter-mile wide. When the Crusaders attacked Tyre in A.D. 1123, it was again a great city and port, with a ditch dug across the peninsula for defense. This was filled during the Crusaders' siege.[1]

The fulfilment of Ezekiel's (chap. 26) prophecy that the Lord would make even "Tyrus . . . of perfect beauty" to become "like the top of a rock . . . a place for the spreading of nets in the midst of the the sea" could not be more dramatically confirmed than in the flat words of the *Sailing Directions for the Mediterranean* (United States Navy, 1951, p. 226):

The remains of a mole extend some distance into the sea, with numerous granite columns along the coast. On the northeastern side of the town are the remains of the moles which inclosed the ancient port; they were constructed of hewn stones of considerable size; little, however, remains,

1. For history of Tyre see Fleming, 1915, *passim.*

FIG. 106.—Harbor at Alexandria, Egypt, about the beginning of the Christian Era. (After Lehmann-Hartleben, 1923, Plan XXI; co-ordinates from United States Navy, 1952, Chart 2553.)

and the port, now filled with sand, affords shelter only to the smallest coasting boats.

The idea of a wall, breakwater, mole, or jetty to give shelter where it was needed thus was very old, and its significance was to grow with the spread of the idea, the growth of commerce, and man's engineering skill. Of the 277 ports listed in *World Port Index* (United States Navy, 1953) for the island of Britain, 51 are classified as "Coastal (Breakwater)." Among the nearly 100

larger, the number of harbors which could accommodate them naturally became fewer. Faced with this dilemma, some ports lost trade or ceased to function, and others spent increasing sums on artificial deepening if the trade—or the naval significance of the harbor—justified it.

Depth of water in a harbor affects the size of ships that may enter, the size of the safe anchorage available, and the size of craft that may come alongside

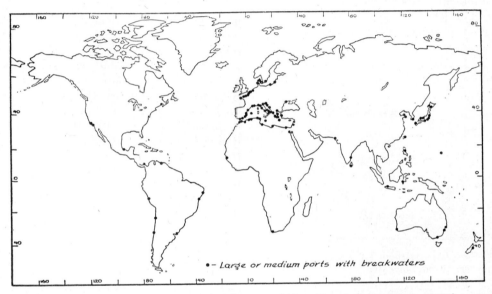

FIG. 107.—Important ports with breakwaters. (After United States Navy, 1953.)

of the world's large ports which would be of decidedly limited use without breakwaters (Fig. 107) are such important ones as Los Angeles, Montevideo, Callao, Cherbourg (Fig. 104, *b*), Gibraltar, Barcelona, Marseilles, Venice, Odessa, Cape Town, Madras, and Yokohama (*ibid., passim*). Nearly all the important ports of the Great Lakes depend for all or most of their shelter on breakwaters.

Depth

The depth of the harbors has been running a race with the draft of ships for several centuries. As ships became

the piers. There are few ports, even those with the best natural harbors, that do not have problems of insufficient depth for one of these functions and must, therefore, continue to dredge or else limit their usefulness. If dredging were to cease for a few years, such great ports as Montreal, Philadelphia, or Hamburg would be faced with considerable curtailment of shipping, and even New York might have to exclude the largest and fastest of the transatlantic passenger ships.

Ports in the estuaries of rivers, and particularly those well upstream, have found artificial deepening especially necessary. Some—such as Amsterdam, Manchester, Houston, and Leningrad—have remained or become seaports only by digging ship canals which are largely artificial channels.

River ports have been especially handicapped by the natural tendency for bars to form at river mouths. In addition to dredging, training walls or jetties have been used to narrow the channel and force the river, through increased velocity, to carry its load of sediment farther to sea.

The jetties at the mouth of the Mississippi are examples of the successes

Fig. 108.—Methods of dredging by manpower. (From Stevenson, 1886, pp. 228, 229.)

and complications of such works. They were started in 1876 and cleared a deeper channel and removed a then existent bar almost at once. But the deeper channel increased the volume and slowed down the water, and the channel had to be narrowed further. There have been several relocations of the jetties, and supplementary dredging has had to be used.

Man increases and maintains the depth of water and thus changes his physical environment only at a cost. For example, to June 30, 1948, the United States government had spent the following:

To dredge and maintain a channel 35–40 feet deep and 96 miles long in the Del-

aware River between Philadelphia and the sea—78 million dollars.

To dredge and maintain the Houston Ship Channel, 36 feet deep and 50 miles long—22 million dollars.

To dredge and maintain a 30–40 foot channel in the Mississippi River for 268 miles from Baton Rouge past New Orleans to the Gulf of Mexico—50 million dollars.

To dredge and maintain entrance channels and anchorage areas in New York harbor to 1950—16 million dollars [United States Congress, 1953, pp. 554 and 556].

Any major deepening of channels in areas permanently covered with water has been possible only since the development of power dredges. Stevenson (1886, pp. 227 ff.) reports that both the Dutch and the Italians were credited with first developing dredging and that the early dredges were powered with human labor. Figure 108 shows two of these old hand-dredging schemes. Stevenson thinks (*ibid.*, p. 229) that the first steam dredge was used on the Wear River in England in 1776. Then from about 1800 there was a race between ship size and the capabilities of the dredges.

Tidal Range

Where the tidal range averages 10 feet or more, its effect on the usefulness of a port becomes significant. There are, of course, advantages associated with a considerable rise and fall of tide. Tidal currents furnish motive power to help move ships in and out of ports, and those same currents may have a scouring action which helps to keep channels open. In general, however, a high tidal range is a handicap, and some of man's more spectacular port works have been built to overcome this feature of the natural environment.

Within a radius of 400 miles of the middle of the Strait of Dover lies the world's most active maritime trading area; all the important ports have had to be largely remade to overcome the handicap of tidal range. Table 5 gives figures for a few of the largest.

The problem of the tidal port is two-fold. First, large vessels can enter or leave only for a limited period at, or near, high tide. There seems to be no solution for this, and the entrances to great tidal ports are crowded with traffic for short periods and very quiet at others—especially at spring tides, when the range is greatest.

The second problem is that of inconvenience in handling cargo between wharves and the ships lying alongside. The relation between the deck or cargo ports of the ship and the level of the wharf varies sharply with the state of

land was constructed at Rotherhithe on the Thames and is described by Vernon-Harcourt (1885, I, 489) as follows:

Excavations are recorded to have been made at Rotherhithe for diverting the course of the river, and were subsequently utilized for a dock, which existed as the Howland Great Wet Dock in 1660 and was the first dock in Great Britain. It was 1070 feet long and 500 feet wide and had a depth of water of 17 feet.

Jones (1932, p. 50) claims that this dock had little commercial significance, being used mainly for fitting out and masting ships, and that the real use of docks on London River began in the earliest years of the nineteenth cen-

TABLE 5*

TIDAL RANGE OF SOME IMPORTANT PORTS

Port	Tidal Range (Feet)	Port	Tidal Range (Feet)
Liverpool	21	Bordeaux	14
Cardiff	28	Brest	15
Bristol	31	Le Havre	18
Southampton	11	Antwerp	14
London	19	Bremerhaven	11

* Source: United States Navy, 1953.

the tide. At spring tides the variation may be so great as to force cessation of cargo handling. Working cargo to and from lighters on the off side of the ship is restricted. In many instances, at the lowest tides, the ship has to "dry out" or "take the ground," as the sailor describes the vessel resting on the bottom. "Taking the ground" often causes damage and always requires vigilance. To this second problem there is a solution—the "dock," or "wet dock," as it is sometimes called.

The idea of putting a gate across the entrance to maintain the water level of a "hithe" or slip dug into the channel bank must have occurred very early, but probably its use had to await the development of satisfactory locks and gates. The earliest such dock in Eng-

tury. Certainly that century saw dock construction occupy many of the alluvial flats and large bends of the river, creeping downstream as the size and draft of ships increased, and culminating with the great Tilbury Docks, 26 miles below London Bridge, opened in 1886. These had an entrance lock 80 feet wide, 700 feet long, and 30 feet deep (*ibid.*, p. 117) and could be reached by ships drawing 26 feet of water at any state of the tide.

As they grew in size, such docks became virtually self-contained ports, in which tugs moved lighters and other craft around at will, and ships loaded and discharged cargo at all times—locked in as they were against the rise and fall of the tide.

Le Havre completed a dock in 1667

(Vernon-Harcourt, 1885, p. 569), Honfleur in 1690 (*ibid.*, p. 576), and Liverpool in 1709 (*ibid.*, p. 504). All these ports had their greatest activity in dock construction after the beginning of the nineteenth century. The great port of Antwerp opened its first docks in 1811 and 1813 and by 1880 had an inclosed dock area of 105 acres (*ibid.*, p. 602).

Bristol, with its great tidal range, is a special case. It is located 7 miles above the mouth of the river Avon. Here, in the first decade of the nineteenth century, a large bend of the river was cut off to form a "floating harbor," over 2 miles long, locked in, and the river was diverted across the neck of the bend (*ibid.*, p. 529). However, the access is so restricted that an additional port—with docks—has been built at Avonmouth on the Bristol Channel.

AIDS TO NAVIGATION

Sailor men the world over hate low coasts. It is therefore no wonder that one of man's earliest improvements on such a coast was a high tower to furnish a bearing. What is often referred to as the first "lighthouse" in the world (e.g., Semple, 1932, p. 591) was on the island of Pharos which protected the harbor of Alexandria (Fig. 106, p. 526). Writing at the beginning of the Christian Era, Strabo says:

This extremity itself of the island is a rock—with a tower upon it of the same name as the island admirably constructed of white marble, with several stories. . . . For as the coast on each side is low and without harbours, with reefs and shallows, an elevated and conspicuous mark was required to enable navigators coming in from the open sea to direct their course exactly to the entrance of the harbour [1903, trans. Hamilton and Falconer, xvii. 1, 6].

In most of the other river deltas, from the Mississippi to the Ganges, the highest points in the present landscape are the lighthouses, beacons, and bearings man has erected to put features on a featureless land. From this it was a simple step to make low, and even submerged, rocks and shoals, on any coast, high enough to see by putting beacons on them. Then, equipped with lights, bells, or horns, they could be seen in the dark or heard through fog.

★   ★   ★

In the eyes of engineers, the defects of natural geography were made to be corrected by their skill, experience, and ingenuity.—J. S. JEANS, *Waterways and Water Transport in Different Countries* (1890), p. 12.

ANCIENT CANALS

Canal-building is one of man's older means of making substantial changes in his environment. When the written records began, canals had been used for untold ages in Mesopotamia and Egypt. A recent issue of *Science* (August 20, 1954, pp. 292, 293) records the discovery of a canal system parallel to the Euphrates which was in existence in 4000 B.C. and was abandoned in the time of Hammurabi about 1800 B.C. This canal not only was used for irrigation—thus changing the distribution of water and agriculture—but was also a major transportation artery. So, too, the Nile and the canals which Herodotus (1928, Book ii) says Sesostris (*ca.* 1850 B.C.) built in the delta to distribute water became channels for boats. Indeed, Strabo says (1903, xvii. 1. 3), "the attention and care bestowed upon the Nile is so great as to cause industry to triumph over nature."

In China serious canal-building may not have begun until about 500 B.C., when dikes and water diversions were being used as instruments of war. In that period, when irrigation was limited to small ditches and furrows, the object was to prevent the irrigation water from getting to the enemy's land —or to divert a flood and drown him out (Chi, 1936, pp. 64, 65). A modern instance of this practice was the breaking of the Hwang Ho dike west of Kaifeng in 1938 by the Chinese as a defense against the Japanese. The Hwang poured southward into the basin of the Hwai and was not returned to its pre-1938 bed for a dozen years.

Chi (*ibid.*, p. 65) believes that the techniques learned in these water battles in the "Period of the Warring States" (481–255 B.C.) sparked a technical revolution that was to have tremendous effect on Chinese history. It gave a method of transforming the alluvial areas by furnishing irrigation water for crops, and it resulted in waterways for transport which bound the river valleys together and made central government possible.

In China, man has interfered with drainage and dug canals for so long— and with so little foresight—that the distinction between river and canal loses its significance over wide areas. Man is by no means in entire control of the situation, but he has certainly modified his environment.

THE PRESENT WATERWAYS

The mid-twentieth-century reader probably finds it difficult to understand how significantly man has modified his environment by making artificial inland waterways or improving on natural ones. Equipped with the railroad and the motor truck, our contemporary fails to realize that the inland transport of cheap, heavy goods was limited to waterways until about 1840, when the railroad began to be significant; it was after 1920 that the motor truck came into its own. Previously, inducing navigability where it had not been was to bring the economically life-giving transportation to regions where it had not been available and to connect regions formerly held apart by natural obstacles.

Canals in Alluvial Plains

The alluvial plains and deltas were, as has been seen, the early schools of canal engineering. Making water widely available where the climate was dry and draining water off where it was overabundant were the dominant problems presented by the environment. The prevalence of light, river-laid soil made digging relatively easy. The deltas and flood plains of the Nile, Tigris-Euphrates, Ganges, Hwang, Hwai, Si, Yangtze, and Po and the streams flowing across Belgium and the Netherlands all are crisscrossed with canals. These are, over wide areas, the farm lanes, streets of the villages, the roads between them, and the highways to the outside world. They are in many cases also the water supply and the sewers. To a remarkable degree this amphibious world is man-made and man-preserved.

Intracoastal Canals

The two monumental examples of intracoastal canals are the Grand Canal in China and the Intracoastal Waterway of the eastern United States. The purpose of such canals is to connect the lower courses of rivers and bays and allow craft designed for inland navigation to pass along the coast without being exposed to the hazards of the open sea.

The so-called "Grand Canal" of China is a connected line of canals, lakes, natural river courses, and canalized rivers. It is usually spoken of as stretching nearly a thousand miles from Peiping in the north to Hangchow on the coast south of Shanghai. Sections were built or improved at widely separated times and have been rejuvenated or neglected at long intervals. Various dates are assigned for "the building of the canal," but perhaps the earliest section of what is now called the Grand Canal was the first connection between the Hwai and the Yangtze in 456 B.C. (*ibid.*). As the centers of power moved about over the face of China, numerous canals were dug connecting river valleys, but it was the establishment of the capital of Peiping by the Tartar invaders about A.D. 1280 that created the necessity for connecting that city with the Yangtze Valley by a more direct route. Thus, a series of new canals was dug more or less directly from Peiping southward and southeastward, intersecting the Hwang, Hwai, and Yangtze rivers and Hangchow Bay. South of the Hwai this utilized many old channels, but they were improved. The principal function of this waterway was described by Marco Polo (1926, chap. lxxii) in the thirteenth century as follows:

Kay-Gui is a small town on the southern bank of the before-mentioned river [the Yangtze], where annually is collected a very large quantity of corn and rice, the greatest part of which is conveyed from thence to the city of Kanbalu [Peiping], for the supply of the establishment of the Emperor. This place is in the line of communication with the province of Cathay, by means of rivers, lakes, and a wide and deep canal which the Great Khan has caused to be dug, in order that vessels may pass from one great river to the other, and from the province of Manji, by water, as far as Kanbalu, without making any part of the voyage by sea.

It is difficult to tell from the literature whether this great line of communications ever remained operational throughout its length for any very long periods. There is little doubt about the portions south of the latitude of Suchow (Tungshan). These are old canals in low-lying country and, while they suffer from floods and breakouts, are relatively stable. The real problem,

which has never been satisfactorily solved, is the section within about 40 miles of the Hwang River crossing. This part is high, and water supply is precarious. It is also an area with dry winters. There has never been any aqueduct carrying the canal across the Hwang. Boats had to use the water of that river, which varies greatly in depth from season to season and is often absent (Carles, 1896–97, *passim*). When this writer was studying aerial photos of North China taken during World War II, the canal, here, was seen to be dry and partially filled in.

One of the great handicaps to the permanency and usefulness of Chinese canals is the absence on the older ones of locks of the type known in the West. Boats are dragged up and down between levels on stone "sluices" or "planes," or different boats are used on different levels. A description of a passage of one of these sluices was given by the early Jesuit traveler Le Compte (as quoted by Phillips, 1793, pp. 12, 13):

They are called by the name of sluices in the relations of travellers, notwithstanding they are very different from ours; they are rather waterfalls, and as it were torrents that are precipitated from one canal into another, and more or less rapid according to the difference of their level. To cause barks or barges to ascend, they make use of a great company of men, who are maintained for that purpose near the sluice: after they have drawn cables and ropes to right and left, to lay hold of the bark in such a manner that it cannot escape them, . . . they have several capstans, by the help of which they raise it by little and little by exerting the utmost strength of their arms, and employing levers, till they have raised it into the upper canal, in which it may continue its voyage. The labour is tedious, toilsome, and exceedingly dangerous. They would be wondrously surprised could they behold with what ease and facility one man alone, who opens and shuts the gates of our locks and sluices in Europe, makes the longest and heaviest laden barks and barges securely to ascend and descend.

The cost in human labor of constructing even these imperfect and often ephemeral waterways was tremendous. It is not necessary to accept the figures of "The Record of the Opening of the Canal" (quoted in Chi, 1936, pp. 123, 124) that 5,430,000 people participated in the building of the Pien Canal with baskets and shovels in A.D. 609. More dependably, perhaps, a portion of the Grand Canal about 60 miles long is said to have cost the labor of 20,261 men from the spring of 1292 to autumn of the following year, and another, dug about the same time, was 83 miles long and cost 2,510,748 man-days (Chi, 1936, p. 141). This would work out at 30,250 man-days per mile.

The Intracoastal Waterway of the United States is favored by the fact that most of the Atlantic coast south of New York and most of the coast line of the Gulf of Mexico is what the geologist calls a "barrier-beach coast." The typical occurrence is a series of long, narrow, sandy islands or peninsulas, parallel to the coast and backed by shallow bays or lagoons. Occasional inlets connect these bays with the sea. It is relatively simple to dredge and maintain channels connecting these inclosed bays and thus to make a relatively continuous protected waterway. There are really two separate sections. Along the Atlantic coast from New Jersey to Florida is a 1,200-mile waterway with a prevailing depth of 12 feet or more. While it connects the mouths of many rivers, these rivers have little commercial water traffic destined for other river valleys. The main use of this waterway is by pleasure craft. The Gulf Intracoastal Waterway is of more significance. Here is nearly another thousand miles of waterway which connects rivers having much more barge traffic, and it has become an important transportation artery.

Improved Rivers

Outside the alluvial deltas not much could be done to improve a river until the development of locks. On many rivers most of the bulkier traffic passed only downstream and awaited water enough to carry boats over obstacles. Upstream navigation against the current was usually very difficult and flourished only after the utilization of steam at the end of the eighteenth century.

There was some narrowing of channels by wing dams to increase water depths in shallow sections and even the development of crude temporary weirs above which boats would wait for water to pile up and then, when the obstruction was suddenly removed, proceed on the accumulated water (Stevenson, 1886, pp. 166–68). There are very few large streams in Europe that have not been modified for centuries—some mainly for flood control.

The modifications man has made on the Nile and the Mississippi systems for flood control, navigation, or irrigation must rank among his major engineering achievements. The control is not complete, but it is substantial.

Locks and Canals

When man developed the idea of the lock—a double set of gates across a waterway by which boats could be raised or lowered between levels—he acquired a tremendous new power to modify natural waterways and build artificial ones. It is probably not too much to say that this was one of the major advances in technology.

There is dispute as to where the idea developed. The first true, double-gate lock has been claimed both for Italy in 1488 (Jeans, 1890, p. 411) and for Holland a century before (Stevenson, 1886, pp. 4, 5). The solution of engineering problems associated with the use of locks must have progressed gradually, but, by 1666, Italian and French engineers had confidence enough to start the Languedoc Canal connecting the Bay of Biscay and the Mediterranean. Finished in fourteen years, it was 125 miles long, conquered a 600-foot drainage divide by means of a hundred locks, and employed tunnels, cuts, sluices, aqueducts, and bridges (Jeans, 1890, pp. 100–105).

This probably marked the coming-of-age of canal engineering. From here on it was possible to canalize swift-flowing rivers and turn them into a series of planes, with slack-water navigation in

a canal. On a watershed between two drainage basins this becomes a major problem—as it is on the Panama Canal. Two devices have been used to overcome this difficulty on small canals. One is an inclined plane with tracks upon which runs a crib which carries boats up and down. This crib may be operated by winches or by counterbalancing with another crib on a parallel track. Such planes were features of the Morris Canal between the Delaware River and New York Bay in the nineteenth

TABLE 6*

NAVIGABLE WATERWAYS OF WESTERN EUROPE, 1952
(In Miles)

Country	Canals	Navigable Rivers	Total Navigable Waterways
Austria...............	10	211	221
Belgium..............	487	445	932
France...............	3,177	4,760	7,937
Germany (West)........	814	1,862	2,676
Ireland...............	293	145	438
Italy.................	736	847	1,484
Netherlands...........	3,479	671	4,150
Sweden..............	188	539	727
Switzerland...........		13	13
United Kingdom.......	1,570	736	2,306
Yugoslavia...........	115	1,106	1,221
Total.............	10,770	11,335	22,105

* Source: United Nations, 1953.

each plane. It demonstrated the feasibility of connecting rivers flowing in opposite directions and led eventually to canals between the Rhine and the Danube, the Rhine and the Rhone, the Seine and the Rhone, etc. Locks also made possible the interconnection of waterways where their courses approached each other, even though there was a considerable difference in their levels—for instance, the Volga and the Don. In addition, as has been pointed out above, the lock made possible the dock, or wet dock, which has so transformed the tidal ports.

The use of locks requires a plentiful supply of water at the highest levels of

century (Harlow, 1926, p. 304). On some canals virtual elevators have been installed that convey boats between levels with the least possible loss of water (Stevenson, 1886, pp. 17, 18).

The cumulative, total mileage of the canals and navigable rivers of the world would be impressive if it could be arrived at with any degree of accuracy. For western Europe (outside the Iron Curtain) and for the United States, some pertinent figures are shown in Tables 6 and 7.

Isthmian and Interoceanic Canals

Herodotus (1928, Book i) tells how the Cnidians, who lived on a peninsula in southwestern Asia Minor, were warned by the Delphic Oracle:

> Fence not the isthmus off, nor dig it through—
> Jove would have made an island, had he wished.

The Cnidians obeyed, but most men seem to have regarded an isthmus as one of Jove's mistakes and have proceeded to correct it. The long sea voyage around creates a temptation to cut through the base of the peninsula, especially if it is narrow. The challenge pre-

same purpose are the Canal du Midi (or Languedoc, above), connecting the Bay of Biscay and the Mediterranean; the line of canals, rivers, and lakes across Sweden from Göteborg to Stockholm; and the White Sea—Baltic, or "Stalin," Canal. In the United States two major proposals have been made: to dig a ship canal across New Jersey from New York Bay to the Delaware River, and one across the base of the Florida peninsula. In addition to cost, considerations of effect on local freshwater supply and of interruptions to

TABLE 7*

NAVIGABLE INLAND WATERWAYS UNDER FEDERAL CONTROL
IN THE UNITED STATES, 1950

Waterway	Miles
Mississippi River system	12,073
Atlantic coastal rivers	5,834
Gulf coastal rivers	4,000
Intracoastal waterways	2,966
St. Lawrence River (International Section)	62
Pacific coastal rivers	1,378
Other	799
Total, excluding Great Lakes	27,112
Great Lakes and connecting channels	1,479
Total waterways	28,591

*Source: United States Congress, 1950, p. 199.

sented by the 4-mile waist of the Isthmus of Corinth was recognized very early. The time saved on the busy trade route by crossing the isthmus was so great that the Corinthians early established a shipway of rollers and charged tolls to drag small ships across (Strabo, 1903, viii. 6. 4). Julius Caesar, Caligula, and Nero all started to dig through the isthmus. When the ship canal was finally opened in 1893, it saved two days in a voyage from Italian ports to Asia Minor or the Black Sea (Jeans, 1890, p. 348).

Other canals enabling ships to save distance or avoid the dangers of rounding peninsulas are the Cape Cod, Delaware-Chesapeake, and Kiel. Among the barge or small-ship canals serving the

land traffic have been stated in opposition.

Suez and Panama

The world is, in effect, divided into four compartments by the distribution of the continents and the oceans (Fig. 109). Eurasia-Africa extends 7,600 miles from north to south, separating the Atlantic Basin from that of the Pacific-Indian Ocean. Westward across the Atlantic, North–South America, 8,800 miles long, also separates the two great basins. Water communication around the north end of these barriers is, because of the climate, so difficult as to be almost impossible; only at their southern ends is ocean navigation uninterrupted around the world.

Each of these great north-south land barriers is pinched down to a width of less than 100 miles at a point about 4,800 miles north of its southern end. Most of the world's population and the active maritime nations are in the middle latitudes of the Northern Hemisphere; the bulk of the world's trade has, therefore, been east-west. As a consequence, the temptation to regard these two isthmuses as "Jove's mistakes" has been strong from very early times.

routes, a railroad in 1860, and, finally, the modern 88-mile Suez Canal, completed in 1869, testify to man's opinion of the importance of this "hyphen" in the waterways of the world.

The isthmus between the Americas is really a zone of isthmuses 1,400 miles long in a northwest-southeast direction from the Isthmus of Tehuantepec in Mexico to the mouth of the Atrato River in Colombia. Here there are four principal possible crossings: the Isthmus of Tehuantepec (125 miles), San

Nearest Liverpool via Panama
Nearest Liverpool via Suez
Nearest Liverpool without using either

FIG. 109.—The effect of the Suez and Panama canals on distances from Liverpool. (After United States Navy, 1948.)

That at Suez was the first to be breached. Herodotus (1928, Book ii) says that Necos (Necho, *fl.* 610–594 B.C.) was the first to attempt a canal from the Nile to the Red Sea and that a hundred and twenty thousand Egyptians lost their lives in its construction. Apparently he was only one of a number who attempted to build or actually did build canals from the eastern branch of the Nile to the head of the Red Sea, thus giving contact between that body and the Mediterranean via the Nile.[2] Caravans along a variety of

Juan River route in Nicaragua (184 miles, some of it natural waterway), the Isthmus of Panama (50 miles), and the Atrato River route in Colombia (100–300 miles, depending on route chosen).

It must be remembered that most of the exploration of the New World around the end of the fifteenth century had as its object a route to the Indies as an alternative to the one from

2. For a summary of canal-building in this route from 1900 B.C. to A.D. 767 see Semple, 1932, p. 167.

the eastern end of the Mediterranean. Thus, Balboa's crossing of the Isthmus of Panama in 1513 was but the beginning of a long search for a water route through the barrier. As early as 1520, Charles V of Spain is said to have had a search made for a possible canal route, and the Spanish pursued the search for a natural water connection, or a route for a canal, until Philip II put a stop to it, saying, "God has shown His will by creating a continuous isthmus" (quoted in Siegfried, 1940, p. 208).

of Magellan and the Cape of Good Hope 4,800 miles to the northward and has opened an east-west water route around the world in the Northern Hemisphere, where most of the world's people and commerce are to be found. Any action of man that decreases the water distance between important places in the world by 1,000–8,000 miles must be one of his major accomplishments. Some comparative figures for distances by common sailing routes from New

TABLE 8*

ROUTES AND MILEAGE SAVINGS VIA SUEZ AND PANAMA CANALS
(In Nautical Miles)

Liverpool to	Via Cape of Good Hope	Via Suez Canal	Saving
Aden	10,243	4,601	5,642
Bombay	10,844	6,250	4,594
Hong Kong	13,170	10,308	2,862
Sydney (Australia)	12,696	11,531	1,165

New York to	Via Strait of Magellan	Via Panama Canal	Saving
San Francisco	13,122	5,263	7,859
Valparaiso (Chile)	8,366	4,634	3,732
Sydney (Australia)	12,332	9,692	2,640
Yokohama	16,576†	9,700	6,876

* Source: United States Navy, 1948.
† 15,269 by Cape of Good Hope.

Over all but the Atrato River route there had been canoe and bateau travel, trails, roads, railroads, and surveys for canals before the barrier was finally breached by the opening of the Panama Canal in 1914. The other routes remain possibilities for supplementary canals, with the Nicaraguan route most likely.

By the Suez and Panama ship canals—130 miles in combined length—man has made a major change in the distribution of land and water on this earth. In effect he has moved the Strait

York and Liverpool around the southern continents and by the canals are given in Table 8.

These changes came in two stages. For the half-century that intervened between the openings of the Suez and of the Panama canals (1869–1914) the change affected principally Europe and the Orient, although even New York to Bombay was 3,000 miles shorter by Suez than by the Cape of Good Hope, and New York to Yokohama was 2,000 miles shorter. The opening of the Panama Canal had its major impact on relations between the east and west coasts of North America, between the

east coast of North America and the
west coast of South America, and between western Europe and the eastern
portions of the Pacific Ocean. The effects of the two canals are indicated in
a graphic manner, considerably simplified, in Figures 109 and 110.

The Great Lakes Waterway

The inland waterway with the world's
heaviest traffic is that constituted by
the Great Lakes, which lie between the
United States and Canada. They have

1952 traffic through the locks of the
Sault Sainte Marie Canals amounted to
94,889,000 long tons (United States
Department of Commerce, 1954, p.
602) as compared with 33,611,000
(*ibid.*, p. 604) through the Panama
Canal and 83,448,000 (Chamber of
Commerce, United Kingdom, 1953, p.
149) through the Suez Canal.

The Welland Canal between Lakes
Erie and Ontario was first opened in
1887, enlarged in 1932, and will be further enlarged as a part of the projected

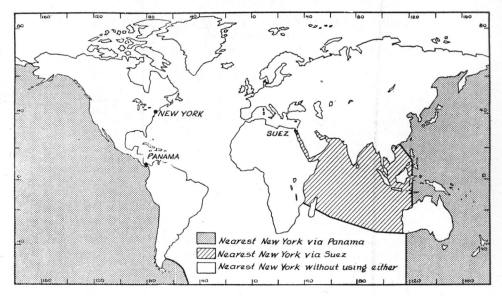

FIG. 110.—The effect of the Suez and Panama canals on distances from New York. (After
United States Navy, 1948.)

the advantage of needing little improvement by man, and they also connect regions of iron ore and wheat production on the west with markets and coal
fields to the east. The obstacle of the
falls in the St. Marys River (the "Soo")
between Lake Superior and Lake Hu-
ron was so slight as to encourage the
Northwest Fur Company to build a
small canal on the Canadian side as
early as 1797. In 1855 the first American canal was built, and this has become the world's busiest waterway. In

Great Lakes–St. Lawrence Seaway. This
latter improvement will bring ocean
shipping drawing up to 27 feet into the
Great Lakes. There is already a canal
of 9-foot draft connecting Lake Michigan with the Illinois River and the Mississippi River navigation. These constitute another major man-made change
in the waterways of the world.

Waterways as Barriers

The motto on the official seal of the
Panama Canal Zone reads: "A land di-

vided; the oceans united." This emphasizes the fact that an artificial waterway —like a natural one—is a barrier to land travel and that man has also changed his environment by separating lands. Herodotus (1928, Book ii) noted this result of the early canalization in Egypt:

By these forced labours the entire face of the country was changed; for whereas Egypt had formerly been a region suited for both horses and carriages . . . it is now unfit for either horse or carriage, being cut up by the canals, which are extremely numerous and run in all directions.

Those who have driven automobiles in the Netherlands will realize what he meant.

Not only do small canals cut up local circulation; large ship canals become major barriers. The Pulaski Skyway was built across the Newark meadows to avoid the traffic jams due to opening of drawbridges on the improved channels of the Hackensack and Passaic rivers. The enlargement of the Delaware and Chesapeake Canal necessitated the construction of new high-level bridges to carry main roads over the tallest ships without interrupting either route. Railroad-builders, especially, like to cross waterways at the lowest level, with the shortest span, and cordially detest drawbridges, which are expensive to build and upset schedules when open.

CONCLUSION

Port and harbor works, being protective and local in effect, have a rare distinction among man's activities in changing the face of the earth; they are almost universally beneficial, and it is seldom possible for their effect to be harmful. That great American student of man's modification of nature, George P. Marsh (1874, p. 401), concluded that, in them, "man has achieved some of his most remarkable and most honorable conquests over nature."

The construction of canals is not so universally and permanently beneficial. The barriers they set to land communication are always present. In addition, they may, as in China, unleash forces that man cannot completely control. The two great isthmian canals have been of unqualified benefit. It is interesting to note that Marsh (*ibid.*, p. 612) dismissed a sea-level canal across the Isthmus of Panama as impossible, was not interested in a locked canal because he was only concerned with "geographical" changes made by man, but considered the Suez Canal "the grandest and most truly cosmopolite physical improvement ever undertaken by man."

REFERENCES

BARTHOLOMEW, J., & SON (Comp.)
   1927   *Bartholomew's Survey Gazetteer of the British Isles.* 7th ed. Edinburgh: John Bartholomew & Son, Ltd. 768 pp. (plus 47 maps).
CARLES, W. R.
   1896–97   "The Grand Canal of China," *Journal of the China Branch, Royal Asiatic Society,* XXXI, 102–15.
CHAMBER OF COMMERCE, UNITED KINGDOM
   1953   *Annual Report, 1952–1953.* London: Witherby & Co., Ltd. 216 pp.
CHI CH'AO-TING
   1936   *Key Economic Areas in Chinese History: As Revealed in the Development of Public Works for Water-Control.* (Auspices of the American Council, Institute of Pacific Relations.) London: George Allen & Unwin, Ltd. 168 pp.
EKWALL, E.
   1951   *The Concise Oxford Dictionary of English Place Names.* 3d ed. Oxford: Clarendon Press. 530 pp.
FLEMING, W. B.
   1915   *The History of Tyre.* ("Columbia University Oriental Studies," Vol. X.) New York: Columbia University Press. 166 pp.

HARLOW, A. F.
   1926   *Old Towpaths.* New York: D. Appleton & Co. 403 pp.

HERODOTUS
   1928   *The History of Herodotus.* Trans. GEORGE RAWLINSON; ed. MANUEL KOMROFF. New York: Tudor Publishing Co. 544 pp.

HOMER
   1948   *The Odyssey.* Trans. S. H. BUTCHER and ANDREW LANG. Chicago: Great Books Foundation (Henry Regnery Co.). 389 pp.

JEANS, J. S.
   1890   *Waterways and Water Transport in Different Countries: With a Description of the Panama, Suez, Manchester, Nicaraguan, and Other Canals.* London: E. & F. N. Spon. 507 pp.

JONES, L. R.
   1932   *The Geography of London River.* New York: Dial Press. 184 pp.

LEHMANN-HARTLEBEN, K.
   1923   "Die antiken Hafenanlagen des Mittelmeeres," *Klio* (Beiträge zur alten Geschichte), N.F., Beiheft XIV, Heft I. 304 pp. (plus 3 pls. plus 39 plans). Leipzig.

MARSH, G. P.
   1874   *The Earth as Modified by Human Action: A New Edition of "Man and Nature."* New York: Scribner, Armstrong & Co. 656 pp.

PHILLIPS, J.
   1793   *General History of Inland Navigation Foreign and Domestic: Containing a Complete Account of the Canals Already Executed in England, with Considerations on Those Projected.* New ed. London: I. & J. Taylor. 371+33 pp.

POLO, MARCO
   1926   *The Travels of Marco Polo.* Revised from Marsden's Translation and Edited, with an Introduction, by MANUEL KOMROFF. New York: Boni & Liveright. 370 pp.

ROWE, R. S.
   1953   *Bibliography of Rivers and Harbors and Related Fields in Hydraulic Engineering.* Princeton, N.J.: Rivers and Harbors Section, Department of Civil Engineering, Princeton University. (This is a modern and exhaustive bibliography, covering history as well as specific engineering subjects and geographical divisions.)

SEMPLE, E. C.
   1932   *The Geography of the Mediterranean Region: Its Relation to Ancient History.* London: Constable & Co., Ltd. 737 pp.

SIEGFRIED, A.
   1940   *Suez and Panama.* New York: Harcourt, Brace & Co. 400 pp. (plus maps).

STEVENSON, D.
   1886   *Principles and Practice of Canal and River Engineering.* 3d ed. Edinburgh: A. & C. Black. 406 pp.

STRABO
   1903   *The Geography of Strabo.* Trans. H. C. HAMILTON and W. FALCONER. ("Bohn's Classical Library.") 3 vols. London: George Bell & Sons. 519+410+422 pp.

UNITED NATIONS
   1953   *Annual Bulletin, Transport Statistics, 1952.* Geneva: United Nations Economic Commission for Europe, Transport Division. 110 pp.

UNITED STATES CONGRESS
   1950   *Study of Domestic Land and Water Transportation: Hearings before the Senate Subcommittee on Domestic Land and Water Transport of the Committee on Interstate and Foreign Commerce, Pursuant to Senate Resolution 50, April 14–July 28, 1950.* (81st Cong., 1st sess.) Washington, D.C.: Government Printing Office. 1,574 pp.

   1953   *St. Lawrence Seaway: Hearings before the Senate Subcommittee of the Committee on Foreign Relations on S 589, etc., April 14, 15, 16, May 20 and 21, 1953.* (83d Cong., 1st sess.) Washington, D.C.: Government Printing Office. 565 pp.

UNITED STATES DEPARTMENT OF COMMERCE
   1954   *Statistical Abstract of the United States, 1954.* Washington, D.C.: Government Printing Office. 1,056 pp.

UNITED STATES NAVY
   1948   *Table of Distances between Ports.* (Hydrographic Office Publica-

tion No. 117.) Washington, D.C.: Government Printing Office. 485 pp.

1951   *Sailing Directions for the Mediterranean,* Vol. IV. (Hydrographic Office Publication No. 154A.) 2d ed. Washington, D.C.: Government Printing Office. 294 pp.

1952   *Sailing Directions for the Mediterranean,* Vol. V. (Hydrographic Office Publication No. 154B.) 2d ed. Washington, D.C.: Government Printing Office. 510 pp.

1953   *World Port Index.* (Hydrographic Office Publication No. 950.) Washington, D.C.: Government Printing Office. 230 pp.

VERNON-HARCOURT, L. F.

1885   *Harbours and Docks: Their Physical Features, History, Construction, Equipment, and Maintenance with Statistics as to Their Commercial Development.* 2 vols. Oxford: Clarendon Press. 702 pp. (plus 16 pls.).

VITRUVIUS

1931   *On Architecture.* Trans. from the Latin by F. GRANGER. 2 vols. New York: G. P. Putnam's Sons. 317+384 pp.

Changes in Quantities and Qualities of Ground and Surface Waters

HAROLD E. THOMAS*

Several years ago a comprehensive survey was made of Lake Mead, the reservoir formed by Hoover Dam on the Colorado River (see Figs. 31 and 32, pp. 29 and 30). One major objective of that survey was to determine the amount of sediment that had accumulated in the lake during the first fourteen years of its existence (Thomas, 1954). Specialists in many scientific fields and from numerous federal agencies and scientific institutions had been assembled for the survey. For the specific job of calculating the sediment there were maps showing the original lake bed, sonar equipment for accurate measurement of the depth of the lake bed beneath the water surface, and means for accurate location of the echo-sounding craft at all times. The measurement of the amount of sediment was a complicated process. The lake level fluctuated through a wide range, and each depth measurement had to be keyed to the contemporaneous stage of the lake as recorded at Hoover Dam.

---

* Dr. Thomas has been geologist and ground-water hydrologist in the United States Geological Survey since 1931, except for three years of service as engineer intelligence officer in the Southwest Pacific during World War II. His recent survey of the national ground-water situation, under the sponsorship of the Conservation Foundation, has been published under the title *The Conservation of Ground Water*, 1951. Other publications include *Ground-Water Regions in the United States— Their Storage Facilities*, 1952, and *The First Fourteen Years of Lake Mead*, 1954.

But the stage record first had to be corrected for instrumental errors. Other corrections had to be applied whenever the lake surface varied from level by reason of seiche action, pile-up due to wind, or large inflow at the upper end of the reservoir. And the maps showing the prelake surface were incomplete, so that they had to be extrapolated in many areas.

This determination of the sediment accumulation in Lake Mead, difficult though it was, was a simple matter in comparison with the evaluation of the effects of man's activities upon the ground- and surface-water resources of the earth, our present topic. Nevertheless, there are several pertinent analogies. Like the levels of Lake Mead, the quantities of water in streams, lakes, and ground-water reservoirs are continually fluctuating. Many of these fluctuations are due to natural causes, and the changes resulting from those causes must therefore be identified and evaluated before we can evaluate with any assurance the effects of man. It is necessary also to scrutinize our methods of measurement throughout the period of record, in order to be assured that apparent changes in the water resource are not traceable to changes in techniques and equipment over the years.

In the evaluation of the total effects of man's activities upon water resources there is no counterpart for the maps that showed the conditions prior to the creation of Lake Mead. It is rare indeed to find any evidence of the natural hydrologic conditions prior to man's occupancy of a region. Necessarily, then, the total effects of man's activity in most places are in the realm of extrapolation, assumption, generalization, and, sometimes, expostulation.

The records that show the changes in quantities and qualities of surface and ground water are obtained as part of a continuing inventory of water resources: stream discharge, lake stage, water levels in wells, spring discharge, temperature, and chemical and bacteriological analyses of ground and surface waters. These records show the composite effects of all factors—natural and artificial—that affect the quantity or quality of ground and surface waters. The discrimination of the effects of individual factors may be possible in detailed studies of small areas, but it is generally less conclusive in larger areas where the changes result from a greater variety of causative factors. However, there is abundant evidence in hydrologic literature that both man's use of water and his use of the land can modify the water resource.

Practically all of man's uses of water can be expected to change either the quantity or the quality, or both, of the resources of ground and surface water. If water is consumed in the use and returned to the atmosphere as vapor, those resources are correspondingly reduced. If water is non-consumptively used, it remains in a liquid state and is eventually returned to a ground- or surface-water body, but generally the chemical or physical properties of the water are changed by the use.

Consumptive use of ground and surface water accounts for only a fraction of the water in the major categories of use by man. It is negligible in production of power, navigation, disposal of wastes, and recreational use, except for the evaporation from water surfaces exposed for those uses. Of the water ap-plied for irrigation, as little as half may be used consumptively, and probably considerably less than half the municipal and domestic water is actually consumed. Generally, only a small proportion of industrial water is used consumptively, but there is a wide range among the different industries. In the United States the total consumptive use of water in irrigation, industry, and public supply may be of the order of 50–80 billion gallons a day, which is about 4–6 per cent of the average streamflow. However, one should not expect this amount of reduction in the streamflow from the nation's borders, because much of the consumptive use is in lieu of the natural return of water to the atmosphere by evaporation or by transpiration of native vegetation.

It is more difficult to place an upper limit on the possible effect of non-consumptive use upon the qualities of ground and surface waters. Non-consumptively used waters include especially sewage, industrial wastes, and irrigation return flows; but, when these are added to a stream or ground-water reservoir, they may render far larger quantities of water unsuitable for some uses. Even the non-consumptive uses for generation of hydroelectric power, river navigation, or recreation may be pre-emptive in the sense that they require storage of water or flows of water that could otherwise be used for other purposes. Thus practically every type of use of water may reduce the quantity or impair the quality of the water resources available for other water-users.

Mankind has not always been aware that uses of water must change the natural resources. The hallowed riparian doctrine of water rights in streams, stemming from an English court decision in 1833, specifies that water-users shall not reduce the quantity or impair the quality of the water in the stream —which, if strictly interpreted, would prevent any use of the water. Many humid regions can nevertheless adhere to the doctrine, because the progressive gain in streamflow offsets the reductions by consumptive use and dilutes the impurities resulting from non-consumptive use. Because of our increasing understanding of the effects of water use on the natural resources, more and more of the new water-development projects are producing changes of which the responsible parties can say, "It was planned that way." There is still room for improvement, of course.

Changes in the surface- and ground-water resources resulting from man's occupancy and modification of the land generally are less direct and less well documented than those resulting from water use. Most of these changes have been inadvertent, and many may have been in progress for years, or even centuries, before anyone recognized the possibility of a relation between the water resources and the land modifications wrought by man.

THE HYDROLOGIC CYCLE

Any changes wrought by man in the quantities or qualities of ground or surface water represent modifications in the natural pattern of circulation of water. Because of this natural circulation—the hydrologic cycle—water is generally a renewable resource, and it is therefore exceptional among the mineral resources of the earth and similar to the animal and vegetable resources. Ground water and surface water are only two of several phases in the hydrologic cycle, but they are exceedingly important to man, because they provide his fresh-water supplies.

The science of hydrology embraces all phases of the hydrologic cycle. So complex is each of these phases that hydrologists must also be specialists in one or more of the closely related sciences of climatology, soil science, geol-

ogy, chemistry, physics, biology, and agronomy. Partly because of the complexities of the hydrologic cycle and partly because of the high degree of specialization of technical research, there are only a few small areas where we yet have a reasonably complete and quantitative description of the operations of the hydrologic cycle. We know how variable the paths of a particle of water in the hydrologic cycle can be in various parts of the earth. The ceaseless and somewhat capricious circulation of water is depicted in Figure 111. Of the water that reaches the land surface by precipitation, some may evaporate where it falls; some may infiltrate into the soil; some may run off overland to evaporate or infiltrate elsewhere or to enter streams. Of the water that infiltrates into the ground, some may be evaporated; some may be absorbed by plant roots and then transpired; some may percolate downward to ground-water reservoirs. Of the water that enters ground-water reservoirs, some may move laterally until it is close enough to the surface to be subject to evaporation or transpiration; some may reach the land surface and form springs, seeps, or lakes; some may flow directly into streams or into the oceans. Of the water in streams, some may accumulate in lakes and surface reservoirs; some may be lost by evaporation or transpiration of riparian vegetation; some may seep downward into ground-water reservoirs; some may continue on to a salt lake or the ocean. The hydrologic cycle is completed by evaporation from these saline-water bodies and by circulation of water vapor in the atmosphere.

Obviously, change is fundamental in all aspects of this natural circulation of water: geographic variations (from place to place on all the land masses of the earth) and also secular changes (from time to time at any point). Because of the interrelations of the various phases of the hydrologic cycle, the ground- and surface-water resources vary in response to climatic changes either in rates of precipitation or in rates of return of water to the atmosphere. Man's development of and use of water necessarily modify the natural circulatory pattern, and by various means he may also change the rates of infiltration or evapotranspiration at the land surface or the flow of water upon or under the land surface.

transpiration draft or in snow-melt which result from day-to-night changes in air temperature; storm runoff from intense or long-continued precipitation; seasonal fluctuations corresponding to seasonal variations in precipitation or temperature; annual variations in runoff reflecting in part the variations in

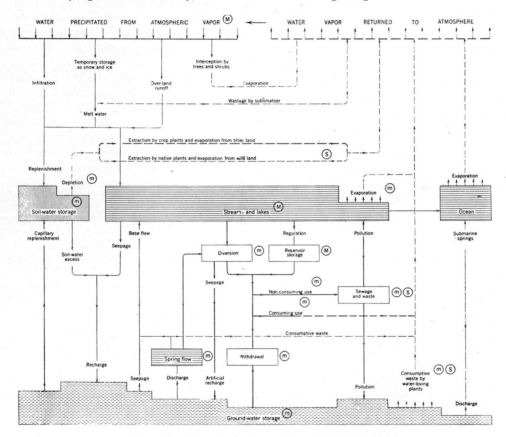

FIG. 111.—Water's complex pattern of circulation

CHANGES CORRELATED WITH NATURAL FACTORS

Many fluctuations in stream discharge are directly correlative with climatic factors: diurnal fluctuations resulting from the differences in evapo-

yearly precipitation over the drainage basin. Certain fluctuations of water levels in wells in many areas have also been correlated with climatic fluctuations—recharge from a single storm, from the precipitation of a rainy season, or from a stream at high stage because of abundant rainfall or snowmelt. Floods and droughts represent the effects of extremes in precipitation, which are clearly reflected in many records of runoff, lake and reservoir storage, and storage in many ground-water reservoirs.

Most of the secular changes in ground and surface waters attributed to natural causes are changes in quantity, because they result from increments (or the lack of increments) of the relatively pure water of precipitation. However, some significant changes in quality also result from natural causes. Thus, in arid regions, water in lakes and reservoirs increases in concentration of dissolved solids when the rate of evaporation exceeds the rate of inflow from streams and direct precipitation. Changing rates of runoff may also be accompanied by changing quality of water in some streams. For example, the Saline River in Kansas receives mineralized water from the ground at a fairly constant rate, but, because of variations in storm runoff, the concentration of dissolved solids has ranged from 210 to more than 4,400 parts per million in a single year (Durum, 1953). The total chemical denudation by water of the land masses of the earth is large; it is estimated to be of the order of 60 tons per square mile annually (Clarke, 1924, pp. 114–21).

The fluctuations in surface-water resources, and in many ground-water resources, in response to climatic variations are so commonplace that they are taken for granted by water-users, and the variations from "normal" precipitation provide an index to the water supplies that can be expected from streams, reservoirs, and some wells. So long as the "normal" remains constant —even though there are marked variations from day to day, season to season, and year to year—these variations can doubtless be discriminated from the changes caused by man, which are likely to be progressively greater in response to the increasing tempo of man's operations. However, with increasing length of records of precipitation and

temperature, there is increasing evidence of progressive changes, or time trends, in the climate of many regions.

Cyclic climatic fluctuations have been discussed by many scientists, and there is general agreement that, if cyclic fluctuations exist, they are certainly not yet sufficiently well defined to provide a basis for reliable long-range forecasting of precipitation or temperature. Otherwise the opinions vary greatly, some concluding that there is no definite evidence of climatic cycles (Henry, 1931), others believing that meteorological conditions tend to recur in more or less obscure cycles (Horton, 1899), and still others finding cycles of varying length, which necessarily create a complex pattern of time trends in any long-term record of precipitation or temperature. As pointed out by Willett (1953, p. 55):

There is continually in progress an entire spectrum of cyclical fluctuations of climate, cycles of shorter period and smaller amplitude being superposed on those of longer period and larger amplitude. These cycles include one whose half period, at least in Europe, extends from the Climatic Optimum at about 3000 B.C. to the peak glaciation from A.D. 1600 to 1900; a second cycle of smaller amplitude and a period of some 2000 years, cool-wet from 500 B.C. to A.D. 100, warm-dry from 400 to 1000, and cool-wet from the thirteenth century to the present; and shorter and smaller cycles, from a few centuries in period to the 80-year, the double sunspot, and the single sunspot cycles observed during the past two centuries.

The records of precipitation at numerous localities in the western United States now cover more than a half-century, and many of these indicate alternation of wet and dry periods of several years' duration. Thus in southern California, where most of the precipitation comes from the Pacific Ocean and occurs in winter, alternating wet and dry periods commonly ten to fifteen years in duration have been identified (Stafford and Troxell, 1953). In Texas, Oklahoma, and Kansas, where precipitation is derived principally from the Gulf of Mexico and occurs chiefly in the summer (Kansas Water Resources Committee, 1955), there are indications of cyclic fluctuations in summer precipitation at several localities. These fluctuations are of length similar to those in California, but they are opposite in phase. In some localities in the intervening southern Rocky Mountain region, the trends in summer and winter precipitation have some similarity to those in localities dominated, respectively, by the Gulf and Pacific types of precipitation. Thus at Salt Lake City the winter precipitation appears to reflect the Pacific cyclic trends and the summer precipitation agrees fairly well with the Gulf trends.

Of the several cyclic fluctuations mentioned by Willett, only the shortest —the sunspot and double sunspot— would be shown completely on most of the available precipitation records, although the records for some localities are long enough to cover the period of an eighty-year cycle. Records pertaining to surface or ground water are generally far shorter than those of precipitation, although a few exceptionally long records are available for interpretation. For example, Abbot (1935) reports periodicities in climate integrally related to the twenty-three-year sunspot cycle, and he finds the effects of this cycle in the records of discharge of the Nile River and the levels of the Great Lakes.

From various sources there are indications of long-term changes in the climate of the earth, which may be the effects of climatic cycles having periods of several centuries. Kincer (1946) shows that temperatures at the stations of longest record have been increasing progressively for eighty years or more; drawing upon records from Canada, Europe, Asia, South America, and the

East Indies, he concludes that "the practically unanimous testimony of these graphs not only establishes the realness of these upward trends but shows that they are operative on an extensive geographical scale." In the years since 1940 there has been a slight downward trend at many localities, but it is not yet known whether this represents a reversal of the long-term trend. The argument that most records are obtained in cities where an upward temperature trend might result from man's occupancy was anticipated by Kincer, and he has shown that the increase in temperature is as marked in Lynchburg and Dale Enterprise, Virginia, and Easton, Maryland, as in the city of Baltimore.

Glaciers provide excellent evidence as to the balance between precipitation and evaporation. If the precipitation is heavy enough or the temperature low enough to retard the rate of evaporation, the glacier will advance; if precipitation is light or temperature sufficiently high, the glacial front will recede. The long-term trends as shown by glacial advances and recessions result entirely from natural conditions and need not be adjusted for man's activity. The data summarized by Matthes (1946) show that glacial recession has been general since the middle of the nineteenth century and that it is world wide. The data, like those of temperature, suggest a rough synchronism in long-term climatic trends throughout the world; these trends in the last century would cause a decrease in net water supplies, and probably a deterioration of quality, of both surface water and ground water. Since 1940, many glaciers have been advancing, as might be expected with the decreasing temperatures. The glacial advances in Glacier Park, Montana, have coincided with forecasts based on sunspot cycles (Dightman and Beatty, 1952).

Measurements by the United States

Coast and Geodetic Survey since 1900 show that there has been a gradual but progressive rise in sea level along the Atlantic, Gulf, and Pacific coasts of the United States—slight in the first three decades of the century and at an increased rate since 1930 (Marmer, 1949). It is not known to what extent these changes may be due to changes in the relative position of continental blocks and the ocean floors of the earth's crust. However, a decrease in the water held on the continents in streams, lakes, subsurface storage, or in arctic regions in ice masses, would result in a corresponding increase in the water of the oceans. The rise in sea level therefore is not in conflict with other hydrologic evidence that in the past century the trend has been toward decreasing net water supplies on the continents. Indeed, the pronounced rise in ocean level beginning about 1930 may reflect the widespread depletion of surface-water and ground-water supplies in the drought of the 1930's. It is well known that during the glacial epochs, when vast quantities of ice were stored on the continents, the sea level was several hundred feet lower than it is today.

Research in tree-ring hydrology (Schulman, 1951) gives promise of providing a basis for detailed analysis of changes in arid regions during the past several centuries—changes that may have been in progress for periods far longer than are covered by recorded data on precipitation, runoff, ground-water storage, glacial advances and recessions, or sea-level changes.

CHANGES CORRELATED WITH WATER USE

It is possible to look at water or to float upon it without changing its natural course through the hydrologic cycle, but practically all other uses of water require some modification of the natural circulation; and even for con-

tinuing enjoyment of recreation or navigation it may be desirable to make some changes in the natural conditions. Consequently, many changes in quantity and quality of ground and surface waters are clearly correlated with water development and use. Among the most obvious of these are the effects of the storage and regulation of streamflow by artificial reservoirs. Natural variations in the quantity and quality of inflowing water tend to disappear in a reservoir, so that the outflowing water has greater uniformity of quality and can be released at rates best suited for man's purposes.

The development and sustained use of ground water similarly modify the natural circulation of water by diverting through wells the water that would naturally be discharged into streams, springs, and seeps or, at the land surface, by evapotranspiration. Gravity is the controlling force in the natural circulation and also causes the flow toward a well as water is withdrawn. Water tables and artesian pressures must be lower than they would be without the development and use of wells, and they will continue to decline until a new equilibrium is established in the hydrologic cycle, in which the well discharge is balanced by decreased natural ground-water discharge or by increased recharge. "Falling water tables" are likely to constitute significant progressive changes during increasing development and use of ground water.

Water is being withdrawn from some ground-water reservoirs at rates in excess of the natural replenishment, and the result is that the storage in the reservoir is being progressively depleted. In these areas water is being mined, just as the non-renewable resources of iron, copper, or petroleum are mined. In the United States the principal areas of ground-water mining are in the southwestern states (Thomas, 1951, Pl. II). In any area of ground-water mining there are progressive changes in quantity of ground water because of man's development. Doubtless the cessation of withdrawal from wells in most of these areas would be followed by gradual refilling and eventual restoration of the natural storage and circulation in the ground-water reservoir (Nelson and Thomas, 1953). However, in some areas near the seacoast, the withdrawal of fresh water has been accompanied by inflow of ocean water,[1] with the result that the quality of water in the ground-water reservoir has been changed, perhaps permanently.

Subsidence of the land surface has been reported in many areas of heavy ground-water draft, and it may well be occurring in most regions of progressive depletion of ground-water storage. Measured subsidence attributed to ground-water withdrawal has been as great as 1.5 feet at Las Vegas, Nevada (Thomas, 1954), 3 feet near Texas City, Texas (Winslow and Doyel, 1954b), and 6 feet at San Jose, California (Tolman and Poland, 1940). In Mexico City the annual rate of subsidence increased from 1.6 inches in 1937 to 5.5 inches in 1948 and 11.5 inches in 1954, and the Palace of Fine Arts has been lowered 16 feet since 1937 (Ortiz, 1953; Anonymous, 1954). The obvious effects of land subsidence are disruption of drainage and, particularly in urbanized areas, potential damage to structures. A less obvious but ultimately more important effect may be the permanent loss of underground water-storage capacity.

Artificial recharge constitutes an important effort by man to adapt the natural water resources to his needs, on the basis that, if the natural replenishment to a ground-water reservoir is insufficient for the demand (as in any area of ground-water mining), he will augment the inflow by artificial means. Notable progress has been made in artificial recharge in some regions, as in Sweden, where artificial ground water now constitutes about 10 per cent of all water used for municipal supplies (Jansa, 1951). In the United States there are numerous examples of artificial recharge (Todd, 1955), but in comparison with the magnitude of ground-water development these would represent no more than experimental or pilot projects. Nevertheless, artificial recharge has increased the storage in some ground-water reservoirs (Blaney and Donnan, 1945) and has reduced the rate of depletion in many others. Artificial recharge is achieved in many places through wells, shafts, or other excavations, but the most common method is by water-spreading in the recharge area of a ground-water reservoir, either in natural channels, constructed basins or ponds, or ditches and furrows which may serve also to irrigate crops in the spreading area. A water-spreading area in southern California is shown in Figure 112. Studies indicate that the consumptive use of water by vegetation in a spreading area generally is negligible in comparison with its beneficial effect upon the percolation rate (Mitchelson and Muckel, 1937), and more recent research has developed other means of increasing the rate of infiltration in water-spreading areas (Muckel, 1951).

The changes in ground and surface water summarized in preceding paragraphs result from man's withdrawal of water for use or from his efforts to regulate the natural resource for sustained withdrawal. These are also the principal changes that result from consumptive use of water, because consumptive use involves withdrawing of water from natural sources and combining it with other matter or passing it as vapor to the atmosphere. However, any water that is returned to the

1. Todd, 1952; Banks and Richter, 1953; Winslow and Doyel, 1954a; Parker, 1955.

FIG. 112.—Water-spreading area for artificial ground-water recharge

atmosphere must leave a residue of the salts that were dissolved in it. This residue may be left in water remaining as ground or surface water, in the soil, or in boilers or other heated vessels. For many water-users, as, for example, those using water for irrigation in arid regions, an important use of water is the non-consumptive one of flushing away the residues left by water used consumptively.

Non-consumptive use of water has resulted in significant increases in quantities of ground water in numerous areas, especially in arid regions where surface water has been diverted and used for irrigation. These effects of irrigation are identical with the artificial recharge achieved by water-spreading, except that they generally have been unintended and unforeseen. In some places the increased ground-water storage has been welcome, because it has provided water for increased development and use. As a general rule, however, the introduction of irrigation to arid and semiarid regions has been followed by drainage problems. In the valleys of the western United States there are thousands of acres of water-logged and abandoned land, larger areas where productivity has decreased because of a rising water table and of salinization and structural changes in soils, and extensive drainage projects to overcome these difficulties.

The Imperial Valley of southern California provides an excellent example of progressive deterioration of irrigated lands and also of man's ability to overcome these difficulties (Donnan *et al.*, 1954). The Imperial Irrigation District embraces about 500,000 acres of irrigable land and uses nearly 3,000,000 acre-feet of water annually. The water comes from the Colorado River and contains nearly a ton of salts per acre-foot. Irrigation water was first brought into the valley in 1901, and the need for drainage became evident as early as 1902. By 1919, about 25 per cent of the irrigable land had become affected by a high water table and salt accumulation, and soon thereafter an extensive system of open drains was constructed at a cost of $2,500,000. Nevertheless in 1940 the water table was less than 6 feet below the land surface in 44 per cent of the area, and in an average year salt was accumulating in the soil at a rate of about a ton per irrigated acre. During the next ten years, however, methods for adequate drainage were developed by research, and more than 100,000 acres were successfully drained; the entire area is now well along toward complete reclamation.

Non-consumptive uses of water have caused a wide variety of changes in the qualities of surface and ground waters. With increasing population, increasing industrialization, and increasing agricultural use of the land, it is inevitable that the non-consumptively used waters —sewage, industrial wastes, and return flow from irrigation—will cause progressive deterioration in quality of the water to which they are returned unless effective countermeasures are undertaken. These effective countermeasures are the essence of pollution control, and for a discussion of corrective measures the undesirable elements in non-consumptively used water may be logically grouped as organic wastes, dissolved inorganic wastes, solid or semisolid refuse, and heat.

Organic wastes are putrescible and eventually are fully decomposed by nature. Organic wastes have caused progressive deterioration in quality of surface water in many places, reflecting increasing rates of waste disposal. But this form of pollution is curable, for the cost of adequate treatment facilities, and need not represent a permanent change in any water.

The soluble chemicals or minerals comprising the inorganic wastes largely remain in the water, and their effects are usually diminished only by dilution. Many industries must dispose of soluble inorganic wastes, and many mines and oil fields must dispose of natural waters that are saline or acid in order to develop fuels and mineral resources of economic value. As examples, 6,500 gallons of mineralized water must be pumped per ton of anthracite coal mined in Pennsylvania, for an average of 470 million gallons a day in 1951 (Ash *et al.*, 1953); and with each gallon of petroleum produced in Kansas there is a by-product of 5 gallons of brine, so that about 65 million gallons a day of brine must be disposed of (Kansas Water Resources Committee, 1955). Some waste products can be injected into deep wells or piped directly to the ocean, but a large proportion has been dumped into streams, with the general result that the quality of water in those streams has deteriorated markedly because of man's activities.

Solid or semisolid wastes may be flushed on out to sea or, like the sediment carried naturally in streams, may accumulate in reservoirs or fill the stream channel: the sediment from placer mining in California filled stream beds and aggravated the flood hazard until the placer operations were subjected to rigid control. The deleterious effect of heat is perhaps best demonstrated by the Mahoning River in Ohio, where, through repeated industrial use of water, the total diversions for cooling may be as much as ten times the flow in the river and where the river temperatures may sometimes become so high as to render normal sewage-purification processes ineffective.

The quality of stream waters is indicated by continuing measurements of temperature, dissolved solids, suspended sediment, and organic content. These data indicate the suitability of the water for various types of use— drinking and culinary, sanitary and service, cooling, processing, boiler feed,

irrigation, etc.—and comparison with earlier data (where available) may show the effects of man's use. As a rule, both the volume of waste and the volume of water in the stream vary through a wide range during a year.

The suitability of stream water for aquatic life, and therefore for recreation, cannot be fully evaluated on the basis of the measurements as to quality. Pollution of a stream has diverse effects upon the biodynamic cycle: sediment destroys the habitats of, or is directly injurious to, certain organisms; sewage removes oxygen; some chemicals have toxic effects; high temperatures are injurious to many forms of life (Patrick, 1949). The composite effect of pollution upon aquatic life is a resultant of these several factors and requires analysis of changes in the biologic equilibrium. Commonly, the first effect of pollution is to eliminate some species but to increase the abundance of those remaining. More severe toxic effects eliminate additional groups, and very severe toxic effects kill all organisms. Recently a continuous sampler of diatom flora has been developed which gives promise of serving as a reliable indicator of the biologic effects of pollution (Patrick *et al.*, 1954).

The quality of ground water has been affected by waste disposal in many places, chiefly by dissolved mineral matter. Such effects have been traced to percolation of water from contaminated streams, to the discharge of wastes into pits or wells, or to their distribution over the ground. The evidences of pollution may not appear for many years, because of the characteristically slow movement of water underground. Some uncommon and unnatural industrial by-products have acted as tracers, revealing paths of underground movement of water that had not been previously known or even suspected. The disposal of radioactive wastes in the United States, supervised to date by the Atomic Energy Commission, is preceded by studies to insure that these wastes will not appear in places where they are not intended and definitely not wanted. As the use of radioactive materials becomes more widespread, it will be important to maintain this assurance that waste disposal will not affect the usable water resources.

The unconsumed water from irrigation generally impairs the quality of the water to which it returns, whether by flow to a stream or by downward percolation to a ground-water reservoir. As already mentioned, the non-consumptive use of water is essential for maintenance of a satisfactory salt balance in the soils of arid regions, and it may be concluded that some deterioration is inevitable as a price for the multiple use of water that is characteristic of many irrigated regions.

The history of the Gila River Basin in Arizona exemplifies many changes in quantity and quality of ground and surface waters as a result of water use (Halpenny *et al.*, 1952). Reservoirs were constructed more than twenty-five years ago on the Salt and Gila rivers to store and regulate the streamflow, and the use of water within the basin has been so intensive that there has been practically no outflow from the basin into the Colorado River for thirteen years. Diversion and non-consumptive use of the surface water soon caused an increase in ground-water storage, and a rising water table caused difficulties in the vicinity of Phoenix more than thirty years ago; but these difficulties were successfully overcome by pumping from wells. The pumping provided water for increasing the irrigated acreage, and further ground-water development was undertaken with enthusiasm, so that in recent years ground water in the Salt River Valley has been mined at increasing rates for irrigation of larger and larger areas. Non-con-

sumptive use and re-use of ground water have caused a progressive deterioration in quality of water in the lower part of the basin, and as a result lands were being abandoned in the vicinity of Wellton and Mohawk until recently, when the purer water of the Colorado River was imported for irrigation.

Individual developments and uses of water have made innumerable changes in the quality or quantity of the water available to other water-users, even though there has been no significant change in the regional water resources. This is to be expected, inasmuch as each development results in some modification of the natural circulation of water. Such modifications are likely to cause controversies among the water-users affected, and many court decisions involving water have been concerned entirely with local hydrologic details. The term "interference" has been applied to the reduced yield of one well caused by withdrawal from a near-by well, and this term might be extended broadly to many other local changes resulting from development: the reduction of streamflow or spring discharge due to pumping from wells; the reduction in ground-water recharge due to diversion of surface water to other areas; the reduction in ground-water recharge due to regulation of streamflow for purposes of flood control, navigation, or other use; and many other instances in which ground-water use may affect surface-water resources, or vice versa.

CHANGES CORRELATED WITH LAND OCCUPANCY

In numerous localities the quantities and qualities of the water resources have been changed by enterprises of civilization not related to the use of those resources. Generally, the changes pertain to ground water, although in some instances the surface water has been modified. Some of these changes have been intentional and some have been beneficial, but others have been detrimental either to the user of land or to the user of water in the affected area.

The total acreage of cultivated land has been increased materially by artificial drainage of swampy areas and lakes. Some such areas occur in practically every one of the United States, but they are especially numerous where Pleistocene glaciation left thousands of lakes, swamps, and undrained depressions. In Michigan about 14,000 square miles of land have been artificially drained by some 23,000 miles of open ditches or tiled drains. The regional water table has been lowered significantly in about one-third of this area.

In many places in the United States the drainage has not been as beneficial as anticipated. Some drains have made land suitable for plowing earlier in the spring but have also reduced the available water supplies for crops in the critical late-summer months. Commonly, the effects of drainage have extended considerably beyond the troublesome swampy area, and the water table has been lowered to the disadvantage of the surrounding areas. Drainage of many natural depressions has aggravated the flood capabilities of streams by providing an outlet for surplus runoff which, prior to drainage, had been held within the area.

On the other hand, some drainage projects have produced valuable water in addition to their principal objective of improving the usability of the land. For example, the shallow water table was lowered several feet by drains prior to construction of the Geneva Works of United States Steel Corporation near Provo, Utah. These drains have reduced the natural evapotranspiration within the plant area, and they now discharge water equivalent in quantity to the consumptive use of water within the plant. Thus Utah has gained a major industry

having a large water requirement but with practically no depletion of the state's developed water resources. By economical water management, the Geneva Works return to other water-users in the drainage basin more water than had been returned to them by former occupants when the same area was agricultural land (Thomas, 1952b).

In many areas the natural infiltration to the soil has been modified by structures that serve to "waterproof" the land surface. The effect of impermeable surfacing is evident along paved highways in the desert, for the vegetation adjacent to the pavement characteristically is more luxuriant than the same species at greater distance from the highway, because of the water flowing from the pavement during rains. In urban areas, buildings, streets, and parking lots may cover a large proportion of the total land area; about half of the area of Brooklyn, New York, has been thus waterproofed, and the recharge to the underlying ground-water reservoir is now probably about half as great as under natural conditions. The precipitation on these constructed impermeable surfaces may be carried by storm sewers to streams and thus may contribute to flood peaks.

In some regions, constructed impermeable surfaces provide water for beneficial use, including culinary use by people who are not allergic to birds. The water supply for Gibraltar is a notable example, and many farm homes in the United States have cisterns which store water collected from house roofs.

In many agricultural areas there is evidence that the soil permeability has been modified by man sufficiently to reduce infiltration from precipitation. Changes, for example, in vegetative cover, tillage practices, and irrigation that increases the exchangeable sodium in the soil have also changed soil permeability (Barksdale and Remson, 1954). These modifications may have reduced the natural recharge to some ground-water reservoirs and thus re- duced the volume of ground water in storage, but generally the evidence is inconclusive. Statements as to the effect of agricultural land use upon ground- water resources commonly lack one or more of the following essential ele- ments of proof: (1) that there is a ground-water reservoir beneath the soil whose permeability has been modified; (2) that the storage in that reservoir has decreased since the modification; (3) that this decrease cannot be ascribed to natural causes; and (4) that this decrease is not caused by man's development and use of the ground water. Most of the effects of agricul- tural use of the land upon ground- water resources, therefore, are properly included in the next section.

THE REALM OF UNCERTAINTY AND GENERALIZATION

Land use is only one of many areas in which we have not yet the evidence to draw quantitative conclusions as to the effect of man upon the quantities and qualities of ground and surface waters. Indeed, it is quite possible that several paragraphs contained in the preceding sections will be shown by further research to have a greater ele- ment of uncertainty than has been indi- cated. This is a common weakness of summary papers of this sort, which tend to present broad generalizations on the basis of a very few cited exam- ples.

Nature in the past has reversed some of man's best judgments. Several years ago the city of Chicago was the recipi- ent of protests from other users of the Great Lakes, who said that the diver- sions through the Chicago Sanitary and Ship Canal were lowering the lake lev- els and reducing the natural outflow from the lakes. The large diversions were primarily for the purpose of dilut- ing the city's raw sewage, which was

discharged into the canal and carried into the Mississippi River Basin. The decision of the city to provide treat- ment for its sewage—predicated upon a Supreme Court decision—permitted a substantial reduction in diversions and also benefited a segment of humanity by improving the quality of the water resources. But, with rising lake levels in recent years, the importance of natu- ral factors has been more fully realized than it was during the controversy over the drainage canal.

Some of our longest records of lake levels or of stream discharge indicate progressive changes that have not yet been certainly correlated either with natural factors or with man's activities. Thus, the level of Devils Lake in North Dakota dropped progressively from 1867 to 1940, and the storage in it dwindled from 1,500,000 to 20,000 acre- feet (Thomas, 1951). This decline has been attributed by some workers to the change from grassland to cultivated land in the drainage basin, although the lake level had begun to recede before that change took place. Recent studies (Swenson and Colby, 1955) indicate that the fluctuations in lake level reflect fluctuations in climate, including both precipitation and temperature. After the effects of these natural factors are assessed quantitatively, the influence of man can be evaluated.

There is as yet no complete explana- tion for the changes in runoff of the Columbia River. The runoff at The Dalles, Oregon, declined progressively from an annual average of 167 million acre-feet in the ten years 1893–1902 to an average of 113 million acre-feet in 1936–45. During this period of decline the use of water for irrigation increased, particularly in the Snake River Basin in Idaho. But recent studies (Simons, 1953) show that the total consumptive use is currently less than 7 million acre- feet, a very small part of the measured decline in runoff. The runoff of the Columbia has trended upward since 1943, and several more decades of record may show whether the changes are due to cyclic fluctuations in climate.

There are several ground-water reservoirs in Kansas which, in the memories of the present generation, have always yielded water unfit for use, although similar aquifers in the vicinity yield potable water (Kansas Water Resources Committee, 1955). Is the poor quality of water due to pollution that occurred many decades ago, or is it a natural condition? In the absence of data for those early years, the question may remain unanswered. But, if periodic resampling shows a gradual improvement of quality in some of these sources, there is at least an inference of pollution that has since been abated, and there are prospects that the water some day may become usable.

In some developed ground-water reservoirs, even though water levels in wells are known to have been lowered by pumping, it cannot be said with assurance that the reservoir is overdeveloped, because an unknown proportion of the decline is caused by below-normal precipitation, streamflow, and recharge (Waite and Thomas, 1955).

The "falling water tables" reported in many regions are matters of great concern to many people, especially those who are not familiar with the peculiarities of ground water. A falling water table can be evidence of ground-water mining, but it can also be the result of drawing upon storage during drought where the average use does not exceed the safe yield, and it can also be a product of interference among closely spaced wells. The water table can be lowered also because of natural factors.

Use (or "abuse") of land that tends to reduce soil permeability may well be a factor in reducing ground-water storage in some areas, but from present information this factor has been emphasized out of all proportion to its true importance (Bernhagen, 1950). And, similarly, the slogan for correcting "abuse" of the land—"hold the raindrop where it falls"—is a generalization that ignores the great natural variations in permeability of soils and underlying rock materials.

PROBLEMS FOR THE FUTURE

The incomplete answer that must be given to the question as to man's role in changing the natural resources of ground and surface waters is a clue to the problems facing hydrologists in the future. For the historian, the record of these changes is meager but probably on a par with records of many other activities of man, particularly if one is considering several centuries. But, for the hydrologist, there is need to know as accurately as possible the modifications that man makes in the hydrologic cycle—past, present, and future—in the hope that man can progressively increase his ability to modify the hydrologic cycle to his advantage. By working with nature, adapting his needs to the natural cycle or adapting that cycle to his needs, man can obtain the greatest beneficial use of the water resources. The question discussed here, as to the effects of man's activities to date, is an essential element in the quest for knowledge on which to base these adaptations in the future.

The progressively increasing use of water and land has created a great variety of problems. Many of these problems arise through man's efforts to adapt an irregular water supply to his demands, and many others are by-products of his progress toward accommodating an increasing population and raising the standard of living for all. Most problems in the past have been concerned with water in a single phase of the hydrologic cycle—precipitation, soil moisture, ground water, surface water—and they have required increasing specialization on the part of engineers, geochemists, geologists, geophysicists, meteorologists, and soil scientists. Obviously, there is a continuing need for highly specialized talents in hydrology.

On the other hand, the "specialist" approach is not enough to meet the needs of the future. The movement of water through the hydrologic cycle can be fully described only by the combined efforts of men having the separate disciplines of many scientific specialties. No person who has limited his studies to ground water or soil water or surface water or precipitation, or to the development and use of water, can have all the answers, because the water eventually moves out of his field in its course through the hydrologic cycle. The announced purpose of this symposium—to emphasize "stimulation of interdisciplinary thought"—is an important objective within the field of water resources alone: the objective of fully comprehending the interrelations of the hydrologic cycle and determining the quantities of water involved in its different phases accurately enough to serve the needs of contemporary stages of planning and development.

Many of the cited uncertainties as to man's influence on the water resources stem from inadequate data, and reliable conclusions may be forthcoming with increasing length of records. Many other uncertainties result from lack of quantitative information as to the interrelation of soil-water, ground-water, and surface-water storage. This lack of knowledge is a serious handicap in comprehensive planning for water-resources development. As an example, it has been found in Kansas that, although data on surface water are sufficient for planning storage and flood-control projects, comprehensive planning for over-all water-resources development is handicapped by the inadequacy of knowledge of the potentials for soil-water or ground-water storage

(Kansas Water Resources Committee, 1955, pp. 163–80). Controversies such as those over big dams versus little dams (Leopold and Maddock, 1954) or upstream versus downstream engineering may have their origin in competition for use of water, but they are nurtured best in fields of inadequate knowledge.

It is not the intent of this paper to belittle the accomplishments of man in research leading to a better understanding of the water resources. There are many such accomplishments, and they have led to major improvements in the development and use both of water and of agricultural land. But there are still outstanding opportunities for hydrologists of the future, who can take our present knowledge as merely the commencement for their work.

Recent and current studies show the trend toward broader comprehension of water resources and of the interrelations of the natural cycle and of man's utilization of water. The possibilities of utilization of ground-water storage in over-all water resource development have been discussed in several papers (Conkling *et al.*, 1946; Thomas, 1952a), and the complementary nature of flood-control and water-supply problems has been pointed out (Laverty, 1945; Kansas Water Resources Committee, 1955).

The importance of water in the process of photosynthesis has recently been summarized in papers by Mahoney *et al.* (1952), and the utilization and control of vegetation for obtaining maximum water yields have been discussed in a book by Colman (1953) and in numerous papers.[2] Special study has been devoted to the problem of phreatophytes, which waste significant quantities of water in arid regions (Gatewood *et al.*, 1950; Robinson *et al.*, 1952).

The problems pertaining to quality of waters available for use have been

2. Hoover, 1944; Dunford and Fletcher, 1947; Wilm and Dunford, 1948.

the subject of comprehensive study in many regions, of which recent studies in California (Banks and Lawrence, 1953) are noteworthy because that state plans to overcome the natural water deficiency of its arid regions by full utilization of all its water resources (Berry, 1950). One possible method of increasing the usability of water resources is the reclamation of sewage and industrial waste waters (Rawn, 1952; California Water Pollution Board, 1953). In the East, used waters have been successfully reclaimed in many localities; a recent accomplishment is the disposal of organic wastes and recovery of usable water through woods irrigation (Mather, 1953).

Partly because of current progress in hydrologic research and partly because of the replenishment that is inherent in the hydrologic cycle, I am inclined to look to the future with optimism. Admittedly, many of man's activities have affected the water resources to his detriment, and some of these operations appear to be irreversible—as, for example, the subsidence of land and resulting reduction in underground storage capacity caused by pumping in some areas, the introduction of contaminated water into ground-water reservoirs

whose water was formerly suitable for use, or the collection of sediment in reservoirs. And some of the detrimental operations can be reversed only at some sacrifice to the economy of the region. Thus, where pumping from wells is causing a progressive depletion in storage, cessation of pumping and waiting for replenishment by natural means may be the only way to renew the natural resource, and that will doubtless be costly to the economy. However, in some such regions, artificial recharge may provide a means of increasing the supply to balance the demand.

Generally, in so far as water is concerned, modern technology has many weapons to combat the difficulties that faced earlier civilizations—turbine pumps to raise water from great depths in times of shortage or to remove water from waterlogged areas; concrete and steel to hold water where it is wanted and away from places where it is not wanted; purification plants to remove the undesirable constituents from water; agricultural equipment to modify the land surface so that water can be of maximum benefit to crops. As with many other products of the machine age, however, man *does* need to develop and increase his skill in using these materials.

REFERENCES

ABBOT, CHARLES G.
  1935 "Weather Governed by Changes in the Sun's Radiation," pp. 93–115 in *Smithsonian Institution Annual Report*. Washington, D.C.: Government Printing Office.
AHLMANN, H. W.
  1953 *Glacier Variations and Climatic Fluctuations.* (Bowman Memorial Lectures, Series Three.) New York: American Geographical Society. 51 pp.
ANONYMOUS
  1954 "Mexico City Sinking Faster as Wells Are Tapped Heavily," *Engineering News Record*, CLII, 74–76.

ASH, S. H., *et al.*
  1953 *Mine Pumping Plants, Anthracite Region of Pennsylvania.* (U.S. Bureau of Mines Bulletin No. 531.) Washington, D.C.: Government Printing Office. 151 pp.
BANKS, H. O., and LAWRENCE, J. H.
  1953 "Water Quality Problems in California," *Transactions of the American Geophysical Union*, XXXIV, 58–66.
BANKS, H. O., and RICHTER, R. C.
  1953 "Sea-Water Intrusion into Ground-Water Basins Bordering the California Coast and Inland Bays," *Transactions*

of the American Geophysical Union, XXXIV, 575–82.

BARKSDALE, H. C., and REMSON, IRWIN
1955 "The Effect of Land-Management Practices on Ground Water," pp. 520–25 in *Publication No. 37 de l'Association Internationale d'Hydrologie.* ("Assemblée générale de Rome," Vol. II.)

BERNHAGEN, RALPH J.
1950 "Program, Responsibilities, and Problems concerning Water Resources in Ohio," *Ohio Journal of Science,* L, 168–76.

BERRY, WILLIAM L.
1950 "The California Water Plan," *Journal of the American Water Works Association,* XLII, 381–85.

BLANEY, H. F., and DONNAN, W. W.
1945 "Ground-Water Situation in San Fernando Valley, California." Washington, D.C.: U.S. Soil Conservation Service. 56 pp. (Mimeographed.)

BROADHURST, WILLIAM L.
1953 "Coastal Plain near Houston, Texas," pp. 51–69 in *Subsurface Facilities of Water Management and Patterns of Supply-Type Area Studies.* ("Physical and Economic Foundation of Natural Resources," Vol. IV.) Washington, D.C.: U.S. Congress, House Interior and Insular Affairs Committee. 206 pp.

BRYAN, KIRK
1928 "Change in Plant Associations by Change in Ground-Water Levels," *Ecology,* IX, 474–78.

CALIFORNIA WATER POLLUTION BOARD
1953 *Field Investigation of Waste Water Reclamation in Relation to Ground Water Pollution.* (California State Water Pollution Board Publication 6.) Sacramento: California State Water Pollution Board. 124 pp.

CLARKE, FRANK W.
1924 *Data of Geochemistry.* (U.S. Geological Survey Bulletin No. 770.) Washington, D.C.: Government Printing Office. 783 pp.

COLMAN, E. A.
1953 *Vegetation and Watershed Management.* New York: Ronald Press Co. 412 pp.

CONKLING, HAROLD, *et al.*
1946 "Utilization of Ground-Water Storage in Stream System Development," *Transactions of the American Society of Civil Engineers,* III, 275–354.

COOPER, H. H., JR., and KENNER, W. E.
1953 "Central and Northern Florida," pp. 147–61 in *Subsurface Facilities of Water Management and Patterns of Supply-Type Area Studies.* ("Physical and Economic Foundation of Natural Resources," Vol. IV.) Washington, D.C.: U.S. Congress, House Interior and Insular Affairs Committee. 206 pp.

DIGHTMAN, R. A., and BEATTY, M. E.
1952 "Recent Montana Glacier and Climate Trends," *Monthly Weather Review,* LXXX, 77–81.

DONNAN, W. W.; BRADSHAW, G. B.; and BLANEY, H. F.
1954 *Drainage Investigation in Imperial Valley, California, 1941–51.* (U.S. Soil Conservation Service Report SCS-TP-120.) Washington, D.C.: U.S. Department of Agriculture. 71 pp.

DUNFORD, E. G., and FLETCHER, P. W.
1947 "Effect of Removal of Streambank Vegetation upon Water Yields," *Transactions of the American Geophysical Union,* XXVIII, 105–10.

DURUM, WALTON H.
1953 "Relationship of the Mineral Constituents in Solution to Stream Flow, Saline River near Russell, Kansas," *Transactions of the American Geophysical Union,* XXXIV, 435–42.

GATEWOOD, J. S.; ROBINSON, T. W.; COLBY, B. R.; HEM, J. D.; and HALPENNY, L. C.
1950 *Use of Water by Bottom-Land Vegetation in Lower Safford Valley, Arizona.* (U.S. Geological Survey Water Supply Paper No. 1103.) Washington, D.C.: Government Printing Office. 210 pp.

GAUM, CARL H.
1953 "High Plains, or Llano Estacado, Texas–New Mexico," pp. 94–104 in *Subsurface Facilities of Water Management and Patterns of Supply-Type Area Studies.* ("Physical and Economic Foundation of Natural Re-

sources," Vol. IV.) Washington, D.C.: U.S. Congress, House Interior and Insular Affairs Committee. 206 pp.

HALE, W. E.; HUGHES, L. S.; and COX, E. R.
1954   "Possible Improvement of Quality of Water of the Pecos River by Diversion of Brine at Malaga Bend." (U.S. Geological Survey Report.) Carlsbad, N.M.: Pecos River Commission, New Mexico and Texas. 43 pp. (plus 7 tables). (Multilith.)

HALPENNY, LEONARD C., et al.
1952   *Ground Water in the Gila River Basin and Adjacent Areas, Arizona: A Summary.* (U.S. Geological Survey Report.) Tucson, Ariz.: U.S. Geological Survey. 224 pp.

HARSHBARGER, J. W.; REPENNING, C. A.; and CALLAHAN, J. T.
1953   "The Navajo Country, Arizona–Utah–New Mexico," pp. 105–29 in *Subsurface Facilities of Water Management and Patterns of Supply-Type Area Studies.* ("Physical and Economic Foundation of Natural Resources," Vol. IV.) Washington, D.C.: U.S. Congress, House Interior and Insular Affairs Committee. 206 pp.

HENRY, A. J.
1931   "Meteorological Data and Meteorological Changes," pp. 15–34 in KIMBALL, H. H., et al., *Meteorology.* ("Physics of the Earth," Vol. III.) Washington, D.C.: National Research Council. 289 pp.

HOOVER, MARVIN D.
1944   "Effect of Removal of Forest Vegetation upon Water Yields," *Transactions of the American Geophysical Union,* XXV, 969–77.

HORTON, ROBERT E.
1899   "Report on the Runoff and Water Power of Kalamazoo River," p. 29 in LANE, A. C., *Water Resources of the Lower Peninsula of Michigan.* (U.S. Geological Survey Water Supply Paper No. 30.) Washington, D.C.: Government Printing Office. 97 pp.

HOYT, W. GLENN, et al.
1936   *Rainfall and Runoff in the United States.* (U.S. Geological Survey Water Supply Paper No. 772.) Washing-

ton, D.C.: Government Printing Office. 301 pp.

HURSH, CHARLES R.
1943   *Local Climate in the Copper Basin of Tennessee as Modified by the Removal of Vegetation.* (U.S. Department of Agriculture Technical Bulletin No. 774.) Washington D.C.: Government Printing Office. 38 pp.

JANSA, O. V. E.
1951   "Artificial Ground-Water Supplies in Sweden," pp. 102–4 in HATHAWAY, GAIL A., et al., *United Nations, Department of Economic Affairs, Scientific Conference on Conservation and Utilization of Resources,* Vol. IV. 466 pp.

KANSAS WATER RESOURCES FACT-FINDING AND RESEARCH COMMITTEE
1955   *Water in Kansas.* (Report to the 1955 Legislature.) Topeka, Kan. 216 pp.

KINCER, JOSEPH B.
1933   "Is Our Climate Changing?" *Monthly Weather Review,* LXI, 251–60.
1946   "Our Changing Climate," *Transactions of the American Geophysical Union,* XXVII, 342–47.

LAVERTY, FINLEY B.
1945   "Correlating Flood Control and Water Supply, Los Angeles Coastal Plain," *Proceedings of the American Society of Civil Engineers,* LXXI, 831–48.

LEOPOLD, LUNA, and MADDOCK, THOMAS, JR.
1954   *The Flood Control Controversy.* New York: Ronald Press Co. 255 pp.

LOHMAN, STANLEY W.
1953   "High Plains of West-Central United States," and "Sand Hills Area, Nebraska," pp. 77–91 in *Subsurface Facilities of Water Management and Patterns of Supply-Type Area Studies.* ("Physical and Economic Foundation of Natural Resources," Vol. IV.) Washington, D.C.: U.S. Congress, House Interior and Insular Affairs Committee. 206 pp.

McGUINNESS, C. LEE
1951   *The Water Situation in the United States with Special Reference to Ground Water.* (U.S. Geological Survey Circular No. 114.) Washing-

ton, D.C.: U.S. Geological Survey. 138 pp.

MAHONEY, JOHN R.
1953 *Water Resources of the Bonneville Basin*, Part I: *The Water Crop and Its Disposition.* ("Utah Economic and Business Review," Vol. XIII, No. 1-A.) 56 pp.

MAHONEY, JOHN R., *et al.*
1952 *Photosynthesis—Basic Features of the Process.* ("Physical and Economic Foundation of Natural Resources," Vol. I.) Washington, D.C.: U.S. Congress, House Interior and Insular Affairs Committee. 33 pp.

MARMER, HARRY A.
1949 "Sea Level Changes along the Coasts of the United States in Recent Years," *Transactions of the American Geophysical Union,* XXX, 201–5.

MATHER, JOHN R.
1953 "The Disposal of Industrial Effluent by Woods Irrigation," *Transactions of the American Geophysical Union,* XXXIV, 227–39.

MATTHES, FRANCOIS E.
1942 "Glaciers," pp. 190–215 in MEINZER, OSCAR E. (ed.), *Hydrology.* New York: McGraw-Hill Book Co. 703 pp.
1946 "Report of the Committee on Glaciers," *Transactions of the American Geophysical Union,* XXVII, 219–33.

MEINZER, OSCAR E. (ed.)
1942 *Hydrology.* ("Physics of the Earth," Vol. IX.) New York: McGraw-Hill Book Co. 703 pp.

MEYER, ADOLPH
1942 *Evaporation from Lakes and Reservoirs.* St. Paul, Minn.: Minnesota Resources Commission. 111 pp.

MITCHELSON, A. T., and MUCKEL, D. C.
1937 *Spreading Water for Storage Underground.* (U.S. Department of Agriculture Technical Bulletin No. 578.) Washington, D.C.: Government Printing Office. 80 pp.

MUCKEL, DEAN C.
1951 "Research in Water Spreading," *Proceedings of the American Society of Civil Engineers,* LXXVII, 1–11.

NELSON, W. B., and THOMAS, H. E.
1953 "Pumping from Wells on the Floor of the Sevier Desert, Utah,"

Transactions of the American Geophysical Union, XXXIV, 74–84.

NICHOLS, H. B., and COLTON, F. B.
1952 "Water for the World's Growing Needs," *National Geographic Magazine,* CII, 269–86.

ORTIZ, SAINT
1953 "Hundimiento de la ciudad de Mexico, una problema de presiones y no de volumenes," *Ingenieria hidraulica en Mexico,* VII, 57–60.

PALEY, W. S., *et al.*
1952 *Resources for Freedom.* (President's Materials Policy Commission.) 5 vols. Washington, D.C.: Government Printing Office.

PARKER, G. G.
1955 "The Encroachment of Salt Water into Fresh," pp. 615–35 in STEFFERUD, ALFRED (ed.), *Water: Yearbook of Agriculture, 1955.* Washington, D.C.: U.S. Department of Agriculture. 723 pp.

PATRICK, RUTH
1949 "A Proposed Biological Measure of Stream Conditions, Based on a Survey of the Conestoga Basin, Limestone County, Pennsylvania," *Proceedings of the Academy of Natural Sciences of Philadelphia,* CI, 277–341.

PATRICK, RUTH; HOHN, N. H.; and WALLACE, J. H.
1954 *A New Method for Determining the Pattern of the Diatom Flora.* ("Notulae Natural," No. 259.) Philadelphia: Academy of Natural Sciences of Philadelphia. 12 pp.

PIPER, ARTHUR M.
1948 "Runoff from Rain and Snow," *Transactions of the American Geophysical Union,* XXIX, 511–20.

PIPER, ARTHUR M., *et al.*
1953 "The Nation-wide Water Situation," pp. 1–20 in *Subsurface Facilities of Water Management and Patterns of Supply-Type Area Studies.* ("Physical and Economic Foundation of Natural Resources," Vol. IV.) Washington, D.C.: U.S. Congress, House Interior and Insular Affairs Committtee. 206 pp.

PIPER, A. M.; GARRETT, A. A.; *et al.*
1953 *Native and Contaminated Ground Waters in the Long Beach–Santa Ana Area, California.* (U.S. Geological

Survey Water Supply Paper No. 1136.) Washington, D.C.: Government Printing Office. 315 pp.

RAWN, A. M.
1952 "Reclamation of Water from Sewage and Industrial Wastes," pp. 89–93 in *The Physical Basis of Water Supply and Its Principal Uses*. ("Physical and Economic Foundation of Natural Resources," Vol. II.) Washington, D.C.: U.S. Congress, House Interior and Insular Affairs Committee. 93 pp.

ROBINSON, THOMAS W., *et al.*
1952 "Symposium on Phreatophytes," *Transactions of the American Geophysical Union*, XXXIII, 57–80.

SCHULMAN, EDMUND
1951 "Tree-Ring Indices of Rainfall, Temperature, and River Flow," pp. 1024–29 in MALONE, THOMAS F. (ed.), *Compendium of Meteorology*. Boston: American Meteorological Society. 1,334 pp.

SIMONS, WILBUR D.
1953 *Irrigation and Streamflow Depletion in Columbia River Basin above The Dalles, Oregon*. (U.S. Geological Survey Water Supply Paper No. 1220.) Washington, D.C.: Government Printing Office. 123 pp.

SIMONS, WILBUR D., *et al.*
1953 "Spokane–Coeur d'Alene River Basin, Washington-Idaho," pp. 164–85 in *Subsurface Facilities of Water Management and Patterns of Supply-Type Area Studies*. ("Physical and Economic Foundation of Natural Resources," Vol. IV.) Washington, D.C.: U.S. Congress, House Interior and Insular Affairs Committee. 206 pp.

STAFFORD, H. M., and TROXELL, H. C.
1953 "Coastal Basins near Los Angeles, California," pp. 21–50 in *Subsurface Facilities of Water Management and Patterns of Supply-Type Area Studies*. ("Physical and Economic Foundation of Natural Resources," Vol. IV.) Washington, D.C.: U.S. Congress, House Interior and Insular Affairs Committee. 206 pp.

SWENSON, H. A., and COLBY, B. R.
1955 *The Quality of Surface Waters in Devils Lake Basin, North Dakota*.

(U.S. Geological Survey Water Supply Paper No. 1295.) Washington, D.C.: Government Printing Office. 82 pp.

THOMAS, HAROLD E.
1951 *The Conservation of Ground Water*. New York: McGraw-Hill Book Co. 321 pp.

1952a *Ground-Water Regions in the United States—Their Storage Facilities*. ("Physical and Economic Foundation of Natural Resources," Vol. III.) Washington, D.C.: U.S. Congress, House Interior and Insular Affairs Committee. 78 pp.

1952b "Utah Valley," pp. 71–76 in *Status of Development of Selected Ground-Water Basins in Utah*. (Utah State Engineering Technical Publication No. 7.) Salt Lake City. 96 pp.

1954 *The First Fourteen Years of Lake Mead*. (U.S. Geological Survey Circular 346.) Washington, D.C.: U.S. Geological Survey. 27 pp.

1955 *Water Rights in Areas of Ground-Water Mining*. (U.S. Geological Survey Circular 347.) Washington, D.C.: U.S. Geological Survey. 16 pp.

TODD, DAVID K.
1952 *An Abstract of Literature Pertaining to Sea-Water Intrusion and Its Control*. Berkeley: California University Engineering Research Institute. 72 pp.

1956 *Bibliography of Artificial Recharge of Ground Water*. (U.S. Geological Survey Report.) Washington, D.C.: U.S. Geological Survey. (In preparation.)

TOLMAN, C. F., and POLAND, J. F.
1940 "Ground Water, Salt-Water Infiltration, and Ground-Surface Recession in Santa Clara Valley, California," *Transactions of the American Geophysical Union*, XXI, 7, 23–34.

WAITE, H. A., and THOMAS, H. E.
1955 "Effect of the Current Drought upon Water Supplies in Cedar City Valley, Utah," *Transactions of the American Geophysical Union*, XXXVI, 805–12.

WEHRLY, M. S., and FORTH, M. L.
1951 *Water for Industry: A Review of*

Water Resources Affecting Industrial Location. (Urban Land Institute Technical Bulletin No. 17.) Washington, D.C. 32 pp.

WHITE, WALTER N.

1932   *A Method of Estimating Ground-Water Supplies Based on Discharge of Plants and Evaporation from Soil.* (U.S. Geological Survey Water Supply Paper No. 659A.) Washington, D.C.: Government Printing Office. 105 pp.

WILLETT, HURD C.

1953   "Atmospheric and Oceanic Circulation as Factors in Glacial-Interglacial Changes of Climate," pp. 51–71 in SHAPLEY, HARLOW (ed.), *Climatic Change.* Cambridge, Mass.: Harvard University Press. 318 pp.

WILM, H. G., and DUNFORD, E. G.

1948   *Effect of Timber Cutting on Water Available for Stream Flow from a Lodgepole Pine Forest.* (U.S. Department of Agriculture Technical Bulletin No. 968.) Washington, D.C.: Government Printing Office. 43 pp.

WINSLOW, A. G., and DOYEL, W. W.

1954a   *Salt Water and Its Relation to Fresh Ground Water in Harris County, Texas.* (Texas Board of Water Engineers Bulletin No. 5409.) Austin: Texas Board of Water Engineers. 37 pp.

1954b   "Land-Surface Subsidence and Its Relation to the Withdrawal of Ground Water in the Houston-Galveston Region, Texas," *Economic Geology,* XLIX, 413–22.

WRATHER, WILLIAM E.

1952   "A Summary of the Water Situation with Respect to the Annual Run-off of the United States," pp. 36–41 in *The Physical Basis of Water Supply and Its Principal Uses.* ("Physical and Economic Foundation of Natural Resources," Vol. II.) Washington, D.C.: U.S. Congress, House Interior and Insular Affairs Committee. 93 pp.

Alterations of Climatic Elements

Alterations of Climatic Elements

Modification of Rural Microclimates

C. W. THORNTHWAITE[*]

Nowhere is the theme of this confer-ence better phrased than in the preface of a book entitled *The Earth as Modified by Human Action* by George Perkins Marsh, in which he states that his purpose is "to indicate the character and . . . extent of the changes produced by human action in the physical conditions of the globe . . . ; to point out the dangers of imprudence and the necessity of caution in all operations which . . . interfere with the spontaneous arrangements of the organic or the inorganic world; [and] to suggest the possibility and the importance of the restoration of disturbed harmonies and the material improvement of waste and exhausted regions" (Marsh, 1874, p. iii).

Marsh was particularly concerned with man's capacity to bring about changes in climate either deliberately or involuntarily. He marshaled an imposing mass of support for the thesis that precipitation and the temperature

[*] Dr. Thornthwaite is Director of the Laboratory of Climatology, Centerton, New Jersey, and Professor of Climatology at Drexel Institute of Technology, Philadelphia. He was a member of the faculty of the University of Oklahoma (1927–34), of the University of Maryland (1940–46), and of The Johns Hopkins University (1946–55). Since 1951 he has been president of the Commission for Climatology, World Meteorological Organization. He was president (1941–44) of the Section of Meteorology, American Geophysical Union, and was the recipient of the Outstanding Achievement Award for 1952 of the Association of American Geographers. His publications include: *The Climates of North America*, 1931, and *The Climates of the Earth*, 1933.

and moisture of air and soil are altered as the vegetation cover of the earth is changed by clearing or burning and replanting and as the hydrologic regime is modified by draining lakes, swamps, and wet soils and by irrigation. But in the main his evidence was only circumstantial and thus inconclusive.

Much emphasis has been placed on the variability of the elements that combine to make climate. Precipitation and temperature are known to vary greatly from day to day, from one month to another, and from one year to another. Wind velocity, cloudiness, and evaporation likewise vary. Since climate is an integration of these many complexly varying elements, it is obvious that climate must also vary from one year to another. Indeed, variation may be thought of as a natural element of climate.

What are the conditions that may cause a change in climate? Climate may change if there is a variation in the general circulation of the atmosphere, if there is a variation in the incoming radiation, or if there are changes in the surface features. These causal factors are interrelated and, when operating in unison, can produce large changes.

Over the world there have been wide fluctuations in climate during the past several centuries. Superimposed on these fluctuations is the recognized long-period change in climate over the world since the Pleistocene periods of glaciation. These changes have been very gradual, occupying at least twenty-five thousand years, and in certain regions they have been practically nonexistent. Mather (1954) has recently shown, on the basis of a study of the present climatic fluctuation, that each local region has experienced its own magnitude of climatic variation.

The evidence from history, botany, archeology, and geology relating to the last two thousand years is indicative of climatic fluctuations such as those we experience today and confirms the meteorological axiom that the more or less random interactions of air masses that determine present climatic variations are the same as those of the past. Evidence for or against long-period climatic changes must necessarily be indirect or circumstantial, and it is impossible to identify the variations as climatic changes.

Thus we must conclude that, by its own nature of constant variation, climate imposes a serious limitation on any attempt to discover the quantitative effects of man's influence upon it. Quite wide fluctuations in climate are possible as a result of fluctuations in the meteorological parameters themselves, and these may mask almost entirely the influence of man's activities unless long periods of time are considered.

How might man be successful in changing the climate? Only through manipulation and modification of the causal factors. No responsible scientist seriously believes that man can alter the general atmospheric circulation in any significant way. When man produces a forest fire or a dust storm, he can blot out the sun and temporarily reduce the amount of incoming solar radiation. The dome of smoke that man has created over many of the larger cities is a permanent agency of climatic change. However, man's greatest potentialities in changing the climate lie in changing the characteristics of the earth's surface over a considerable dis-

tance. Generally, the influence of man upon climate is displayed over normally small areas where some obvious change has been made on the surface. The resultant changes in climate will be visible only in the layer of air near the ground.

HISTORICAL REVIEW

During the last couple of decades sensational and irresponsible stories have created the impression that weather control was imminent through rainmaking and through dissipation of clouds and that hurricanes could be broken up with atom bombs and tornadoes and hailstorms with dry ice. The impression has been given that arid and semiarid climates could be made humid and drought periods prevented by artificial inducement of precipitation. It has also been implied that cloudseeding could dissipate certain types of cloud which are widespread in some seasons and thereby increase incoming radiation and change the climate over extensive areas.

These are only modern manifestations of a type of thinking that has exerted a powerful influence on many of man's activities during the last two centuries. Marsh, for example, in referring to the belief that vegetation and precipitation are reciprocally necessary to each other, quotes the following (1864, p. 182):

Afric's barren sand,
Where nought can grow, because it raineth not,
And where no rain can fall to bless the land,
Because nought grows there.

The idea that vegetation influences rainfall—in fact, determines its amount and distribution—is so firmly rooted that it has been the basis of action programs in many lands. In our country the Timber Culture Act of 1873 was passed in the belief that, if settlers were induced to plant trees in the Great Plains and the prairie states, rainfall would be increased sufficiently to eliminate the climatic hazards to agriculture (Thornthwaite, 1936, p. 209). This belief still persists among some western farmers, and during the great drought of the 1930's more than one blamed his difficulties on his own failure to plant trees.

It was the same idea that activated President Roosevelt in his decision to authorize the Shelter Belt Project for tree-planting in the Great Plains in 1934. At the same time the governors of several of the plains states advocated the creation of thousands of ponds and reservoirs for the purpose of augmenting evaporation, which, in turn, was expected to increase precipitation.

Similar ideas have appeared in many forms. Aughey, writing of Nebraska in 1880, credited the increased rainfall then being experienced to the spread of cultivation. He said (1880, pp. 44–45):

It is the great increase in absorptive power of the soil, wrought by cultivation, that has caused, and continues to cause, an increasing rainfall in the State. . . . After the soil is "broken," a rain as it falls is absorbed by the soil like a huge sponge. The soil gives this absorbed moisture slowly back to the atmosphere by evaporation. Thus year by year as cultivation of the soil is extended, more of the rain that falls is absorbed and retained to be given off by evaporation or to produce springs. This, of course, must give increasing moisture and rainfall.

A long drought period setting in shortly thereafter, while Nebraska was still being settled, demonstrated the fallacy of Aughey's hypothesis but apparently failed to lead to a critical examination of its premises. In 1923 Clements and Weaver conducted an investigation to determine the relative moisture contributions to the atmosphere from native grasslands and field crops. In 1936 Clements made use of the results of the investigation to shed light on the sources of moisture for local rainfall. He says (Clements and Chaney, 1936, p. 41): "The outcome demonstrated that there was no material difference in transpiration and evaporation from the two types of cover, and hence that cultivation could have had no favorable influence upon precipitation."

Clearly, the implication of this quotation is that there is a direct relation between an increase in atmospheric moisture and precipitation. There is no question that various types of vegetation and land use do contribute varying amounts of water to the atmosphere. A great mass of experimental evidence demonstrates this, but there is no similar demonstration that the moisture added to the atmosphere in this way is reprecipitated later in the same area. This is a matter that is now being settled through a detailed study of the actual sources of moisture for precipitation (Holzman, 1937; Thornthwaite, 1937).

The ideas expressed by Aughey seventy-five years ago and by Clements thirty-two years ago still find support. For example, Schwerdtfeger and Vasino (1954) published a paper on the secular variation of precipitation in central Argentina in which they pointed out that an increase in precipitation had occurred during a period when there was a great increase of land under cultivation. They stated as an established fact that the increase of precipitation accompanied and was caused by the expansion of agriculture in the region. From this they concluded that, since there would be no retraction of agriculture, there would be no danger of a diminution of precipitation in the decades to come.

In Geiger's *The Climate near the Ground* there is a section of three and one-half pages that deals with the unintentional effect of man on the microclimate (1950, pp. 375–78). The only climatological work that I have seen which formally discusses man's effect upon climate is a chapter in a Russian textbook published in 1952 (Alisov *et al.*, 1952). It seems to me that in this chapter the chief concern of the authors is to persuade the policy-makers in the Soviet Union that climates can be changed, that it is most necessary to change them, but that only climatologists know how. The following quotation presents the point of view (*ibid.*, pp. 317–18):

Man's influence upon climate through the burning and clearing of the forest, through tilling the soil, and through pasturing cattle began even in prehistoric times . . . ; in proportion to man's technical advances . . . the primitive effect of man upon the functioning of the earth's surface, and thereby upon climate, gradually increased, reaching especially great proportions under capitalism. At this point it is essential to note the criminal nature of exploiting of natural wealth, especially under capitalism, when carried as far as despoiling of forests, developing of ruinous gullies, pulverizing and washing away of topsoil, etc. (especially in U.S.A., where about 30 per cent of the land has been cast to utter ruin). The effect of such radical changes upon climate, too, is without doubt unfavorable.

Planned measures for the improvement of climate began first to be tried out on a small scale in the first half of the nineteenth century. . . . However, under the existing conditions of czarist Russia or contemporary capitalism embracing individual land ownership and an over-all lack of planned development, it was impossible to take measures for the influencing of climate on any appropriately broad scale. Only under socialism has it become possible to exert a systematic and planned influence upon nature: draining marshes, lowering the level of permanent ice, irrigating deserts, and planting forests.

The supreme form of planned influence upon nature and climate is a system of scientific procedures which the people have named Stalin's Plan for Reforming Nature.

A huge category of these operations will apply first of all to the arid zone. Magnificent enterprises will follow in the draining of marshes. . . . It should not be forgotten that these steps toward reforming nature in our Fatherland constitute the one and only determined stand of mankind against conditions of nature unfavorable to man, and partially, those of climate. . . . The systematic care which our party and our leadership have taken in this struggle against aridity, commencing with the first days of the inauguration of Soviet power, has culminated during recent years in a series of historical decisions as to the reforming of nature in the U.S.S.R. arid regions. . . . Also of note [in these decisions] is the short time set for completion by communism of its innumerable majestic achievements.

The main feature of the so-called "Stalin Plan" is the struggle against aridity which employs grass-covered northern slopes, wood strips to protect the fields, and irrigation through the impounding of local runoff. The full program is described as follows (*ibid.*, p. 318):

All the arid territory of this plan by 1965 will be covered with a grillwork of wooded strips which in the generally pasture-type of agriculture should prevent the washing or blowing away of soil, should conserve the winter's moisture in the ground, should protect the fields from needless evaporation especially under desert winds, and should catch in ponds and reservoirs that moisture which will always run off over the surface (number of planned reservoirs being 44,288) so as to return moisture to the soil by an irrigating process.

Little can be said of this program except that it is highly speculative and is mainly for the future (see also the discussion by Burke, pp. 1042–44 below). Whatever part of the program may have been completed by 1965, it may be assured that there will be only trivial changes in climate.

MEASUREMENT OF MAN'S INFLUENCE
ON THE MICROCLIMATE

The basic difficulty in determining the magnitude of man's effect on the microclimate has been the lack of instruments and observation techniques of sufficient precision to permit identification of any climatic modification that has occurred in two comparable areas that have been treated differently or in a single area before and after some environmental change has been made. Marsh appreciated this difficulty when he wrote the following (1874, p. 25):

There is one branch of research which is of the utmost importance . . . but which . . . has been less successfully studied than almost any other problem of physical science. I refer to the proportions between precipitation, superficial drainage, absorption, and evaporation. Precise actual measurements of these quantities upon even a single acre of ground is impossible; and in all cabinet experiments on the subject, the conditions of the surface observed are so different from those which occur in nature, that we cannot safely reason from one case to the other. . . . In discussing the climatology of whole countries, or even of comparatively small local divisions, we may safely say that none can tell what percentage of the water they receive from the atmosphere is evaporated; what absorbed by the ground and conveyed off by subterranean conduits; what carried down to the sea by superficial channels; what drawn from the earth or the air by a given extent of forest, of short pasture vegetation, or of tall meadow-grass; what given out again by surfaces so covered, or by bare ground of various textures and composition, under different conditions of atmospheric temperature, pressure, and humidity; or what is the amount of evaporation from water, ice, or snow, under the varying exposures to which, in actual nature, they are constantly subjected.

For the last seven years my associates and I at the Laboratory of Climatology have been continuing a comprehensive study of microclimatology which I initiated in the Soil Conservation Service just two decades ago. During this period there has been a growing awareness of the problems of microclimatology, and our efforts are now only a part of a world-wide attack against them. Both instruments and theory have now reached a point where observations can be made to record any changes which may occur in the microclimate.

Climates owe their individual characteristics to the nature of the exchanges of momentum, of heat, and of moisture between the earth's surface and the atmosphere. Any region is a composite of innumerable local climates —the climate of the ravine, of the south-facing slope, of the hilltop, of the meadow, of the cornfield, of the woods, of the bare rocky ledge. Both the heat and the moisture exchange vary from the ravine to the hilltop and to the rocky ledge because of a variance in the physical characteristics, position, exposure, and aspect of these diverse surfaces. The color, apparent density, heat capacity, moisture content, and permeability of the soil; the characteristics of the vegetation cover; the albedo and roughness of the surface— these are all factors that influence the heat and moisture exchange and are thus important climatic factors (Thornthwaite, 1954, p. 228).

Accordingly, these are the factors on which man must operate and which must be measured to verify his success in producing change in the climate. Although it is possible to make large changes in certain of these factors, and some of them have been changed profoundly, the resultant climatic change has been small and unimportant. With better instruments, more precise observations can be made, and they may reveal for the first time small microclimatic changes which may be attributed to man and which would not otherwise have been visible.

THE WATER BUDGET—MAN'S MAJOR INFLUENCE ON CLIMATE

Any review of the ways in which man may influence the climates brings clearly into focus several important facts. While man's influence on his environment can be great, it is generally of limited areal extent and duration and, in the main, does little to the climate. The cities he builds, the lakes he creates, or the swamps he drains will not change the climate over any more than a restricted area. For example, the construction of the Ribinsky Dam in Russia produced almost no perceptible change in the monthly averages of air temperature on the shore—scarcely a few tenths of a degree. The average wind speed doubled over the water surface and along the shore, but the effect was only local. In the United States there are the examples provided by Salton Sea and Lake Mead, two large lakes with surface areas of about 300 and 175 square miles, respectively. The creation of these water bodies in the dry southwestern part of the country has resulted in scarcely any change in the climate even in the immediate vicinity. For instance, 2,000 feet from the Salton Sea shore line the moisture content of the air itself is relatively unaffected. The use of heaters, smoke generators, or intensive watering for protection against frost likewise results in only minor local changes in climate. These may be important to a farmer or orchardist, but in the sense of permanence and far-reaching effect they are trivial.

I pointed out at the beginning of this chapter that the three important causal factors in climate which, if influenced by man, would result in some climatic modification were solar radiation, the general circulation, and surface features. Any realistic appraisal of the ways in which man might influence the first two of these shows that such influence must be transitory and of small effect. Most of the changes man can produce on the surface features, too, result in only local or temporary climatic changes. There is, however, one significant area—the water economy—where man can significantly influence climates over large areas and on a more permanent basis.

Almost every change in environmental conditions which man can make results in some change in the water economy or water budget at the earth's surface. In the regions where precipitation is continuously excessive and where drainage is the principal modification which man makes in the hydrologic regime, there is little possibility of bringing about any significant change in climate. Similarly, where precipitation is continually deficient, irrigation is man's means for changing nature. However, water is in such short supply that only a small fraction of the area can be irrigated. In the oases which result, there are important local microclimatic changes but no changes that have any widespread influence.

There are, however, large areas of the world which have excessive precipitation during one season of the year and a lack of water during another. It is these areas, with their relatively abundant supplies of water, in which really significant climatic changes can be produced through the use of perhaps only a small amount of irrigation at just the proper time and in the correct amounts. These areas may have only a small water deficiency and yet may produce crops with poor yields or no crops at all. However, they have potentialities for future development not to be found in the desert areas with great water deficiencies or in the areas where drainage is necessary because of large water surpluses.

Since the water budget is such an important area of human influence, it is desirable to discuss it in some detail and to consider how it can be used in irrigation scheduling. The water temporarily stored in the land surface as ground water and soil moisture is a balance between what is contributed to the supply through precipitation and what is removed from it as evapotranspiration—the combined evaporation from the soil and transpiration from plants. Since rainfall and evapotranspiration are due to different things, they are not often the same either in amount or in distribution through the year. In some places more rain falls month after month than the vegetation can use. The surplus water moves through the ground and over it to form streams and rivers and flows back to the sea. In others, month after month, precipitation is less than potential evapotranspiration, there is not enough moisture in the soil for the vegetation to use, and a water deficit occurs. Regions with alternating wet and dry seasons, or with cold seasons of low water need, normally show (1) a period of full storage, when precipitation exceeds water need, and a *water surplus* accumulates; (2) a drying period, when stored soil moisture and precipitation are used in evapotranspiration, storage is steadily diminished, the actual evapotranspiration falls below the potential, and a *water deficiency* occurs; and (3) a moistening season when precipitation again exceeds water need, and soil moisture is recharged (Thornthwaite and Hare, 1955).

Precipitation is easily measured by means of rain gauges and has been recorded in most settled areas of the world. It is not easy to measure evapotranspiration, however; in fact, no weather service in the world yet determines this important element, and the little we know about its areal distribution has been pieced together from various scattered determinations.

Scientists have tried various ways to determine the amount of water used by plants. Experiments which attempt to measure the water loss from a leaf or a branch detached from the plant, or from isolated plants in special pots, are highly artificial, and generalizations from such studies have sometimes been greatly in error. The only method that measures the evapotranspiration from a field or any other natural surface without disturbing the vegetation cover in any way is the so-called "vapor-transfer" method (Thornthwaite and Holzman, 1942). Water vapor when it enters the atmosphere from the ground or from plants is carried upward by the moving air in small eddies or bodies of air that are replaced by drier eddies from above. If we determine the rate at which the air near the ground is mixing with that above it and at the same time measure the difference in water-vapor content at the two levels, we can determine both the rate and the amount of evapotranspiration.

This method is not easy to understand or to use. It requires physical measurements of temperature, humidity, and wind that are more precise than are usually made. However, the method can and should be perfected, for it will answer many important questions for climatology and biology.

There are other ways of determining both water use and water need. In some irrigated areas rainfall, irrigation water, and water outflow are all measured. The fraction of the applied water that does not run off is the evapotranspiration. In a few isolated places, mostly in the western United States, irrigation engineers have determined the evapotranspiration from plants growing in sunken tanks filled to ground level with soil in which water tables are maintained at different predetermined depths beneath the soil surface (Young and Blaney, 1942).

Since 1946, increasing thought has been devoted to the problem of measuring the water use of plants under optimum soil-moisture conditions—the potential evapotranspiration—and an improved instrument to do it has been developed and standardized (Thornthwaite *et al.*, 1946; Mather, 1950). It consists of a large soil tank so constructed that plants can be grown in it under essentially field conditions and can be provided with water as they need it. The tanks are 4 square meters in area and contain soil to a depth of approximately 70 centimeters. They have means for subirrigation from a supply tank designed so that actual amounts of water used can be accurately measured, or they can be irrigated by sprinkling from above. This latter method proves to be much more satisfactory in practice. When it rains, any excess water drains through the soil and is similarly measured. Thus, the potential evapotranspiration can be determined as a difference, since every other term in the hydrologic equation is measured. A number of these evapotranspirometers are now in operation in widely scattered areas of the world. There is, however, a need for many additional installations if we are to understand the variation of evapotranspiration from one area to another (Mather [ed.], 1954).

There are three possible sources of energy for evaporation or evapotranspiration: solar radiation, heat that reaches the evaporating surface from the air, and heat that is stored in the evaporating body. With no external source of energy, however, the surface temperature of an evaporating body would quickly drop to the dewpoint of the air, and evaporation would cease. Consequently, evaporation can occur as a continuing process only while energy is being received from some outside source.

The sun is the original source of all energy that is involved in the transformation of water from liquid to vapor. Not all the energy that is received from the sun is used in evaporating water,

however. Some of the incoming solar radiation is immediately reflected from the surface back to the sky. For a vegetation-covered surface about 25 per cent of the incoming radiation is lost in this way. Also a certain percentage of the incoming radiation is radiated from the surface back to the sky, the amount depending upon the temperature of the earth's surface and on the sky above. It is often between 10 and 15 per cent of the incoming radiation.

After deducting the losses due to reflection and back radiation, the remainder, which is known as the net radiation, is used in heating the soil surface. This heat is then partitioned into three parts: that which heats the deeper layers of the soil, that which heats the lower layers of the air by conduction and convection, and that which is utilized in evaporation. Recent measurements have shown that, when the soil is very moist, more than 80 per cent of the net radiation is used in evaporation. As the soil becomes dry, the evaporation rate declines, and more of the net radiation is devoted to heating the air and the soil, with less remaining for evaporation.

The potential rate of evapotranspiration is realized only when the area of the evaporating surface is adequately supplied with water and is large enough so that all the energy for evaporation comes from radiation and none from advection. Obviously, the area of a standard evapotranspirometer (4 square meters) is too small and could give reliable values only when it is surrounded by an extensive buffer area identical in vegetation cover and soil moisture. If the area of the evaporating surface is large, the influence of the air passing over it becomes small, and solar radiation is the primary source of energy for evaporation. Under these circumstances the atmospheric humidity is unimportant. If the air is moist, the temperature of the evaporating surface will rise to a point above the dewpoint of the air such that the evaporation will just use the energy that is available. Similarly, in dry air, rapid evaporation will lower the temperature of the evaporating surface until the evaporation is in balance with the available energy.

Although the various methods of determining evapotranspiration have many faults, and the determinations are scattered and few, we get from them an idea of how much water is transpired and evaporated under different conditions. We find that the rate of evapotranspiration depends on five things: climate, soil-moisture supply, plant cover, soil type and texture, and land management. There is considerable evidence to show that, when the root zone of the soil is well supplied with water, the amount used by the vegetation will depend more on the amount of solar energy received by the surface and on the resultant temperature than on the kind of vegetation growing in the area. Soil type and texture and farming practices likewise have little effect on the rate of evapotranspiration under high moisture conditions. The water loss under optimum soil-moisture conditions, the potential evapotranspiration, thus appears to be determined principally by climatic conditions.

Using the most reliable measurements of evaporation and transpiration that are available, we have obtained a valid and practical relationship between certain climatic parameters and potential evapotranspiration. This relationship permits the computation of potential evapotranspiration for any place from information on air temperature and latitude alone. The relationship is given and its use described elsewhere (Thornthwaite, 1948). Work is proceeding toward the development of a new formula that is based on sound physical principles; in the meantime, the present empirical formula is being

widely used in various water-balance studies.

If we compare the monthly march of precipitation and potential evapotranspiration, it is possible to obtain an insight into the water budget of an area (Fig. 113). For instance, at Seabrook, New Jersey, the potential evapotran-

Fig. 113.—Average march of precipitation, potential evapotranspiration, and actual evapotranspiration through the year at Berkeley, California, and Seabrook, New Jersey. Diagrams also show other factors of the moisture balance: water surplus (4); water deficit (5); soil-water utilization (6); and soil-water recharge (7).

spiration is negligibly small in winter, but in early spring it begins a rapid rise which reaches the high point of the year of more than 6 inches in July. It falls rapidly during the autumn months. The corresponding precipitation is far more uniformly distributed through the year, being very close to 3½ inches in nine of the twelve months. The rainiest months are July and August, each of which receives about 4½ inches; November, the driest month, has only 2¾ inches.

In this example, rainfall and water need do not coincide. There is too much rain in winter and too little in summer. Thus, at the time of maximum rainfall in July and August, there is a water deficiency, whereas in November, when rainfall drops to the lowest value of the year, there is a water surplus. In early autumn, water need falls below precipitation. For a while the surplus rainfall replaces soil moisture that had been used up previously. From then on the surplus water raises ground-water levels and produces surface and subsurface runoff. In spring, both transpiration and evaporation increase rapidly, and soon water need surpasses precipitation. When the soil moisture is at field capacity, actual and potential evapotranspiration are the same, and all precipitation in excess of the potential evapotranspiration is realized as water surplus. When precipitation does not equal potential evapotranspiration, the difference is made up in part from soil-moisture storage; but, as the soil becomes drier, the part not made up is larger. This is the water deficit, the amount by which actual and potential evapotranspiration differ.

Both water surplus and water deficit can be derived from the comparison of the monthly precipitation with the monthly potential evapotranspiration. The water surplus occurs in winter in Seabrook and amounts to about 15 inches; the water deficit occurs in summer and amounts to about 1 inch. Through the course of the year there is a net water surplus amounting to 14 inches. Through this system of monthly water bookkeeping it is possible also to determine the water that must be accounted for as soil-moisture storage.

In Berkeley, California, in a different climatic zone, nearly all the rainfall comes in winter, and there is almost no rain in summer. Here the winter water surplus is 4 inches and the summer water deficit is 7 inches.

A comparison of the water balance for Seabrook and Berkeley reveals some interesting facts. Both places have water surpluses and deficits during the year. The surplus at Seabrook, however, is considerably greater than at Berkeley. In addition, the net water balance shows an annual surplus of 14 inches at Seabrook and an annual deficit of 3 inches at Berkeley. Thus, at Seabrook and in other areas with similar water balances, there is a large supply of readily available water which may be stored in the water table beneath the earth's surface—a supply which can be used for widespread irrigation and which will be replenished each year. On the other hand, at Berkeley subsurface water taken for irrigation is not all replaced, and there would be a year-to-year lowering of the water table. Full irrigation of all land in such areas would not be possible. These two stations are illustrative of two different situations; in one area man might be able to produce widespread climatic changes through irrigation, but in the other his influence could be of only local significance.

SOIL MOISTURE AND THE IRRIGATION SCHEDULE

When the moisture content of the soil is at field capacity or above, any water that is added to it by precipitation percolates downward through it to the ground water table. This gravitational water is only detained briefly, the period depending on its amount and on the permeability of the soil. When the soil moisture is below field capacity, precipitation first brings the soil-moisture storage back to that level. The amount of water that can be stored in the root zone of the soil depends on its depth and on the soil type and structure. With shallow-rooted crops on a sandy soil, only 1–2 inches of water can be stored for free use of the plants. On the other hand, with deep-rooted crops on a fine-textured soil, 6–8 inches or more of water will be readily available.

Evaporation from a moist soil immediately begins to lower the moisture content of the soil (Fig. 114). As the soil dries, the rate of evapotranspiration diminishes. At first, evapotranspiration goes on uniformly at nearly the maximum rate from all soils, but, by the time an inch of water has been removed, the rates from different soils begin to differentiate. When one-half of the water is gone, the rate of evapotranspiration falls to one-half of the potential rate, and plants begin to suffer from drought. With a constant rate of potential evapotranspiration of 0.2 inch per day, the half-rate would be reached after seven days in coarse sand but not until after thirty-seven days in fine-textured soil. Within twenty days the soil moisture in coarse sand would be reduced to a point where the evapotranspiration is only 25 per cent of the potential rate. Long before this much water has been lost, the plants are suffering severely from lack of water, and growth is seriously retarded. In soil with water-storage capacity of 11 inches, this same degree of drought would be reached only after seventy-five days. Tables have been prepared which give the daily rates of soil-moisture depletion under varying rates of evapotranspiration for soils holding different amounts of water at field capacity.

It is clear that many of man's activities can influence in one way or another the soil-moisture relations. Many of these activities have resulted in a decrease in the amount of water which a soil can hold and hence tend to make it even more susceptible to droughts than

it might otherwise be. For instance, the cultivation of soil greatly disturbs the soil structure, and, when wheeled vehicles move over moist soil, some rearrangement of the soil particles occurs which results in a compaction of the soil. This compaction reduces the permeability of the soil and lowers its ability to hold water. It becomes extremely difficult for water or plant roots to penetrate the compacted layer.

Fig. 114.—Actual rates of soil-moisture depletion from soils holding different amounts of water in the root zone, assuming a constant rate of potential evapotranspiration of 0.2 inch per day.

For example, the water available to plants in the upper layer of a Sassafras silt-loam soil in a cultivated field in southern New Jersey has been found to be 2.17 inches per foot depth. The sod-covered soil along the border of this field holds 3.15 inches of water per foot. Thus, the loss of water-holding capacity due to cultivation in this field is nearly an inch of water per foot of soil.

Light sandy soils, of course, are able to hold less water than heavy silt or clay soils. To a considerable extent plants compensate for the lower water-holding capacity of sandy soils by deeper root penetration and more rapid root development. There is no similar compensation, however, when the water-holding capacity of a soil is reduced by misuse. Misuse destroys the soil structure and reduces air capacity, which inhibits root development. Thus, as water-holding capacity diminishes, aeration does also, and the root zone becomes shallower.

The effects of vegetation changes— by grazing, burning, cropping, substitution of species, and clearing—on the amount of water which enters or is retained in the soil, and hence on the water economy of an area, are also noteworthy (Colman, 1953). The elimination of transpiration by stopping plant growth will always result in making more water available for soil-moisture storage or for runoff. Whether the water enters the soil or runs off over the surface, producing harmful erosion, depends on the type of surface cover that remains. Uncontrolled burning of vegetation, of course, destroys not only the aerial parts of the plants but also much of the surface organic material and, hence, will lead to more runoff and less soil storage of the increased water supply. Grazing or overgrazing will result in two changes in the environmental conditions which will influence the microclimate. First, the removal of vegetation by the grazing animal will reduce transpiration and result in more of the precipitation being made available for soil storage or runoff. Second, however, the compaction of the soil by the hoofs of the animals will reduce the capacity of the soil to absorb water and hence make it less able to store water. The additional water made available by reduced transpiration will run off the surface and may result in erosion damage.

One of the limitations of the current soil-conservation program is that it does not attempt to get at the real seat of the trouble. The real task is to restore soil structure and increase the permeability and water-holding capacity of soil to eliminate runoff rather than to attempt to conduct the runoff water away from the field with a minimum of erosion through grassed waterways and terraces.

Results obtained for a number of places (Figs. 115 and 116) and for different years support the conclusion that soil moisture can be computed with all needed precision from climatological data. It is apparent from the agreement found between measured and computed values that the climatologic approach will permit the accurate determination of the movement of water through soils and the amount of storage in any selected layer in the soil. The method of computing is empirical, however, and it is still necessary to make certain assumptions in order to obtain the computed values. Further work should make it possible to refine the method and to base it on sound physical principles.

An irrigation schedule is a natural outgrowth of this method of determining soil moisture (Fig. 117). One can set up limits below which the soil moisture will not be allowed to fall for the particular crop and depth of root zone in question. Then, by keeping daily account of how much water has been lost from the soil, it is possible to know exactly when the predetermined level of soil-moisture depletion is reached and to know just how much to irrigate to bring the moisture level back to a safe value. Shallow-rooted crops will have to be irrigated more frequently, but with smaller amounts of water, than will deeper-rooted pastures or orchards. If irrigation is scheduled by keeping continuous account of the soil moisture, no great moisture deficiency can develop in the soil to limit growth, and there will be no overirrigation to damage both soil and crop and to result in a wasteful misuse of water (Thornthwaite and Mather, 1955).

With the solution to the problem of

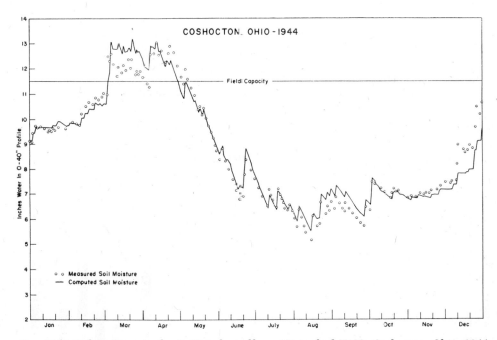

Fig. 115.—Soil moisture in the 0–40-inch profile on Watershed Y102, Coshocton, Ohio, 1944. Measured values obtained by Soil Conservation Service from soil samples and by use of weighing lysimeter. Computed values from daily climatological data using water-budget method.

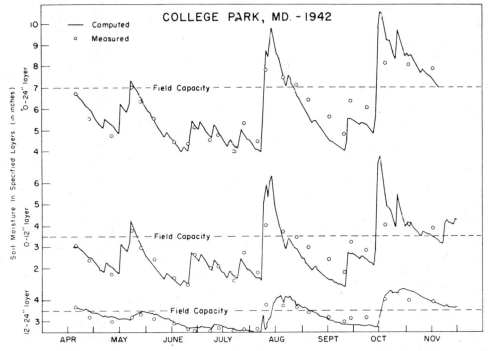

Fig. 116.—Soil moisture in specified layers of soil profile, College Park, Maryland, 1942. Measured values obtained by Soil Conservation Service from soil samples. Computed values from daily climatological data using water-budget method.

when to irrigate, a great forward stride toward scientific irrigation has been made. But irrigation farming is not just ordinary farming with irrigation added. In order to perfect a system of irrigation farming, we must fit irrigation into other necessary farming practices, such as cultivation, weed and pest control, and fertilization. In order to attain the high yields that are possible under irrigation, the whole complex of farming

the remaining New Jersey farm land under irrigation offers a great challenge. But I feel that there is a much greater challenge for scientific irrigation in southern New Jersey. There is an opportunity through irrigation to reclaim and develop the extensive empty areas which are unsettled and which now produce nothing.

The southern counties of New Jersey contain more than 2,500,000 acres of

Fig. 117.—Irrigation schedule for three different types of crops, Seabrook, New Jersey, 1954. Soil holds 3 inches of water at field capacity per foot depth of soil. Rain on May 21 brought soil up to field capacity, so that computations of deficiency start from 0 on that day.

practices must be revised to harmonize with the condition of abundant soil moisture at all times that results from irrigation. For example, under irrigation it is necessary to revise fertilizer practice and modify row spacing.

FUTURE DIRECTION OF MAN'S INFLUENCE ON RURAL ENVIRONMENTS

In 1949 the irrigated acreage in New Jersey stood at 28,117, less than 3 per cent of the land in harvested crops in that year. The possibility of bringing

land, but only 400,000 acres were in harvested crops in 1949, and, of these, only 13,000 were irrigated. At least 1,500,000 acres are considered nonarable waste land. The soils of this area, which is a part of the Atlantic coastal plain, are generally sandy and incapable of storing much water for use of crops during periods of summer drought. The soils dry out so completely in summer that the vegetation frequently is ravaged by fire. This vegetation is made up of stunted and fire-damaged pine and oak scrub, large sections of which are known as the "barrens" and are considered worthless.

There is an area of poor sandy soil on Seabrook Farms which closely resembles the barrens. It is covered with a woodland of scattered pine and jack oak. Although the woodland has been burned over many times, it was never cleared and cultivated, because the soil was considered to be too poor for crop production. We have recently had some experience in irrigating this kind of land and have learned that it possesses great hidden potentialities.

All the industrial waste water from Seabrook Farms has been disposed of in this woods since 1950. It is pumped into irrigation lines and discharged onto the land surface through giant nozzles, each of which irrigates more than an acre. Through the six seasons that this system has been operating, the water applied averaged about 35 inches a week. The average artificial rainfall in the woods has been about 600 inches a year, and the maximum in a part of the woods in 1950 was 1,200 inches. These large quantities of water have brought about a great change in the vegetation. The open woodland has been transformed into a jungle of weeds and other plants new to the area. Furthermore, the organic material in the soil has increased greatly. The rapidity of the change has been phenomenal.

The objective of this work has been to dispose of large quantities of water economically. We have attained this objective fully, and at the same time we have stumbled upon the means greatly to increase the agricultural production in the state.

A large part of southern New Jersey has the same sandy and droughty soils as the Seabrook Farms water-disposal area. Almost everywhere, however, ground water is within a few feet of the surface and readily available for irrigation. Therefore, the land is ideal-

ly situated to profit from scientific irrigation. Although this vast area is non-arable by ordinary standards, when water is applied to it by proper irrigation and its mineral deficiencies are rectified by correct fertilization, it can be highly productive. If this waste area, which now produces nothing, were reclaimed and planted to potatoes, it could easily produce five hundred million bushels a year—more than has ever yet been produced in the whole United States. This is only an illustration of the potentialities of this neglected region (Thornthwaite, 1953).

This huge job of reclamation in southern New Jersey can be done more cheaply and with less risk and uncertainty and would be economically more defensible than many of the large reclamation works of the West. It is not a job for the Federal Bureau of Reclamation, however, but for private interests. Since the task is expensive, most of the development will probably be done by large farming corporations. Insurance companies might take note of this opportunity for profitable investment of large sums of money.

What I have said of the possibilities of changing the climate in southern New Jersey by counteracting drought through supplemental irrigation applies almost equally to the entire Atlantic and Gulf coastal plains and the Mississippi Delta from Long Island to Louisiana and Arkansas. In this vast area, consisting of approximately 200,000,000 acres, soil moisture becomes deficient during the summer, but ground water is abundant within a few feet of the surface. It is not my task to discuss the benefits to crop production that will result from scientific irrigation of humid lands where water can be secured easily when it is needed. It is rather to point out that the counteracting of drought on a large scale is probably the principal way in which man can modify climate.

Over the earth's surface there are many other areas as large as our own coastal plain where the climate exhibits the defect of a large water surplus in one season and a large deficiency in another and where irrigation provides the means to correct this defect.

Technical developments have greatly improved irrigation practice. Fifty years ago farmers had to resort to windmills and coal-fired steam engines for power. Now electric motors and gasoline and diesel engines especially adapted to the purpose are available. There have been great developments in small pumps. Light aluminum pipe of greatly improved design is now available in large quantity, and, with the tremendous growth of facilities for the production of aluminum, it should become increasingly inexpensive. Modern portable irrigation pipe is a great improvement over the "clay tile wound with wire and laid in concrete" that was being used in New Jersey as recently as 1920. And, with the new methods of scheduling irrigation, it is possible to apply correct amounts of water at the right time; thus drought can be overcome fully, so that crop plants need never experience a deficiency of water.

In this survey I have attempted to be non-technical and have avoided giving tables of data to illustrate man-made changes in climate. I have stated that man is incapable of making any significant change in the climatic pattern on the earth; that the changes in microclimate for which he is responsible are so local and some so trivial that special instruments are often required to detect them. Through changes in the water balance which man brings about, sometimes deliberately and sometimes inadvertently, he exercises his greatest influence on climate. Through destruction of the natural ground cover and cultivation of the soil, he reduces the water-holding capacity of the soil and increases the incidence and severity of drought. In regions of seasonal drought, where there are alternating wet and dry periods, scientific irrigation can eliminate drought. This is where man is able to remedy a defect in climate and, in so doing, will do more to increase the food supplies of the world than he has ever done before in any other way.

REFERENCES

ALISOV, B. P.; DROSDOV, O. A.; and RUBENSTEIN, E. S.
  1952 *Kurs Klimatologii* ("Course in Climatology"). Leningrad: Publishing Institute of Hydrometry. 487 pp.

AUGHEY, S.
  1880 *Sketches of the Physical Geography and Geology of Nebraska.* Omaha, Neb.: Daily Republican Book and Job Office. 326 pp.

CLEMENTS, F. E., and CHANEY, R. W.
  1936 *Environment and Life in the Great Plains.* (Carnegie Institution Supplement Publication No. 24.) Washington, D.C.: Government Printing Office. 54 pp.

COLMAN, E. A.
  1953 *Vegetation and Watershed Management.* New York: Ronald Press Co. 412 pp.

GEIGER, R.
  1950 *The Climate near the Ground.* Cambridge, Mass.: Harvard University Press. 482 pp.

HOLZMAN, B.
  1937 *Sources of Moisture for Precipitation for the United States.* (U.S. Department of Agriculture Technical Bulletin No. 589.) Washington, D.C.: Government Printing Office. 41 pp.

MARSH, G. P.
  1864 *Man and Nature.* London: Sampson, Low & Son. 560 pp.
  1874 *The Earth as Modified by Human Action.* New York: Scribner, Armstrong & Co. 656 pp.

MATHER, J. R.
  1950 *Manual of Evapotranspiration.* ("Publications in Climatology, The Johns Hopkins University Laboratory

of Climatology," Vol. III, No. 3.) Centerton, N.J. 29 pp.

1954 "The Present Climatic Fluctuation and Its Bearing on a Reconstruction of Pleistocene Climatic Conditions," *Tellus*, VI, No. 3, 287–301.

MATHER, J. R. (ed.)

1954 *The Measurement of Potential Evapotranspiration*. ("Publications in Climatology, The Johns Hopkins University Laboratory of Climatology," Vol. VII, No. 1.) Centerton, N.J. 225 pp.

SCHWERDTFEGER, WERNER, and VASINO, CESAR J.

1954 "La Variación secular de las precipitaciones en el este y centro de la República Argentina," *Meteoros*, IV, No. 3, 174–93. Buenos Aires.

THORNTHWAITE, C. W.

1936 "The Great Plains," pp. 202–50 in GOODRICH, C.; ALLIN, B. W.; THORNTHWAITE, C. W., et al., *Migration and Economic Opportunity*. Philadelphia: University of Pennsylvania Press. 763 pp.

1937 "The Hydrologic Cycle Re-examined," *Soil Conservation*, III, No. 4, 85–91.

1948 "An Approach toward a Rational Classification of Climate," *Geographical Review*, XXXVIII, No. 1, 55–94.

1953 *Climate and Scientific Irrigation in New Jersey*. ("Publications in Climatology, The John Hopkins University Laboratory of Climatology," Vol. VI, No. 1.) Centerton, N.J. 8 pp.

1954 "Topoclimatology," pp. 227–32 in WORMELL, T. W., et al., *Proceedings of the Toronto Meteorological Conference 1953*. London: Royal Meteorological Society. 294 pp.

THORNTHWAITE, C. W., and HARE, F. K.

1955 "Climatic Classification in Forestry," *Unasylva* (Forestry Division, FAO, Rome), IX, No. 2, 50–59.

THORNTHWAITE, C. W., and HOLZMAN, B.

1942 *Measurement of Evaporation from Land and Water Surfaces*. (U.S. Department of Agriculture Technical Bulletin No. 817.) Washington, D.C.: Government Printing Office. 75 pp.

THORNTHWAITE, C. W., and MATHER, J. R.

1955 "The Water Budget and Its Use in Irrigation," pp. 346–58 in STEFFERUD, ALFRED (ed.), *Water: Yearbook of Agriculture, 1955*. Washington, D.C.: U.S. Department of Agriculture. 723 pp.

THORNTHWAITE, C. W., et al.,

1946 "Report of the Committee on Evaporation and Transpiration, 1945–1946," *Transactions of the American Geophysical Union*, XXVII, No. 5, 721–23.

YOUNG, A. A., and BLANEY, H. F.

1942 *Use of Water by Native Vegetation*. (California Department of Public Works, Bulletin No. 50.) Sacramento. 160 pp.

The Climate of Towns

H. E. LANDSBERG[*]

INTRODUCTION

One of the primary purposes of man's shelter is protection against biologically adverse climatic influences. Even though most houses are compromises, they fulfil this purpose in first approximation (Landsberg, 1954). However, when man's gregariousness, his need for common defense, and the trend toward division of labor bring many houses into close proximity, the end result is a modification of local climate —with often far from pleasant results.

For the present discussion we shall extend the definition of the term "town" to cover all large, concentrated settlements from several hundred dwellings up to cities and metropolitan areas. It is quite difficult to decide, in an objective fashion, at what point of population and building density a notable influence upon climate begins. Any change in the natural ground cover destroys existing microclimates (Geiger, 1950). Every farm, every house, and every road causes a new microclimate.

In many cases an assessment of the change in climate a settlement has caused is quite difficult. This stems from the fact that many towns and cities have been built in spots in which the conditions governing the climate are quite complicated. The coastal positions which make good ports, the valleys which favor traffic and trade, and the heights and promontories which are natural fortresses often have already a local climate quite distinct from the surroundings. City development may tend to accentuate or eliminate these differences caused by position and topography. Our task here shall be to filter out and discuss the extent of climatic change which has been caused by settlements per se.

PRIOR WORK

Early students of climate were quite conscious of the fact that man's activities were likely to cause changes of climate. Thomas Jefferson, who was much interested in this problem, recommended to his correspondent, Dr. Lewis C. Beck, of Albany, New York, in a letter dated at "Monticello," July 16, 1824, that climatic surveys "should be repeated once or twice in a century to shew the effect of clearing and culture towards the changes of climate."

The early instrumental records began to show differences between town and countryside which were commented upon from the earliest specific study of a city climate (Howard, 1833)—that of London—and have continued to be commented on up to current monographs on the climate of individual cities. However, for a century the climatological studies were content to

---

[*] Dr. Landsberg is Chief of the Climatic Service of the United States Weather Bureau, Washington, D.C. He has taught in the meteorology departments of Pennsylvania State University (1934–40) and the University of Chicago (1941–43). He also directed military research work in the Research and Development Board (1946–51) and in the Air Force Cambridge Research Center (1951–53). His book, *Physical Climatology*, 1941, is now in its fifth printing, 1950.

point out in individual cases what differences happened to exist. With the growth of conscious town-planning, we find also an expanding literature on the influence of settlements and industry on climate. Among the authors who have studied the problem from a fundamental point of view, we want to single out only four: Louis Besson, Wilhelm Schmidt, Rudolf Geiger, and Albert Kratzer.

Out of his Munich doctoral dissertation, the Benedictine priest, Father Kratzer, developed a comprehensive survey (1937) of the existing literature which contains 225 specific and 25 statistical references to source data. This is today still the most authoritative text on our subject matter. A further excellent guide is Brooks's bibliography on urban climates (1952), which contains 249 abstracts and covers the literature between 1833 and 1952. In addition to works on the effects of towns on climate and the relation of climate to town-planning, this bibliography includes the most important climatographies of individual localities.

THE PROBLEM

At first sight, it might appear simple to get at the differences between the climate of the town and that of the undisturbed countryside. Yet, quite aside from the difficulty of topographic site peculiarities, already mentioned, it is not easy to obtain strictly comparable records from a city and from its surroundings. In fact, quite a few of the earlier studies suffer from an inadequate evaluation of the data used in obtaining the results. When authors, with considerable indifference, compared data obtained from roof stations with others where the instruments were exposed on the ground, they likely masked the very information they searched for. Or, in other instances, comparisons of earlier with later records are not entirely satisfactory unless

care is taken to eliminate regional climatic fluctuations. This is by no means an easy task, yet it is indispensable if tenable results are to be obtained. Because observations made specifically for the purpose of comparison are scarce, the present study is not entirely free from these objections.

Before entering into the discussion, a brief review of basic causes for a change in climate by urbanization seems in order. The first is the alteration in surface. In the most radical case a dense forest will have been replaced by a formation of rocklike substances, such as stone, brick, and concrete; naturally moist areas, such as swamps and ponds, will have been drained; and the aerodynamic roughness will have been increased by obstacles of varying size. The second cause for climatic change is the heat production of towns, ranging from the metabolism of the mass of humans and animals to the heat liberated by furnaces in homes and factories, enhanced in recent years by the millions of internal combustion engines of an ever increasing number of motor vehicles. The third major city influence upon climate, often reaching far beyond the confines of the settlement, is the change produced in the composition of the atmosphere. Addition of inert solid matter, gases, and active chemicals has caused Kratzer (1937) to liken the effect, in part, to that of an active volcano. The total impact of these changes upon climatic conditions has been adverse in most cases. Only in a few instances can one assume that urbanization has decreased climatic stresses. In some localities the draining of swamps has been beneficial. There is also some reason to believe that in hot, sunny desert areas the cities with their narrow streets have contributed to the comfort of the inhabitants. Unfortunately, there are no quantitative data to prove this. In most other urban areas of our industrialized civilization the over-all climatic result has been an unhealthy one.

In the following detailed analysis of town climate the influence of these basic man-made changes upon the various elements will be dealt with. Inasmuch as we consider the changes basically induced by air pollution as the most far-reaching and fundamental ones, the discussion will start with the modification induced by this component.

AIR COMPOSITION

The greatest climatic aberration from natural conditions brought about by urbanization is caused by changes in

TABLE 9*

CONCENTRATIONS OF CONDENSATION NUCLEI
AS INFLUENCED BY ENVIRONMENT

(Number of Aitken Nuclei per Cubic Centimeter)

Type of Locality	No.	Average Count	Extreme Count
Cities (>100,000 population).....	28	147,000	4,000,000
Towns (<100,000 population).....	15	34,300	400,000
Countryside......	25	9,500	330,000

* Source: Landsberg, 1937.

the composition of the atmosphere. The term "pollution" encompasses it in one word. It is nothing new. The first real metropolitan area of the world suffered from it centuries ago. Evelyn (1661, p. 18), in his description of London conditions, put it quite succinctly: "For when in all other places the Aer is most Serene and Pure, it is here Ecclipsed with such a Cloud of Sulphure, as the Sun itself, which gives day to all the World besides, is hardly able to penetrate and impart it here; and the weary Traveller at many Miles distance, sooner smells, than sees the City to which he repairs."

Not much has changed in the nearly three centuries since this was written.

If anything, pollution has worsened. Individual episodes—the Meuse Valley in 1930; Donora, Pennsylvania, in 1948; London in 1952—have been widely discussed because of their disaster-like consequences, but they were just peaks in a continuous, insidious process. Pollution adversely affects plants, including valuable crops, causes untold corrosive damage, and is undoubtedly detrimental to human health. In less dangerous stages it causes eye and bronchial irritation. In its worst manifestations it causes premature death among the aged who are afflicted with chronic pulmonary or cardiovascular ailments. There is even a suspicion that it contributes to the notable increase in lung cancer.

Almost all climatic elements are affected by pollution—radiation, cloudiness, fog, visibility, and the atmospheric electric field. In a secondary way temperature, precipitation, and humidity also are influenced. Pollution climate is certainly at present the basic problem of the climatology of industrialized modern towns.

The concentrations of particulate matter contained in city air illustrate the situation in a gross way. A fairly simple measure of total suspensoids are the so-called condensation (or Aitken) "nuclei," with diameters between about 0.01 and 0.1 micron. A summary of many thousands of observations showed the conditions listed in Table 9.

For the larger *dust* particles (about 0.5–10 microns), which are also indicative of the degree of pollution, though likely to be more a nuisance than a menace, Löbner (1935) has given some values for the city of Leipzig. He found high concentrations of 25–30 particles per cubic centimeter in the center of the city and only 1–2 per cubic centimeter near the outskirts. Schmidt (1952) in a later study in the same locality found an average of 7 particles per cubic centimeter in the most polluted area. This at least fixes the order of magnitude. A tenfold increase in dust particles in town areas can be accepted as the doubtful contribution of the community to the air.

From publications of Berg (1947) and Reifferscheid (1954) we can deduce that, whereas clean country air contains only about 4–10 microörganisms in each 10 liters, city air has ten times as many in the same volume. The relative proportion of pathogenic organisms has not been determined, but there is no reason to assume that the ratio is less.

In some cities detailed surveys cn

a trace to 3 per cent (among them being Al_2O_3, PbO, TiO_2, Cr_2O_3, V_2O_5, NiO, MnO_3, CaO, MgO, ZnO, CnO, MoO_3, SnO_2, and As_3O_3). Oxides of sulfur and phosphorus are aso present. Several of these are definitely worse than just a nuisance!

The topography in which the towns are located often causes unfavorable microclimatic or macroclimatic conditions which contribute heavily to accumulation of smoke and fumes in the lower layers of the atmosphere. Light winds and temperature inversions are usually meteorological adjuvants of the topographical controls. An example

TABLE 10*

SOME SOURCES AND QUANTITIES OF POLLUTANTS IN DONORA, PENNSYLVANIA
(Pounds per Day)

Source	Particulate Matter	Sulfur Dioxide	Carbon Dioxide	Carbon Monoxide	Chlorides	Fluorides
Domestic fuels	12,600	12,600	1,400,000	74,000	15	30
Trains and boats	3,860	3,860	446,000	5,370	4.7	2.4
Automobiles (3,000)			70,000	30,000		
Steel mills†	7,420	200		696,000	140	44

* Source: Anonymous, 1949*a*.

† Other steel-mill pollution products: iron oxides, 3,110; total sulfur compounds, 1,135; other metal oxides, 125.

solid suspensions give a similar picture. For example, over the industrial city of Pittsburgh an average of about 610 tons of dust settle per square mile each year. In the summer months this amounts to about 1½ tons per square mile a day; in winter it is over 2¼ tons per square mile a day (Ely, 1952). Of this quantity, about 5 per cent is carbon soot. In earlier years, prior to the widespread introduction of domestic oil-burners and diesel engines and other "smoke control," this component was closer to 25 per cent of the total. In this steel and smelter town the largest constituent of the solid-dust deposits— around 20 per cent—is iron oxide (Fe_2O_3). Silica (SiO_2), with 16 per cent, is next. Other metal oxides are found in concentrations ranging from

each of a microclimate and of a macroclimate favorable to air pollution follows.

Microclimatic setting heavily contributed to the October, 1948, smog episode in the town of Donora, Pennsylvania (12,000 inhabitants), near Pittsburgh. A United States Public Health Service survey (Anonymous, 1949*a*) disclosed that about 42 per cent of the population had suffered adverse health effects. The twenty fatalities attributed to the smog in the borough represented six times the normal death rate. The pollution products added by various sources to the atmosphere are shown in Table 10.

In Los Angeles a macroclimate of frequent temperature inversions coupled with sunshine has intensified the smog menace. A special inquiry by Stanford Research Institute (1954) has shown that various combustion processes furnish tremendous quantities of pollution products to the air, as shown in Table 11. This Stanford study indicated that the sunlight produces active oxygen—ozone (O_3)—and causes photochemical reactions in the oxides of nitrogen and sulfur as well as in other organic compounds which accumulate under the inversion layer. Various secondary reactions produce some of the irritating aldehydes. Table 12 gives the concentrations of various pollutants in Los Angeles as established by numerous analyses.

From measurements in ten other big cities both in Europe and in America we can establish the ranges found for some of the most universal pollutants, as shown in Table 13. The thresholds of

TABLE 11*

POLLUTION SOURCES AND PRODUCTS IN LOS ANGELES, CALIFORNIA

Fuel Type	Consumption (Tons per Day)	Some Products Resulting	Quantities (Tons per Day)
Gas	20,400	Aldehydes	85
Oil	7,300	Ammonium	14
Gasoline (2,000,000 cars)	11,550	Nitrogen oxides	463
Refuse	9,165	Sulfur oxides	411
Other	260	Acids	157
		Organics	1,534

* Source: Stanford Research Institute, 1954.

TABLE 12*

AIR POLLUTANTS IN LOS ANGELES, CALIFORNIA

Gases	Parts per Million of Air	Aerosols	Milligrams per Cubic Meter of Air
Carbon monoxide	0–25	Aluminum compounds	0.018
Acrolein	Trace	Calcium compounds	0.007
Lower aldehydes	0.3–1.1	Carbon	0.132
Formaldehyde	0.09–0.3	Iron compounds	0.010
Hydrocarbons	0–3	Lead compounds	0.042
Ozone	0–0.8	Ether solubles	0.120
Nitric acid	0.2–0.4	Silica	0.026
Sulfur dioxide	0.1–0.4	Sulfuric acid	0.05–0.2

* Source: Stanford Research Institute, 1954.

TABLE 13

RANGE OF CONCENTRATIONS OF POLLUTANTS IN CITY AIR

Gas	Parts per Million	Aerosols	Milligrams per Cubic Meter
Carbon monoxide	10–30 (100)*	Sulfuric acid	0.1–7 (3)*
Carbon dioxide	50–400	Hydrochloric acid	1–4 (5)*
Sulfur dioxide	0.1–2 (3)*		
Nitrogen oxides	1–6 (25)*		

* Threshold of dangerous concentration.

dangerous concentrations, accepted in industrial establishments, are added in parentheses. This table indicates that some of the observed values either come close to or occasionally exceed the safe thresholds. For sensitive and old persons the thresholds may lie lower.

A series of comparative analyses for sulfur dioxide by the Air Hygiene Foundation (1937–38) showed that, in seven eastern United States cities, their centers invariably had higher concentrations than the countrysides 25 miles away. In the towns with least pollution the ratio was 3:1; in the worst setting it was 10:1. The average of all measurements yielded a ratio of about 5:1.

At the doorstep of an era energized by nuclear fuels we can just barely guess what the future may have in store. If coal and hydrocarbons vanish as fuels, many of the above-described ill-smelling and irritating substances may disappear as admixtures of city air. However, they may be replaced by radioactive gases, fumes, and particulates. At present we have but a rather vague idea of what might be tolerable for some of the compounds which are likely to show up in our atmosphere as effluents from atomic reactors. They are listed in Table 14.

After this review of changes in the composition of the air produced by industrial urbanization, we shall attempt to answer the question of how these changes affect the climatic elements. Several of the latter—radiation intensity, visual range, atmospheric electric properties—are modified to a considerable degree by atmospheric pollution.

Atmospheric Radiation

Various measurements of the reduction in total radiation received at the surface in a number of cities as compared to the countryside are in substantial agreement. For the total annual radiation the reduction averages about 15–20 per cent. This quantity of energy is partly absorbed and partly reflected and scattered by the dust haze above the city. Actually, most of the radiation is lost in a relatively shallow layer.

TABLE 14*

MAXIMUM PERMISSIBLE CONCENTRATIONS OF RADIOACTIVE EFFLUENTS FOR 24-HOUR CONTINUOUS EXPOSURE

Element	Microcuries per Cubic Centimeter
Ar^{41}	10^{-8}
I^{131}	10^{-8}
C^{14}	10^{-8}
Xe^{133}	10^{-7}
Kr^{85}	?

* Source: Wolman, 1952.

TABLE 15*

PERCENTAGE LOSS OF SOLAR RADIATION IN CITY AIR COMPARED TO COUNTRYSIDE AIR

SEASON	HEIGHT OF SUN ABOVE HORIZON			
	10°	20°	30°	45°
Winter	36	26	21	.....
Spring	29	20	15	11
Summer	29	21	18	14
Winter	34	23	19	16

* Source: Steinhauser, 1934.

Lauscher and Steinhauser (1932) reported on some measurements in Vienna which were taken in midsummer simultaneously at the surface and 236 feet higher on the tower of St. Stephen's Cathedral. This layer of city air reduced the radiation received at the surface by 5.7 per cent. A combination of data obtained by Steinhauser (1934) for three cities—Vienna, Leipzig, and Frankfurt—as a function of season and solar altitude is shown in Table 15.

As regards change in *spectral distribution,* there is some question about the influence of city air. Büttner (1929) found in Berlin and Potsdam, Germany, that all wave lengths are equally weakened proportional to the total reduction in intensity. In contrast to this, Maurain (1947) reported for Paris the relative spectral distribution shown in Table 16. This table indicates an almost complete elimination of the ultraviolet radiation in that city.

An air-pollution survey made by the Department of Scientific and Industrial Research (1945) in the city of Leicester, England (population 260,000),

TABLE 16*

PARTITION OF ENERGY IN SOLAR RADIATION
IN AND NEAR PARIS, FRANCE

(Percentage of Total Intensity)

	Ultra-violet	Extreme Violet	Visible	Infra-red
Paris center...	0.3	2.5	43	54
Outskirts......	3.0	5.0	40	52

* Source: Maurain, 1947.

showed a reduction of ultraviolet radiation around 3,000 angstroms of about 30 per cent in winter and 6 per cent in summer.

The great scattering of incoming radiation by the smoke pall is also indicated by observations of *sky blue*. In cities the data show much paler shades than those for the country. Lettau (1931) related for Königsberg (Kaliningrad) a difference of three scale divisions on the Linke-Ostwald blue scale. *Illumination* likewise is less in the city. Among the worst examples are Leningrad and London, where mean reductions of 50 and 40 per cent, respectively, have been found (Galanin, 1939; Kratzer, 1937).

Visual Range

Most obvious in all climatological records is the conspicuous decrease of visual range in cities and towns. As cities and industrialization grew, so did the number of days with fog.

In the first monograph devoted to the climate of a city, Howard (1833, II, 357) probably introduced the term "city fog." He relates a number of cases which, because both of the historical interest and of the acuteness of the observations, shall be quoted in full. He describes the fog of January 10, 1812, in the following words:

London was this day involved, for several hours, in palpable darkness. The shops, offices, &c. were necessarily lighted up; but the streets not being lighted as at night, it required no small care in the passenger to find his way, and avoid accidents. The sky, where any light pervaded it, showed the aspect of bronze. Such is, occasionally, the effect of the accumulation of smoke between two opposite gentle currents, or by means of a misty calm. I am informed that the fuliginous cloud was visible, in this instance, for a distance of forty miles. Were it not for the extreme mobility of our atmosphere, this volcano of a thousand mouths would, in winter be scarcely habitable [*ibid.*, pp. 162–63].

In the next observations Howard notes the limited extent of the city fog in a paragraph referring to January 16, 1826:

At one o'clock yesterday afternoon the fog in the city was as dense as we ever recollect to have known it. Lamps and candles were lighted in all shops and offices, and the carriages in the streets dared not exceed a foot pace. At the same time, five miles from town the atmosphere was clear and unclouded with a brilliant sun [*ibid.*, III, 207].

In another place, in quoting a contemporary newspaper on the fog of November 12, 1828, he indicates that adverse health effects were recognized even then:

The fog of Wednesday has seldom been exceeded in opacity in the metropolis and its neighborhood. It began to thicken very much about half past twelve o'clock, from which time, till near two, the effect was most distressing, making the eyes smart, and almost suffocating those who were in the street, particularly asthmatic persons [*ibid.*, p. 303].

Four generations later the situation in London had become, if anything, even more aggravated. The episode of December 5–9, 1952, as discussed at a meeting of the Royal Meteorological Society (1954), eloquently documents this. In central London the "smog" lasted for 114 hours. It was extremely dense for 48 hours, with visibility at times less than 30 feet. Particulate matter was measured to reach temporarily

of them the number of *days with fog* doubled in the half-century prior to the depression of the early 1930's. Paris offers a typical example on the decrease of visual range in the morning hours, and Table 17 shows the steady decrease in the number of days when visual range exceeded 4 miles. The subsequent standstill of many factories

TABLE 17

AVERAGE NUMBER OF DAYS WITH
VISUAL RANGE OF 4 MILES
IN CENTER OF PARIS

Decade	No. of Days
1901–10	95
1911–20	82
1921–30	60

TABLE 18*

PROBABILITIES OF LOW VISIBILITIES IN PARIS AND ENVIRONS
(0900 Data—in Number of Cases per 1,000)

VISIBILITY RANGE TYPE	OCTOBER–MARCH			APRIL–SEPTEMBER		
	City	Suburbs	Country	City	Suburbs	Country
Light fog ($\frac{1}{4}$–1 mile)	350	219	60	49	49	6
Moderate fog (300 feet–$\frac{1}{4}$ mile)	49	43	28	3	3	2
Dense fog (<300 feet)	8	14	5	0	1	0

* Source: Besson, 1931.

values of 4.5 milligrams per cubic meter. This is ten times the value observed in the same locality in December when no fog is present. Sulfur dioxide reached seven times its normal value, and, under the meteorological conditions prevalent at the time, accumulation exceeded dissipation by 70 tons of sulfur dioxide per day. Deaths jumped from 250 to 900 per day. A total of 4,000 fatalities was attributed to this fog.

London, while perhaps afflicted with the most notorious city fogs, does not stand alone. Almost all million-inhabitant cities in latitudes requiring heating experience the condition. In many

caused a temporary improvement. In the last decade the values have teetered. Enforcement of antismoke ordinances and use of control equipment and fuels producing less pollutants have helped in many localities to check the rise.

Paris also offers a good example of the difference between the city and the country in the number of cases of low visual ranges. The figures shown in Table 18 were compiled by Besson (1931). This characterizes especially the light and moderate fogs as typical phenomena of the densely populated metropolis.

A rather interesting case can be related from observations near Detroit. Hourly visibility observations were made there both at the Municipal Airport, which is located 6 miles northeast of the center of town at an elevation of 619 feet, and at the Wayne County Airport 17 miles southwest of the center, elevation 632 feet. The typical city smogs generally develop when winds are weak, 5 miles per hour or less. Under those conditions low visibilities of less than a mile were reported on an average of 149 hours per year at the Municipal Airport. The County Airport had only 89 such hours. At the Munic-

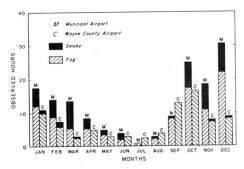

FIG. 118.—Annual variation of visual range less than a mile at two neighboring airports in Detroit, Michigan, one being under city influence (simultaneous wind speeds less than 5 miles per hour).

ipal Airport the cause of the low visibility was attributed to smoke on 49 observations annually, but at the County Airport only 5 hours, on an average, were caused by this element. Figure 118 shows the annual variation of both fog and smoke at the two airports. Winter is the main season when pollution affects visual range. The prevalence of pure radiation fogs at the County Airport from July through October is also notable. The difference shown between the two airports can be taken as rather typical for the city-countryside contrast of fog types in our latitudes.

Atmospheric Electricity

Some of the more subtle effects of pollution on the atmosphere escape our senses. Among these are changes produced in the atmospheric electrical properties. In pure air there is always a substantial number of small ions of both signs present, usually around several hundred per cubic centimeter. They have high mobility and cause a fairly high conductivity. In the city small ions have a very short lifetime. As soon as generated, they attach themselves to aerosol particles and become large ions. Thus we find that the number of small ions per unit volume in cities is usually 50–75 per cent less than in the countryside. On the other hand, the large ions are higher by a factor of ten or more in the polluted areas. This reduces the conductivity, and hence there is a marked increase in potential gradient (see, e.g., H. Kuhn, 1933; U. Kuhn, 1954; Maurain, 1947; Mühleisen, 1953). To give an order of magnitude, typical winter values of potential gradients in the city are around 200 volts per meter in winter and 100 volts per meter in summer. The corresponding rural values are, respectively, about 70 and 40 volts per meter. The pollution cycles, both diurnal and annual, are fully reflected in the measurements of the electric field. The Sunday lull in industrial activity and vehicular traffic, compared with other days of the week, shows in a definite minimum in the potential gradient.

It is not known whether or not the atmospheric electric conditions exert an influence upon human beings, but hypotheses claiming such bioclimatic effects have been advanced from time to time.

TOTAL PRECIPITATION

The question of influence of towns on precipitation seems, upon analysis, to be quite intimately related to the problem of air pollution, although other parameters enter into the very complex phenomena encountered here. Precipitation is a very fickle element, and the degrees of variation, as well as differences between stations, often are hard to establish. This is partly caused by the relatively poor sampling inherent in the usual rain-gauge measurements. Nevertheless, one can state that there has been an increase in rainfall over metropolitan areas compared to less densely populated and industrialized areas. This is stated with the reservation that there is hardly any case of really undisturbed natural surface, with its original forest or plant cover, within distance of a city that would make a valid comparison possible.

Schmauss (1927), in the case of the city of Munich, was one of the first to discover a definite surplus in the number of *days with small amounts of precipitation* in the city compared to outlying stations. He found that the mean annual number of days with precipitation of 0.004–0.2 inch was 144 in the city and only 130 in the country. This is an increase of 11 per cent. The city of Munich also showed a very definite surplus of heavy showers of between 0.8 and 1.6 inches. The eastern sector of the city was more affected than the western portion, in accordance with the prevailing westerly winds. The frequency of *hail* and *thunderstorms* showed a similar increase. Analogous findings were reported by Berkes (1947) for Budapest, with greater thunderstorm activity over Pest being attributed to city influence. Kratzer (1937) gave for Nürnberg, Germany, an average of 32.3 days per year with thunderstorms over the city against only 27.8 days per year for the airport, a difference of 14 per cent.

For *total rainfall* amounts an early report by Bogolepow (1928) compares seventeen-year simultaneous records at the city station of Moscow, and at a near-by country station. He reports annual mean values of 23.95 and 21.22 inches, respectively, a difference of 10 per cent. There was some scoffing at these earlier data. They were variously interpreted as resulting from doubtful observations or microclimatic differences. The influence of air pollution on precipitation, however, seemed to become more substantiated by the analysis of rainfall data for the industrial town of Rochdale, England, presented by Ashworth (1929). In three decades a monotonous increase in rainfall was noted, as shown in Table 19. Nothing

TABLE 19*

RAINFALL AVERAGES FOR
ROCHDALE, ENGLAND

Decade	Mean Annual Value (Inches)
1898–1907	42.81
1908–17	45.83
1918–27	48.65

* Source: Ashworth, 1929.

like it was observed in the non-industrial neighborhood.

Table 19 shows a total increase of 5.84 inches, or 13 per cent. Particularly noteworthy is the fact that there was a marked difference between the mean rainfall observed on weekdays in contrast to Sundays during the thirty-year period. The difference of the mean gave 0.37 inch less for Sundays, a value of three times the probable error. No difference of this magnitude was found at less industrialized towns near by.

Wiegel (1938) adduced further evidence for the effect of industrial activity on precipitation. He studied the conditions in the Rhenish-Westphalian area. This includes the famous Ruhr region, one of the most industrialized spots on the earth. He used a thirty-five-year record, from 1891 to 1925. In undisturbed areas the mean annual rainfall averaged 30 inches; in the industrial zones it was 1.5 inches per year more, an excess of 5 per cent. He also noted a marked increase in the number of days with small amounts of precipitation (0.004–0.2 inch) in the industrial areas. The total annual number of days with precipitation there rose by 20–30 days over the value of 170 days per year in the non-polluted portions, an increase of 12–18 per cent.

We have searched the files of United States climatological records to find

TABLE 20

DECADAL POPULATION CENSUS
FIGURES FOR TULSA, OKLAHOMA

Year	Population
1890...............	....
1900...............	1,390
1910...............	18,182
1920...............	72,075
1930...............	141,258
1940...............	142,157
1950...............	182,740

The precipitation values observed in Tulsa were correlated with records maintained at other localities in the region—Claremore, Cleveland, Bacone, and Broken Arrow, Oklahoma—and, for the earlier parts of the record, with Fort Gibson, Oklahoma, and Fort Smith, Arkansas. In the last two decades data from the Tulsa airport were also available. From the correlations there was obtained an "estimated" value, based on the general regional variation, and assumed to represent Tulsa minus the town effect. In Table 21 the observed and these estimated values are compared for six decades. The increase of the observed over the estimated values is quite notable. There would seem to have been a slight dip in the depression decade 1931–40.

For the fourteen-year period 1939–52 we can also carry out a comparison between values observed in town and

TABLE 21

MEAN ANNUAL PRECIPITATION OBSERVED FOR TULSA AND ESTIMATED CITY INFLUENCE

	DECADE					
	1891–1900	1901–10	1911–20	1921–30	1931–40	1941–50
Observed inches.......	34.93	36.75	37.91	42.10	38.15	42.91
Estimated inches......	35	36	34	39	36	40
Percentage of excess....	0	2	10.5	7.2	4.8	6.8

additional material which might throw further light on the problem. One of the objectives was to obtain data for a locality where topography would inject a minimum of complications. Another was to locate a town which essentially was a point source of pollution rather than to use cases of vast industrialized regions or metropolitan areas, which complicate the analysis. The best example we could find was Tulsa, Oklahoma, a town which has grown explosively, developing from an Indian trading post into an industrial city in a few decades (Table 20).

at the airport, 6 miles to the northeast. This comparison was carried out for individual monthly values and later combined for the warmer and colder halves of the year and for yearly totals (Table 22). Aside from the general increase in the city amounts, already noted in the preceding trend analysis, this table shows a fairly marked differentiation between warm and cold seasons. In the warm season, most precipitation is likely to be in shower form and hence more irregular. We may also deal with rain from warm cumulus clouds, upon which pollution products may have less influence. In the cold season, frontal rains (and supercooled clouds) are more frequent, and hence nucleating properties of pollution products might become more effective. It may be well to insert here that cloud nucleation is not the only hypothesis which can explain the increase in rainfall. In the first place, many combustion processes add water vapor to the atmosphere, so there may be more precipitable water available over urban areas in spite of the surroundings. Furthermore, the added impetus to turbulence over the city, because of temperature convec-

amount of precipitation which falls in the form of snow. Kassner (1917) reported such a situation, for example, for Berlin. He found over periods of years that, when it snowed in the country, the city had snow in only 72 per cent of the cases; in 14 per cent of the cases the city snow was mixed with rain; and in 7 per cent only rain was observed in the city. (In the remaining 7 per cent no simultaneous precipitation was reported for the city.) Maurain (1947) indicated the same for Paris, where snow, however, is rather infrequent. That city had snowfall, on

TABLE 22

COMPARISON OF PRECIPITATION FOR TULSA: CITY VERSUS AIRPORT STATIONS

	April–September	October–March	Year
Average precipitation in city (inches)........	27.73	13.95	41.68
Difference between city and airport (inches)..	1.27	1.57	3.20
Percentage excess in city..................	4.7	11.5	7.7
No. of months in which city had higher amounts.............................	55 (66)*	61 (73)*	116 (69)*
No. of months in which airport had higher amounts.............................	29 (34)*	23 (27)*	52 (31)*

* Percentage of cases in parentheses.

tion and increased roughness, might explain equally well the greater amounts of precipitation. In the writer's opinion, nucleation and turbulence each contribute to the increases but under different synoptic situations. Later paragraphs will bring out further facts in support of this position.

Snowfall

Precipitation in the form of snow deserves some special attention in a discussion of the special properties of urban climates. It is often a rather sensitive indicator of climatic differences and changes. The frequency of snowfall is, of course, influenced by variations in air temperature. These temperatures, as we shall see later, are generally higher in towns than in their surroundings. This decreases the relative

an average, a little over 10 days per year, while the near-by country had 14.

The pollution influence on snowfall was suspected first by Kratzer (1937) for Munich. From his own visual observations on several trips from the outskirts to the center of the city, he reported that there was slight snowfall from the fog, or stratus, over the city but none in the surroundings. This was in the days when only a few meteorologists were paying any attention to cloud nucleation problems.

A particularly convincing case of this type has been placed on record by Kienle (1952). This one occurred over the heavily industrialized cities of Mannheim and Ludwigshafen, Germany, on January 28 and 30, 1949. Snowfall was entirely restricted to the city area. A ground fog and low stratus

1,500 feet thick were settled over the towns; surface air temperature was 25° F., and calm prevailed. Above the stratus was a sharp temperature inversion, with temperatures above freezing, and completely clear sky. On the two mentioned days, for about 4 hours each, light snow fell out of the fog. In the first instance it left about ¼ inch of snow on the ground. It is very probable that under the prevalent synoptic conditions the effect was caused essentially by nucleation of a supercooled local fog.

TEMPERATURE

Although a considerable volume of data and discussions has accumulated in the literature, the essence of the effect of cities on temperature was set forth clearly by Howard (1883, I, 236–37) in his classic text, *The Climate of London . . . :*

The Mean Temperature of the Climate, under these circumstances, is strictly about 48.50° Fahr.: but in the denser parts of the metropolis, the heat is raised, by the effect of the population and fires, to 50.50°; and it must be proportionately affected in the suburban parts. The excess of the temperature of the city varies through the year, being least in spring, and greatest in winter; and it belongs, in strictness, to the nights; which average three degrees and seven-tenths warmer than in the country; while the heat of the day, owing without doubt to the interception of a portion of the solar rays by a veil of smoke, falls, on a mean of years, about a third of a degree short of that in the open plain.[1]

Only in the last few years has there been an attempt to underbuild the observed facts by a theory. This was done by Sundborg (1951) on the basis of observations of the temperature differences between the town of Uppsala,

1. It is evident from the text that the same statement was included in the first edition of Howard's book, in 1818, which was not available to the writer.

Sweden, and the surrounding countryside. The underlying causes for the temperature differences are changes in radiative processes, absorption, conversion of latent heat, convection, and turbulence. In most instances none of these primary elements is being routinely measured. Some of them enter into the picture essentially as constants of the locality. All of them can be approximately expressed, for the purpose on hand, as functions of the usually observed meteorological elements. Sundborg arrives at an empirical equation of the following form:

$$\Delta t = a + b_1 n + b_2 V + b_3 T + b_4 e \, ,$$

where Δt is temperature difference between city and country in degrees centigrade; n is cloudiness in 1/10 sky cover; V is wind velocity in meters per second; T is temperature in degrees centigrade; e is vapor pressure in millimeters; and a, b_1 to b_4, are constants.

Sundborg determined the constants by regression for the Uppsala conditions. It is instructive to show his results, which are encompassed in two equations, one representing the daytime, the other the nighttime, conditions.

Day: $$\Delta t = 1.4° - 0.01n - 0.09V - 0.01T - 0.04e \, ,$$

Night: $$\Delta t = 2.8° - 0.10n - 0.38V - 0.02T - 0.03e \, .$$

Particularly noteworthy is the increase in influence of the cloud and wind factors at night; the former is ten times, the latter four times, larger than during the day. The value of a includes essentially all the static city influences, such as self-screening of built-up areas, albedo, and heat conductivity. These formulas show quite clearly that the vapor pressure and the level of temperature are quite small and that in daytime only the wind parameter has some modifying effect over and above the basic "city factor" *a*. At night both wind and cloudiness have an influence which far outweighs all other factors. The nighttime formula can therefore be reduced to these two modifiers. For Uppsala this results in the following:

$$\Delta t = \frac{a - bn}{V} = \frac{4.6 - 0.28n}{V}.$$

Similar formulas can, of course, be developed for other cities. Sundborg points out that the "city factor" changes radically, and the contrasts sharpen, when the country is snow-covered while the city has no snow. This is a not uncommon event.

The observational material on city temperatures is extensive. We restrict ourselves here to presenting a few salient facts. The excess of *mean annual temperature* of city over country, by size of cities, is shown in Table 23.

There is considerable variation from place to place in the *annual march* of the city-country difference. In Paris, for example, the minimum occurs in June (1.2° F.) and the maximum in September (2.2° F.). In contrast, Tulsa, Oklahoma, has the maximum excess in autumn (1.3° F.) and the minimum in spring (0.7° F.).

As has already been pointed out, the *diurnal variation* of the difference in temperature is particularly pronounced. Minima are usually a great deal lower in the country than in the city. Sometimes, on clear calm days a few hours after sunset, temperature differences of 10 degrees between the two are not unusual. The heat retained by masses of buildings and pavements, in part radiating toward each other rather than toward the sky, is only slowly dissipated. In comparison, grass, in the open, with small heat capacity and poor heat conductivity from below, will cool rapidly. A rather striking example of this type, with a 20-degree temperature difference between the business dis-

trict of San Francisco and the outlying parkland, was recently provided by Duckworth and Sandberg (1954). Figure 119 shows one of the cases presented by these authors. They also showed for several California cities, by means of low-level soundings, to what height the city thermal effect extended in the evening. It is generally of the order of only a few hundred feet.

In Duckworth and Sandberg's study, as well as in numerous others, which yielded isothermal patterns for whole city areas, one is confronted with very complex phenomena. Many of the ob-

TABLE 23*

AVERAGE EXCESS OF MEAN ANNUAL TEMPERATURES: CITY VERSUS COUNTRY

No. of Cities	Size of City	Average Temperature Excess (° F.)
10	1,000,000	1.3
10	500,000–1,000,000	1.1
10	100,000– 500,000	1.0

*Source: Bogolepow, 1928; Besson, 1931; Kratzer, 1937; Bider, 1940; Liljequist, 1943; Berg, 1947; Maurain, 1947; Mitchell, 1953.

served contrasts would probably occur even if no city were present. They are simply microclimatic results of topography and position. These may become accentuated or diminished, as the case may be, by the city development. It is often quite difficult to ascertain the city effect per se.

We have searched for some data which are relatively free from such meso- and microclimatic differences. For the diurnal variation of temperature in and near a moderate-sized city on a clear day, Figure 120 presents a typical set of thermograph records for a clear day with light winds at Richmond, Virginia (population 230,000). The observations, both from ground exposures, were taken at the Weather Bureau offices in the city park and at the airport. The figure shows three main features of comparison: the lower night temperatures at the outlying station followed by a rapid rise in the morning; the nearly identical values during the midday period; and the rapid, almost exponential, drop of temperature after the maxima down. Others believe that the highest temperature level in cities is located at the upper surface (namely, the roof level), analogous to the condition in forests, where the highest values are often noted at tree-crown level.

Fig. 119.—City temperatures of San Francisco (temperature contrasts at 2-meter level, observations at 2320 PST, April 4, 1952). (After Duckworth and Sandberg, 1954.)

sunset at the airport, compared to the rather gradual and more sinusoidal change at the city station.

The effect of a medium-sized town on extreme temperatures is shown for Lincoln, Nebraska (population 100,000), in Figure 121. City and airport observations are about as free from complicating terrain factors as can be found. The data for a year, for the warm and cold seasons, are presented as frequency diagrams. These diagrams show that the minima throughout the year are for the vast majority of cases lower at the airport and that during the cold half of the year there are often quite substantial differences. For the maxima the situation is quite different. In the cold season the values cluster very closely around zero deviation. In the warm season, however, there is a very definite preponderance of higher maxima at the airport. Some investigators have suggested that the increased convection over the city keeps

Fig. 120.—Typical thermograph traces at town and country station-pair on a clear day with low wind speed (Richmond, Virginia, June 2, 1953).

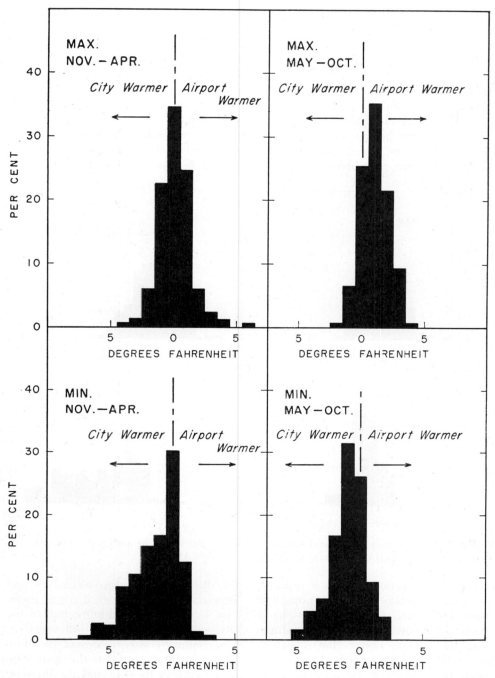

FIG. 121.—Frequency of differences of daily extreme temperatures at town and country station-pair—uncomplicated case (Lincoln, Nebraska, 1953).

In Figure 122 data for another city are shown. These are observations for Cleveland, a city close to a million inhabitants. For the minima the city-country contrast is considerably magnified. During the cold season the maxima are also usually higher in the city. During the warm season a new factor of local climate becomes quite preponderant—the lake breeze. This small-scale circulation, possibly reinforced by

Mitchell (1953), at New Haven, Connecticut, that Sundays showed less "city effect" than weekdays. He found for the winter season a mean temperature difference of 1.0° F. for city-airport values. The mean value of the difference on weekdays was 1.1° F. but was only 0.5° F. for Sunday. Undoubtedly, there is less heat and pollution produced by factories and motor vehicles on Sundays. If we are to attribute

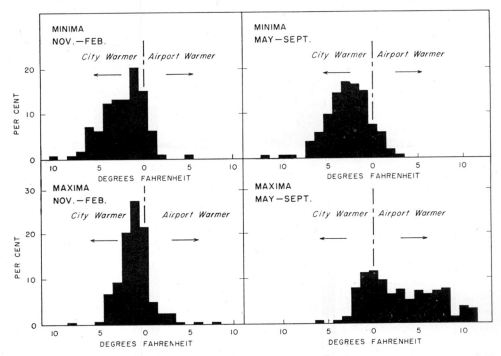

Fig. 122.—Frequency of differences of daily extreme temperatures at town and country station-pair—case complicated by lake influence (Cleveland, Ohio, 1950).

the city convection, brings a different air mass into the city, but normally it does not reach the airport, which is somewhat more inland. This illustrates the point made above that city temperature comparisons have to be used with discrimination because of interaction of meso- and microclimatic factors other than the city influence itself.

Returning to the problem of the temperature field of towns in general, it is interesting to relate the observation by

the difference between weekdays and Sundays to these factors, it would mean that they are responsible for half of the city-country temperature difference.

Secondary consequences of the temperature differential are the reduction in snowfall in the city and the increase in the freeze-free season. The former has already been discussed. The latter is, of course, the more pronounced the closer to freezing point the spring and autumn temperatures are. In some localities the mean interval between the last freezing temperature in spring and the first in autumn is three to four weeks longer in the city than in the country. Here again microclimatic factors, rather than city influence, are often the real reason; the same applies to the frequency of days with minimum temperatures below freezing. The differences can be substantial. For example, in Cologne the average annual number of days with minimum below freezing is 19, compared to 29 in the country—a reduction of 34 per cent for the city. In Basel, Switzerland, the corresponding figures are 64 and 85 days per year, respectively—a 25 per cent reduction.

These conditions are, of course, also reflected in quantities derived from temperatures, such as degree-days. Heating degree-days, in particular, are usually lower in the city. Cooling power, a combined effect primarily of temperature and wind speed, also is substantially reduced in the city.

HUMIDITY

Towns have a lower humidity than the countryside. This applies both to relative and to absolute humidities. Apparently, the water vapor added by combustion processes rapidly diffuses upward and, near the surface, does not contribute to moisture in the air except in cases of strong ground inversions of temperature.

Actually, there are only a few reliable sets of comparative measurements. These have been summarized by Kratzer (1937). They show for the city an average reduction of 6 per cent in the relative humidity and a half-millibar lower vapor pressure. In the annual variation the least difference is found in winter (around 2 per cent lower) and the most in summer (about 8 per cent lower). This is not entirely an effect of the higher city temperatures. It is caused in part by the rapid runoff of precipitation through storm sewer systems and also by the great expanse of impervious surface materials, such as roofs and streets. These do not hold moisture, as is the case with ordinary soil. There is relatively little vegetation in most cities, so that the processes of evapotranspiration are completely different from those occurring over natural surfaces.

CLOUDINESS

The climatological records for most cities show an increase in cloudiness over the years. This is to some extent a consequence of the more frequent occurrence of fog. The city pollution and the added water vapor, under otherwise favorable meteorological conditions, will lead to condensation, occasionally even before saturation is reached. At other times the increased convection and turbulence over city areas also will cause cloud formation. These effects are usually operative to a sufficient degree over large metropolitan areas. Even so, the average increase is less than 1/10 in mean sky cover, or a few percentage points of the total mean cloudiness. In most localities the effect is more pronounced in winter than in summer. There are other patterns too. Munich, for example (cf. Kratzer, 1937), has an 8 per cent increase of cloudiness over the city in summer and only a 3 per cent increase in winter.

In diurnal variation, increases in cloudiness in the early-morning hours are particularly notable. This is caused by the higher number of city fogs. In midday there is another increase, particularly in cumulus formation caused by convection. In the late-afternoon and early-evening hours little difference between city and country exists.

The records for nearly all major cities in the middle latitudes of the Northern Hemisphere show a decrease in clear days and an increase in cloudy days over the decades. Some of this is caused by a universal climatic change. However, the clear days have decreased by 40 per cent and the cloudy days have increased by 50 or even 60 per cent in a half-century. Comparison with country stations indicates that a substantial fraction of this change is chargeable to city influence. As an over-all average, large cities have 25 per cent less clear days and 5–10 per cent more cloudy days than their rural environs.

WIND FIELD

The city influence on the wind field is both mechanical and thermal. In the

TABLE 24

SEASONAL AVERAGE WIND SPEEDS AT
CENTRAL PARK OBSERVATORY AND
LA GUARDIA AIRPORT, NEW YORK

SEASON	MILES PER HOUR		
	La Guardia	Central Park	Difference
Spring.........	12.5	9.9	2.6
Summer........	10.5	8.0	2.5
Autumn........	11.2	8.4	2.8
Winter.........	14.4	11.1	3.3

first category it is not much different from that of any large obstacle placed in the wind path. Locally, there is usually a decrease in wind speed at the surface, because of increased friction and the radically enlarged roughness parameter. An early interesting account on city influence on *wind speed* is owed to Kremser (1909). He reported on anemometer records obtained from a tower 105 feet above the surface, located at the outskirts of Berlin. This installation was originally free on all sides but became enveloped in the next two decades by apartment houses, the rooftops of which were only 23 feet below the anemometer. The mean wind

speed in the first decade (1884–93) was 11.4 miles per hour; in the second (1894–1903), 8.8 miles per hour. This is a reduction of 25 per cent.

In Paris, according to Maurain (1947), the mean wind speed in the center of the city is 5.1 miles per hour and on the outskirts 10.1 miles per hour, a value which is nearly twice as large.

A comparison in New York City between the Central Park Observatory and La Guardia Airport shows for the two years 1952 and 1953 the values given in Table 24. For the whole year the mean observed reduction at the Central Park location is 23 per cent. The height of the anemometer at La Guardia Airport is 82 feet above the ground; at Central Park, 62 feet. The value expected at Central Park because of the height difference would be about 4 per cent less. Hence we can ascribe the remainder of 19 per cent to environmental influence. For the peak speeds (around 60–70 miles per hour) the environmental influence is even less, namely, about 12 per cent.

In most cities the frequency of calms is increased. The values compared to country surroundings range between 5 and 20 per cent. This again is a factor very much influenced by microclimatic conditions. Reduction in wind speed especially during winter diminishes cooling power but at the same time decreases dissipation of polluting substances.

There are statements in the literature to the effect that a city sets up its own circulation, comparable to land and lake breezes, because it is generally warmer. Such a local small-scale wind system as envisaged by this hypothesis starts over the warm city with ascending currents, a pressure gradient ensues, and a cool country wind converging on the city from all sides is supposed to result. Berg (1947) calculates that a temperature difference of

5 degrees would cause a 7-mile-per-hour wind at the edge of town, provided the general synoptic wind field is weak. His own observations in Cologne did not show the existence of such a country breeze. The weak pressure gradients are probably unable to overcome the friction. It is therefore more common for the country air, especially in the early night, to enter the city in discrete pulses like a miniature cold front.

However, there is always considerable turbulence over cities, induced partly by the large-scale roughness features and narrow columns of ascending vertical thermal currents. These are noticeable even at considerable heights. They are well known to airline passengers as marked bumpiness and have even been used by glider pilots for soaring. In summer these ascending columns are often marked by cumulus clouds which dissolve as they drift to the lee of the city.

Inside the larger wind field there are also some small-scale circulations stimulated by microinfluences, such as differential heating of different sides of streets or thermal differences among roof, courtyard, street, and park surfaces.

CONCLUSIONS

It is quite clear that our cities at moderate and high latitudes have, by and large, caused a rather undesirable deterioration of climate. A few changes may be considered favorable, such as the higher winter nighttime minimum temperatures. These are far outweighed by increase in pollution, increase in cloudiness, and reduction in illumination and ultraviolet radiation. Construction practices have aggravated rather than alleviated the situation.

Only in recent years has there been more attention to macro- and microclimatological factors in city planning such as the Kitimat case (Anonymous, 1954c). The adverse effects can be minimized without prohibitive cost if the climatic aspects are adequately considered in plans for new settlements or for the reconstruction of old ones. This, coupled with adequate community action against air pollution, could without doubt lead to at least a tolerable if not an optimal bioclimate for the inhabitants.

REFERENCES

AIR HYGIENE FOUNDATION OF AMERICA, INC.
1937–38 *Concentrations of Volatile Sulphur Compounds in Atmospheric Air.* ("Special Research Series," Bulletin No. 1.) Part I, pp. 1–80; Part II, pp. 83–132. Pittsburgh.

AMERICAN METEOROLOGICAL SOCIETY
1951 *On Atmospheric Pollution.* ("Meteorological Monographs," Vol. I, No. 4.) Boston: American Meteorologica! Society. 55 pp.

ANONYMOUS
1949a *Air Pollution in Donora, Pennsylvania.* (U.S. Public Health Bulletin No. 306, A-239.) Washington, D.C.: Government Printing Office. 173 pp.

1949b "Atmospheric Contamination and Purification," *Industrial and Engineering Chemistry,* XLI, 2384–2493.

1954c "Kitimat: A New City," *Architectural Forum,* July, August, and October, pp. 128–47, 120–27, 158–61.

ASHWORTH, JAMES REGINALD
1929 "The Influence of Smoke and Hot Gases from Factory Chimneys on Rainfall," *Quarterly Journal of the Royal Meteorological Society,* LV, 34–350.

BERG, HELLMUT
1947 *Einführung in die Bioklimatologie.* Bonn: H. Bouvier & Co. Verlag. 131 pp.

BERKES, ZOLTAN
1947 "A Csapadek eloszlasa Budapest teruleten," *Idöjaras,* LI, 105–11.

BESSON, LOUIS
1931 "L'Alteration du climat d'une grande ville," *Annales d'hygiène publique, industrielle et sociale,* IX, No. 8, 1–34.

BIDER, MAX
1940 "Temperaturunterschiede zwischen Stadt- und Freilandstationen," *Helvetica physica acta,* XIII, 5–7. Basel.

BOGOLEPOW, M. A.
1928 "Über des Klima von Moskau," *Meteorologische Zeitschrift,* XLV, 152–54.

BROOKS, CHARLES ERNEST PELHAM
1952 "Selected Annotated Bibliography on Urban Climates," *Meteorological Abstracts and Bibliography,* III, No. 7, 734–73.

BÜTTNER, KONRAD
1929 "Der Einfluss des Grosstadtdunstes auf die Sonnen- und Himmelsstrahlung," *Meteorologische Zeitschrift,* XLVI, 521–25.

DEPARTMENT OF SCIENTIFIC AND INDUSTRIAL RESEARCH
1945 *Atmospheric Pollution in Leicester: A Scientific Survey.* (Atmospheric Pollution Research Technical Paper No. 1.) London. 161 pp.

DUCKWORTH, FOWLER S., and SANDBERG, JAMES S.
1954 "The Effect of Cities upon Horizontal and Vertical Temperature Gradients," *Bulletin of the American Meteorological Society,* XXXV, No. 5, 198–207.

ELY, SUMNER B.
1952 *Report on Stationary Stacks, Year 1951.* Pittsburgh: Bureau of Smoke Prevention. 15 pp.

EVELYN, JOHN
1661 *Fumifugium: or the Inconvenience of the Aer, and Smoke of London Dissipated.* Oxford. (Reprinted. Manchester: National Smoke Abatement Society, 1933.) 43 pp.

FOULGER, J. H.
1954 "Smog and Human Health," *Meteorological Monographs,* II, No. 8, 111–17.

GALANIN, N. F.
1939 "Osveshchennost rasseiannym sve-

tom atmosfery v Leningrade po nabliudeniiam za chetyre goda," *Meteorologiia i Gidrologiia,* No. 4, pp. 8–12.

GEIGER, RUDOLF
1950 *The Climate near the Ground.* Cambridge, Mass.: Harvard University Press. 482 pp.

HOWARD, LUKE
1823 *The Climate of London Deduced from Meteorological Observations Made in the Metropolis and at Various Places around It.* 2d ed. 3 vols. London: J. & A. Arch, Cornhill; Longman & Co.

KASSNER, CARL
1917 "Der Einfluss Berlins als Grosstadt auf die Schneeverhältnisse," *Meteorologische Zeitschrift,* XXXIV, 136–37.

KIENLE, J. VON
1952 "Ein stadtgebundener Schneefall in Mannheim," *Meteorologische Rundschau,* V, 5, Nos. 7–8, 132–33.

KRAMER, HARRIS P., and RIGBY, MALCOLM
1950 "Cumulative Annotated Bibliography on Atmospheric Pollution by Smoke and Gases," *Meteorological Abstracts and Bibliography,* I, No. 1, 46–71.

KRATZER, ALBERT
1937 *Das Stadtklima.* ("Die Wissenschaft," Vol. XC.) Braunschweig: Friedrich Vieweg & Sohn. 143 pp.

KREMSER, V.
1909 "Ergebnisse vieljähriger Windregistrierungen in Berlin," *Meteorologische Zeitschrift,* XXVI, 259–65.

KUHN, H.
1933 "Studie über das luftelektrische Potentialgefälle und dessen Unruhe unter besonderer Berücksichtigung des Einflusses einer Grosstadt," *Zeitschrift für Geophysik,* IX, 238–52.

KUHN, UDO
1954 "Die Beinflussung der luftelektrischen Elemente durch Luftverunreiningungen," *Zeitschrift für Meteorologie,* VIII, Nos. 7–8, 236–43.

LANDSBERG, H. E.
1937 "The Environmental Variation of Condensation Nuclei," *Bulletin of the American Meteorological Society,* XVIII, Nos. 4–5, 172.
1950 "Microclimatic Research in Re-

lation to Building Construction," pp. 23–28 in BUILDING RESEARCH ADVISORY BOARD, *Research Conference Report*, No. 1. Washington, D.C.

1954 "Bioclimatology of Housing." *Meteorological Monographs*, II, 81–98.

LAUSCHER, FRIEDRICH, and STEINHAUSER, FERDINAND

1932 "Strahlungsuntersuchungen in Wien und Umgebung," *Akademie der Wissenschaften, Mathematisch-naturwissenschaftliche Klasse, Sitzungsberichte*, Abt. 2a, CXLI, 15–320. Vienna.

LAWRENCE, E. N.

1954 "Microclimatology and Town Planning," *Weather*, IX, No. 8, 227–32.

LETTAU, HEINZ

1931 "Uber den meteorologischen Einfluss der Grosstadt," *Zeitschrift für angewandte Meteorologie*, XLVIII, 263–73.

LILJEQUIST, GOSTA H.

1943 *The Severity of the Winters at Stockholm, 1757–1942*. ("Statens Meteorologisk-Hydrografiska Anstalt," Meddelanden No. 46.) Stockholm. 24 pp.

LÖBNER, ALFRED

1935 "Horizontale und vertikale Staubverteilung in einer Grosstadt," *Leipzig Universität Geophysikalisches Institut, Veröffentlichungen*, 2d ser., VII, 53–100.

LONGLEY, RICHMOND W.

1954 *The Climate of Montreal, Canada*. Ottawa: Meteorological Division, Department of Transport. 46 pp.

McCABE, LOUIS C. (chairman)

1952 *Air Pollution: Proceedings of the United States Technical Conference on Air Pollution*. New York: McGraw-Hill Book Co. 847 pp.

MAURAIN, CHARLES HONORÉ

1947 *Le Climat parisien*. Paris: Presses Universitaires. 163 pp.

MITCHELL, J. MURRAY, JR.

1953 "On the Causes of Instrumentally Observed Secular Temperature Trends," *Journal of Meteorology*, X, 244–61.

MÜHLEISEN, R.

1953 "Die luftelektrischen Elemente im Grosstadtbereich," pp. 142–60 in BROCKAMP, B. (ed.), *Zeitschrift für Geophysiks, Sonderband*. Braunschweig: Friedrich Vieweg & Sohn. 192 pp.

REIFFERSCHEID, HELLMUT

1954 "Die Bestimmung des Luftkeimgehaltes als Voraussetzung der Luftentseuchungshygiene," *Zeitschrift für Aerosolforschung*, III, No. 3, 268–72.

ROYAL METEOROLOGICAL SOCIETY

1954 "Discussion of 20 January 1954: Smog," *Quarterly Journal of the Royal Meteorological Society*, LXXX, 261–78. (Opening papers: ABSALOM, H. W. L., "Meteorological Aspects of Smog," pp. 261–66; WILKINS, E. T., "Air Pollution Aspects of the London Fog of December 1952," pp. 267–71; OSWALD, N. C., "Physiological Effects of Smog," pp. 271–72; "General Discussion," pp. 272–78.)

SCHMAUSS, AUGUST

1927 "Grosstädte und Niederschlag," *Meteorologische Zeitschrift*, XLIV, 339–41.

SCHMIDT, GERHARD

1952 "Zur Nutzbarmachung staubklimatischer Untersuchungen für die städtebauliche Praxis," *Berichte der Deutschen Wetterdienstes U.S.-Zone*, Weickmann Heft, No. 38, pp. 201–5.

SCHMIDT, WILHELM, and BREZINA, ERNST

1937 *Das Künstliche Klima in der Umgebung des Menschen*. Stuttgart: Friedrich Enke. 212 pp.

SHELEIKHOVSKII, G. V.

1949 *Zadymlenie Gorodov* ("Smoke in Cities"). Moscow: Ministerstvo Kommunal'nogo Khoziaistva. 234 pp.

STANFORD RESEARCH INSTITUTE

1954 *The Smog Problem in Los Angeles County*. Los Angeles: Western Oil & Gas Association. 134 pp.

STEINHAUSER, FERDINAND

1934 "Neue Untersuchungen der Temperaturverhältnisse von Grosstädten: Methode und Ergebnisse," *Meteorologische Zeitschrift, Bioklimatische Beidlatter*, I, 105–11.

SUNDBORG, ÅKE

1951 *Climatological Studies in Uppsala, with Special Regard to the Temperature Conditions in the Urban Area*. ("Geographica," No. 22.) Uppsala: Universitet Geografiska Institutionen. 111 pp.

Topitz, Alois
1952 "Über den Wandel der Luftverunreinigung in Wien in der Zeit von 1900 bis 1950," *Wetter und Leben,* IV, Nos. 5–7, 95–101.

Wiegel, H.
1938 *Niederschlagsverhältnisse und Luftverunreinigung des Rheinisch-Westfälischen Industriegebiets und seiner Umgebung.* ("Veröffentlichungen des Meteorologischen Instituts, Universität Berlin," Vol. III, No. 3.) Berlin: Verlag von Dietrich Reimer. 52 pp.

Wolman, Abel
1952 "Effects of Ionizing Radiation in Air Pollution," pp. 489–92 in Mc-Cabe, Lee C. (ed.), *Air Pollution.* New York: McGraw-Hill Book Co. 147 pp.

Artificially Induced Precipitation and Its Potentialities

VINCENT J. SCHAEFER*

Water is man's most precious natural resource. There are few, if any, who will disagree with that oft-repeated statement. Down through the centuries, as man has slowly forged his way, the importance of water has grown hand in hand with his advance in knowledge, agriculture, and technology. That man is wasteful of this important resource cannot be denied. In most regions where water resources are reportedly marginal or submarginal, it is often possible to show that such water emergencies are based on imprudent uses, wasteful practices, or improvident exploitation.

We have only to consider the amount of water used from the well or spring on a backwoods farm, still untouched with so-called "modern conveniences" —electric pumps and related gadgets— and compare it with the much greater quantities used in a modern apartment, with its hot baths or showers, air-conditioning units, automatic laundry, and flush-toilet facilities! The pump handle and the carrying of a water bucket were conservation tools of the first magnitude.

The tremendous increase in the use of water is not necessarily bad—in fact, it seems to be a direct measure of our advance in technology and of the modern standard of living. There are, however, limits to the primary sources of water. Those communities which use this potentially renewable resource in such a manner that the reserves show a steady decline of supply are heading for trouble.

Since essentially all water currently used by civilized man comes from atmospheric sources, it is of considerable importance that we become thoroughly familiar with the mechanisms which control this supply. While some persons will insist that such studies are a complete waste of time, since we are at the mercy of the elements, the more scientific-minded will venture the opinion that any scientific subject which is not well understood has many potentially important discoveries awaiting the inquiring researcher. Thus, when we consider the inadequacy of our

* Dr. Schaefer since 1953 has been Director of Research of the Munitalp Foundation, Inc., Schenectady, New York, developing a program of basic research in meteorology with emphasis on atmospheric physics and chemistry. From 1929 to 1953 he was associated with the General Electric Research Laboratory, successively as research assistant (1931) and research associate (1938) to Dr. Irving Langmuir, collaborating in studies of surface chemistry. Studies in 1943 of aircraft radio static caused by snow and aircraft-icing phenomena led to studies of supercooled clouds. In 1946 a practical method was developed of seeding natural supercooled clouds with dry ice. This discovery led to the formation of Project Cirrus, a joint General Electric–Army–Navy five-year research program for studying the possibilities and limitations of experimental meteorology. His recent publications include: *Experimental Meteorology*, 1950; *Clouds of the Jet Stream*, 1953; and *Thunderstorms, Jet Streams, and Project Skyfire*, 1955.

knowledge of atmospheric processes, it seems likely that many advances in our understanding of these phenomena will be forthcoming.

Man's dream of controlling the weather extends far back into antiquity. Until very recent times, however, this was little but a dream. The primitive medicine men, in most cases, did little to arouse our scientific curiosity. However, we have evidence that some of them would scatter mysterious powders into hot fires built on mountaintops. In view of our current knowledge of the potential importance of a few grams of heat-vaporized silver iodide, we must be careful in saying that all "medicine men" were ineffective in their rainmaking activities!

It is only within the past half-century that scientific advances have been made toward a better understanding of precipitation processes and the potentialities of affecting them. The names of Gathman (1891), Wegener (1911), Veraart (1931), Bergeron (1935), and Findeisen (1938) are associated with these early imaginative steps. In a prophetic statement, shortly before World War II, Findeisen said (1938):

> The recognition of the fact that quite minute, quantitatively inappreciable elements are the actual cause setting into operation weather phenomena of the highest magnitude gives the certainty that, in time, human science will be enabled to effect an artificial control on the course of meteorological phenomena. It would be going beyond the limits of the present work to discuss in detail the possibility of exercising a kind of technical control over the course of weather conditions. From the considerations under survey here, we have now come to quite new points of view on this. It can be boldly stated that, at comparatively moderate expense it will, in time, be possible to bring about rain by scientific means, to obviate the danger of icing and to prevent the formation of hailstorms. Through the energy transformations thus secured various other weather phenomena (e.g. temperature, wind) will be brought under a certain kind of control, which perhaps never, in a direct manner, could, to an appreciable extent, be acted upon in the atmosphere. The colloido-meteorological investigations by themselves with only the assistance of research work as the means to get some control over the weather factors have opened up a new field for their efforts. They obviously only can solve those various problems with the close assistance of aerology.

Unfortunately, Findeisen mysteriously disappeared at the end of the war and is now presumed to be dead.

In July, 1946, at the end of four years of basic research in the fields of precipitation static and aircraft icing (Schaefer, 1946), the writer discovered that small bits of dry-ice particles dusted into a supercooled cloud would quickly and completely change its nature. The experiment was so simple and the effect so striking that a considerable number of research-minded persons quickly tested the results and in some instances made immediate plans to start experimental studies of atmospheric clouds.

Vonnegut, a co-worker of Schaefer, discovered (1947) that silver iodide could also be used to convert supercooled clouds to ice crystals. These two discoveries were responsible for the inauguration of the tremendous worldwide interest which has developed in atmospheric physics and experimental meteorology during the last nine years.

INADEQUACY OF PRESENT KNOWLEDGE IN METEOROLOGY

In observing and forecasting the weather, meteorologists have developed many techniques—some of them based on long experience and some on an extrapolation of today's weather to some future time by assuming that a storm or other phenomenon will continue across the country at about the same rate and intensity as those of the observed condition. Others consider the general circulation, some the behavior of jet streams, while yet others plot the geographic position of high- or low-pressure cells and correlate their locations with the behavior pattern of a historical series of weather developments. A currently favored procedure is the so-called "analogue method," in which fifty or more years of weather data are classified into a small number of storm types and related to the weather occurring over subsequent periods. This method assumes that a specific weather pattern will be followed by about the same resultant developments. The most recent of all methods depends on the use of giant computing machines which automatically receive current weather reports, digest them apply the observed changes to the equations of motion, vorticity, advection, and related weather parameters, and then indicate the weather patterns to be expected.

Despite these diverse methods and many combinations and permutations of them, weather forecasting is still beset with failures and near-misses. Unfortunately, the "busts" tend to be associated with the sudden appearance of an unexpected storm or, in some cases, the rapid deterioration of a loudly heralded storm, so that the failures are often quite embarrassing to the forecasters. Many reasons may be advanced for these difficulties, many of which may be ascribed to a simple lack of an adequate understanding of basic weather phenomena. Until weather forecasts reach a level of accuracy considerably better than at present, new avenues of research must be explored with enthusiasm and active imagination.

Among the factors which are not currently used in preparing weather forecasts are the concentration and type of condensation and ice nuclei in the air masses under consideration. It is easily shown that the concentration of effective ice-crystal and condensation nuclei

in the world's atmosphere varies greatly from place to place and from time to time. The most intensive and extended study of ice nuclei in the atmosphere has been conducted at the Mount Washington Observatory, New Hampshire (Schaefer, 1954), where more than eighteen thousand observations have been made at three-hour intervals during the last six and one-half years. These observations show that the concentration of ice-crystal nuclei in the air passing the summit of Mount Washington varies by a factor of at least a million fold, as measured at an average temperature of $-18°$ C. Thus, the air at times contains as many as ten million nuclei per cubic meter. At other times not a single nucleus can be detected.

These large variations in ice-nuclei concentrations suggest explanations as to why, at times, the atmosphere will contain a profusion of large supercooled clouds, while, at other times, even the smallest clouds shift quickly to showers of snow crystals. Efforts have been made to discover the reason for these large variations and the source of those which are observed (Schaefer, 1950; Isono and Komabayasi, 1954).

By gathering samples of fine soils obtained in regions where dust storms and dust devils are commonplace occurrences, the writer has shown that some terrestrial soils act as fairly effective ice-crystal nuclei. Certain volcanic soils, pumice deposits, and clays have been found to serve as effective ice-crystal nuclei in the temperature range of $-12°$ to $-22°$ C. Not all particles are effective at a particular temperature, although the number which are active increases with a decrease in temperature, until most will initiate ice-crystal formation in the range of $-30°$ to $-35°$ C. Even at this temperature, however, there are many solid particles which have no effect whatever when introduced into a supercooled cloud.

It is easily demonstrated that water droplets will supercool to a temperature of about —38° C. Attempts to go to colder temperatures fail because of the spontaneous nucleation effects which occur at about —40° C. (Schaefer, 1946; Cwilong, 1947). At this temperature cloud droplets freeze spontaneously and under some conditions produce many additional submicroscopic ice crystals (Schaefer, 1952).

Cirrus clouds generally form in the temperature range of —40° to —60° C. and, consequently, consist of pure ice. Such crystals slowly settle earthward and under many atmospheric conditions continue to grow throughout their fall. During major storm developments this prolific source of ice nuclei exercises a dominant control of the precipitation process. At the point of contact between falling cirrus crystals and cumulus, alto-cumulus, or stratus cloud masses, radar studies show the development of major precipitation areas (Gunn *et al.*, 1954).

Because of the heterogeneous nature of natural ice-crystal nuclei and the great variability in their concentration, the introduction into the atmosphere of large numbers of superior ice nuclei, under controlled conditions, is likely to exert a pronounced effect on supercooled clouds and possibly on the synoptic situation.

Both dry ice (solid carbon dioxide) and silver iodide may be used to produce colossal numbers of nuclei. When introduced into a supercooled cloud under optimum conditions, dry ice may produce 1×10^{16} ice crystals per gram of material. Silver iodide has similar effectiveness, plus the added advantage that it may be formed at warm temperature and in cloudless air but will then become effective when encountering suitable atmospheric conditions (Vonnegut, 1949).

Many types of silver iodide generators have been devised (Vonnegut, 1950), ranging from the burning of string or paper impregnated with powdered silver iodide, the burning of a solution of silver–sodium iodide dissolved in acetone and sprayed into a gas flame, the burning of coke or charcoal soaked in a silver iodide solution, or the electric arcing of silver electrodes in a vapor of free iodine. Generators have been devised which will operate on the ground, suspended from balloons or kites, shot high into the air as exploding shells or rockets, or transported on reciprocating or jet-engine aircraft.

A few pounds of dry ice or a few ounces of silver iodide, if properly introduced into supercooled clouds, will exert profound effects on the precipitation cycle in supercooled clouds. By controlling particle size and volume concentration, and depending on the method of introducing the seeding materials into cloud masses, many different effects may be achieved. Large holes may be cut into solid stratus or strato-cumulus overcasts, supercooled ground fogs may be intensified or dissipated, an ice-crystal overcast may be produced in air which is supersaturated with respect to ice, and large, vigorously growing supercooled cumulus clouds may be caused to produce a fairly extensive local rainstorm or snowstorm (Schaefer, 1953*a*). Some evidence has been obtained that a combination of dry ice and silver iodide, when introduced into a cumulus cloud system, may serve to stimulate cyclogenesis (Langmuir, 1950). Widespread effects of this kind are likely to be favored when the air is deficient in natural nuclei.

It is only within the past few years that meteorologists have reached some degree of agreement that heavy rains may fall from clouds which are not high enough or sufficiently cold to produce ice crystals (Schaefer, 1949*b;* Mordy and Eber, 1954). Studies of subtropical clouds show that they are often prevented from reaching the 0° C. level by the trade-wind inversion. Consequently, the clouds reach maximum vertical thicknesses with minimum temperatures of 8° to 10° C. Rain intensities equal to an inch an hour were measured during our Project Cirrus flight studies (see below), using rain scoops flown below the bases of precipitating clouds along the Puerto Rican coast.

Subsequent studies have provided further evidence of the widespread nature of coalescence in the formation of so-called "warm-cloud rain." In one of our earliest seeding flights, during the late fall of 1946, we observed light, misty rain falling from supercooled clouds, all parts of which were colder than 0° C.

In most instances where rain forms by coalescence without resort to the ice-crystal mechanism, the air contains "giant" sea-salt particles and relatively low levels of effective condensation nuclei. In a number of instances at Puerto Rico we estimated that the air contained only from fifty to a hundred effective condensation nuclei per cubic centimeter. Over continental areas similar measurements show values which are often ten to fifty times greater, especially in regions having smoke and haze from industrial sources or from natural sources such as forest fires.

Many new discoveries may be expected in relation to the role played by condensation nuclei in the initiation and development of storms. While such particles are rarely, if ever, absent in the atmosphere, there are regions where the concentrations are very low.

In the rain forests of the Hawaiian Islands, Mordy has shown (1955) that the introduction of additional condensation nuclei produces an increase in the number of cloud droplets in a sample of air. This could happen only under conditions in which the air is slightly supersaturated with respect to water.

It is, therefore, of considerable interest to discover the effect that may follow the introduction of large numbers of effective condensation nuclei into subtropical clouds, which normally produce rain when only a few thousand feet thick. If rain prevention could be exercised in this manner, it might be possible to delay the inception of rain until the cloud moved to a region where it would be more useful.

There is some evidence that this occurs. Over the high mountainous ridges of Puerto Rico, clouds often grow to much greater dimensions without producing any rain than they do over the sea. While this might in some manner be due to the greater vertical turbulence in such clouds, it is commonly observed that these larger clouds, which do not rain often, have large numbers of condensation nuclei flowing into their bases as smoke, produced by sugar *centrales,* cement plants, and burning cane fields.

In areas where coalescence rainfall develops in supercooled regions of clouds, research is needed to determine the methods which could be employed to control the precipitation process, using efficient ice nuclei.

Under atmospheric conditions in which warm clouds commonly form without producing rain, there is a strong possibility that the release of large salt particles in air moving into the clouds might accelerate the development of coalescence and lead to precipitation (Woodcock, 1949; Fournier d'Albe, 1955). The introduction of water droplets into clouds may initiate coalescence or a chain reaction (Langmuir, 1948*a*, 1948*b*; Bowen, 1950). However, it is doubtful whether this is economically feasible with aircraft. By using large salt particles from ground generators or in certain favored topographical situations, such types of warm-cloud–seeding may be effective.

Notable in the latter connection is the Keanae Valley experiment on the island of Maui, Territory of Hawaii (Mordy, 1955). At that location a cloud "river," consisting of a mass of northeast trade-wind cloud, is projected against the steep mountain slopes rising to 10,000-foot Haleakala. The line of moisture-laden air encounters a steep escarpment and is forced upward at velocities greater than normally encountered in trade-wind clouds. At this location a pipe line leads water from a stream draining the slopes of the mountain and sprays the water into the cloud-laden air. These particles are carried upward in the rapidly rising air, grow by coalescence with the smaller cloud droplets, and then fall out as rain several miles downwind from the spray site in a region where it may be collected by a series of conduits and flumes.

With experimental setups of this type, much important data may be collected on precipitation mechanisms of warm clouds. It should also be feasible to study electrification phenomena—a field in which many important discoveries will be made within the next few years.

EXPERIMENTAL METEOROLOGY

Since the four exploratory seeding flights made by the writer in the fall and early winter of 1946, many interesting developments have occurred. The results of preliminary flights at Schenectady led to the formation of Project Cirrus, a joint Army- and Navy-sponsored research study in the field of experimental meteorology. Aircraft were supplied by the Air Force and Navy, and technical guidance was supplied by Langmuir, Schaefer, and Vonnegut of the General Electric Research Laboratory. Project Cirrus research studies extended from early 1947 until September, 1952. Further laboratory studies continued until July, 1953

(Schaefer, 1953*b*). During this period 225 experimental flight studies were conducted. A breakdown into the several experimental categories and the number of flights devoted to each follows: dry-ice–seeding studies, 92; observational flights for sounding, sampling, and photographing clouds and cloud systems, 62; flights for testing new instruments, 40; silver iodide–seeding studies, 21; water-seeding studies, 17; flights for checking aircraft, 5; and flights for training purposes, 4. Some flights had dual purposes and for this reason are included twice in this accounting. The record, minus such duplications, shows that the number of flights made specifically for cloud-seeding was 116—slightly more than half of the total number of flights made.

The major objectives of the Project Cirrus flight program were of an exploratory nature and designed to determine the possibilities and limitations of cloud-modification activities. They were planned on a broad base, since it was our belief that more basic information was needed before large-scale cloud-seeding should be attempted under government auspices. The several objectives might be enumerated in order of importance as follows: (1) evaluation of the effectiveness of various seeding materials and techniques; (2) exploration of various cloud types in terms of supercooling, structure, or other physical properties; (3) development of procedures for studying clouds and obtaining quantitative information about them; (4) the working-out, on the basis of observed results, of flight procedures for producing specific effects in unstable clouds; and (5) design and development of new instruments for measuring various properties of the atmosphere while in flight.

Shortly after the initial experiments conducted by Schaefer, other groups in various parts of the world also initiated flight studies. Some of these, like the Commonwealth Scientific and Industrial Research Organization group in Australia (Smith, 1949), set up an extensive and excellent long-range research program. Others, such as local service organizations and publicity-seekers, were satisfied with single or a few simple flights.

A most important development at this time in the United States was the formation by private meteorologists of commercial cloud-seeding organizations with the announced purpose of engaging in "precipitation-increasing" activities. By 1951, these groups had become so well organized that more than a third of all the land west of the Mississippi was under contract for cloud-seeding activities. So widespread had been the publicity given to cloud-seeding that these organizations had little, if any, "selling" to do to gather contracts from farmer-rancher organizations.

This demand for cloud-seeding action, out of proportion to the state of basic knowledge concerning the possibilities and limitations of the methods in use, inevitably led to disappointments and dissatisfaction among many of these groups. Most of them had oversold themselves! Consequently, by 1953, a considerable number of the enthusiasts had lost faith in cloud-seeding programs and abandoned further activities along such lines. This was not the situation with all groups, however, especially those with a long-range vision of the potential importance of such activities if they could be made successful.

Much has been said about the waste of money and the unwarranted claims of cloud-seeding organizations and about their "get-rich-quick" schemes. While it may be true that the potentialities of cloud-seeding were oversold in the 1949–52 period, it was our experience in meeting with many farmer-rancher groups that *they* were the ones primarily responsible for this situation. Many had a tendency to show little or no interest in the basic facts concerning experimental meteorology. Moreover, individual assessments were relatively low. The owner of a wheat ranch of 5,000 acres in most cases paid less than a hundred dollars a year for cloud-seeding activities in his area. If cloud-seeding resulted in an increased amount of moisture and led to an increased yield of a bushel an acre, this "gamble" paid off twenty-five to fifty fold!

While it is unfortunate that better scientific data were not obtained during this early period, this situation has gradually improved, so that, at present, a considerable mass of important scientific data is being gathered. The present use by commercial organizations of radar, cold chambers, potential-gradient meters, time-lapse photography, and similar scientific equipment indicates an important trend and should contribute to an increase of scientific knowledge from field operations. It should be encouraged.

By now, the major commercial organizations have from three to six years of field experience and are in a good position to exploit new discoveries as they are made. This is an important factor in the development of new ideas and techniques in any new science. It means that advances will be made without delay and that the spirit of competition will tend to discourage apathy and will serve as a positive force, encouraging the steady development of the new science of experimental meteorology.

WORLD-WIDE RESEARCH IN EXPERIMENTAL METEOROLOGY

One of the important aspects of meteorology is its world-wide relationships. Nothing happens in the atmosphere of one area without having some effect on the weather around the world.

Whether it is a local rain shower, an air-mass thunderstorm, a regional cold front, or an extensive cyclonic storm, all are reflected in global weather. As a consequence, most competent meteorologists consider weather patterns and sequences without heed to political subdivisions or other artificial boundaries.

Owing to this global aspect of weather, the new field of experimental meteorology was quickly appraised and investigated by research scientists in many parts of the world. In some countries this interest did not proceed beyond the university level; in others it became part of intensive government-sponsored research. Some of the outstanding research in other countries is typified by scientific papers published in Australia (Kraus and Squires, 1947), Hawaii (Leopold and Halstead, 1948), Japan (Wadati, 1954), and Africa (Davies, 1951). In addition to the formally published papers, workers in many other countries conducted experiments and studies, accounts of which, because of limited issue, are not as easily available for study and evaluation. Typical of these is the work described in reports from Honduras (Silverthorn, 1950) and Mexico (Siliceo, 1953).

The popular appeal of rainmaking, storm modification, precipitation-increasing, or weather control, as such activities have been labeled, has given rise to exaggerated and unscientific claims for the potentialities of these new techniques. In addition to unwarranted claims and reckless public statements, which, in the United States, marked the period of 1948–52, some cloud-seeding activities were conducted by individuals and small groups purporting to have discovered new materials and techniques which were far superior to dry ice and silver iodide. Unfortunately, these purported new discoveries were surrounded with an aura of mystery. Persons interested in

the advance of basic knowledge in the field of atmospheric physics and experimental meteorology were unable to find out the basis for the new methods, so that a considerable amount of distrust developed concerning some of these commercial activities. As generally happens in such cases, no matter what the field of science, failures to perform as claimed soon led the mysterious methods into disrepute.

Seeding operations using dry ice and silver iodide have not been free of skepticism and question either! However, in a number of instances where extensive field operations have been reported as unsuccessful, an investigation has indicated that those responsible for the planning either neglected to follow the known facts, set up operational procedures which were basically unsound, saw fit to change the experimental conditions to such a radical degree that the experiences of the past were disregarded, or initiated such an ambitious project that large amounts of effort and money were expended in getting organized and ready to operate, with the monetary support failing soon after the crucial operations got under way.

APPLIED EXPERIMENTAL METEOROLOGY

Large-Scale Cloud-seeding Activities

Commercial cloud-seeding activities seem to be settling down into a fairly definite pattern. In the high mountain areas, where snow deposits serve to provide stable water supplies until midsummer, hydroelectric power companies are sponsoring attempts to increase the depth of the snow pack and thus augment what is termed "multipurpose water." In such regions snow crystals falling on a high mountain slope represent a potential water source, which, upon the melting of the snow in July, August, or September, not only provides water power to turn a half-dozen or more turbine wheels during its descent from the high mountain slopes but also, at lower levels, before reaching sea level, provides water for drinking purposes, irrigation, and industrial uses.

By effectively seeding supercooled orographic clouds in the wintertime with silver iodide ground-based generators, there is strong evidence that considerable success attends such activities, as indicated by Elliott and Strickler (1954). Among the points which favor successful operations are:

1. Supercooled orographic clouds commonly occur in the wintertime on high mountains in the middle latitudes, especially in regions downwind from oceans.

2. Observations of riming, the frequency of graupel snow particles, and the evaporation of clouds on the downwind side of the mountains all indicate a lack of effective concentrations of suitable ice nuclei in the air forming the clouds on the mountains.

3. The deactivation of silver iodide from ground generators by the temperature, low humidity, and ultraviolet effects are minimized under winter conditions in mountainous regions.

4. Orographic clouds cover high mountains for extensive time periods in the winter. Proper control of seeding effects should offer many opportunities for successful operations.

5. By controlling the particle size and concentration of silver iodide smokes, it may eventually be feasible to determine the temperature at which the seeding effect begins and the location where the first snow will fall.

6. High mountain areas are ideal locations for storing moisture in the form of snow and holding it for extended periods of the summertime.

Modification of Storms

Another application of experimental meteorology is in the possible modification of storm clouds. This activity may range from the prevention of hail and lightning in local convective clouds of the air-mass type to the prevention of hurricanes.

Much more research remains to be done to make even the simplest of these activities a certain success. However, local storms have already been profoundly modified (Schaefer, 1953a). Certain physical conditions must obtain if a reasonable degree of success is to follow. For example, it is much easier to modify a lightning storm before it reaches the lightning stage than when the storm is fully developed, since a large storm of this sort depends to a great extent on the degree of instability which develops before it is triggered off. Thus, if a large amount of supercooled cloud develops in a cloud system, there is a much greater chance that a violent storm will occur than if the potential energy is continuously bled away by the removal of the unstable, supercooled cloud masses.

The same reasoning may apply with respect to hurricanes, but, since they are so much more complicated than local thunderstorms, much field research will be required before a successful effort at modification may be expected. A preliminary study of a hurricane was made by our Project Cirrus group in 1948 (Langmuir, 1948b). This study showed that an active hurricane contains many clouds and extensive cloud systems which exist in a supercooled state and are, therefore, susceptible to modification by cloud-seeding techniques. These storms are so extensive and contain such potential energy that the most logical approach to hurricane modification would seem to consist in learning to recognize the initial stages of the storm and finding ways to prevent the development of the closed, self-perpetuating system of the mature hurricane.

LARGE-SCALE WEATHER CONTROL

In a series of papers Langmuir (1953) has described a remarkable chain of rainstorms which recurred at seven-day intervals over the United States. By statistical methods, he showed a high correlation between these and a weekly schedule of silver iodide–seeding conducted in New Mexico as part of Project Cirrus in late 1949, 1950, and part of 1951. Although some of the cause-and-effect relationships described by Langmuir have aroused considerable controversy, no one has yet provided a better explanation for the observed seven-day periodicities in precipitation, temperature, and pressure which occurred over large areas of the United States and in some instances extended across the Atlantic into Europe.

Recent studies by Langmuir of physical mechanisms possibly responsible for these remarkable effects have led him to conclude that the storm patterns show a developmental pattern similar to certain electronic circuits of the feedback type such as are used in controlling frequency-modulated radio. The basic principle resides in the postulate that atmospheric phenomena related to precipitation, pressure, and temperature tend to occur with a harmonic rhythm. Under natural conditions the large variations in atmospheric ice-crystal nuclei—which, from day to day, may vary a million fold in concentration (Schaefer, 1954)—produce random effects which tend to suppress the natural periodicities. If these natural nuclei are supplanted by sufficient concentrations of more effective particles, such as silver iodide (which may have effects at temperatures 10°–15° C. warmer than natural nuclei), then more uniform reactions occur over more extensive areas and thus permit the natural periods to emerge, develop, and dominate the synoptic weather patterns.

The critical test of the theory proposed by Langmuir would consider the year 1948 as a dividing line. Langmuir states that, if his theory is correct, there will have been many more instances of an extended series of periodic weather phenomena since 1948 than in any equivalent period previous to 1948. These periodic cycles may have frequencies in the range of six to ten, or more, days per cycle and, once started, will recur for periods of several months or more. A systematic study of the historical weather records should be made as soon as possible to test this important idea.

CONCLUSION

Experimental meteorology is a new science. We are probably at the threshold of many important and exciting new discoveries. As so often happens in scientific research, the current objectives may never be achieved or may dwindle into insignificance as new facts are uncovered. The advance in understanding and achievement will depend on the enthusiasm, imagination, curiosity, perseverance, and "will to do" of those scientists and others who will work hard but at the same time direct their eyes toward the sky.

Experimental meteorology is a science which depends primarily on the experimental ability of its devotees. Progress will not be made at the work table unless it is preceded by good work in the field. As in all phases of science, advancement depends on people. If the science of experimental meteorology is favored by having a few good ones, a successful future is assured.

REFERENCES

BERGERON, T.
1935 "On the Physics of Cloud and Precipitation," *Meteorologie und Geodetik Geophysik International*, Part II, pp. 156–78.

BOWEN, E. G.
1950 "The Formation of Rain by Coalescence," *Australian Journal of Scientific Research*, Series A, III, No. 2, 193–214.

CWILONG, B. M.
1947 "Sublimation in a Wilson Cloud Chamber," *Proceedings of the Royal Society*, Series A, CXC, 137–43.

DAVIES, D. A.
1951 "Report on Experiments at Kongwa on Artificial Stimulation of Rain," *Memoirs of the East African Meteorological Department*, II, No. 9, 1–31.

ELLIOTT, R. D., and STRICKLER, R. F.
1954 "Analysis of Results of a Group of Cloud Seeding Projects in Pacific Slope Watershed Areas," *Bulletin of the American Meteorological Society*, XXXV, 171–79.

FINDEISEN, W.
1938 "Colloidal Meteorological Processes in the Formation of Atmospheric Precipitation," *Meteorology*, II, 55, 121–33.

FOURNIER D'ALBE, E. M.
1955 "Giant Hygroscopic Nuclei in the Atmosphere and Their Role in the Formation of Rain and Hail," *Archiv für Meteorologie Geophysik und Bioklimat*, Series A: *Meteorologie und Geophysik*, Vol. VIII, No. 3.

FOURNIER D'ALBE, E. M.; LATEEF, A. M. A.; RASOOL, S. I.; and ZAIDI, I. H.
1955 "The Cloud Seeding Trials in the Central Punjab, July–September, 1954," *Quarterly Journal of the Royal Meteorological Society*, LXXXI, No. 350, 533–662.

GATHMAN, LOUIS
1891 *Rain Produced at Will*. Chicago: The Author. 62 pp.

GUNN, K. L. S., et al.
1954 "Radar Evidence of a Generating Level for Snow," *Journal of Meteorology*, XI, 20–26.

ISONO, K., and KOMABAYASI, M.
1954 "The Influence of Volcanic Dust on Precipitation," *Journal of the Meteorological Society of Japan*, Ser. II, XXXII, 345–53.

KRAUS, E. B., and SQUIRES, P.
1947 "Experiments on the Stimulation of Clouds To Produce Rain," *Nature*, CLIX, 489–94.

LANGMUIR, I.
1948a "The Production of Rain by a Chain Reaction in Cumulus Clouds at Temperatures above Freezing," *Journal of Meteorology*, V, 175–92.
1948b *The Growth of Particles in Smokes and Clouds and the Production of Snow from Supercooled Clouds*. ("Proceedings of the American Philosophical Society," Vol. XCII.) 167 pp.
1950 *Results of the Seeding of Clouds in New Mexico*. (Project Cirrus, Occasional Report No. 24, General Electric Research Laboratory Report No. RL-364.) Schenectady. 20 pp.
1953 *Analysis of the Effects of Periodic Seeding of the Atmosphere with Silver Iodide*. (Final Report, Part II, Project Cirrus, General Electric Research Laboratory Report No. RL-785.) Schenectady. 340 pp.

LEOPOLD, L. B., and HALSTEAD, M. H.
1948 "First Trials of the Schaefer-Langmuir Dry Ice Cloud Seeding Technique in Hawaii," *Bulletin of the American Meteorological Society*, XXIX, 525–34.

MORDY, W. A.
1955 *The Keanae Valley Experiment*. (Pineapple Research Institute Report.) Honolulu: Pineapple Research Institute. 48 pp.

MORDY, W. A., and EBER, L. E.
1954 "Observations of Rainfall from Warm Clouds," *Quarterly Journal of the Royal Meteorological Society*, LXXX, 48–57.

SCHAEFER, V. J.
1945 *Final Report on Icing Research up to July 1, 1946*. (A.T.S.C. Contract No. W-33-038 ac 9151, General Electric Research Laboratory.) Schenectady. 45 pp.
1946 "The Production of Ice Crystals

in a Cloud of Supercooled Water Droplets," *Science*, CIV, 457–59.

1949*a* "The Formation of Ice Crystals in the Laboratory and the Atmosphere," *Chemical Review*, XLIV, 291–320.

1949*b* *Report on Cloud Studies in Puerto Rico*. (Project Cirrus, Occasional Report No. 12, General Electric Research Laboratory Report No. RL-190.) Schenectady. 16 pp.

1950 "The Occurrence of Ice Crystal Nuclei in the Free Atmosphere," pp. 26–33 in *Proceedings of the First National Air Pollution Symposium, Pasadena, California*, Vol. I.

1952 "Formation of Ice Crystals in Ordinary and Nuclei Free Air," *Industrial and Engineering Chemistry*, XLIV, 1300–1304.

1953*a* *Laboratory, Field and Flight Experiments*. (Final Report, Part I, Project Cirrus, General Electric Research Laboratory Report No. RL-785.) Schenectady. 170 pp.

1953*b* *Final Report ONR Project*. (General Electric Research Laboratory Report. No. RL-1007.) Schenectady. 102 pp.

1954 "The Concentration of Ice Nuclei in Air Passing the Summit of Mount Washington," *Bulletin of the American Meteorological Society*, XXXV, 310–14.

SILICEO, E. P.

1951 *Lluvia artificial en la cuenca hidrologica de Necaxa, Estado de Puebla, Mexico*. (Mexican Light and Power Report.) Mexico City. 8 pp. (plus 47 figs.) (Different material with same title in 1949 and 1953 issues.)

SILVERTHORN, J.

1950 "Reports on Seeding Cumulus Clouds with Water and Dry Ice in Honduras." (Private communications, United Fruit Co.)

SMITH, E. J.

1949 "Experiments in Seeding Cumuliform Cloud Layers with Dry Ice," *Australian Journal of Scientific Research*, Series A, II, 78–92.

VERAART, A. W.

1931 *Meer Zoneschyn in het Nevelig Noorden meer Regen in de Tropen*. Amsterdam: Seyffardts' Boek en Muziekhandel. 32 pp.

VONNEGUT, B.

1947 "The Nucleation of Ice Formation by Silver Iodide," *Journal of Applied Physics*, XVIII, 593–95.

1949 "Nucleation of Supercooled Water Clouds by Silver Iodide Smokes," *Chemical Review*, XLIV, 277–89.

1950 "Techniques for Generating Silver Iodide Smokes," *Journal of Colloid Science*, V, 37–48.

WADATI, K.

1954 *Report of Rainmaking in Japan*. Tokyo: Committee for Rainmaking in Japan, Meteorological Research Institute. 160 pp.

WEGENER, A.

1911 *Thermodynamik der Atmosphäre*. Leipzig: J. A. Barth. 331 pp.

WOODCOCK, A.

1949 "Sampling Atmospheric Sea Salt Nuclei over the Ocean," *Journal of Marine Research (Sears Foundation)*, VIII, No. 2, 177–97.

Slope and Soil Changes through Human Use

Slope and Soil Changes through Human Use

The Nature of Induced Erosion and Aggradation

ARTHUR N. STRAHLER[*]

* Dr. Strahler is Associate Professor of Geomorphology in the Department of Geology, Columbia University, New York. In addition to giving graduate instruction and research supervision in geomorphology, he represents physical geography on the university's committee in charge of advanced degrees and instruction in geography. His research and publications deal largely with the development of quantitative and dynamic aspects of geomorphology and the application of statistical methods to landform analysis. He is author of *Physical Geography*, 1951.

INTRODUCTION

To set forth adequately the nature of induced erosion and aggradation would require that we summarize a sizable science developed in the past quarter-century by a large body of competent engineers, hydrologists, soil scientists, and geologists. To offer a somewhat different treatment of erosion and aggradation than is usually seen, an attempt is made here to synthesize the empirical observations of the engineer on particular cases and in restricted physical limits with the more generalized rational theories of fluvial erosion and deposition formulated by the geomorphologist, who views landforms as parts of evolving systems adjusted to given sets of environmental factors.

DEFINITION OF EROSION AND AGGRADATION

It will be necessary first to define the terms "erosion" and "aggradation" and then to make a suitable distinction between normal geological processes and those accelerated processes induced by man.

In the broadest sense generally acceptable to the geomorphologist, *erosion* is the progressive removal of soil or rock particles from the parent-mass by a fluid agent. Entrainment of the particles into the fluid medium of transportation is thus implicit, but the form of transportation—whether by suspension or bed-load traction—and the distance of transportation are not specified. By introducing mention of the fluid agent, the definition excludes mass-gravity movements such as thick mudflows, earthflows, landslides, and slump, which are plastic flowage or slip movements not requiring a suspending fluid medium. Excluding these phenomena by no means implies that they lack importance in the scheme of landmass denudation; they are excluded in this paper because of lack of space. The fluid media acting upon landforms are water, air, and glacial ice. Here, again, limitations of topic and space require that only water erosion be treated. The omission of wind erosion is serious from the standpoint of the total problem of induced erosion but does not otherwise interfere with a treatment restricted to water erosion.

In this discussion water erosion will be recognized as taking two basically different forms: (1) *slope* erosion and (2) *channel* erosion. The first is the relatively uniform reduction of a fair-

621

ly smooth ground surface under the eroding force of overland, or sheet, flow which, although by no means uniformly distributed in depth or velocity, is more or less continuously spread over the ground and is not engaged in carving distinct channels into the surface. The second form of erosion consists of the cutting-away of bed and banks of a clearly marked channel which contains the flow at all but the highest flood peaks. Channel erosion takes place in and produces both the gullies and deep shoestring rills incised into previously smooth slopes and the valley-bottom stream channels which have long been permanent features of the landscape. Too often, in the writer's opinion, the distinction between slope erosion and channel erosion is not clearly drawn in soil-erosion publications deploring the high sediment yield from a watershed.

In defining slope erosion, the question of inclusion of surficial soil creep requires consideration. By surficial creep is meant the slow, usually imperceptible, downslope movement of unconsolidated soil or weathered mantle caused by the disturbance or agitation of the particles and their subsequent rearrangement under the force of gravity (Gilbert, 1909, p. 345). The importance of this creep is extremely great in normal geological land-surface denudation and is responsible in part for the form of the slope profile. Nevertheless, it is excluded here because the rates at which detritus would be supplied to a stream by creep are assumed to be extremely slow and to produce a negligible increment to stream loads in comparison with quantities involved in accelerated slope erosion induced by radical changes in surface treatment. One mechanism of the creep process is not so easily surrendered, however. This is the process of downslope movement induced by rain-beat (splash erosion) on a poorly protected soil surface

(Ellison, 1950). On a perfectly horizontal surface the impacts of vertically falling drops would produce no general soil movement in one direction, but on a slope a vector is added to the otherwise random movement, and a residual downslope movement of particles is inevitable. On broadly rounded divides and gentle slopes, splash erosion by rain-beat may be considered quantitatively to be of prime importance.

Aggradation, like water erosion, occurs in two basic forms: (1) sheet deposition, or slope wash, at the slope base and (2) channel deposition. In the first form, a slow accretion of soil particles occurs on the lower parts of the valley-side slopes where the gradient diminishes. It is brought down by sheet runoff from the slopes immediately above. The second form, channel deposition, includes the building of bars of well-sorted and stratified grains on the channel floor. This type of aggradation may be extended to include alluvial deposits spread broadly upon alluvial fans and flood plains by overbank flow of streams in flood. Debris flows and mudflows, commonly interbedded with sorted and stratified deposits of stream flows, may be included.

The term "sedimentation" is broader than the term "aggradation" and includes not only slope wash and channel aggradation but also deposition of sediment in reservoirs, lakes, or the oceans in the form of deltas, fine layers of sediment produced by settling, or turbidity current layers. This type of sedimentation, while of major concern to conservationists and engineers, is not treated in this paper.

NORMAL VERSUS ACCELERATED EROSION AND AGGRADATION

Much has been written about a distinction between a certain benign regimen of erosion, transportation, and deposition that characterized our country prior to the white man's spread and a sharply contrasting, usually devastating or impoverishing, white-man-induced regimen termed "accelerated erosion," which has since set in. The first condition has been termed the "geologic norm" by Lowdermilk (1935), Sharpe (1941, p. 236), and others. In many areas the second is clearly shown in the surface forms—particularly gullying—and is obvious to the most untutored layman. Less obvious to the eye are rapid accelerations in sheet erosion and aggradation which seem to have set in following deforestation and cultivation.

A survey of papers discussing the distinction between normal and accelerated erosion gives the definite impression that doubt exists as to the validity of the distinction mostly in reference to the semiarid and arid lands of the West. Apparently nearly everyone accepts the severe gullying of the Piedmont and of the Middle West loess regions as an example of accelerated erosion brought about by man. Where the question is with arroyo trenching in the Navaho country, sedimentation of the Rio Grande Valley, or occurrence of mudflows at the foot of the Wasatch, however, some seriously raise the question whether such radical changes are actually "normal" for the prevailing climatic, topographic, and vegetative environment or whether man's activities have been only coincidental with upsets brought about by natural factors. Such skepticism is not entirely unwarranted. The sedimentary contents of many alluvial fan deposits show histories of debris floods and mudflows throughout the construction of the fans (Blissenbach, 1954). Bailey (1935) found evidence of a history of repeated epicycles of erosion and filling in certain valleys of the Colorado Plateau, though not in all valleys or to such great depths as the recent trenching which he attributes to overgrazing. Such periods of accelerated erosion

and deposition are entirely expectable in regions where steep slopes and a naturally poor vegetative cover place large amounts of soil and rock debris at the disposal of sporadic heavy storms.

Taking these things into consideration, the adjective "accelerated" as applied to erosion and aggradation will be intended to mean merely a very considerable increase in rate of these processes, quite irrespective of whether the acceleration is brought about by natural causes or man-made causes or by a combination of both. Where caused by man or his livestock, the qualifying expression "man-induced" will be used, and this may be shortened to "induced."

What are the physical criteria for distinguishing between a present-day period of accelerated erosion and deposition and a previous regimen constituting the geologic norm? One is suggested by Bailey (1941) on the basis of conspicuous changes in texture in sections of alluvial deposits found at the base of the Wasatch Range. A change to coarser texture is evidence of accelerated watershed erosion, because, as we shall see later, increases in transporting capacity and competence of the stream result from increases in runoff. As a second criterion, the existence of any steep-banked stream channel or axial gully in whose walls fine-textured soils (often with soil profiles) are exposed is ample proof of a recent upset in stream regimen.

DYNAMICS OF SLOPE EROSION

The geomorphologist and hydraulic engineer see erosion and aggradation processes from somewhat different points of view, each appropriate to the aims of his field of study. To the engineer concerned with accelerated erosion on a cultivated hillside, the problem relates to a sloping patch of ground. This particular area is often regarded as an independent plot and is in fact often physically isolated with artificial sides and a trap for runoff and sediment at the lower edge. To the geomorphologist the plot is merely an indistinguishable part of a continuous geometric surface formed into a drainage basin bounded by a natural drainage divide and centered upon an axial stream. It is the gross aspect of the whole system operating over a long period of time that interests the geomorphologist, but he realizes that he cannot fully understand the morphology without a knowledge of the principles of erosion operative upon any given small plot within the whole. We shall therefore consider first the dynamics of the slope erosion processes and then turn to the total basin morphology.

Following the cue given by Knapp (1941, p. 255), we recognize that "fundamentally, erosion is a mechanical process, whose vital components are the forces which cause erosion, those which resist it, and the resulting motion of the eroded material." We add to this the concept of a natural slope as an open dynamic system tending to a steady state (Strahler, 1952a, pp. 934–35). A slope plot of unit width and of any desired segment of the length between the limits of a drainage divide and the axial stream channel at the base is considered to form the open system. Water and rock waste pass through the system in one general direction only (downslope, or vertically downward). Added to by direct precipitation and by rock disintegration at all points in the system, the water and debris thus proceed cumulatively to the line of discharge at the slope base. When the system has achieved a steady state of operation, the rates at which materials enter, pass through, and leave the system become constant, or independent of time, and the form of the system is stabilized. The nature of this steady state is determined by the relative magnitude of the forces of resistance and the forces tending to produce downslope movement.

Forces tending to produce entrainment by sheet flow are given by Knapp (1941, p. 257) as uniform boundary shear, local intensified shear from eddies, fluid impacts, and particle impacts. All these are expressions of the downslope component of the gravitational force. To this is added the force of buoyancy, which makes entrainment easier. If force of raindrop impact is added, this, too, is a result of the action of gravitational force. Other forces which tend to disrupt or otherwise weaken the soil or rock near the surface are molecular rather than gravitational in nature (Strahler, 1952a, p. 932). Adsorption of water by colloids, hydrolysis of silicate minerals, growth of capillary films at grain contacts, thermally induced expansion and contraction, reactions between acids and mineral crystals, direct solution, and growth of ice or salt crystals are all processes tending to reduce the strength of the soil and rock. The forces responsible for them are not related to the gravitational field but are of the general group of intermolecular or interatomic forces.

Forces of resistance to entrainment include intergrain friction in the coarse sediments (proportional to the component of gravitational force normal to the surface), capillary film cohesion in silts and clays, and forces of intercrystal cohesion in rocks. Breaking, or shearing, resistance of plant roots and stems and of organic litter is a major force and differs from the inorganic forces in being continually restored through photosynthesis and conversion of solar energy. Equivalent to a resistive force is capacity of the soil to transmit precipitation through the surface to the ground-water system and thus to reduce or prevent the accumulation of surface runoff. This type of "resistance" is analogous to a fighter side-stepping a blow and letting it go harmlessly past. Volcanic cinders and permeable coarse sands may prove surprisingly resistant to sheet erosion simply because runoff cannot form.

We may say, then, that there exist two major groups of opposed forces: those which tend to produce movement or shear and those which tend to resist movement or shear. These may be formed into a dimensionless ratio with resistive forces in the denominator. Where this force ratio exceeds unity, entrainment will set in, and, in general, the higher the ratio, the more rapid will be the rate of erosion.

Horton (1945, p. 319) has cited the DuBoys formula as a rational expression relating the eroding force to slope and to depth of runoff:

$$F = wd \sin \alpha \, , \qquad (1)$$

where F is force per unit area (stress) exerted parallel with the soil surface; w is the specific weight of water (weight per unit volume); d is depth of overland flow; and α is angle of slope. Horton (*ibid.*, p. 320) sums the forces of resistance to erosion in the term "resistivity," R_i, expressed in pounds per square foot of surface. He assigns to R_i values ranging from .05 on newly cultivated bare soil to as high as 0.5 for well-developed grass sod. He observes that erosion will not occur on a slope unless the available eroding force exceeds the resistance of the soil to erosion (*ibid.*).

In addition to the resistivity, R_i, as a measure of susceptibility of a surface to erosion, Horton (*ibid.*, p. 324) introduces an "erosion proportionality factor," k_e, which we shall define as mass rate of removal per unit area divided by force per unit area:

$$k_e = \frac{e_r}{F}, \qquad (2)$$

where e_r is mass of soil removed per unit time per unit area and F is eroding force per unit area. Horton defines depth of soil erosion in inches per hour, whereas, for reasons which will be apparent later, it is here defined as mass removed per unit time per unit area. With terms as defined above, the proportionality factor has the dimensions of inverse of velocity. The proportionality factor is the ratio between the erosion rate and the eroding force being applied to produce that rate and will increase in value as susceptibility of the surface to erosion increases. Resistivity, by contrast, will decrease in value when susceptibility to erosion increases.

If eroding force is proportional to both depth and sine of slope angle, as the DuBoys formula requires, and if we assume for the moment that a particular surface plot has a fixed slope, then the next step in our analysis is to consider what factors control depth of runoff. Depth of overland flow may be related to runoff intensity and slope length, for a plot of unit width, by the following dimensionally correct equation (*ibid.*, p. 309):

$$d = \frac{aLQ_s}{V}, \qquad (3)$$

where d is depth of flow; a is a dimensionless numerical constant; L is length of slope; Q_s is runoff intensity, defined as volume rate of flow per unit area; and V is average velocity of flow.

From this equation we see that depth of overland flow will increase directly with both length of slope and runoff intensity but is inversely proportional to the velocity. We shall therefore wish to transfer our attention to the term Q_s, because this is most directly related to precipitation intensity.

The empirical Manning formula states that

$$V = \frac{b}{n} R^{2/3} S^{1/2}, \qquad (4)$$

where V is mean velocity; R is hydraulic radius or, in this case, equivalent to depth of flow, d, of equation (3); S is slope, measured as tangent of slope here (but approximately the same as sine of slope for angles up to 15°); n is Manning's roughness number; and b is a numerical constant. Horton (*ibid.*, pp. 309–10) shows that by simple substitution of the value of V from the Manning equation (4) into equation (3) and by combining slope, the Manning number, slope length, and the numerical constants into one constant, K_s, runoff intensity may be expressed as a function of depth by

$$Q_s = K_s d^{5/3} . \qquad (5)$$

Although this relationship applies to turbulent flow only, it has been generalized by Horton to include laminar and mixed flow by a simple power function of depth:

$$Q_s = K_s d^m , \qquad (6)$$

where m is an exponent which has the value 5/3 only for turbulent flow. Horton (*ibid.*, p. 311) found that the power function agrees remarkably well with values obtained from experimental plots: the values of m ranged between 1.0 and 2.0.

Continuing the chain of analysis, consider next what factors determine the magnitude of runoff intensity, Q_s. Expressed as discharge per unit area of ground surface, Q_s is dimensionally the same as precipitation intensity, I; both are independent of total surface area of the given plot or watershed. If no rainfall were lost through infiltration and evaporation, intensities of runoff and precipitation would be equal. Neglecting evaporation and other losses, the principal loss with which we are concerned is infiltration, expressed also in the velocity dimension, length (depth) per unit time. Horton's (*ibid.*, pp. 306–9) infiltration theory of runoff states that runoff can occur only when precipitation rate exceeds infiltration rate and that the latter is itself a function of time such that

$$f = f_c + (f_0 - f_c) ^{-Kt} , \qquad (7)$$

where f is infiltration rate at a given time, t; f_c is constant infiltration rate approached with time; f_0 is initial infiltration rate; and K is a numerical constant. The sharp drop-off in infiltration rate, described in equation (7) as exponential, is well known from field observations (Sherman and Musgrave, 1949, p. 247). The term f_c has been shown to vary considerably with different surface conditions of the same soil and is a major factor in determining whether or not rapid erosion will occur under a given precipitation regimen. Whereas rainfall intensity rarely exceeds infiltration capacity in undisturbed soils under dense forest cover and surface litter, it does so readily on bare soils whose infiltration capacity has been greatly reduced by rain-beat or livestock trampling. A prime cause of man-induced accelerated soil erosion is therefore the reduction in permanent infiltration capacity, because man has no control over the other variable, precipitation intensity, which also determines runoff intensity, or over slope (unless by terracing), which, along with runoff intensity, determines eroding force.

If, as the foregoing discussion has indicated, the rate at which erosion proceeds depends upon susceptibility of the surface to erosion, expressed as the erosion proportionality factor, k_e; upon the runoff intensity, Q_s, determined, in turn, by ratio of precipitation intensity to infiltration capacity; and upon the slope of the ground surface, S, we may conveniently combine these three terms into one dimensionless product:

$$N_H = Q_s k_e S . \qquad (8)$$

I propose that the number N_H be designated the *Horton number*, after the investigator who contributed so extensively to the research on erosion and surface runoff.

Although the Horton number has not been quantitatively investigated, this appears feasible and will lead to a series of numbers summarizing the erosional qualities of given regions. To obtain k_e, measurements of sediment yield will supply values of the term e_r in equation (2); the eroding force, F, may be estimated from the DuBoys formula, which requires data on runoff depth and slope. Runoff intensity can be measured directly from field installations, but a representative value must be stated in terms of storms of a particular intensity. Slope may be generalized for a given watershed by a mean slope or similar statistic derived from slope maps or random slope sampling by methods discussed elsewhere (Strahler, 1956b). We might anticipate that the observed range of the Horton number would show a critical value, analogous to the critical value of the Reynolds number, above which severe erosion would set in.

RELATION OF SLOPE EROSION TO TOTAL DRAINAGE BASIN MORPHOLOGY

In the preceding discussion slope erosion was considered as operating on a patch of ground, or slope plot, regarded as an open system within arbitrary boundaries. To satisfy the geomorphologist, this scope should be expanded to treat all the surface of a complete drainage basin lying within the limits of the watershed and terminated at the lower end by a stream channel through which all water and rock waste is discharged. The question now is: What does man-induced, accelerated sheet erosion and gullying mean in terms of the adjustment of the drainage-basin morphology to a steady state of operation?

A concept of the drainage basin as a natural open system whose geometrical form is delicately adjusted under normal, or prevailing, geological and climatic conditions to maintain a steady state of operation was adapted by the writer (Strahler, 1950, p. 676) from analogous biological systems described by Bertalanffy (1950). Attempts to determine the characteristic hypsometric curves and integrals of basins in the steady state have been carried out (Strahler, 1952b). Further studies of the nature of slope frequency distributions over an entire drainage basin (Strahler, 1956b) have added to existing knowledge on the characteristic morphology. All these studies are based upon Horton's (1945, pp. 281–82) theory that drainage systems can be analyzed according to a system of orders of magnitude of the channel branches and that certain exponential laws of dimensional increase relative to increase in order of magnitude are observed. Fundamental to such a treatment is the concept of the *first-order drainage basin*, or *unit basin*, which may be likened to the cell in living organisms. The first-order basin is defined as that basin contributing directly to a permanently situated fingertip stream channel to the downstream point where this channel joins with another permanent channel, whether of similar order or larger. The first-order basin is usually elliptical or ovate in outline.

The principal distinction between any two first-order basins taken from each of two regions differing in climate, vegetative cover, underlying lithology, and relief is in dimensions. Basin outlines and general surface forms are often surprisingly similar despite great inequalities in scale. While there are various ways in which scale of a basin can be stated, the most valuable general scale index has proved to be *drainage density, D_d*, defined by Horton (*ibid.*, p. 283) as total length of stream channels divided by total area, or

$$D_d = \frac{\Sigma L}{A}, \qquad (9)$$

where ΣL represents the summation of all channel lengths in miles and A is the area in square miles. Drainage density thus has the dimensions of inverse of length and increases in value as the channel network becomes finer in texture with channels closer together. Because of its dimensional quality, a linear scale must be specified; Horton used miles, and this unit has subsequently been adopted. Observed drainage density values range from as small as 2–3 miles per square mile in regions of massive sandstones to as high as 500–1,000 or more for badlands in weak clays.

Our problem now will be to tie together the principles of erosion with drainage density, which is an index of the scale of the basic landform units. From this we may be able to secure some insight into the fundamental meaning of accelerated erosion.

First of all, there are rational grounds, substantiated by field observation, for supposing that drainage density is a function of several variables already shown to be factors controlling the intensity of the slope-erosion process. The prevailingly high values of drainage density in regions underlain by impervious clays and marls, in contrast to density on more permeable rocks, is clearly seen where the differing rock types lie adjacent to one another, but at essentially the same level, under essentially the same vegetative cover, and subject to the same previous geologic history. This leads us to conclude that drainage density would be an increasing function of runoff intensity, Q_s.

The striking contrast in drainage densities where rocks of differing strength are exposed side by side is well known to all geomorphologists. Clays and marls invariably form fine-textured badlands in contrast to large, full-bodied slope forms of such dense hard rocks as sandstone and limestone. This we can attribute to differences in resistivity to erosion or, inversely, to the erosion proportionality factor, k_e.

Slope is also considered by geomorphologists to be an independent variable in controlling drainage density, although this is difficult to confirm by observation. The presumption is that, in regions of steep slope, channel gradients will also be steeper and hence that first-order streams can persist with smaller watershed areas than are required by a system of lower gradients. It is true that the highest drainage densities are recorded in badlands, and these are regions of excessively steep slope.

Relief, or average difference in elevation between divides and adjacent channels, is a scale factor which may vary independently of either drainage density or average slope. It is introduced here to give a characteristic vertical dimension to the drainage basin, analogous with channel depth or hydraulic radius in a stream channel. In general, it seems reasonable to suppose that regions of high relief are subjected to more intensive rates of erosion than are regions of low relief, because the potential energy of the former system will be higher and will tend to produce steeper ground slopes and channel gradients.

We are now prepared to introduce the following general equation showing the several variables of which drainage density is a function:

$$D_d = \phi\,(Q_s,\ k_e,\ S,\ H,\ \nu,\ g)\,. \quad (10)$$

Definitions of the terms and dimensional analysis of each are given in Table 25. Kinematic viscosity of the runoff, ν, is added as a significant property of a system operated by hydraulic flow. Acceleration of gravity, g, is introduced as the force field within which the entire hydraulic system operates.

By means of the Buckingham Pi Theorem we may combine the variables in equation (10) into a set of dimensionless groups. Mathematical details of this procedure are presented elsewhere (Strahler, 1956a), and it must suffice here to give the final result only, which is a function containing four groups:

$$\phi \left(D_d H, Q_s k_e S, Q_s \nu H, \frac{Q_s^2}{Hg} \right) = 0 . \quad (11)$$

the Reynolds number in which relief, H, is the representative length dimension of the system and Q_s is the velocity term. The fourth group, Q_s^2/Hg, is recognizable as a form of the Froude number. These last two numbers, while not the subjects of immediate concern in this discussion, are of prime importance in considerations of dynamic similarity of drainage systems of various scales (Strahler, 1956a).

Having decided that drainage density is a function of the various elements comprising the dimensionless

TABLE 25

DIMENSIONS OF VARIABLES IN DRAINAGE DENSITY EQUATION

Symbol	Term	Dimensional quality	Dimensional symbol
D_d	Drainage density (Horton)	Length divided by area	$L/L^2 = L^{-1}$
Q	Runoff intensity (Horton)	Volume rate of flow per unit area of cross-section	$L^3 T^{-1}/L^2 = L T^{-1}$
k_e	Erosion proportionality factor (Horton)	Mass rate of removal per unit area divided by force per unit area	$M L^{-2} T^{-1}/M L^{-1} T^{-2}$ $= L^{-1} T$
S	Slope	Dimensionless	0
H	Average relief	Length	L
ν	Kinematic viscosity of fluid	Absolute viscosity divided by density	$L^2 T^{-1}$
g	Acceleration of gravity	Distance per unit time per unit time	$L T^{-2}$

The first number, $D_d H$, is the product of drainage density and relief; it is here termed the *ruggedness number*. It gives a measure of over-all ruggedness, because it increases directly both with relief and with increasing detail of the drainage net. The second number, $Q_s k_e S$, is the Horton number, already derived in the discussion of dynamics of slope erosion, and is the measure of over-all intensity of the erosion process. The slope term, S, in this product is dimensionless and could be added to any one of the groups without disturbing their dimensionless quality. Nevertheless, it seems most desirable in the Horton number, where the mechanical influence of slope is required.

The third group, $Q_s \nu H$, is a form of

groups, we may solve for D_d in equation (11):

$$D_d = \frac{1}{H} f \left(Q_s k_e S, Q_s \nu H, \frac{Q_s^2}{Hg} \right) . \quad (12)$$

This tells us that drainage density is inversely proportional to relief times some function of the remaining three dimensionless groups. To determine this function, an extensive program of experimentation would be required. We can, however, now outline the principles relating accelerated slope erosion to the over-all basin morphology.

The essential point is that accelerated erosion in which a gully system is developed on previously smooth, unchanneled slopes is an adjustment of the drainage system toward a higher drainage density and a system of steeper slopes. When a relatively resistant vegetative cover is destroyed and the soil over a weak bedrock exposed, two changes occur in the Horton number, both tending to increase this number: the erosion proportionality factor, k_e, is greatly increased, which means simply that more material is eroded from the bare surface by a given runoff depth and velocity than in the previous condition of high resistance; and the runoff intensity, Q_s, is greatly increased for a given precipitation regimen because the stripping of the vegetative cover leaves the soil susceptible to direct rainbeat, which seals the surface openings and reduces infiltration rates. Additional breakdown of the soil structure by man or animals may further reduce infiltration capacity.

We must assume that the relations between increased sediment load entrained and increased overland flow are such that the flow at points where it is concentrated by favorable undulations of slope is capable of deep scour and begins to carve a gully, which is actually an extension of the stream-channel system and is the means by which drainage density is increased. As gullies are deepened and ramified, a system of steep slopes is formed, and these quickly replace the original surface. The rising grade of the newly formed channels lowers the relief, where this relief is measured from channel to immediately adjacent divide. Each gully end now becomes a new first-order stream segment, and the slopes draining into it are molded into new, small, first-order drainage basins. Presumably, the newly formed system would now achieve a new steady state of operation, which would persist as long as the ground surface continued to be barren and the physical quality of the material beneath the surface remained unchanged. Neither of these qualifica-

tions would be likely to be met for long in the humid regions of the eastern United States. Removal of the layer of weathered rock, even though thick, would in most places expose a more resistant bedrock. Vegetation would probably take hold long before the steady state could be achieved.

An interesting case illustrating the drainage-density adjustment theory of severe slope erosion is the Ducktown, Tennessee, locality (Fig. 123). Here the long-continued production of noxious fumes has prevented the recovery of vegetation and allowed the development of a nearly complete erosional topography in a stage that would be termed "mature" by the geomorphologist.

In general, it may be noted that severe erosion leading to extensive gullying can be expected in any region where the contrast in resistivity of a vegetated surface and a barren surface is great, because the low-resistivity surface will demand a high drainage density and because the erosion system will "take" such measures as it "needs" to adjust its morphology to a new steady state. Where difference in surface resistivity before and after surface denudation is not so marked and there is introduced only a small increase in runoff intensity, we may expect the uppermost ends of existing stream channels to be increased in length but with only limited occurrence of new gullies on side slopes.

DYNAMICS OF AGGRADATION

In the introductory definition aggradation was considered to take two basic forms: (1) slope-wash, or colluvial, deposition and (2) channel deposition and associated valley-bottom deposits. In both cases the dynamics are fundamentally similar. The problem is to explain why a sheet or stream of water engaged in bed-load transport should on the average drop more particles than it picks up from a given area of the bed and therefore raise the level of its bed. We assume that, if the transportation system is in a steady state of operation, it would neither aggrade nor degrade but would transport the load supplied to it through the system without changes in vertical position of the bed and without changes in transverse form of the bed or channel. This steady state is essentially the same as the state of operation of a graded stream with an equilibrium profile, to use the geomorphologists' conventional terminology.

FIG. 123.—Severe erosion near Ducktown, Tennessee. Complete denudation of vegetation has been followed by transformation to a morphology characterized by high drainage density and steep slopes.

The occurrence of persistent aggradation is itself primary evidence of a change in the factors whose balance determines a steady state and is a manifestation of the self-adjustment of any open dynamic system to restore a steady state. If raising the height of the bed alone were involved—that is to say, merely lifting the entire profile by addition of a constant increment at all points—the operation of the system would not be appreciably affected in a short period of time. Instead, the aggradation must be viewed as increasing in depth upstream or downstream to produce a wedgelike deposit which increases or decreases the slope of the bed and therefore influences the velocity of flow and hence also the ability of the stream to transport. Only by producing changes in slope can aggradation restore a steady state of operation. Upstream increase in depth of aggradation is the characteristic change in fluvial systems, and we may say that aggradation is generally associated with increase in slope of the fluvial system. Reduction of slope may conceivably be accomplished for a short period by downstream increase in depth of aggradation but requires the special case of introduction of a raised or rising base level in the path of the flow (Mackin, 1948, pp. 496–97). As a general rule, in the absence of such base-level changes, reduction of slope is accomplished by erosional reduction of the bed, the depth of removal increasing upstream to yield a wedge of removal which thickens upstream.

Both the bed-load capacity for a given size grade and the competence (ability to move, stated in terms of particle size) are functions of bed velocity, which in a general way varies with mean velocity in a stream (Gilbert, 1914). Aggradation can thus be initiated by a reduced velocity of flow, and we shall need to inquire into those external changes which may on the average substantially reduce the velocity of flow, both overland and in channels. One such change is reduction of discharge, which, through a decrease in depth of flow, reduces velocity. Reduction in magnitude of flood discharges may be general over an entire watershed through climatic change in which runoff-producing rains of given high intensities become less frequent. Aggradation reflects not so much the inability of reduced discharges to keep the channel cleared of debris as it does a steepening of gradient undertaken by the system to restore its transporting ability and to restore a steady state of operation on a reduced budget of discharge. Loss of discharge by influent seepage through the stream bed and by evaporation is important in lower reaches of channels and on fans in the dry climates. Progressive loss of stream discharge by increasing diversion of flow to underground solution channels is important in limestone regions (Strahler, 1944) and is accompanied by aggradation in valley floors. An improvement in infiltration capacity on watershed surfaces would also tend to reduce peak discharges and hence might seem to be a cause of aggradation, but, because this is normally part of a sequence of events in which vegetation becomes more dense and consequently holds back sediment load, it is generally followed by channel erosion rather than aggradation.

Excessive decrease of slope of the stream bed or ground surface in the downstream direction is a second cause of velocity reduction. The concavity commonly present at the base of a valley-side slope provides a continually lessening declivity over which sediment-ladened sheet flow must pass. Deposition of sediment in this zone is easily attributed to the decrease in velocity forced by the decrease in slope, but in terms of open-system dynamics it would be more meaningful to say that the aggradation is an attempt to steepen the slope to the point where increased velocity will permit the sediment to be transported across the slope with no further aggradation.

In a channel the downstream decrease in slope, which is approximately of a negative exponential form, may be delicately adjusted for a steady state of operation under a given regimen of climate and watershed characteristics. If discharge is reduced, this slope will prove to be insufficient. Aggradation will provide the means of steepening the stream slope, thereby increasing its transporting power, and consequently will tend to restore a steady state in which the debris is carried through the entire system on a fixed grade.

Quite apart from changes in velocity of flow, the load itself is the fundamental independent variable to which the stream slope is appropriately adjusted when a steady state of transportation exists. Necessity for aggradation which will steepen the slope is brought about either by (1) an increased rate of supply of debris of a given size distribution (because the capacity for bed-load transport is limited) or by (2) an increase in coarseness of the debris (because the competence is also limited). Assuming that the overland flow and channel flow are adjusted to transport a given quantity of debris of a given coarseness per unit time, an increase in either the quantity or the coarseness will require that the flow be adjusted to supply greater transporting ability. This can be done only by an increase of slope through aggradation. Normally, the depletion of watershed vegetative cover accompanied by cultivation or other disturbance of surface will simultaneously increase not only the quantity of debris but also its mean grain size.

Discharge and load are not normally varied independently of each other. The same depletion of vegetative cover that causes greater quantity and larger caliber of load will also be expected to be associated with reduced infiltration capacity of the soil, and this in turn yields greater peak runoff and stream discharge. What is of prime importance is therefore the ratio between load and discharge. In general, an excessively high load-to-discharge ratio will be met with aggradation and steepening of slope; a low ratio, with scour of the bed and lowering of the slope. Whereas accelerated sheet erosion with severe gullying of slopes is most commonly associated with aggradation in valley floors, this would not necessarily have to be so in all cases. If the acquisition of debris by the runoff did not continue to excess in the downstream direction not only might there be no aggradation down the valley but erosional deepening of the entire drainage system (diminishing of course to zero at the mouth) might conceivably result.

Velocity may be reduced independently of changes in discharge and load by deterioration in the efficiency of the channel form and by increase in the irregularity of the bed (Mackin, 1948, pp. 487, 504). In the case of overland flow on slopes, or of subdivided flow over alluvial fans and alluvial valley flats, the development of a cover of grass or small bushy shrubs will be expected to retard the flow appreciably and to cause the velocity drop necessary to produce aggradation. While this effect may be deemed beneficial on hillside and valley-side slopes, where retardation of sediment movement is desired, it forms part of a vicious cycle in aggradation of valley bottoms, as described below.

In streams, deterioration of channel efficiency may be expected to reduce velocity and bring on aggradation at increased rates. Assuming first that a marked increase in bed load relative to discharge has caused rapid aggradation in the channel of a stream, the building of sand and gravel bars will be expected to decrease the depth of flow at the same time that the channel is broadened or actually subdivided. Leopold and Maddock (1953, p. 29) point out that an alluvial channel which is broad and shallow probably carries a relatively large bed load. A steep slope would, however, be required in compensation for reduced depth. The temporary loss of transporting power would be expected to intensify the rate of aggradation still further and to set off a vicious cycle wherein the flow spreads over the banks and is distributed over the entire valley floor. The rapid formation of channel-plug deposits with upstream sediment accumulation and overbank spreading has been described by Happ *et al.* (1940, pp. 71–73, 94–95). In the absence of a deep, strongly scoured channel in the valley axis vegetation can take hold, further impeding the flow and at the same time increasing the resistance of the valley floor to scour. Eventually, however, the valley-floor slope is built up by aggradation to the point where an unusual flood, deficient in bed load, can quickly incise the alluvium and initiate cutting of a relatively narrow, deep channel requiring a lower slope. That such cycles of aggradation and trenching are the normal deviations from a uniformly maintained steady state of operation in a semiarid environment has been under consideration by geomorphologists for many years, one of the earliest discussions being by McGee (1891), who introduced the term "varigradation" for normal development of alluvial accumulations in the course of a stream.

The role of man in such cycles of aggradation and intrenchment may prove, most rationally viewed, to be one of setting off changes that might otherwise be long delayed and of intensifying the extremes of the cycle. Deforestation, cultivation, or overgrazing might be expected to increase the load so greatly in relation to discharge as to force channel aggradation and initiate the aggradation cycle. In humid regions responsibility for such aggradations seems to rest almost solely upon man; in semiarid regions the responsibility is less clearly his. By the reasoning invoked above, trenching of alluvial fills to produce narrow arroyos is a reflection of either increased discharge or reduced bed load, or a reduction in ratio of load to discharge, and is thus the diametric opposite of the change invoked to explain aggradation. Under these circumstances it is difficult to accept the blanket explanation of man-induced depletion of vegetative cover to account for valley aggradation in one part of the country and for valley incision in another part.

Another aspect of aggradation dynamics deals with textural differences between parent-material and aggraded products. In general, the slope-wash and valley alluvium produced in the aggradational cycle will be the coarser fraction of the parent-material from which the fine clays and silts, readily carried in suspension to distant downstream points, have been sorted. The initial erosion velocity required to entrain the fine-grained materials is great, because of initial cohesion. Once in suspension, however, they remain in motion at relatively low velocities and will settle out only in reservoirs or lakes or when flocculated in contact with sea water. This accounts for the coarseness of aggradational deposits formed as aprons at the base of valley-side slopes and in the floors of the smaller stream valleys. Happ *et al.* (1940, pp. 86–88) state that sand or coarser sediment causes most of the sediment damage to valley agricultural land.

RELATION OF AGGRADATION TO TOTAL DRAINAGE-BASIN MORPHOLOGY

In a previous section of this paper dealing with relation of slope erosion to total drainage-basin morphology the principle was developed that, when severe erosion accompanied by gullying sets in, following breakdown of initial surface resistivity and reduction of infiltration capacity, the channel system is undergoing a change from low- to high-drainage density. Streams are lengthening and are increasing greatly in number by development of new branches. Slopes are being steepened and at the same time greatly shortened in length from divide to channel. We shall now attempt to integrate into this general theory of drainage-basin transformation the occurrence of aggradation of the channel and valley floor of the main stream. Such a development is illustrated in Figure 124, representing the case where severe slope erosion is concomitant with channel aggradation.

The drainage basin outlined represents a single unit, or first-order basin, prior to the induced modifications. It has one axial channel without branches. The slopes are long and smooth from

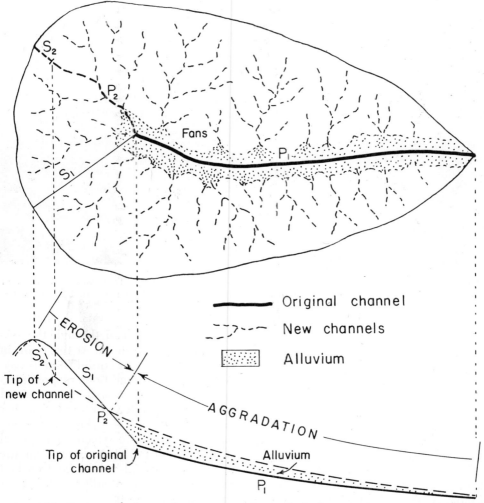

Fans

Original channel

New channels

Alluvium

EROSION

Tip of new channel

AGGRADATION

Tip of original channel

Alluvium

FIG. 124.—Drainage-basin transformation from low to high drainage density. Severe gullying and badland development on slopes accompanied by aggradation in main valley axis. Profiles show that channel gradient and slope gradient are both increased by the transformation.

divide to channel, although ephemeral shoestring rills may from time to time be carved on these slopes by unusual storms and subsequently rehealed. With the onset of severe erosion, a greatly ramified drainage network develops, with a large number of new first-order basins of small size replacing the single large basin. This is strikingly illustrated in the Ducktown, Tennessee, locality shown in Figure 125. The chan-

cause the ratio of load to discharge has increased during this development, the slope of the channel of the main axial stream will have from the beginning required steepening, and this will take the form of coalescent fans built out from the base of each new gully into the floor of the main valley (*ibid.,* p. 92). This aggradation will be extended down the valley as a wedge until the entire gradient is steepened to allow

Fig. 125.—Transformation of slopes by severe erosion near Ducktown, Tennessee, 1949. Smooth, long, vegetated slopes are being transformed by an extended channel network into regions of short, steep, bare slopes.

nels are extended headward into surfaces previously part of the smooth slopes. The new channel system transports greater quantities of debris, including coarser material than formerly, because the increased proportion of surface runoff greatly increases the transporting capacity of the system at the same time that the resistivity of the surface has been greatly reduced, and the load is more easily entrained by the runoff. As the gully incision progresses, more and more of the surface is transformed into steep badland slopes. Be-

discharge of the load through the system and out the mouth. At this point in time a stabilized, or equilibrium, profile is produced. If conditions of precipitation and surface resistivity remained constant thereafter, the only further change would be a slow lowering in elevation of the entire system as required by removal of the landmass. In time the aggraded material would be trenched and dissected, eventually to disappear from the entire basin.

The transformation outlined above would represent an extreme case, comparable to change from landforms appropriate to humid climates with dense vegetative cover to badland forms in semiarid regions. We might suppose that moderate changes in resistivity of surface or in rainfall regimen would bring about correspondingly moderate changes in drainage density and that in some cases the growth of new channels and aggradation of the main valley floor would be observable only from careful observations of long duration.

CONCLUSION

The principal objective of this discussion has been to attempt to develop certain rational, qualitative principles of land erosion and aggradation in which the phenomena observed by engineers studying soil erosion and sedimentation on small plots of ground or on limited reaches of streams are related to a general geomorphological theory based upon consideration of an entire drainage basin as an open system tending to achieve a steady state of operation but responding by erosion and aggradation when the steady state is upset by man's treatment of the land or by natural changes in physical environment. Perhaps such a theory relating all parts of a fluvial system, if proved sound, will permit more accurate prediction of the downstream consequences which may be expected from changes in watershed conditions. Perhaps, also, such a theory will help to resolve some of the seemingly anomalous cause-and-effect relationships among erosion, aggradation, land use, and climatic change in the semiarid grazing lands of the West.

REFERENCES

BAILEY, REED W.
1935 "Epicycles of Erosion in the Valleys of the Colorado Plateau Province," *Journal of Geology*, XLIII, 337–55.
1941 "Land Erosion—Normal and Accelerated—in the Semiarid West," *Transactions of the American Geophysical Union, 1941*, pp. 240–50.

BERTALANFFY, LUDWIG VON
1950 "The Theory of Open Systems in Physics and Biology," *Science*, CXI, 23–28.

BLISSENBACH, ERICH
1954 "Geology of Alluvial Fans in Semiarid Regions," *Bulletin of the Geological Society of America*, LXV, 165–90.

ELLISON, W. D.
1950 "Soil Erosion by Rainstorms," *Science*, CXI, No. 2880, 245–49.

GILBERT, GROVE KARL
1909 "The Convexity of Hilltops," *Journal of Geology*, XVII, 344–50.
1914 *The Transportation of Debris by Running Water.* (U.S. Geological Survey Professional Paper No. 86.) Washington, D.C.: Government Printing Office. 263 pp.

HAPP, STAFFORD C.; RITTENHOUSE, GORDON; and DOBSON, G. C.
1940 *Some Principles of Accelerated Stream and Valley Sedimentation.* (U.S. Department of Agriculture Technical Bulletin No. 695.) Washington, D.C.: Government Printing Office. 134 pp.

HORTON, ROBERT E.
1945 "Erosional Development of Streams and Their Drainage Basins: Hydrophysical Approach to Quantitative Morphology," *Bulletin of the Geological Society of America*, LVI, 275–370.

KNAPP, ROBERT T.
1941 "A Concept of the Mechanics of the Erosion Cycle," *Transactions of the American Geophysical Union, 1941*, pp. 255–57.

LEOPOLD, LUNA B., and MADDOCK, THOMAS, JR.
1953 *The Hydraulic Geometry of Stream Channels and Some Physiographic Implications.* (U.S. Geological Survey Professional Paper No. 252.) Washington, D.C.: Government Printing Office. 57 pp.

LOWDERMILK, W. C.
  1935 "Acceleration of Erosion above Geologic Norms," *Transactions of the American Geophysical Union*, 15th Annual Meeting, pp. 505–9.
McGEE, W J
  1891 "The Pleistocene History of Northeastern Iowa," pp. 187–577 in *U.S. Geological Survey: Eleventh Annual Report (1889–1890)*, Part I. Washington, D.C.: Government Printing Office.
MACKIN, J. HOOVER
  1948 "Concept of the Graded River," *Bulletin of the Geological Society of America*, LIX, 463–512.
SHARPE, C. F. STEWART
  1941 "Geomorphic Aspects of Normal and Accelerated Erosion," *Transactions of the American Geophysical Union, 1941*, pp. 236–40.
SHERMAN, LEROY K., and MUSGRAVE, GEORGE W.
  1949 "Infiltration," pp. 244–58 (chap. vii) in MEINZER, OSCAR E. (ed.), *Physics of the Earth*, Vol. IX: *Hydrology*. New York: Dover Publications, Inc. 712 pp.
STRAHLER, ARTHUR N.
  1944 "Valleys and Parks of the Kaibab and Coconino Plateaus, Arizona," *Journal of Geology*, LII, No. 6, 361–87.
  1950 "Equilibrium Theory of Erosional Slopes Approached by Frequency Distribution Analysis," *American Journal of Science*, CCXLVIII, 673–96, 800–814.
  1952a "Dynamic Basis of Geomorphology," *Bulletin of the Geological Society of America*, LXIII, 923–38.
  1952b "Hypsometric (Area-Altitude) Analysis of Erosional Topography," *ibid.*, pp. 1117–42.
  1956a "Dimensional Analysis in Geomorphology," *ibid.*, LXVII, 571–96.
  1956b "Quantitative Slope Analysis," *ibid.* (In press.)

Land Use and Sediment Yield

LUNA B. LEOPOLD[*]

INTRODUCTION

When the vegetal cover is removed from a land surface, the rate of removal of the soil material, at least initially, increases rapidly. So well known is this principle that it hardly needs restatement.

If attention is focused on any individual drainage basin in its natural state, large or small, and inquiry is made as to the rate of denudation, a quantitative answer is not easily obtained. The possible error in any computation of rate of sediment production from any given drainage basin is considerable. Significant variations are found in sediment yields from closely adjacent watersheds which appear to be generally similar. To make a quantitative evaluation of the change in the rate of denudation when the natural vegetation is disturbed is, therefore, even more difficult. Considering the fact that "soil conservation" has been promoted to the status of a science, our lack of ability to answer what is apparently so simple a question may seem surprising. Let us look at some of the reasons.

[*] Dr. Leopold is a Hydraulic Engineer in the United States Geological Survey, Washington 25, D.C. He was formerly Head (1946–49) of the Department of Meteorology in the Pineapple Research Institute and Experiment Station of the Hawaiian Sugar Planters' Association, Honolulu, Hawaii. His publications include (with Thomas Maddock, Jr.): *The Hydraulic Geometry of Stream Channels and Some Physiographic Implications*, 1953, and *The Flood Control Controversy*, 1954.

METHODS OF MEASURING EROSION RATE

Sheet erosion cannot be accurately measured by observing directly the gradual lowering of the ground elevation as a function of time. The lowering is not areally uniform; on a microscale, erosion here is offset by deposition there. The process is slow in terms of a man's span, even in a badland area (King and Melin, 1955). To judge the amount of erosion in terms of loss of a certain portion of a complete soil profile supposed to have originally existed is crude at best (though widely employed) and hardly satisfies the desire for an objective, quantitative measure.

To measure rate of degradation of a landscape by gully erosion through computation of the volume of the gully network is possible, though few good data exist. But such estimates are plagued by the importance of local deposition (temporary storage) of the eroded material in fans near the mouth of the gully (Hadley, 1954). Furthermore, there is no assurance that at least some of the gullies did not exist prior to the beginning of the period under consideration. Leopold and Miller (1954) have emphasized that many gullies in Wyoming which appear to have been formed since the opening of the West are in fact at least pre-Columbian and may be several thousands of years old.

It is theoretically possible to estimate net rate of removal of soil material from a watershed on the basis of the sediment load of the main stream draining the area. But present techniques are adequate to measure only the suspended portion of a stream's load, and then only if the material is not coarser than sand. There is no practical method at present for measuring that part of the load moving along or close to the bed of the stream. Though the suspended portion of the sediment load may constitute three-quarters or more of the total debris in many streams, the suspended load is still only a portion. The load of gravelly streams cannot be accurately measured in the channel at all.

The rate of sediment deposition in a reservoir provides the best measurement of total load and, therefore, of average denudation rates. Though some suspended sediment does not deposit in the reservoir but passes through the gates or over the spillway, this spill usually can be estimated with an accuracy commensurate with that of other necessary measurements. Currently, some four hundred reservoirs in the United States have been surveyed and have ranges established for resurvey. But this number is hardly adequate to describe the diversity of watersheds in the river basins of the United States. Moreover, reservoir surveys do not furnish information on the relative amounts of debris from various parts of the basin upstream.

Excellent measurements of rates of soil loss are available from experimental plots and watersheds, but the data cover only a small fraction of the many possible combinations of soil type, slope, and vegetal cover. Moreover, it is very difficult to extrapolate from the measurements on small areas to large natural drainage basins.

The scope of the available experimental data dealing with the interrelation of vegetation, soils, rainfall, runoff, and erosion may be judged from a review of federally sponsored research.

This represents not all, but the major portion, of such experimentation. A recent survey (Leopold and Maddock, 1954) showed that investigations by federal agencies included work on about 1,700 experimental plots and on some 560 natural watersheds, together comprising 464 experiments. Of the total, 86 per cent of the experiments dealt with areas of less than 100 acres in size. Such experiments provide a quantitative measure of the effect of particular vegetal changes on sediment production only in similar watersheds of like size.

Rate of degradation of a landscape is not measured solely by the movement of discrete particles of debris, for the constituents dissolved in the runoff water may be a significant part of the whole. Measurements of reservoir sediment deposits do not include the dissolved fraction.

Clark (1924) estimated that the annual rate of chemical denudation in the United States is approximately 100 tons per square mile, though this figure needs revision on the basis of new data. From fifty representative records of sediment yield in the United States, chosen by Glymph (1951, Table 1), the median value was 900 tons per square mile annually. It appears from this rough comparison that chemical degradation may be of the order of 10 per cent of the total. In the Wind River Basin, Wyoming (Colby *et al.*, 1955), the dissolved load of streams constitutes about 13 per cent of the total dissolved and sediment load. It is possible that dissolved loads may be more important in landscape reduction than indicated by Glymph.

Changes in water quality as a result of successive use by irrigation are well known, and in the Wind River Basin, for example, Colby *et al.* (1955, p. 192) believe that irrigation "is greatly accelerating the normal processes of erosion and transport of water-soluble minerals from the Wind River formation, alluvial terraces, and associated soils." Such effects of human activity generally apply to only portions of the drainage basin. We are forced, however, from both lack of data and lack of personal knowledge, to restrict the present discussion to landscape degradation products carried by streams as sediment.

EFFECT OF HUMAN USE

The relative extent to which human use has increased sediment yield probably varies inversely with the rate of the original yield. This is suggested by measurements and appears logical from general considerations. Brune's (1948) estimates of increase for areas in the north central states are much larger than those of Rosa and Tigerman (1951) for areas in the Colorado River Basin. The eastern edges of the prairie and the hardwood associations of the upper Mississippi were originally characterized by nearly complete vegetal cover, whereas large areas in the West and Southwest included badlands, poorly vegetated scarps, and generally low vegetation density. The well-vegetated mountain areas, though contributing most of the water, comprise only a minor part of the total drainage area.

The presettlement sediment yield of drainage basins in the West is particularly difficult to evaluate. The original density of vegetation in woodland and semidesert shrub association was characteristically low even in presettlement times. However, this low density need not necessarily be interpreted as coincident with high sediment yield. The species composition now extant is often quite different from that originally found over great areas, even where vegetation *density* has not changed appreciably. Furthermore, in the Southwest the relatively good observational record of early American exploration came only after two centuries of land use by the Spanish (Leopold, 1951). The Span-

ish were poor observers of natural history, and their records are of little use in reconstructing original conditions.

There are but few good accounts of vegetation as it affects sediment yield in areas essentially untouched until white exploration. The Lewis and Clark journals are among the best. From them we learn that the Missouri was certainly high in sediment load. But even the best expedition accounts do not provide a clear picture of where the sediment originated. Bank-cutting on the Missouri was described as an active source, but bank-cutting is usually a process of sediment-trading—erosion in one place and deposition in another.

Even in Montana, where vegetation on the plains areas is generally far more dense than that in comparable topography of the Southwest, Lewis and Clark (Coues, 1893, p. 347) made the following observation near the foot of the Bear Paw Mountains:

A high, level, dry, open plain . . . [constitutes] the whole country to the foot of the mountains. The soil is dark, rich, and fertile; yet the grass is by no means so luxuriant as might have been expected, for it is short and scarcely more than sufficient to cover the ground. There are vast quantities of prickly-pears, and myriads of grasshoppers. . . .

In the same place during a rain, they observe (*ibid.*, p. 348) that they

found the bed of a creek 25 yards wide at the entrance, with some timber, but no water, notwithstanding the rain. It is indeed astonishing to observe the vast quantities of water absorbed by the soil of the plains, which, being opened in large crevices, presents a fine rich loam.

A thorough review of the methodology and of the results of attempts to determine the total sediment yield from natural watersheds would be out of place in the present discussion. A few examples will, however, provide some picture of the difficulties involved and the possible order of magnitude of the effect of human activities on land degradation.

One technique is illustrated in a study by Brune (1948), using primarily rates of accumulation of sediment in reservoirs. By modifying these results with supplemental suspended sediment records and experimental data from plots and small watersheds, Brune derived figures on the rate of annual sediment movement from some particular drainage basins of various sizes. It is generally recognized that the sediment yield is a function of drainage-basin size even in an area of relatively uniform characteristics. But the figures on sediment yield for basins of a given size in the Brune study showed a variation of approximately a hundred times between minimum and maximum sediment yield. He attempted to relate this variation to land use as well as to physical characteristics of the individual basins. The first step was to segregate the data in terms of land use. Three categories were used to represent the percentage of the drainage area which was in cultivation. An adjustment for effect of soil type, degree of slope, length of slope, and type of rotation was made on the basis of a somewhat subjective classification of the whole area into zones chosen to represent relative uniformity in respect of these variables. A further step was to apply a factor to the sediment yield to represent the mean annual runoff.

On the basis of such analysis, Brune showed that on the average, for a drainage area of 100 square miles, in north central United States, as an example, basins within which one-third of the total area is cultivated or "idle" are characterized by a long-term sediment concentration in runoff equal to .015 per cent by weight. He concluded that the concentration is increased by six and one-half times when cultivated and "idle" land represents one-third to two-thirds of the drainage area. It is increased by thirty-five times when more than two-thirds of the drainage area is cultivated or "idle." Brune estimated that the present rate of sediment production in the Ohio and the Great Lakes drainage basins is roughly fifty times the geologic norm. He stated further (*ibid.*, p. 16) that "in the upper Mississippi River drainage basin where about 42 per cent of the land is now cultivated or idle, the present rate of sediment production and erosion is approximately seventy-five times the geologic norm."

Another approach to the problem is illustrated in a study by Gottschalk and Brune (1950). A multiple correlation was used to express the relationship between total sediment accumulation in a reservoir (considered a dependent variable) as a function of net watershed area, age of the watershed in years, rate of gross erosion, and the ratio of reservoir capacity to watershed area. The regression is greatly influenced by the value of the parameter used to represent the rate of gross erosion. Estimates of this factor were obtained by adding results of two kinds of measurements. Gully erosion was determined by field observations, using rate of gully development measured on successive aerial photographs. Sheet erosion was estimated by an empirical interrelation among average length of slope, average degree of slope, and type of cultivation, based principally on the results of plot and small-watershed experimentation.

The nature of the problem unfortunately necessitates this kind of roundabout analysis. Any studious attempt to correlate the many variables is commendable; nevertheless, we should not gloss over the fact that the results obtained can be considered nothing better than general approximations.

Still another type of methodology is illustrated by the study of Rosa and

Tigerman (1951), who attempted to estimate the sediment contribution from various portions of the Green and Colorado drainage basins. These workers began by restricting their attention to surface runoff from storms, separating out base flow. The sediment load obtained from daily averages of suspended sediment was correlated with mean daily discharge during the passage of individual hydrograph rises. Using forty such flood occurrences, a relation between sediment load and daily discharge was derived. For a given discharge the sediment load was then correlated with vegetal cover types on the watershed to which approximate values of cover condition had been assigned. It was found that there was good agreement between the estimates of sediment yield so derived and estimates based on a subjective classification map of erosion conditions compiled from general field observation. The same authors studied six small drainage basins which had different vegetal covers under varied land use. The watersheds were mapped and categorized by subjective field observations which attempted to take into account vegetal cover, erosion, soils, slope, and other factors. Sediment measures so derived were compared with analyses based on suspended-load sampling in the Boise River Basin.

Rosa and Tigerman made further comparisons with measurements on the amount of sheet erosion from infiltrometer studies where water is sprinkled onto plots varying in size from 12 by 30 inches to 6 by 12 feet. They concluded (*ibid.*, p. 17) that "if all watersheds could be improved from fair to a good condition [of vegetal cover], sedimentation rates might be expected to be reduced to about one-half of the present rate from large drainage basins. . . . If it were possible to restore all poor watershed areas to a good condition the future sedimentation would be

only one-third to one-fourth the existing rate." It should be realized, however, that such a statement can apply only to areas of uniform characteristics.

Experimental data indicate that changes in land use have a greater effect on sediment yield than on either total runoff or runoff intensity (Leopold and Maddock, 1954, p. 81). Yet it must be admitted that available data do not permit quantitative generalizations about the effect of human activity on landscape degradation. Both cultivation and grazing have, without question, for a time increased sediment yield over that obtaining in the natural or original condition, but the amount is variable and highly dependent on local conditions.

This cursory description of attempts to generalize relations of geology, topography, vegetation, and climate to sediment contribution can do no more than indicate the complexity of the problem. All the methods used are, basically, forms of correlation between observed sediment yields and several controlling factors. In any such correlations an unexplained variance remains, and this margin of error may be quite large. It is clear, therefore, that any attempt to estimate the change in sediment yield resulting from a change of the controlling variables depends for validity on the relative magnitude of the anticipated consequences of and the error inherent in describing the original condition.

The preceding discussion dealt with the problem of ascertaining the present rate of sediment production from natural watersheds. To summarize, one of the most satisfactory methods of measuring sediment yield consists of successive measurements of deposition in reservoirs adjusted for outflow of sediment on the basis of suspended-load measurements. Such measurements are available on only a small number of streams relative to the total number in the continent. The values of sediment yield may vary markedly even between basins which superficially appear similar. Some of this variation can be quantitatively accounted for by differences in type and condition of plant cover, soil, slope, and other factors. This variability, however, causes most estimates of sediment yield under virgin conditions to be quite imprecise. It is difficult, then, to know how much reliance may be placed on the computed values of sediment yield under virgin conditions. Subject to this error, the magnitude of which is unknown, the estimates available indicate that in the areas for which studies have been made human activity has increased sediment production from as little as twice to as much as fifty times the original value. These figures are meant only to indicate orders of magnitude.

EVALUATION

With this background in mind, let us examine some of the over-all implications of changes in sediment yield.

The first and most obvious economic reason for an interest in sediment yield relates to erosion on the land. So extensive is the literature on this subject that no review is attempted here. In the present context the rate of sediment removal from a watershed should not be assumed to be in direct ratio to loss of land productivity. Crop yield as it is affected by soil removal is also distinct from loss of "irreplaceable" topsoil. Baver (1950) provided a commendable way of thinking about the erosion problem when he indicated that some topsoil is replaceable. The seriousness of a given amount or rate of erosion depends on the thickness of the regolith, the kind of rock from which it is derived, and the profile characteristics—in other words, on many local factors.

That soil erosion tends to reduce soil productivity is not disputed. Gully erosion may in many places be of even greater importance than sheet erosion by reducing channel storage of runoff water and by the physical dissection of arable land. It is generally believed that sheet erosion is more important, on the average, as a sediment source than is gullying.

No extensive comment is necessary on the effects of reservoir sedimentation. The recent survey of sediment deposits in Lake Mead showed that in the first fourteen years of operation sediment deposits comprised 5 per cent of the reservoir capacity below spillway-crest elevation. The sediment weight is computed to be about two billion tons (Gould, 1951). A particularly interesting result of this survey was the information that about half of the weight of sediment deposit, or 64 per cent of the volume, consists of fine-grained material transported by turbidity currents. This indicates the importance of the fine-grained portion of the total load. Again, we can merely speculate on the question of whether soil erosion which results primarily from human use would result in increased or decreased percentage of a particular size fraction of the load.

The Lake Mead survey provides a specific example of the difficulties in interpretation of reservoir accumulation data. The allocation of the sediment to various portions of the upper Colorado Basin can be made only roughly, and it is virtually impossible to ascertain what percentage of the measured sediment yield can be attributed to effects of land use. Methods such as those described earlier represent the only available bases for estimating this quantity.

RELATION OF CHANGES IN SEDIMENT LOAD ON RIVER CHANNELS

The literature on rates of reservoir sedimentation is extensive. The economic aspects of this problem are patent.

I wish to direct attention to an aspect of the effects of sediment yield which is less well known and more speculative than the problems of accelerated erosion and reservoir sedimentation. This is the change in stream channels produced by change in sediment yield. The river channel is constructed by the river itself. The channel system is the route by which runoff and erosion products are carried from the land to the ocean or to some intermediate basin. As such, it is logical to suppose that any channel system would be of such configuration and size that it is capable of performing this function. Considerable speculation has been directed at the question of how efficient the channel net is for this function. Natural channels generally have a larger width-to-depth ratio than a semicircle, which is known to be the most efficient hydraulic cross-section for discharge of water. The fact that natural channels carry erosion products, as well as water, appears to be the underlying cause of observed channel shapes.

Increasing attention recently has been devoted to the problem of explaining river-channel characteristics. Studies of channels in general led to the conclusion that a quasi-equilibrium tends to exist between the discharge and sediment load emanating from a drainage basin and the natural channel which carries these products (Leopold and Maddock, 1953). Detailed study of a channel system of a single drainage basin confirmed this generalization and demonstrated that such quasi-equilibrium tends to characterize small headwater tributaries in youthful topography as well as the major stream channels (Wolman, 1955). A generally similar tendency for quasi-equilibrium was shown to typify even ephemeral headwater channels and rills in a semiarid area (Leopold and Miller, 1956).

The river flood plain is a particularly important feature in the equilibrium picture. The level area bordering a stream is built by the stream itself and at such a level that it is overflowed during high stage. Of greatest interest is the concept that the frequency of such overbank flow is essentially constant for small rivers and large ones in the same basin and between rivers of different basins (Wolman, 1955; Wolman and Leopold, 1956). This similarity in frequency of overflow of the flood plain, which in essence is also the frequency of the bankfull stage of the river, is a consequence of the characteristics of sediment load and sediment action in flows of various magnitudes. Small flows carry small sediment loads and are essentially ineffective in scour and deposition. The greatest floods are the most effective in shaping the channel and altering existing shape, but these extreme flows are so infrequent that, in the long run, they are less important than the lesser floods. The level of the river flood plain is, therefore, controlled primarily by floods of such magnitude that they are capable of significant erosion and deposition but still frequent enough to have cumulative effects of importance. This combination appears to characterize flows of that magnitude which recur about twice each year (Wolman, 1955; Wolman and Leopold, 1956).

This apparent consistency in the recurrence interval of bankfull floods in combination with the concept of a river channel in quasi-equilibrium lead to a provocative hypothesis: If a change occurs in the relation of sediment yield to water discharged from a drainage basin, forces exist which would, over a long period, tend to readjust the height of the flood plain, so that the frequency of the flood stage would remain constant. If activities of man, therefore, tend to increase markedly the sediment yield relative to discharge characteristics of a drainage basin, the river channel will, given sufficient time, adjust its channel in such a manner that floods over the flood plain will recur at about the same frequency which originally prevailed.

This concept has its first and primary application to the field of flood control through land management. Programs for land-use improvement generally anticipate marked reduction in sediment yield from a drainage basin. It should be expected that a consequence of this reduction of sediment would be a channel readjustment. This readjustment may be such that overbank floods do not, in the long run, occur any less seldom than originally.

However, man's work directly on river channels has been and probably will continue to be a far more important determinant of future channel conditions than the natural operation of river mechanics in response to man's changes on the watershed. It is probable that long before the effects of the latter can occur, river conditions will have been so altered by dams that the latter will be the primary factor in controlling river-channel characteristics. The degradation of the channel of the Colorado River after the construction of Hoover Dam is a well-known example of one type of change. There will probably be extensive changes of a more subtle nature distributed widely over rivers in this country as the dams, already planned, are built. Bank-cutting, channel-shifting, and other effects not so obviously connected with reservoir construction as bed degradation should be expected. In the Mississippi Basin alone ninety-six new dams are contemplated even at this time (Leopold and Maddock, 1954). This figure indicates the trend in river work. This trend can probably be expected to continue at least until the best reservoir sites have been utilized and for as long as there remains economic justification for hydroelectric and irrigation development.

Projects are considered justifiable, under present laws, if the computed benefits exceed the costs. Most projects will yield benefits equal to costs during their economic life, but there will come a time when great lengths of major river valleys will consist of reservoirs more or less filled with sediment. When that time comes, the problems of water control and of water use will be of a distinctly different character from those which concern us today, though this will not occur until several generations hence.

SUMMARY

In summary, then, we may conclude that man's use of the land can have a marked effect on sediment yield. Because of the difficulties of measurement of the initial conditions, it is extremely difficult to evaluate quantitatively this effect. Although increased erosion affects soil productivity, this effect is influenced by many variables in the dynamics of soil formation. The effects of high sediment yields on reservoir capacity are well known and have obvious economic implications. Less well known are the effects on river channels of changes in sediment yield. The present trend is toward ever increasing numbers of dams on the rivers of the United States. The effect of these structures on changes in the channels greatly overshadows the effects due to varying proportions of sediment to water produced by man's use of the land.

REFERENCES

BAVER, L. D.
    1950 "How Serious Is Soil Erosion?" *Proceedings of the Soil Science Society of America, 1950*, pp. 1–5.

BRUNE, G. M.
    1948 *Rates of Sediment Production in Midwestern United States.* (U.S. Soil Conservation Service, SCS-TP-65.)

Washington, D.C.: Government Printing Office. 40 pp.

CLARK, F. W.
1924 *The Data of Geochemistry.* (U.S. Geological Survey Bulletin No. 770.) Washington, D.C.: Government Printing Office. 841 pp.

COLBY, B. R.; HEMBREE, C. H.; and RAINWATER, F. H.
1956 *Sedimentation and Chemical Quality of Surface Waters in the Wind River Basin, Wyoming.* (U.S. Geological Survey Water Supply Paper No. 1373.) Washington, D.C.: Government Printing Office. (In press.)

COUES, ELLIOT
1893 *History of the Expedition under the Command of Lewis and Clark.* 4 vols. New York: Harper & Bros.

GLYMPH, L. M., JR.
1951 *Relation of Sedimentation to Accelerated Erosion in the Missouri River Basin.* (U.S. Soil Conservation Service, SCS-TP-102.) Washington, D.C.: Government Printing Office. 20 pp.

GOTTSCHALK, L. C., and BRUNE, G. M.
1950 *Sediment Design Criteria for the Missouri Basin Loess Hills.* (U.S. Soil Conservation Service, SCS-TP-97.) Washington, D.C.: Government Printing Office. 21 pp.

GOULD, H. R.
1951 "Some Quantitative Aspects of Lake Mead Turbidity Currents," *Society of Economic Paleontologists and Mineralogists, Special Publication No. 2*, pp. 34–52.

HADLEY, R. F.
1954 "Reconnaissance Investigations on Sources of Sediment in Southern Part of Cheyenne Basin above Angostura Dam." (Unpublished report for the Bureau of Reclamation, U.S. Geological Survey, open file.) 31 pp.

KING, N. J., and MELIN, K. R.
1956 "Sediment Accumulations in Small Reservoirs," in COLBY, B. R., *et al.*, *Sedimentation and Chemical Quality of Surface Waters in the Wind River Basin, Wyoming.* (U.S. Geological

Survey Water Supply Paper No. 1373.) (In press.)

LEOPOLD, L. B.
1951 "Vegetation of Southwestern Watersheds in the Nineteenth Century," *Geographical Review*, XLI, 295–316.

LEOPOLD, L. B., and MADDOCK, THOMAS, JR.
1953 *The Hydraulic Geometry of Stream Channels and Some Physiographic Implications.* (U.S. Geological Survey Professional Paper No. 252.) Washington, D.C.: Government Printing Office. 56 pp.
1954 *The Flood Control Controversy.* New York: Ronald Press Co. 278 pp.

LEOPOLD, L. B., and MILLER, J. P.
1954 *A Postglacial Chronology for Some Alluvial Valleys in Wyoming.* (U.S. Geological Survey Water-Supply Paper No. 1261.) Washington, D.C.: Government Printing Office. 90 pp.
1956 *Ephemeral Streams: Hydraulic Factors and Their Relation to the Drainage Net.* (U.S. Geological Survey Professional Paper No. 282A.) Washington, D.C.: Government Printing Office. 40 pp.

ROSA, J. M., and TIGERMAN, M. H.
1951 *Some Methods for Relating Sediment Production to Watershed Conditions.* (U.S. Department of Agriculture Forest Service, Intermountain Forest and Range Experiment Station Research Paper No. 26.) Washington, D.C.: Government Printing Office. 19 pp.

WOLMAN, M. G.
1955 *The Natural Channel of Brandywine Creek, Pennsylvania.* (U.S. Geological Survey Professional Paper No. 271.) Washington, D.C.: Government Printing Office. 56 pp.

WOLMAN, M. G., and LEOPOLD, L. B.
1956 *River Flood Plains: Some Observations on Their Formation.* (U.S. Geological Survey Professional Paper. Washington, D.C.: Government Printing Office. (In press.)

Physical, Chemical, and Biochemical Changes in the Soil Community

WILLIAM A. ALBRECHT[*]

For generations, the conquest of Nature has been accepted as man's prerogative. But man is a part of Nature, it being his essential environment, and unless he can find his rightful place in it he has poor hope of survival. Man's present behavior often resembles that of an over-successful parasite which, in killing its host, accomplishes also its own death.

Man's environment is the whole natural scene, the earth with its soil and water, its plants and its animals. In many places these have reached a natural balance which man disturbs at his peril.—C. L. BOYLE, "Mother Earth," *Journal of the Soil Association*, VIII (1954), 3.

INTRODUCTION

If we accept a state of natural balance, or a kind of momentary equilibrium, in the soil community at that date in its geological development when man arrived on any particular virgin scene, then man may well be viewed as a force upsetting that equilibrium. Since the soil is a temporary interlude for rocks and minerals on their way to solution and to the sea—in suspension if not in solution—man's activities in working the soil hasten the traverse by rocks from their higher potential energies and chemical dynamics to lower ones.

* Dr. Albrecht is Professor of Soils and Chairman of the Department of Soils at the University of Missouri, Columbia. In addition to his studies in the United States, he has conducted soils research in Great Britain, Australia, and on the European continent. He is the author of many articles on soils and soil fertility and is a consulting editor for publications on soils and general agriculture. For a number of years he has emphasized the need of proper soil treatment to insure healthy plants and healthy people, stressing the relation of soil fertility to human nutrition.

Increasing Populations and Soil Conservation—a Paradox

Man's survival in a situation in which he can be fed only by means of rocks and minerals en route to the sea appears to be a paradox. Those rocks must be put into solution. Their nutrient elements must be extracted from stable mineral forms. They must be brought into ionic activity in solutions if they are to be adsorbed into the soil colloidal complex and to be held there for exchange to the roots of plants upon which animals and men feed. Yet, in our concern with conservation, especially of the soil, we are apt to believe that rocks should not be allowed to weather and thus go into solution and into the sea. However, only by this dynamic behavior of rocks and minerals can life-forms survive on earth. This is a fact that cannot be gainsaid.

Soil conservation, to some degree, can reduce excessive movements to the sea of the nutrient elements after they enter into the ionic activities of solution. Under virgin conditions the minerals weathering within the soil are not moved hastily to the sea. Instead, they are quickly taken up by soil microbes and by plant roots. The accumulated organic matter resulting within and on top of the soil serves as a microbial diet of excess energy food, holding the microbial population down to the levels of the supplies of more soluble inorganic elements and nitrogen. Soluble inorganic elements are always quickly taken out of solution and made insolu-

of their passage into the sea through erosion, sewage disposal, and other ways. Man, in changing the face of the earth, has altered the soil community by moving it, both directly and indirectly, more rapidly into the sea. It is in this respect that "man's . . . behavior . . . resembles that of an oversuccessful parasite." While exploiting his soils, man is destroying his host and accomplishing slowly his own death.

Fig. 126.—Excessive erosion—man-wrought. Erosion is a symptom of a fertility level of the surface soil too low to grow cover equal to the stresses and strains of the falling rain and runoff water.

ble in the microbial and plant cells. Thereby, not much of the virgin soil and of its active chemical contents is on its way to the sea. Continuous plant cover, even in the humid regions with much water going into the soil, does not result in speedy soil depletion (Fig. 126). Neither is there a rapid soil erosion. The rates of solubles and suspensions going to sea are low.

Man must increase the rate of mineral solution if he is to feed himself. But his neglect of conservation of those soluble elements has increased the rate

The speed of these changes in the soil community brought on by man is astounding. As Sears puts it (1954, p. 959):

The earth as a separate planet is at least 2000, perhaps 3000, million years old. The species of mammal—to which we belong—has been present for only the last 30 seconds of the 24th hour of the earth's existence, while modern power technology based on fossil fuel compares with a very fast instantaneous snapshot.

For the first time in earth history, a single species has become dominant, and we are it. The power and intensity of our pressure upon environment is without precedent. Our numbers increase at the net rate—conservatively—of 1 per cent a year. This means a net gain of more than 50,000 a day, doubling in a generation. This also means increasing demand for space in which to live and move, and increasing demand for food and other necessities from the space that is left.

PHYSICAL CHANGES DUE TO
MAN'S ACTIVITIES

More Soil for Site Value, Less for Food Services

Urban man—85 per cent of the population in the United States—now uses much soil exclusively for sites on which to live and move. The remaining space on which to produce food and other biotic necessities for everyone is occupied by only 15 per cent of that population—the rural folk. In the recent shift from a rural family to an urban crowd, man has lost sight of the significance of the biological behavior and services of the soil community as our food source. With emphasis on economics, technologies, and industries, he has built big cities on soil and so exploited its site value only. The soil community has had the attention of agricultural and chemical technologies to make it more highly productive per farm operator or to hasten the rocks and minerals into solution, so as to be potentially creative of more crops and more livestock. The higher agricultural efficiency per farm worker has, in turn, made possible the urban congestion where, as the Indian said, "You ought to put a town here; nothing will grow here." Now we must soon face the dilemma of feeding ourselves on paved streets, because the rural soil community is about to be the dead victim of a parasitic, technical soil exploitation that has failed to appreciate the biological aspect of the soils in the creative business of feeding all of us. It is time that more of us paid attention to the physical, chemical, and biochemical changes wrought by man in the soil community, for soils represent either assets or liabilities for man's survival.

Physical changes which cultivated soils undergo are not sudden and readily recognized, save for occasional landslides or natural flooding-in of sands or of deposits of clay on top of the soil. Such coverings add new horizons to the top of the profile, making for abrupt transitions in texture and other properties between the top horizons. These are decided hindrances to plant root-feeding and to root penetration, and they put much soil out of cultivation. The physical changes in soils over long periods of cultivation by man are not so sudden. Rather, the changes are more insidious, with no suddenly visible symptoms of the transformation.

Man has been covering soil not only with cities but with connecting highways of concrete, to remove much soil entirely from potential food production. Alongside the soil covered by concrete, there is the right of way serving as shoulders and as drainage ditches. When a two-lane highway parallels a railroad, as is common when the railroad's location represents past experience in judicious grade selections, a strip of land as much as 25 rods wide is taken out of food production by agriculture. This represents 50 acres for every mile of such transportation facilities.

Much of our soil area is also being blotted out of service in food production by expanding urbanization. Urbanites are moving into rural areas around the cities to an increasing extent, owing to the automobile, which makes possible long commuting distances. This expansion does not represent a "back to the soil" movement aimed toward independent agricultural production by families contributing to city food supplies as well as providing their own. On the contrary, covering the soil by more urban expansion, more parking spaces, more airports, more military reservations, more defense plants, more industrial developments, and more superhighways represents a decided physical change in the soil community brought on by man. Instead of growing vegetation, loading itself with organic matter, and breaking down its rock content—the whole forming the active assembly line of food creation—the soil is shorn of this biological service and represents no more than site value. This physical change of the soil community is now one of geometric dimension and no longer one of arithmetic dimensions only.

Tillage Means Less Construction, More Destruction of the Soil

Putting virgin soil under cultivation initiates a breakdown of what may be called the "body" of the soil. Virgin soil, when plowed, takes on a granular body which only slowly slakes out under successive rains. The granular units of soil have a remarkable stability. They do not pack together under machinery traveling over the soil. The entrance of air in consequence of tillage starts microbial decay action. There is an increase in the carbon dioxide released. Runoff of rain water is slow and, instead, the rainfall filters in readily. Significant amounts of water are stored in the greater depths of the profile to support vegetative growth over extended rain-free periods.

It was this character of granular yet stable body by which the pioneer judged the potential productivity of the land when he took a handful of soil, allowed it to run between his fingers, and said, "This will be a good place to farm."

The shift in our soils to a body which rainfall disperses readily is a major physical change in the soil community. Continuously cultivated soils, when plowed and mechanically put under granular form by tillage machinery, are quickly hammered by the rainfall into surface slush. This seals the pores and prevents rapid infiltration of water. Water that would be beneficial were it stored in the soil is compelled to run off and represents not only loss of water but also a force for serious erosion of the surface, the very place where maximum returns and additions of organic residues are always made by nature to maintain potential productivity. Thus the advent of increased erosion, about which we have recently become concerned, is merely evidence of the previous breakdown of the soil body (Fig. 127).

This breakdown or degeneration of the soil body is not, however, a physical change alone. Rather is it the physical manifestation of chemical and biochemical changes which the soil suffers under tillage. It is the reverse of the soil construction under virgin conditions. The chemical force bringing about granulation of significant stability is exercised by salts of the divalent cations like calcium and magnesium, or even by the trivalent and multivalent ones. The monovalent ones, like hydrogen, sodium, potassium, and others adsorbed on the clay colloid, have quite the opposite effect, that is, they are dispersing agents rather than granulating and flocculating ones. The loss of fertility salts through crop removal, and by water percolating through the soil where increased decay under tillage has given more carbon dioxide and more acidity for their removal, represents more dispersion. Thus, granulating agencies are replaced by dispersing ones, and the soil is consequently shifted from a physically stable body to an unstable one and from one that takes water and has little erosion to one taking little water and having much erosion.

Another chemical change acting as

cause for the decreasing physical stability of the granular structure is the loss of much of the organic matter originally in the virgin soil. Tillage of the soil serves to fan the microbial fires burning out carbon and leaving instead inorganic ash of past generations of dead plants. This seasonal provision of ash by decay is the means for growing large crops. A rising delivery rate of

We could not expect to keep virgin organic matter preserved in the soil indefinitely. Its decay is a requisite for agricultural production. But more organic matter must always be returned and incorporated if production is to be maintained. Organic matter manifests pronounced physical effects on the soil in bringing about granular structure, but these are the results of chemical

FIG. 127.—Unreplenished cultivated soil contrasted with soil regularly replenished. Man's continuous cropping breaks the soil down chemically and physically to where nature fails to grow cover (*upper right*), and a single rain puts the plowed soil into slush (*lower right*). Similar cropping and manure returned regularly give the soil winter cover (*upper left*) and a granular structure holding the plow-turned farm under rain (*lower left*).

such ash, running parallel with the advance of the growing season and with the mounting temperatures, is nature's way of providing more nourishment for the growing crop in synchronization with its increasing demands. This represents a uniquely co-ordinated set of processes. This inorganic part of the soil organic matter must continue in its cycle of decay, incorporation into the new growing plants, return to the soil, and then decay again if crops are to be grown continually.

effects by both the inorganic and the organic components of the soil. The desirable physical condition of the soil is a matter not only of a fine physique. Rather is it also one of nutrition of the plants grown on that soil, of nutritional support for the fungal and bacterial crops within the soil, of the suite of inorganic nutrient elements required by the growing vegetation, and of the regular incorporation of organic matter into the soil by which alone this condition is maintained.

A physical change, this one consequent on cultivation, in the soils of humid regions is the increase in clay content of profiles when the top of the profile is truncated by erosion and when the successive cultivations cut more deeply into the lower horizon of higher clay concentrations. As a result of the truncation of the profile the physical condition gradually shifts to one of more clay (Fig. 128). Since the been, that agricultures survived longest (Fig. 129).

Soil Moisture Required for Ionic Activities That Nourish Plants

One of the physical conditions of the soil required for its proper tillage is the presence of water. Water is required in a physicochemical setting for the ionic activities of the nutrient elements and for their entrance into the

Fig. 128.—Rate of soybean growth in soils containing varying amounts of clay. More clay (*left to right in sand in glass containers*) with more adsorptive capacity to hold calcium for the soybean roots gave more and healthier plants. Soils "heavy" in clay have supported crops longest under cultivation.

deeper horizons, or the more acid subsoils, are less fertile in both inorganic and organic essentials, the top layer gradually becomes not only less tillable because of the high clay content but also less productive. If this increase in clay content were an addition of a more fertile or less weathered clay, then the gradual change would be an asset rather than a liability (Fig. 128). Potentially, the more clay, the more active fertility that can be held. It was on the fertile clay soils of some parts of the Old World, intractable and difficult to cultivate though they may have plant roots, into the microbial cells, and into the other living forms within the soil. It is in the aqueous atmosphere, or the very thin film of water, surrounding the colloidal clay particles that the chemodynamics of the nutrient elements occur. It is in that limited area that the positively charged elements like calcium, magnesium, potassium, sodium, hydrogen, and others—when once broken out of the rock and put into solution—are held rather than lost to the water passing through the soil. It is within that atmosphere, blended into the corresponding colloidal atmosphere of the root hair enshrouded by its hydrogen carbonate, that the root exchanges its very active hydrogen for any of the list of the clay's nutrient cations just cited. Water is then the ionizing medium required in any fertile soil so that its nutrient salts may be active suites of many essentials serving in proper nutrition of different plant species.

Fertile soils must contain the salts

trated general farming—they do not contain enough moisture to serve together with air to complete an electrical circuit when the radio switch is turned.

Droughts Are Becoming More Disastrous

Man has changed decidedly the high degrees of fluctuation against which the moisture content of the surface soils

FIG. 129.—Tillage of clay soils in France. Heavy clay soils in the Old World (France) require much power for tillage but have supported agriculture over the many years.

in the presence of water if the electrical performances of exchange between the root and the soil are to occur. As an interesting and suggestive illustration, there is in the United States a close similarity between the areas of maximum concentration of farming and of high efficiency of radio reception (Fig. 130). Areas of excessive soil moisture are neither good for farming nor good for radio reception. Such soils are too highly developed, and their fertility salts are too nearly washed out. While arid soils contain plenty of salts for radio reception—though not necessarily in the proper combination for concen-

was once maintained. For the pioneer farmer in the eastern United States, water in excess, or standing water, was the problem. He concerned himself seriously with drainage, in order to allow air to enter the soil and the sun's heat to raise its temperature for crop production. Now that we have cleared the land so that little permanent plant cover is left to hold the water where it falls, we have unwittingly moved into excessive drainage. Hasty runoff by water cuts small rills into our barren soils, and each is soon the equivalent of a drainage ditch. Our land areas, now cut up into smaller units,

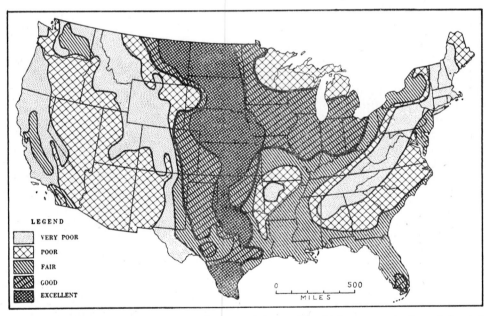

FIG. 130a.—Land in farms in the United States, 1945

FIG. 130b.—Ground conductivity in the United States. The higher concentration of farms in the mid-continent and the higher efficiency of radio reception there are both the result of the higher concentration of chemical dynamics in the soil by which, respectively, larger crops are grown and the soil is a better conductor.

make each owner thereof an opponent of standing water, scarcely permitting it to stand long enough for infiltration sufficient to provide water for crops from one rain to the next.

Our hydrophobia is exhibited by the drainage ditch alongside every highway and roadway draining each unit of land area. All-weather roads to fulfil automobilist demands have encircled about every section, however small, of productive land. Those drainage ditches, dug to depths of three or more feet around a square mile, have lowered the water table to nearly that extent. They have literally lifted the soil that much higher out of contact with the water table. This is desiccating our soil and our country. Roots are not nourished by a dry soil, and we are bringing the deserts around ourselves by hastening the drying of the surface soil. Unfortunately, that soil layer so highly dried is also the soil horizon to which both man and nature are most regularly adding and returning the fertility elements so as to maintain production.

Man's excessive drainage and change of soil conditions under which less water enters the profile to store itself are the reasons why there is less water to evaporate and so hold down summer temperatures, which, consequently, rise to record-breaking figures year by year. Our drought disasters have pushed themselves eastward into the national treasury, while the western deserts are on a rapid march eastward, too.

Shortage of Stored Water Is Increasing

That the deserts are on the march, because man has been changing the earth to absorb less water from rainfall, is a physical phenomenon with significant chemical and biochemical consequences. Temperature falls when the evaporation of a gram of water spends 540 calories of heat, but that reduction

of temperature fails to take place when there is no soil water to evaporate. Consequently, the thermometer climbs to the disaster point for plants and animals. This amounts to giving us record-breaking heat waves, commonly characterized by the broad term "drought," as if it were a matter wholly of weather when we are bringing it on ourselves.

Droughts are not just rain-free periods. They cannot be defined from standard meteorological observations, since the intensity and the length of the drought depend on characteristics of crops, soil water, and soil-fertility conditions as well as on meteorological parameters. Consequently, we need to recognize the soil as a major factor in those disturbances to crops which we call "droughts." These are in reality dry periods that bring about crop disaster through chemical and biochemical irregularities.

Since water's services to plants are exercised mainly after rain water has entered the soil, the soil should be considered more than merely a water reservoir. The many services of water to crops need to be understood before we use water shortage as the alibi for poor crops.

Continental Effects of Climate Are Becoming More Severe

The areas between the humid and the semiarid soil regions are the climatic settings for most droughts. In general, these are regions of mineral-rich soils, since low rainfall has not developed them excessively or removed the calcium and other minerals of similar soil behavior from the profile to replace them by hydrogen. These are the soils where agriculture grows protein-rich forages, where soils are wind-blown, and where animals grow readily on what are apt to be called "the prairie and the plains soils."

Droughts are also geographically located in the midst of larger land areas where the effects of what is called "continentality" are pronounced. This represents the degree of variability of the weather or the daily meteorological condition. The larger the body of land, that is, the more continental the area, the more the weather or the daily condition will vary from the climate or average. This is the "law of continentality" in brief. Droughts, then, are "continental" manifestations and may be expected more commonly in the mid-continent of the United States.

Columbia, Missouri, for example, is reported to have an annual rainfall of 39.33 inches. This mean annual rainfall from records covering nearly a half-century says nothing about how high or how low the amount for any single year may be. Because of the continentality of Missouri—it being located a thousand miles from any seacoast—Columbia, according to recorded data, has a continentality effect of 50 per cent. That is, while the rainfall is reported to average 40 inches, it actually varies over a range of 50 per cent, namely, 25 per cent, or 10 inches, below 40; and 25 per cent, or 10 inches, above 40. Precipitation ranges, then, from a low of 30 inches to a high of 50 inches in different years.

But that figure, once established for continentality, is the fact no longer. The record was broken in 1953, when the annual rainfall was but 25.12, rather than 39.33 inches, or 36.1 per cent below the mean. This is a continentality effect of twice 36.1, or 72.2 per cent.

If one considers the rainfall for only the summer months of 1953—May to September, inclusive—when the effects of the extended rain-free period on vegetation were exaggerated by high temperatures, then Columbia, Missouri, suffered under a continentality effect amounting to 86 per cent. This was a most severe disaster to an agricultural area devoted extensively to livestock and heavily dependent on grass for their feed. The law of climatic averages applied to Missouri may leave us content, but the law of continentality is disturbing, yet revealing, when droughts such as that of 1953 are experienced in record-breaking dimensions.

We have, to repeat, been bringing our droughts, as they represent shortage of supplies of soil water, upon ourselves. Droughts are disastrous in terms of deficiency of that liquid mineral in the soil and, thereby, of the food it grows. The more fertile, high-protein-producing soils are exhibiting the more serious droughts. Man is thus pushing himself off the soils which are best for nutrition. He is crowding himself into areas of higher rainfall and onto soils yielding feeds and foods of high-fattening rather than high-feeding values. He has not noticed this, since hidden hunger is registering all too slowly. But now that he is crowding himself out of drink, which registers more quickly, since thirst is more speedily lethal than hunger, droughts take on more meaning. Droughts, moreover, are moving from the country to the towns and to the cities, where they are known as water shortages. They register as thirst disasters, regardless of whether humans or vegetation are concerned.

Fertility Shortages Are Confused with Water Shortages

The shortage of plant nutrition for our crops has too commonly been mistaken for water shortage. When the farmers said, "The drought is bad, since the corn is 'fired' for four or five of the lower leaves on the stalk," they were citing the plant's translocation of nutrients, especially nitrogen, from the lower, older, nearly spent leaves in order to maintain the upper, younger, and growing leaves. Now that we can apply fertilizer nitrogen along with other nutrient elements, we know that in the confusion about plant nutrition we made too much of the drought as a direct shortage of liquid for the plants, at the expense of the more common deficiency of nitrogen to be synthesized into protein and all that compound represents in crop production.

In this case the shortage of nutrition in the soil and not of water was responsible for what was called "drought." With the drying-out of a fertile surface soil underlain by an acid, infertile clay horizon, the roots of the crops were compelled to leave the surface horizon that originally provided both fertility and water and to penetrate into the subsoil, which had water but no qualities of fertility. That shallow surface layer was dried not only by the sun's heat but also by the roots of the growing crop—corn, for example, being estimated to take from 0.15 to 0.25 of an inch of water per day by transpiration alone (Decker, 1954). Some hold that 0.10 inch of water is transpired daily by a corn crop, and so they define a drought for corn as rainfall of less than an inch every ten days. This gives no consideration to the soil fertility concerned. When the lower leaves of a cornstalk "fire," we need only to note the growing tip of the stalk, which will be wilted too if water shortage is responsible. The growing tip will not commonly be wilted, since the roots, going deeper into the subsoil, are delivering water to maintain that active plant part (Albrecht, 1954a).

Data from the Soil Conservation Research project at McCredie, Missouri, compiled during the drought of 1953, showed the corn crop exhausting the soil moisture to a depth of 3.5 feet where the soil was well fertilized. The equivalent of only 1.04 inches of water remained in that entire depth. Where the soil was not fertilized, the crop dried the soil to a lesser depth, leaving the equivalent of 4.5 inches of water in the upper 3.5 feet. On the unfertilized corn, which took a total of 14 inches of water from the soil, the yield was only 18 bushels per acre. It required 26,000 gallons of water to make a bushel of grain. On the fertilized soil, with a yield of 79 bushels, only 5,600 gallons of water per bushel were required. The drought was a case of plant hunger rather than one of plant thirst (Albrecht, 1954c).

Soil's Physical and Chemical Changes Are Becoming Biochemically Intolerable

That water shortage in the soil is detrimental to biochemical activities in the crops and in the animals was demonstrated in the mid-continental drought of 1954. The effects of that disaster on the different levels of soil fertility of the plots on Sanborn Field, at the Missouri Agricultural Experiment Station, suggested forcefully that drought disturbs plant processes because of high temperatures. It suggested also a more severe injury to plant tissues according as the higher soil fertility represented more actively growing plants (*ibid.*).

Where corn had been grown continuously since 1888 with crop removal and no soil treatment, the plants remained the greenest of all corn plots on the entire field. Only the lower two leaves on the stalks were "fired." The other eight leaves, though much rolled, showed no visible irregularities. The stalks were tasseled but were without shoots. This was about the customary "short" crop which that plot has been producing for many years.

On the adjoining plot, where 6 tons of manure per acre annually have been used, the much taller and heavier stalks had the lower five leaves badly "fired." The remaining six leaves were rolled, but they were not visibly injured. The stalks were well tasseled, but the plants were without shoots, suggesting no grain production.

The physiological strain on these dioecious plants by the heat seemingly did not disrupt the masculine efforts of the plant to reproduce but eliminated the female contribution to the survival of the species. This suggests that the female phase of reproduction is a much heavier physiological load or a more extensive integration of biochemical processes than is the male phase.

On another near-by plot where heavy crop residues are turned under and the soil given full fertilizer treatment—including nitrogen—only a single lower leaf per plant was "fired." The other thirteen or more leaves were closely bunched on the shortened stalk. The tassel had not emerged. Neither were there any shoots or signs of ears. More significant, however, was the fact that the leaves were badly bleached from their tips back to almost their midlength. This part of the leaf tissue was dead. Save for its widely different appearance, the damage duplicated the pattern of the leaf area involved when the plant suffers from nitrogen deficiencies in the soil. It suggested death in the area where the extra nitrogen was involved in rapid growth rather than where there was a deficiency of it.

Since the more vigorous plant growth for seed production involves more physiological functions than growth for fodder production only, it seems reasonable that high temperatures might be more disturbing to the living processes centered in the expectably higher protein content of the cells than to those in plants growing less vigorously and doing little more than making the minimum of carbohydrates. Processes of growth and life are activated by enzymes, compounds resembling proteins in some respects. They are decidedly thermolabile, or are killed by temperatures going above 45° C. (113° F.). The proteins of vigorously growing plants may not be very widely different in their responses to high temperatures from fertile eggs under incubation. Eggs give a good hatch when the temperature is held at 100° F. But a few hours at 10° F. above that temperature will ruin the hatch even if the egg protein is not coagulated or coddled. No signs of injury are visible until the egg dies and processes of decomposition have had time to give the evidence. In the case of the corn leaf, time was also required for the disturbed plant metabolism to reveal itself.

High Temperatures Disrupt Biochemical Processes and Result in Death of Plants and Animals

This disruption of the metabolic processes in the leaves of corn plants was not corrected by the next rain, which moved nitrogen, for example, as nitrate from the revived soil into the corn plants. Also, this nitrate was not reduced significantly. Nor did it move well up into the plant and become changed into organic forms of nitrogen. Instead, it accumulated toward the lower part of the stalk. Those concentrations were high enough to be lethal to the cattle consuming the fodder. More than two hundred head of cattle were reported killed in the state of Missouri as a result of this biochemical irregularity in the corn plants due to the disruption of physiological processes when the air temperatures went above 110° F.—and this because there was not enough water stored in the soil.

Some other biochemical disturbances resulted from the high temperatures. The heat wave in Missouri in 1954 was disastrous to animals as well as to plants, killing both poultry and rabbits. The correlation of increasing temperatures with increasing deaths of experimental rabbits fed on wheat in conjunction with hay grown on soil of different treatments suggested that the nutrition of the animal and not the high temperature per se was the responsible factor in the fatalities associated with the heat.

Seven lots of nine rabbits each, separated from the larger original group, were fed on wheat of a single lot and on timothy hays grown on soil given different treatments: (1) full fertilizer treatment; (2) this supplemented by copper; (3) by boron; (4) by cobalt; (5) by manganese; (6) by zinc; and (7) by all these trace elements.

With the mounting temperatures of the heat wave, many of the experimen-

and a mean maximum of 99.4° F. during the fortnight closing July 17.

On that date the wheat–timothy hay ration was supplemented with 10 grams per rabbit per day of commercial, dried skim-milk powder. No more deaths occurred during the extension of the experiment for nine days, where maximum daily temperatures ranged from 89° to 111° F., with a mean high of 98.2° F.

A repeat of this test was started on July 26, using corn, oats, and wheat in

Sanborn Field, Missouri Agricultural Experiment Station

Fig. 131.—The difference in quality between legumes seeded in manured soil and those seeded in soil without manure. Sixty years of cropping resulted in chemical and biochemical effects differing according to a six-year rotation with manure (*Plot 12, left*) and without manure (*Plot 13, right*), as illustrated by the difference in emergence of newly seeded legume.

tal rabbits died, and, at the weighing dates after each fortnight, replacements were made from those remaining in the original group (which had suffered no heat fatalities) fed on the same wheat as the experimental rabbits, but on the roughage of green grass growing on soil fertilized with rabbit manure. During the period June 11–July 17, 1954, a total of fifty-seven rabbits (70 per cent) died on the timothy-wheat ration, while in the same room there were no deaths among the original group remaining on their wheat-grass ration and tolerating the same heat wave. This represented maxima ranging from 88° to 113° F.

equal parts by weight along with the same timothy hays. This trial exhibited again the fatalities with the high temperatures until August 23, when the feeding of the timothy hay was discontinued and red-clover hay substituted. No deaths occurred during the extension of this test with red-clover hay from August 23 to September 6, during which the maxima of temperatures ranged from 79° to 102° F., with a mean maximum of 97.6° F. for those fourteen days. For the fortnight preceding the date of change to red clover, the maxima ranged from 70° to 98° F., with a mean maximum of 82.5° F. At the close of this test there still remained all eight rabbits of the original group kept on the wheat-grass ration during the entire summer.

These deaths of the experimental rabbits represent differing fatalities according to nutrition of the animal. They were merely another part in the reaction chain of many biochemical processes pointing to man's manipulations of the soil community to his own detriment, whereas, ultimately, the soil must give the nutrition of all life (Fig. 131).

CHEMICAL CHANGES DUE TO MAN

Man's Survival Demands Reconstructive Changes in the Soil Community

Man has pulled down the levels of virgin-soil fertility to the point where those predatory acts will not continue to feed him and his growing numbers.

Courtesy of United States Forest Service

Fig. 132.—The development of mesquite as a result of soil exploitation. Soil exploitation by livestock removal and reduced return of organic matter brought in the mesquite (*lower photo, 1943*) where forty years previously there had been a cattleman's paradise (*upper photo, 1903*).

He must now change his soil communities physically, chemically, and biochemically by construction instead of by continued destruction. Instead of exploiting nature's work, he must now co-operate in re-establishing that work.

We may well observe the principles underlying natural conservation and be guided by them toward wiser soil management (Fig. 132). The study of man's exploitation of soil under agricultural cropping reveals resulting chemical soil conditions similar to those where excessive development has resulted naturally under higher rainfall. Our exploitation of soils under higher rainfall and lower temperatures was less rapid than that of soils under similar rainfall and higher temperatures. Virgin soils in the northeastern United States, with clays of high exchange capacity and much acidity, suffered less exploitation under cultivation than that by virgin soils of equal clay content, less exchange capacity, and less acidity but developed under similar rainfall and higher temperatures in the southeastern United States. Soils farther west, developed under corresponding longitudinal temperatures but under lower rainfalls, like those near the mid-continent, soon ap-

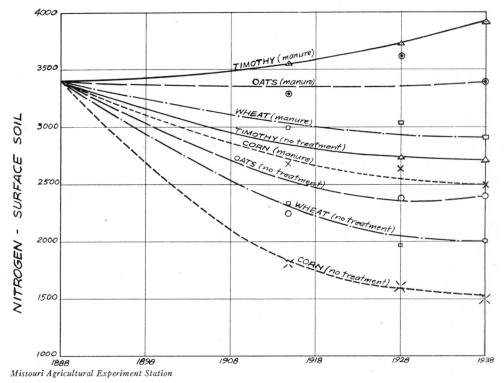

Missouri Agricultural Experiment Station

Fig. 133.—Some declines in the total nitrogen of the soil during fifty years of continuous cropping with and without manure.

proach (under exploitation) the fertility array illustrated in soils farther east but naturally more highly developed under higher rainfalls (Albrecht, 1951b, p. 384). When man uses the soil under rainfalls generous enough for large crop yields, he depletes the fertility rapidly. He encourages leaching to enlarge its toll. He brings the soil to a much higher degree of development and more rapidly than nature would under his absence in that climatic setting (Fig. 133). Its depletion leads him to believe that the climate (average of weather) has become worse in terms of the contrast between the nutritional quality of the present vegetation and of that which was virgin in the area. The vagaries of the weather are much more disastrous to his agriculture via poorer soil as poor nutrition than they once were. Nutrition in the fullest sense must, then, be declining along with the fertility of the soil and with the successive harvests of crops.

Successive stages of increasing soil development under higher rainfall give decreasing soil fertility under natural conditions. The increasing rainfall (temperatures constant) in the United States as we go east toward the Atlantic from the soils that once grew proteins for the bison's body makes for a decreasing supply of the total essential elements coming from the soil as nutrition for microbes, plants, animals, and men. However, the relative decrease in supply of calcium, which element the soils must give generously for the production of protein-rich forages (illustrated by lime for legumes and better grasses), is much greater than the decrease in potassium, which serves in the plant's production of carbohydrates. Thus, with increasing soil development, the fertility supporting the plant's biosynthetic processes of converting the carbohydrates into protein is lost first (relatively high calcium loss from the soil), while the fertility supporting the photosynthesis of carbohydrates continues to give crops of considerable vegetative bulk (illustrated by sufficient potassium).

The changing ratio between amounts of calcium and potassium shifts the ecological pattern from the grasses and legumes of high nutritional value per acre (providing proteins along with carbohydrates for the original herds of bison) eastward to deciduous forests able to support only a few browsing animals and then to the coniferous for-

ests on which even such life cannot survive. This is a principle of soil fertility in relation to the climatic pattern of natural soil development that controls the ecological patterns of different life-forms via protein production by the soil. It tells us to expect the nutritional values to dwindle as we intensify the soil's use without concern about maintaining fertility adequate for the plant composition and the food values we expect the soil to deliver. This principle is basic in outlining the rebuilding of the soil now that almost every corner of the earth has been exploited.

Managed Agriculture Demands Uplift and Integration of More Soil Factors than the Limiting One

Attempts to offset exploitation of the soil have brought on the practice of using chemical and mineral fertilizers. A major practice is the liming of the soil (originally to remove soil acidity) in order to restock it with calcium and magnesium (Fig. 134). These two elements are required in the highest active amounts within the soil for exchange to the plant roots. Phosphorus has been used both as the natural mineral and in chemically treated forms. Others, like potassium, serving among the cations in smaller active amounts in the soil, are now more commonly required as treatment if soils are to produce. Nitrogen, a fertilizer of the crop more than of the soil, and available now as the result of advances in chemical processing of this inert gaseous element from the atmosphere, is serving extensively as a soil treatment. It has two alternatives: (1) offsetting soil exploitation when we purposely use nitrogen to build up the organic matter in the soils at the same time that the crop production is increased and (2) increasing soil exploitation for increased crop production in disregard of the need to rebuild soils in both their organic and their inorganic essentials (Fig. 135).

In line with the latter view of increased production by soil treatments, research in soil chemistry and plant nutrition has made progress in its efforts to offset soil exploitation in the inorganic essentials. Experimental studies using colloidal clay as the medium for well-controlled plant nutrition have demonstrated that differences in the bohydrates but also differences in the sugars, starches, hemicelluloses, etc., composing them. Likewise, the ratios of the different amino acids composing the proteins, and the amino nitrogen, as part of the total nitrogen, will be variable according as the ratios and amounts of inorganic fertility are varied for movement into the root as plant nourishment from the soil (Reed, 1953).

Up to this moment the operation in

Fig. 134.—Field of soybeans spotted by streaks of better crops where calcium compounds were supplied. Liming the soil serves the crop because it fertilizes with calcium (or magnesium) and not because it reduces soil acidity. Streaks of better crops of soybeans resulted (*right to left*) from (*a*) calcium chloride, (*b*) calcium nitrate, and (*c*) calcium hydroxide because they all provided calcium and not because each (*a*) made the soil more acid, (*b*) made it more acid, or (*c*) made it less acid.

ratios of the several inorganic fertility elements active on this soil fraction bring about differences in both the proteins and the carbohydrates as plant composition. Thus, by different ratios, or variable balance, of calcium and potassium, we can grow either much plant bulk mainly of high carbohydrate with low protein content or, vice versa, less bulk of higher protein concentration and low carbohydrate content. By varying the fertility ratio in only these two cations in the soil, there are brought about not only different amounts of car- agriculture of this basic principle of soil fertility in relation to crop production has exemplified itself in (1) the introduction of crops mainly for increased yields of carbohydrates and in (2) managed crop composition and improved yield under the program of testing of soils for the appropriate application of inorganic fertility. While the introduction of the corn hybrids covered itself with some semblance of glory, their yield increase comes at the loss of their power to procreate themselves by their own seed. They suffer also in being of lesser value in animal nutrition because of their reduced concentration of crude protein and its deficiency in certain required amino acids, notwithstanding their reputation as the crop giving high farm income.

More particularly, the principle of the ratios to one another of the many active

for production of plants of certain nutritional value in their proteins in balance with their carbohydrates as well as (2) generous total yields of them mainly as carbohydrates per acre (*ibid.*).

As a result, 75 per cent of the soil's exchange capacity might well be satu-

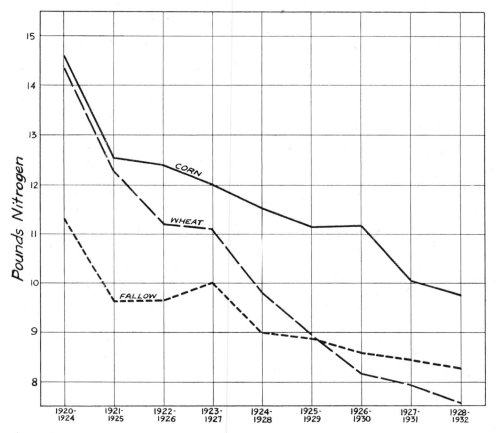

Fig. 135.—Biochemical activities in the soil, as illustrated by the level of nitrate nitrogen during the growing season for advancing five-year means, show serious decline under soil exploitation by tillage without soil restoration.

inorganic fertility elements in the soil for control of the biosynthetic services by crops has offered decided promise when applied in relation to increased protein production along with the carbohydrates. Thus we can use the soil to grow more nearly balanced nutrition. It has given us the concepts of (1) specific ratios of active fertility elements

rated by calcium; 7.5–10 per cent by magnesium; and 2.5–5 per cent by potassium for the growth of forages rich in protein and carrying also the quota of the many other inorganic elements— the vitamins, enzymes, hormones, and other essential compounds associated with proteins and required for proper animal nutrition. Thus, via soil management, there becomes possible the production of crops with nutritional purposes in mind. By such management soil moves into the food-creating category rather than growing only filler feeds for fattening values (Albrecht, 1954*b*).

While man has been bringing about destructive chemical changes in his soil community, he has also learned much about constructive soil management. This is the exception rather than the rule in practice. It is hoped that constructive soil management will dominate, so that improved soil communities will result in better nutritional support of man. Research evidence from soil study has outlined many essentials, pointed out hazards, and suggested the high costs of maintaining a soil community for the continued nutrition of sedentary man (Figs. 136 and 137).

BIOCHEMICAL CHANGES IN THE SOIL COMMUNITY VIA MAN

When the soil community is viewed as a biochemical entity, we recognize within it many microscopic living forms and their life-processes, including the use by the plant roots of the sunlight on the plant top to derive energy. Plant roots bring a stream of carbon dioxide down into the soil by way of their respiration. To this, there is added what comes from the microbial forms oxidizing the returned organic remains. Consequently, the soil air represents a concentration of 1 per cent of carbon dioxide, to give a high acid concentration along with all the other decomposition products of both catabolic and anabolic origin. The exploitation of the soil in disregard of a generous return of organic matter represents biochemical destruction of the virgin soil much in advance of, and in a higher degree than, that under chemical and physical exploitation. Unfortunately, our observations on the biochemical changes of the soil community have been few. The

tools for their recognition and critical inventory have not yet been so plentifully designed. When inorganic chemistry has developed as a phase of soil science so late, we should not be surprised that organic chemistry has not yet turned its light more strongly on plant physiology as modified by the organic aspects of the soil.

Because we can grow certain plants in water cultures of purely chemical salts, the erroneous conclusion has been drawn that plants do not therefore take organic compounds from the soil for their physiological service. Plant studies have demonstrated that a great variety of organic compounds is absorbed by the plant root from the soil, since their soluble amounts within the soil may represent as high a concentration as that of the inorganic compounds (Miller, 1938, p. 297). A long list of carbohydrates has been assembled from tests, showing them taken up by the roots and serving the plant as an energy source in the absence of light.

With the addition of certain vitamins to sterile, mineral-nutrient solutions, excised root tips have been grown over long periods of time in the dark with sugars, via root absorption, supplying the energy (Robbins and Schmidt, 1938). Organic acids are also absorbed by plant roots. Nitrogen in organic compounds is no exception when the extensive list of amino acids may serve as well as many other organic nitrogenous compounds. These experiments suggest that organic substances very commonly supplement, but in few cases replace, the inorganic nitrogenous salts. But, when man and his herds have been so closely associated and interdependent on soils (Albrecht, 1952*a*), the return of the animal manure may have been more significant in terms of organic compounds returned for crop production than we commonly recognize. Manures suggest fertility values transcending those represented by their ash contents only.

Fig. 136.—Trends of yields of corn and wheat under various treatments with "nothing" returned to the soil (*above*), compared with yields where manure, limestone, phosphate, and potash were combined (*below*).

Observations are accumulating to suggest that, in the synthesis by plants of the proteins complete in all the essential amino acids for man and his livestock, some organic compounds must be returned to the soil or kept in cycle. It seems a logical theory that, for the synthesis of the more complex amino acids by the plants, some complex organic compounds must be absorbed from the soil as starter compounds (Albrecht, 1952b). For example, this seems a suitable theory in regard to that very commonly deficient

NONE   75   150   300   600

NONE   75   150   300   600

Photos courtesy of John Bushnell, Ohio Agricultural Experiment Station

FIG. 137.—The effects of different chemical fertilizers on the growth quality of plants. Chemical fertilizers manifest wide differences in their chemical and biochemical effects at the same rates of application: ammonium sulfate (*above*) and superphosphate (*below*).

amino acid—tryptophan. The indole ring seems to be a requisite when bean plants have demonstrated their absorption of this compound from the soil and have deposited it into the seed, with the fecal odor of the indole detectable there. It is also significant when the indole ring is so much of the indole-acetic acid and related compounds serving as the major growth hormone of plants (Thimann, 1954).

The significance of indole as a fecal waste, resulting from the digestion of the amino acid tryptophan, impressed itself in some observations on the vol-

unteer weed crops and the planted bean crops in the sand of abandoned, experimental cat pens (Fig. 138). The cats had buried their dung during two years while being kept under study for differential development because of a cooked diet in which milk was the only variable. The cats were segregated in pens according as they were fed on (1) condensed, (2) evaporated, (3) pasteurized, and (4) raw milk. No other soil treatment or fertilizer was used (Pottenger, 1946).

The weeds, showing wide differences in amount of growth, were removed,

Photos courtesy of Francis M. Pottenger, Jr., M.D.

FIG. 138.—The effects derived from controlled diets on the growth quality of a weed and a bean crop. Cat dung, buried in sand during two years of experimental feeding of male cats on evaporated milk (*left*) and raw milk (*right*), when all else in the diet was cooked and constant, brought differences in the volunteer weed crop (*upper photos*) and shifted the "dwarf" bean to a "pole" bean (*lower photos*).

and each of the pens (male cats separate from the female) planted with two rows of a "dwarf" bean, all from the same lot of seed. Wherever the cat's diet contained the heated milks, the plant growth characters were those of what one would call the "bush" or the "dwarf" kind of bean. But, where the dung from the cats fed the raw milk was the fertilizer, the plants were "pole" beans, with vines climbing the screened sides as high as 6 feet.

Since the indole odor was present in the seeds of the dwarf-bean plants and no such odor was detectable in the seeds of the pole-bean plants, there is the suggestion that intake of the cooked milk led to excretion of indole by the cats, its absorption by the roots of the bean plants, and its mobilization without change into the seed, where the protein would be the expected deposit guaranteeing survival of the plant species. There is the suggestion that drinking the raw milk also led to indole excretion, but there followed its later synthesis into indoleacetic acid as a hormone to shift the "dwarf" growth characters of the ancestor beans into the "pole" growth characters. There may have followed the synthesis of some of the indole into tryptophan and its deposition into the seed, for which no tests were made.

All this points up that there are some biochemical behaviors in the soil related to plant nutrition and to animal nutrition in a degree of refinement we have not yet envisioned. It raises the question whether man did not bring on serious disturbances in the nutritional values of his foods coming via animals, plants, microbes, and the soil when he put the plow ahead of the cow to the point where he has now almost forgotten the cow. This question is all the more challenging, since the nomad had the cow ahead of the plow as a kind of perambulating soil-tester for its health and reproduction, to say nothing of the nomad's, and since prevailing degenerative human diseases are now suggesting that we ought to expect such troubles in accepting in our nutrition almost any foods on caloric values alone and "crude" proteins in our nutrition in place of the complete array of required amino acids (Figs. 139 and 140).

Man has become aware of increased needs for health preservation, interpreted as a technical need for more hospitals, drugs, and doctors, when it may be simply a matter of failing to recognize the basic truth in the old adage which reminded us that "to be well fed is to be healthy." Unfortunately, we have not seen the changes man has wrought in his soil community in terms of food quality for health, as economics and technologies have emphasized its quantity. Man is exploiting the earth that feeds him much as a parasite multiplies until it kills its host. Slowly the reserves in the soil for the support of man's nutrition are being exhausted. All too few of us have yet seen the soil community as the foundation in terms of nutrition of the entire biotic pyramid of which man, at the top, occupies the most hazardous place.

SUMMARY

The physical, chemical, and biochemical changes in the soil community brought about by man have represented soil destruction so much more than soil construction that they have brought into sharp focus the problem of food for population numbers mounting geometrically. This focus is all the sharper when land areas are not only shrinking as areas but in food quality per unit produced.

Man has changed the soil to reduce its services in the absorption and storage of rainfall. These changes have increased our droughts. Those are now starting—from the soil—a set of chain reactions amounting to near-national

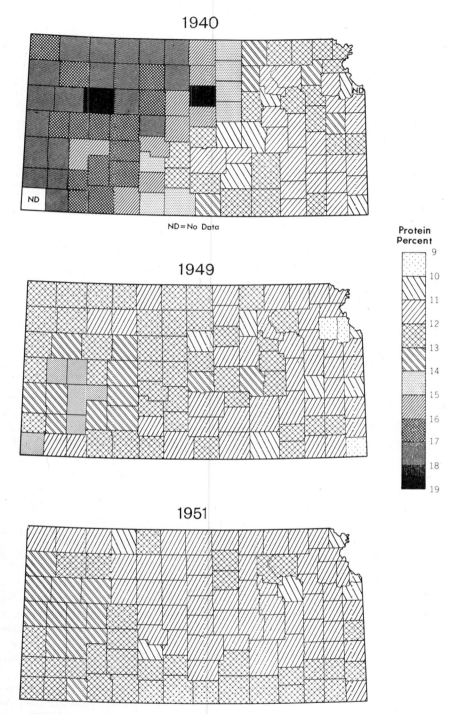

FIG. 139.—The concentration of crude protein in the wheat of Kansas, by county averages, has been declining during successive years of sampling.

emergencies. The soil exploitation, destructive of that creative resource, is lowering the quality per unit of agricultural output. Lowered protein content of crops grown is the major single, summarized report of what man has brought about via the several soil changes.

When the population pressures on ogy for us to manage conservatively all the natural phenomena via agricultural soils. In consequence, continued soil exploitation must eventually be recognized as causative of many biotic manifestations which are simply hidden hungers originating in the deficiencies of the soil. As the shrinkage of the supporting soil areas under each of us con-

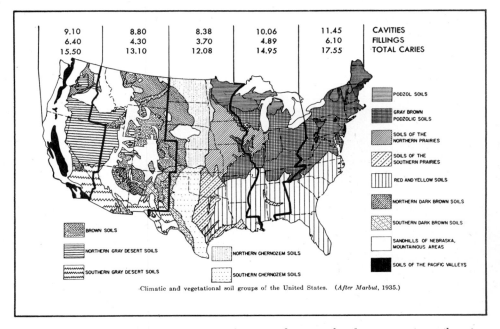

9.10	8.80	8.38	10.06	11.45	CAVITIES
6.40	4.30	3.70	4.89	6.10	FILLINGS
15.50	13.10	12.08	14.95	17.55	TOTAL CARIES

PODZOL SOILS

GRAY BROWN PODZOLIC SOILS

SOILS OF THE NORTHERN PRAIRIES

SOILS OF THE SOUTHERN PRAIRIES

RED AND YELLOW SOILS

NORTHERN DARK BROWN SOILS

SOUTHERN DARK BROWN SOILS

SANDHILLS OF NEBRASKA, MOUNTAINOUS AREAS

SOILS OF THE PACIFIC VALLEYS

BROWN SOILS

NORTHERN GRAY DESERT SOILS

SOUTHERN GRAY DESERT SOILS

NORTHERN CHERNOZEM SOILS

SOUTHERN CHERNOZEM SOILS

Climatic and vegetational soil groups of the United States. *(After Marbut, 1935.)*

FIG. 140.—Results of teeth examinations of Navy inductees related to respective soil regions. The above numbers revealed cavities, fillings, or total caries per inductee, as a mean, of 69,584 inductees into the Navy in 1942 from respective soil regions. These were lowest in the mid-continent of moderate development of the soil according to the climatic forces but were higher to the west, with underdevelopment under low rainfall, and higher also to the east, with overdevelopment and higher rainfall.

the soil give it no rest for natural reconstruction, and when the farmer's economic entanglements similarly preclude such rest, the depletion of the fertility of the soil, by which it gives biochemical as well as chemical activities in food service, must push this service to a lower and lower potential.

Science, having given so much to technology, has not yet collected and organized enough knowledge of biol- tinues, or as more of our lifelines back to the soil are shortened and severed, we hope we shall gather sufficient knowledge soon enough to balance increased population against the pressure of increased food output, while still maintaining the productivity of the soil. For that, knowledge gained from our past soil destruction may well contribute some principles of wise management for sustained soil construction.

The Moving Finger writes; and, having writ,
Moves on: nor all your Piety nor Wit
Shall lure it back to cancel half a Line,
Nor all your Tears wash out a Word of it.

Rubáiyát of Omar Khayyám, trans. FitzGerald

REFERENCES

ALBRECHT, W. A.

1951a "War: Some Agricultural Implications," *Organic Farmer,* LXXXII, 36 ff.

1951b "Nutrition via Soil Fertility According to the Climatic Pattern," pp. 384–97 in *Proceedings, Special Conference in Agriculture on Plant and Animal Nutrition in Relation to Soil and Climatic Factors, Australia, 1949.* London: H.M. Stationery Office. 490 pp.

1952a "The Cow Ahead of the Plow," *Guernsey Breeders' Journal,* LXXXIV, 1173–77.

1952b "Protein Deficiencies via Soil Deficiencies. II. Experimental Evidence," *Oral Surgery, Oral Medicine and Oral Pathology,* V, 483–99.

1954a "Droughts: The Soil as Reasons for Them," pp. 42–55 in *Proceedings of the Eleventh Annual Meeting of the American Institute of Dental Medicine, Palm Springs, California, November, 1954.* 185 pp.

1954b "Soil and Nutrition," pp. 24–40, *ibid.*

1954c "Drought," *Better Crops with Plant Food,* XXXVIII, No. 9, 6–9.

BOYLE, LT. COL. C. L.

1954 "Mother Earth," *Journal of the Soil Association,* VIII, 3.

DECKER, WAYNE L.

1954 "Sixth Annual Progress Report of the Missouri Climatological Research Project." (University of Missouri in co-operation with the U.S. Weather Bureau.) Columbia, Mo.: U.S. Department of Commerce. 21 pp. (Mimeographed.)

MILLER, EDWIN C.

1938 *Plant Physiology.* New York: McGraw-Hill Book Co. 1,201 pp.

POTTENGER, FRANCIS M.

1946 "Effect of Heat Processed Foods and Metabolized Vitamin D Milk on Dento-facial Structures of Experimental Animals," *American Journal of Orthodontics and Oral Surgery,* XXXII, 467–85.

REED, LESTER W.

1953 "Biosynthesis in Plants as Influenced by the Nutrient Balance in the Soil." Unpublished Ph.D. thesis, Department of Soils, University of Missouri. 190 pp.

ROBBINS, W. J., and SCHMIDT, MARY BARTLEY

1938 "Growth of Excised Roots of the Tomato," *Botanical Gazette,* XCIX, 671–728.

SEARS, PAUL B.

1954 "Human Ecology: A Problem in Synthesis," *Science,* CXX, 959–63.

THIMANN, KENNETH V.

1954 "The Physiology of Growth in Plant Tissues," *American Scientist,* XLII, 589–606.

Modifications of Biotic Communities

Modifications of Biotic Communities

The Re-creative Power of Plant Communities

EDWARD H. GRAHAM[*]

The purpose of this paper is to discuss human dependence and impact upon vegetation and particularly to point to the possibility of environmental improvement by using the re-creative power of plant communities. The word "vegetation" is here used to mean plant communities as they occur in nature, whether or not disturbed by man. Plant communities represent and are a part of an environmental situation. They have botanical characteristics that identify them, and they possess dynamic qualities expressed by certain biological processes. Among the most important of such qualities is the power of plant communities to reconstitute themselves when the cause of disturbance disappears. We shall comment on this dynamic quality of vegetation later. The paper deals not with plants of arable or cultivated lands but with plants in natural communities either native to the site they occupy or ecologically related to such a site.

THE EARTH'S VEGETATION

As background, we may first consider James's estimate of the distribution of world vegetation. Admittedly a generalization, it helps to orient us. There are few parts of the world which have not supported communities of higher plants, although in extreme deserts, as the central Sahara, and in polar areas, vegetation may be absent. The world's vegetation, prior to historically widespread human disturbance, may have been distributed approximately as follows (James, 1935): tropical forest, 13 per cent; boreal forest, 9 per cent; mid-latitude mixed forest, 7 per cent; Mediterranean scrub forest, 1 per cent; dry lands, 17 per cent; grasslands, 19 per cent; mountain, 18 per cent; polar, 16 per cent (total, 100 per cent).

Estimates by the Food and Agriculture Organization of the United Nations indicate that about one-fourth of the world's land area today is forested. While this is less than James's estimate of land originally forested, it would seem that the bulk of the world's land suited to forest persists in trees. Most natural grazing lands also remain vegetated, for the FAO estimates that 20 per cent of the earth's land surface is now in "grassland," that is, vegetation consisting of grasses, legumes, herbs, and shrubs. Today, according to the FAO, about 10 per cent of the world's land is in crops, while 40–45 per cent is barren desert, polar, or high mountain areas (Semple, 1951).

But it is important to recognize that, while the *extent* of land supporting natural vegetation has not materially changed, the *composition* of most of

* Dr. Graham is Director of Plant Technology, Soil Conservation Service, United States Department of Agriculture, Washington, D.C. In 1954 he was awarded a John Simon Guggenheim Memorial Foundation Fellowship for a comparative study of the use of land resources in selected countries of the New and Old Worlds. His publications include: *Botanical Studies in the Uinta Basin of Utah and Colorado*, 1937; *Legumes for Erosion Control and Wildlife*, 1941; and *Natural Principles of Land Use*, 1944.

the earth's vegetation has been substantially altered within historic time. It will be useful to consider some of the factors that have influenced this change.

MAN'S DEPENDENCE UPON VEGETATION

Man has long depended upon plants as his primary source of nourishment, although wild animals, from both the land and the sea, yield valuable food. Domesticated livestock of various kinds also furnish food, but today 85 per cent of the world's food is derived from plants (Pearson and Harper, 1945).

Not only food but much shelter and clothing come from plants. Ever since the development of weaving, fiber plants have produced the raw materials for cloth. Synthetic fibers continue to be derived largely from cellulose. Wood has long been the most readily available fuel and the most easily adaptable building material. Plants have produced, in both the ancient and the modern world, many other materials needed by man. Vegetable oils, medicines, intoxicants, perfumes, dyes, gums, resins, spices, plastics and other synthetics, alcohol, furniture, and many other essential adjuncts of civilization come from plants.

Less obvious than the products of plant species, but more germane to our discussion, is the value of plant communities. After thousands of years of use in many parts of the world, natural plant communities still support livestock on the open range and produce timber in the world's forests. These plant communities, while not often now constituted entirely of species that were part of the undisturbed vegetation, have a floristic composition related to their original one and to the site upon which they grow.

Nor will the wizardry of modern science and technology remove us from our reliance upon vegetation. Technology itself feeds upon raw materials. A rising world population increases the demand for food, clothing, and shelter. Through struggles for higher levels of living, social orders become accustomed to more and more material goods. The reports of national and international bodies point almost monotonously to the need for greater production. And much of this needed production will of necessity derive from plant resources and from the world's vegetation.

MAN'S IMPACT UPON VEGETATION

The influence of man upon native vegetation is the most conspicuous modification of his environment. Land in cultivation, being maintained by constant care and attention, is always different in aspect from its appearance before cultivation, which in this paper refers to the process of maintaining an area in tilled crops, hay, pasture, vineyards, or orchards. Forests that are lightly cut and range land that is lightly grazed may show little change in aspect, although there may be some difference in species composition. Heavily used range land shows a much greater change and may finally support only a scattered stand of shrubs or annual plants largely non-palatable to stock. Forests destroyed by lumbering, fire, and grazing may become transformed into low-yield grazing land.

Severe depletion of natural plant cover often results in soil erosion and sedimentation of streams, lakes, and reservoirs. The result in some parts of the world has been to render the land no longer capable of supporting the type of vegetation naturally occurring on the site or even the plants which were cultivated there before the accelerated erosion rendered the site useless. Thus an irremediable change may be rendered in the capacity of human environment to provide the plant resources needed by man.

Fire

In spite of controversies as to its exact impact, fire has probably modified the composition of vegetation for a longer time than any other influence mentioned in this paper. Lightning may always have set fires in forests and grasslands and may well control vegetation types in some regions. Primitive existence of this vegetation depends upon the burning, as proved by the dense deciduous forest that develops wherever an area is protected from fire. Fire was and still is widely used in attempts to improve brush- or tree-covered land for livestock or wild game.

Throughout the humid tropics shifting cultivation has been possible only

Fig. 141.—Shifting cultivation in Panama. Note the cornfield in lower left, forest in upper right, and intermediate stages of reforestation on the slope between.

tation types in some regions. Primitive man undoubtedly caused fires, by accident if in no other way, as by deserted campfires. More often he set fires purposely. This he did in native grasslands to provide fresh growth for his grazing herds. The American Indian, and the white settlers who succeeded him in the southeastern United States, regularly burned the pine-broomsedge vegetation of the coastal plain. The with the use of fire. Forest trees, girdled or felled, in the dry season are burned. In the areas thus opened, crops may be grown for a few years before production drops and the plot is abandoned to revert to trees. The cultivator then shifts to a new area cleared and burned for the same purpose (Fig. 141). Here is use of fire in a type of vegetation which does not burn unless it is first altered by man.

Clearing for Cultivation

All the land now devoted to the raising of cultivated plants, both annual food plants and perennials that provide economically valuable products, was once occupied by some type of native vegetation. Some six thousand years ago or more, cereal grains had been sufficiently developed from wild grasses that they could be sowed and grown in open, tilled fields. Perhaps the first areas to be cleared for cultivation were the great river deltas of the Nile, Tigris-Euphrates, and Indus. By drainage and irrigation these estuaries were made suitable for wheat, barley, and other early crops, with tilled fields replacing the marsh vegetation that must have occupied such habitats. Alluvial areas in the Orient were transformed to rice fields by water-spreading. It is of considerable interest that even today, when so much cultivation has moved to the uplands, one-fourth of the world's inhabitants get their food from irrigated crops (Pearson and Harper, 1945).

As the need for food grew with the spread of ancient civilizations, and as tools were developed and new plants were added, land in trees and grass were cleared for cultivation. The forests of China, Europe, and eastern North America, the grasslands of Russia and the United States, yielded to the agricultural pressures of expanding populations. In spite of the increasing demands of the modern world for plant products from cultivated land, not more than one-tenth of the earth's land surface has the combination of climate, topography, and soil adapted to food crop production (*ibid.*). We have already noted this to be the percentage that the FAO estimates is now in crops. Although this proportion of land area is small, it is inherently the world's most productive land and furnishes 90 per cent of our food supply (Semple, 1951).

Grazing

Along with the development of cultivated crops, man domesticated a number of animal species. While some of these are carefully husbanded, as the chicken and hog, man has depended largely on native vegetation as sustenance for most of them, as camels, goats, sheep, cattle, and horses. The cultivated river valleys of the ancient world are bordered by semidesert areas which undoubtedly once supported vegetation far different in both composition and density from what it is today. These arid lands still support livestock of nomadic tribes, as they did the herds of antiquity. As man spread with his crops and flocks, any accessible area of natural grassland made useful pasture. Brushland and forest were grazed for the stock feed they provided. The intensity and type of grazing determined the very composition of the vegetation until, in many parts of the world, the result was a large number of poorly nourished animals barely existing on an equally poorly nourished type of vegetation maintained by the constant pressure of the livestock themselves (Fig. 142). One of the terrific impacts upon vegetation has been that of the domesticated grazing animal.

Lumbering

Use of wood from the time man first gathered it for fuel has made demands upon woody vegetation. It is of interest to note that two-thirds of the people of the world still use wood for cooking their food (Orr, 1946). In this respect wood and the land that produces it become an integral part of the world's food supply. The demand upon forests for building materials is age-old. During the Third Dynasty—nearly five thousand years ago—Egypt drew upon the forests of the eastern Mediterranean for timbers to supplement stone in the building of its cities. The timbers were carried in wooden ships, some of them 170 feet in length (Childe, 1950). Solomon, for the construction and ornamentation of his famous temple and palace, had "fourscore thousand hewers in the mountains" to get the cedars from the hills of Lebanon. Today these hills are treeless (Fig. 143). Mediterranean shipping during the Roman period, unsurpassed until modern time, was in wooden bottoms. Some of the grain ships carried 1,200 tons and transported yearly to Rome alone as much as 15,000,000 bushels of grain from Egypt and North Africa (Casson, 1954).

As civilizations pushed from arid lands to temperate areas, forests were cleared for living space, fields, and pastures. In Europe, when mining became important, forests were destroyed near the mines to furnish mine props, carts, water pipes, and fuel. The most important of machine tools, the lathe, was originally made of wood, the woodman becoming father to the engineer. And, in the tropics, forests were changed by the use of shifting cultivation, already mentioned. Shantz (1948, p. 67) has stated that "in tropical Africa today the forest area is about a third of what it could have been except for the ravages of fire and the destructive practices of the agriculturists."

Our demands for wood are still tremendous and are increasing as we find new ways of using it. The destruction of forest vegetation, especially as it exposes soil to erosion and deterioration,

Fig. 142.—*Anabasis* desert, northeast of Damascus, Syria, characteristic of much of the world's semiarid vegetation, controlled by the heavy pressure of nomadic flocks.

is another of the important influences rendering land less fit for human use.

Water Control

One of the human impacts upon vegetation that is at least locally significant, and is constantly assuming wider importance, is the flooding of land or the removal of water from or near its the ancient and in the modern world, denudation of forested hills and mountains has increased stream sedimentation. Frequently one of the results is the creation of large detrital fans of coarse material that smothers rich alluvial soils and existing vegetation (Fig. 144, *a, b*). In other places finer material may be so distributed over flood

FIG. 143.—The grove of *Cedrus libani* at Les Cedres, Lebanon, protected remnant of a forest that once covered the intermediate slopes of the Lebanon Range.

surface. The changing of the marsh vegetation of deltas and other alluvial lands by the ancients has already been cited. The careful application of water to irrigated fields, such as the rice terraces of the Philippines, alone makes it possible to maintain those areas in agricultural production and to prevent revegetation by plant communities that would otherwise occur there. This is, of course, true wherever irrigation has been practiced. In many places, both in plains as to change the existing plant cover to communities of marsh plants.

More recently the construction of artificial ponds, lakes, reservoirs, and large river impoundments has become widespread. Flooding by the reservoir behind a dam destroys all higher plants in the area covered by the water, prohibiting the growth of natural plant communities or cultivated crops on the inundated land. Comparatively small in relation to the total land in cultiva-

Fig. 144.—Erosional deposits as a result of disturbed vegetation of watersheds. In both the New and Old Worlds, disturbance of the vegetation of a watershed results in accentuated runoff and erosion.

a) Detrital fan of stream entering Lake Atitlan in the highlands of Guatemala.

b) Heavy erosional debris, washed from the valley into the Portaikos River, near Trikkala, Greece.

tion, the amount of land inundated by the works of man is nevertheless significant. In the United States not less than 10,000,000 acres have been covered by artificially impounded water (according to unpublished estimates by the United States Soil Conservation Service and the United States Geological Survey). While the compensating values of water use are in no way denied, it is suggested only that the effect of water control upon vegetation, whether it results from drainage, irrigation, or impoundment, is real and often important.

Urban Developments

A contemporary demand for land and an influence upon the vegetation it supports are seen in the rapidly expanding acreage of urban and other non-rural developments. Throughout the world these demands are evident in varying degrees. In England a most important land-use problem is the conflict between urban and rural demand for land. In the Low Countries criteria are being developed as guides for preserving highly productive truck-crop soils where they are threatened by expanding cities. In the period 1910–50, 40,000,000 acres in the United States were absorbed by towns, cities, and urban industrial developments (Wooten, 1953), and there is little reason to believe that this rate of 1,000,000 acres per year needed for such purposes will decrease appreciably in the immediate future. A single modern airport requires 5,000 acres or more. Modern highways are scheduled to absorb millions of acres of land in the United States. When the human population increases, the demand for food, clothing, and shelter increases. In the Western world particularly, the trend toward suburban living and dispersed industry, together with the establishment of more airports, highways, parks, and recreational areas, requires land. Some of this acreage will come from land now in cultivation, some from grassland, and some from forest. In any event, this new and growing impact of man upon nature is in many instances a major influence upon vegetation. (See Harris, pp. 882–85 below.)

RESULT OF HUMAN IMPACT

Let us briefly summarize some of the results of man's influence upon the earth's plant cover, before pointing to the value and use of an understanding of the dynamic qualities of vegetation.

The extreme effect of man upon natural vegetation is illustrated by his maintenance of the tilled field. The farmer exerts the maximum control of natural vegetation. That this dominance is far from absolute is shown by the time and cost involved in weed control, even in modern agriculture. In spite of annual plowing and repeated cultivation throughout the growing season, annual weeds—initiating the process of revegetation—will invade the fields. In the United States nearly four billion dollars' damage occurs annually from weeds on agricultural land (Shaw, 1954).

Where he has removed the native vegetation and restricted the plant cover to a single species of annual plant, man has created conditions on cultivated fields that cause accelerated soil erosion. On slopes with erosive soils the result has often been disastrous. This subject has been adequately treated elsewhere (Bennett, 1939; Jacks and Whyte, 1939), but it may be well to reiterate that accelerated soil erosion with the attendant loss of tilth and fertility, due to cultivation, overgrazing, and lumbering, is undoubtedly the most serious result of man's disturbance of the earth's vegetation.

Forests have not only been replaced by cultivation; they have been transformed to other kinds of plant communities. The once-timbered hills of Attica, Greece, are clothed now with scattered woody shrubs and weedy perennials like *Asphodelus,* unpalatable to goats and other livestock which exert a pressure upon the vegetation as positive in its way as the control of the agriculturist in his crop fields. In the British Isles and northwestern Europe a uniform cover of heather, maintained by grazing sheep, supplants the temperate forest. When the sheep are removed, birch and pine immediately invade the heather.

In many places where the forest has not been destroyed, changes are nevertheless real. Cutover land is often reoccupied by forest communities quite different in tree species from the ones there when the timber was first cut. For example, after cutting, a mixed deciduous-coniferous forest in northeastern North America may be replaced by deciduous species, owing to their ability to reproduce by stump sprouts. If the ax is followed by the plow, and the land is subsequently abandoned, the old fields will, throughout most of the eastern United States, become populated with various species of pine, depending upon the region. Ultimately, hardwoods are seeded among the pines by birds and mammals. When the pines die or are cut, they will be replaced by deciduous species or a mixed hardwood-coniferous stand.

Woodlands are frequently pastured, and the grazing may eliminate reproduction by many tree species. The trampling of the animals may decrease infiltration of water into the soil and increase runoff and erosion, not only changing the species composition of the woods but creating a different microclimate as well.

In grassland, desert shrub, or savanna, the grazing of stock maintains vegetation quite different from that which occupies the site without grazing, as already noted. No one knows what the semiarid range lands of North Africa and the Middle East, grazed for millen-

niums, once were like. In the United States we can reconstruct native grassland from records of early explorers, travelers, and botanists. And usually, in protected spots, there are relicts—species of the aboriginal plant communities—to be found that lend a clue. Thus we are able to reconstruct native plant communities and understand the process involved when they move to reconstitute themselves. Here is the key to our ultimate manipulation and management of vegetation.

Let us look at an illustration in the grazing land of southern Idaho (Fig. 145, *a–d*). Today in this area well-drained bottom lands and alluvial fans support woody sagebrush (*Artemisia tridentata*) and rabbit brush (*Chrysothamnus* sp.), which may occupy 70 per cent of such sites. Perennial and annual weeds compose most of the remainder of the vegetation. This plant community dominated by shrubs and weeds is referred to by range-management technicians as "poor condition" for grazing livestock because 15 acres are required to support one cow for a month. Yet scattered in the protection of the shrubs and in other spots where grazing stock cannot reach them are perennial grasses such as blue bunch wheat grass (*Agropyron spicatum*) and Indian rice grass (*Oryzopsis hymenoides*), constituting not more than 5 per cent of the stand.

If grazing pressure is lessened to where 5 acres will support a cow for a month, the wheat grass and rice grass, plus other perennials such as Nevada blue grass (*Poa nevadensis*), increase to compose 25 per cent of the vegetation, with correspondingly fewer weeds and woody shrubs. These grasses, more nutritious and palatable to stock, so change the nature of the vegetation that the range is said to be in "fair condition."

Where the perennial grasses occupy 50 per cent of the site, it then supports

a

b

FIG. 145.—Changes in quality of range vegetation, produced by intensity of grazing pressure. Vegetation often responds rapidly to change in use. In southern Idaho, this change is illustrated by the condition of vegetation corresponding to the intensity of grazing.

a) Under moderate use a preponderance of perennial grasses palatable to livestock constitutes "excellent" range condition.

b) The same site changes to "good" condition where heavier use reduces the grasses.

c

d

c) More intensive utilization changes the vegetation to a "fair" condition, with woody shrubs and weeds evident, the grasses scarce.

d) "Poor" condition is indicated by a plant community dominated by shrubs and weeds, the result of very heavy grazing.

a cow on 3.5 acres, and the range is said to be in "good condition."

In some places 75 per cent of the vegetative cover consists of perennial grasses—blue bunch wheat grass, Nevada blue grass, Indian rice grass, and Idaho fescue (*Festuca idahoensis*). This is "excellent condition," for the site then supports a cow per month on only 1.8 acres, and shrubs like sagebrush and rabbit brush are uncommon —never more than about 15 per cent of the total. Such excellent range supports a thick stand of the perennial grasses with accompanying litter and mulch, and soil erosion is reduced to a minimum (Dyksterhuis, 1949; Renner, 1948).

What is the significance of this example? Excellent condition represents vegetation comparatively undisturbed by man even after seventy-five years of use. The greater the pressure of man's use—in this case his grazing herds—the greater the change in the composition and character of the vegetation. The plant species most palatable to cattle are eliminated. The resulting vegetation is less able to support grazing animals, as seen by the increase in the acreage of vegetation required—from 1.8 acres per cow per month for excellent range to 15 acres per cow per month for range in poor condition. Much of the grazing land of the world is in poor condition and is an expression of the kind and intensity of use placed upon it. Both the prevailing vegetation where no use is made of it by man and its potentiality for use depend upon the site—soil, climate, and the total of environmental factors. When use is involved, it often becomes the factor that determines the existing condition of the vegetation (Graham, 1944). Wind, avalanche, ice, fire, insects, and other non-human influences also change the composition of vegetation, but their effect is usually less extreme than use by man.

HUMAN REACTION TO IMPACT

The one great law of vegetation dynamics is that the composition of vegetation tends always to constitute itself in relation to the environmental factors that influence the site occupied by the vegetation. Use by man is an environmental factor. Where use by man is intensive, that factor overshadows all others. When use becomes less intensive, vegetation tends to reconstitute itself in relation to other factors. Thus it appears that, while man's impact upon vegetation is essentially destructive, by control of use man can influence the composition of plant communities within the limits of the natural factors influencing the site. The biological process involved is never regressive or deteriorative in so far as the vegetation is concerned. It is always progressive, because plant communities tend to reconstitute themselves in response to the environment. Recovery may not always be fulfilled, of course, as in cases where the once dominant plant species have been extirpated and where there is no source of seed. Artificial seeding of a desired species brought from other areas, however, or seeding of ecologically similar species, may help to fill the niche. On the other hand, where the destruction of vegetation has resulted in soil erosion sufficient to remove all or the upper horizons of the soil profile, revegetation with the plant communities previously existing on the uneroded soil is all but impossible (Fig. 146, *a, b*).

Nearly a century ago George P. Marsh, in his pioneer work *Man and Nature,* subsequently published under the title *The Earth as Modified by Human Action* (1874), called attention to the terrific impact of man upon nature. He wrote (p. 34) that "man is everywhere a disturbing agent. Wherever he plants his foot, the harmonies of nature

a

b

FIG. 146.—Soil erosion, with attendant loss of tilth and fertility, the most serious result of man's disturbance of the earth's vegetation.

a) Severely eroded area now being revegetated by protection from grazing and lumbering, near Serrai, northern Greece.

b) Wheat is still planted on portions of this slope, most of which has been rendered useless by continuous planting. San Rafael de Mucuchies in the Venezuelan Andes (9,000 feet).

are turned to discords." Man, he stated (*ibid.*), is "essentially a destructive power" in nature. Since the days of Marsh, we have learned a great deal. The very situation that led Marsh to write his book has gradually become more generally recognized. The "conservation movement" in America, for example, is a social awareness of the need for more careful management of resources. Our attitude toward natural resources is entirely different today from what it was in Marsh's time. The first century of the industrial age was indeed one of resource destruction—of waste in the use of coal, iron, timber, and soil. Today great energy is devoted to attempts at understanding resources —their nature, use, and development. There is widespread support for directing our inventive genius at the sustained production and intelligent utilization of the things in nature that we use.

Soil conservation, forestry, wildlife management, range conservation, and modern agronomy, with remarkable techniques for care of the land and its productivity, have all evolved in the past half-century. Today colleges and universities provide professional training in these fields—all dealing at least in part with vegetation. Governments have established bureaus whose sole function is the proper use and development of the biological resources. International organizations direct attention to such subjects, and technical assistance programs including attention to

vegetation are generally supported throughout the world.

Compared to the support given military activity, and in relation to the exact sciences, such as physics and chemistry, the biological sciences and technologies are poorly indorsed. With respect to vegetation, the great needs are (1) study and observation that will increase our fundamental knowledge of vegetation—its behavior and relation to human impact; (2) better understanding of vegetation, its value, and the processes involved in its management on the part of the informed public; and (3) improved techniques of working with the man on the land in order that he can apply those practices pertinent to the use and management of vegetation.

When we contemplate the condition of much of the world's grazing, timber, and other lands that either now or once supported native vegetation, the productive management of them seems remote and nearly out of reach. Yet successful management has been demonstrated both in the United States and abroad. The greatest allies we have in this task are the dynamic nature of vegetation itself and the understanding of the fact that plant communities possess the power to reconstitute themselves. A fuller understanding of this process, and exact application of its knowledge to practical affairs, can help materially to reduce damage to vegetation and to move toward utilizing its productive potential.

REFERENCES

BENNETT, H. H.
  1939 *Soil Conservation.* New York: McGraw-Hill Book Co. 993 pp.
CASSON, LIONEL
  1954 "Trade in the Ancient World," *Scientific American*, CXCI, 98–104.
CHILDE, V. GORDON
  1950 *What Happened in History.* Harmondsworth, Middlesex: Penguin Books. 288 pp.

DYKSTERHUIS, E. J.
  1949 "Condition and Management of Range Land Based on Quantitative Ecology," *Journal of Range Management*, II, 104–15.

GRAHAM, EDWARD H.
  1944 *Natural Principles of Land Use.* New York: Oxford University Press. 274 pp.

JACKS, G. V., and WHYTE, R. O.

1939 *The Rape of the Earth: A World Survey of Soil Erosion.* London: Faber & Faber. 313 pp. (American ed.: *Vanishing Lands: A World Survey of Soil Erosion.* New York: Doubleday, Doran & Co. 332 pp.)

JAMES, PRESTON E.

1935 *An Outline of Geography.* Boston: Ginn & Co. 475 pp.

MARSH, GEORGE P.

1874 *The Earth as Modified by Human Action.* New York: Charles Scribner's Sons. 629 pp. (First published in 1864 as *Man and Nature.*)

ORR, JOHN BOYD

1946 Preface (pp. 5–9) in *Forestry and Forest Products: World Situation, 1937–1946.* Stockholm: United Nations Food and Agricultural Organization. 93 pp.

PEARSON, FRANK A., and HARPER, FLOYD A.

1945 *The World's Hunger.* Ithaca, N.Y.: Cornell University Press. 90 pp.

RENNER, F. G.

1948 "Range Condition: A New Approach to the Management of Natural Grazing Lands," pp. 527–34 in *Proceedings of the Inter-American Conference on Conservation of Renewable Natural Resources.* (U.S. Department of State Publication No. 3382.) Washington, D.C.: Government Printing Office. 782 pp.

SEMPLE, A. T.

1951 *Improving the World's Grasslands.* ("FAO Agricultural Studies," No. 16.) Rome: United Nations Food and Agriculture Organization. 147 pp.

SHANTZ, H. L.

1948 "An Estimate of the Shrinkage of Africa's Tropical Forests," *Unasylva,* II, 66–67.

SHAW, B. T. (ed.)

1954 *Losses in Agriculture.* (U.S. Department of Agriculture, ARS-20-1.) Washington, D.C.: Government Printing Office. 190 pp.

WOOTEN, H. H.

1953 *Major Uses of Land in the United States.* (U.S. Department of Agriculture Technical Bulletin No. 1082.) Washington, D.C.: Government Printing Office. 100 pp.

Fire, Primitive Agriculture, and Grazing in the Tropics

H. H. BARTLETT[*]

THE EARLY RECORDS

The use of fire to clear land of felled forest for agriculture, as well as the burning-over of grassland or brushland in hunting and to improve grazing, is so ancient that its beginning in time or place never can be known with certainty. This is obviously true of tropical countries, for which records are scanty or lacking. One often-cited fragment that bears upon the subject is the *Periplus* of Hanno. That ancient Carthaginian voyager sailed through the Pillars of Hercules and down the west coast of Africa, some centuries before Christ, with the object of founding a Carthaginian commercial colony. He saw mysterious and terrifying fires by night in an inhabited region, and, though he did not discover their cause, the modern explanation is that he saw the annual burning-over of the grazing region south of the Sahara.[1]

There is archeological evidence, as well as some evidence in classical literature, of the former greater extent of agriculture in the region of the upper Nile. Stebbing (1922–26) states that the Greek observers in Alexander's army recorded that east of the Jhelum River in extratropical northwestern India there was stately forest of wide extent where now, in this subarid country, there are only scattered trees of *Dalbergia* and *Acacia*. Although these records are very important as indicating extension of subarid conditions in historical time, there seems to be no specific indication of the agency of man in deforestation. Man's actions, however, must be inferred, because ancient ruins prove that there was formerly a greater population in the arid lands than such lands could now support.[2]

Although ancient records are not very

* Mr. Bartlett is Professor of Botany and Director of the Botanical Gardens at the University of Michigan. He has conducted botanical and agricultural field work and research in Sumatra, the Philippines, Formosa, Mexico, Guatemala, British Honduras, Panama, Haiti, Argentina, Uruguay, and Chile under the auspices of the University of Michigan, the United States Rubber Company, the Smithsonian Institution, the Gorgas Memorial Institute, the Carnegie Institution of Washington, the University of the Philippines, and the Office of Rubber Plant Investigations, Bureau of Plant Industry, United States Department of Agriculture. He has contributed to various journals.

1. This explanation was originally proposed by Bruce (1790) and accepted by Falconer (1797), who has been followed by most modern authors (Busse, 1908; Chipp, 1927; Schnell, 1950) but not by Auguste Mer (1885), who considered the "fires" to be lava flows.

2. In the lack of actual historical records of what has occurred through the agency of man in many regions, reasonably close chronological dating of archeological materials is being accomplished by means of the carbon-14 method. This will be especially important in India and will supplement such datable records as exist. For pre-Columbian America the dated stelae of the Yucatán Peninsula are the only historical records that may be correlated with vegetational changes.

helpful so far as fire is concerned, it is possible to learn much from the literature of modern exploration and discovery. Because we are concerned here with *primitive* agriculture, we have sometimes preferred accounts of a century or more ago to the possibly more complete later ones.

ACTIVITIES OF CONTEMPORARY TROPICAL PEOPLES

Much of the effect of man on the face of the earth can only be inferred from the persistence of ancient folkways among primitive peoples today. It is to be assumed that anthropological processes, like geological, are subject to Lyell's fundamental rule that we can best interpret the past in the light of our observation of agencies now in operation. It is still possible to study primitive agricultural survivals, including the employment of fire, in many tropical regions.

Primitive man's reasons for the burning-over of land have been stated many times. They have been (1) to clear forest (or, rarely, grassland) for agriculture; (2) to improve grazing land for domestic animals or to attract game; (3) to deprive game of cover or to drive game from cover in hunting; (4) to kill or drive away predatory animals, ticks, mosquitoes, and other pests; (5) to repel the attacks of enemies or to burn them out of their refuges; (6) to expedite travel; (7) to protect villages, settlements, or encampments from great fires by controlled burning; and (8) to gratify sheer love of fires as spectacles.

Shifting Cultivation

Wherever there are sparse populations of primitive man within the tropics there is also a peculiar type of shifting agriculture which exhibits only minor variations around the world. In Malaya and much of the East Indies it is based upon the *ladang* (Marsden,

1783; Crawfurd, 1820; Begbie, 1834). A *ladang* is a clearing in the forest which is used for only one, two, or maybe four years and then abandoned.[3]

The chief American writer on shifting agriculture was O. F. Cook (1908, 1909, 1921). As he observed it in Guatemala, the *milpa* system (Maya equivalent of Malay *ladang*) was based on the felling and burning of new areas of forest each year to make temporary clearings. It was adapted to sparsely inhabited regions, where forest was so extensive that there could be long intervals of "forest fallow" between burnings. Land burned over too frequently became overgrown with perennial grasses, which rendered it useless for agricultural purposes with primitive implements.[4]

3. In the Batak lands of northern Sumatra such a clearing is called *juma* (*djoema*) (Joustra, 1926; Bartlett, 1919). A possible cognate of this word is found among the hill tribes of Assam where the clearing is *jhum* (Gurdon, 1914). In the Philippines it is *kaingin* (Finley, 1913); in Java *tagal* (Crawfurd, 1820); in Indochina, *ray* (Chemin-Dupontès, 1909); in Burma, *taungya* (Kurz, 1875); in central India, *bewar, dippa, erka, jara, kumari, podu,* and *penda* (authorities cited in Bartlett, 1955); in Ceylon, *chena* (Parker, 1910); in Madagascar, *tavy* (Humbert, 1923, 1927); locally in Mexico, *coamile* (Cook, 1909); in Yucatán and Guatemala, *milpa* (Cook, 1909); formerly in Guadeloupe, *ichali* (Ballet, 1894); in Venezuela, *conuco* (Pittier, 1936). In Uganda *chitemene* (Richards, 1939) is a modification of the system which also exists in India under the names *dahi* and *parka* (Hislop, 1886; Grigson, 1938). Doubtless dozens of other designations are locally used for various primitive systems. From the standpoint of geographic distribution the most interesting of the words is *uma*, with clear cognates in languages all the way from Fiji to Madagascar (Bartlett, 1955).

4. Persons who have had no tropical experience frequently express surprise that grasslands should be generally used by primitive man only for grazing and not for agriculture. The reason is that the soil of freshly cleared and burned-over forest land is soft, readily planted, fertilized by the soluble mineral constituents of the ashes, and initially almost entirely free from pernicious weeds. Grass-

Ladangs and *milpas,* or their equivalents, have been described many times.
An excellent description of *milpa* agriculture is that of Lundell (1937). Its
main features are that the land is prepared for planting by felling or deadening forest, letting the debris dry during the hot season, and burning it before the rains begin. With the first rains,
holes are dibbled in the soft ash-
covered earth with a planting stick.
Then it is necessary to pull weeds until the crops are ready for harvesting.
Ordinarily, a *milpa* in Mexico, Central
America, or northern South America
contains maize and beans. In Brazil,
however, the chief crop is manioc. In
the *ladang* of the Malayan countries
the primary crop is generally upland
rice. In both the New World and the
Old a root crop is likely to follow the
grain. From New Guinea eastward root
crops have not been supplanted by
grains as the mainstay of agriculture.
Africa often has one or more small
grains, vaguely called "millet," or
sorghum, as the grain crop, and in
many parts of the Old World manioc
has largely replaced yams and is widely known by the Malay name *ubi kayu,*
"tree" yam, to distinguish it from the
ordinary vine yams (*ubi*). After the
primary harvest of rice a Malayan *la-*

---

land, on the contrary, has a deep sod of intricately interwoven tough rhizomes and roots,
which can be turned only by inordinate labor
with hand tools and which will quickly
sprout again because superficial fires during
the dry season when grasses are dormant do
not destroy them. Grassland can be, and is,
utilized on a small scale for gardens, e.g., in
Sumatra (Brenner, 1894), and on a larger
scale in the Sudan by a specially controlled
system of preagricultural burning called *hariq*
(Burnett, 1948), which is timed to use old
grass as fuel to destroy the new growth when
the stored underground reserve foods have
been exhausted by the fresh sprouting after
the rains. Tropical grassland has of course
been successfully conquered by the adoption
by tropical man of modern methods and implements, introduced by colonial governments.

dang produces a succession of foods
until the fertilizing effect of the ashes
wears off and the weeds become too
numerous and bothersome. Then comes
abandonment and either reversion to
some sort of forest or degradation to
grassland, depending upon whether or
not forest is in an unstable equilibrium
with climate and upon whether or not
man interferes with normal ecological
succession by repeated burning.

Aside from the crops grown, pre-
Columbian shifting agriculture was remarkably similar in the Old World and
the New. The differences in crops were
promptly obliterated by voyagers who
introduced such various major economic plants as maize, manioc, sweet potatoes, pineapples, and tobacco from
America to Asia and Africa. Conversely, rice and sugar cane were quickly
established in America from the Orient.
The interchange extended to many useful field and horticultural crops, probably within a half-century after the discovery of tropical America, but many
interesting minor varieties remained
localized.

Replacement by grassland of all the
forests in any tropical region would set
a natural limit to agricultural occupation under the *ladang* or *milpa* systems,
but, before that limit would be reached,
the population would have entered into
decline, because only the previously
neglected poorer lands and those of insufficient extent would be available. A
district that once might have supported
an agricultural population would have
been entirely denuded and sterilized,
except for hunting and, in the Old
World, grazing. Cities and villages
might have developed horticulture as
a secondary food source, but that
would only supplement the basic diet.

Cooke (1931) applied the idea that
the consequences of deforestation,
shifting agriculture, and fire were the
same in the past as in the present to
explain the abandonment of ancient

seats of civilization in the Mayan area of Central America. The temples and dated sculptured monuments of the Mayan Old Empire show that relatively large, centralized communities existed six hundred to a thousand years ago, and the limitations of the *milpa* system of agriculture explain in part why the cities did not persist longer. It is a fact, however, that the water supply of the Petén at places such as Tikal and Uaxactún has failed, as the streams and shallow ponds (*aguadas*) now dry up during the hot season, because, if one theory is correct, former shallow lakes were silted up during a period of great agricultural activity, when the forest was extensively cleared and the topsoil was eroded away (*ibid.*). A long swing of erosional or climatic change, or both, must be considered to have been a factor in the depopulation of the area of the Mayan Old Empire, though this would not be true of modern Indian towns elsewhere in Guatemala, which, Cooke said, were surrounded by such wide belts of unproductive grassland that the difficulty of transportation of food from distant *milpas* on the backs of the people led to dispersal of population from old villages. Cooke thought that silting of the lakes had stopped transportation by waterways in the Petén.

Permanent Cultivation

The alternatives to agricultural abandonment of tropical grassland in the Old World have been the adoption of a pastoral existence or the development of permanent cultivation. Among peoples in the tribal or village state of culture, the latter has taken, in the main, two forms: (1) the cultivation of irrigated land and (2) the planting of village groves and gardens. The former depends upon the annual impounding of flood water in diked stream flats or upon the building of terraces on slopes which can be irrigated with divertible water from higher ground.

The fortunate areas of the tropics where permanent flood-plain agriculture has long supported large populations are located in Thailand and Burma, but there are similar areas of lesser extent in the Philippines, Borneo, and elsewhere. Terrace cultivation exists in numerous places. Many illustrated descriptions have been written of the famous rice terraces of the Bontoc of Luzon—a marvel of primitive engineering (Jenks, 1905). The Javanese and Sundanese of Java, as well as the Batak and Malay of Sumatra, also have notable terrace cultivation. Tropical peoples who depend chiefly upon permanent irrigated fields engage in shifting agriculture also, as a secondary resource, which may again become the primary means of subsistence for colonists who drift too far away from irrigable land. There are places around Lake Toba in Sumatra where the deforestation of upper slopes has brought about a too rapid runoff and has destroyed the utility of terraces at a lower altitude. Permanent terrace cultivation depends upon the maintenance of a dependable water supply. In Malay-speaking countries the irrigated fields are called *sawah*—as good a term as any for irrigated rice-growing in the tropics—to contrast with *ladang* agriculture on dry land.

The second chief form of permanent cultivation in the tropics—village groves and gardens—is in large part primitive horticulture rather than agriculture. It depends, obviously, upon whether or not a people has permanent habitation. Some seminomadic peoples move so often that they can have little in the way of horticulture. Others have permanent villages which have become transformed into groves of fruit trees interspersed with small patches of other useful plants which are maintained regardless of the great labor of hand cultivation. An old village site is a place that is constantly and unconsciously fertilized by man (partly through his domestic animals), for it is a center of deposition of organic material drawn far and wide from the surrounding region. "Wastes" are not wasted, but their valuable fertilizer constituents turn up again and are transformed by beneficent nature into the form of fruits and vegetables. So a tropical village is often a medley of grove and garden, the products of which supplement a living gained from shifting or permanent agriculture, fishing, hunting, or any combination of these. The most delightful tropical landscapes are those in which ancient village centers of industry and art display primitive horticulture and gardening, perhaps separated by a bamboo hedge from surrounding lands in permanent *sawah* cultivation, around which the forest retains its proper place, regulating streamflow, preventing excessive erosion, yielding forest products, and affording sanctuary to the wild animals and plants. A reasonable amount of grassland suffices for grazing of domestic animals.[5]

No matter where we go we find that primitive shifting agriculture was carried on at the expense of forest. Trees were killed by fire or ringing and eventually burned or were felled and burned. The ashes fertilized the soil, and one, two, or a few crops were obtained from a clearing before it was abandoned. Permanent agriculture on periodically overflowed or terraced ir-

rigated land tended to stabilize population. Village gardening and horticulture had the same effect, whereas shifting agriculture led to shifting of population and to disproportionate development of pastoral pursuits.

Grazing and Burning

In many parts of the Old World tropics the grazing of domestic animals has been as vitally important for thousands of years as it became in the Americas after European colonization. Throughout Africa and tropical Asia, the annual burning-over of formerly agricultural clearings has prevented their reversion to forest and has extended the area of grazing land. As in America before there were domestic animals, hunting was an important food resource, and fresh, tender, green forage would be more quickly and easily available on land cleared of dried-up vegetation by fire than on land covered by hard, dead, largely inedible remnants of the previous seasons' vegetation.

There has been endless dispute about whether the burning-over of grassland actually improves pasturage. The dense accumulation of inedible dead stems makes the tender new growth very difficult for animals to graze, so that they may actually suffer from malnutrition in the presence of nutritious fodder. This is a strong argument in favor of burning. Another is that burning is absolutely essential in some regions if shrubs and trees are not to eliminate the grass.[6] However, burning destroys

5. Primitive tropical horticulture and gardening, as distinguished from agriculture, have been alluded to or written about by Ames (1939), Bates (1864), Gurdon (1914), Powell (1883), Terra (1953), and many others. Terra has developed a theory that will interest social anthropologists, i.e., that primitive permanent land utilization in the form of village horticulture and gardening was typically women's work, but field agriculture, on the contrary, was men's work.

6. The judicious and controlled use of more goats, which are by habit browsing rather than grazing animals, instead of cattle, might aid in keeping down the growth of woody vegetation, but it is to be borne in mind that in Africa, as elsewhere, goats may become destructive pests. They have the advantage of not being sacred or a symbol of social status, whereas in many African tribes (including some in Madagascar) possession of cattle is the basis of social distinction, and cattle are even worshiped. As cult objects

organic nitrogen compounds, and the excessive leaching of tropical soils during the rainy season results in constant loss of salts from the ashes of the burned grass and burned animal manure. It is a curious thing that the mowing of tender grass at the right time and the making of hay have seldom, if ever, been resorted to by primitive man in the tropics.

Vegetational history shows that, in general, deserted tropical agricultural clearings not burned over after abandonment, if surrounded by damp forest, quickly become seeded and reforested by quick-growing, light-loving trees. These are gradually replaced by many less readily disseminated trees, and a process of succession is begun which results in the re-establishment of a new forest, ideally becoming, in time, more or less similar in composition to the old and a variant of the "regional climax." The degree of similarity which may be attained depends upon many factors, the most important of which is man's intervention with fire. This may

interrupt the stages of progress toward climax forest to produce permanent savanna or treeless prairie. The most rapid deflection from normal ecological succession occurs in clearings which border regularly burned grassland. Here, deflection of the succession to grassland is almost certain.

If a clearing becomes weedy enough before abandonment so that dry grass and other inflammable material can be burned off annually during the dry season, the seedlings or sprouts of most woody plants will be killed and their place will be taken by coarse perennial grasses, which die above ground and provide fuel for fierce annual fires. However, they will have stored food supplies below ground to provide for resumption of growth during the rainy season. The only woody plants able to compete with coarse grasses are those that combine the characteristics of fire resistance above ground with food storage and vegetative renewal of growth below ground. There seem to be a few trees and shrubs with such an adaptive combination of characteristics in almost every flora. At any rate, they always seem to be near enough at hand to move in from the nearest drier floristic zone. Thus, the forest vegetation of Brazil seems to have little in common with that of the great treeless grasslands (*campos*), but actually there are areas that are floristically intermediate between them, in that they contain species which can survive in either *campo* or forest, to multiply greatly in land subject to annual fires but well enough supplied with water so as to be capable of supporting forest.[7]

---

cattle are kept so uneconomically that they are a detriment rather than a help to the people. Of their own accord, however, many Africans are as averse to changing ancient attitudes toward cattle, no matter how irrational they may be, as are the Hindus.

The problem of devastation of land and poverty of people caused by non-economic and cult cattle has been dealt with for Africa by Gourou (1947), Hailey (1945), Hall (1930), Harten (1953), Matheson and Bovill (1950), and Tothill (1940). For Madagascar a few of many references are Catat (1895?), Charon (1897), and Marcuse (1914). For India so much has been written that a bibliography for that country alone would be lengthy. Much of the literature is so complicated by religious prejudice as to indicate that many Hindus remain untouched by arguments of science or economics. Needless to say, some of the more enlightened Hindus would restrict sacred cattle to reasonable numbers and insist that they be not maltreated, starved, or allowed to become a public nuisance. The danger arising from unregulated goat-raising in India has been touched upon by Coventry (1929).

7. The trees and shrubs of the savanna have been termed "pyrophytes" by Kuhnholz-Lordat (1939). Their greater mass below ground than above in the burned-over (*chana*) land of Angola is commented upon by Gossweiler and Mendonça (1939). They all have some structural feature of the stem which gives them unusual qualities of fire resistance,

In the tropics, just as in temperate latitudes, there are climatic and edaphic zones where the balance of factors determining closed forest as opposed to savanna, or dry savanna as opposed to thorn scrub, is unstable and where the addition by man of a single, potent factor—fire—could transform and has transformed cleared forest land into grassland. Conversely, the discontinuance of the use of fire could result in the transformation of prairie into forest.[8] Of the latter change, one of the best-attested examples was the westward extension of the coastal forest of subtropical southern Texas and the extinction of the old, abrupt boundary of the prairie by outward diffusion of the forest when prairie-burning was discontinued (Cook, 1908).

REGIONAL EXAMPLES OF GRASSLAND
EXPANSION AT THE EXPENSE
OF FOREST

Northern Equatorial Africa

The point is frequently made that man's most devastating effects on tropical vegetation occur where gradual climatic change already may have produced a condition of unstable equilibrium. If the climate is steadily becoming drier, as so many believe of northern equatorial Africa, and as evidence indicates, we would expect to find persisting effects of primitive man in the zone of transition from natural prairie

or savanna to natural closed forest, on the one hand, and from grassland or savanna to open xerophytic thornbush, on the other.

Man's activities accelerate the effect of climate in shifting the position of whole vegetational zones rather than in creating them. Change of zonal boundaries is so slow that it has been seriously debated whether or not the Sahara is advancing and the equatorial African forest retreating. The evidence is clear that both are occurring.[9]

In Africa there are vast areas of savanna of such artificial aspect that the English term them "parkland," for they

8. Because of the existence of desert floras and faunas, it must be admitted that desert has also existed through geological time and that between desert, in which the ground cover of plants is too sparse to transmit fire, and humid closed forest, in which the undergrowth is not subject to forest fires, there have been various habitats in which grasses prevailed and were sufficiently dense to burn over wide areas after ripening and drying. At the mesophytic edge of a savanna or grassland there would be a more gradual transition to thorn forest or scrub depending upon the occurrence in time and space of enough grass to transmit a prairie fire. In between the two extremes the effect of fire would be to transform savanna into grassland. In between would also be found the tropical pinelands, in which the trees are usually isolated from each other by enough grass and fallen pine needles to transmit fire. In the United States we think of savanna as at least seasonally humid and characterized by palms, but tropical American pinelands may be grassland in the main, with both pines and palms interspersed among other fire-resistant trees, and they may be at times very dry. For descriptions of tropical and subtropical pineland and its relation to fire in Assam see Bor (1938, 1942); in Sumatra, Hagen (1903); in the Philippines, Merrill (1926); in Mexico, Gentry (1946), La Farge (1927), Hartmann (1897), and Stephen White (1948); in Haiti, Holdridge (1947).

9. Aubreville (1937, 1949*a*, 1949*b*), Bégué (1937), Duveyrier (1864), Gourou (1947), Hailey (1945), Harroy (1949), Stanhope White ["Sabiad"] (1944*b*), Shantz and Marbut (1923), and Stebbing (1937) are among those who have made important contributions to the subject.

but still they may be killed above ground and forced to sprout anew, so that the bulk of accumulated wood below ground is much greater than above. Many are palms, but others belong to extremely diverse families of plants. They characterize tropical and subtropical areas between typical forest and prairie or between forest and thorn scrub. In addition to many other references to such plants, the reader will find especially interesting information about those of India in works by Brandis (1906) and Gamble (1875). Those of the Philippines were discussed by W. H. Brown (1919) and those of Brazil by Hoehne (1914). These authors have been followed by many later ones.

contain scattered, single, fire-resistant trees and island-like groups of trees that look as though they had been planted. In the main, the woody plants that give savanna its characteristic appearance are those of the Sudanese flora of an arid to semiarid zone bordering the desert. Parkland or savanna may be traversed by streams which are bordered by true tropical forest. An extensive landscape may show transition from forest, by way of savanna and prairie, to thorn scrub and then to desert. Botanists have come to very different conclusions about what is man-made through the agency of fire and pastoral pursuits and what is "natural" in this type of landscape. Almost all agree, however, that man has brought about great vegetational degradation and that the result of his activities has been wide extension of desert and prairie and corresponding contraction of forest.

Man has transformed much of the central African equatorial forest into grassland by primitive agriculture, fire, and grazing. By overgrazing and repeated burning, he has moved the zone of thornbush into the grass and has encouraged the deterioration of thornbush to actual desert.[10]

10. The reader may refer to an excellent and copiously illustrated work by Shantz and Marbut (1923) for a general description of African vegetation. They were especially concerned with classification of vegetation and soils from the standpoint of utility for agriculture, grazing, and forestry. Their general conclusions are therefore especially important; namely, that the forests had shrunk as a result of the use of fire in primitive agriculture; that in some places forests would spread again if human interference ceased but that it was very doubtful if forest would ever replace all the grassland; and that, if fire were eliminated, the dry forests would ultimately have a different composition from those now existing.

The area of forest which, if human depredation were to continue, might practically all be transformed into grassland or savanna was estimated by Shantz and Marbut at over

Madagascar

As a result of a finely illustrated memoir by Humbert (1927), in which he accepted and extended the views of Perrier de la Bathie (1917, 1927), Madagascar has come to be thought of as the typical and best-studied example of the destruction of a tropical flora by fire, primitive agriculture, and grazing.

Since Madagascar is now largely deforested, Humbert assumed that the same processes which are today gnawing away the last of the forest are those which have operated for hundreds of years and that we see now almost the final stage in the transformation of a fine forest, with a highly indigenous flora and fauna, into a grassland largely of weedy and useless species. His evidence indicated that the entire island, an area of 600,000 square kilometers, formerly had been forest except for the arid district of the extreme southwest, which had probably always been low thorn scrub.

Upon review, Humbert's conclusions seem valid only if we classify as forest all plant associations containing even a few trees of any nature whatsoever. It would be necessary to regard as forest those tracts of seasonally semiarid land on which the trees were normally widely spaced species, such as doom palms (*Hyphaene*) and the anomalous baobabs (*Adansonia*). In continental Africa these are characteristically genera of parkland savanna and thornbush habitats situated between true forest and desert. This is true both on the southern fringes of the Sahara, toward the equatorial forest, and on the southwestern borders of the Congo, where

2,000,000 square miles. Of grassland of non-desert type, i.e., not closely alternating with desert scrub, there are about 4,700,000 square miles that may have been originally derived from forest by the use of fire in primitive agriculture and maintained as such by fire after it became useful only for hunting and grazing.

there is transition to the northward coastal extension of actual desert.

In Madagascar the endemic species of both genera have special adaptations to semiarid conditions, and the conclusion would seem sound that speciation in both genera took place under semidesert conditions and that the common ancestry of the continental African and Madagascar species would be found before the Pleistocene. The similar plant associations of the semiarid areas of both these regions afford the strongest possible evidence that the general outlines of plant geography are the same today in Madagascar as they were before human depredation began.

Nevertheless, one may accept certain conclusions of Perrier de la Bathie and Humbert, to wit: that there is clear evidence of great loss of forest land to prairie; of deterioration of primary forest and substitution by impoverished *savoka* flora or secondary forest; of increasing rarity of most endemic species and probable extinction of many; of increase of semidesert or desert; of soil deterioration and consequent floristic impoverishment by burning and erosion; and of increasing dominance of cosmopolitan plants of a weedy nature. All this is bad enough without accepting the more extreme position of Lavauden (1931) that almost the entire island was uniformly forested (in the usual sense of the word) when man appeared upon the scene.

Perrier de la Bathie (1917) called attention to the importance, in the study of vegetational change, of his discoveries of swamp deposits containing identifiable plant remains in association with the bones of such recently extinct members of the fauna as *Aepyornis*. Such deposits should be investigated anew in order to trace, if possible, by pollen analysis and radiocarbon (C^{14}) dating, a paleobotanical sequence down to times of occupation by men and domestic animals.

During the last few hundred years of human occupation of Madagascar, cattle have increased to such vast numbers that overgrazing and trampling have broken down protective vegetation, with erosion as the result. Before man's introduction of domestic cattle, there may possibly have existed a now extinct "slender-legged form of Zebuox." Sibree (1915) seems to have thought at first that certain supposedly fossil bones were those of a zebu of human introduction but later concluded that a zebu relative was at least early enough to have been contemporary with the giant flightless birds and the pygmy hippopotamus. Aside from this record, there seems to be no evidence for that time of any grazing mammal tied in its evolution to the existence of prairie. Grazing damage has probably, therefore, taken place during the human period. Among the extinct birds, however, the ten-foot-high *Aepyornis titan* and its lesser relatives, related even if somewhat distantly to the ostrich and to the great extinct moa of New Zealand, probably lived in prairie or in largely open savanna.

Sumatra

We may now turn from the depressing literature on Africa and Madagascar, where forest is being replaced by grassland and the desert is advancing, to countries of ample rainfall throughout, where, although great retrogressive changes have taken place through the agency of man, there is no desert and where practicable measures have been initiated for agricultural utilization of excessive grassland or its restoration to forest.

In normally forested tropical countries the extent of grassland may almost be taken as a measure of the cumulative effect of human occupation. Although there are exceptional areas where seasonal drought and local edaphic conditions result in grassland or brush, Sumatra in the main is a well-watered, naturally forested land where most areas of *lalang* grass (*Imperata* and its associates) are man-made. Such areas, called *padang*, have been described by many writers (Junghuhn, 1847; Forbes, 1885; Bartlett, 1919, 1935). They have become productive as rubber plantations. The great Deli tobacco plantations used old *ladangs* with cropping, followed by a long fallow, much in the native fashion, except that the shorter fallow might have been brush with grass between crops or just grass, instead of secondary forest, old enough for *lalang* grass to have died out from shading.

The Philippines

Another country in which most of the grassland is man-made is the Philippines, where clearings for shifting agriculture, called *kaingin*, have resulted in grasslands (*cogonales*) of such great extent that their return to forest or agricultural productivity is a national problem.

The Philippine grasslands, although used for grazing, are of very low economic productivity. The prevailing grass, *cogon*, is the same as the *lalang* or *alang-alang* of the Malay Archipelago and Peninsula, namely, *Imperata*, associated with *Sorghum spontaneum* and other coarse grasses. *Kaingin* agriculture was described over two centuries ago, in a long unpublished manuscript, by Delgado (1892). In addition to the *cogonales*, almost uniformly of grass two to six feet high, *kaingin* agriculture has created enormous areas of another type of forest-replacement vegetation, called *parang* (Whitford, 1906), which is more jungle-like, consisting largely of bamboo, shrubs, and a few species of quick-growing, soft-wooded trees (W. H. Brown *et al.*, 1917; W. H. Brown, 1919).[11]

Since the concept of individual ownership of wild land was probably not general in the pre-Spanish Philippines, it does not surprise us to find that it was the Spanish, very late in their occupancy, who established public lands under government ownership and in 1867 promulgated with little success the first law for restricting *kaingin* agriculture (Nano, 1939). The Americans built upon the foundations of Spanish rule by more precisely delimiting the public domain and then proceeded to the great task of land classification on an economic and conservational basis. Down through 1931 (Fischer, 1932) this had resulted in the establishment of forest reserves, national parks, and the Makiling National Botanic Garden; the complete or partial mapping of 899 areas from among 1,219 that were to be set aside from the public domain for municipally controlled communal forests and grazing reserves; and the allotment of lands for the exclusive use of non-Christian groups who still practiced primitive shifting agriculture. Rapid progress was being made in the segregation of timberland from "alienable and disposable" land for allotment to individuals for agricultural use. In order to be as sympathetic as possible with people whose ancient traditions of forest waste were being violated, forest-covered areas that had little prospective value for timber were being designated for *kaingin* when necessary to relieve emergencies caused by earthquakes, storms, and floods. The use of these areas was by specific permit, and the grantees (*caingineros*) had to undertake, under direction of the Forest Service, to plant the *kaingin* areas with valuable trees after agricultural use.

11. It may be noted that bamboo thicket as a successional alternative to ordinary grassland occurs not only in the Philippines (Marche, 1887; Merrill, 1926) but likewise in India (Hodson, 1911; Troup, 1926), Ceylon (Hooker, 1909), Burma (Stamp, 1925), Madagascar (Flacourt, 1661; Copland, 1822), and Brazil (Dansereau, 1948). The writer has seen it in Formosa and Sumatra, and it doubtless occurs throughout the wet tropics.

The Forest Service had jurisdiction over approximately 5,600,000 hectares of *cogon* land, of which 1,000,000 hectares were to be reforested, another 1,000,000 devoted to permanent agriculture, and the remainder improved for grazing purposes.

In the reforestation program some six hundred kinds of trees had been tried. For the initial planting of old grassland, the most successful species of considerable commercial value for posts, firewood, etc., was the tropical American *Leucaena glauca,* called by the Filipinos *ipil-ipil.* This tree also was recommended by Pendleton (1933) for reforestation of the grasslands of Kwangtung, the subtropical province of China. These Chinese grassland areas are similar to the Philippine *cogonales* and of the same origin. Much of subtropical China is dominated by the same grass, *Imperata.*

Before the war the California Packing Corporation ("Del Monte") led the way in developing the Philippine *cogon* lands for permanent agriculture. The company's great pineapple plantations in Bukidnon, Mindanao, illustrated how agricultural use of *cogonales* could add a great industry to the national economy. Power plowing and scientific fertilization were essential to success.

There is a need to rework part of the Philippine grasslands into good grazing land, and it is possible that persistent mowing and haymaking would produce it. Curiously enough, however, there is a strange aversion to mowing throughout the tropics. Wherever that curious breed of humanity, the white man, has had to have his golf grounds, though, regardless of economy, *Imperata* has been replaced with soft, nutritious grass at the expense of ridiculously inefficient hand labor. Why not do it for the sake of utility as well as play? Mowing would provide hay during the dry period when the *cogon* is too coarse for grazing, and thus a limiting factor in

beef production would be eliminated. Return of animal manure to the land instead of burning it with the grass would take the place of fertilization by ashes. Systematic mowing at the right time, when the grass was still soft, might make it possible to kill out *cogon* (*lalang*) and its equally coarse, normal ecological associates and to replace them with grasses of greater forage value.

Brazil

An enormous area of tropical American prairie probably climatic and edaphic in origin is the central *campo* of Mato Grosso in Brazil. This has been so much extended by man that phytogeographic and floristic evidence that the whole *campo* is not man-made is obscure. Seeking a Brazilian parallel with conditions in Africa which favor the extension of grassland, we find that the tropical subarid or at least seasonally very dry area of Brazil is toward the northeast, and it is precisely from there that areas of grassland and savanna extend to the mouths of the Amazon and along the Tocantins River almost to its confluence with the Amazon. Westward there are prairies along the Tapajoz River, but they are considerably farther upstream. Thence to the west the great Amazonian forest has mostly isolated patches of man-made prairies. Great deposits of pottery fragments near the mouth of the Amazon indicate long human occupation, but how much savanna is entirely natural and how much is man-made is not clear from studies thus far made.[12] The an-

12. For references to Amazonian prairies near the coast see Bates (1864), Bouillenne (1926), Dansereau (1948), Froés Abreu (1931), Lange (1914), and Sampaio (1945). Notes on the man-made openings along the Xingu and westward will be found in the writings of many authors, including Hoehne (1916), Rondon (1916), Roosevelt (1914), and Steinen (1886). For discussion of the view that the central *campo* of Mato Grosso is natural see Hoehne (1910), Löfgren (1898),

tiquity of human occupation there should be established by carbon-14 datings of debris such as charcoal from archeological sites.

How Much Grassland Is Man-made?

Since shifting agriculture followed by repeated fire in forest clearings gives rise to artificial grassland, and since so much tropical grassland is man-made, it seems almost axiomatic to some botanists that, wherever we find tropical grassland within the altitudinal range of forest, it is man-made. Many, however, have described what would seem to the present writer to have been natural grassland, as, for instance, the grasslands of Durango, habitat of a Pleistocene grazing fauna, studied carefully by Gentry (1946), which the writer has also visited and about which he has formed a somewhat independent judgment.[13]

and Waibel (1949). Nearly all the authors cited refer to man-made *campo* and fire, but a classical discussion, citing earlier writings from St. Hilaire (1837) and Martius (1840–65) on, is that of Warming (1892). See also Lindman (1900).

13. Burbridge (1880) on the island of Jolo, Sulu archipelago, observed a lava flow that resembled a mass of clinkers covered with *lalang* grass (*Imperata*) four feet high. It seems unlikely that such a place would ever have been cleared. The writer encountered a similar locality (a cycad savanna) on the island of Culion, also in the Philippines, when visiting the type locality of the local cycad, *Cycas wadei* Merrill. Another sea-level example is that of the region around Taal Volcano, on Luzon, created not by lava but by volcanic mud and ash (Chamisso, n.d.; W. H. Brown *et al.*, 1917). There must have been large areas of what was essentially grassland or savanna in Africa to provide a habitat for the evolution of the magnificently developed grazing fauna, to say nothing of such specialized plants as the baobab. Johnston (1884), describing the beautiful undulating region of scattered forest and grassy plains south of the Congo, said of the parklike zone that it was the country of the large game animals and that "the rhinoceroses, zebras, giraffes and many antelopes never enter the

Some savannas and prairies evidently represent natural, persistent climatic and edaphic plant associations in which prevention of fire would not result in reforestation. This view has been opposed, however, and some scientists believe that practically all grassland is maintained by fire and, if fire in grassland is always kindled by man, that there is no "natural" grassland. This extreme view has led to more or less futile discussion of whether or not man is a part of "nature." The present writer is obviously one of those who defines primitive man as having been thoughtless of the future and therefore a natural ecological factor for millenniums.

As causes apart from man for the occurrence of fire, much has hinged upon whether grass fires originate from lightning, as do forest fires in coniferous forests, but there has been an astonishing dearth of dependable observation. Writers have quoted the most flimsy evidence of ancient date. For evidence of a convincing nature, only very recently at hand, we turn to an admirable report by Robertson (1955) on the subtropical Everglades National Park. He indicates that it may now be considered proved that grassland fires can be started by lightning and, moreover, that such open grasslands and sedgelands as the prairies of the Florida Everglades might remain such by the agency of fire ignited by lightning. Moreover, there are endemic non-weedy species in the periodically fire-swept southern part of Florida that drop out of the flora if fires are controlled so long that woody vegetation supersedes prairie,

forest belt that clothes much of Western Africa." The writer believes that during recent geological time there have always been tropical grasslands and savannas, some on marshland maintained as such by lightning, others of volcanic origin, such as those around Taal Volcano in Luzon, others edaphic, and the greater ones mainly determined by climatic factors. Otherwise there is no way to explain how the mammalian fauna evolved.

savanna, or open pineland. These species would seem to indicate that the
fire-controlled flora is an ancient one
that presumably preceded man's occupancy of the land.

APPROACHES TO PERMANENT CULTIVATION

Nothing is more interesting about
primitive agriculture than the tentative and halting steps toward permanent land utilization made by many
peoples. When population increased to
the point at which new forest for clearing was no longer available, it became
necessary to use the same land repeatedly and, eventually, in a regularly recurrent cycle. Some observers of
African primitive agriculture have not
considered it bad at all but merely a
system of doing as well as possible with
leached-out sterile soil. So the system
of shifting agriculture has been looked
upon, at its best, as permanent land
utilization for agriculture with a long
fallow between crops. Primitives have
made efforts to make the long fallow of
some immediate yearly profit.

There has been mention of tropical
man's beginnings in the development
of continuous utilization of non-irri-
gated village land by primitive horticulture. Aside from the probably quite
unconscious fertilization of horticultural plants that resulted from the
proximity of human beings and domestic animals, there were approaches
to continuous field agriculture from
several directions: (1) improvement of
tools; (2) renewed application of ashes
as fertilizer on currently used fields;
(3) sod- or soil-burning; (4) alternation of cropping and a controlled grass
fallow; (5) control by planting selected trees so that the "forest fallow"
would be productive; and (6) the intelligent use of animal manure.

Improvement of Tools

Improvement of tools took place by
the replacement of wood and stone by
iron and the development of spade,
hoe, fork, and plow from the primitive
digging stick.

Examples of the use of the digging
stick as an agricultural tool are found
in many surviving cultures, for even
where its most ancient use in uproot-
ing yams and other wild root crops has
not been actually reported, its later use
has been for digging cultivated root
crops and as a dibble for planting.
More complete geographic coverage of
surviving use of the digging stick could
be found by a more thorough review
of the literature, for, as Ames (1939)
said, it must have been man's first agricultural implement.[14] In Borneo,
Nieuwenhuis (1904–7) reported the
use of the digging stick in planting by
the coastal Malays. In Sumatra it is
used by the Menangkabau (Maass,
1910), in Atjeh (Jacobs, 1894), in Gayo-
land (Hazeu, 1907), by the Batak of
Asahan (Bartlett, 1919), Simeloengoen
(Tideman, 1922), and Karoland (Brenner, 1894). In addition to the regular
planting stick (*parlobong*, "hole-
maker"), Tideman reported a bamboo
stick with two prongs (*gogo*) used in
weeding, which might be the precursor
of a fork, and Brenner described a row
of Karo women with digging sticks
working side by side to turn a furrow
in grassland, this being an almost

14. Fürer-Haimendorf (1943), commenting
on the survival of the digging stick among
tribes of primitive culture in Hyderabad, said
that, if we were to name existing cultures
from the most characteristic artifact, as prehistorians name archeological cultures, the
Chenchu of Hyderabad would exemplify an
ancient "digging-stick culture" of hunting and
collecting forest tribes. Other Indian examples
are from Khondistan (Campbell, 1864) and
Assam (Hodgson, 1880). In Annam (Baudesson, 1919) the sowing was not done by
the irregular punching of holes in the soft
ashy earth but in rows, by the scratching of
furrows with the planting stick. This improvement (which would facilitate weeding) had
a parallel in Indochina, where, although holes
were punched, they were kept in line by laying a bamboo on the ground to serve as a
ruler (Mouhot, 1864).

unique instance of digging-stick cultivation among the Malayan peoples that
was not at the expense of forest. It has
been verified by the writer's personal
observation that Karo women undertake great labor of this sort in gardening. As might be expected, peoples who
depend largely or entirely on root crops
rather than grain are those most likely
to retain the digging stick. So the Papuans and Melanesians use it, as reported from New Guinea (Chalmers
and Gill, 1885), New Britain (G. Brown,
1910), and Fiji (Williams, 1858). The
Malayan-type upland rice culture of
Madagascar was described by Flacourt
(1661) as employing the planting stick.
Examples from the New World of its
use are less easily found but may be
cited from Chiapas, southern Mexico
(La Farge, 1927), and the Yucatán
Peninsula (Lundell, 1937).

Turning to the literature on continental Africa, we find that most of the
agricultural descriptions are of hoe cultivation, and we get the impression
(this appears to have been also the
conclusion of Bews, 1935) that at the
time of the European explorers of a
century or more ago the hoe had long
replaced the digging stick among Bantu
cultivators. Livingstone (1875) encountered in what was to become
Northern Rhodesia a miserable tribe
(the Babisa) who lived on many wild
fruits, roots, and leaves, but who also
practiced the most primitive type of
hoe cultivation with a wooden V-shaped
implement made from a branch with
another springing out of it, with which
they clawed the soil after scattering
seed. This primitive tool might almost
as well have been regarded as a surviving precursor of the plow as of the
hoe. In other districts of the same general region, however, Livingstone found
evidence of smelting of iron and possession of iron tools from very ancient
times.

The next higher type of tool after the
hoe was the plow, but this in its primi-

tive forms was too ineffective and fragile an implement for breaking sod. Introduction of modern types opened a
period of plowing of grassland though
with no regard to contours or erosion,
which resulted in great soil damage.

Ashes and Termite Debris as Fertilizer

Leached ashes, from concentrated
fertilizer salts in trees, afforded the
only fertilizer that the primitive agriculturist had. This was absorbed only
partially by his crops, the remainder
was lost in drainage, and the supply
was sufficient for only a crop or two.
After primitive man discovered the
value of the ash, he conceived the idea
of lopping branches from near-by trees
to burn on his field. So came about the
system which in Africa is known as
chitemene. This corresponds to an ancient practice in Europe, though its
origin is unknown. In Northern Rhodesia, the region which contributed the
word *"chitemene"* to agricultural literature, lopping and pollarding trees on
fallow land to burn on the fields has
become standard practice in the cycle
of land use, for the great part of the
land in forest fallow contributes part of
its growth increment each year to the
fertilization of the smaller part under
cultivation.[15]

15. The Livingstones (1866) and Livingstone
(1875) seem to have been the first to observe and describe what must have been
chitemene in Nyasa along the Rovuma River.
An excellent, and the most complete, description of the method as applied to growing a
specific crop is that of Clements (1933) for
finger millet (*Eleusine coracana*) in Nyasaland. Accounts by Hailey (1945), Richards
(1939), and Trapnell and Clothier (1937)
for Northern Nigeria and of Burnett (1948)
for the Sudan are especially important.
Burnett (1948) described for the Sudan a
most amazing modification of *chitemene*,
which depends upon the reduction of the
accessory wood to fertilizer through the action of termites instead of fire. The land to
be regenerated is piled with branches and
leaves from adjacent areas to a thickness of
a couple of feet. In four months the termites

In India the aboriginal tribes of the peninsula have practiced an equivalent of *chitemene*. It was described for the Korku of the Central Provinces by Forsythe (1889); it is called *parka* or *dippa* by the Maria Gonds of Bastar in the Central Provinces (Grigson, 1938); it has been studied by Fürer-Haimendorf (1949) among the Reddi of Hyderabad.

Sod- or Soil-burning

Similar to fertilization by burning of vegetation to secure ash is the system of sod- or soil-burning which is resorted to in India and Africa. It is believed to improve the texture of the soil as well as to fertilize it, and it apparently was met with approval by Crowther (1948), one of the contributors to Tothill's volume (1948) on *Agriculture in the Sudan*, although Tothill himself dissented.

In Nyasaland, Livingstone (1875) found that hoe cultivation of grassland was accompanied by soil-burning. Ma-

---

will have reduced it to dust, and this purely biological process will not have destroyed or dissipated valuable manurial constituents. This system is practiced by the Dinka, but neighboring tribes, instead of using fire, let the termites dispose of felled material on clearings which are not enriched by additional loppings.

In West Africa (Alawa district, Niger Province) Taylor (1942) found that pagan villagers were keeping plots in permanent cultivation by the use of broken-up termite mounds as fertilizer and that the same people (doubtless of Bantu affinity) arranged for the pastoral Fulani to "kraal" their cattle on land which was thus rendered fertile and productive. Other African groups did the same without saving animal manure and transporting it to their fields.

Copland (1822) wrote of what may have been the equivalent of the *chitemene* system in Madagascar. His work was based upon the archives of the London Missionary Society, and the particular account was of burning bamboo to procure ashes for fertilizing rice fields in the vicinity of Tamatave, where Flacourt had first described the burning of bamboo to make rice fields.

ravi or Mananja people made flat heaps of dry grass and weeds. On top they piled sods and soil. Igniting the heap from below resulted in combustion of the vegetable matter and humus. Livingstone said: "The burning is slow, and most of the products of combustion are retained to fatten the field; in this way the people raise large crops." Similar accounts are found for the Sudan and for India (Crowther, 1948), where sod-burning extended to Assam. There, according to Gurdon (1914), the Khasi turned over sods, allowed them to dry, and piled them with bundles of grass in sufficient quantity to insure that the ignited pile would be slowly reduced to denatured soil and ashes. This was a procedure which, Gurdon said, persisted even in England as the "paring and burning" process. In Africa it was apparently confined to the northeast, where it was probably an introduction from Asia.

Sod- or soil-burning is not associated with the most primitive agriculture, which utilizes only wooded land, but with hoe agriculture, which includes grassland as well.

The Hariq System of Grass-burning

Associated with agricultural use of grassland is not only sod-burning but also a specialized type of grassland-burning which actually destroys the grass. Known in the Sudan as *hariq*, the Arabic word for burning, it is an introduction from Asia (Burnett, 1948; Crowther, 1948).

In ordinary burning of grassland the firing is done during the dry season when the grasses are dormant and the rhizomes below ground are full of stored food to provide for the first rapid renewal of growth when the rains come. If burning takes place just when the new growth has exhausted the stored food, the rhizomes cannot renew growth, and the grass dies. So the *hariq* system of cultivation depends upon waiting until the stored food is nearly exhausted. Old dead grass must provide enough fuel to kill the lush new growth at the time when the latter cannot be renewed.

Alternation of Cropping and Controlled Fallow

In some sparsely populated districts of Africa where there was sufficient land to allow cropped plots to lie fallow long enough to restore soil fertility, there was often replacement of primary forest by secondary forest. As population increased and primary forest was no longer available, the agricultural tribes fell into a system of using the land in a more or less regular rotation of crop with secondary-forest fallow. They protected from fire adjoining land which had already been degraded to "parkland savanna," so that it reverted to forest, and took it into the rotation also. In this way the extent of land occupied by some sort of protective covering of forest was actually increased. This could take place deep enough within the closed forest region, so that there was excess moisture to permit natural reforestation; it could hardly happen in a marginal zone where clearing had taken place under conditions of unstable equilibrium.

According to Vanderyst (1924), whose views are expounded at considerable length by Kuhnholz-Lordat (1939), certain Bantu tribes in the western Congo developed the system of shifting agriculture into a regular rotation by protecting their fallow clearings from fire, and their procedure (the "Bantu system" of agriculture) even resulted in reclaiming to forest some of the savanna land adjoining their clearings. In the main, however, the great majority of observers have concluded that there has been general progress of savanna and grassland into the former forest zone, even though

there may have been exceptional instances of forest recovery on the border. Furthermore, there is general agreement that, as the forest has retreated, so, in the main, has agriculture, although there is some hoe agriculture of grassland, and recently the plow has been widely adopted, chiefly under European influence. The historical trend, however, was for seminomadic, partially Hamitic, pastoral tribes to push southward and to displace the dominant Bantu agriculturists.

In Africa there is seldom a happy mean between agricultural and pastoral pursuits. Hamitic tribes, often referred to as the "Fulani," were generally almost purely pastoral. Pressing southward from the Mediterranean region and the Sahara, they amalgamated by slave-raiding with some of the Bantu and often imposed their pastoral culture upon a mixed population. More equatorial Bantu tribes have remained almost entirely agricultural. The nomadic pastoral groups at the edge of the Sahara are as devastating as swarms of locusts, and those Bantu who have adopted pastoral life have often been burdened with unproductive, non-economic cattle, which are a measure of social distinction and of wealth without prosperity.

Before the advent of European colonialism, the economy of tropical Africa was usually suited only to a sparse population. Of course there were exceptionally fertile areas, but in the main a subsistence economy prevailed, with no surplus or facilities for trade. Production of agricultural products for export has created a demand for labor, and detribalized laborers have had to be fed, which has required more rational and scientific land use.

Control by Planting Selected Trees

Advocates of modification of the "Bantu system" of agriculture maintain that alternation of agricultural and silvicultural crops would be the best system of land management for certain areas which are suitable for growing uniform plantings of useful timber trees. The early forestry officials and advisers in India and Burma believed that such a system of rotation could be based upon shifting agriculture and that the agricultural phase would provide for subsistence of the relatively sparse population permanently employed to care for the forest. Areas cleared of mature forest on a successional basis could be planted to crops for a season or two and then planted with useful trees. At times of planting, the nursery-grown seedlings of valuable species, such as teak, would be too small to interfere with agricultural crops. As the planted trees grew, competing "weed" trees could be cleared out and used for fuel, poles, etc. In Burma the natives sometimes planted disused clearings with useful woody plants such as orange trees, tea, and betel-nut palms, so that a beginning seemed to have been made in enrichment of secondary jungle which might be adapted to an orderly rotation. So arose the so-called *taungya* forestry system, essentially of European inception, which has been widely talked about and advocated in Africa. Actually, there is nothing about it for which African precedent and an African name could not easily have been found: witness the conservation and planting of oil palms in agricultural clearings from West Africa to almost across the continent.

On the east coast of Sumatra the Pardembanan Batak sometimes planted exhausted clearings with sugar palm to be utilized years later. Sugar palms would mature and come into flower at about the same time. When the inflorescences had been tapped to make sugar and the abundant black fiber had been harvested for thatching, the productivity of the old clearing ended, for all the palms die at the conclusion of flowering. The land-use cycle then would end, and the old *ladang* (Malay) or *juma* (Batak) would be cleared again for dry-land rice, maize, manioc, bananas, and other food plants. The same natives somewhat systematically enriched forest with rattan seedlings grown in nursery beds from seeds procured while gathering mature rattan. Such a cycle of agricultural utilization and reversion to forest could not be indefinitely repeated, for increase in amount of grass led to closely repeated burnings which ended with a patch of grassland in which the *lalang* (*Imperata*) sod was too compact to be cultivated, except in a very limited way. In the course of ages of human occupation much of Sumatra has been transformed from forest into artificial prairie (*padang*). Of course, the densely populous parts of the central Batak lands have depended mainly on permanent cultivation of wet-rice terraces (*sawah*). The *djoema* or *ladang* system of temporary agriculture has been replaced by *sawah* cultivation, except on submarginal or distant, peripheral land. This was undoubtedly a development that took place hundreds or thousands of years ago.

In Burma and Sumatra enrichment of the forest fallow intergrades with enrichment of the secondary forest-at-large, and both are not far removed from village plantings of useful trees which we have regarded as primitive horticulture. There would seem to be no insuperable psychological impediment to the ultimate replacement of shifting agriculture by an agricultural-silvicultural cycle. Among primitive agriculturists antipathy to forest reserves is marked, especially, in Africa, but is being overcome by the establishment of village woodlands where people may obtain building materials and fuel. At any rate, the accelerated denudation of tropical lands has come to present a problem of first magnitude.

Civilized Destruction of Forests

It is an interesting fact that, wherever a few colonists of a higher culture have gone into countries of primitive culture, they have largely dropped to the primitive level of agriculture. This is well demonstrated by the history of the colonization of the eastern United States, where land was ruthlessly cleared, with waste of the forest, and eventually with waste of much of the soil by erosion. The best tropical example is provided by Cuba, where the situation was early complicated by the addition of an African slave population to the original vanishing Carib population on about the same cultural level. In the presence of what seemed inexhaustible resources of forest and land, and with slave labor, supposedly civilized man dropped back to the agricultural level of primitive tribesmen. This also took place along the coast of Brazil. If an example were to be chosen from the Orient, it might be pointed out that the agricultural procedure of Europeans in the famous Deli tobacco region of Sumatra was at first merely an extension of the indigenous *ladang* agriculture, which had already reduced much of the forest in the most fertile area of Sumatra's east coast to useless *lalang* grassland (*padang*). That is to say, it was useless to the native, who could not turn the heavy sod with the resources at his command, but it could be employed under European management. Even considering its long-fallow rotation, the Deli tobacco system was no great improvement on native *ladang* agriculture, and, in recognition of its devastation of a disproportionate amount of forest for the amount of land actually producing a crop at any one time, it was not a credit to civilized culture.

Replacement of overmature rubber trees on plantations in the Far East might well be preceded by a season or two of cropping, but permanent land use in the tropics is likely to utilize woody plants almost exclusively and to resemble forestry in its procedures. There are many who believe that the most profitable agriculture for non-industrialized tropical regions will always be production for export of distinctively tropical products, such as rubber, coffee, and bananas, with only a minimum of subsistence crops for local consumption. The tropics, if a peaceful world and freedom of trade could be maintained, might provide a quite satisfactory standard of living by their export trade for a population adjusted to the productivity of its land.

There are many persons in cultured communities who see nothing harmful about destruction of forest in shifting cultivation. The prevailing philosophy among the administrative class in many colonial countries has been (1) that deforestation was not harmful if the forest contained many different species and the commercially valuable ones among them were too infrequent to make exploitation "pay"; (2) that there was so much forest that it would never "pay" to preserve even potentially valuable inaccessible forest; (3) that forest harbored noxious animals or that it was "unhealthy"; (4) that land had to be cleared preliminary to utilization (it was almost a law of nature that it should be, so why try to prevent it?); (5) that forest was less profitable than grazing land; and (6) that shifting cultivation was "customary," and ancient customs should not be interfered with.

Primitive Conservation of Forests

Some of the most interesting phenomena in connection with the preservation of primary forest in the tropics are the little reserves left here and there by aborigines, which, except for the advance of "civilization," would have sufficed as sources of seed for the restoration of some species of the original flora. These were sacred groves, often occupying hilltops, or places where there were unusual manifestations of nature that were attributed to wild or ancestral spirits.

Such sacred spots have been reported from a good many distant regions. To take some random examples from Asia and Indonesia, on the island of Timor, Forbes (1885) found it difficult to secure botanical collections from the places richest in interesting species because they were *luli*, that is, under a taboo. In Borneo, Nieuwenhuis (1904–7) found the same taboo, there termed by a cognate word, *lali*.[16] Jenks (1905) pictures a sacred grove of the Bontok of Luzon. In India some areas occupied by the aboriginal tribes had many sacred groves. A most regrettable feature of missionary activity among these tribes is that converts were encouraged

by their teachers to desecrate sacred places by cutting wood and by other depredations.[17] The *Gazetteer of India* (1908, XV, 255) said that the highest peaks of the Khasi Hills of Assam were clothed with indigenous forest "which superstition has preserved from the axe of the wood cutter." Gurdon (1914) said of the numerous sacred groves (*ki'law kyntang*) that they were a remarkable feature of the same region, that they were generally located near the summit of hills or just below the brows of the hills, and that it was an offense to cut wood in them except for cremations. They still persisted in 1938, when Bor (1942) visited them. He gave an excellent account of these sacred patches of evergreen forest which just before World War II were the only

16. In Sumatra (Asahan) places on flat land inhabited by the Pardembanan Batak were found by the writer to be considered sacred to forest spirits if lateral growth of superficial roots and fallen leaves had made a roof over a little forest stream and thus concealed it from view except at short intervals. Sometimes there would be just a little aperture, a foot or so across, where the swiftly flowing stream appeared, running over a white sand bottom through a black muck swamp. Or, at other places, the stream could be heard murmuring along under the spreading superficial roots of a tree. The curious gentle noises filled the Batak with what seems to a conservationist a most commendable feeling of reverence. Nothing would induce them to clear such a spot, and, if it was necessary in connection with preparing a plantation site, Chinese had to be employed for the work. Ypes (1932) stated that the Dairi Batak maintained "island-like places of prayer" (*poelo-poelo sĕmbahĕn*), or sacred groves, in which a particular "prayer tree" (*Kajoe sĕmbahĕn*) was considered to be the exact residence of the spirit that was prayed to.

17. Bor remarked (1942, p. 159): "It has always been a matter of great regret to me that the spread of Christianity in the hills tends to involve the complete destruction of all that is most interesting in the lives and customs of primitive peoples. . . . The Khasi attitude of mind being what it is it is unreasonable to expect that the sacred groves will last forever." With their disappearance goes the last remnant of the "climax forests of the Khasi Hills." In Chota Nagpur, Bradley-Birt (1910) said that the superstitions of the Kols had preserved in the sacred groves (*sarna*) what little remained of primitive forest. The same author (1905, pp. 257, 279) had said of the Santals of Dravidian stock that each village preserved a sacred grove (*jaher than*), scene of communal sacrifices. Roy (1912) wrote of the Mundas of Chota Nagpur that their only temples were the village *sarnas*, or sacred groves, and that in some Mundari villages no other original forest had escaped the *jara* fire. The *jara* was the forest clearing of shifting agriculture.

As an example from India of the protection of a single sacred species, Hahn (1906) tells us that the *karm* tree (*Nauclea parvifolia*) was worshiped by the Oraon and Kharwar of Chota Nagpur and was preserved even when all other trees were cleared away for shifting agriculture. The same author said that, of the sacred groves of the Munda, only a few trees were left and that some *sarna* had been pre-empted for Christian mission stations. Thus the traditional conservation was negated by the advance of civilization!

remnant of ancient vegetation. There has been extraordinary destruction since then in that region, partly caused by intrusive population with no local traditions.

Sacred groves and mountains have likewise been reported in various parts of tropical Africa, from the Ivory Coast at the west to Mozambique at the east.[18] In Madagascar, as we learn from Lord (1900), the most ancient traditional site of habitation in Imerina, the capital province, was still preserved as a sacred grove in 1853. In general, places traditionally associated with the spirits of the Vazimba or most ancient inhabitants were regarded with awe and were not devastated except through European influence. The same was true of the burial places of the Hova kings and other ancient burial sites.

As already indicated, the veneration for sacred groves and wooded burial places is related to worshipful regard for certain species of trees or for individual trees which are accounted sacred. Such limited regard is not so efficacious for conservation of all vegetation of a sacred place, but it has doubtless accounted for the preservation of

18. As an example one may cite Livingstone's (1875) observation of a tree called "*bokonto*," which was preserved in a "dark sepulchral grove" near Tamiala in the middle of what is now Nyasaland and which seemed to have been exterminated elsewhere. Livingstone also (1866) noted, near Motunta in the country from which the Batoka tribe had been driven by slave-raiders, that the sites of deserted villages were marked by stone circles on which corn safes had stood, as well as by fruit trees and gigantic wild fig trees. From Livingstone's later work (1875) we learn that on the eastern shore of Lake Nyasa (barely within Mozambique) the sites of old villages were marked by the "sacred fig." Bégué (1937) mentioned as vegetational vestiges the sacred forests near certain village sites in the Ivory Coast. Schnell (1950) says that certain mountain crests in the same country are refuges of the native flora because they are held sacred to mountain spirits. He cites similar observations of Bouys and Chevalier.

seed trees of certain species which might otherwise have been destroyed. In Formosa and Sumatra the custom has prevailed of propagating certain trees from the parent-village at a new village site. In all countries where Buddhism has been important certain sacred trees have been propagated at new religious centers. In this way the pipal (*Ficus religiosa*) has been widely spread in southern Asia, and other species, such as *Ficus benjamina*, have spread throughout Indonesia.

Forest Renewal and Continuous Productivity

Overcoming formerly natural limitations on population growth goes on apace. The progress of medical science keeps people alive longer; the progress of agricultural science provides more food; the development of engineering projects improves control over floods and drought; and the spread of civilization tends to stop limitation of population by minor warfare. All these trends produce overpopulation. If there is to be no present restraint on population, no looking to the future, no doubt that science will always find a substitute for depleted natural resources, then there is no hope for success of those who would conserve the earth's endowment for the future.

Yet it would seem almost axiomatic that, if human life is so valuable a thing, its long future should be assured. In fact, it would seem to those of us who believe in conservation that the difference between civilized and uncivilized man is that truly civilized man feels an obligation to leave the world as good as, or better than, he inherited it, for the benefit of future generations. Though humane, man may nevertheless be uncivilized if he cannot take thought for the future as well as for the present, and, if ruthless in destruction of natural resources, he is merely a barbarian.

We may ask: What is the bearing of all this on the effect of primitive agriculture and fire on tropical vegetation? The bearing is simple. The rise of man from brute to savage, from savage to barbarian, and from barbarian to the semicivilized man of today has come at great expense to the resources of the world as it was, let us say, before man's mastery of fire and tools enabled him to dominate the earth. He knew no better than to do what has been found to be harmful. Now he knows better. He can take stock of what he has done and can plan for the future, before everything has been destroyed. He is now entering upon a new age in which his very knowledge, without wise planning, may bring about retrogression and loss of what he has gained.

One cannot argue that man should not strive to retain his dominance. It would be idle to attempt to taboo all interference with nature, in so far as nature can be modified for the ultimate good of man. But ruthless destruction now for only fleeting advantage, followed by the everlasting depreciation of resources for the future, can only be condemned. The wastefulness of shifting agriculture must be condemned by those who look to the future. The goal of our efforts now should be to return land, already greatly deteriorated through unwise predatory utilization, to the state of forest and to elevate the remainder to the state of continuous productivity.

The chief objective of this chapter has been to point out what man has done by primitive agriculture and fire in tropical lands around the world to bring about deterioration. Frank realization of what has happened must be the first step toward reform.

REFERENCES

AMES, OAKES
  1939 *Economic Annuals and Human Cultures.* Cambridge, Mass.: Botanical Museum of Harvard University. 153 pp.
AUBREVILLE, A.
  1937 "Dix années d'expériences sylvicoles en Côte d'Ivoire," *Revue des eaux et forêts,* LXXV, No. 4, 289–302; No. 5, pp. 385–400. Paris: Société des Amis et Anciens Elèves de l'École Nationale des Eaux et Forêts.
  1949a *Climats, forêts et désertification de l'Afrique tropicale.* Paris: Société d'Éditions Géographiques, Maritimes et Coloniales. 352 pp.
  1949b *Contribution à la paléohistoire des forêts de l'Afrique tropicale.* Paris: Société d'Éditions Géographiques, Maritimes et Coloniales. 98 pp.
BALLET, JULES
  1894 *La Guadeloupe: Renseignements sur l'histoire, la flore, la faune, la géologie, la minéralogie, l'agriculture,* Vols. I–III: *1625–1715.* Basse-Terre:

Imprimerie du Gouvernement. 369 pp.
BARTLETT, H. H.
  1919 "The Manufacture of Sugar from *Arenga saccharifera* in Asahan, on the East Coast of Sumatra," *Twenty-first Report, Michigan Academy of Science,* pp. 155–65.
  1935 "The Batak Lands of North Sumatra, from the Standpoint of Recent American Botanical Collections," *Natural and Applied Sciences Bulletin,* IV, No. 3, 211–323. Manila: University of the Philippines.
  1955 *Fire in Relation to Primitive Agriculture and Grazing in the Tropics: Annotated Bibliography.* Ann Arbor, Mich.: University of Michigan, Botanical Gardens. 568 pp.
BATES, HENRY WALTER
  1864 *The Naturalist on the River Amazons.* 2d ed. London: John Murray. 466 pp.
BAUDESSON, HENRI
  1919 *Indo-China and Its Primitive Peoples.* Trans. E. APPLEBY HOLT.

London: Hutchinson & Co.; New York: E. P. Dutton Co. 328 pp.

BEGBIE, P. J.
1834 *The Malayan Peninsula, Embracing Its History, Manners and Customs of the Inhabitants, Politics, Natural History, etc., from Its Earliest Records.* Printed for the Author at the Vepery Mission Press. 521 pp.

BÉGUÉ, LOUIS
1937 *Contribution à l'étude de la végétation forestière de la Haute-Côte d'Ivoire.* ("Publications du Comité d'Études Historiques et Scientifiques de l'Afrique Occidentale Française," Series B, No. 4.) Paris: Librairie Larose. 126 pp.

BEWS, J. W.
1935 *Human Ecology.* London: Oxford University Press. 312 pp.

BOR, N. L.
1938 "A Sketch of the Vegetation of the Aka Hills, Assam: A Synecological Study," *Indian Forest Records,* I, No. 4, 103–221. Delhi: Government of India Press.
1942 "The Relict Vegetation of the Shillong Plateau, Assam," *Indian Forest Records* (N.S.), *Botany,* III, No. 6, 152–95. New Delhi: Government of India Press.

BOUILLENNE, RAY
1926 "Savanes équatoriales en Amérique du Sud," *Bulletin Société Royale de Botanique de Belgique,* Series 2, LVIII, 217–23.

BRADLEY-BIRT, F. B.
1905 *The Story of an Indian Upland.* London: Smith, Elder & Co. 354 pp.
1910 *Chota Nagpore: A Little-known Province of the Empire.* London: Smith, Elder & Co. 327 pp.

BRANDIS, DIETRICH
1906 *Indian Trees: An Account of Trees, Shrubs, Woody Climbers, Bamboos, and Palms Indigenous or Commonly Cultivated in the British Indian Empire.* London: Constable & Co., Ltd. 767 pp. (4th impression, 1924.)

BRENNER, JOACHIM FREIHERR VON
1894 *Besuch bei den Kannibalen Sumatras: Erste Durchquerung der un-abhängigen Batak-Lande.* Würzburg: Verlag von Leo Woerl. 388 pp.

BROWN, GEORGE
1910 *Melanesians and Polynesians: Their Life-Histories Described and Compared.* London: Macmillan & Co. 451 pp.

BROWN, WILLIAM H.
1919 *Vegetation of Philippine Mountains.* Manila: Bureau of Printing. 434 pp.

BROWN, WILLIAM H.; MERRILL, E. D.; and YATES, HARRY S.
1917 "The Revegetation of Volcano Island, Luzon, Philippine Islands, since the Eruption of Taal Volcano in 1911," *Philippine Journal of Science, C. Botany,* XII, No. 4, 177–248.

BRUCE, JAMES
1790 *Travels To Discover the Source of the Nile, in the Years 1768 . . . 1773.* 5 vols. Edinburgh: G. G. J. & J. Robinson.

BURBIDGE, F. W.
1880 *The Gardens of the Sun: Or a Naturalist's Journal on the Mountains and in the Forests and Swamps of Borneo and the Sulu Archipelago.* London: John Murray. 364 pp.

BURNETT, J. R.
1948 "Crop Production," pp. 275–301 in TOTHILL, J. D. (ed.), *Agriculture in the Sudan.* London: Oxford University Press. 974 pp.

BUSSE, WALTER
1908 "Die periodische Grasbrände im tropischen Africa, ihr Einfluss auf die Vegetation und ihre Bedeutung für die Landeskultur," *Mitteilungen aus den deutschen Schutzgebieten,* XXI, No. 2, 113–39. Berlin: Ernst Siegfried Mittler & Sohn.

CAMPBELL, JOHN
1864 *A Personal Narrative of Thirteen Years Service amongst the Wild Tribes of Khondistan for the Suppression of Human Sacrifice.* London: Hurst & Blackett. 320 pp.

CATAT, LOUIS
N.d. *Voyage à Madagascar (1889–1890).* Paris: L'Univers Illustré. 410 pp.

CHALMERS, JAMES, and GILL, WILLIAM WYATT
1885 *Work and Adventure in New Guinea, 1877 to 1885.* London: Religious Tract Society. 342 pp.

CHAMISSO, ADELBERT VON
N.d. *Reise um die Welt mit der Romanzoffischen Entdeckungs-Expedition in den Jahren 1815–1818 auf der Brigg Rurik, Kapitän Otto v. Kotzebue,* Vol. I: *Tagebuch;* Vol. II: *Anhang, Bemerkungen und Ansichten.* (Vols. III and IV in *Chamissos gesammelte Werke* . . . , ed. MAX KOCH.) Stuttgart: Verlag der Cotta'schen Buchhandlung. Vol. III, 279 pp.; Vol. IV, 304 pp.

CHARON, A.
1897 "Étude sur les prairies et l'élevage du bœuf dans le pays Sihanaka et le Haut-Bouéni, Colonie de Madagascar," *Notes, reconnaissances et explorations,* II, No. 12, 561–91. Tananarive: Imprimerie Officielle.

CHEMIN-DUPONTÈS, PAUL
1909 "La Question forestière en Indochine," *Bulletin de Comité de l'Asie Française,* IX, No. 101, 340–48. Paris: Comité Asie Française.

CHIPP, T. F.
1927 *The Gold Coast Forest: A Study in Synecology.* ("Oxford Forestry Memoirs," No. VII.) Oxford: Clarendon Press. 94 pp.

CLEMENTS, J. B.
1933 "The Cultivation of Finger Millet *(Eleusine coracana)* and Its Relation to Shifting Cultivation in Nyasaland," *Empire Forestry Journal,* XII, No. 1, 16–20.

COOK, O. F.
1908 *Change of Vegetation on the South Texas Prairies.* (U.S. Department of Agriculture, Bureau of Plant Industry, Circular No. 14.) Washington, D.C.: Government Printing Office. 7 pp.
1909 *Vegetation Effected by Agriculture in Central America.* (U.S. Department of Agriculture, Bureau of Plant Industry, Bulletin No. 145.) Washington, D.C.: Government Printing Office. 30 pp.
1921 "Milpa Agriculture, a Primitive

Tropical System," *Annual Report of the Smithsonian Institution for 1919,* pp. 307–26. Washington, D.C.: Government Printing Office.

COOKE, C. WYTHE
1931 "Why the Mayan Cities of the Petén District, Guatemala, Were Abandoned," *Journal of the Washington Academy of Science,* XXI, No. 13, 283–87.

COPLAND, SAMUEL
1822 *A History of the Island of Madagascar, Comprising a Political Account of the Island, the Religion, Manners and Customs of Its Inhabitants, and Its Natural Productions.* London: Burton & Smith. 369 pp.

COVENTRY, B. O.
1929 "Denudation of the Punjab Hills," *Indian Forest Records,* XIV, Part II, 49–78. Calcutta: Government of India, Central Publication Branch.

CRAWFURD, JOHN
1820 *History of the Indian Archipelago.* 3 vols. Edinburgh: Archibald Constable & Co.

CROWTHER, FRANK
1948 "A Review of Experimental Work," pp. 439–592 (chap. xx) in TOTHILL, J. D. (ed.), *Agriculture in the Sudan.* London: Oxford University Press. 947 pp.

DANSEREAU, PIERRE
1948 *The Distribution and Structure of Brazilian Forests.* (Bulletin du Service de Biogéographie, No. 3.) Montreal: University of Montreal. 17 pp. (Repaged reprint from *Forestry Chronicle,* XXIII [1947], 261–77.)

DELGADO, JUAN J.
1892 *Historia general sacro-profana, política y natural de las Islas del Poniente Llamadas Filipinas.* Manila: Imp. El Eco de Filipinas de D. Juan Atayde. 1,012 pp. (First publication of MS of 1751–54.)

DUVEYRIER, HENRI
1864 *Exploration du Sahara: Les Touareg du Nord.* Paris: Challamel aîné. 499 pp.

FALCONER, THOMAS
1797 *The Voyage of Hanno Translated and Accompanied with the*

Greek Text; Explained from the Accounts of Modern Travellers; Defended against the Objections of Mr. Dodwell, and Other Writers; and Illustrated by Maps from Ptolemy, D'Anville, and Bougainville. London: T. Cadell Jun. & Daviss. 105 pp.

FINLEY, JOHN PARK
1913 *The Subanu: Studies of Sub-Visayan Mountain Folk of Mindanao, Part I: Ethnographical and Geographical Sketch of Land and People.* (Carnegie Institution of Washington Publication No. 184.) Washington, D.C. 4 pp.

FISCHER, ARTHUR F.
1932 "Annual Report of the Director of Forestry of the Philippine Islands for the Fiscal Year Ended December 31, 1931," *Annual Report of the Department of Agriculture and Natural Resources for the Year 1931,* pp. 523–905. Manila: Bureau of Printing.

FLACOURT, ESTIENNE DE
1661 *Histoire de la Grande Isle Madagascar ... avec une relation de ce qui s'est passé és années 1655, 1656, et 1657, non encor veuë par la première impression.* 2 vols. Paris: Chez Pierre Bien-fait.

FORBES, HENRY O.
1885 *A Naturalist's Wanderings in the Eastern Archipelago: A Narrative of Travel and Exploration from 1878 to 1883.* New York: Harper & Bros. 536 pp.

FORSYTHE, JAMES
1889 *The Highlands of Central India: Notes on Their Forests and Wild Tribes, Natural History and Sports.* London: Chapman & Hall. 475 pp.

FROÉS ABREU, SYLVIO
1931 *Na Terra das Palmeiras.* Rio de Janeiro: Officina Industrial Graphica. 287 pp.

FÜRER-HAIMENDORF, CHRISTOPH VON
1943 *The Aboriginal Tribes of Hyderabad,* Vol. I: *The Chenchus.* London: Macmillan & Co. 391 pp.

FÜRER-HAIMENDORF, CHRISTOPH and ELIZABETH VON
1943 *The Aboriginal Tribes of Hyderabad,* Vol. II: *The Reddis of the Bison Hills.* London: Macmillan & Co. 364 pp.

GAMBLE, J. SYKES
1875 "The Darjeeling Forests," *Indian Forester,* I, No. 2, 73–99.

GENTRY, HOWARD SCOTT
1946 "The Durango Grasslands." University of Michigan thesis, Ann Arbor. Ann Arbor: University Microfilms. 165 pp.

GOSSWEILER, JOHN, and MENDONÇA, F. A.
1939 *Carta fitogeográfica de Angola.* Lisbon: Republica Portuguesa, Ministério das Colónias, Edição do Govêrno Geral de Angola. 243 pp.

GOUROU, PIERRE
1936 *Les Paysans du delta Tonkinois: Étude de géographie humaine.* Paris: Éditions d'Art et d'Histoire. 666 pp.
1947 *Les Pays tropicaux: Principes d'une géographie humaine et économique.* Paris: Presses Universitaires de France. 196 pp.

GRIGSON, W. V.
1938 *The Maria Gonds of Bastar.* London: Oxford University Press. 350 pp.

GURDON, P. R. T.
1914 *The Khasis.* London: Macmillan & Co. 232 pp.

HAGEN, B.
1903 "Die Gajo-Länder auf Sumatra," *Jahresbericht des Frankfurter Vereins für Geographie und Statistik,* Nos. 66–67, pp. 29–85. Frankfurt on the Main: Gebrüder Knauer.

HAHN, FERDINAND
1906 *Blicke in die Geisteswelt der heidnischen Kols. Sammlung von Sagen, Märchen und Liedern der Oraon in Chota Nagpur.* Gütersloh: C. Bertelsmann. 116 pp.

HAILEY, LORD
1945 *An African Survey: A Study of Problems Arising in Africa South of the Sahara.* 2d ed. London: Oxford University Press. 1,838 pp.

HALL, A. DANIEL
1930 *The Improvement of Native Agriculture in Relation to Population and Public Health.* London: Oxford University Press. 104 pp.

HARROY, JEAN-PAUL
1949 *Afrique: Terre qui meurt. La Dégradation des sols africains sous*

l'influence de la colonisation. 2d ed. Brussels: Marcel Hayez. 557 pp.

HARTEN, J. A.
1953 "Beknopt Overzicht van de Landbouw der Bantu's in de Unie van Zuid-Afrika en zÿn Problemen," *Indonesië,* VI, No. 4, 317–29.

HARTMANN, C. W.
1897 "The Indians of Northwestern Mexico," *Congrès Internationale des Américanistes, Comptes-rendus de la Dixième Session, Stockholm, 1894,* pp. 115–36. Stockholm: Imprimerie Ivar Haeggström.

HAZEU, G. A. J.
1907 *Gajōsch-Nederlandsch Woordenboek met Nederlandsch-Gajōsch Register.* Batavia: Landsdrukkerij. 1,148 pp.

HISLOP, STEPHEN
1886 *Papers Relating to the Aboriginal Tribes of the Central Provinces, Left in MSS by the Late Revd. Stephen Hislop. . . . Edited . . . by R. Temple.* Nagpore(?). N.p.

HODGSON, BRIAN HOUGHTON
1880 *Miscellaneous Essays Relating to Indian Subjects,* Vol. I. London: Trübner & Co. 407 pp. (Section I, essay on the Kocch, Bódo, and Dhimál tribes, pp. 1–160. Original ed., Calcutta, 1847.)

HODSON, T. C.
1911 *The Naga Tribes of Manipur.* London: Macmillan & Co. 212 pp.

HOEHNE, F. C.
1910 *Historia natural,* Part I: Botânica. (Annex No. 5.) Rio de Janeiro: Commissão de Linhas Telegraphicas e Estrategicas de Matto Grosso ao Amazonas. 71 pp.
1914 *Expedição scientifica Rosevelt-Rondon: Botânica.* (Annex No. 2.) Rio de Janeiro. 81 pp.
1916 *Relatorios dos trabalhos de botânica e viagens executatos durante os annos de 1908 e 1909, apresentados ao Sr. Tenente Coronel de Engenharia Candido Mariano da Silva Rondon.* (Publication No. 28, Annex No. 4.) Rio de Janeiro: Commissão de Linhas Telegraphicas e Estrategicas de Matto Grosso ao Amazonas. 54 pp.

HOLDRIDGE, LESLIE RENSSELAER
1947 "The Pine Forest and Adjacent Mountain Vegetation of Haiti, Considered from the Standpoint of a New Climatic Classification of Plant Formations." University of Michigan thesis, Ann Arbor. Ann Arbor: University Microfilms. 186 pp.

HOOKER, J .D.
1909 "Botany," pp. 157–212 (chap. iv) in *The Imperial Gazetteer of India,* Vol. I. New ed. Oxford: Clarendon Press. 568 pp.

HUMBERT, HENRI
1923 *Les Composées de Madagascar.* Caen: Imprimerie E. Lanier. 337 pp.
1927 *La Destruction d'une flore insulaire par le feu: Principaux aspects de la végétation à Madagascar.* ("Mémoires de l'Académie Malgache," Vol. V.) Tananarive. 79 pp.

JACOBS, JULIUS
1894 *Het Familie- en Kampongleven op Groot-Atjeh: Eene Bijdrage tot de Ethnographie van Noord-Sumatra.* 2 vols. Leiden: E. J. Brill. 408+271 pp.

JENKS, ALBERT ERNEST
1905 *The Bontoc Igorot.* ("Department of Interior, Ethnological Survey Publications," Vol I.) Manila: Bureau of Public Printing. 266 pp.

JOHNSTON, H. H.
1884 *The River Congo, from Its Mouth to Bólóbó, with a General Description of the Natural History and Anthropology of Its Western Basin.* London: Sampson Low, Marston, Searle, & Rivington. 470 pp.

JOUSTRA, M.
1926 *Batakspiegel: Tweede, vermeerderde Druk.* ("Uitgaven van het Bataksch Instituut," No. 21.) Leiden: S. C. Van Doesburgh. 382 pp.

JUNGHUHN, FRANZ
1847 *Die Battaländer auf Sumatra: Im Auftrage Sr. Excellenz des General-Gouverneurs von Niederländisch-Indien Hrn. P. Merkus in den Jahren 1840 und 1841 untersucht und beschrieben. . . . Aus den holländischen Original übersetzt vom Verfasser,* Vol. I: *Chorographie;* Vol. II: *Völkerkunde.* Berlin: G. Reimer. 300+388 pp.

KUHNHOLTZ-LORDAT, G.
1939 *La Terre incendiée: Essai d'agro-*

nomie comparée. Nîmes: Éditions de
la Maison Carrée, Ateliers Brugier.
362 pp.

KURZ, SULPICE
1875 *Preliminary Report on the Forest
and Other Vegetation of Pegu.* [Cal-
cutta:] C. B. Lewis, Baptist Mission
Press. 97+95+34 pp.

LA FARGE, OLIVER
1927 "Observations of the Indians of
the San Martin Pajápan Region" and
"The Coatzacoalcos Basin," pp. 49–
92; "Pines," pp. 329–43; "The Oco-
singo Valley," pp. 245–57; and "The
Northern Tzeltal Tribes," pp. 325–75
in BLOM, FRANS, and LA FARGE,
OLIVER (eds.), *Tribes and Temples:
A Record of the Expedition to Middle
America Conducted by the Tulane
University of Louisiana.* 2 vols. New
Orleans: Tulane University of Louisi-
ana.

LANGE, ALGOT
1914 *The Lower Amazon.* New York
and London: G. P. Putnam's Sons.
468 pp.

LAVAUDEN, L.
1931 "Le Déboisement et la végétation de Madagascar," *Revue de la
botanique appliquée et agriculture
coloniale,* No. 122, pp. 817–24. (Seen
only in abstract; reference not verified.)

LINDMAN, C. A. M.
1900 *Vegetationen i Rio Grande do
Sul (Sydbrasilien).* Stockholm: Nordin
& Josephson. 239 pp.

LIVINGSTONE, DAVID
1875 *The Last Journals of David Livingstone in Central Africa, from Eighteen Hundred and Sixty-five to His
Death, Continued by a Narrative by
Horace Waller.* Chicago: Jansen, Mc-
Clurg & Co. 541 pp.

LIVINGSTONE, DAVID and CHARLES
1866 *Narrative of an Expedition to
the Zambesi and Its Tributaries; and
of the Discovery of the Lakes Shirwa
and Nyassa, 1858–1864.* New York:
Harper & Bros.; London: J. Murray.
608 pp.

LÖFGREN, ALBERTO
1898 *Ensaio para uma distribuição dos
vegetaes nos diversos grupos floristicos*

no Estado de São Paulo. 2d ed. ("Bo-
letim da Commissão Geographica e
Geologica de São Paulo," No. 11.)
São Paulo: Typographia, Vanorden
& Cia. 50 pp.

LORD, T.
1900 "The Early History of Imerina
Based upon a Native Account," *An-
tananarivo Annual and Madagascar
Magazine,* No. 24, pp. 451–75. An-
tananarivo: Press of the London Missionary Society.

LUNDELL, CYRUS LONGWORTH
1937 *The Vegetation of Petén.* With
an Appendix, "Studies of Mexican
and Central American Plants. I."
Washington, D.C.: Carnegie Institution of Washington. 244 pp.

MAASS, ALFRED
1910 *Durch Zentral-Sumatra.* Berlin:
Wilhelm Susserott. 851 pp.

MARCHE, ALFRED
1887 *Luçon et Palaouan: Six années
de voyage aux Philippines.* Paris:
Hachette & Cie. 406 pp.

MARCUSE, WALTER D.
1914 *Through Western Madagascar in
Quest of the Golden Bean.* London:
Hurst & Blackett, Ltd. 318 pp.

MARSDEN, WILLIAM
1783 *The History of Sumatra, Con-
taining an Account . . . of the Native
Inhabitants, with a Description of the
Natural Productions.* London: The
Author. 375 pp.

MARTIUS, C. F. P.
1840–65 *Flora Brasiliensis: Enumera-
tio plantarum in Brasilia hactenus de-
tectarum . . . Argumentum Fascicu-
lorum I–XL.* Leipzig: F. Fleischer.
CX coll.; LIX tabb.

MATHESON, J. K., and BOVILL, E. W.
1950 *East African Agriculture: A
Short Survey of the Agriculture of
Kenya, Uganda, Tanganyika, and
Zanzibar, and of Its Principal Prod-
ucts.* London: Oxford University
Press. 332 pp.

MER, AUGUSTE
1885 *Mémoire sur le Périple d'Hannon.*
Paris: Librairie Académique Didier,
Emile Perrin, Librairie-Éditeur. 156
pp.

MERRILL, ELMER D.
1926 "General Ecology of Philippine

Plants and Animals," pp. 56–71; "Bibliography of Philippine Botany," pp. 155–239, in *An Enumeration of Philippine Flowering Plants.* Vol. IV. Manila: Bureau of Printing. 515 pp.

MOUHOT, HENRI
  1864   *Travels in the Central Parts of Indo-China (Siam), Cambodia, and Laos, during the Years 1858, 1859, and 1860.* 2 vols. London: John Murray. 303+301 pp.

NANO, JOSÉ F.
  1939   "Kaingin Laws and Penalties in the Philippines," *Philippine Journal of Forestry,* II, No. 2, 87–92.

NIEUWENHUIS, A. W.
  1904–7   *Quer durch Borneo: Ergebnisse seiner Reisen in den Jahren 1894, 1896–97, und 1898–1900.* 2 vols. Leiden: E. J. Brill. 557 pp.

PARKER, H.
  1910   *Village Folk-Tales of Ceylon.* 3 vols. London: Luzac & Co. 396+466+479 pp.

PENDLETON, ROBERT L.
  1933   "Cogonals and Reforestation with *Leucaena glauca,*" *Lingnam Science Journal,* XII, No. 4, 555–60.

PERRIER DE LA BATHIE, H.
  1917   "Au sujet des tourbières de Marotampona," *Bulletin de l'Académie Malgache* (N.S.), I, 137–38. Tananarive: Imprimerie Officielle.
  1927   *Le Tsaratanana, l'Ankaratra et l'Andringitra.* ("Mémoires de l'Académie Malgache," Vol. III.) Tananarive: G. Pitot et Cie. 71 pp. (Appendix II, "Historique de la destruction de la végétation de la cime de Tsaratanana et ses conséquences," pp. 26–28.)

PHILLIPS, JOHN
  1930*a*   "Some Important Vegetation Communities in the Central Province of Tanganyika Territory (Formerly German East Africa): A Preliminary Account," *Journal of Ecology,* XVIII, No. 2, 193–234.
  1930*b*   "Fire: Its Influence on Biotic Communities and Physical Factors in South and East Africa," *South African Journal of Science,* XXVII, 352–67. Johannesburg.

  1931   "The Biotic Community," *Journal of Ecology,* XIX, No. 1, 1–24.

PITTIER, H.
  1936   "Consideraciones acerca de la destrucción de los bosques e incendio de las sabanas," *Boletin de la Sociedad Venezolana de Ciencias Naturales,* III, No. 26, 291–302. Caracas.

POWELL, WILFRED
  1883   *Wanderings in a Wild Country; or, Three Years among the Cannibals of New Britain.* London: Samson Low, Marston, Searle & Rivington. 284 pp.

RICHARDS, AUDREY I.
  1939   *Land, Labour and Diet in Northern Rhodesia: An Economic Study of the Bemba Tribe.* (Published for the International Institute of African Languages and Cultures.) London: Oxford University Press. 423 pp.

ROBERTSON, WILLIAM B., JR.
  1955   "A Survey of the Effects of Fire in Everglades National Park." (Submitted to United States Department of the Interior, National Park Service, February 15, 1953.) 169 pp. (Mimeographed.) [Homestead, Fla., 1955.]

RONDON, CANDIDO MARIANO DA SILVA
  1916   *Conferencias realizadas pelo Sr. Coronel Candido Mariano da Silva Rondon . . . referentes a trabalhos executadas sob sua chefia pela expedição scientifica Roosevelt-Rondon e pela e, commissão telegraphica.* (Commissão de Linhas Estrategicas de Matto Grosso ao Amazonas, Publicação No. 42.) Rio de Janeiro.

ROOSEVELT, THEODORE
  1914   *Through the Brazilian Wilderness.* New York: Charles Scribner's Sons. 383 pp.; London: J. Murray. 374 pp.

ROY, SARAT CHANDRA
  1912   *The Mundas and Their Country.* With an Introduction by E. A. GAIT. Calcutta: Jogendra Nath Sarkar at the City Book Society. 546 pp.

"SABIAD"; *see* WHITE, STANHOPE

ST. HILAIRE, AUGUSTE DE
  1837   *Tableau géographique de la végétation primitive dans la province de Minas Geraes.* Paris: P. de la Forest. 49 pp.

SAMPAIO, ALBERTO JOSÉ DE
  1945   *Fitogeografia do Brasil.* 3d ed. ("Bibliotheca pedagogica brasileira," Series 5*a*, Vol. XXXV.) São Paulo: Companhia Editora Nacional Brasiliana. 372 pp.

SCHNELL, RAYMOND
  1950   *La Forêt dense: Introduction à l'étude botanique de la région forestière d'Afrique Occidentale.* (Publié sous le patronage de l'Institut Français d'Afrique Noire.) Paris: Paul Lechevalier. 531 pp.

SHANTZ, HOMER LEROY, and MARBUT, C. F.
  1923   *The Vegetation and Soils of Africa.* ("American Geographical Society Research Series," No. 13.) New York. 263 pp.

SIBREE, JAMES, JR.
  1915   *A Naturalist in Madagascar. . . .* London: Seely, Service & Co. 320 pp.

STAMP, L. DUDLEY
  1925   *The Vegetation of Burma from an Ecological Standpoint.* Calcutta: Thacker, Spink & Co. 65 pp.

STEBBING, E. P.
  1922–26   *The Forests of India.* 3 vols. London: John Lane.
  1937   *The Threat of the Sahara.* (Journal of the Royal African Society, Extra Supplement.) 35 pp.

STEINEN, KARL VON DEN
  1886   *Durch Central Brasilien: Expedition zur Erforschung des Schingú in Jahre 1884.* Leipzig: F. A. Brockhaus. 372 pp.

T[AYLOR], J. E.
  1942   "Termite Mounds Used for Manure," *Farm and Forest, or Land Use and Rural Planning in West Africa,* III, No. 1, 49.

TERRA, G. J. A.
  1953   "Some Sociological Aspects of Agriculture in Southeast Asia," *Indonesië,* VI, No. 4, 297–316; No. 5, pp. 439–63.

TIDEMAN, J.
  1922   *Simeloengoen: Het Land der Timoer-Bataks in zijn vroegere Isolatie en zijn Ontwikkeling tot een Deel van het Cultuurgebied van de Oost-kust van Sumatra.* Leiden: Louis H. Becherer. 306 pp.

TOTHILL, J. D. (ed.)
  1940   *Agriculture in Uganda.* London: Oxford University Press. 551 pp.
  1948   *Agriculture in the Sudan: Being a Handbook of Agriculture as Practised in the Anglo-Egyptian Sudan.* London: Oxford University Press. 974 pp.

TRAPNELL, C. G., and CLOTHIER, J. N.
  1937   *The Soils, Vegetation and Agricultural Systems of North Western Rhodesia.* (Report of the Ecological Survey.) [Lusaka?] 81 pp.

TROUP, R. S.
  1926   "Problems of Forest Ecology in India," pp. 283–313 (chap. xv) in TANSLEY, A. G., and CHIPP, T. F., *Aims and Methods in the Study of Vegetation.* London: British Empire Vegetation Committee and the Crown Agents for the Colonies. 383 pp.

VANDERYST, H.
  1924   "L'Évolution des formations botanico-agronomique dans le Congo Occidental," *Revue des questions Scientifiques,* pp. 65–83. (Not seen; discussion based on the review by Kuhnholtz-Lourdat [1939].)

WAIBEL, LEO
  1949   "A vegetaçao e o uso da terra no planalto central," *Revista brasileira de geografia,* X, No. 3, 335–80. Rio de Janeiro: Instituto Brasileiro de Geografia e Estatística, Conselho Nacional de Geografia.

WARMING, EUG.
  1892   *Lagoa Santa: Et Bidrag til den biologiske Plantegeografi . . . Med en Fortegnelse over Lagoa Santas Hvirveldyr, . . .* ("Det Kongelige Danske Videnskapernes Selskab Skrifter," Series VI, Vol. VI, No. 3.) Copenhagen: Blanco Lunos Kgl. Hof-Bogtrykkeri (F. Dreyer). 488 pp.

WHITE, STANHOPE
  1944*a*   "Agriculture Economy of the Hill Pagans of Dikwa Emirate, Cameroons (British Mandate)," *Farm and Forest, or Land Use and Rural Planning in West Africa,* V, No. 3, 130–34.
  1944*b*   "Climatic Change in West Afri-

ca, and Its Relation to Erosion Problems and Soil Deterioration," *Farm and Forest, or Land Use and Rural Planning in West Africa,* V, No. 4, 186–92.

WHITE, STEPHEN
1948   "The Vegetation and Flora of the Region of the Rio de Bavispe in Northeastern Sonora, Mexico," *Lloydia,* XI, No. 4, 229–312.

WHITFORD, H. N.
1906   "The Vegetation of the Lamao Forest Reserve," *Philippine Journal of Science,* I, No. 4, 373–431.

WILLIAMS, THOMAS
1858   *Fiji and the Fijians,* Vol. I: *The Islands and Their Inhabitants,* ed. GEORGE STRINGER ROWE. London: Alexander Heylin. 266 pp. (Volume II, by another author, is a history of the Fijian missions.)

YPES, W. K. H.
1932   *Bijdrage tot de Kennis van de Stamverwantschap, de inheemische Rechtsgemeenschappen en het Grondenrecht der Toba— en Dairibataks.* The Hague: Martinus Nijhoff. 553 pp.

The Modification of Mid-latitude Grasslands and Forests by Man

JOHN T. CURTIS[*]

Man's actions in modifying the biotic composition of mid-latitude grasslands and forests can best be studied by separating them into two groups of processes. In the first group are the effects induced by pioneer cultures in areas peripheral to main population centers. These areas may be peripheral because the main population has not had time to spread out over the entire region, as was the case during the European settlement of North America, or they may be peripheral because the severity of the environment more or less permanently prohibits the development of intensive civilization, as in rugged mountains, deserts, or taiga. In either case the exploiting peoples have economic ties with the main population in the sense that the latter furnishes both the tools for exploitation and a market for the products.

The second group of effects is composed of those that are produced by the intensive utilization of land for agricultural and urban purposes within the regions of high population. These typically follow the pioneer effects in time and are influenced by the earlier

* Dr. Curtis is Professor of Botany at the University of Wisconsin, Madison, and Research Director of the University Arboretum. He was a Guggenheim Fellow (1942) and was research director of the Société Haitiana-Americaine de Development Agricole, Gonaives, Haiti (1942–45). He is the author of papers on plant ecology, especially on the continuum concept of community relationships.

changes. Most of the available evidence on the nature of the changes induced by man is concerned with impact of European man on his environment, but it is probable that both older civilizations and aboriginal cultures exerted similar effects whenever their populations were sufficiently high.

MODIFICATIONS OF MID-LATITUDE FORESTS

The mid-latitude forests are typified by the deciduous forest formation, although several kinds of conifer forests are also to be found within the strict geographical boundaries of the mid-latitudes. In the interests of simplicity, this discussion will be concerned almost solely with the deciduous forest.

Peripheral Effects

Ordinarily, the first products of a peripheral wilderness to be exploited by an adjoining civilization are derived from the animal members of the community, especially the fur-bearers. The French *voyageurs*, the Hudson's Bay Company, and John Jacob Astor and his fur-trading competitors are familiar agents of such exploitation in America. Ecologically, the effects were not very great, since the rather minor population changes brought about in the animal species concerned were not radically different from those experienced in natural fluctuations. Of far greater significance was the utilization of the forest for its timber. The first stages in this utilization were concerned with the harvest of products of high value, such as shipmasts, spars, and naval timbers in general, followed by woods of importance in construction of houses and furniture. When the tree species suitable for these needs were common and especially when they grew in near-ly pure stands, as was the case with the white pine in eastern North America, the impact of the exploitation was great. This was true both of the mag-nitude of the changes and of the rela-tive size of the area affected. White pine was a favorite goal of the early American lumberman and was ruthless-ly harvested far from the scenes of its ultimate use.

Some forest types were composed mostly of trees of lesser value, such as the oaks and maples. These were com-monly by-passed, or their more valu-able members, used as cabinet woods, were selectively logged. This emphasis on special products rather than on com-plete utilization was mainly a feature of young expanding cultures whose demands were small relative to the size of the resource base in the peripheral area. The phenomenon is present in current times, as exemplified by the utilization of only a few of the host of tropical species for special veneers and by the selective harvest of spruce in the conifer forests of Canada and the non-utilization of the equally abundant bal-sam fir and other species.

All these exploitations were and are dependent upon certain definite phys-ical properties of the wood as it occurs in the trunks of natural trees produced under natural conditions. These proper-ties are commonly unrelated to the eco-logical behavior of the species in the sense that no special growth habits or reproductive capacities are concerned. The primitive exploiter was not worried about whether or not a second or con-tinuing crop of the species would be available. In many respects, the selec-tive harvest resembled mining in that it was the utilization of a non-renew-able resource or at least was treated as such.

As the economic demands of the main population centers grew and espe-cially as the population centers spread out in area, the utilization of the pe-ripheral resources became more in-tense. In non-industrial civilizations or non-industrial stages in the develop-ment of any culture, the forest is called on to produce a considerable share of the fuel used by that culture. This might be in the form of firewood or in the form of charcoal. Even in those countries or stages where coal was used for fuel, the forest was a source of tim-ber for mine props and for ties or sleep-ers on the railroads used for hauling the coal. All these uses were more or less dependent upon a near-by source of supply. The biological significance of this lies in the fact that the harvest-ers now became desirous of gathering more than one crop from the same land. The ecological behavior of the species thus came to be of greater importance than the physical structure of the wood. Species were utilized regardless of be-havior, but only those which possessed the ability to resprout or otherwise to reproduce themselves remained in the forest. Firewood, charcoal, and mine props all utilize small-dimension stock by preference, and thus a premium was placed on those species which could quickly return to a merchantable size. The technique of coppicing, so widely used in Eurasia, is a direct result of this situation.

In many places in the world the more intensive utilization of the trees in the subperipheral areas was accompanied by the introduction of grazing animals to the forest community. The wood-choppers, charcoal-makers, and lime-burners were more permanent inhabit-ants of a region than the earlier lum-bermen, and they commonly broadened the base of their economy by the use of cattle, sheep, or goats. These animals were allowed to roam the woods on free range and to make use of such forage and browse as might be available there. The livestock pressure was rarely as great as that which accompanied the agricultural economies of subsequent times, but its effects cannot be overlooked (Steinbrenner, 1951). In addition to the growth behavior patterns selected by the harvesting techniques, the successful species were also those best able to withstand the effects of grazing.

Thus we find in the areas peripheral to major population centers a gradually increasing intensity of utilization, either in space or in time, from a negligible pressure with little effect on the biotic composition of the forest to a severe pressure which selectively favored species with particular behavior patterns and eliminated other species which did not conform.

Let us now inquire into the actual nature of the changes that accompanied this increase in utilization. The earlier stages in the process are best studied by examples from the United States, since these stages occurred so long ago in Asia and Europe as to have left almost no record. In the United States the fur-trapping stage was roughly a seventeenth- and eighteenth-century phenomenon, while the lumber-harvest stage was most prominent in the nineteenth century.

The later, more intensive stages began in the latter half of the 1800's in the eastern portion of the United States. In much of Europe the intensive utilization began in the 1200's and continues in marginal areas up to the present. Thus, in England, extensive forests were utilized chiefly for hunting purposes through the period of Norman domination. Later timber-harvesting resulted in such a severe depletion of suitable trees that large-scale imports from the Baltic region were required by 1300. Widespread utilization of the forests for pasturage of swine and cattle, combined with intensive cutting of fuelwood, made further inroads on the peripheral areas. By 1544 a series of laws was passed regulating the procedures by which a coppiced woods should be managed (Tansley, 1939). In the Balkans utilization of the forests for construction timber and marine products was active in the 1200's, with many areas depleted by 1620. Intensive utilization for firewood, charcoal, and lime-burning still continues in the more mountainous regions (Turrill, 1929). In China peripheral exploitation is much older and has long since been completed in all but the most rugged and inaccessible terrain. Clearing of forests for agricultural purposes was widespread during the Shang dynasty beginning in 1600 B.C. (Needham, 1954).

The most obvious biotic change in the forest is the great shift in species composition, both qualitative and quantitative. This is best seen today in the northern states of the United States, where the original forest was a mosaic of patches of hardwoods with a few conifers and patches of conifers with a few hardwoods (Brown and Curtis, 1952). Those portions of the northern forests originally covered with hardwoods underwent a relatively slight alteration. They were composed of a mixture of species, none of which was ever in great economic demand. Large areas, therefore, were rarely cut over in anything like the intensity so common in the neighboring pine forests. In addition, fires were much less frequent and usually not so severe as those in the coniferous area. Many of the component species had the ability to resprout after cutting, like the maple and the beech, and most of them had very efficient means of reproduction, so that a stand was able to regenerate itself following partial destruction. Here and there, selective pressure reacted against one or more species. Millions of board feet of hemlock were cut in the region solely for the bark, which was used in the tanning industry. The logs were allowed to rot where they fell after they had been peeled (Goodlett, 1954). In more recent times, yellow birch has been intensively exploited because of its value as a veneer wood, and a few other species have experienced similar selective pressures. The major change resulting from all this has been an increase in the relative importance of sugar maple (*Acer saccharum*) in the remaining stands. This species is ecologically the most vigorous of all. The normal subordinate rank of the other species, accentuated by the added pressure from man, has resulted in their gradual disappearance in favor of the maple.

In contrast to this shift in relative importance of one member of the hardwood forest at the expense of others, the pine forests suffered a much more severe alteration. The march of the lumbermen from Maine in the late 1700's, to New York in 1850, to Michigan in 1870, to Wisconsin in 1880, and finally to Minnesota in 1890 was primarily a quest for white pine (*Pinus strobus*). This species, like the majority of pines, is a "fire tree" and was found in essentially pure stands in large blocks on lands subject to widespread burns. Profitable harvesting enterprises could be centered in regions where such blocks were common and where adequate facilities for transportation by river driving were available. In such regions the initial harvest obviously made great changes in forest composition by the removal of 90 per cent or more of the dominant trees. Of even greater importance were the frequent fires which broke out in the slash following the lumbering operations. These fires were allowed to burn unchecked and were often actually encouraged.

White pine is adapted to seeding-in following a fire but has no mechanism for sprouting from a burned stump. The first fire, therefore, often produced a new crop of pine seedlings, but a second fire before the trees had matured destroyed the entire population. The land became covered with weedy tree species like the aspens, birches, and oaks and with shrubs like the hazelnut, all of which could resprout following fire and thus remain in control of the ground. Excessive burning sometimes produced the so-called "barrens"—desolate tracts almost devoid of large woody plants, such as occupy extensive portions of Michigan and Wisconsin.

Accompanying the changes in species composition have been changes in the micro-environment within the forest. Selective logging or other mild harvesting practices result in an opening-up of the canopy of the forest, a breaking of the former more or less complete cover. The openings thus created possess a very different microclimate from the remaining portions of the forest. The most significant change is an increase in the rate of evaporation, and this increase is proportional to the intensity of the harvest, reaching maximum values in clear-cut and particularly in cut and burned woods.

With the exception of those lightly harvested forests containing sugar maple in which the net result is an increase in maple, practically all the environmental changes induced by the peripheral harvesting sequence are in the direction of a more xeric habitat, with greater light, more variable temperatures, more variable moisture, and much greater transpirational stress. The internal, stabilizing mechanisms of the community that lead toward homeostasis are upset or destroyed. The new environment tends to resemble that normally found in adjacent, hotter and drier regions (the "preclimax conditions" of Clements, 1936). Such conditions are most suitable for the ecologically pioneer plants of the region, which are those species that grow vigorously under the unstable climatic conditions and that possess adaptations to make use of the high light intensities. Ordinarily, such species possess highly effective means of reproduction and dispersal and, in addition, are likely to survive under severe disturbance, as by cutting or fire, through the ability to sprout from stumps or roots. The initial invaders of the disturbed areas, therefore, tend to be the pioneer species. Subsequent harvesting, as by coppicing, favors the persistence of these species and the gradual elimination of those with more climax tendencies. Thus, the original mixed forests come to be replaced by large areas of scrub oaks, aspen, box elder, sassafras, and similar species. The final selection under grazing pressure may eliminate or depress some of these, since there are very few species in the biota with the necessary combination of attributes to resist all the decimating influences. A fertile field for future investigation would be the study of the characteristics of various plants which enable them to survive under the conditions just outlined.

Agro-urban Effects

As the main centers of populations expanded into the peripheral areas, a considerable change in the land-use pattern followed. In the mid-latitudes, with their generally favorable climate during the growing season, agriculture became the dominant feature. The forests, already modified by peripheral utilization, were cleared to make room for fields with an initial selection of the best sites, followed by gradual encroachment onto less favorable land types. The actual nature of the best sites naturally varied from place to place, but the ideal appeared to be a large area of level or gently rolling land, with well-drained soils of high fertility. Frequently, the land was chosen on the basis of indicator species, black walnut being a favorite of the American settler, as it grew in rich forest stands well supplied with moisture and available nutrients. On these preferential sites the trees were killed by girdling or cutting, the logs and tops burned, the stumps pulled, blasted, or otherwise removed, and the ground plowed. Any member of the original community which persisted under the treatment was subsequently eradicated by the clean cultivation practices employed on the fields. The impact of man on these agricultural fields was thus one of total destruction with respect to the original community.

Marginal lands which were remote, difficult of access, or topographically unsuited for crop agriculture were commonly employed for intensive grazing. A continuing pressure was also exerted on them for lumber and firewood harvest. The distinction between peripheral and central activities is least clear at this stage, which is usually rather short in duration. With long-term occupancy of the land by an agro-urban culture, the remnants of the original forest come to be restricted to sites which are totally unusable for agriculture, such as cliffs, rocky ground, barren sands, ravines, or swamps. These habitats all differ markedly from the bulk of the land in their physical environment and hence also in their community composition. For various reasons, successional development is retarded in these extreme sites, and they retain a very high proportion of ecologically pioneer species. Consequently, they are less subject to drastic change by man's disturbance, since this disturbance usually leads to an increase in pioneers which are here the natural dominants.

The rate and the extent of the destruction of original cover by agricultural clearing are well demonstrated by a case history covering the first century of use of a township of land in Green County, Wisconsin, along the Wisconsin-Illinois border. The vegetation in 1831 before agricultural settlement began, as derived from records of the original Government Land Survey, was mostly upland deciduous forest, dominated by basswood, slippery elm, and sugar maple except for an area of oak-hickory forest in the northwest. A small portion of prairie with surrounding oak savanna was present in the southwest corner. The extent of forest cover in 1882 and 1902 was mapped by Shriner and Copeland (1904), while that in 1935 was recorded by the Wisconsin Land Economic Survey. The present condition was determined from aerial photos taken in 1950 and from personal inspection. The changes are shown in Figure 147 and in Table 26. While the very first clearings may have been confined

1831

1882

1902

1950

Fig. 147.—Changes in wooded area of Cadiz Township, Green County, Wisconsin (89°54′ W., 43°30′ N.), during the period of European settlement. The township is six miles on a side and is drained by the Pecatonica River. The shaded areas represent the land remaining in, or reverting to, forest in 1882, 1902, and 1950.

to the best lands, by 1882 the most evident factor influencing the pattern of land clearing was the unfortunate system of land survey which resulted in square landholdings independent of terrain. Not until the forest had been reduced to less than 10 per cent of its original extent did the remaining wood lots begin to reflect the topography. Currently, the majority of the remnant forests still have one or more straight boundaries, although most of them are confined to rocky outcrops and thin-soil hilltops. The statistics for the township show a reduction in forest cover to

by 36 per cent in 1935. This was due largely to the drying-up of springs in their original headwaters, thus reflecting a decrease in subsoil water storage from the reduced infiltration on agricultural fields and pastured wood lots.

A number of important changes occur in forested regions under the impact of agriculture aside from the obvious destruction of most of the forest. Under aboriginal use or peripheral exploitation, fire was a common occurrence, with large areas involved at each burn, since both the means and the desire to stop the fires were absent. Fol-

TABLE 26

CHANGE IN WOODED AREA, CADIZ TOWNSHIP, GREEN COUNTY, WISCONSIN (89°54′ W., 43°30′ N.), FROM 1831 TO 1950

	1831	1882	1902	1935	1950
Total acres of forest...............	21,548	6,380	2,077	1,034	786
Number of wood lots...............	1	70	61	57	55
Average size of wood lot in acres..	21,548	91.3	34.0	18.2	14.3
Total wooded area as a percentage of 1831 condition...............	100	29.6	9.6	4.8	3.6
Total periphery of wood lots in miles............................		99.0	61.2	47.2	39.8
Average periphery per wooded acre in feet.........................		82	155	241	280

29.6 per cent of the original by 1882, to 9.6 per cent by 1902, to 4.8 per cent by 1936, and to 3.6 per cent by 1954. The existing forests are used by their owners as sources of firewood and occasional saw timber. In addition, 77 per cent of the present wooded area is heavily grazed by cattle to the point where no regeneration of the trees is taking place. Thus only 0.8 per cent of the land under forest cover in 1831 is still in what might be called a seminatural state, and this tiny portion is broken up into even more minute fragments, widely scattered throughout the area.

Concomitant with the reduction in forest cover in a presumed cause-and-effect relation was a decrease in total length of the streams draining the area. The permanently flowing streams had decreased by 26 per cent in 1902 and

lowing the dissection of the landscape and the interpolation of farm land between remnant forest stands, fires were more or less automatically stopped by the bare fields or were consciously suppressed by the farmers. In consequence, the forests that escaped clearing received a degree of protection far greater than they had normally experienced. In addition, the high cost of fencing wood lots in many instances prevented their use for grazing animals. As a result of these two influences, the forest, although gradually reduced in size and contiguity, actually improved in structure, with an increased density of trees per acre and an increase in cover and hence in humidity. On many marginal sites which had been reduced to brush by recurrent presettlement fires, mature forests subsequently developed. Since the species which were able to persist through the fires were the extremely vigorous pioneers, the first forests that developed were dominated by these pioneer species. In much of the central United States, where the recovery of marginal and remnant sites has been under way for about a century, the natural processes of succession are just beginning to convert the forests to a more climax condition (Cottam, 1949).

The conversion frequently is hastened in regions where mixed forests are present by the selective utilization of the mature pioneer members of the community for farm timber and firewood. Species of oaks are most commonly involved in the process in the United States and in Europe, although other pioneer species of high economic value are sometimes important. Since these trees are removed only a few at a time as the farmer needs them, environmental conditions are not greatly altered. The major result is a liberation of the understory layer of climax species like maple, beech, and basswood and the consequent repression of regeneration of the original pioneer trees.

The early period in the agro-urban utilization of forest land, therefore, presents the anomaly of severe reduction in total amount of forest but considerable improvement in the stands that did survive. These remnants commonly suffered severe damage from grazing at a later date.

Another change accompanying agricultural occupation of forested land is in what might be called the physiognomic result. Instead of an essentially continuous forest cover, with infrequent meadow-like openings along watercourses or small grasslands where fires had been unusually severe, the landscape now presents the aspect of a savanna, with isolated trees, small clumps or clusters of trees, or small groves scattered in a matrix of artificial grassland of grains and pasture grasses, unstable and frequently devoid of plant cover as a result of regular plowing. The physical conditions of the intervening "grasslands" are such as to prevent the successful growth of practically all members of the forest biota. A few of the plant members persist along fence rows and other places of relatively infrequent disturbance, and a very few are sufficiently weedlike actually to compete in the farmer's fields, especially in the permanent pastures (bracken fern, hazelnut, etc.).

Among the animal members of the community is a group that normally made use of the original forest edges. Some birds, for example, nested within the forest but sought their food in the open places and in the tangle of vines and shrubs that commonly bordered the openings. Such animals were greatly benefited by the increased "edge" provided by the fragmented wood lots, and their relative populations increased accordingly. As shown in Table 26, the average length of the periphery per acre of forest increased from 82 feet in 1882 to 280 feet by 1950.

The artificial savanna condition provided a suitable habitat for a number of species which originally occurred in grasslands and natural savannas on the dry margin adjacent to the mid-latitude forests. A number of birds, like the prairie horned lark (Forbush, 1927, pp. 336–70) and the western meadow lark, extended their range well into the original forest country of the eastern United States. Aggressive prairie plants, like ragweed, black-eyed Susan, and big bluestem similarly advanced far beyond their original areas of prominence and became conspicuous features of the vegetation along roadsides and in agricultural fields. Similar migrations of steppe plants westward into the forests of Central Europe are known (Oltmanns, 1927, pp. 104–56). These migrations resulted in a partial blending of the components of two or more major biotic communities and served to lessen their inherent differences.

Within the remnant forest stands, a number of changes of possible importance may take place. The small size and increased isolation of the stands tend to prevent the easy exchange of members from one stand to another. Various accidental happenings in any given stand over a period of years may eliminate one or more species from the community. Such a local catastrophe under natural conditions would be quickly healed by migration of new individuals from adjacent unaffected areas (the "gap phase" concept of Watt, 1947). In the isolated stands, however, opportunities for inward migration are small or nonexistent. As a result, the stands gradually lose some of their species, and those remaining achieve unusual positions of relative abundance.

The lack of interchange of plant individuals also applies to plant pollen. Those members of the community which are regularly or usually cross-pollinated no longer have the opportunity of crossing with a wide range of individuals. It is probable, therefore, that opportunities for evolution of deviant types by random gene fixation will be increased in the future, as the isolating mechanisms have longer times in which to operate. In heavily utilized stands selection pressures engendered by the frequent disturbance, together with the shift toward pioneer conditions resulting directly from the small size of the stands, would tend to favor those ecotypes which have pioneer tendencies and to reject the more conservative climax strains. The study of this micro-evolution should be one of the most fertile fields for future investigations.

EFFECTS ON MID-LATITUDE GRASS-
LANDS AND SAVANNAS

Peripheral Effects

The plant members of the mid-latitude grasslands for the most part are of no direct use to man. Their main value comes after they have been converted to high-protein foods in the form of animals. The earliest utilization of grasslands, therefore, was by hunting cultures or by peripheral exploitation for the benefit of a remote agro-urban civilization. The slaughter of the bison on the prairies of mid-continental North America is a familiar example of this process (Garretson, 1938). In the absence of adequate information as to the influence of the bison on the structure of the remainder of the grassland community, little of value can be said about the effects of their removal. In any case, such effects would have been temporary, for intensive agricultural use of much of the eastern area followed quickly afterward, while domesticated cattle were introduced in the drier ranges to the west and began to exert an effect of their own.

The nature of the changes induced by cattle were probably different from those formerly resulting from the bison. The cattle were kept on limited ranges, so that the vegetation was subject to pressure over a long season, year after year. The bison, on the other hand, may have exerted an even greater pressure for brief periods, but a recovery period of several years commonly intervened before the wandering herd revisited any particular area. The long-term effects of the two types of grazing animals thus were very different.

Cattle begin to utilize the prairie grasses as soon as growth starts in the spring. Utilization of regrowth occurs during the summer and is particularly damaging when the reproductive stems begin to elongate in the later months. The continual reduction in photosynthetic area due to leaf removal results in a decreased storage of reserves in the underground organs. At the same time, the normal control of dormant buds by growth hormones is upset by the removal of stem tips, with a resultant stimulation of new growth which further depletes the stored reserves. The bluestems (*Andropogon* sp.), Indian grass (*Sorghastrum nutans*), and switch grass (*Panicum virgatum*) are typical species which respond in this way, and the gradual weakening leads to their eventual elimination and replacement by others. The replacing forms, under normal circumstances, are grasses which are recumbent, with their stems on or near the ground surface and with a large proportion of their leaves in a similarly protected position. They accordingly escape destruction by cattle, which do not graze closely. The grama grasses (*Bouteloua* sp.) and buffalo grass (*Buchloe dactyloides*) are good examples. In the absence of competition from the former dominants, these forms rapidly increase their populations. In range parlance, they are said to be "increasers" as opposed to the species which decline under grazing, which are called "decreasers" (Dyksterhuis, 1949). Both types were present in the prairie before grazing began, but the decreasers, because of their erect habit and greater size, were dominant over the increasers.

When the carrying capacity of the grasslands is greatly exceeded, either by too many cattle per unit area or by a reduction in productivity of the grasses due to drought, then the increasers themselves begin to suffer. Their decline results in a breaking of the continuous plant cover. The bare soil thus exposed becomes available for invasion by weedy annuals, which were formerly excluded from the closed community. In the American grasslands these newcomers, termed "invaders," are frequently exotics which originated in similar situations in the grasslands of the Old World, like cheat grass, Russian thistle, and halogeton. Native invaders are typically plants indigenous to the drier shrub deserts toward the west and are frequently unpalatable as a result of spines and thorns, like prickly poppy and prickly-pear cactus. Continued

overgrazing results in the almost complete eradication of the original prairie flora and its replacement by an unstable community of annuals and thorny perennials.

The entire degradation process involves a shift from climax to pioneer plants and from mesic to xeric conditions. The upgrading effects of the original flora with respect to organic-matter accumulation in the soil, to nutrient pumping, and to water-entrance rates and other constructive activities are greatly lessened or reversed. The soil becomes compacted, less easily penetrated by rain, and much more subject to erosion, especially by wind.

Accompanying these direct effects of cattle on the plant community are a number of important secondary effects deriving from the disruption of the animal community. Misguided efforts at predator removal in the form of wolf and coyote bounties and other more direct means allow the rodent populations to get out of balance. Mice, pocket gophers, prairie dogs, and jack rabbits frequently reach epizootic levels and further add to the already excessive pressures on the plants. Control by extensive campaigns of rodent poisoning is usually temporary in effect and often serves to accentuate the unbalanced condition and to make return to stability more difficult.

In the more humid eastern portion of the grasslands in North America, the better sites were soon used for crop agriculture rather than for grazing, but marginal lands on thin soils, steep hills, or rocky areas frequently remained in use as pastures. In this region the decreasers behaved in the same manner as those farther west, and a few of the same increasers were also present. The major difference, and a very important one for the economy of large sections of the country, was the fact that the most important increaser was in reality an invader—Kentucky bluegrass (*Poa pratensis*). This species has a growth habit similar to the grama grasses and the buffalo grass of the western plains but thrives under a humid climate. It differs from the usual invaders in that it does not require bare soil or a broken cover to become established and is neither an annual nor an unpalatable perennial. The time and conditions of its origin in Eurasia are unknown. In all probability it developed under the influence of man and his pastoral habits, since it is found in the Old World in those regions where grazing has been practiced for long periods. In America it demonstrates a vigor scarcely exceeded by any other plant of similar size and has come to dominate most of the unimproved pasturages in the eastern half of the continent. This domination is virtually total in many areas, so that the original grassland species are completely lacking. The forbs and the few other grasses that do accompany bluegrass (dandelion, white clover, oxeye daisy, quack grass, timothy, etc.) are themselves exotic and serve to replicate on this continent a man-made community that is very widespread in Europe. In fact, this great expansion of the world range of a particular community under the unintentional influence of man is one of the most powerful examples of man's role as the major biotic influence in the world today. Investigation of the origin of the component species and intensive studies of the dynamics of the assemblage in its new environment should be highly rewarding. (See the chapter by Clark below, pp. 737–62.)

Agro-urban Effects on Grasslands

The extensive utilization of the major mid-latitude grasslands for crop agriculture was restricted to those portions adjacent to the deciduous forest where the rainfall, although irregular, was usually sufficient for grain crops. The most favored places were those grasslands which had been extended into the forest during the postglacial xerothermic period (Sears, 1942) and which had subsequently been maintained by fire when the climate again favored forest. The Corn Belt in the prairie peninsula of the United States and the European breadbasket in the steppes of the Ukraine and in the *puzta* of Hungary are outstanding examples. In the climatically suitable areas utilization of the grassland for crops instead of for pasture was dependent upon the development of the steel plow for subjugation of the tough prairie sod. The invention and widespread manufacture of such an instrument occurred in the second quarter of the nineteenth century. Hence we find that the American prairies and the European steppes were both converted to cropland at about the same time (Conard, 1951), although the inhabitants of the former were scarcely past the stage of a hunting economy, while the latter had been used for grazing for centuries or millenniums.

The conversion from grassland to cropland was far more complete than the equivalent conversion from forest. In large part this was a result of the fact that the grasslands were flat or gently rolling and presented far fewer topographical obstacles to the plow than did the forest. The destruction of the entire prairie community by clean cultivation over extensive tracts of land means that remnants of the original vegetation are very rare. The major agency preventing complete eradication in much of the American prairie is the railroad system which was extended throughout the area contemporaneously with the advance of the settler (Shimek, 1925). The railroad right of way in many instances was laid on grade and was protected by fences. The tracks themselves were placed in the middle of the right of way, thus leaving a strip of virgin grassland on either side. The only maintenance operations which affected the vegetation was an occasional burning. Since this merely continued the normal practices of aboriginal times, these linear strips of prairie have been maintained in more or less primeval condition except for the random destruction of certain species and their failure to re-enter (Curtis and Greene, 1949).

Contrary to the case of the forest remnants, these railside prairies are not necessarily on pioneer or otherwise deviant sites but rather sample the full range of environment originally present. This is indeed fortunate, since over millions of acres of middle western prairie the only prairie plants to be found are on these railroad prairies. The much-needed research on prairie ecology has been and will continue to be conducted there.

The savannas between the grasslands and the surrounding forests are physiognomically intermediate between the two major formations. In the mid-latitudes they are largely the result of repeated advances and retreats of the prairie-forest border. Along the prairie peninsula of the United States, the characteristic savanna was the oak opening, a community of widely spaced orchard-like oak trees with an understory of prairie plants and a few forest shrubs. All available evidence indicates that these savannas were created by an advance of the prairie into the forest under the driving force of fire. Their maintenance was similarly effected by recurrent fires set by the Indians. They were but little used during the peripheral period except by the early hunters. A very brief period of open-range grazing was quickly followed by agricultural settlement. The potential yields of timber were so low and the quality of the gnarled oaks so poor that no extensive lumbering was ever practiced.

Within a decade or two of settlement, the remnant oak openings that escaped

the ax and plow suddenly began to develop into dense, closed-canopy forests. In large part, this rapid increase in number of trees was due to the liberation of previously suppressed "grubs" or oak brush which had been repeatedly killed to the ground by fire and which had persisted through production of adventitious buds from underground rootstocks (Cottam, 1949). One of the major tribulations of the early settler on the savannas was the laborious hand removal of these underground growths which effectively stopped the best plow and the strongest oxen.

Agricultural occupation of the oak openings thus resulted in two very different effects. On the one hand, the majority of the land was cleared and cultivated, thus destroying the entire community. On the other, the remnant portions rapidly changed over from savanna to forest under the influence of fire protection. Those few areas which continued to be kept open by fire or other means were ordinarily thus treated so that they might be used as pasture, with consequent destruction of the understory vegetation. As a result, an oak savanna, with its full complement of original vegetation, is one of the rarest vegetation types in the United States today.

A similar release of woody vegetation by excessive fire protection has produced the mesquite stands now so common on the savannas of the southwestern range land (Humphrey, 1953).

GENERAL CONSEQUENCES OF MAN'S UTILIZATION

Changes in Environment

The changes induced in native vegetation by man, either through peripheral, pioneer, or primitive utilization or through more intensive agro-urban occupation, range from simple modification through severe degradation to complete destruction and replacement. All these changes in plant cover are accompanied by changes in the environment within and adjacent to the affected vegetation.

Whether or not widespread deforestation can influence the amount or distribution of rainfall has been debated for decades. No satisfactory proof that such influence exists has appeared so far, but the question remains unresolved. The most convincing arguments concerning the influence of vegetation removal on over-all regional climate are those connected with the energy balance as it is influenced by the albedo or reflecting power of the earth's surface. The value of this factor is very similar for any green vegetation, whether it be forest, prairie, or corn crop. In deciduous forests it may drop during the winter, especially in regions without a permanent snow cover. In grasslands, on the other hand, it actually increases during the winter, owing to the light color of the dead and matted grasses. When the grasslands are plowed, particularly where the land is fallowed or fall-plowed, the dark prairie soils cut down reflection tremendously. The absorption of solar energy is thereby increased, with a possible appreciable change in the total energy increment and hence in the local temperature. This could be of major significance in the spring months in the northern grasslands.

The soil factor of the environment has also been altered by man's activities. Trampling and other disturbances incident to the harvesting operation, combined with activities of livestock, tend to compact the soil, destroying its loose structure and impeding the free entrance of water from rainstorms. The amount of surface runoff is thereby increased. The partial or total absence of tall trees reduces the amount of subsoil water which would normally be lost by transpiration. The excess finds its way to the stream system of the region by way of springs. The initial result of forest-cutting is an increase in the total volume of streamflow, but the complete destruction of the forest, as by fire, greatly increases the flash-flood potential of the watershed and decreases its usable water-producing abilities.

One of the major consequences of the agricultural utilization of mid-latitude forests and prairies has been the very great decrease in soil stability. The resultant soil erosion, both by water and by wind, reached terrifying proportions in many sections of the United States before concerted efforts were made to bring it under control. For the most part, this erosion is unrelated to the previous vegetation and is largely due to the misguided attempt to apply an agricultural system developed under one set of environmental and economic conditions to a totally different situation. The current severe "nutrient erosion" now accelerating in the Corn Belt under the influence of hybrid grains is another example of a faulty socioeconomic farm philosophy and is unrelated to the original prairie vegetation except in so far as the inherited soil richness, which hides the folly of the system, is a result of millenniums of prairie activity.

General Changes in Community Composition

In those cases where man's utilization has not completely destroyed the original biotic community, whether under peripheral conditions or in remnants within agricultural areas, it is possible to detect a recurrent pattern in the compositional changes that have occurred. In both forest and grassland the more conservative elements of the vegetation (the "upper middle class" and the "aristocrats" of Fernald, 1938) have tended to disappear. These are the plants that are most demanding in their requirements, with low tolerance of fluctuations in moisture, with high nutrient requirements, and with low ability to withstand frequent disturbance. They commonly have only limited powers of vegetative reproduction and usually have specialized requirements for germination. They make up the most advanced communities of a given region from the standpoints of degree of integration, stability, complexity, and efficiency of energy utilization (Sears, 1949). They are "climax" plants in the basic sense of the word.

Under the impact of man these climax plants tend to decline in numbers and importance. Their retrogression leads to decreased stability and to disorganization of the community pattern. The environmental changes accompanying the decline are in the direction of more xeric, lighter, and more variable conditions. These encourage the expansion of less conservative plants with such pioneer tendencies as the ability to withstand greater fluctuations in temperature and available moisture, the capacity for resisting disturbance through production of proliferating shoots or adventitious buds, and the possession of efficient means of rapid population increase. Particular harvesting techniques of man, either directly through logging and coppicing or indirectly through the medium of grazing animals, tend to exert a selective influence on the pioneer plants which do succeed. A premium is placed on those species which can resist the particular pressure and still maintain their populations. All others tend to decline or disappear.

This reduction in species complement increases in proportion to the intensity and duration of the utilization. In the final stages the communities completely dominated by man are composed of a small number of extremely vigorous, highly specialized weeds of cosmopolitan distribution, whose origin and distribution are in themselves man-induced phenomena. The subfinal

stages are a mixture of these weeds and the most aggressive elements of the native flora. The relative proportion of indigenous and exotic elements varies with the climate, those regions most like the ancient centers of agricultural development (semidesert or Mediterranean climates) having a vegetation which is more completely exotic than that of the cool humid regions.

The highest vegetational product of evolution is the tropical rain forest. In the mid-latitudes the climax deciduous forest as found in the southern Appalachians and in the mountains of China is the ultimate in complexity, stability, and integration. Large numbers of species grow in intimate interrelationship, with maximum capture and reutilization of incident energy consistent with the seasonal nature of the climate. Many niches exist, and each has its adapted species with the necessary modifications in nutritional, growth, or photosynthetic habit to enable it to make the most of its specialized opportunities. Not only is energy capture at a maximum in this highly organized community but normal processes of peneplanation are reduced to a minimum. Indeed, there may be a decrease in randomness of the local habitat due to intake of highly dilute mineral elements from the subsoil or bedrock by tree roots and their subsequent accumulation in the humus-rich topsoil. In the sense that entropy means randomness or "mixed-up-ness" in the universe as a result of highly probable events, the climax deciduous forest may be said to possess a very low entropy, since it is an incomprehensibly improbable phenomenon existing in a dynamic steady state.

Man's actions in this community almost entirely result in a decrease in its organization and complexity and an increase in the local entropy of the system. His activity in reducing the number of major communities, climax or otherwise, and in blurring the lines of demarcation between them by increasing the range of many of their components likewise reduces the non-randomness of his surroundings. Man, as judged by his record to date, seems bent on asserting the universal validity of the second law of thermodynamics, on abetting the running-down of his portion of the universe. Perhaps the improbability of the climax biotic community was too great to be sustained, and man is the agent of readjustment. Let us hope his new powers for total entropy increase are not employed before the readjustments can be made.

REFERENCES

BROWN, R. T., and CURTIS, J. T.
1952 "The Upland Conifer-Hardwood Forests of Northern Wisconsin," *Ecological Monographs*, XXII, No. 3, 217–34.

CLEMENTS, F. E.
1936 "Nature and Structure of the Climax," *Journal of Ecology*, XXIV, No. 1, 252–84.

CONARD, H. S.
1951 *The Background of Plant Ecology*. Ames, Iowa: Iowa State College Press. 238 pp.

COTTAM, GRANT
1949 "The Phytosociology of an Oak Woods in Southern Wisconsin," *Ecology*, XXX, No. 3, 171–287.

CURTIS, J. T.
1951 "Hardwood Woodlot Cover and Its Conservation," *Wisconsin Conservation Bulletin*, XVI, No. 1, 11–15.

CURTIS, J. T., and GREENE, H. C.
1949 "A Study of Relic Wisconsin Prairies by the Species-Presence Method," *Ecology*, XXX, No. 1, 83–92.

DYKSTERHUIS, E. J.
1949 "Condition and Management of Range Land Based on Quantitative Ecology," *Journal of Range Management*, II, No. 3, 104–15.

FERNALD, M. L.
1938 "Must All Rare Plants Suffer the Fate of Franklinia?" *Journal of the Franklin Institute*, CCXXVI, No. 3, 383–97.

FORBUSH, E. H.
1927 *Birds of Massachusetts and Other New England States*. 2 vols. Boston: Massachusetts Department of Agriculture.

GARRETSON, M. S.
1938 *The American Bison*. New York: New York Zoölogical Society. 254 pp.

GOODLETT, J. C.
1954 *Vegetation Adjacent to the Border of the Wisconsin Drift in Potter County, Pennsylvania*. (Harvard Forest Bulletin No. 15.) Petersham, Mass.: Harvard Forest. 93 pp.

HUMPHREY, R. R.
1953 "The Desert Grassland, Past and Present," *Journal of Range Management*, VI, No. 3, 159–64.

KITTREDGE, JOSEPH
1948 *Forest Influences*. New York: McGraw-Hill Book Co. 394 pp.

NEEDHAM, JOSEPH
1954 *Science and Civilization in China*, Vol. I. Cambridge: Cambridge University Press. 318 pp.

OLTMANNS, F.
1927 *Das Pflanzenleben des Schwarzwaldes*. Freiburg: Badischen Schwarzwaldverein. 690 pp.

SEARS, P. B.
1942 "Xerothermic Theory," *Botanical Review*, VIII, No. 10, 708–36.
1949 "Integration at the Community Level," *American Scientist*, XXXVII, No. 2, 235–42.

SHIMEK, B.
1925 "The Persistence of the Prairies," *University of Iowa Studies in Natural History*, XI, No. 5, 3–24.

SHRINER, F. A., and COPELAND, F. B.
1904 "Deforestation and Creek Flow about Monroe, Wisconsin," *Botanical Gazette*, XXXVII, No. 2, 139–43.

STEINBRENNER, E. C.
1951 "Effect of Grazing on Floristic

Composition and Soil Properties of Farm Woodlands in Southern Wisconsin," *Journal of Forestry*, XL, No. 12, 906–10.

TANSLEY, H. G.
  1939 *The British Islands and Their Vegetation.* Cambridge: Cambridge University Press. 930 pp.

TURRILL, W. B.
  1929 *The Plant-Life of the Balkan Peninsula.* London: Oxford University Press. 487 pp.

WATT, A. S.
  1947 "Pattern and Process in the Plant Community," *Journal of Ecology*, XXXV, No. 1, 1–22.

The Impact of Exotic Invasion on the Remaining New World Mid-latitude Grasslands

ANDREW H. CLARK*

FOREWORD

The evidential basis for an assessment of man's role in changing the face of the earth is to be derived especially from careful historical research in particular kinds of areas. Much has been written of the effect of man on grasslands, but a great deal of this has lumped together too wide a variety of grasslands or has considered too limited a period of time. This paper takes a view more sharply focused as to kind of grassland and kind of use by man. At the same time we will consider the history of operation of specific factors generally supposed to have contributed substantially to change. It will be argued that there is no clear picture, over all, of destructive exploitation by man and that change has varied widely in dimension and direction even within the set limitations.

The writer's experience in field investigation, reading, and writing has been rather closely identified with new worlds overseas, invaded and occupied by Europeans in the last four centuries.

* Dr. Clark is Professor of Geography at the University of Wisconsin, Madison. Previously, he was chairman of the Department of Geography at Rutgers University, New Brunswick, New Jersey. In his historical study of agricultural and pastoral geography he has worked primarily in New Zealand and Canada. He is the author of *The Invasion of New Zealand by People, Plants and Animals*, 1949.

It seemed wise, therefore, to restrict attention to those regions.

These worlds have included several areas which were grasslands in 1600 or thereabouts: substantial regions, largely devoid of trees, with only occasional shrubby growth, dominated in vegetation cover by a variety of grasses. Such was the South African Veld, the Argentine Pampa, the tussock grassland of the South Island of New Zealand, the Pacific bunch grasslands of California and the Columbia Basin, and the great mid-continent grassland of North America. There were others which almost qualify. The Patagonian tussock and the parklands of Victoria and New South Wales in Australia were finally excluded because of special problems involved by the presence of a large amount of woody growth. The Manchurian grassland, though in a true sense a "new world" grassland, was not settled by Europeans and is therefore also excluded.

By limiting our attention to those parts of the chosen grasslands which still have a substantial area remaining which has not been plowed, the focus thus finally settled on the unplowed stretches of the Great Plains, on the margins of California's central valley and adjacent coastal mountains, and on New Zealand's South Island high country. The plowing of most of the Pampa, the Prairies, the Palouse, and, for that matter, much of the more attractive margins of the Great Plains, the California grassland, and the New Zealand tussock, is one of the great epics of invasion and settlement of our time; it is a story too complex to be summarized here, and the invasion involved, in effect, the large-scale obliteration of the original grassland as such.

The limitations as defined have the great virtue of allowing us to speak throughout about *grassland* areas. We are not involved in study of the transition from forest to grassland or cropland, or grassland to arable, nor are we concerned with grasslands artificially and deliberately created by man. We shall not estimate how long any of these areas have been grassland, although there are tempting avenues in paleoecology and culture history to be explored. Assuming that the nature of the biome was in reasonable internal balance and in external balance with the habits of the occupying culture in each area, as we first view it, and assuming that no significant advent of exotic plants or animals had occurred in any of them for long centuries before, we will review briefly fact and opinion as to effects of the European invasions of the last few centuries.

In each case the invasion precipitated large-scale displacement or destruction of the pre-European peoples and their culture. Native grazing fauna were considerably altered; the principal grazing animals in the largest of the areas were all but obliterated. Millions of horses, cattle, sheep, and goats were introduced. Animals were imported for sport, or by accident, and became noxious pests. There were weeds and birds, with bacteria and viruses in train. Fences appeared as well as hedges and groves of exotic trees; wells were sunk, and windmills were erected to pump them; irrigation channels and stock-watering races were etched in the surface of plain, terrace, or river flat. And

there were houses, villages, and towns; trails, roads, and railroad lines; dams and power lines.

With these changes came the alteration of the grasslands. It is our purpose to try to describe some of the latter changes and to suggest something of their dimension, significance, and cause. Two kinds of study are involved: historical and processual. The former is concerned with establishing the fact of circumstance and change; the latter aims to assign relationships between the characteristics and changes and the processes observed or hypothesized. Processual research is more advanced, but its wells of historical material are running dry. There is observable an increasing tendency to hypothesize the characteristics or changes themselves and thus to replenish those wells. By guessing what may have been the vegetation cover of North Africa, or the prairie peninsula of North America, or the Llanos of the Orinoco five thousand years ago, we have gone on to argue the role of the goat, the plow, hoe or digging stick, fire, or changing climate in the changes assumed. All of this has its place in the development of theory, else all of our knowledge remains disorderly. Yet we really do not have the evidence to be as dogmatic as we have been (or sounded) in many of our goat-garrigue, precipitation-prairie, or similar single-factor interpretative emphases.

The limited focus here on a period of three or four centuries is not intended to suggest that we should not give as much or more attention than we have done to more distant historical studies (documentary, archeological, or ecological) in either these or other areas or that we should not attempt to erect processual theory on the basis of such reconstruction. But the restriction does allow us a much more comprehensive array of evidence and, by directing attention to the remaining grasslands, may allow a firmer base for backward extrapolation. Historical fact and processual theory will appear here intermixed as they are in the words and writings of most students of the grasslands and of their settlement by European man. The emphasis on exotic invasion is both the most logical and the most convenient method of examining directly the impact on the pre-invasion biome. It directs our attention to the most spectacular, and probably most significant, vectors of change.

THE NORTH AMERICAN GREAT PLAINS

The Vegetation Cover in 1600 and the Remaining Grassland Area of 1950

The accompanying map (Fig. 148) indicates the extent of the pre-European short-grass area in the interior of the continent and (somewhat roughly, for there is a great deal of interfingering on the margins and many enclaves and exclaves) that which is still largely unplowed in the mid-twentieth century. Commonly, the whole sixteenth-century central grassland has been reconstructed as tall prairie grasses to the east and short "plains" grasses to the west, with associated forbs and woody growth. There was, however, a considerable zone of gradation, which has been reported as a region of "mid-grasses" or, more specifically, a zone of intermixture of taller or shorter grasses with the dominance of one or the other apparent in years of greater or less rainfall. In fact, most of the tall-grass and mid-grass zones, as well as some parts of the short-grass plains, have been plowed, although agricultural occupation of many such areas has been temporary. The remaining unplowed grassland is largely within the presumed short-grass area, originally some two hundred million acres, the southern part of which Coronado and his associates traversed four centuries ago.

There have been many botanical and ecological descriptions of the plains (Malin, 1947). Carpenter (1940) interpreted the area as essentially a region of short grass, with grama grasses (*Bouteloua* spp.) and buffalo grass (*Buchloe dactyloides*) as dominants, on which bison and pronghorn grazed: briefly the *Bouteloua–Bulbilis* [*Buchloe*]-*Bison–Antilocapra* biome. Weaver and Clements (1938, p. 524) identified this short-grass area as a disclimax materially altered by grazing pressure of sheep and cattle. The judgment was based in considerable part on exclusion grazing studies, the observation of the extension of taller grasses in wetter years, and evidence of earlier travel accounts (Hayden, 1870). Larson (1940) feels that this interpretation ignores grazing pressure of bison, and he questions some of the evidence used (e.g., his view that the year of the Hayden expedition, 1870, was atypical).

In general, the middle of the short-grass area (western Kansas and eastern Colorado) is believed to have had a predominantly grama-grass sod at higher levels, with more buffalo grass appearing at lower levels and on slopes and being mixed with bluestems (*Andropogon* spp.) in the lowest spots. Wheat grasses (*Agropyron* spp.) and needle grasses (*Stipa* spp.) were more prominent in the northern plains reaching up into Canada (Coupland, 1953). In the sandhills of Nebraska the shorter grasses tended to be replaced by the taller bluestems, a dropseed (*Sporobolus cryptandrus*), and prairie sand grass (*Calamovilfa longifolia*). To the south the gramas were mixed with *Hilaria* species, notably, curly mesquite grass (*H. belangeri*) and galleta grass (*H. jamesii*).

Throughout the grasslands there were leafy herbaceous plants (the forbs of the ecologist and the "weeds" of the cattleman) and shrubs. The latter increased in density toward the west and southwest, and, where the grassland grades into the desert-shrub associa-

Sand Hills

Edwards Plateau

UNPLOWED GRASSLANDS
OF WESTERN NORTH AMERICA

GREAT PLAINS AND CALIFORNIA

16ᵗʰ Century boundaries of grasslands

Chief areas still unplowed

0   100   200   300   400
MILES

GEOGRAPHY DEPARTMENT, UNIVERSITY OF WISCONSIN

FIG. 148.—Unplowed grasslands of western North America: Great Plains and California tions, shrubs became dominant. The northern desert was remarkable for the dominance of the sagebrushes (*Arte-misia* spp.), and these were the principal shrubs of the northern plains. To the south, mesquite (*Prosopis juliflora*) extended similarly from the southern desert. Prickly pear (*Opuntia* spp.) had a rather wide distribution.

These are the broadest of generalizations. The grass usually formed a continuous sod, but even this was not universal. The local habitats varied greatly with the parent-material of the soils, broken ground, exposure, elevation, and hydrological situation. Along the river flats, forests of a kind, dominated by cottonwoods, pushed far into the plains. There were, literally, hundreds of species of grasses, herbs, shrubs, and trees in the region. If there was a balance in the whole biome, one would expect it to have been a shifting one, for the climate is capricious. Sharp contrasts in rainfall were noticed from one place to another in particular years and in individual localities from year to year. There were also periodic (though unpredictable and non-cyclical) fluctuations, resulting in series of relatively dry or relatively wet years. A drier phase must inevitably have allowed the short grasses to extend eastward (and appeared to do so rather spectacularly because of the mixed character of the "mid-grass" association), and with them the sagebrush, cactus, and mesquite. Wet years would have reversed the trend and given a "prairie" aspect to much of the short-grass region.

Climatic fluctuation extended beyond rainfall to include temperature, not only in great annual extremes and year-to-year differences, but, with the changing surge of air masses, in rapid changes from day to day and week to week. Levels of sunshine and wind speed are higher than in the areas to the east, as average rainfall is markedly lower. The surface itself is far from uniform. To the

north and west of the Black Hills there is a substantial degree of local relief; sometimes the plains are multilevel, with sharp breaks between. South of the Nebraska sandhills the high plains are, in general, a country of little slope and broad, uninterrupted sweeps. In such expanses the valleys of the major rivers from the mountains are incised far below the plains level, and surface water is little and far between; the water table is generally at substantial depth, and streams run intermittently in drier seasons. The soils share with nearly all the other soils of the dry mid-latitude grasslands a high potential fertility for most crops, otherwise suitable, if water (by irrigation or higher than usual rainfall) becomes available. Irrigation water is, however, very limited, and higher rainfall years (like those of the 1940's) are sandwiched in between others (like those of the mid-1930's and the early 1950's) when the annual totals are of desert dimensions locally.

Entry of the Horse and Destruction of the Bison

The most obvious change in the remaining grasslands of the Great Plains is the presence of cattle and sheep which graze the grasses and browse the shrubs. The first exotic invader of importance, however, was the horse, which entered the plains to stay far ahead of the Europeans themselves or any other of their animals. Assuming no permanent introductions from the expeditions of De Soto or Coronado, the general consensus is of a slow seventeenth-century spread north and east from Santa Fe and other centers by escape, trade, and Indian capture.[1] The horses of pre-European times on the plains should be considered in two categories: the truly feral mustangs, which bred freely and increased rapidly in numbers, and those which were incorporated into the cul-

1. Aiton, 1939; Denhardt, 1947, 1951; Haines, 1938.

ture and economy of the Plains Indians. Although it has been argued that the wild horses were at one time to be counted "in the millions" (Wyman, 1945, p. 21), it is generally concluded that they were not a major element leading to change in the grassland. It is believed that they had declined greatly in numbers by 1870.

The greatest contribution of the horse to the rate and nature of grassland change was the increase of war potential among the Plains Indians which proved a major deterrent to European occupation for a period of nearly two centuries.[2] The evidence hardly suggests that it contributed substantially to reduction of bison numbers. Perhaps the increased pressure through horse-grazing was of similar proportion to the decrease of foraging bison. Thus the question of changes in the bison population is begged, and again we lack the historical research essential to any degree of certainty. The effect of changes in numbers on grazing pressure is little clearer. Bison-grazing has been carefully observed only under conditions so changed as to make comparisons of doubtful value. But there were very numerous bison that grazed grass, and the question at issue is whether their replacement by cattle and sheep has resulted in a substantial change in grass cover or other "natural" characteristics. The gamut of opinion runs from the viewpoint that the present plains cover is a disclimax resulting from a quite different, and more severe, grazing pressure of cattle and sheep, as compared with bison and pronghorn, to that which questions the whole concept of a stable climax and insists that bison-grazing may well have matched that of sheep and cattle (Larson, 1940). Unquestionably, the weight of opinion is that the bison did not graze as heavily (see relevant quotations in Trexler,

1921, esp. p. 350), but it is equally true that pronghorn-grazing was probably much heavier than has been assumed; some estimates would rate pronghorn equal in number to bison, at least on the plains (Skinner, 1922).

Debate is particularly sharp as to bison numbers.[3] It now seems safe to conclude that an average figure of some fifty million for the grasslands over all, with perhaps ten million on the area here considered, in an intermediate (what we illogically call "normal") rainfall year, is a conservative estimate. Clements and Shelford (1939, pp. 264, 273) assumed a much higher figure. Although the bison were virtually eliminated before 1890, the reduction in numbers was slow at first. With an assumption that the average yearly kill was about two million in the 1830's, the 15–20 per cent annual net replacement should have been ample to replenish the herds, even if the killing of cows was as much as the estimated eight to one in comparison with bulls. In the next decade, however, the kill began to far outstrip annual increase. The systematic destruction during the 1840–80 period has been well studied.[4] It was completed in the early eighties, somewhat earlier north of the forty-ninth parallel. The discovery in 1871 that the hides could make commercial leather greatly broadened the demand, and the destruction, toward the end, of two or three million a year was even greater than it had been a half-century earlier.

Although there was little delay in the replacement of bison by cattle—the great cattle invasion beginning after the Civil War—there probably was some

3. The best recent studies, which bring Allen (1876) and Mair (1890) up to date and winnows some wheat from the writings of such dubious reporters as Hornaday (1887) and Seton (1909, 1929), are those of Roe (1937, 1951).

2. Roe, 1939; Linton, 1940; Webb, 1931; Wissler, 1914, 1920.

4. Branch, 1929; Garretson, 1938; Rister, 1929.

lessening of grazing pressure in the replacement period 1840–80, which possibly may have given the plains a different aspect to visitors of that time than would have been shown in a time of more usual bison or cattle numbers. What has been overlooked in general, however, is the probability that grazing pressure by bison may well have increased in the first three or four decades of the century. If we accept the reasonable point of view that the bison were always more numerous where the forage was better (in the prairies and mixed grasslands), the early years of the century should have seen greater pressure on them in just those areas, partly from European advance in Texas and Illinois, but more particularly from the enforced invasion of Indians, pushed west by the flooding trans-Appalachian movement of American population. It is possible, thus, that some of our earliest systematic descriptions of the plains country (e.g., Marcy, 1849; Wislizenus, 1848, 1912) and the many more popular descriptions (e.g., Parkman, 1849) may have reported on an area subjected to heavier grazing in the immediately preceding decades than that experienced in any earlier century or since.

The possible effect of the horse on nature in the plains thus remains a lively topic for further historical research and processual reconstruction and speculation. It is inextricably linked with the matter of bison numbers, for it was ultimately an indispensable agency both in destroying and in replacing bison, but its effects as a grazer must surely have been small compared with the effect of changing numbers of bison.

The Invasion of Cattle

The spread of cattle over the plains is one of the best-documented stories of American expansion from the oceans to the interior.[5] In the southern plains, cattle spread northward from the Texas reservoir in the 1830's, 1840's, and 1850's. At the end of the Civil War there were five million cattle in Texas alone. Other sources of cattle, especially for the northern plains, were Oregon and the present Corn Belt states. By 1880, cattle had effectively occupied the plains (Table 27), and the short-lived open range was giving way to fenced ranches.

This cattle invasion has generally

TABLE 27

INVASION OF CATTLE AND SHEEP INTO THE
NORTHERN PLAINS STATES, 1860–1950*

STATE OR TERRITORY	CATTLE (IN THOUSANDS)			SHEEP (IN THOUSANDS)	
	1860†	1880‡	1950	1880	1950
Kansas	93	1,115	3,509	630	511
Nebraska	37	952	3,629	247	314
Colorado		763	1,776	1,091	1,657
Wyoming		517	1,028	450	1,829
Montana		417	1,758	279	1,337
North Dakota		166	{1,588}	84	{ 386
South Dakota			{2,513}		{ 889

* Source: United States Bureau of the Census, 1952.
† Few in plains.
‡ Omitting milch cows.

5. Briggs, 1934; Dale, 1930; Osgood, 1929; Pelzer, 1936; Webb, 1931; Wellman, 1939; etc.

been considered to be the principal immigrant factor which altered the character of the grassland. There is a very rich, if uneven, literature concerned with some of these effects. We should unquestionably give more attention here to the impedimenta of the invasion: men, their buildings, cities, and towns; transportation lines, agriculture on both margins (prairie and irrigation) and spottily in the plains themselves; fences; windmills; and a host of immigrant plants, animals, insects, bacteria, and viruses, many of them noxious to the men and the major animal immigrants. But, again, our focus demands rigid limitation to the changes in the grasslands as such. These include changes in physiognomy and density of the association, the expansion or contraction of the range of certain species, the appearance of new species and the disappearance of older ones, correlative changes in the fauna, and changes in soil or water conditions, including erosion and gullying.

Most attention in study of the change in the biome associated with the entry of cattle has centered on the problem of "overgrazing." It has been accepted doctrine by a good many conservationists (and indeed by most cattlemen and other students of the area) that, from the 1880's onward (and before then in the southern plains), we have had, recurrently, the grazing of one or another portion of the range at a pressure causing serious deterioration of the cover. When these changes have reduced forage by thinning, replacement of more by less palatable graze or browse, substitution for grass of woody plants and "weeds" (i.e., forbs), or obvious blowing, washing, or gullying of soil as protective cover has been removed, the expressions "overgrazing," "depletion," or "erosion" have been applied as processual descriptions or explanations of the circumstances.

That short-term changes have oc-

curred, in the terms described, is not in question.[6] But that the unplowed shortgrass plains have, as a result, an essentially different character from those of an eighteenth-century (and earlier) presumed grama grass—buffalo grass—bison—pronghorn *cum* Plains Indian assemblage is quite another thing. To begin, we cannot accept the idea of a nicely balanced climax suddenly and substantially overturned by the entry of cattle and sheep. Culture does not suddenly enter a cultureless sphere, and grazing animals do not appear for the first time on the grassland areas. Moreover, the short-grass—bison biome probably had no continuous local or general stability in its numbers and distributions of plants, major or minor animals, or insects. With broad fluctuations in climate, with more or less natural and cultural burning (Sauer, 1950), with fluctuations in rodent or insect population not clearly related to rainfall or temperature trends, with some outward migration of bison, pronghorn, and, latterly, mustangs to mountains or prairies and parklands in "desert years" and heavier influxes in "prairie years," most of the kinds of changes ascribed to cattle- or sheep-grazing pressure must have occurred without it (Crawford, 1842, pp. 420–22). Thus, it is possible, for example, to see in the depletion of productive forage, the dust storms, rainwash, and gullying, the spread of shrubs at the expense of grass, or the increase of rodents or insects, not an example of destructive cultural exploitation of a valuable natural resource, but an expectable phase of a widely swinging pendulum which might have been observed many times in recent centuries.

With the substitution of fenced ranches for the open range, which followed the invasion of cattle in a brief

6. This literature is so widely known and available that citation is perhaps pointless, but we may mention the bibliography in Stefferud *et al.,* 1948.

quarter-century. it is true that a new factor was introduced. The improvement of transportation for the outward movement of animals in poor years, or the inward movement of feed, together with the local production of supplementary forage by irrigation or dry-farming technology, have interfered with the presumed safety valves of migration and large-scale die-off. There is a tendency to continue an intensity of grazing pressure in drier years, which might well have been much lighter under the bison-pronghorn regime. The significance of these things is, however, comparative, and we are left with possibilities, not facts.

Since we can only guess at pre–cattle-grazing pressure, attempts at comparison, for example, of pressures between the beginning and end of the nineteenth century must be rather tentative. In fact, we do not have a clear picture of optimum grazing pressure for cattle and sheep in the twentieth century. The extensive literature reveals not only a very wide variation in estimates of the optimum between one or another part of the plains but much uncertainty in specific areas, even when attempts are made to allow for climatically induced fluctuations of forage yield.[7] What also may be overlooked is that optimum grazing pressure is not a concept associated with the maintenance of a presumed climax; the desired goal may be something quite different. "Overgrazing" thus is applied to departures from the optimum—an agronomic rather than an ecologic ideal (Clarke *et al.*, 1943).

Many attempts have been made to assess the significance of climatic fluctuations in steadily grazed lands. Perhaps the most comprehensive study ever made of drought in relation to grass cover was that by Weaver and Albertson (1940; also 1936, 1939, 1944) of

7. Black and Savage, 1948; Larson and Whitman, 1942; Sarvis, 1941; Savage and Heller, 1947; Williams and Post, 1945.

eighty-eight ranges in western Kansas and Nebraska, western South Dakota, eastern Wyoming, eastern Colorado, and the Oklahoma Panhandle. The decade-long period of lower-than-average rainfall saw the loss of much topsoil, blowing, burial by dust, damage by grasshoppers, and general grass depletion, chiefly noticeable as thinning. *Opuntia* and other cactus and shrubs, Russian thistle, and other weeds increased greatly. The recovery of grama and buffalo grasses with improving rainfall was slow, for they are not good seeders; of the two, buffalo grass recovered more rapidly and replaced grama grasses on many areas. The most interesting aspect of these studies is, however, that even under continued grazing pressure (and perhaps much heavier than drought-year grazing by bison and pronghorn) the tendency with improved rainfall was return of the "normal" short-grass cover. Experimental pastures at the United States Range Livestock Experiment Station in eastern Montana took some eight years to recover from the 1934–36 drought under "conservative" grazing, but recover they did (Chapline, 1948).

In drier years the plains have experienced locally, under cattle-grazing, a degree of depletion of cover which is unlikely to have occurred under the free-ranging bison-pronghorn (or bison-pronghorn-mustang) regimes and a similarly exaggerated extension of brush and weeds. It is undemonstrated, however, that we have changed the potential of restoration of something very like the presumed early nineteenth-century cover by grazing pressure alone or that, even in the sorriest "desert" years of the thirties, an actual alteration which was more that an extra kick to the swing of the pendulum in a normally "oscillating equilibrium" had in fact occurred. "Overgrazing," "depletion," and "erosion" are actual, observable phenomena; they may have been endemic in kind, if not recent degree, for many long centuries in the Great Plains—as much a part of "natural" characteristics of plains as any phenomenon we care to name.

It is clear that "overgrazing" is associated principally with drought years, and, in this connection, we do need a closer examination of the degree to which dust storms or floods are associated with the unplowed plains, a comparison in this context of dust storms of the nineteenth and twentieth centuries (Malin, 1946; Sears, 1947, chap. xiii) and particularly whether their severity has been, in any sense, increased by heavier grazing. Malin (1947, pp. 131–48) has made a most exhaustive examination of the problem, and his tentative conclusions are that there has been no distinct long-term trend toward more dust storms or floods, or more severe ones. He suggests that we should not ascribe to cattle invasion the "climatic catastrophes" of the Dust Bowl era with the evidence we now have at hand. That cattle, the entrepreneurs who manage them, and the economy of the area have suffered severely from such disasters is clear; to our problem these facts would have relevance only if they documented a thesis of long-term change.

Other Invaders

Sheep.—The short-grass areas have received sheep and goats as well as cattle. There are, however, distinctly fewer of them and, equating their grazing pressure to that of cattle (and chiefly wool-type, high-Merino-blood sheep, compared with Hereford and similar beef-type cattle) at seven, or ten, to one, they are of very much less significance. The effect of sheep pressure can be interpreted in general in the same terms as cattle pressure, as considered above. Perhaps the vulnerability of sheep to attack by predators (chiefly coyotes and wolves on the plains) has led to more widespread and systematic attack on predators in the sheep country and thus

tended to disturb more substantially broader balances of the ecosystem in general (Connor, 1921; Towne and Wentworth, 1945).

Grasses, weeds, and shrubs.—Some attempt has been made to control the character of the association by regulation of grazing pressure by the animals, but there have been other deliberate attempts to "engineer" changes in the vegetation cover. These involve in part the deliberate suppression of some types of vegetation and the introduction or encouragement of others. The extent of reseeding of the short-grass area has been obscured by the rather larger effort to turn land once plowed out of short grass, for grain production, back to a satisfactory forage sod. How much of the true short-grass land has been plowed in non-irrigation areas is uncertain. The supposed large-scale plowing-under of such land during World War I for grain production has been greatly exaggerated. Jorgensen (1949), with some careful calculations, estimates that, of an often-quoted (and misleading) figure of eleven to twelve million acres for the west North Central states, only about five million acres were plowed in the short-grass lands of that area in the war decade. Taking this and various other estimates on the plains area for land plowed in high-price, good-rain years (which coincided during two World War periods), and which has been allowed to revert to volunteer vegetation or has been deliberately reseeded to grass, we should arrive at between ten and fifteen million acres for the whole short-grass plains. The area of deliberate reseeding of unplowed grass is smaller, but as of seven or eight years ago some five million acres of such land had been reseeded (Pearse *et al.*, 1948).

Some of the seeds planted are natives, but there has been a substantial attempt to introduce such exotics as crested wheat grass (*Agropyron cris-*

tatum), Russian wild rye (*Elymus junceus*), and Hungarian smooth brome (*Bromus inermis*) in the north; three South African lovegrasses—weeping (*Eragrostis curvula*), Boer (*E. Chloromelas*), and Lehmann (*E. lehmanniana*)—in the south; and Caucasian and Turkestan bluestems (*Andropogon intermedius* var. *caucasius* and *A. ischaemum*) in higher-moisture sites. With this program a considerable alteration of cover has been achieved, and it has been going ahead with some momentum since 1947. Concurrent with the recent severe drought in the southern plains especially, something approaching a hundred million acres of depleted land are being recommended for reseeding.[8]

Other methods of deliberately inducing changes in the grassland include the mowing and "railing" of weeds and shrubs, the widespread use of chemical weed- and brush-killers, and fertilization, especially by air-dusting, although the last presents serious problems in areas of such low rainfall. A great deal has been attempted in fencing, in spacing waterholes and salting points to avoid concentration, and in keeping sheep scattered instead of clustered; but these are methods of controlling grazing intensity, and the major hope of students of range improvement in the short-grass area is to introduce new grasses or to improve old ones.

The major program of breeding, selection, and reseeding is now a half-century old. Crested wheat grass, introduced in 1906, is hardly a paragon; it is being improved by mass selection, and other *Agropyron* species (*A. elongatum, A. Trichophorum*, and *A. intermedium*) are also being imported (Graham, 1944, pp. 203 ff.). Actual breeding has been rather slow. One of the more interesting possibilities arises from the substantial degree of interspe-

cific hybridization which goes on in the grasslands. Although the offspring are sterile, they are more vigorous and long-lasting, and the deliberate planting-together of parent-species to produce such hybrids is now being undertaken (Keller, 1948).

Few truly exotic forbs and shrubs have become widely established in the short-grass area. The variation of density or distribution of *Artemisia, Prosopis*, or *Opuntia* is a "natural" phenomenon of fluctuating conditions of the grasslands; they have been present at all times and are in no sense exotic to any part of it. Most of the plants considered noxious for one reason or another, either as poisonous (e.g., larkspur), inedible (e.g., orange sneezeweed), unpalatable (e.g., bitterweed, etc.), or as fire hazards when dry (e.g., cheatgrass) are, like the shrubs, native; Malin (1953) has presented evidence to suggest in the case of mesquite, sagebrush, and cactus some doubt as to current theories of wider spread associated with "overgrazing."

Most of the serious exotic "weed" problems are in fact outside of the unplowed, short-grass plains proper; some weeds, like Russian, Canada, and sow thistles in particular, have occasionally been problems in the plains, but they have never become permanent additions to the ecosystem to alter its essential long-term character.

Trees.—The short-grass plains were, and still are, largely treeless regions, except for the larger mesquite in parts of the southern plains and the cottonwood river-bottom strips fingering their way west into the plains of the center or north. One of the most difficult adjustments of "deciduous forest man" (Shelford, 1943) in the plains was to learn to live without trees, and he did not learn without making great efforts to bring his trees with him and to maintain them in the unfriendly environment. Despite a wide variety of efforts

8. Hanson, 1928; Nelson and Shepherd, 1940; Savage, 1934; Short, 1943.

to introduce trees, it is, however, a safe generalization to make that the un-plowed plains and many millions of acres once plowed and allowed to re-vert to something like their original character are still treeless.

Reaction of Minor Grazing Fauna, Predators, and Insects to the Invasions

As a footnote to the story of the in-vasions, much has been written of the change in the pre-European fauna. The bulk of it has been concerned with the effect of the change in numbers and kinds of wildlife on the productivity of the range. As competitors for forage with sheep and cattle, there have al-ways been hares and rabbits and the "true rodents": prairie dogs, ground squirrels, pocket gophers, and kangaroo rats in particular. Despite much study, their role in the ecology of modern range use is not well understood. They do consume much grass. The Zuñi prairie dog, for example, was found to feed on 78 per cent forage grasses and to be somewhat selective of the best species (Kalmbach, 1948). Kalmbach quotes an estimate of Grinnell and Dixon that California ground squirrels ate herbage and grass which, if fully utilized, could have supported 160,000 cattle or 1,600,000 sheep. Actually it is doubtful if the competition means much in good years, but in bad years it not only may be serious for cattle and sheep but also may speed range deterioration through change in the density and kind of plants in the cover (Taylor, 1930).

Most of the observations have to be treated with great care. Accepting an apparent increase in rabbits, hares, and rodents as contemporaneous with de-pletion and change in vegetation is cer-tainly not to establish cause and effect and, indeed, raises the question of which *is* cause or effect if a causal re-lationship be accepted. It is entirely possible, if not probable, that rodents thrive better on land where grasses are depleted and shrub growth is encour-aged. Scrub control operations, by mowing, railing, burning, etc., remove protective cover and allow coyotes and hawks to prey on rodents. Jack rabbits are observed to congregate, not where the range is best, but where it is poor-est. Of particular relevance is the con-clusion that such fluctuations in rodent numbers should have been a long-term characteristic of plains history, far ante-dating the entry of cattle and sheep.

We have little better understanding of the relation of insect numbers to the replacement of bison and pronghorn by cattle and sheep. The insects of most interest to graziers, and therefore most studied, have been grasshoppers, Mor-mon crickets, cutworms, army worms, range caterpillars, and leaf-cutting ants. Major attention has been given to the grasshoppers, the attack of which at various times has assumed the dimen-sions of a national calamity (Le Duc, 1878; Brown, 1948). When they swarm to the degree that they are called "lo-custs," they consume a great deal and create a serious pressure on the vegeta-tion. This is, of course, most evident when drought, rodent-grazing, and heavy cattle- or sheep-grazing are com-bined with the locust swarms.

THE CALIFORNIA GRASSLANDS

"The original appearance of the Cali-fornia Grassland is not a matter of his-torical record" (Beetle, 1947, p. 343). The reconstructions have varied a good deal, but the most general assumption is that the Great Valley (except for the drier south-central area of the southern portion) and many of the valleys of the coastal mountains south of San Fran-cisco Bay had a dominant cover of per-ennial bunch grasses. It is also assumed that these grasses occurred extensively in the parklands and scrublands of the none-too-well-named "chaparral" associ-ation which covered most of the re-mainder of the southern coastal moun-tain-and-valley complex, as well as portions of the lower slopes of the southern Sierra Nevada. Much of this area has been brought under cultivation, particularly as irrigated land at lower elevations of the Sacramento Valley and the broad eastern fans of the southern valley. Also, many valleys, irrigated or not, and areas marginal to the valley irrigated lands or at higher levels in the coastal ranges have been used for rainfall-farming. Throughout the southern coast ranges and in a border of fluctuating width surrounding the valley, there are still unplowed areas which were, however, presumably grassland in the seventeenth century (see Fig. 148, p. 740).

If the cover was indeed perennial bunch grass, a very great change has occurred, for today these unplowed areas are dominated by annual grasses mostly exotic to the area and even to the continent. Whatever the original cover, it is at least likely that there were strong contrasts between the California grasslands and those of the Great Plains. The latter, undoubtedly, have always been subject to a much heavier grazing pressure. They presumably have been predominantly perennial sod grass and have had, we believe, a high degree of stability within a considerable range of periodic fluctuation. The original California grassland was "grazed" only by deer, rabbits, and rodents. There must have been a great deal of variation in the presumed needlegrass–bluegrass (*Stipa-Poa*)–bunchgrass association, but it is thought to have been dominated by California, or purple, needlegrass (*S. pulchra*) and other needlegrasses and to have included species of bluegrass (*Poa*), medic (*Melica*), squirreltail (*Sitanion*), wild rye (*Elymus*), fescue (*Festuca*), bromes (*Bromus*), bentgrass or browntop (*Agrostis*), bluestem (*Andropogon*), three-awn (*Aristida*), muhly (*Muhlenbergia*), Panicum, Danthonia, and prairie June grass (*Koeleria cristata*), the last the only species known

to be common to both the grassland of California and the mid-continent prairies.[9]

There were some native annuals, and there have been some successfully introduced perennials (e.g., colonial bent [*Agrostis tenuis*] and perennial rye grass [*Lolium perenne*]), but a conversion from predominant native perennials to predominant exotic annuals is nearly complete. The entry of the latter is presumed to be associated with the successive spread of missions and cattle graziers in the later eighteenth century (Parish, 1920). Why contact of missions and graziers in New Mexico and Texas should not have led to a similar exotic invasion of grasses into the Great Plains has never been satisfactorily determined. Differences between bunch-grass and sod cover, in climates (both in reduction of lower temperature extremes and in reversal of season of rainfall), in soils, in the occupying Indian cultures, and in both Indian and European cultural burning practices— all have been argued. The most significant contrast, perhaps, is that between the grazing pressure of many bison east of the Rockies and of a few deer west of the Sierra, but the actual application of this to the problem remains to be worked out in detail.

Our assurance that most of the present grasses are immigrants rests on far better evidence than does the assumed pre-Spanish character of the grassland. Present dominant plants are readily identifiable as exotics, and their time of entry and rate of spread have been established by some highly ingenious detective work in examination of grasses imbedded in adobe bricks in structures of known age.[10] Annual bluegrass (*Poa annua*), common foxtail (*Hordeum murinum*), and Italian ryegrass (*Lolium multiflorum*) became established

9. Beetle, 1947; McArdle *et al.*, 1936; Robbins, 1940.

10. Hendry, 1931, 1934; Hendry and Bellue, 1936; Hendry and Kelly, 1925.

early. The now ubiquitous wild oat (*Avena fatua*) is thought to have arrived somewhat later (about 1800). Although the last is still of great importance, it, in turn, has been greatly reduced from its earlier nineteenth-century dominance among the annuals (Newberry, 1857), though Aldous and Shantz (1924) listed it with three species of brome grass and alfileria, or red-stemmed filaree (*Erodium cicutarium*), as of greatest importance among annuals of only thirty years ago. Certainly it has provided a significant amount of range forage for well over a century. Fifteen or more bromes have been introduced, but, of these, soft chess (*Bromus mollis*) is much the most important for forage; ripgut grass (*B. rigidus*) and red brome (*B. rubens*) are almost as common if not as welcome. Annual bluegrass (adobe-dated 1797) and common foxtail (adobe-dated 1775), two of the earliest, are still very widespread.

The grassland contains many non-grassy annuals. Red-stemmed filaree appears to have been in California before 1769.[11] Filaree is certainly a very important range fodder plant, often cut for hay as well as grazed. The two major types of filaree (red stemmed and white stemmed, *E. moschatum*) have somewhat different areas of concentration, although they are mixed on most ranges. Davy (1902) has told us something of the general mechanism of grassland change in California by his report on the northwestern ranges. There he reconstructed replacement of the original perennial bunch grasses chiefly by wild oats and red-stemmed filaree; common foxtail, squirreltail, and soft chess followed; and, finally, in the twentieth century, came white-stemmed filaree.

11. Hendry and Kelly, 1925. Robbins (1940) quotes Frémont (1845), Torrey (1859), and Brewer and Watson (1880), among others, on the extent of alfileria and on their general erroneous conclusion that it was a native.

The invaders have included many truly noxious plants: St.-John's-wort or Klamath weed (*Hypericum perforatum*), Russian knapweed (*Centaurea repens*), Canada thistle (*C. arvense*)—which had the honor of inducing California's first noxious weed act in 1872 —and sow thistle (*Sonchus asper*), with an adobe history dating back to 1771. Russian thistle (*Salsala kali,* var. *temifolia*), vinegarweed (*Trichostema lanceolatum*), the peppergrasses (*Lepidium* spp.), and the plantains (*Plantago* spp.) might also be mentioned. Some exotics came via the eastern United States, like Johnsongrass (*Sorghum alepense*) and the puncture vine (*Tribulus terrestris*), which was also a nuisance on the Great Plains. The list of adventive plants now found in or near the grasslands is of course very long and includes shrubs and perhaps trees in, or at least on the border of, the grasslands: the Australian saltbushes (*Atriplex* spp.) and eucalypts. Curiously, the predominance of the exotics has led to the consideration of many native forbs (and some grasses) as undesirable weeds in the present grassland.

The significance of invading horses, cattle, and sheep in this substantial alteration of the unplowed California grassland is not clear. The transmission of seeds in the wool of the sheep and the droppings of the cattle, the pressure of grazing, and the early and repeated burning as a range management practice may have been the principal factors in the change. Yet the speed with which so many annuals spread suggests that, even without grazing pressure or animal help, a substantial invasion of the grassland might have occurred, granted the entry of annuals by some means. The point may not be very important; with the invasion of man, his plants and his animals, came a change in the plant cover almost as substantial as that achieved by plowing or cutting and burning of forest.

Associated questions are those of acceleration of soil erosion, lowering of water tables, drying-up of streams, flooding, etc. On the whole it is doubtful if we have any clear direct association of these questions with grassland change. The elaborate irrigation systems, the extensive cutting of forest, the many dams, channels, and levees—all have had incidental effects on the grasslands. But the direct contribution of exotic plants and animals to the change is obscure.

Studies of reseeding and the place of rodents and insects reveal nothing essentially new or significant. California's grasslands are more easily reseeded largely because they are annuals, but the new seeds face an even more difficult problem of establishment because of the aggressive weedy nature of the exotic cover (Chapline, 1920).

The remaining grassland plays a very small part in the whole economic structure of California. Yet a little over a century ago the grassland, as it then was, formed the principal base of the regional economy. In general, the same things are true of the interior North American grasslands, although the sod grasses of the high, dry plains, generally very much less altered by the seventeenth- to nineteenth-century invasions and displacements, are of more regional importance today than are those of California. In both cases, with a minimum of deliberate attempt to change the nature of the grassland (and with much effort to avoid change), the invasions occurred. In the Great Plains the essential change has been small; in California it has been nearly complete.

GRASSLANDS OF THE SOUTH ISLAND OF NEW ZEALAND

The writer has made only one detailed investigation of the invasion of a grassland and of resulting changes— that of the South Island of New Zealand (Clark, 1949). Figure 149 (*top*) is reproduced from that study (p. 24). Figure 149 (*bottom*) is a generalization of the remaining areas of grassland unplowed and unaltered by deliberate seeding operations, as given by the map accompanying Hilgendorf (1935) and adjusted in part by Cumberland (1941). Grass is still the most extensive single kind of vegetation cover on the island, clothing some one-third of the total area, or about thirteen million acres. (The island as a whole is about the size of Illinois.)

The grassland, as its character has been reconstructed, was a bunch-grass association (locally "tussock grassland," or simply "tussock") dominated by perennial bluegrasses (*Poa* spp., esp. *P. caespitosa* var. *laevis*, and *P. colensoi*) and fescues (esp. *Festuca novae zelandiae*), with two or three *Danthonias* of minor importance. There was originally an understory of herbaceous plants and other grasses which sheep must have fed on largely as they first invaded the grassland. It was not comparable in density, variety, or importance to the present substratum which comprises the chief sheep forage today but which has been greatly changed by invasion and internal plant migration as burning and grazing have created entirely new microclimates in the intertussock areas. Scattered through the grassland were coarse savanna-grass types (*Aciphylla, Arundo,* and *Celmisia* spp.), clumps of New Zealand flax (*Phormium tenax*), shrubs (as *Leptospermum* and *Discaria*), and occasional lone cabbage trees (*Cordyline*) (L. Cockayne, 1928).

The existence of such a grassland in a region enjoying, in general, a precipitation well in excess of that established by Köppen for a grassland boundary is an anomaly comparable to that of the grasslands of the Argentine Pampa or the "prairie peninsula" of North America. The bunch-grass vegetation is most

FIG. 149.—Pre-European vegetation cover and remaining tussock grasslands, South Island, New Zealand.

nearly like that presumed for the Pacific Coast grasslands in general, and California in particular, but it had no close parallel anywhere. Few, if any, of the explanations offered for the existence of humid-climate grasslands elsewhere apply to this one. The vegetation was unique not only in enjoying isolation from competition for periods which are measured in geological, rather than historical, time but also in having no associated grazing or browsing fauna except for the indigenous flightless birds. These were of many genera and species. The most spectacular were the giant moas (*Dinornithiformes*), the largest land birds of recent millenniums and among the largest of paleontological record. They may have "grazed" extensively in the grassland. They were, however, completely exterminated by the Polynesian Maori sometime before the first Europeans visited the island.

The remaining tussock grassland is almost entirely occupied and used for grazing; the grazing animals are virtually all sheep. Actually, even most of the sheep now graze improved (largely plowed, rotational) pastures on the various plains and "downs" areas which are usually close to the northern, eastern, or southern coasts; such areas also contain most of the cattle and pigs not in grassland established on burned forest. But vast stretches of the higher plains, foothills, lower mountain slopes, and intermontane basins east of the main drainage divide are still covered with a grassy vegetation in which the original tussock grasses are the physiognomic dominants. They are grazed largely by sheep with varying proportions of Merino blood (Buchanan, 1935; Belshaw, 1936).

The evolution of the organization of sheep husbandry, always sensitive to changing prices and demand, is still in active development. Sheep began grazing the original tussock grasslands on the coasts in the early 1840's and pushed to the ultimate limits of the grassland within three decades. Most of the grassland has thus been under grazing pressure for a century—not quite so long as cattle and sheep have been in California but somewhat longer, in general, than cattle and sheep on the Great Plains.

Standard practices in range management included regular burning. That it contributed to deterioration of the range in markedly reducing forage production (in the long run) is accepted by most students of the area (A. H. Cockayne, 1910; Zotov, 1939; Cumberland, 1945). So, too, did heavy sheep-grazing and rabbit infestation. This change in forage production has involved a great reduction in the size and number of individual tussocks of grass, a serious depletion of the original subtussock grasses and forbs, and a widespread change in the type and character of the latter. The ultimate form of depletion was reached within a few decades in the dry central Otago hill country of the south, where little but mats of scabweed (*Raoulia lutescens*) are scattered around over otherwise nearly bare ground (L. Cockayne, 1919–22; Clark, 1949, Fig. 57, p. 262).

The burning controversy has, figuratively, fully lived up to its name. The justification most generally given for the practice is that regular burning is necessary to protect flocks; if one "run" (i.e., the owned or, more usually, leased land of one grazier) is left unburned, fires, spreading from neighboring runs, may incinerate the home flock. But burning also removes the coarse, unpalatable, dead tussock leaves and makes much forage available from the tussocks which would otherwise be avoided by the sheep. Despite many experimental exclusion studies, it has proved impossible to disentangle the separate effects of burning and sheep- and rabbit-grazing; but, taken together, they have greatly altered the grass cover, economically for the worse.

In this alteration history the entry of the European rabbit and its rapid spread may be of more importance than sheep-grazing. In the course of the last seventy-five years scores of millions of rabbits have regularly occupied large areas of the grasslands and scrublands of the island. All the usual protective devices (fences, poisoning, introduction of predators, disease control) have been used. Up to twenty million rabbit skins a year have been exported from New Zealand; with Australian rabbit skins, they were basic staples for the world's fur-felting industries. The rabbits certainly competed with sheep for grass; the degree, however, is problematical. Estimating a rather conservative normal figure of fifty million for the island's rabbit population, with the majority in the remaining tussock grasslands, they probably displaced at least a million sheep. The effect of the rabbits, however, has been much more in their contribution to long-term decline in range forage production; in those terms, their economic effect on the sheep industry was incalculable but certainly very much larger. Until very recently, fluctuations in rabbit numbers have borne very little obvious relation to attempts to bring them under control (Thomson, 1884, 1922; Wodzicki, 1950).

There are no domesticated animals of importance other than sheep in the South Island tussock grasslands except for horses, used to help herd sheep, and a relatively few beef cattle. Stray pigs, which quickly became feral, spread rapidly in certain forest and brush areas and somewhat into the grasslands before formal settlement and were present in tens of thousands as late as the 1860's (Hochstetter, 1863). The feral pigs, a considerable supplementary food resource for the early settlers, were, however, quickly eliminated from the grassland, and farm swine are not important there.

Like pigs, the goats have become feral, but, unlike pigs, the feral goat is still present in large numbers in two major concentrations in the tussock: near Lake Wakatipu in the southwest and in Marlborough Land District of the northeast. The writer estimated not less than 50,000 feral goats for the whole island in the early 1940's. The modesty of that figure is suggested by an export of 34,136 goatskins in 1946 and destruction of more than 73,000 by extermination teams of the Department of Internal Affairs in 1947, mostly on South Island. As with rabbits and deer, control efforts have not been very successful. The precise effect of the goats on the plant cover of the grassland is not too well understood; most attention has been paid to their effect on forest and brushland. They do add grazing pressure and must have contributed their share to change.

Among wild animals, rabbits were not, however, the only exotic animals of importance to be introduced. The acclimatization fever, so disastrous in its encouragement of rabbit importation, also brought various species of deer, chamois, thar (or tahr)—even wapiti and moose—to the island. In 1942 these animals were estimated to total well above 100,000, and it was the dominant red deer which most notably extended its grazing pressure from the remnants of *Nothofagus* forest into the tussock grasslands. In the 1944–46 period well over 100,000 deerskins were exported each year from New Zealand, most of them from South Island (Donne, 1924; Wodzicki, 1950).

The change in the grassland has involved the decline, thinning, or virtual disappearance of certain original species, the spread of other natives to take their place under the altered ecological conditions, and the entry of many exotics. Thus *Agropyron scabrum,* the only one of the three native wheatgrasses of any original importance in the South Island tussock and believed to have been a substantial member of the original subtussock stratum, is now confined to the shelter of the remaining dominants. Similar fates have befallen many of the others, and the tussock dominants themselves (*Poa caespitosa* and *Festuca novae-zelandiae* on the plains, downs, and lower mountain slopes and two *Danthonias—D. flavescens* and *D. raoulii* var. *rubra*—of the tall tussock grassland above the "scrub line") are much depleted. A native bluegrass, *Poa maniototo*, has stood up better than others, is relatively more important now, and may even have spread a little in some of the drier interior basins. The most aggressive native clearly has been the oatgrass, *Danthonia pilosa*, which was always important but has spread widely in an improved competitive position under burning and grazing. Another aggressive native under similar pressures has been ringed danthonia (*D. semi-annularis*). In many parts of the present grassland these have clearly taken over from the *Poa* and *Festuca* dominants reported by the earliest observers (Allan, 1936).

But exotics *have* moved in over many broad areas. Browntop (*Agrostis tenuis*, the colonial bent of American terminology) has been the leader. Other invading grasses of importance include sweet vernal (*Anthoxanthum odoratum*), red fescue (*Festuca rubra*, var. *fallax*), Yorkshire fog (*Holcus lanatus*, or common velvetgrass), and the world-wide camp follower of European man, *Poa pratensis* (twitch or Kentucky bluegrass). And with the grasses came the many "weeds," with sorrel (*Rumex* spp.) and cat's-ear or capeweed (*Hypochaeris radicata*) in the van. Most of the invaders have provided valuable grazing; indeed, they may form the chief sheep forage over many areas.

However, one invading grass has become a noxious nuisance in North Canterbury (*Nasella* spp., esp. *N. trichotoma* from Argentina) and for a time necessitated local control boards like those organized to combat rabbits.

Since tussock areas are fenced largely with wire, the spread of gorse (*Ulex europaeus*) has not been extensive in the tussock areas, but it has "got away" locally. In the right places it is a useful invader for sheep shelter, but it is remarkably aggressive and is a real pest when out of control. Otherwise, there are a few afforestation projects of woody growth which have done remarkably well in the tussock lands, principally with Monterey, Corsican, and Pondosa pines (*P. radiata*, *P. laricio*, and *P. ponderosa*) and European larch (*Larix decidua*). Here and there on the tawny sweeps of the grasslands the headquarters of the "stations" are picked out by groves of darker exotic trees, especially the two most successful invading trees in all of New Zealand: Monterey pine and Monterey cypress (*Cupressus macrocarpa*).

CONCLUSION

This has been a thumbnail sketch of changes in some unplowed grasslands associated with recent exotic invasion. Few generalizations can be drawn. Indeed, we should be wary of the generalization "grassland," for similar histories of exotic invasion have not led to similar changes. Where the exotic invasion involved a replacement of wild by domesticated grazing animals, the real change may have been small; where the new grazing pressure clearly was greater than before, or was virtually a new phenomenon, more substantial changes have occurred. But, again, the contribution of the grazing of the animals, as distinct from related burning or rabbit or rodent attack, has never been established. If there had been no sheep- or cattle-grazing, the exotic annuals might still have taken over much of California's original grassland, given the opportunity of spread by man. This is suggested clearly in the early adobe-dating of many of them. In New Zealand it is entirely possible that any one of the new elements in the grassland (sheep, fire, and rabbit) alone, or any two in combination, might have achieved substantial change. The precise change which, in fact, occurred as a result of the triple attack is doubtless different in kind, but not necessarily in degree, from what has been achieved by the other alternatives. And, unlike California, South Island retains a dominant perennial cover on its grassland.

There is, we can say, no clear over-all picture of destructive exploitation of the grasslands; it is most nearly recognizable in some parts of the New Zealand tussock, but even there ingenuity may demonstrate that it was temporary. It can also be seen that heavy grazing in poor grass years anywhere tends to reduce the most profitable types of forage and may lead to some accelerated soil erosion and gullying. It is perhaps fair to assume that this was rare before the invasions in New Zealand and California and can be attributed to them; such an assumption is by no means clearly justified in the Great Plains.

Man's really significant alteration of the mid-latitude grasslands has occurred where he has destroyed and replaced them by plowing and planting. The impact of culture on nature by grazing of unplowed mid-latitude grasslands has been far less than, and on the whole different from, what has generally been implied in conservational writing. These grasslands *have* changed, but they are still essentially grasslands, and, assuming that they were to be used for grazing, they are perhaps not seriously impaired, as yet, for that purpose. If they had not been grazed, they might have been quite different; in the case of New Zealand and California we can suggest the approximate degree of that difference. But, if they had not been used for grazing, they would not have served even the rather minor auxiliary economic purpose they now serve in their general regional economies. Judged in terms of long-range economic benefits and in terms of technologies available in their less than two (in one case scarcely one) centuries of use, the invasions may have been clearly a net gain.

REFERENCES

AITON, ARTHUR S.
  1939 "Coronado's Muster Roll," *American Historical Review*, XLIV, No. 3, 556–70.
ALDOUS, H. E., and SHANTZ, H. L.
  1924 "Types of Vegetation in the Semi-arid Portion of the United States and Their Economic Significance," *Journal of Agricultural Research*, XXVIII, No. 2, 99–128.
ALLAN, H. H.
  1936 *An Introduction to the Grasses of New Zealand.* (New Zealand Department of Scientific and Industrial Research Bulletin No. 49.) Wellington, N.Z.: Department of Scientific and Industrial Research. 159 pp.

ALLEN, JOEL A.
  1876 *The American Bison, Living and Extinct.* ("Memoirs of the Museum of Comparative Ethnology," Vol. IV, No. 10.) Cambridge, Mass.: Harvard University Press. 246 pp.
BEETLE, ALAN A.
  1947 "Distribution of the Native Grasses of California," *Hilgardia*, XVII, No. 9, 309–55. Berkeley.
BELSHAW, HORACE, *et al.* (eds.)
  1936 *Agricultural Organization in New Zealand: A Survey of Land Utilization, Farm Organization, Finance and Marketing.* Melbourne: University of Melbourne Press. 818 pp.

BLACK, W. H., and SAVAGE, D. A.
1948 "Grass for the Production of Beef," pp. 103–19 in STEFFERUD, A., *et al.* (eds.), *Grass: Yearbook of Agriculture, 1948.* Washington, D.C.: Government Printing Office. 892 pp.

BRANCH, E. DOUGLAS
1929 *The Hunting of the Buffalo.* New York: D. Appleton & Co. 239 pp.

BREWER, W. H., and WATSON, SERENO
1880 "Polypetalae," Vol. I, Part I, of *California Geological Survey: Botany.* 2d ed. (1st ed. 1876.) 2 vols. Cambridge, Mass.: J. Wilson & Sons, University Press. 622+559 pp.

BRIGGS, HAROLD E.
1934 "The Development and Decline of Open-Range Ranching in the Northwest," *Mississippi Valley Historical Review,* XX, No. 4, 521–36.

BROWN, RALPH H.
1948 *Historical Geography of the United States.* New York: Harcourt, Brace & Co. 596 pp.

BUCHANAN, R. OGILVIE
1935 *The Pastoral Industries of New Zealand.* (Institute of British Geographers Publication No. 2.) London: Geo. Philip & Son. 99 pp.

CARPENTER, J. R.
1940 "The Grassland Biome," *Ecological Monographs,* X, No. 4, 617–84.

CHAPLINE, W. R.
1920 "Range Reseeding," *California Countryman,* III, No. 15, 26–30; No. 16, pp. 28–30.
1948 "Grazing on Range Lands," pp. 212–16 in STEFFERUD, A., *et al.* (eds.), *Grass: Yearbook of Agriculture, 1948.* Washington, D.C.: Government Printing Office. 892 pp.

CLARK, ANDREW HILL
1949 *The Invasion of New Zealand by People, Plants and Animals: The South Island.* New Brunswick, N.J.: Rutgers University Press. 465 pp.

CLARKE, S. E.; TISDALE, E. W.; and SKOGLUND, N. A.
1943 *The Effects of Climate and Grazing Practices on Short-Grass Prairie Vegetation in Southern Alberta and Southwestern Saskatchewan.* (Canadian Ministry of Agriculture Publication No. 747, Technical Bulletin No. 46.) Ottawa: King's Printer. 53 pp.

CLEMENTS, F. E., and SHELFORD, V. E.
1939 *Bioecology.* New York: John Wiley & Sons. 425 pp.

COCKAYNE, A. H.
1910 "The Effect of Burning on Tussock Country," *New Zealand Journal of Agriculture* (Part I of "The Natural Pastures of New Zealand"), I, No. 1, 7–15. Wellington.

COCKAYNE, LEONARD
1919–22 "An Economic Investigation of the Montane Tussock Grassland of New Zealand" (fourteen articles), *New Zealand Journal of Agriculture,* Vol. XVIII, No. 1, to Vol. XXV, No. 3. Wellington.
1928 *The Vegetation of New Zealand.* (*Die Vegetation der Erde,* Vol. XIV, No. 2.) Leipzig: W. Engelmann. 456 pp.

CONNOR, L. G.
1921 "A Brief History of the Sheep Industry in the United States," pp. 89–197 in *Annual Report of the American Historical Association for the Year 1918,* Vol. I. Washington, D.C.: Government Printing Office. 487 pp.

COUPLAND, ROBERT T.
1953 "Grassland Communities of the Western Canadian Prairies—Climax and Subclimax," pp. 625–31 in *Proceedings of the Sixth International Grassland Congress (State College, Pennsylvania, 1952).* Washington, D.C.: Government Printing Office. 1,801 pp.

CRAWFORD, T. HARTLEY
1842 *Annual Report of the Commissioner of Indian Affairs for 1842.* Washington, D.C.: Government Printing Office. 158 pp.

CUMBERLAND, KENNETH B.
1941 "A Century's Change: Natural to Cultural Vegetation in New Zealand," *Geographical Review,* XXXI, No. 4, 529–54.
1945 "Burning Tussock Grassland: A Geographic Survey," *New Zealand Geographer,* I, No. 2, 149–64.

DALE, EDWARD E.
1930 *The Range Cattle Industry.* Nor-

man, Okla.: University of Oklahoma Press. 216 pp.

DAVY, JOSEPH BURTT
1902   *Stock Ranges of Northwestern California: Notes on the Grasses, Forage Plants and Range Conditions.* (U.S. Bureau of Plant Industry Bulletin No. 12.) Washington, D.C.: Government Printing Office. 81 pp.

DENHARDT, ROBERT M.
1947   *The Horse of the Americas.* Norman, Okla.: University of Oklahoma Press. 286 pp.
1951   "The Horse in New Spain and the Borderlands," *Agricultural History,* XXV, No. 4, 145–50.

DONNE, T. E.
1924   *The Game Animals of New Zealand: An Account of Their Introduction, Acclimatisation and Development.* London: J. Murray. 322 pp.

FRÉMONT, J. C.
1845   *Report of the Exploring Expedition to the Rocky Mountains in the Year 1842, and to Oregon and North California in the Years 1843–44.* Washington, D.C.: Gales & Seaton, Printers. 693 pp.

GARRETSON, MARTIN S.
1938   *The American Bison: The Story of Its Extermination as a Wild Species and Its Restoration under Federal Protection.* New York: New York Zoölogical Society. 254 pp.

GRAHAM, EDWARD H.
1944   *Natural Principles of Land Use.* New York: Oxford University Press. 274 pp.
1947   *The Land and Wildlife.* New York: Oxford University Press. 232 pp.

HAINES, FRANCIS
1938   "Where Did the Plains Indians Get Their Horses?" *American Anthropologist,* XL, No. 1, 112–17.

HANSON, H. C.
1928   *Revegetation of Waste Range Land.* (Colorado Agriculture Experiment Station Bulletin No. 332.) Fort Collins, Colo. 9 pp.

HAYDEN, FERDINAND V.
1870   *Sun Pictures of Rocky Mountain Scenery, with a Description of the Geographical and Geological Fea-* tures, and Some Account of the Resources of the Great West; Containing Some Thirty Photographic Views along the Pacific Railroad, from Omaha to Sacramento. New York: J. Bien. 150 pp.

HENDRY, GEORGE W.
1931   "The Adobe Brick as an Historical Source," *Agricultural History,* V, No. 3, 110–27.
1934   "The Source Literature of Early Plant Introduction into Spanish America," *ibid.,* VIII, No. 2, 64–71.

HENDRY, GEORGE W., and BELLUE, M. K.
1936   "An Approach to Southwestern Agricultural History through Adobe Brick Analysis," pp. 1–8 in *Proceedings of a Symposium on Prehistoric Agriculture, Flagstaff, Arizona.* ("University of New Mexico Bulletin, Anthropological Series," Vol. I, No. 5, Whole No. 296.) Albuquerque, N.M.: University of New Mexico Press. 72 pp.

HENDRY, GEORGE W., and KELLY, MARGARET
1925   "The Plant Content of Adobe Bricks," *California Historical Society Quarterly,* IV, No. 4, 361–73.

HILGENDORF, F. W.
1935   *The Grasslands of the South Island of New Zealand: An Ecological Survey.* (New Zealand Department of Scientific and Industrial Research Bulletin No. 47.) Wellington, N.Z.: Government Printer. 24 pp.

HOCHSTETTER, FERDINAND VON
1863   *Neu-Seeland.* Stuttgart: Cotta'scher Verlag. 556 pp. (Translated by EDWARD SAUTER and revised by HOCHSTETTER and SAUTER as: *New Zealand: Its Physical Geography, Geology and Natural History.* Stuttgart: Cotta'scher Verlag. 1867. 515 pp.)

HORMAY, AUGUST L.
1944   *Moderate Grazing Pays on California Annual-Type Ranges.* (United States Department of Agriculture Leaflet No. 239.) Washington, D.C.: Government Printing Office. 8 pp.

HORNADAY, WILLIAM T.
1887   "The Extermination of the American Bison, with a Sketch of Its Discovery and Life History," pp. 367–548 in Part II of *Annual Report of*

the United States National Museum (*Smithsonian Institution*). Washington, D.C.: Government Printing Office. 771 pp.

JORGENSEN, LLOYD P.
1949 "Agricultural Expansion into the Semiarid Lands of the West North Central States during the First World War," *Agricultural History*, XXIII, No. 1, 30–40.

KALMBACH, E. R.
1948 "Rodents, Rabbits and Grass," pp. 248–56 in STEFFERUD, A., *et al.* (eds.), *Grass: Yearbook of Agriculture, 1948*. Washington, D.C.: Government Printing Office. 892 pp.

KELLER, WESLEY
1948 "Wanted: A Paragon for the Range," pp. 347–51 in STEFFERUD, A., *et al.* (eds.), *Grass: Yearbook of Agriculture, 1948*. Washington, D.C.: Government Printing Office. 892 pp.

LARSON, FLOYD
1940 "The Role of the Bison in Maintaining the Short-Grass Plains," *Ecology*, XXI, No 2, pp. 113–21.

LARSON, FLOYD, and WHITMAN, WARREN
1942 "A Comparison of Used and Unused Grassland Mesas in the Badlands of South Dakota," *Ecology*, XXIII, No. 4, 438–45.

LE DUC, WILLIAM G.
1878 "The Rocky Mountain Locust or Grasshopper of the West," pp. 264–333 in *Report of the Commissioner of Agriculture for the Year 1877*. Washington, D.C.: Government Printing Office. 592 pp.

LINTON, RALPH (ed.)
1940 *Acculturation in Seven American Indian Tribes*. New York: D. Appleton–Century. 526 pp.

MCARDLE, RICHARD F., *et al.*
1936 "The White Man's Toll," pp. 81–116 in UNITED STATES FOREST SERVICE, *The Western Range* (74th Cong., 2d sess.; Senate Document No. 199). Washington, D.C.: Government Printing Office. 620 pp.

MAIR, CHARLES
1890 "The American Bison, Its Habits, Methods of Capture and Economic Uses in the Northwest, with Reference to Its Threatened Extinc-

tion," *Proceedings and Transactions of the Royal Society of Canada*, VIII, Sec. II, 93–108.

MALIN, JAMES C.
1946 "Dust Storms, 1850–1900," *Kansas Historical Quarterly*, XIV, No. 2, 129–44; No. 3, pp. 265–96; No. 4, pp. 391–413.
1947 *The Grassland of North America: Prolegomena to Its History*. Lawrence, Kan.: Privately published. 398 pp. (Note bibliography, pp. 336–94.)
1952 "Man, the State of Nature and Climax: As Illustrated by Some Problems of the North American Grasslands," *Scientific Monthly*, LXXIV, No. 6, 29–37.
1953 "Soil, Animal, and Plant Relations of the Grassland, Historically Reconsidered," *ibid.*, LXXVI, No. 4, 207–20.

MARCY, (CAPT.) RANDOLPH B.
1849 "Report of Exploration and Survey of Route from Fort Smith, Arkansas, to Santa Fe, New Mexico, Made in 1849," pp. 26–89 in House Executive Document No. 45 (31st Cong., 1st sess.). Washington, D.C.: Government Printing Office. 89 pp. (Bound in Vol. VIII, Public Document No. 577, of the same session.)

NELSON, E. W., and SHEPHERD, W. O.
1940 *Restoring Colorado's Abandoned Croplands*. (Colorado Agricultural Experiment Station Bulletin No. 459.) Fort Collins, Colo. 31 pp.

NEWBERRY, JOHN S.
1857 "Report upon the Botany of the Route," pp. 9–94 in UNITED STATES WAR DEPARTMENT, *Reports of the Explorations and Surveys To Ascertain the Most Practical and Economical Route for a Railroad from the Mississippi River to the Pacific Ocean, 1854–1855*, Vol. VI, Part III: "Botanical Report." Washington, D.C.: Beverly Tucker, Printer. 305 pp. and 137 pls.

OSGOOD, ERNEST S.
1929 *The Day of the Cattleman*. Minneapolis: University of Minnesota Press. 283 pp.

PARISH, S. B.
1920 "The Immigrant Plants of South-

ern California," *Bulletin of the Southern California Academy of Sciences,*
XIX, No. 4, 3–30.

PARKER, J. R.
1952 "Grasshoppers," pp. 595–605 in
STEFFERUD, A., *et al.* (eds.), *Insects:
Yearbook of Agriculture, 1952.* Wash-
ington, D.C.: Government Printing
Office. 780 pp.

PARKMAN, FRANCIS
1849 *The California and Oregon Trail.
. . .* New York: G. P. Putnam. 448
pp. (Many times reprinted and republished; *see* 8th ed., revised, 1886,
under title: *The Oregon Trail.* Boston: Little, Brown & Co. 381 pp.)

PEARSE, C. K.; PLUMMER, A. P.; and
SAVAGE, D. A.
1948 "Restoring the Range by Re-
seeding," pp. 227–33 in STEFFERUD,
A., *et al.* (eds.), *Grass: Yearbook of
Agriculture, 1948.* Washington, D.C.:
Government Printing Office. 892 pp.

PELZER, LOUIS
1936 *The Cattlemen's Frontier: A
Record of the Trans-Mississippi Cattle
Industry from Oxen Train to Pooling
Companies, 1850–1900.* Glendale,
Calif.: Arthur H. Clark Co. 351 pp.

RISTER, CARL C.
1929 "The Significance of the Destruction of the Buffalo," *Southwestern Historical Quarterly,* XXXIII
(July, 1929, to April, 1930), 34–49.

ROBBINS, W. W.
1940 *Alien Plants Growing without
Cultivation in California.* (University
of California Agricultural Experiment
Station Bulletin No. 637.) Berkeley:
University of California. 128 pp.

ROE, FRANK GILBERT
1937 "The Numbers of the Buffalo,"
*Proceedings and Transactions of the
Royal Society of Canada, Series III,*
XXXI, Sec. II, 171–203.
1939 "From Dogs to Horses among
the Western Indian Tribes," *ibid.,*
XXXIII, Sec. II, 209–71.
1951 *The North American Buffalo:
A Critical Study of the Species in Its
Wild State.* Toronto: University of
Toronto Press. 957 pp.

SARVIS, J. T.
1941 *Grazing Investigations on the*
Northern Great Plains. (North Dakota Agricultural Experiment Station Bulletin No. 308.) Fargo, N.D.
110 pp.

SAUER, C. O.
1950 "Grassland Climax, Fire, and
Man," *Journal of Range Management,* III, No. 1, 16–21.

SAVAGE, D. A.
1934 *Methods of Reestablishing Buffalo Grass on Cultivated Land on the
Great Plains.* (U.S. Department of
Agriculture Circular No. 328.) Washington, D.C.: Government Printing
Office. 20 pp.

SAVAGE, D. A., and HELLER, V. G.
1947 *Nutritional Qualities of Range
Forage Plants in Relation to Grazing
with Beef Cattle on the Southern
Plains Experimental Range.* (United
States Department of Agriculture
Technical Bulletin No. 943.) Wash-
ington, D.C.: Government Printing
Office. 61 pp.

SEARS, PAUL B.
1947 *Deserts on the March.* 2d rev.
ed. Norman, Okla.: University of
Oklahoma Press. 178 pp. (1st ed.,
1935.)

SETON, ERNEST THOMPSON
1909 *Life History of Northern Animals: An Account of the Mammals
of Manitoba.* 2 vols. New York:
Charles Scribner's Sons. 1,220 pp.
1929 "Hoofed Animals," pp. 413–780
(Part II) in *Lives of Game Animals,*
Vol. III. New York: Doubleday,
Doran & Co. 780 pp.

SHELFORD, V. E.
1943 "Deciduous Forest Man in the
Grassland of North America," pp.
203–6 in *Proceedings of the Eighth
American Scientific Congress, Washington, 1940,* Vol. IX. 12 vols. Washington, D.C.: Government Printing
Office.
1944 "Deciduous Forest Man and the
Grassland Fauna," *Science,* C, No.
2590, 135–40; No. 2591, pp. 160–62.

SHORT, L. R.
1943 *Reseeding To Increase the Yield
of Montana Range Lands.* (U.S. Department of Agriculture, Farmer's
Bulletin No. 1924.) Washington,

D.C.: Government Printing Office. 25 pp.

SKINNER, M. P.
1922 "The Pronghorn," *Journal of Mammalogy,* III, No. 2, 82–105.

STEFFERUD, ALFRED, *et al.* (eds.)
1948 *Grass: Yearbook of Agriculture, 1948.* Washington, D.C.: Government Printing Office. 892 pp.
1949 *Trees: Yearbook of Agriculture, 1949.* Washington, D.C.: Government Printing Office. 944 pp.
1952 *Insects: Yearbook of Agriculture, 1952.* Washington, D.C.: Government Printing Office. 780 pp.

TAYLOR, WALTER P.
1930 "Methods of Determining Rodent Pressures," *Ecology,* XI, No. 3, 523–42.

THOMSON, G. M.
1884 "The Rabbit Pest," *New Zealand Journal of Science,* II, 79–80. Wellington.
1922 *The Naturalisation of Plants and Animals in New Zealand.* Cambridge: Cambridge University Press. 607 pp.

TORREY, JOHN
1859 "Botany of the Boundary," pp. 11–270 (+ 61 plates) in *Report on the United States and Mexican Boundary Survey,* Vol. II, Part I (34th Cong., 1st sess.; Executive Document No. 135). Washington, D.C.: Cornelius Wendell, Printer.

TOWNE, CHARLES W., and WENTWORTH, EDWARD N.
1945 *Shepherd's Empire.* Norman, Okla.: University of Oklahoma Press. 364 pp.

TREXLER, H. A.
1921 "The Buffalo Range of the Northwest," *Mississippi Valley Historical Review,* VII, No. 4, 348–62.

UNITED STATES BUREAU OF THE CENSUS
1952 *United States Census of Agriculture: 1950,* Vol. II: *General Report (Farms, Farm Characteristics, Livestock and Products, Crops, Fruits and Values).* Washington, D.C.: Government Printing Office.

WEAVER, JOHN ERNEST
1954 *North American Prairie.* Lincoln, Neb.: Johnsen Publishing Co. 348 pp.

WEAVER, J. E., and ALBERTSON, F. W.
1936 "Effects of the Great Drought on the Prairies of Iowa, Nebraska and Kansas," *Ecology,* XVII, No. 4, 567–639.
1939 "Major Changes in Grassland as a Result of Continued Drought," *Botanical Gazette,* C, No. 3, 576–91.
1940 "Deterioration of Midwestern Ranges," *Ecology,* XXI, No. 2, 216–36.
1944 "Nature and Degree of Recovery of Grassland from the Great Drought of 1933 to 1940," *Ecological Monographs,* XIV, No. 4, 393–479.

WEAVER, J. E., and CLEMENTS, F. E.
1938 *Plant Ecology.* 2d ed. (1st ed., 1929.) New York: McGraw-Hill Book Co. 601 pp.

WEBB, WALTER PRESCOTT
1931 *The Great Plains: A Study in Institutions and Environment.* Boston: Ginn & Co. 525 pp.

WELLMAN, PAUL I.
1939 *The Trampling Herd: The Range Cattle in America.* New York: Carrick & Evans, Inc. 433 pp.

WILLIAMS, RALPH M., and POST, A. H.
1945 *Dry Land Pasture Experiments at the Central Montana Branch Station, Moccasin, Montana.* (Montana Agricultural Experiment Station Bulletin No. 431.) Bozeman, Mont. 30 pp.

WISLIZENUS, ADOLPHUS (FRIEDRICH ADOLF)
1848 *Memoir of a Tour to Northern Mexico, Connected with Colonel Doniphan's Expedition, in 1846 and 1847.* (30th Cong., 1st sess.; Senate Miscellaneous Document No. 26, Serial No. 511.) Washington, D.C.: Government Printing Office (or Tippin & Streeter, Printers). 141 pp.
1912 *A Journey to the Rocky Mountains in the Year 1839.* Translated from the German, with a sketch of the author's life, by FREDERICK A. WISLIZENUS, ESQ. St. Louis: Missouri Historical Society. 162 pp.

WISSLER, CLARK
1914 "The Influence of the Horse in the Development of Plains Culture,"

American Anthropologist (N.S.), XVI, No. 1, 1–25.

1920 *North American Indians of the Plains.* 2d ed. New York: American Museum of Natural History. 167 pp. (1st ed., 1912; 3d ed., 1934.)

WODZICKI, K. A.

1950 *Introduced Mammals of New Zealand: An Ecological and Economic Survey.* (New Zealand Department of Scientific and Industrial Research Bulletin No. 98.) Wellington, N.Z.: Department of Scientific and Industrial Research. 255 pp.

WYMAN, WALKER D.

1945 *The Wild Horse of the West.* Caldwell, Idaho: Privately published. 348 pp.

ZOTOV, V. D.

1939 "Survey of the Tussock-Grasslands of the South Island, New Zealand," *New Zealand Journal of Science and Technology,* XX, Part A, 212A–44A. Wellington.

Man as a Maker of New Plants and New Plant Communities

EDGAR ANDERSON[*]

That man changes the face of nature may be noted by any casual observer; not even the ablest and most experienced scholar can yet estimate just how far this has reclothed the world. Whole landscapes are now occupied by man-dominated (and in part by man-created) faunas and floras. This process began so long ago (its beginnings being certainly as old as *Homo sapiens*) and has produced results of such complexity that its accurate interpretation must await research as yet scarcely begun. Though answers to many basic questions remain unknown, they are by no means unknowable.

The average thoughtful person has little inkling of this reclothing of the world; even professional biologists have been tardy in recognizing that in the last analysis a significant portion of the plants and animals which accompany man is directly or indirectly of his own making. The ordinary American supposes that Kentucky bluegrass is native to Kentucky and Canada bluegrass native to Canada. A few historians and biologists know that these grasses (along with much of our meadow and pasture vegetation) came to us from Europe. The research scholar inquiring

critically into the question realizes that some of this vegetation was as much a Neolithic immigration into Europe as it was a later immigration into the New World. Like Kentucky mountaineers, this vegetation has its ultimate roots in Asia and spread into Central and Western Europe at times which, biologically speaking, were not very long ago.

It is obvious that landscapes such as the American Corn Belt have been transformed by man. Other man-dominated landscapes do not betray their origin to the casual observer. Take the grasslands of California, the rolling hills back from the coast, the oak-dotted savannas of the Great Valley. Here are stretches of what look like indigenous vegetation. Much of this mantle is not obviously tended by man; it has the look of something that has been in California as long as the oaks it grows among, yet the bulk of it came, all uninvited, from the Old World along with the Spaniards. Most of it had a long history of association with man when it made the trip. Wild oats, wild mustards, wild radishes, wild fennel— all of these spread in from the Mediterranean, yet over much of the California cattle country they dominate the landscape. Native plants are there, even some native grasses, but it takes a well-informed botanist going over the vegetation item by item to show how small a percentage of the range is made up of indigenous California plants.

* Dr. Anderson is Director of the Missouri Botanical Garden, St. Louis, Missouri, and Engelmann Professor of Botany at Washington University, St. Louis. His works include: *Introgressive Hybridization*, 1949, and *Plants, Man, and Life*, 1952.

For those parts of the tropics where plants grow rapidly it will take careful research before we can have an informed opinion about such questions. Thorn scrub, savannas, bamboo thickets, weedy tangles of quick-growing trees and shrubs are known to have covered vast areas in the last two or three millenniums. Yet Standley, our greatest authority on the vegetation of Central America, digging up a small tree in what appeared to him to be a truly indigenous forest in the Lancetilla Valley, came upon a layer of potsherds (Standley, 1931). What is the relation between the supposedly wild avocados of such a forest and the avocados eaten in the village that once covered that site? We now have various techniques (pollen profiles, carbon-14 datings, chromosome analysis, extrapolated correlates) which can give critical answers, but they are time-consuming, and their application to such problems has just begun.

The total number of plants and animals that have moved in with man to any one spot on the earth's surface is way beyond what even a biologist would estimate until he looked into the problem. There are the cultivated plants both for use and for display, the domesticated animals, the weeds, and their animal equivalents such as house-flies, clothes moths, rats, and mice. A much larger class of organisms is those not purposely introduced by man, which are neither eyesores nor plagues, but which, like weeds, have the capacity to get along in man's vicinity. Such are the daisies and yarrows and buttercups of our meadows. Such in a sense are even those native species that spread under man's influence. Take, for example, the sunflowers of Wyoming. They are certainly native to North America and may possibly in part be prehuman in Wyoming. They line the roadways yet seldom are elsewhere prominent in the native landscape.

They appeared along with the road, even though they may have moved in from not so far away. But how did they get into the spot from which they spread, and did pioneers or primitive man have anything to do with making this previous niche? This is the sort of question we are now making the subject of decisive experiments; we do not yet have enough results for decisive answers.

For microörganisms the problem of the species which travel about with man staggers the imagination. Microorganisms seemingly fall into the same general categories as macroörganisms. Brewers' yeasts are as much cultivated plants as the barleys and wheats with which they have so long been associated for brewing and baking. The germs of typhoid and cholera are quite as much weeds as are dandelions or Canada thistles. The microörganisms of our garden soil are apparently the same mixture of mongrel immigrants and adapted natives as our meadow and pasture plants. Soils are good or bad quite as much because of the micro-communities they contain as because of their composition. Man's unconscious creation of new kinds of microörganisms is an important part of his total effect on the landscapes of the world. Think, then, of this total composite mantle of living things which accompanies man: the crops, the weeds, the domesticated animals, the garden escapes such as Japanese honeysuckle and orange day lily, the thorn scrub, the bamboo thickets, the English sparrows, the starlings, the insect pests. Think of the great clouds of algae, protozoa, bacteria, and fungi—complex communities of microörganisms that inhabit our soils, our beverages, our crops, our domesticated animals, and our very bodies.

If we turn to the scientific literature for an orderly summary of where these species came from and how, there is a depressing lack of information. The crop plants and domesticated animals have been somewhat studied, the ornamentals and the weeds scarcely investigated. Even for the crop plants one notes that for those which have been the most carefully studied—wheat (Aase, 1946), cotton (Hutchinson *et al.*, 1947), maize (Mangelsdorf and Reeves, 1938)—there is now general recognition that their origins, relationships, and exact histories are much more complex problems than they were thought to be a generation ago. In spite of these wide gaps in our knowledge, I believe the following generalizations will stand:

1. All the major crops and most of the minor ones were domesticated in prehistoric times. *Modern agriculture, classified solely by the plants it uses, is Neolithic agriculture.*

2. For none of the major crops can we point with certainty to the exact species (or combination of species) from which it was derived: for some we can make guesses; for a number we can point to closely related weeds. This merely complicates the problem. We then have to determine the origin of the crop, the origin of the weed, and the history of their relationships.

The world's knowledge of crop plants, in other words, does not tell us very much. All we know is that we are dealing with man's effects on certain plants in the Neolithic or before. Yet for weeds and ornamental plants even less is known. A few general observations may be offered, parenthetically, about their origins.

1. We can now point to crops which are definitely known to have been derived from weeds. For instance, rye as a crop originated from a grainfield weed (Vavilov, 1926). As barley and wheat spread farther north onto the sandy Baltic plain, the weed gradually replaced the crop. The origin of rye as a weed is a far older and more complex problem. Stebbins and his students are

far enough into it to tell us that it is a story with several chapters, most of them unsuspected until recently.

2. We can point to weeds which originated from crop plants. The bamboo thickets that cover whole mountainsides in the Caribbean came from cultivated bamboos. It now seems much more probable that teosinte the weed was derived from maize the crop than that maize was derived from teosinte.

3. Crop plants and their related weeds frequently have a continuing effect upon each other. We have documented evidence of weeds increasing their variability by hybridizing with crop plants and of crop plants consciously or unconsciously improved through hybridization with weeds. These processes recur repeatedly in the histories of weeds and crop plants. For wheat it is clear that a minor grain was in very early times built up into one of the world's great cereals through the unconscious incorporation of several weeds from its own fields (Anderson, 1952, pp. 57–64).

As a whole, ornamentals (though little studied as yet) provide the simplest keys and the clearest insights into the basic problems of domestication of any class of plants or animals. Some have been domesticated within the last century, the African violet, for instance, but are already distinct from the species from which they arose. Such recent domesticates provide unparalleled experimental material for determining what happens to the germ plasm of an organism when it is domesticated. Others of our garden flowers originated in prehistoric times. They seem to have been associated with magic and ceremony; some of them may have been with us for as long or even longer than our crop plants. Take woad, *Isatis tinctoria,* now known only as a garden flower, though it persisted as a commercial dye plant until Victorian times (Hurry, 1930). When Caesar came to

Britain, he found our semisavage ancestors using it to paint their bodies. There are various other ornamentals (*Bixa, Amaranthus, Helianthus*) whose earlier associations were with dyes and body paints. Which is older, agriculture or body painting?

The cultivated grain amaranths (known to the Western world mainly through such bizarre late-summer annuals as love-lies-bleeding) demonstrate that we shall be in for some rude shocks when we make serious studies of these apparently trivial plants. J. D. Sauer found (1950) that this whole group was domesticates, divisible into several different species, none of which could be equated to any wild amaranth; that the whole group was of American origin; and that the varieties cultivated since ancient times in Kashmir, China, and Tibet were not (as had previously been taken for granted) derived from Asiatic amaranths. They are instead identical with those cultivated by the Aztecs and the Incas.

It is now becoming increasingly clear that the domestication of weeds and cultivated plants is usually a process rather than an event. None of them rose in one leap from the brain of Ceres, so to speak. The domestication of each crop or weed went on at various times and places, though by bursts rather than at a regular rate. For many it still continues. Our common weed sunflowers, for example, are at the moment being bred into superweeds. In California, by hybridization with a rare native sunflower, these weeds are increasing their ability to colonize the Great Valley (Heiser, 1949). In Texas (Heiser, 1951), by similar mongrelizations with two native species, they are adapting themselves to life on the sandy lands of the Gulf Coast (see Figs. 150–152).

The story of the American sunflowers is significant because it demonstrates the kinds of processes which went on in the Stone Age and before, when our major crops were domesticated. It is because the domestication of weeds and cultivated plants (using the word "domestication" in its broadest sense) is a continuing process that it came to my professional attention. Thirty years ago I started out to study (and if possible to measure) such evolution as was still going on. As I analyzed example after example, the fact became increasingly clear that evolutionary activity is concentrated in (though by no means confined to) disturbed habitats—to times and places where man's interference with the prehuman order of things has been particularly severe. Post-Pleistocene evolution, it seems, has been very largely the elaboration of weedlike plants and animals.

Now why should this be? What is there about the presence of man that stimulates his plant and animal companions into increased evolutionary activity? A growing body of observational and experimental data bears directly upon that question; rather than summarizing it, let me describe in considerable detail one particularly illuminating example. It concerns the hybridization of two California species of wild sage, *Salvia apiana* and *S. mellifera*. They have been meticulously studied by Epling—in the field (1947), the herbarium (1938), the laboratory, and the experimental plot (Epling and Lewis, 1942). Burton Anderson and I (1954) have made an exhaustively detailed analysis of the variation pattern of several populations, confirming and extending Epling's conclusions.

These two species of sage are so unlike that any ordinary amateur would immediately recognize them as radically different plants; only an occasional botanist would see that they are really quite closely related and that their differences, though conspicuous, are superficial. This was what first drew Epling's attention to them. He found that they hybridized readily when artificially cross-pollinated. The hybrids grew vigorously in an experimental plot and were fertile enough to produce abundant and variable offspring. In spite of this fertility, hybrids were ordinarily not found in nature or occurred mainly at spots where the native vegetation had been greatly altered by man's activities. Yet on the rocky slopes where they were native, these two kinds of sage frequently grew intermingled. Burton Anderson and I worked with samples of wild populations of both species so intensively that eventually we could distinguish between mongrels, seven of whose great-grandparents were from one species and one from the other, and plants with all eight grandparents from one species. With this yardstick we learned that, though the plants on the mountainside were prevailingly of one species or the other, yet along the pathway from which we collected them we could find a few mongrels. These were mostly plants closely resembling typical *Salvia mellifera* but showing slight indications of *S. apiana* in one character or another. Apparently the very rare hybrids which Epling had found were not completely without issue. Some of them had crossed back to *S. mellifera*, and, of these three-quarter bloods, a few of those similar to the recurrent parent had been able to fend for themselves.

At one point along the path we found conspicuous hybrids resembling those produced by Epling; careful investigation of this area gave us new understanding. With repeated visits we gradually realized that these bizarre mongrels were limited to a definitely circumscribed plot having a greatly altered habitat. It was at a point where the trail swung down along the slope. Originally a forest of live oaks had abutted on the rocky, sunny slopes where the salvias grow. The oaks had

been cut and a small olive orchard planted and then abandoned—abandoned so long ago that native plants had flowed in and the whole site looked quite natural. A collection of salvias made exclusively from among the olives was almost entirely hybrids and hybrid descendants. Though the bulk of the plants looked somewhat like *Salvia apiana*, there was not a single plant which in all its characters agreed exactly with the *apianas* outside this plot. Furthermore, they resembled artificial backcrosses in that their differences from *apiana* were all in the direction of *S. mellifera*. These "sub-*apianas*" graded into plants closely resembling the first-generation hybrids raised by Epling. There were a few "sub-*melliferas*" similar to those we had detected along the pathway on the mountainside and a few plants which on our index scored as typical *melliferas*. However, in the field *none* of them looked quite average. Dr. Anderson and I had to work in St. Louis on pressed and pickled material previously collected in California. Had we been able to go back and add characters such as flower color and flower pattern to our battery of measurable differences between *S. mellifera* and *S. apiana*, I believe we could have demonstrated that the entire plot was colonized with hybrids and mongrels, most of them first or second or third backcrosses from the original hybrids to one or the other species.

These results indicate that hybrids are being constantly produced on this mountainside, but one does not ordinarily find them, because there is no niche into which they can fit. The native vegetation had a long evolutionary history of mutual adaptation. Plants and animals have gradually been selected which are adapted to life with each other like pieces of a multidimensional jigsaw puzzle. It is only when man, or some other disruptive agent, upsets the whole puzzle that there is any place where something new and different can fit in. If a radical variant arises, it is shouldered out of the way before it reaches maturity. In a radical-

ly new environment, however, there may be a chance for something new to succeed. Furthermore, the hybrids and their mongrel descendants were not only something new; they varied great-

FIG. 150

FIG. 151

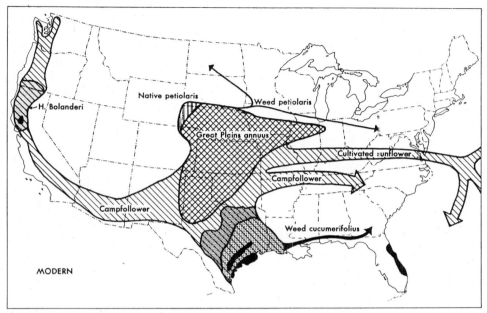

FIG. 152

FIGS. 150, 151, and 152.—A diagrammatic and greatly simplified demonstration of the extent to which the domestication of the sunflower as a cultivated plant and its development as a weed are processes rather than events. Data from Heiser (1949, 1951) and personal communications and from my own observations. The history of the cultivated sunflower, complicated though it is shown to be, will be simpler than that of most cultivated plants when these histories have been worked out in accurate and documented detail. Various complications have been ignored altogether to keep the diagram intelligible, as, for instance, the continuing intercrossing between the "camp-follower" weed and the cultivated ornamental and field-crop sunflowers.

FIG. 150.—Annual species of North American sunflowers as presumed to have existed in pre-human times: (1) *Helianthus exilis*, a highly localized endemic in the serpentine areas of California; (2) *H. petiolaris* on bare sandy areas in the western Great Plains; (3) *H. annuus* in playas and other raw-soil habitats of the southwestern deserts; (4) *H. argophyllus* on the sands of the Texas coastal plain; and (5) *H. debilis* in Florida and Texas.

FIG. 151.—Hypothetical origin of the North American sunflower as a weed and as a cultivated annual in pre-Columbian times. In the areas where *annuus* and *petiolaris* had begun to introgress, this process is being unconsciously accelerated by the activities of early man.

FIG. 152.—Spread of annual species of North American sunflowers in modern times. In the Great Plains extensive introgression of *annuus* and *petiolaris* produced the Great Plains race of *Helianthus annuus*, which has spread eastward through the prairies as a somewhat weedy native. The camp-follower weed (sometimes mixed with Great Plains *annuus*) has spread as a weed throughout the East and to irrigated lands in the West. In California, by extensive and continuing introgression with *exilis*, it has created the semiweedy *H. bolanderi*, which is still actively spreading. Similarly on the sands of the Texas coast and the Carrizo ridge, *H. argophyllus* is introgressing actively with *H. annuus* to produce weedier strains. Over an even wider area in Texas extensive introgression of *annuus*, *petiolaris*, and *cucumerifolius* is producing a coastal plain weed sunflower which is actively spreading along the coast. In spots it has already reached the North Carolina coastal plain. Eventually this will react actively with *H. debilis* var. *debilis*, breeding a superweed for the American Southeast but, fortunately, a not unattractive one. The Texas and California phenomena have already been documented by Heiser (1949 1951), and research on other facets of the problem is going forward rapidly.

ly among themselves. If one of them would not fit into the strange new habitat, another might. Though virtually all of them had been at a selective disadvantage on the mountainside, a few of them (aided and abetted no doubt by the vigor which is characteristic of these and many other hybrids) were now at a selective advantage. They consequently flowed in and occupied the old olive orchard to the virtual exclusion of the two original species.

Furthermore, to take up an important fact about which biology as yet knows very little, the habitat among the olives was not only something new; it was *open*. It was not full of organisms which had been selected to fit together. Remember that for the mountainside, on those rare occasions where a first-generation hybrid plant had been able to find a foothold, virtually none of its highly variable descendants was able to persist. Such species crosses can father hundreds if not thousands of distinguishably different types of mongrel descendants. Only along the pathway had *any* of these been able to find a place for themselves and then only those which differed but slightly from *Salvia mellifera*. Hybridization does not advance in closed habitats.

The plants in the olive orchard had no such history of long association. The olives were new to California. The societies of microörganisms in the soil were originally those which go with live oaks, not those accompanying the salvias on the sunny slopes. These must have been greatly changed during the time the olives were cultivated. Furthermore, the olives, being planted at considerable distances, from each other, did not re-create either the fairly continuous shade of the oaks or the open sunshine of the upper slopes. The orchard became the site for evolutionary catch-as-catch-can, and under these circumstances, as we have seen, the new and variable had a decisive advantage.

Now that we know this much about these salvias, it would be interesting to work experimentally with them and the species with which they are associated to determine just what factors allow two different but closely related species to fit together with their associates so perfectly that all hybrid intermediates are excluded. From experience with other similar problems I should predict that among the most important factors would be fairly specific reactions between some of the other associated plants and these two sages. In our experimental work with sunflowers we have discovered that one of the strongest factors in determining where weed sunflowers may or may not grow is their reaction to grass. Many grasses apparently give off a substance highly toxic to weed sunflowers. The various species of weed sunflowers differ in their sensitivity to this poison. When two such sunflowers hybridize, one of the factors affecting the outcome is the grassiness of the site. Such relationships seem to be very general among plants. On the whole, many species grow where they do, not because they really prefer the physical conditions of such a site, but because they can tolerate it and many other organisms cannot.

Generally speaking, the plants which follow man around the world might be said to do so, not because they relish what man has done to the environment, but because they can stand it and most other plants cannot.

Are these salvias weeds? I would put forward the working hypothesis that those in the abandoned olive orchard are on the way to becoming weeds. The small exceptional communities of hybridizing colonies similar to this one, which can be found here and there over southern California, are worth considerably more attention than they have hitherto received. They demonstrate the way in which man, the great weed-breeder, the great upsetter, catalyzes the formation of new biological entities by producing new and open habitats.

The *Salvia* case is not unique. We now have over a score of similar well-documented studies of the connection between hybridization and weedy, disturbed habitats. This relationship had long been known to observant naturalists, though not until the last few decades was its significance stressed or experimental work undertaken. One other example demonstrates the role of man's operations on the habitat. Riley (1938) studied the hybridization of two species of *Iris* on the lower delta of the Mississippi in a neighborhood where the land-use pattern had produced something as demonstrable and convincing as a laboratory experiment (Anderson, 1949; see Fig. 153). Property lines ran

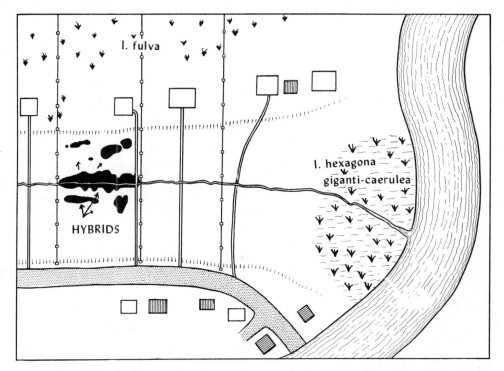

Fig. 153.—A demonstration of man's unconscious role in creating new plants. (From Riley, 1938.) At the far right one of the minor bayous of the lower Mississippi Delta. At right angles to it and running nearly across the figure is the abandoned channel of a former stream, now drained by a ditch. The natural levees of the stream are slightly higher than the surrounding country. Their sharp inner edges are indicated on the map by hachures. The road has been run along the lower levee, and houses have been built along the opposite one. The property lines (as in many old French settlements) produce a series of long narrow farms, which for our purposes serve as so many experimental plots. Each farm has its house on a low ridge with a long entrance drive connecting it across a swale to the public road on the opposite ridge. The farms (including a score of others which are out of sight to the left of the figure) were originally essentially similar. At the point where the ditch joins the bayou is a large population of *Iris hexagona giganti-caerulea*. Behind the levee on which the houses were built, *I. fulva* grows on the lower ground as well as farther upstream along the ditch. The key fact to be noted is that the hybrids are on only one farm, that they are abundant there, and that they go up to the very borders of the property on either side. Nature is evidently capable of spawning such hybrids throughout this area, but not until one farmer unconsciously created the new and more or less open habitat in which they could survive did any appear in this part of the delta. (See Anderson, 1949, pp. 1–11, 94–98, for a more complete discussion.)

straight back from the river; the farms were small, only a few hundred yards wide, and very narrow. Under these conditions it was easy to see that the hybrids between these two irises were virtually limited to one farm. They grew in a swale which crossed several of the farms, yet were nearly all on one man's property. On his farm they went right up to the fences and stopped, and

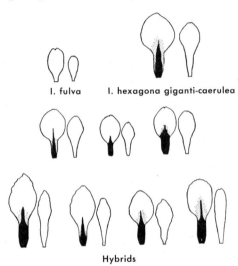

I. fulva   I. hexagona giganti-caerulea

Hybrids

Fɪɢ. 154.—Sepals and petals of some hybrids of *Iris hexagona giganti-caerulea* and *I. fulva* somewhat diagrammatic but accurately to scale. In each case the sepal (the so-called "fall" of iris fanciers) is shown to the left; the petal, "standard," to the right. *I. fulva* has small lax terra cotta sepals and petals. *I. hexagona giganti-caerulea* has large crisp petals and sepals of bright blue. The sepal has a brilliant yellow signal patch (*shown in black*) surrounded by a white area (*shown by stipples*) shading off into the blue. Note that in the various hybrids the small-sized flowers (characteristic of *I. fulva*) tend to be associated with the lack of a white area (another *fulva* characteristic). Note the variability of the hybrids. In color they varied from deep wine to very pale, light blue.

this could be demonstrated at either side of his property. Unlike his neighbors, he had kept the swale heavily pastured. His cattle had held in check the grasses which are serious competitors of swamp irises. They had also,

tramping about in wet weather, turned the swale into more of a quagmire than existed on any of the neighboring farms. They had at length produced an open environment in which the pasture grasses were at a disadvantage and the resulting hybrid swarm of irises at a very real advantage. Hybrids in various patterns of terra cotta, wine, purple, and blue flooded out into this swale until it had almost the appearance of an intentionally created iris garden.

Though Riley never published the sequel, it might be inserted here, parenthetically, since it points up some kind of a moral. The farmer himself did not remove the irises, even though they interfered seriously with the carrying capacity of his pasture. The irises were conspicuously beautiful, and garden-club members from New Orleans dug them up for their gardens, at so much per basket, until they were eventually exterminated. The hybridization which nature began in this and other pastures around New Orleans has been continued by iris fans. These Louisiana irises are now established as cultivated plants both in Europe and in America. Until the arrival of the garden-club ladies, they were nascent weeds (Fig. 154).

A little reflective observation will show that the ways in which man creates new and open habitats, though various, can mostly be grouped under a few headings: (1) dumps and other high nitrogen areas; (2) pathways; (3) open soil; (4) burns. The last is probably the oldest of his violent upsettings of the natural order of things. It must have stimulated evolutionary activity very early—whole floras or certainly whole associations must have come to a new adjustment with it here and there; fire should be, of all man's effects upon evolution, the most difficult to analyze. Until valid experimental and exact historical methods deal with this problem, it inevitably must spawn more polemic activity than scientific analysis.

In contrast to fire, the creation of open-soil habitats as a really major human activity belongs much more to the age of agriculture and industry than to prehistory. It may be that is why it seems to be the simplest to analyze. In Europe and eastern North America, in the humid tropics and subtropics, open soil—bare exposed earth—is scarcely part of the normal nature of things. Most of the flora truly native to these areas cannot germinate in open soil or, having germinated, cannot thrive to maturity. Make a series of seed collections from wild flowers and forest trees and plant them in your garden just like radishes or lettuce. You will be amazed to learn how small a percentage of them ever comes up at all. Make similar collections from the weeds in a vacant lot or from the plants (wanted and unwanted) of your garden. Nearly all of them will come up promptly and grow readily. Where did these open-soil organisms come from in the first place, these weeds of gardens and fields, these fellow-travelers which rush in after the bulldozer, which flourish in the rubble of bombed cities? Well, they must have come mostly from prehuman open-soil sites. River valleys did not supply all of them, but rivers are certainly, next to man, the greatest of weed-breeders. Our large rivers plow their banks at floodtimes, producing raw-soil areas. Every river system is provided with plants to fill this peculiar niche; all those known to me act as weeds in the uplands. One of the simplest and clearest examples is our common pokeweed, *Phytolacca americana*, native to eastern North America. It will be found growing up abundantly in the immediate valleys of our major rivers (Sauer, 1952; see Fig. 155). On the uplands it is strictly limited to raw soil, though, once established in such a habitat, it can persist vegetatively for a long time while other kinds of vegetation grow up around it. Being attractive to birds, its seeds are widely scattered. I remember, from my Michigan boyhood, how pokeweed came in when a woodland near our home was lumbered over. We had never noticed this weed in that community, but the birds had been planting it wherever they roosted. When the felling of the big oaks tore lesser trees up by the roots, pokeweed plants appeared as if by magic for the next few years in the new craters of raw soil. Man and the great rivers are in partnership. Both of them are upsetters. Both of them breed weeds and suchlike organisms. The prehuman beginnings of many of our pests and fellow-travelers are to be sought in river valleys. River valleys also must have been the ultimate source of some of the plants by which we live: gourds, squashes, beans, hemp, rice, and maize.

The examples of the salvias and irises show how quickly evolution through hybridization can breed out something new and different under man's catalytic influence. What we should most like to know is the extent to which weeds and suchlike organisms, created or at least extensively modified through man's influence, are built up into whole associations. It is clear that such things can happen; the *maqui* vegetation of the Mediterranean, the *shiblyak* and *karst* vegetation of the Balkans, the *carbón* scrub of Central America, are obviously very directly the results of man's interference. One would like to analyze the dynamics of these associations. We must do so if man is to understand his own past or to be the master of his own future. For such purposes we need ways of studying vegetation which are analytical as well as merely descriptive —methods not based upon preconceived dogmas. I should like to suggest that the methods used in analyzing the *Iris* hybrids and the *Salvia* hybrids, if com-

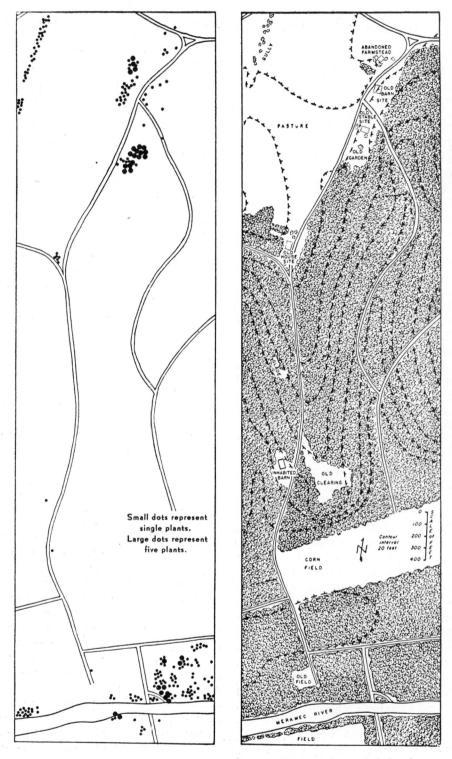

FIG. 155.—Occurrence of pokeweed in two different habitats. Pokeweed (*Phytolacca ameri-cana*) is an example of a species which is apparently native in the open soil along American rivers but a weed in the open soil of disturbed habitats. (Map from Sauer, 1952.) Small dots represent single plants. Large dots represent five plants. It will be seen that the pokeweed is occurring in two quite different kinds of habitats: in the raw soil of repeatedly flooded woodlands on the immediate banks of the river and as a weed around farm buildings, gardens, and the like. (See Sauer, 1952, for further details and discussion.)

bined with other experimental techniques, would allow us to get a long way into these problems. Let me illustrate what I mean by describing some recent studies of *Adenostoma*, a fire-resistant shrub, which is a common component of the California chaparral (Anderson, 1954).

Between the Great Valley and the Pacific Coast, *Adenostoma fasciculatum* is one of the commonest shrubs in the California landscape. Noting that it varied conspicuously from one plant to the next, I made collections of it near Palo Alto and applied to them the methods of pictorialized scatter diagrams and extrapolated correlates. The details of these techniques need not concern us here, since they have been adequately published elsewhere, both in technical journals and in books for the intelligent public. They allow us (through a meticulous examination of variability in such mongrel complexes as the salvias of the abandoned olive orchard) to determine precisely the good species (or subspecies or varieties) from which these complexes must ultimately have arisen. Furthermore, though it takes considerable hard work, these methods can be used successfully by one with no previous knowledge of the organisms or of the faunas and floras from which they may have come.

Using these methods, I have shown that the common *Adenostoma fasciculatum* of coastal California arose from the hybridization of two very different adenostomas. One of these was *A. fasciculatum* var. *obtusifolium*, a low-growing shrub of the headlands and islands along the California coast. The other is now found in its purest form in the Mother Lode country of the Sierra foothills, a tall, branching shrub which, when in flower, somewhat resembles a small-leaved white lilac. Each of these had its own contributions to make to life in coastal California. The coastal shrub brought in a tolerance of brilliant sunlight and the ability to grow in thin, rocky soil. However, it was accustomed to fog and drizzle even during the dry season. The inland form could go months without a drop of water, but it is used to deeper soil and to less extreme radiation. When these two centers of variation had been identified, it was easy to demonstrate that the common *Adenostoma* is a great, plastic, hybrid swarm, including approaches to these two extremes and many intermediates between them. On dry, rocky ridges in sites which are frequently foggy, one finds plants very close to the island extreme. On deeper soils and in the shade of small oaks are bushes scarcely different from those of the Mother Lode country. Around old ranch buildings and in other peculiar habitats one finds strange and bizarre recombinations of various sorts.

Just as these studies came to a close and it was time for me to leave California, I realized that many of the other plants in the chaparral association were similarly variable. There were swarms of hybrid oaks and hybrid ceanothus and hybrid manzanitas. The entire association seemed to be in a state of flux. Unlike the coastal sages which I had studied in southern California, there was room for hybrid recombinations within the association itself. The entire chaparral seemed to be ecologically in the same general class of disturbed habitat as the abandoned olive orchard.

I do not wish to jump to conclusions from one small experiment. I would merely suggest that these methods are appropriate for the analysis of such problems, particularly if combined with experimental work (for instance, the removal of a single specie or species complex from a small area using modern herbicides followed by measurement of the effect of this removal on the other complexes in the association). Here is a field in which we could very rapidly get down to some of the basic principles concerning closed versus open habitats. In my opinion, the degree to which such associations as the California chaparral are man-made is a better subject for study than for debate. They have certainly been greatly affected by man. To learn to what degree, I should prefer to look for more facts rather than to listen to more opinions.

Even among biologists there has been a strong tendency to avoid such problems—to study the plants and plant associations of mountaintops and jungles rather than those of dooryards and gardens, to think of plant and animal communities as they must have been in some blissfully innocent era before the advent of man. It seems to me far healthier and far more logical to accept man as a part of nature, to concentrate one's attention as a naturalist on man's activities, since he is the one species in the world we most nearly understand. It is because we know from inside ourselves the problems in which man is deeply involved that we appreciate their bewildering complexity; experiments with laboratory insects would not seem so beautifully simple if we knew as much about them as we do about man. The population genetics of garbage-pail flies (Dobzhansky, 1949) would appear more complex if we understood from within what it is like to be a *Drosophila*. The apparently standardized environment of flour in a bottle (Park, 1938) would not seem undifferentiated to any investigator who had once been a flour beetle and who knew at firsthand the complexities of flour-beetle existence. Imagine a non-human investigator of human populations recently arrived from Mars. What could he understand of the relationships of Catholics and Protestants? How long would it take him to discover that, though most of the shortest girls in New York City get married, the very

tallest seldom do? Having discovered this phenomenon, how much longer would it take him to understand it? When we attempt to work with laboratory insects, our ignorance of their social complexities makes them seem far simpler material than they really are.

I must confess that when, from being a student of variation in natural populations, I was of necessity led to being a student of man's upsetting effects on his environment, my own thinking was too much colored by this attitude. Only gradually did I come to realize that, though man is now the world's great upsetter, he is not the first. There were others before him, and they played a similar role in evolution. Stebbins and I have recently suggested (1954) that the great bursts of evolutionary activity in the past, the times of adaptive radiation, were caused by such upsets. The formation *de novo* of a great freshwater lake such as Lake Baikal produced a new and open habitat in which the organisms from various river systems could meet and mongrelize and, under the hand of selection, evolve as rapidly into new paths as did the salvias in the abandoned olive orchard. What must have happened when the first land vertebrates at last arrived on continents whose vegetation had no experience of such beasts? What occurred when the giant reptiles of the Mesozoic churned like gigantic bulldozers through the ferny swamps of that period? Must not the plants of those periods have gone through the same general experiences as are now facing the adenostomas of the California chaparral?

Man has been a major force in the evolution of the plants and animals which accompany him around the world, in the midst of which he largely spends his days. The detailed study of this process (1) should illuminate for us the course of evolution in prehuman times; (2) should be as well one of our truest guides to the history of prehistoric man; (3) most importantly,

should enable us at last to understand and eventually to control the living world around us.

REFERENCES

AASE, HANNAH C.
1946 "Cytology of Cereals. II," *Botanical Review*, XII, No. 5, 255–334.

ANDERSON, EDGAR
1949 *Introgressive Hybridization.* New York: John Wiley & Sons. 109 pp.
1952 *Plants, Man, and Life.* Boston: Little, Brown & Co. 245 pp.
1954 "Introgression in *Adenostoma*," *Annals of the Missouri Botanical Garden*, XLI, 339–50.

ANDERSON, EDGAR, and ANDERSON, BURTON R.
1954 "Introgression of *Salvia apiana* and *Salvia mellifera*," *Annals of the Missouri Botanical Garden*, XLI, 329–38.

ANDERSON, EDGAR, and STEBBINS, G. L., JR.
1954 "Hybridization as an Evolutionary Stimulus," *Evolution*, VIII, No. 4, 378–88.

DOBZHANSKY, TH.
1949 "Observations and Experiments on Natural Selection in *Drosophila*," pp. 210–24 in BONNIER, GERT, and LARSSON, ROBERT (eds.), *Proceedings of the Eighth International Congress of Genetics (July 7–14, 1948, Stockholm).* Lund: Berlingska Boktryckeriet. 696 pp.

EPLING, CARL C.
1938 "The California *Salvias*: A Review of *Salvia*, Section Audibertia," *Annals of the Missouri Botanical Garden*, XXV, 95–188.
1947 "Natural Hybridization of *Salvia apiana* and *Salvia mellifera*," *Evolution*, I, Nos. 1–2, 69–78.

EPLING, CARL C., and LEWIS, HARLAN
1942 "The Centers of Distribution of the Chaparral and Coastal Sage Associations," *American Midland Naturalist*, XXVII, No. 2, 445–62.

HEISER, CHARLES B., JR.
1949 "Study in the Evolution of the Sunflower Species *Helianthus annuus* and *H. bolanderi*," *University of California Publications in Botany*, XXIII, No. 4, 157–208.

1951 "Hybridization in the Annual Sunflowers: *Helianthus annuus* × *H. debilis* var. *cucumerifolius*," *Evolution*, V, No. 1, 42–51.

HURRY, JAMEISON B.
1930 *The Woad Plant and Its Dye.* London: Oxford University Press. 328 pp.

HUTCHINSON, J. B.; SILOW, R. A.; and STEPHENS, S. G.
1947 *The Evolution of Gossypium and the Differentiation of the Cultivated Cottons.* London: Oxford University Press. 160 pp.

MANGELSDORF, P. C., and REEVES, R. G.
1938 "The Origin of Maize," *Proceedings of the National Academy of Sciences*, XXIV, No. 8, 303–12.

PARK, THOMAS
1938 "Studies in Population Physiology. VIII. The Effect of Larval Population Density on the Post-embryonic Development of the Flour Beetle, *Tribolium confusum* Duval," *Journal of Experimental Zoology*, LXXIX, No. 1, 51–70.

RILEY, H. P.
1938 "A Character Analysis of Colonies of *Iris fulva, I. hexagona* var. *giganticaerulea* and Natural Hybrids," *American Journal of Botany*, XXV, 727–38.

SAUER, JONATHAN D.
1950 "The Grain Amaranths: A Survey of Their History and Classification," *Annals of the Missouri Botanical Garden*, XXXVII, No. 4, 561–632.
1952 "A Geography of Pokeweed," *ibid.*, XXXIX, 113–25.

STANDLEY, P. C.
1931 *Flora of the Lancetilla Valley, Honduras.* ("Field Museum of Natural History, Botanical Series," No. 10.) Chicago: Field Museum. 418 pp.

VAVILOV, N. I.
1926 "Studies on the Origin of Cultivated Plants," *Bulletin of Applied Botany and Plant Breeding*, XVI, No. 2, 138–248.

Man's Ecological Dominance through Domesticated Animals on Wild Lands

F. FRASER DARLING[*]

The subject of man as an ecological dominant might seem an easy one for an ecologist to elaborate. It is too easy, in that a library of books could be written. My task is to set down in a few thousand words a pivot for discussion and, at the same time, something of a reasoned statement. Everyone is well aware of the manifestations of man as an ecological dominant, and my wish in this chapter is to cut in on an aspect of man's dominance which is not necessarily intentional, which takes a long time to develop its expression, and which is not always conspicuous in process, so that its influence is often unappraised in both biological and administrative assessments in land-use policy and socioanthropological deliberation.

My main theme is pastoralism over wild habitats, a mode of land use which would appear to have developed later in human history than cultivation of food plants. Pastoralism may have arisen primarily not as a means of keeping food animals constantly available but as a means of getting game—with

a few tame animals being kept as decoys. For example, the domestic reindeer was almost certainly developed in this way. True pastoralism of ungulate animals and breeding them in semicaptivity are obvious steps from the decoy stage. At this point man emerges from the hunting and food-gathering stage in which he is not an ecological dominant, though he may be apical in an Eltonian pyramid. Man's persistence in any chosen habitat as a hunter and food-gatherer depends upon his not becoming an ecological dominant; otherwise he changes or destroys his habitat, which would mean either changing his culture—on which point he is in general conservative—or migrating.

By the very nature of the hunting and food-gathering life in which man is apical in the pyramidal structure of numbers and at the end of the food chain, sociality is limited and may not extend beyond the family, though, as we see in Eskimos and American Indians, there may be seasonal gathering at a chosen spot for a short period. But the human being has a definite urge to be social beyond the very small group, and to this end man has developed methods of exploitation of the habitat which have enabled him to aggregate, to be gregarious, and ultimately to civilize. This involves what I think may be taken as axiomatic—that man advances materially and ultimately in his civilization by breaking into the stored wealth of the world's natural ecological cli-

* Dr. Darling is Senior Lecturer in Ecology and Conservation, University of Edinburgh, and a member of the Nature Conservancy (Britain). He was a Rockefeller Special Research Fellow in 1950, and he visited Alaska in 1952 under the auspices of the Conservation Foundation. Dr. Darling received the Mungo Park Medal of the Royal Scottish Geographical Society in 1947. His most recent publication cognate to the symposium is *West Highland Survey*, 1955.

maxes. The process gives him leisure much needed for the art of civilizing. The ecological climax, as opposed to earlier stages of succession, is a conserver of energy, wasting very little; rather it builds up a store of wealth within the ecosystem. Man the climax-breaker is on the way to being an ecological dominant—a very profound change in human behavior, vividly brought to mind by Nietzsche's symbolism of the Dionysian and the Apollonian man. Instead of living with nature, man takes himself out of the biotic community and thereafter is involved in the fight against nature— a fight in which he has become dangerously successful.

In ecological terms, cultivation of cereal food plants consists of setting back the course of succession to a primary stage and of growing a stand of one plant of annual, or at most biennial, character. Early methods involved shifting cultivation, but there can be no doubt that much greater gregariousness was made possible as a result. A definite store of plant nutrients was tapped by man's traumatic impact on the environment. It might well be said that at this early stage man's influence on his whole environment was to enrich it by increasing its variety and by providing successional habitats which might not otherwise have occurred except through the natural catastrophic agencies of fire and hurricane. Man's numbers were insufficient to cause devastation, and export of organic products must have been so limited as to be negligible.

Man the pastoralist would appear to be doing very little to change the habitat in any area of what might seem to him to be grazing country. The grazing of wild lands is often called a natural use of land. But pastoralism means that animals are in proximity to and available to man where and when he wants them, and this usually means that more animals are on the ground and for a longer time than they would be in nature. As we understand it, pastoralism means domestication of animals, a process which slows down natural movement and largely removes the desire for extended fortuitous migration. Some cultures, such as the Reindeer Lapps and the western Asiatic tribes, evolved a definite migratory pastoralism of animals native to the terrain (e.g., reindeer, sheep, goat, and camel). The South American Indians of the Altiplano did much the same with the llama. The habitat has persisted.

Truly wild pastoralism is best typified by the Plains Indians and the buffalo of North America. The native animal, the buffalo, was allowed to go its own way undomesticated, and the tribes followed it as predators. But they were not only predators and therefore of the early hunting and food-gathering type. They were wild pastoralists who extended the range of the buffalo by deliberate burning of the forest edge, which receded. As Sauer has shown and repeats in his chapter (p. 55), the postulated climatic origin of grassland areas is not a satisfactorily authenticated hypothesis. We now know that the Plains Indians very considerably extended the prairies in historical times. The use of fire changed the vegetational character of the land and produced certain graminaceous dominants in the herbage complex. To this extent, the Plains Indians, who should be classed as wild pastoralists rather than as hunters and food-gatherers, became ecological dominants.

Now edges, whether of thought or of country, are revealing places for the inquirer, and, in the example of wild pastoralism we have been considering, parts of Wisconsin show vividly the advance and regression of the Plains Indian and the buffalo. Wooded hills are once more apparent where wooded hills were before; this time the trees are of even age, dating exactly to the time of the recession.

The prairie chicken also extended its

range with the buffalo, to the limit of the bird's range, one may suspect, for it is fast receding in Wisconsin; and its behavior there is incomplete as compared with its type habitat of, say, Missouri. The white man's farming in Wisconsin perhaps gave the prairie chicken a longer hold on a man-dominated habitat; but, in those areas where farming is being given up, the prairie chicken is declining. The spruce grouse will return to its own. It is, of course, interesting to speculate to what extent that exotic animal, the horse, made possible the extended wild pastoralism of the Plains Indian and enabled him to be the ecological dominant he was. The Indian became faster than his quarry and gave up his safety-holds in forest-edge agriculture; he became a specialist, and, when that further ecological dominant, the white man with his plow, came to the prairies, the specialized wild pastoralist was unable to adjust, and his lot has been more pathetic than that of other less specialized Indian cultures.

Pastoralism and the domestication and selection of animals have enabled man to canalize more of the stored wealth of the terrain through his own species: in other words, to increase his own bio-mass and indulge his craving for an extended social life. His use of fire has been very common, almost universal, and, as pastorally used, much more often in incidence than would occur in nature. This in itself impoverishes the variety of the vegetational complex, but the animals have preferences among the food plants and are definitely selective of them. The natural density of wild grazing animals in any habitat was probably insufficient to depress natural increase of desirable food plants from the level to which they had attained; but, under a pastoralism of a higher density and possibly more frequent passage over the ground, the desirable food plants have decreased and in many instances have been exterminated. (When I was in Utah in 1950, a range specialist told me how he was explaining this decline in the incidence of desirable plants to a group of visitors. An Israeli in the company quietly remarked, "In my country there are no desirable plants." That is the difference between a hundred and four thousand years of pastoralism.)

Man's selection of types of domesticated animals has made possible the grazing of habitats which otherwise would not be grazed. Wild goats occupy the highest places to which they can reach in mountainous country and are not found in valleys and on plains. But man has brought them to these habitats, selecting those individuals proving most resistant to helminthic parasitism. Wild sheep occupy the hard green slopes of high hills, quite a special habitat, and nowhere could it be better seen than with the Dall sheep in Alaska. Wild cattle are found in forest or savanna, usually where there is good access to water. But man has been able to move them to other habitats where they are exotics in effect. Moreover, cattle, sheep, and goats become true exotics when man migrates to new countries. These animals must accept that status in America, Australia, and New Zealand, countries which are now the greatest livestock areas of the world.

Man as pastoralist looks to the condition of his stock, and in general it may be said that livestock species have thrived in the countries and habitats to which they have been taken. It is only very recently in the face of some threatened collapses that man has turned his eyes the other way, to study the condition of the habitat. Pastoral memory would seem to be remarkably short, and the ecologist-historian of today has difficulty in arriving at the truth of the status of habitats a thousand, a hundred, or even fifty years ago. It may be said in general that man's ecological dominance by pastoralism of domesticated animals over wild lands has resulted in marked deterioration of habitat. Vegetational climaxes have been broken insidiously rather than by some grand traumatic act, and, just as cultivation of food plants involves setting back ecological succession to a primary stage, pastoralism deflects succession to the xeric, a profound and dangerous change.

It is the thesis of this paper that pastoralism for commercial ends, as we presently understand it, cannot continue without progressive deterioration of the habitat and that, where pastoralism over a long period has not damaged the habitat, it is markedly nomadic in character. Anthropologically studied, the present world trend is to restrict nomadism and transhumance, and I suggest that we are faced with the necessity of deciding what is and what is not biologically possible. The stored wealth of ecological climaxes has sheltered us from these decisions in the past, and the relatively slow rate of change in the habitat has masked the significance. Furthermore, pastoralism as we now understand it means export of calcium phosphate and nitrogenous organic matter; it is not merely the canalizing of energy through a larger social group of residents within the habitat. This fact of export of minerals and organic matter from grazing grounds needs careful consideration before the practice is condemned out of hand. Pastoralism is being practiced in so many different habitats that the loss of material by export may be negligible as compared with the possible losses by the practices of more or less sedentary pastoralism to which Western economic civilization seems to be molding the wild lands for grazing.

Let us consider a few different types of pastoral habitat: first, one which I have studied—the Scottish Highlands and Islands. The terrain is one of acid rocks, steep slopes, and peaty moors, cool in temperature, and with an annual precipitation of 50–100 inches. The original vegetational cover was forest of oak, pine, hazel, birch, alder, and willow to an altitude of 2,000 feet. This largely now has gone, having suffered from burnings for warlike purposes during the infiltration of the Vikings over a thousand years ago, from what might be called predatory burnings, from exploitation for smelting and timber in the seventeenth and eighteenth centuries, and, finally, from removal for the sake of increasing sheep pasturage. The area is still largely under sheep, and regeneration of the old forest is occurring in one or two fragments only. This exploitation by sheep has been enormously profitable in the past; now it is holding together economically by governmental subsidy and the present world meat shortage; biologically it is decrepit.

If we apply Albrecht's train of thought (1952) to contemplation of this kind of terrain of acid rocks, steep slopes, and ample rainfall, what is the obvious natural product? The answer is carbohydrate—cellulose in the form of timber. The Highlands could have continued as a wonderful timber area. But what, in chemical terms, have we done in the last one hundred and fifty years? We have set our faces against cellulose and demanded protein—protein direct as meat and wool from an exotic animal. As Albrecht has demonstrated often enough, we cannot commit such enormities against chemical logic. At least we cannot go on doing it indefinitely without loss and deterioration, but the insidiousness of the attack on the natural wealth of the ecological climax has prevented our seeing the illogic of what we were doing.

There is a further point to consider in this situation: the natural ecological climax of vegetational growth has a characteristic of making good in some measure the natural deficiencies of a habitat. I mentioned acid rocks, steep slopes, peat formation on moors, and fairly high precipitation in a cool climate. Leaching of minerals would be expected and does take place; but, under forest and scrub cover, the deeper-going roots reach the rock face and draw what may be available in the form of calcium, phosphorus, and potassium. Furthermore, the trees keep the mineral matter in circulation. The young leaves are rich in minerals, and some of the leaf crop is eaten by defoliating caterpillars, whose calcareous droppings are worked into the forest soil by earthworms. The autumn leaf-fall gives friable organic matter for conversion by invertebrate animals of many kinds. Ovington (1953) recently has reduced to chemical terms what this means in the way of brown-forest soil production on terrain which might be thought inimical to it. Ecologically, if we examine the flora of these natural woods on acid rocks, it is obvious that there are more calcicolous plants within the woods than outside them. In other words, there is more calcium present in the surface layers. The texture of this forest soil is also such that leaching is not nearly so serious as in the grazing ground outside.

It is well known that efficient protein production by plants calls for adequate calcium and potassium levels in the medium and for a correct calcium-potassium ratio. Equally, herbivorous animals synthesize protein better from plants which have an adequate mineral content. We come to the fact, therefore, that even a typical cellulose-producing area can naturally produce a certain amount of protein as a secondary crop, depending on the maintenance of the area as a cellulose producer. This secondary protein is best realizable as game consisting of animals native to the habitat, following their natural movement within the habitat, and helped to keep up movement and keep down excessive numbers by the presence of their natural predators. Natural accre-

tion in a climax community of this kind would ordinarily be sufficient to allow some removal from the habitat of both cellulose and protein.

Deforestation of such terrain is followed by a greening-over by sedges, grasses, and heather upon which the sheep feed. These plants are superficial in rooting habit as compared with trees, and the deep circulatory system is broken. The grazing ratio between sheep and cattle becomes very wide, sometimes as wide as 70:1 and very commonly 20:1, whereas two hundred years ago it was unity or less. The selective habit of sheep-grazing as opposed to the shearing habit of cattle results in much uneaten top growth. It is burned off. Even here, in a country of high precipitation, such a practice pushes back the floral complex to the xeric. Moor matgrass (*Nardus stricta*) increases on the high ground and where peat erosion sets in, and that xerophyte of wet, acid habitats (the carbonic acid being the ruling factor), purple moor grass (*Molinia caerulea*), becomes dominant.

In addition to the presence of *Calluna*, the more xerophytic forms of ericaceous plants such as *Erica tetralix* become more common. The final degradation of this kind of ground under sheep-grazing and burning is an herbage floor in which the deerhair sedge (*Scirpus caespitosa*) is a dominant. The calcicoles have gone, the herbage is deficient in both minerals and protein, and the attempt continues to extract protein direct in meat and wool. It is in this progressive devastation of a habitat that governments decide to shore up this decrepit wrongheadedness by the award of a ewe subsidy.

The Great Plains of the United States and the steppes of eastern Europe and western Asia maintained their different kinds of pastoralism, the one wild in which the buffalo moved at its own adequate pace for maintenance of the range, and the other under strongly migratory cultures; both maintained their habitat. Both regions are strictly comparable in their chernozem soils, fairly low precipitation, and close precipitation-evaporation ratio. Such soils are not leached, and they can yield protein direct without loss, for the mineral store is immense and the nitrogen is replaced by legume fixation. These soils are the ones which, in both Old and New Worlds, have passed into the production of high-protein wheat and are no longer pastoral. From a land use they could have maintained indefinitely at a pastoral rate of return, they have become subjected to a quickened rhythm of yield which can ultimately be bolstered by the addition of fertilizers.

There are great areas of high western range in America and of similar range in Asia which will not withstand heavy or sedentary pastoralism. This is being well realized in the United States, in that much of such land previously in private ownership has returned to the government and will never again be heavily grazed. The damage which has occurred in less than a hundred years is sometimes remediable, sometimes not; but, where man as an ecological dominant has greatly changed the floral complex and set it back to the extremely xeric, the task of repair is immensely harder. Even when the domesticated livestock is removed, the game-carrying capacity has been much lowered, and this hits back on the standard of living of primitive groups of men. Take, for example, the Hopi Indians of the high mesas of Arizona. They are farmers, not pastoralists, but they were uniquely farmer-hunters, getting their animal protein from wild game of the desert. The surrounding pastoral practices of both white man and Navaho have so far reduced the game-carrying capacity of the desert that the Hopi are suffering a shortage of protein in their diet.[1]

The semideserts of Utah and Arizona have become peopled with persons who have a strong sense of home, making for a sedentary pastoralism which the habitat cannot maintain. Walter Cottam, speaking at the Utah State Centenary Celebrations in 1947, asked a startling question in the title of his paper, "Is Utah Sahara-bound?" Then from historical and factual evidence he proceeded to show that grass as an appreciable constituent of the floral complex had sadly declined since the rise of pastoralism. The Anglo-Saxon races have a sure feeling that grass and livestock are complementary and naturally go together. But not in semidesert where cattle are exotics. Pastoralism must be light and fast if the habitat is to be maintained.

The Navaho Indian is naturally a great mover. One of the objects of making him a pastoralist was to anchor him, so to speak. The Navaho Reservation of Arizona is one of the worst-eroded landscapes in America. Yet it has been said, and probably rightly, that the present tally of livestock is not too great for the total area of the reservation. Work has already begun in the Indian Service to empty sections of land from livestock for a year and then gradually to work the stock back over a period of years, with the proviso that the stock be kept moving. On one section I examined, it was hoped that 140 per cent of the original 1937 stock could now come back so long as migratory pastoralism continued to be practiced. In short, the effort is to make man an ecological concomitant, not an ecological dominant.

Water developments in the Arizona semideserts are for the good of the

1. Is it not interesting that, where the white man ecologically dominates the habitat of brown, black, and red men, he raises the carbohydrate level of diet and very surely depresses the protein? This "quietens" a native race, but possibly scalping and sudden death are replaced by a ripeness for political disaffection and ideological change. The provision of a high-protein diet should be a definite part of education for peaceableness!

stock, not for the good of the range. In addition to this observation, mention should be made of the increasing mobility of stock made possible by the motor truck. The result is not so much the mobility of a strongly migratory pastoralism as the rapid consumption or predation of growth in areas which have received showers. In short, technical advance in the mechanical fields is enabling man to be increasingly dominant in these marginal habitats where formerly there were checks.

I have mentioned pastoral areas of acid rocks with high rainfall, of deep soils with moderate rainfall, and of semideserts and high ranges with low rainfall, showing the variations brought about with such land use. There is, in addition, the limestone area, which, considered ideally, should be an admirable field for stock-raising. In fact, we find that the limiting factors of slope, vegetational cover, rainfall, and soil depth are now even more limiting. These ideas occurred to me in the few limestone areas of Highland Scotland, where, with the pastoral practice of burning, erosion of the peat overlay to the rock was much more rapid than where there was no burning. I compared these observations in my mind with what we know of limestone pavements in Yorkshire and Ireland. Removal of the hazel scrub from such areas in early times resulted in expanses of bare rock intersected with fissures which now hold the only vegetation. Then I saw the Manti section of the Wasatch Plateau in Utah. The Manti is also of limestone, and the deterioration of the habitat under sheep-grazing has been very rapid. Finally, illustrating the point but having nothing to do with pastoralism, I observed the eroded slopes of Mexican mountains in the Sierra Madre Oriental. It was obvious here that, if the rock was a shale or a schist, there was some hope of natural repair; but, where there was complete

slip from the limestone, there was no comeback at all. It would seem that the oxidation rate over limestone is a factor of immense importance. Under a natural climax vegetation of forest, forbs, or grass, there may be great richness, but it is extremely tender. Unless all conditions are favorable, oxidation will exceed the deposition of organic matter. That which seemed particularly desirable to the pastoralist seeking new fields will become the scene of starkest ecological and physical degradation. The limestone pavement is a permanent monument to an aspect of human ecological dominance.

Pastoralism influences the composition of the animal complex of the climax biotic community as well as the vegetational. It is on overgrazed ranges that rodent populations tend to irrupt: ground squirrels in California, kangaroo rats in Arizona, field voles in the Southern Uplands of Scotland, the "mice" of ancient Egypt in the Bible. Rodent irruptions are so characteristic of pastoral areas in several parts of the world that it is my belief that vole plagues in Britain are bound up with this land use. I would go further and state as a principle that violent fluctuations in animal populations are indicators of disturbed ecological norms and that the disturbance is often attributable to human agency, though it may be indirect. Rhythmic cyclicism is evident in nature, and the ecological norm can accommodate it. Not only do plagues or violent fluctuations endanger the species concerned but there is the percussive influence of the "high" on the habitat.

The example of the pocket gopher (*Thomomys*) may serve to illustrate how the influence of a rodent's activity may be injurious to the terrain under conditions of pastorally broken climax, whereas in the ecological norm its activities are highly beneficial. Ellison's study (1946) of this animal on the Wasatch Plateau resolves the conflicting evidences and places them in perspective. The gopher acts as a gigantic earthworm, and in the original richly clothed rendzina soils of the plateau its influence in soil aeration and mixing, and the maintenance of porosity, must be of fundamental importance, for there are no earthworms proper at that elevation of around 10,000 feet. The depth of vegetational cover on virgin range is such as to prevent soil slip; but, as soon as the dense vegetation of forbs and grasses is removed, the gophers' workings are left open and friable to the impact of climatic factors. When gullying has begun, the course of erosion is then accelerated by the presence of gophers. A frontal attack by pastoralists on the gophers in such a situation shows the common failure of land-using interests to make ecological appraisal.

It is the unfortunate paradox of pastoralism that the ameliorative influence of the full complex of predators may not be expressed, as the pastoralist becomes the sworn enemy of many of the predators. I do not wish to differ from those who suggest that populations of animals are self-regulatory and that predation is unimportant in population control. But in a marginal habitat, or in a habitat where man has become the ecological dominant, the predators may, if present as a complex of animals, exercise such influence as to prevent the percussive "highs" which are so damaging.

The last example I shall take of a pastoral habitat in which man has exercised a profound ecological influence is western Alaska, where reindeer have been grazed since 1892. It is a particularly interesting habitat to consider, because Europe has a comparable one in Lapland, where the Lapps have maintained their habitat by strict adherence to nomadism and are only now losing it as they slacken their migratory habit. In arctic Alaska the wild caribou takes the place of the reindeer. It is general knowledge that the reindeer population of Alaska crashed from 650,000 to 25,000 in about ten years. When all is said and done, the reindeer crashed because they ate out their range; there were too many of them. But the process was speeded up by the fact that the strict nomadic movement of the original Lapp herders was not continued. The foliose lichens which are the main winter food of the reindeer were completely grazed off in the coastal areas, and in some places it was burned off. Regeneration of the lichens would take from fifty to three hundred years. The effect of the removal of the climax blanket of lichens has been to let free the arctic shrub flora of dwarf willow and dwarf birch, of *Ledum* and *Vaccinium,* and the cotton sedge *Eriophorum.* The herbage floor today is very different from what it was when the reindeer came, but for once we have to revise the trend of thought which the observer of overgrazing over the face of the world has come to follow. There are many man-made deserts, but in Alaska the too heavy grazing of the lichen ranges has made the tundra bloom. The smothering blanket of lichen has gone. The shrubs, the herbs, the sedges, and the grasses see the sun again and are producing a wealth of growth.

What, then, are we grumbling about? Indeed, the objective ecologist should not grumble overmuch at what has happened on the Reindeer Coast. The removal of the climax of lichen has removed the winter feeding potential of the tundras for one species of grazing animal, the reindeer, or its wild counterpart, the caribou; but this removal has altered the potential for many others. The decline of caribou and reindeer has been followed by a rise in the numbers of moose and a spread in its range. Viewed objectively, the setting-back of succession should not result in the possibilities of loss which we commonly associate with such trauma.

Sociologically, nevertheless, we must be concerned with this great ecological upheaval on the Reindeer Coast. Alaskan Eskimos and Aleuts never arrived at a true nomadic culture with the reindeer, and the Lapp herdsmen who had come early to Alaska shook their heads. Now that the numbers have crashed and there are only 25,000–30,000 deer, all owned by Eskimos or the United States government, it is time to build imaginatively a nomadic grazing culture for the Eskimos which will be of such order that their innate delight in social and family life as well as their equal delight in winter movement can be fulfilled. It is no good for men to be in a herding camp while women languish in Kotzebue. Winter grazing must be one of movement in surviving lichen ranges far back from the coast. Summer grazing on the profusion of herbage of the coastal tundras could be at a much slower tempo of movement, allowing the gathering of the Eskimos at Nome and Kotzebue for those occasions of extended sociality which they love.

It is necessary, perhaps, having mentioned reindeer grazing in western Alaska, to speak of the still great herds of caribou in arctic Alaska. Here the lichen is spread much thinner than it was on the Reindeer Coast. The only blankets are in the thin, forest-edge region south of the Brooks Range. The lichen of the arctic prairie, not hindering the growth of shrubs, sedges, and grasses, is integral to the maintenance of the grazing situation for the herds of caribou. Any form of overzealous wildlife management for the increase of caribou *in the arctic,* where adequate human predation is still impossible, might well result in a crash of the caribou, which would be deplorable. The wildlife manager must always remember that he is not concerned with the production of large numbers; rather should he prevent "highs" which have,

as I have said earlier, percussive effects on the habitat. The caribou in their vast herds move far and fast, conserving their own habitat so long as the ecological complex is maintained. There is some evidence that when the habitat is damaged by man, as by too frequent incidence of fire in subarctic Alaska, the greatly reduced caribou herds lessen the length of their migrations—one herd, in fact, is relatively sedentary in the Nelchina Basin, and it remains to be seen whether the range can withstand the more constant occupancy through a long period of time.

Our minds find it difficult to grasp the immensity of range necessary for reindeer or caribou in Alaska. Those animals and that country provide an extreme example of what has, nevertheless, been a constant phenomenon—that the area of range in relation to domesticated animals over the face of the world has been underestimated. And as the pastoralist tires of being an Ishmael and wishes to build a house rather than to pitch his tent, so does he reduce the possibility of maintaining the pastoral life. The Nunamiut Eskimos of the Brooks Range of Alaska are the only true nomadic Eskimos in Alaska, dependent wholly on the caribou and Dall sheep. Their culture, however, cannot be called wild pastoralism, as was that of the Plains Indians, for they do not interfere with the habitat.

Pastoralism of domesticated animals on wild lands is still providing much of what an increasing world population desires of meat and wool. The lineaments of the wild lands remain more or less constant and mask the extent to which man has been an ecological dominant over them. This paper suggests that pastoralism demands a nomadism to which mankind is becoming increasingly disinclined. Nomadic societies cannot acquire civilization as we understand the process, though their behavior may acquire great polish. A world of sedentary cultures impinges always on nomadic territory not held in fee simple, and the nomadic society is brittle. What is to be the answer?

REFERENCES

ALBRECHT, W. A.
   1952   "Protein Deficiencies via Soil Deficiencies. II. Experimental Evidence," *Oral Surgery, Oral Medicine and Oral Pathology*, XV, 483–99.
DARLING, F. FRASER
   1947   *Natural History in the Highlands and Islands*. London: Collins. 303 pp.
   1955   *West Highland Survey*. Oxford: Oxford University Press. 438 pp.
ELLISON, L.
   1946   "The Pocket Gopher in Relation to Soil Erosion on Mountain Range," *Ecology*, XXVII, 101–14.
LEOPOLD, A. S., and DARLING, F. FRASER
   1953   *Wildlife in Alaska*. New York: Ronald Press Co. 129 pp.
OVINGTON, J. D.
   1953   "Studies of the Development of Woodland Conditions under Different Trees," I, "Soils pH"; II, "The Forest Floor"; III, "The Ground Flora," *Journal of Ecology*, XLI, 13–52; XLII, 71–80; XLIII, 1–21.

Man as an Agent in the Spread of Organisms

MARSTON BATES[*]

If we were discussing the general question of the relationship between human activities and the distribution of organisms, we would have to consider three different sorts of effects. First, as discussed in many chapters of this volume there is man's effect in altering the habitat—clearing, draining, irrigating, and exhausting the soil and (more rarely perhaps) enriching the soil. Second, there is his effect in restricting and exterminating populations. And, third, there is his effect as an agent of dispersal.

Our focus here is on the third effect, but the separation of this from the other two is really quite arbitrary. As our knowledge of ecology increases, it becomes clearer that the introduction of an organism into a new region through human agency, purposeful or accidental, is often possible only because the habitat has been greatly altered by other human activities. This is particularly true of introduced plants, whose status may depend not only on man's clearing of the pre-existing vegetation but also on the maintenance of altered conditions through activities

* Dr. Bates has been Professor of Zoölogy at the University of Michigan since 1952; before that he was a member of the staff of the International Health Division of the Rockefeller Foundation, working on malaria in the Mediterranean and on yellow fever in South America. His books include: *The Nature of Natural History*, 1950; *Where Winter Never Comes*, 1952; and *The Prevalence of People*, 1955.

such as the introduction of grazing domestic mammals. Allan (1936), studying the New Zealand vegetation, and Egler (1942), studying one of the Hawaiian islands, both came to the conclusion that the apparently dominant aliens were really only precariously established and that (to quote Egler, 1942, p. 23), "in the absence of anthropic influences, the evidence strongly favors the view that most of the aliens will be destroyed by the indigenes, such aliens surviving only in greatly reduced numbers and as very subordinate members of the resulting ecosystem."

Hawaii and New Zealand form extreme cases of biotas altered through the agency of the introduction of organisms by man. They are extreme examples in part because their isolation resulted in the development of restricted and peculiar indigenous biotas, so that the alien elements stand out strikingly. Yet the anthropic effect may really be much greater in the densely inhabited parts of the earth's continents—only we have come, there, to take this effect for granted. It is curious, in reviewing general books on ecology, to see how little attention is paid to man as an ecological agent, though European and North American ecologists are almost always studying man-altered habitats.

The man-altered habitats allow for the dispersal and establishment of organisms in new regions, and the introduction of new organisms through human agency contributes to the alteration of the habitats. This makes a nice circle.

Coming to our proper focus on man as the agent of introduction, we may find it most convenient to deal separately with the dispersal of microörganisms, of plants, and of animals. With all three of these categories we find both purposeful or deliberate introduction and accidental introduction. Details of the purposes for which and the ways in which the organisms are introduced, however, differ considerably.

MICROÖRGANISMS

Our chief point of interest here is on man as the agent of dispersal of his own parasites. It seems at first sight that we are dealing with a purely biological system: a specific aspect of the general question of the dispersal relations between host and parasite. Even in this, however, I have come to think that the human situation is peculiar: the geography of infectious disease in man is perhaps best understood not in strictly biological terms but in cultural terms (May, 1954).

In the matter of spread, it is important to distinguish between the contagious diseases and the diseases transmitted indirectly through vectors or alternate hosts. The self-limited contagions of man (things like measles, smallpox, mumps, and the like) present interesting problems in relation both to history and to geography. I have developed elsewhere (Bates, 1955, pp. 154–72) the theory that these contagions are post-Neolithic developments. I do not see how they could have been maintained in the small, dispersed populations of Paleolithic hunting and gathering cultures; they cannot maintain themselves in such population situations today. The cosmopolitan distribution of these diseases is clearly a consequence of post-Columbian intercontinental contacts.

Disease caused by pathogens with indirect transmission mechanisms—such as malaria and yellow fever—move less easily, since they have more exacting environmental requirements than the contagions. On the other hand, they can persist in endemic form in scattered populations, and some of these pathogenic relationships have probably evolved right along with evolving man.

Yellow fever and malaria are particularly interesting cases because both have spread considerably in modern times, despite their complicated epidemiology. I would incline to the theory that Africa was the original home of both diseases. Malaria, whatever its origin, has been present in the Mediterranean for a very long time, since it can be identified in the Hippocratic writings, and its ups and downs in the Greco-Roman world show a nice correlation with economic and political events (Hackett, 1937). Transmission of the pathogen from man to man depends on a particular type of mosquito (*Anopheles*), but mosquitoes of this group, perfectly capable of acting as vectors, are present on all the continents. The disease is not sharply self-limited in man, so that carriers of the parasite, moving into an environment favorable for the parasite, with man-biting anopheles abundantly present, may easily introduce the disease. It seems to me most probable that the parasite was not present in America until the arrival of the Spaniards. The unhealthiness of the lowland American tropics, then, may well be a post-Columbian phenomenon.

In the case of yellow fever, the disease spread in part at least with the spread of the vector. The common vector, *Aedes aegypti*, is a mosquito that breeds readily in all sorts of domestic water containers, so that it could easily go with the sailing ships wherever they went. It is presumably tropical African in origin, but it was soon spread to all the warm parts of the earth by European explorers. The slave trade from Africa to America presumably brought both the vector and the virus—with considerable historic consequences. If this theory is correct, the "jungle yellow fever" of South America would be a secondary development, resulting from the fact that South American monkeys and forest mosquitoes both proved to be good hosts for the virus (Bates, 1946). The disease has never spread to the Orient despite the long-established traffic from Africa across the Indian Ocean; the reason for this failure of spread is not clear.

It would be difficult to overestimate the importance of the changing disease patterns on human history and geography. Man, as the unconscious dispersal agent of his own pathogens, has thus contributed greatly to the shaping of his own destiny. For documentation of this, I can do no better than refer to the delightful book by Hans Zinsser, *Rats, Lice and History* (1935).

The contagiousness of certain diseases was anciently discovered, and man's efforts to prevent spread of disease—quarantines—should get attention in any balanced discussion of the history of man and his pathogens. The literature on quarantines, including the reports on interceptions, is enormous. Magath and Knies (1945) have written a summary of present practices.

The spread of human pathogens has been almost wholly accidental rather than purposeful—though the concept of "germ warfare" brings up the possibility of purposeful spread. This is not a completely new idea. The Stearns (1945) have found records of a few deliberate attempts to introduce smallpox infection into American Indians as an adjunct of war operations in Colonial times.

Man has, of course, spread not only his own pathogens but those of his domesticated animals and plants as well. The consequences of accidental introduction of such pathogens into new regions have sometimes been catastrophic, as in the famous case of the spread of the potato blight in Europe in 1845, the history of which is reviewed by Salaman (1949).

For the last fifty years or so, scientists have been experimenting with the deliberate introduction of pathogens for the biological control of pests. For the most part, these efforts have not been successful because, where conditions were favorable for an epidemic, the epidemic was liable to develop without human interference; and, where conditions were unfavorable, the deliberate introduction of the pathogen was unsuccessful. A striking exception to this is the recent introduction of the virus of rabbit myxomatosis into Australia (Fenner, 1954), which resulted in an immediate and drastic reduction of the rabbit population. Introduction of the virus into France, in an attempt at local and restricted rabbit control, was less successful, in the sense that the virus promptly got out of hand in a region where rabbits were prized.

It is difficult to assess man's importance in relation to the spread of non-pathogenic microörganisms. A good many of these have, in any case, highly efficient means of dispersal through resistant spore forms, so that they may be cosmopolitan without any help from man. Wolfenbarger (1946) has written a general review of the dispersal mechanisms of small organisms, including microörganisms.

The domesticated microörganisms should be mentioned, since we tend to forget them, though yeasts, for instance, are among the most anciently tamed of organisms. With these, as with all cultigens, the spread of useful strains is directly under human control. With the development of microbiology, the list of cultivated microörganisms is constantly growing.

PLANTS

I mean by "plants" the so-called "higher plants"—and discussion might well be restricted to the seed plants, which are so overwhelmingly important in the economy of both nature and man today. The study of the geography and dispersal of the higher plants has interested many people, and it forms the subject matter of an extensive and well-organized literature. But, in surveying this literature from the present point of view, the neglect of studies of the effect of human interference stands out strikingly. This is understandable in terms of the biological preoccupation with evolutionary events, which are seen as taking place on the geological stage, where man appears only in the last few seconds of action. Yet these few seconds comprise very significant action. Anderson has shown in his chapter how significant this action may be from the viewpoint of general evolutionary theory. The weeds and cultigens, scorned as "unnatural," yet may tell us a great deal about nature; their behavior is part of an unplanned but nonetheless significant series of gigantic experiments which, by the very alteration of the geological sequence of events, may teach us much about the operation of that sequence.

Man, as the agent of dispersal, is the initiator, the trigger, of these evolutionary experiments. This action is a relatively small aspect of the total experimental situation, but it is still an important aspect, and one that must be carefully studied for any valid interpretation of the experimental results.

Good (1947), depending largely on the summary by Ridley (1930), has outlined man's activities as an agent of plant dispersal as follows:

A. Deliberate introduction
B. Accidental introduction
  1. Dispersal by accidental adhesion to moving objects
     a) Adhesion to man's person
     b) Adhesion to moving vehicles (e.g., mud on cart wheels, dust carts, trains, etc.)
  2. Dispersal among crop seed (e.g., many cornfield weeds)
  3. Dispersal among other plants (e.g., fodder and packing materials)
  4. Dispersal among minerals (e.g., soil export, ballast, road metal)
  5. Dispersal by carriage of seed for purposes other than planting (e.g., this includes a whole range of possibilities; one mentioned by Ridley is the spread of drug plants from seeds escaping from druggists' shops)

Deliberate Introduction

Deliberate introduction becomes a rather inconspicuous subdivision in a scheme like Good's, but it involves an enormous number of different kinds of plants. I tried to estimate the number by the statistically dubious experiment of counting items on ten random pages in the 1941 edition of the Baileys' *Hortus*, which happened to be at hand. I find that the Baileys here treated some 19,600 "horticultural species" (i.e., forms considered to be distinct enough to warrant a Latinized name), distributed among some 2,700 genera. This is surely a minimum estimate of the numbers of plants that are currently subject to manipulation, to "deliberate introduction" of one sort or another, by American horticulturists, since it includes only items that have gained some currency among gardeners.

Of course a very considerable percentage of these plants could not exist in the United States outside of greenhouses or without constant horticultural attention. Further, these figures include a large number of plants of purely "ornamental" interest—with orchids, irises, and suchlike groups dear to the horticultural heart. This interest in ornamentals, on this scale, is relatively modern and restricted to complex civilizations. But experimental gardening—the exchange of plants and attempts at cultivation of new plants—must have been going on continuously, even though on a small scale, ever since Neolithic times.

The curious thing, in fact, is that modern man, despite his feverish horticultural activity, has not been able to add any item to the list of basic crop plants. The origins of all our major crops are lost in the mists of prehistory, and we cannot really be sure about either the identity of their wild ancestors or the steps in the process of their domestication, despite the great amount of research that has been dedicated to the matter. Recent discussions of these problems have been written by Anderson (1952) and by Sauer (1952).

We might arbitrarily class the plants purposefully dispersed by man as major crops, minor crops, ornamentals, and landscape modifiers (plantings for reforestation, erosion prevention, and the like).

The major crops include the plants that have been most drastically modified by the domestication process. For the most part these plants have come to be completely dependent on man for reproduction and dispersal. In some cases they have lost the capacity for producing viable seeds and depend on man-controlled vegetative propagation (breadfruit and bananas come to mind); in other cases the seed, though viable, may be produced in such a way as to require human intervention for removal and planting (maize is the classical case). With most, the reason for failure of self-production is less clear and definite; the plants, apparently, simply cannot "compete" with wild vegetation and disappear when man ceases to intervene.

The relationship between man and his crop plants, then, is symbiotic. The plants have become completely dependent on man for survival, and man —in his contemporary numbers—has become completely dependent on the plants. We might well call plants of this sort "obligate cultigens." The geography of such plants is an aspect of human geography; the plants do not escape from cultivation to form part of the wild vegetation.

When any such generalization is made, exceptions start coming to mind. These partly involve the clearly artificial distinction between "major" and "minor" crop plants. Surely, however, the coconut is a major crop plant by any definition, yet it seems able to maintain itself independent of man and has become a characteristic element of the coastal flora everywhere in the tropics. The coconut is, however, more dependent on man than it might, at first glance, seem. Its tropicopolitan distribution is now generally acknowledged to be a consequence of deliberate dispersal by man. Where coconuts occur on uninhabited Pacific islands, there is frequently evidence that they were planted by transient visitors; and, where there is no evidence one way or another, it is difficult to rule out the possibility of planting.

The coconut now certainly seems perfectly capable of persisting as a part of strand vegetation with no interference from man. But man does so frequently interfere that it is difficult to be sure what would happen to the coconut if this interference ceased. It is certainly less of an obligate cultigen than most of the other major crop plants—but it is also more of a cultigen than it seems to the casual observer. The considerable literature on the origin and dispersal of the coconut has recently been surveyed by Heyerdahl (1953, pp. 453–65).

As we move from the major crop plants to the minor crop plants and ornamentals, we find an increasing frequency of plants that can best be regarded as facultative cultigens, since they readily "escape" from cultivation to join with the company of the weeds or, under appropriate conditions, that of the native flora. *Lantana* in Hawaii and *Opuntia* in many parts of the world come to mind as examples of escapes that have found themselves all too much at home in new environments.

Plants used for reforestation, for protection against erosion, and the like can hardly be called "cultigens." Perhaps most often indigenous plants are used in such operations, but frequently enough alien species are considered more suitable. The plantings of Australian trees of such genera as *Eucalyptus*, *Casuarina*, and *Melaleuca* throughout the tropics and subtropics of the world are particularly striking.

Accidental Introduction

Ridley (1930) considers that accidental introductions of plants probably outnumber purposeful introductions. This is true only if we disregard plants in a particular area known only under cultivation; but such disregard is surely justified. No one would think that a flora of Massachusetts should include all the plants grown in Massachusetts' greenhouses any more than a fauna should include animals known only from the zoos. But it is far from easy to draw lines between the cultigens, the weeds, the escapes, and the established aliens—and divergence in practice in distinguishing among these various categories makes the compilation of statistics difficult.

The difficulties are nicely illustrated by the discussion of New Zealand aliens given by Allan (1936, p. 188):

It is not possible to state precisely how many species of plants are actually naturalized in New Zealand; much depends on the view taken as to what constitutes naturalization, and for a number of species definite information is lacking. Hooker (1855) listed 61 species, and later (1867) 170. Kirk (1870) recorded 292. Cheeseman ('06) gave 528, and later ('25) 576, but a number of the species in his lists do not conform to his statement that they "appear to be thoroughly well established." Thomson ('22) considered that "over six hundred species have become more or less truly wild, i.e., they reproduce themselves by seed, and appear at the present time more or less denizens of the country." My own estimate of thoroughly naturalized species is 413, based on the evidence that they (1) occupy significant extents of territory, so that they are not liable to extinction by a small local catastrophe, (2) reproduce themselves, whether by seed or vegetatively, (3) are not decreasing in area occupied.

But for the purposes of this paper it matters little which estimate be adopted, and I have accepted 603 species. Now, in regard to competition with indigenes, 324 may be at once put aside. They are either rare or so local and limited in extent as not to play any significant part in the struggle. Of the remainder no fewer than 231 (including 165 annuals or biennials) occur mainly in waste places about settled areas, cultivated lands and man-made pastures, and only 93 of them extend into very much modified indigenous communities (especially low tussock-grassland and coastal sands). None of them sets up any serious competition with the indigenes. There remain to consider 48 species only. Of these 28 are of Old World origin, 9 are from the Americas, 7 from Australia, and 4 from South Africa. The life-forms are: 1 parasitic plant, 4 water plants, 22 shrubs and trees, 4 grasses, and 17 perennial herbs or half shrubs.[1]

Ridley (1930, p. 638) analyzed the probable origins of the 704 alien species of plants reported by Dunn as more or less well established in Great Britain in 1905. He found that 540 of these were from Europe, 68 from temperate Asia, 4 from Africa, 88 from North America, and 4 from Australia. In North America also the greatest number of aliens has come from Europe. These

1. The references cited in this quotation have not been included in the reference list of the present paper.

are also the predominant aliens in Australia and New Zealand.

This man-induced spread of elements from the European flora into other parts of the world with similar climatic conditions has led, since the time of Hooker, to speculation about the "aggressiveness and colonizing power" of this flora (Good, 1947, p. 307). But the contemporary ecological opinion is that these plants do not have any special advantage in competition with local floras. Their ubiquitousness seems to depend on their adaptation to the special habitats created by man. The question then becomes whether this adaptation is a consequence of the relatively long period in which man-made habitats have existed in Europe or whether it is a consequence of some older and more general characteristic of the European flora.

INVERTEBRATES

Man's relations with the vertebrates and the invertebrates are different enough to make it convenient to treat them separately. It is interesting that in both cases the analysis of human interference involves, almost exclusively, terrestrial and fresh-water organisms. This is, in one way, understandable enough, since man himself is a terrestrial organism. He has become intimately involved with the sea in many ways, and many human cultures depend for existence primarily on exploitation of the sea. But these cultures, however advanced technologically, remain essentially "gatherers" in their relations with the inhabitants of the sea. The contrast between man's effect on the terrestrial environment and his effect on the marine environment is so great and so obvious that we are apt to overlook it or to take it for granted.

Of course, man has, in some cases, successfully established marine fish in new regions—the establishment of the Atlantic striped bass (*Roccus*) on the

Pacific Coast is an outstanding example (Scofield, 1931). A great many marine invertebrates must have been moved about with the shipping of modern man, but I have come across no general study of this but only isolated mention, like the appearance of the American oyster drill (*Urosalpinx cinerea*) in English oyster beds (Orton, 1937, p. 155).

In discussing man and the invertebrates in the present context, then, I shall be concerned primarily with man and insects—the predominant terrestrial invertebrates. Among the insects there are a few species that are directly associated with men and their households and a host of others more indirectly associated through their effects on domestic animals, crops, or other aspects of the human habitat. The directly associated insects can conveniently be divided into three groups: the domesticates, the inquilines, and the human parasites.

It is striking that among the millions of insect species so few have been domesticated: the honeybee and the silkworm, with perhaps the cochineal insect, now relegated to the past tense by the development of chemical dyes, and the lac insect, similarly doomed by the plastic resins. The silkworm, too, may not survive chemical developments, but it remains particularly interesting because, like so many other plant and animal domesticates, it is now known only in its domestic form. Its wild ancestors are unknown, and it has never, as far as I know, "escaped" to establish itself independent of human care.

The domestication of the honeybee, like that of the silkworm, is lost in the mists of antiquity, but wild races have persisted in the Asiatic tropics, and the species has been able to establish itself independent of man in many parts of the world where it has been introduced.

Perhaps the standard laboratory animals should be included among the "domesticated" species. In that case an insect, *Drosophila,* could well be considered one of man's most important domesticates.

The insects that have become associated with human habitations form an interesting group. I think they might well be called the "inquilines" by analogy with the "guests" of anthills. Everywhere that man builds habitations (with the possible exception of the Far North) some members of the local insect fauna also find these habitations suitable living places and move in. A few of these (certain species of roaches, silverfish, and ants come to mind) have achieved an almost cosmopolitan distribution through this association, quite comparable with the similar achievement of the household mice and rats.

Two mosquitoes, *Aedes aegypti* and the complex of *Culex fatigans-pipiens,* might well be included in this group of inquilines, since they have spread with man to almost all climatically suitable parts of the world and, over most of this range, breed only in man-made accumulations of water. Both of these kinds of mosquitoes warrant much more biological study than they have received from this viewpoint of association with the human habitat. Why does *Aedes aegypti,* which breeds in tree holes in its native tropical Africa, breed only in domestic water containers in other parts of the world? Is the curious multiplicity of strains among the *pipiens* mosquitoes a consequence of the human association? It seems to me possible that man here has acted as an evolutionary agent in the sense discussed by Anderson in his chapter of this volume. (For bibliography on these species see Bates, 1949.)

I would class the domestic mosquitoes as inquilines rather than parasites, even though the adults do largely depend on human blood. The concept of "parasite" is particularly difficult to de-fine as a category of insect behavior, but I would restrict the term to more intimate associations than that of the mosquitoes—associations like those of the various human lice and the bedbugs. But with these two examples we have a basic behavioral divergence hidden under the label "parasite," since the lice are continuously associated with the body itself, while the bedbugs have the dwelling as a habitat and make contact with the body only for feeding—which makes for differences in the methods of dispersal of the two groups. Fleas have characteristics of each group.

The human lice have accompanied man everywhere from the beginning—probably even evolving with him (*Pediculus,* that is; the history of *Pthirius,* the pubic louse, is less clear). We have direct evidence of the prehistoric universal dispersal of lice from the Peruvian and Egyptian mummies and other similar sources. Much study has gone into comparisons among the lice of different living races, and some students have thought they could detect racial differences in the lice corresponding with the racial differences in the host (Zinsser, 1935).

The domesticates, inquilines, and parasites among the insects and other arthropods form a fascinating field of inquiry but a trivial one from our present viewpoint. Man's major role as an agent of dispersal for invertebrates has been not with these close associates but with the thousands of species that he has incidentally transported with his travels and commerce.

It seems curiously difficult to find figures on the numbers of introduced or adventive species of insects in the different faunas. Such species are generally explicitly omitted from zoögeographical discussions because the focus of interest is on the "natural" affinities of the fauna. The omission from ecological discussion is less understandable but seems to be related to the general ecological aversion to studies of the explicitly man-made biological environments. These are studied by the "applied biologists." But the applied biologists reasonably focus their interest on the significant pests. While these, often enough, are introduced species, they represent but a small fraction of the organisms moved about by human agency.

Hawaii is probably the most changed of the major faunas through man-dependent dispersal, but I have come across no general discussion of the biology of this phenomenon—though, to be sure, only a limited part of the Hawaiian literature is accessible to me. Zimmerman (1948), in his excellent introductory volume to the *Insects of Hawaii*, confines his discussion to the indigenous fauna. In the body of the work he gives tables for each order, showing the numbers of indigenous and adventive species and genera. In the first five volumes (which cover the orders from Thysanura through Homoptera) I find that, of 930 species listed, 421 are considered as certainly or probably adventive. The indigenous fauna of Hawaii presents so many fascinating evolutionary and ecological problems that the neglect of the adventive fauna is understandable. Yet the adventive fauna comprises, really, a sort of gigantic, unplanned ecological experiment that might also yield information of great biological interest.

The concentration of the applied biologists on the pests is also understandable, and considerable proportions of the major insect pests of crops in all parts of the world are adventive species for the particular region in which they act as pests. The very concept of "pest" implies human intervention, in so far as it implies an upset in the ordinary numerical relations of organisms in the "balance of nature." Sometimes the pest is an indigenous insect species that has adapted to introduced crop plants and escaped ordinary population controls in the special ecological situation of cultivation. Often, however, it is an introduced species able to attain destructive abundance because its usual population controls—parasites and predators—are not present in the new region.

Smith (1929) compiled a list of 183 insects considered to be major crop pests in the United States. He found that 81, or 44 per cent of these, were undoubtedly of foreign origin. The situation in the United States is probably typical of continental areas in general; if so, we could make the generalization that nearly half of the major insect pests of any particular region will be found to be species accidentally introduced into that region by human agency. The proportion of introduced species on oceanic islands would undoubtedly be much higher. Really disastrous insect outbreaks are perhaps particularly apt to involve introduced species, free from their usual population controls—hence the great interest in the establishment of quarantines to prevent accidental insect introductions.

The number of insects that become established in new regions through human agency, however, is but a small fraction of the species that are constantly being moved about by modern man, with his automobiles, trains, ships, and airplanes. The statistics published by various quarantine services on insects intercepted show this. Metcalf and Flint (1951), for instance, quote figures from the United States Public Health Service on airplane inspections in the ten-year period from 1937 to 1947. Of 80,716 planes inspected, 28,852 were found to contain arthropods. I doubt whether anyone can estimate the degree of efficiency of such inspection services and thus get an idea of how many insects every year get by the quarantine.

The airplane, with its abolition of distance, is the most potent of man's new agencies for insect dispersal. The danger is particularly great where planes cross barriers between regions of similar climatic environment, as in the Atlantic crossings between Africa and South America. The story of the introduction, spread, and final extermination of the African mosquito, *Anopheles gambiae,* in Brazil, is a striking illustration of the dangerous possibilities of this particular route (Soper and Wilson, 1943).

The establishment of an insect in a new region is not always easy, as has been shown by the history of attempts at deliberate introduction. Since the abundance of adventive pests so often clearly results from the absence of their usual parasites and predators, agriculturists early had the idea of controlling such pests by introducing their natural enemies. This "biological control" is the subject of a considerable literature. Outstanding examples of successful introductions are summarized by Metcalf and Flint (1951, pp. 345–51), but I know of no summary of the failures, which would be equally interesting from the biological point of view.

The insects get the attention because they are so overwhelmingly numerous, but man has also been involved in the dispersal of many other types of invertebrates. Ticks, mites, household spiders, and other arthropods are frequently transported by man just as the insects are. Man has also been an active agent in the dispersal of earthworms and other soil inhabitants as he has carried soil from one place to another for various reasons. There have been several deliberate introductions of crustaceans for food purposes—the introduction of Chinese crabs and American crayfish into Europe has been discussed by Levi (1952).

Fresh-water and terrestrial mollusks have been moved about a great deal by human agency, but there seems to be no recent general summary of the literature on this. Kew (1893) includes a chapter on dispersal by man in his interesting general study of the dispersal of mollusks. A few molluscan introductions have been made deliberately, but most have been accidental. Thus, Thomson (1922) lists twenty-eight introduced species of snails and slugs found in New Zealand, all but one accidental. The exception is an English snail (*Lymnaea stagnalis*) introduced as food for fish. Mollusks have also occasionally been introduced into new regions as human food, the most notorious case being the dispersal of the African snail, *Achatina,* to many Pacific islands by the Japanese (Abbott, 1951).

Thus man has acted in several ways as an agent in the spread of invertebrates. The domesticates have been spread as a matter of course; the inquilines and parasites have accompanied their host; and a great variety of species has been accidentally moved in the course of modern travel and commerce. Many deliberate introductions have been made in connection with biological control operations—usually for the control of previously introduced pest weeds or insects. A few introductions have been made for food purposes. Probably, in the vast majority of cases, the adventives that have become established have, as in the case of adventive plants, come to form parts of the man-dominated environmental situations, though study, from the point of view of competition with indigenous fauna, seems to have been relatively neglected.

VERTEBRATES

Man's role in the dispersal of vertebrates is almost always deliberate and purposeful. The category of "accidental introduction," so important with microorganisms, plants, and invertebrates, is here trivial. The vertebrate human inquilines, rats and mice, have managed, unwanted, to accompany modern man on his travels and to establish themselves almost everywhere; but I think it safe to say that they are the only mammals accidentally dispersed. Among birds, I can think of no cases of accidental dispersal through human agency. Various lizards, however, have managed to achieve a wide distribution by hitching rides on ships and canoes; and burrowing snakes have possibly been transported in some instances with ballast.

Man has been actively involved in the dispersal of fresh-water fish for a great many years now, and the fisheries literature on the subject is considerable. Most of the introductions have been deliberate, and they have frequently been successful. Thomson (1922) has reviewed the history of fish introductions into New Zealand with his usual thoroughness. The paper by Miller and Alcorn (1943) on fish introductions into Nevada provides an example of the sort of activities carried on in all parts of the United States. They discuss attempted introductions of 39 species and subspecies of fish, 24 of which became successfully established.

Man has also been an accidental agent in the distribution of fish, perhaps most often as a consequence of his activity in digging canals between previously unconnected watersheds. Hubbs and Lagler (1947) have summarized the effect of canals on fish distribution in the Great Lakes region. The most notorious case is the inland extension of the range of the lamprey, presumably as a consequence of the construction of the Welland Canal.

Mostly, however, man has moved vertebrates deliberately. These introductions may be classed in one or another of four general categories: (1) species introduced as domestic animals; (2) species introduced for sport, food, or fur; (3) species introduced to control a pest; and (4) species introduced for sentimental reasons.

Domestic Animals

The origins of the domestic animals are, for the most part, as obscure as the origins of cultivated plants, and the animals have in general become as directly dependent on man for survival as have the plants. Still, there are striking cases where the domesticates have become feral in a new environment, getting along quite well without any continuing human interference—dogs, cats, goats, swine, horses, and cattle have perhaps most often been involved. These animals have frequently successfully established themselves in island environments with limited indigenous mammal faunas.

The grazing domesticates, whether managed or feral, have been a very powerful instrument of landscape change in many parts of the world. This is reflected in the continuing controversies among ranchers, farmers, and conservationists. The goat is outstanding in this respect—it might well be called the "ecological dominant" over much of the Mediterranean region, the Venezuelan Andes, and many other parts of the world, including numerous oceanic islands. Yet, running through a series of ecology textbooks, I find no entry of "Goat" in the indexes.

Sport, Food, and Fur

Most attempts to transfer wild vertebrates from one region to another have been made with one of these economic objectives, though it is sometimes difficult to distinguish the economic motive from the sentimental one, especially in the cases of animals introduced for sport. The introduction is made to compensate for alleged deficiencies in the local fauna; but the deficiency may be apparent because man is hankering after some particular kind of sport remembered from "back home" and is unwilling to adapt his habits to the sporting possibilities of the new fauna.

It is not always easy to get a vertebrate species established in a new region, even though the new environment may seem quite suitable. Bump (1951) notes that over a period of seventy-one years many unsuccessful attempts were made to introduce rabbits into Australia. Several attempts were made to introduce the starling into North America before the species was successfully established around New York by the liberation of forty pairs in 1890 and of a similar number in 1891 (Phillips, 1928). (This introduction, of course, belongs under the heading "for sentimental reasons.")

Of the numerous attempts to introduce foreign birds into North America for reasons either of sport or of sentiment, only six have been successful (Wing, 1951, p. 306): the Hungarian partridge, the ring-necked pheasant, the starling, the crested mynah (in British Columbia), the house sparrow, the European tree sparrow (in Missouri), and the Chinese spotted dove (in the vicinity of Los Angeles). In addition to these, the ranges of the valley quail and the bobwhite have been successfully extended by introduction into western states. Phillips (1928) has provided an interesting survey of these attempts at the introduction of wild birds.

The traffic in introductions has not all been one way into the New World. Perhaps the most notorious of the vertebrate introductions into Europe has been the muskrat, released first in the vicinity of Prague in 1905, in the hope of adding a valuable fur animal to the European fauna. The history of its spread and increasing destructiveness on the Continent has been reviewed by Storer (1937). The species escaped, or was released, in England; but there the government took strong measures and succeeded in exterminating it, prohibit-

ing any further introductions. This is interesting as one of the few cases of successful extermination of an established alien.

Similarly, the traffic in vertebrates has not all been one way across the Equator from the Northern to the Southern Hemisphere. An interesting reverse movement is the recent establishment of the nutria (*Myocastor*) from Argentina in the southern and southwestern United States. The animal now seems to be thoroughly established, but it is still not certain whether, in the long run, it will be regarded as a valuable addition to the list of fur animals in the region or as one more pest in the rice-growing region (Ashbrook, 1948; Swank and Petrides, 1954).

There is an extensive literature on these wildlife introductions. It has recently been reviewed, from rather different points of view, by Bump (1951) and Levi (1952). No clear principles and no means of predicting the circumstances under which introduction will be successful or the possible consequences of success seem to emerge. There appears to be a considerable group of wildlife specialists who favor continuing attempts at the introduction of exotic animals, despite the unpredicted and unfortunate consequences in cases like those of carp and starlings in the United States, rabbits in Australia, and deer in New Zealand.

Biological Control

The introduction of the mongoose into Hawaii and the West Indies is the classic case of this type of vertebrate dispersal through human agency. Allen (1911, p. 217) has sketched the history of the spread of this animal in the Caribbean.

In 1872, W. Bancroft Espeut imported four pairs of mongoose from Calcutta to Jamaica, for the purpose of destroying the rats that caused so great a destruction of sugar cane. These four pairs increased so rapidly, and attacked the rats with such ardor, that ten years later it was estimated that they effected an annual saving to the colony of 100,000 pounds sterling. Shortly after, however, they had so reduced the rats that they fell upon the native ground animals, and nearly annihilated certain toads, lizards, birds, and mammals.

Now the mongoose itself is regarded as a first-class pest everywhere that it has been introduced.

Seaman (1952) has written a short but very interesting account of the status of the mongoose in the Virgin Islands, where it was introduced in 1884 from Jamaica, shortly before the Jamaicans started becoming disillusioned about the value of the animal. Again it was effective in reducing the rat population for a few years, and again it was responsible for great reduction in the abundance of other local animals. Seaman, however, reports the gradual re-establishment of a biological balance. The rats, apparently, are now as abundant as ever—but they have taken to nesting high off the ground. He reports that the bridled quail dove, once considered to have been exterminated by the mongoose, has re-established itself, and quail have persisted through the mongoose episode despite their ground-nesting habits. It is clear that various behavior adaptations have taken place, probably both on the part of the mongoose and on the part of persisting local faunal elements. Surely here we have an unplanned but nonetheless interesting ecological experiment that has received nothing like the attention it warrants from the point of view of ecological theory. The present situation of the mongoose in Hawaii, where various faunal adaptations have also occurred, has been described in some detail by Baldwin *et al.* (1952).

The other outstanding example of biological control through vertebrate introduction is the fish *Gambusia,* which

has been widely spread as a mosquito-control measure. The history of this has been reviewed by Krumholz (1948). The *Gambusia* seem nowhere to have caused any unexpected disasters; but I have never been able to see clear proof that they caused any reduction in malaria either.

Sentiment

The starling and the English sparrow are America's heritage from the days of sentimental animal importation—the only two species to become established of the many introduced. Birds are the most frequent animals introduced for sentimental reasons. Thomson (1922) records attempts at introducing 130 species of birds into New Zealand, with success in 24 cases. Eight of the 24 successful introductions (ducks, pheasants, quail) might be classed as game birds; the remainder can be explained only by sentimental desire for birds of the homeland in the new landscape.

THE HUMAN HABITAT

Generalization about man as an agent in the spread of organisms is difficult. This may partly be because we lack the data; careful studies of the adventive elements in a biota, like the book on New Zealand by Thomson (1922), are rare. But, even if we had statistics for several major regions, their interpretation would be difficult, as is shown by the difficulties of interpreting the New Zealand situation (Allan, 1936; Murphy, 1951). The problem turns largely on the definition and analysis of the human habitat itself and on the extent and nature of human influences in local biotic communities.

If we define the "establishment" of an organism in a new situation in terms of its ability to persist in the absence of any other continuing human influence on the environmental situation, it looks as though remarkably few organisms spread through human agency were able to establish themselves in new situations—at least in new continental situations. This, however, is pretty much a theoretical postulation, because we do not, in fact, have the discontinuance of other human influences.

If we look at the organisms that form a direct part of the human habitat in any part of the world, the percentage of aliens, or species spread by human agency, seems remarkably large. There is also, however, a pervasive human influence beyond the direct human habitat, that is, beyond the terrain purposefully manipulated by man for subsistence. We have the effects of clearing and abandonment, of the spread and the control of fire, of selective tree-cutting, of hunting and other activities turning on sport and recreation, of stream manipulation and stream pollution. It becomes difficult to draw a line marking off the human habitat, and there is every degree between human dominance on Manhattan Island and human insignificance in the forest of some remote tributary of the upper Amazon. Yet even in the remote forest we may come across a mango tree, the only trace of a Jesuit mission abandoned a century and a half ago; and there are always the small, shifting clearings of the Indians. Vernadsky (1945) has proposed the word "noosphere" for the part of the earth's envelope dominated by the human mind. On land, at least, the noösphere is coming to correspond with the biosphere.

As biologists, we are apt to deplore this, to brush it off, to try to concentrate on the study of nature as it might be if man were not messing it up. The realization that, in trying to study the effect of man in dispersing other organisms, I was really studying one aspect of the human habitat came as a surprise to me. But, with the realization clear in my mind, I wonder why we do not put more biological effort

directly into the study of this pervasive human habitat.

There are practical considerations. To gain an understanding of the possible effect of accidental or purposeful introductions of organisms, we need primarily to study this human habitat. To estimate the importance and efficiency of our quarantine barriers, we need to study this human habitat. We live in the human habitat, and the interrelations of the organisms associated with us in that habitat affect us at every turn.

But there are also theoretical considerations, and I have tried to emphasize them wherever I could in this paper. The experimental-like situations produced by man's alteration of environmental factors, and by his movement of organisms into different environments, offer possibilities for study that seem to me not to have been fully realized. There are implications here not only for the understanding of ecology in the strict sense but also for the study of key aspects of the behavior of organisms and of the possible mechanisms of organic evolution.

Thomson (1922, p. 503) notes:

The conviction early grew upon me that here in New Zealand was a field in which the accuracy of Darwin's views in certain directions could be put to the test. The way in which certain species of introduced animals and plants seemed to "run away," as it were, from their recognized specific characters, led to the expectation that new forms would spring up in this country under altered conditions, and that we should here observe the "origin" of new species. I certainly was not alone in this half-expectation. It was somewhat generally, though vaguely, held.

Thomson reports disappointment, from this point of view, after his careful survey of the adventive biota. But perhaps he and the other naturalists were expecting too much, too obvious changes. It seems to me that they were clinging to a morphological concept of species and looking too anxiously for morphological changes in the introduced populations. The key, perhaps, lies not in structure but in behavior. Here, in surveying the literature, I am impressed by the number of tantalizing suggestions that seem not to have been followed up or fully analyzed. This human habitat, in which we all live, is a complex, dynamic, elusive, ever changing environment, certainly not easy to study. But it has the immense advantage of being under our noses, and it offers great possibilities for the understanding not only of ourselves but of the system of nature to which we belong.

REFERENCES

ABBOTT, R. TUCKER
  1951 "Operation Snailfolk," *Natural History*, LX, No. 6, 280–85.
ALLAN, H. H.
  1936 "Indigene versus Alien in the New Zealand Plant World," *Ecology*, XVII, 187–93.
ALLEN, GLOVER M.
  1911 "Mammals of the West Indies," *Bulletin of the Museum of Comparative Zoölogy, at Harvard College*, LIV, No. 6, 175–263.
ANDERSON, EDGAR
  1952 *Plants, Man and Life*. Boston: Little, Brown & Co. 245 pp.
ASHBROOK, F. G.
  1948 "Nutrias Grow in the United States," *Journal of Wildlife Management*, XII, 87–95.
BAILEY, L. H. and E. Z.
  1941 *Hortus Second: A Concise Dictionary of Gardening, General Horticulture and Cultivated Plants in North America*. New York: Macmillan Co. 778 pp.
BALDWIN, P. H.; SCHWARTZ, C. W.; and SCHWARTZ, E. R.
  1952 "Life History and Economic Status of the Mongoose in Hawaii," *Journal of Mammalogy*, XXXIII, 335–56.
BARTHOLOMEW, GEORGE A., and BIRDSELL, JOSEPH
  1953 "Ecology and the Protohominids," *American Anthropologist*, LV, No. 4, 481–98.
BATES, MARSTON
  1946 "The Natural History of Yellow Fever in Colombia," *Scientific Monthly*, LXIII, 42–52.
  1949 *The Natural History of Mosquitoes*. New York: Macmillan Co. 379 pp.

  1955 *The Prevalence of People*. New York: Charles Scribner's Sons. 283 pp.
BUMP, GARDINER
  1951 "Game Introductions—When, Where, and How," *Transactions of the 16th North American Wildlife Conference*, XVI, 316–25.
CHILDE, V. GORDON
  1941 *Man Makes Himself*. London: Watts & Co. 242 pp.
CLARK, J. G. D.
  1952 *Prehistoric Europe: The Economic Basis*. New York: Philosophical Library. 349 pp.
EGLER, FRANK E.
  1942 "Indigene versus Alien in the Development of Arid Hawaiian Vegetation," *Ecology*, XXIII, 14–23.
FENNER, FRANK
  1954 "The Rabbit Plague," *Scientific American*, CXC, No. 2, 30–35.
GOOD, RONALD
  1947 *The Geography of the Flowering Plants*. London: Longmans, Green & Co. 403 pp.
HACKETT, L. W.
  1937 *Malaria in Europe: An Ecological Study*. Oxford: Oxford University Press. 336 pp.
HEYERDAHL, THOR
  1953 *American Indians in the Pacific: The Theory behind the Kon-Tiki Expedition*. Chicago: Rand McNally & Co. 821 pp.
HUBBS, C. L., and LAGLER, K. F.
  1947 *Fishes of the Great Lakes Region*. (Cranbrook Institute of Science Bulletin No. 26.) Bloomfield, Mich. 186 pp.
KEW, HARRY WALLIS
  1893 *The Dispersal of Shells: An Inquiry into the Means of Dispersal Possessed by Fresh-Water and Land Mol-*

lusca. London: Kegan Paul, Trench, Trubner & Co. 291 pp.

KRUMHOLZ, LOUIS A.
1948 "Reproduction in the Western Mosquitofish, *Gambusia affinis affinis* (Baird & Girard), and Its Uses in Mosquito Control," *Ecological Monographs,* XVIII, No. 1, 1–43.

LEVI, HERBERT W.
1952 "Evaluation of Wildlife Importations," *Scientific Monthly,* LXXIV, 315–22.

MAGATH, T. B., and KNIES, P. T.
1945 "Modern Concepts of International Quarantine with Special Reference to Military Traffic," *Military Surgeon,* XCVI, 209–22.

MAY, JACQUES M.
1954 "Cultural Aspects of Tropical Medicine," *American Journal of Tropical Medicine and Hygiene,* III, 422–30.

METCALF, C. L., and FLINT, W. P.
1951 *Destructive and Useful Insects: Their Habits and Control.* 3d ed. New York: McGraw-Hill Book Co. 1,071 pp.

MILLER, ROBERT R., and ALCORN, J. R.
1943 "The Introduced Fishes of Nevada, with a History of Their Introduction," *Transactions of the American Fisheries Society,* LXXIII, 173–93.

MURPHY, R. C.
1951 "The Impact of Man upon Nature in New Zealand," *Proceedings of the American Philosophical Society,* XCV, No. 6, 569–82.

ORTON, J. H.
1937 *Oyster Biology and Oyster-Culture.* London: Edward Arnold & Co. 211 pp.

PHILLIPS, J. C.
1928 *Wild Birds Introduced or Transplanted in North America.* (U.S. Department of Agriculture Technical Bulletin No. 61.) Washington, D.C.: Government Printing Office. 63 pp.

RIDLEY, H. N.
1930 *The Dispersal of Plants throughout the World.* Ashford, Kent: L. Reeve & Co. 701 pp.

SALAMAN, REDCLIFFE N.
1949 *The History and Social Influence of the Potato.* Cambridge: Cambridge University Press. 685 pp.

SAUER, CARL O.
1952 *Agricultural Origins and Dispersals.* (Bowman Memorial Lectures, Series Two.) New York: American Geographical Society. 110 pp.

SCOFIELD, EUGENE C.
1931 *The Striped Bass of California (Roccus lineatus).* (California Division of Fish and Game, Fish Bulletin No. 29.) 84 pp.

SEAMAN, G. A.
1952 "The Mongoose and Caribbean Wildlife," *Transactions of the 17th North American Wildlife Conference,* XVII, 188–97.

SMITH, HARRY S.
1929 "On Some Phases of Preventive Entomology," *Scientific Monthly,* XXIX, 177–84.

SOPER, F. L., and WILSON, D. B.
1943 *Anopheles gambiae in Brazil, 1930 to 1940.* New York: Rockefeller Foundation. 262 pp.

STEARN, E. WAGNER and ALLEN E.
1945 *The Effect of Smallpox on the Destiny of the Amerindian.* Boston: Humphries, Inc. 153 pp.

STORER, T. I.
1937 "The Muskrat as Native and Alien," *Journal of Mammalogy,* XVIII, No. 4, 443–60.

SWANK, W. G., and PETRIDES, G. A.
1954 "Establishment and Food Habits of the Nutria in Texas," *Ecology,* XXXV, 172–75.

THOMSON, G. M.
1922 *The Naturalization of Animals and Plants in New Zealand.* Cambridge: Cambridge University Press. 607 pp.

VERNADSKY, W. I.
1945 "The Biosphere and the Noösphere," *American Scientist,* XXXIII, 1–12.

WING, L. W.
1951 *Practice of Wildlife Conservation.* New York: John Wiley & Sons. 412 pp.

WOLFENBARGER, D. O.
1946 "Dispersion of Small Organisms, Distance Dispersion Rates of Bacteria, sphere," *American Scientist,* XXXIII, Incidence Rates of Diseases and Injuries," *American Midland Naturalist,* XXXV, No. 1, 1–152.

ZIMMERMAN, ELWOOD C.
    1948 *Insects of Hawaii,* Vol. I: *Introduction.* Honolulu: University of Hawaii Press. 206 pp.
ZINSSER, HANS
    1935 *Rats, Lice and History: Being a Study in Biography, Which, after Twelve Preliminary Chapters Indispensable for the Preparation of the Lay Reader, Deals with the Life History of Typhus Fever.* Boston: Little, Brown & Co. 301 pp.

Ecology of Wastes

Ecology of Wastes

Disposal of Man's Wastes

ABEL WOLMAN*

As long as life has existed in this world, the disposal of waste has been a problem. All living organisms, by the very nature of their metabolism, produce wastes of varying composition, weight, and hazard to man and to lower animals. This inevitable characteristic of the living organism has in it the elements of danger to the individual if procedures for disposing of wastes are nonexistent or inadequate. With communities of individuals the problem is multiplied.

Among the waste problems of man we normally include the disposal of human wastes—feces and urine—and the disposal of refuse, such as organic garbage, rubbish, weeds, street dirt, small dead animals, and the like. These main classifications are the subject of this discussion.

DISPOSAL OF HUMAN WASTES
In Modern Western Communities

Scientific waste disposal is comparatively recent even in the developed countries of the world, such as England, Germany, and the United States. In the vast underdeveloped areas the problem remains relatively unsolved for well over a billion and a half people.

The great sewers of antiquity were storm-water surface drains rather than true sewers. Their function in the removal of human excreta was purely incidental and unimportant. As a matter of fact, until about 1815 the discharge of any wastes other than kitchen slop into the drains of London was prohibited by law. In Paris the same policy was continued until 1880.

The results of such prohibition of the discharge of human wastes into the great drains were the accumulation of extraordinary amounts of decomposing organic matter in all the cities of the Western world. The classic investigation of sanitary conditions which took place in Great Britain in the mid-nineteenth century provided the basis for the relaxation of these restrictions and the rapid introduction of human excreta into the storm drains. In the United States innumerable storm-drainage systems existed even as far back as the seventeenth century, but

* Dr. Wolman is Professor of Sanitary Engineering at The Johns Hopkins University, Baltimore, Maryland. Previously he was editor-in-chief of the *Journal of the American Water Works Association* (1921–37) and chief engineer of the Maryland State Department of Health (1922–39). He has served as consulting engineer to municipalities, regions, states, and federal agencies in more than ten states and the District of Columbia. Currently he is serving as Consultant to the United States Public Health Service (since 1939); Bethlehem Steel Company (since 1940); Surgeon General, United States Army (since 1944); Association of American Railroads (since 1946); and Atomic Energy Commission (since 1947). Since 1942, he has been Chairman of the Advisory Committee on Sanitary Engineering and Environment, Division of Medical Sciences, National Research Council, Washington, D.C., and Chairman of the Permanent Sanitary Engineering Committee, Pan American Sanitary Bureau. He was president (1939) of the American Public Health Association and (1942) of the American Water Works Association.

their use for the disposal of human wastes did not become accepted on a broad scale until about a hundred years ago. In England, in Germany, and in the United States the design of comprehensive sewerage projects dates from about 1850, with installations in Chicago in 1855, in Hamburg in 1842, and in Berlin in 1860.

With the advent of the water-carriage system for human excreta in the early nineteenth century, the community assumed the responsibility for the disposal of the wastes of the individual. Thus a new set of problems was created in the large communities, which were already plagued by the unsuccessful and dangerous procedures used by the individual. This technological advance corrected promptly the unsanitary conditions surrounding each dwelling by transferring the problem to the outskirts of each city. At these peripheral limits the concentrated filth from the entire population then had to be disposed of. Since the water-carriage system diluted the wastes from the individual by almost one hundred fold, the new problem involved a large volume of water, sullied by the addition of human excreta, kitchen wastes, and bathing wastes.

In general, for each 100 gallons of sewage per capita per day delivered from the average American community, less than one-half of 1 per cent represents the true waste ingredients. In England and in Germany the total unit volume would be of the order of less than 50 gallons per capita per day.

The major problem confronting every community in the developed countries of the world, therefore, is the disposal of vast quantities of water which have been deliberately fouled by the addition of the wastes produced by the average house, business, and industry. On balance the water-carriage system represents the major sanitary advance over the centuries. That the process

brought with it a new set of problems is a reasonable price to pay for the great inherent sanitary advantages.

The undesirable constituents of sewage are generally classified under two main heads: the living germs and the dead organic matter. The first of these create disease, and the second produces nuisances. The great epidemics of the past, such as typhoid fever, cholera, and diarrhea, had their origins in human wastes which polluted private and public water supplies. Where these supplies were inadequately purified, which was often the case in the nineteenth and early twentieth centuries, diseases of intestinal origin were extremely widespread. The details of these great epidemics need not be repeated here, because the public health literature is replete with examples. It is worth recalling, however, that the severe epidemics of Asiatic cholera in Hamburg in 1892–93 probably taught the lesson of the danger of water-supply contamination in a fashion unequaled by any other experience in sanitation. It must be remembered in this connection that the acceptance of the germ theory of disease was at the time less than a year old.

Since sewage contains bacteria, cysts, viruses, and other biological forms capable of causing disease when ingested by man, the significance of its prompt removal from contact with media and materials which may gain access to man is obvious. The routes by which disease may be transmitted are generally through water supplies, shellfish, bathing beaches, and insects.

The second major problem associated with the disposal of water-carried wastes is in the conversion of the organic to stable inorganic matter. Unless this is done, the decomposition will inevitably cause a nuisance. Although all sewage-purification processes generally reduce the number of bacteria present, this accomplishment is incidental, and the real problem is to reduce and to convert the organic matter into stable and unobjectionable form.

This situation is complicated, of course, where the wastes from manufacturing are abundant. Their influence on processes and on ultimate disposal must always be taken into account. Toxic materials, which might influence and deter biochemical processes, also add to the complications of sewage treatment. In the past, most of the large cities of the Western world disposed of their wastes by taking advantage of the natural purification capacities of receiving bodies of water, such as lakes, rivers, and oceans. This method was practiced by New York City, London, Chicago, Cleveland, and other cities. It was and is a legitimate use of such resources, provided the amount and nature of these wastes are carefully and adequately related to the capacities for their assimilation by such waters. Modern technology provides the tools by which to evaluate these balances, and, until these relationships become sharply unbalanced, the discharge of regulated amounts of wastes with only minor treatment into such bodies of water is not only permissible but of great economic value in reducing the investment in sewage treatment.

As is often the case, such natural purification was relied upon in many instances well beyond the point at which it was successful or appropriate. With the growth of communities, the procedures became less and less successful. Most of the great cities of the world have had to supplement the natural purification in near-by waters by artificial processes to prevent these waters from producing a nuisance from odor, sludge deposits, oily surfaces, or objectionable physical appearance.

The development of artificial processes of sewage treatment began approximately a hundred years ago, because it was apparent even then that rivers and harbors were reaching unsatisfactory status. Early investigators turned promptly, therefore, to a search for artificial methods which would accomplish the same purposes as natural purification, would entail minimum costs, and might provide, if possible, for the recovery of important organic constituents.

The great mid-nineteenth-century investigations in England by parliamentary commissions provided the practitioner with important data on the characteristics of the wastes themselves. In general, then and now, the water-carriage wastes of most communities consist of a mixture of inorganic and organic volatile substances of nitrogenous and carbonaceous matter. In the United States the total organic matter of sewage is approximately 0.2 pound per capita per day. A total nitrogen value for American city sewages varies from 15 to 35 parts per million by weight; about one-half of this will be in the form of free ammonia, while the remainder generally is in the form of organic nitrogen. The total carbon of many of the sewages will average about 200 parts per million, of which perhaps 75 parts may be found in the nitrogenous material. Fats represent a considerable problem in municipal sewages and may average approximately 50 parts per million.

Variations in city sewages may account for deviations as much as 50 per cent from these figures. The total organic material ordinarily would represent about 200 parts per million when measured by the biochemical oxygen demand at 20° C. for five days. Suspended material is usually of the same order of magnitude. In those countries in which the per capita use of water is materially less than in the United States, such as in England, Germany, and France, sewage strength is materially greater. Design of treatment processes therefore must take into account the nature of the populations served and of their water uses.

The royal commissions on sewage disposal in England recognized the fact that the only way to prevent the increasing pollution of rivers was to purify community sewage. It was natural for these commissions to decide that the most appropriate way of doing this was to dispose of these wastes on land. They were strongly motivated in this by the assumption that the fertilizer values of nitrogen and phosphorus in sewage would be adequately conserved and used for the benefit of animal and plant life. This emphasis on land disposal probably retarded the development of successful artificial procedures for treating sewage by at least a quarter of a century. The attempted disposal on land of vast quantities of sewage water, particularly in a country having relatively few dry months in a year, was a dismal failure. It was a failure likewise in most other countries in which it was carried out and in which equally inappropriate climatologic conditions prevailed. In addition, great difficulties were encountered with soils too fine to permit adequate absorption of liquid and solid without clogging.

When the scientists and the technologists gradually escaped from both this hope and this emphasis on land treatment, development of artificial procedures moved forward with great rapidity. In each of these artificial methods the same principles, however, were used as were applicable in theory to land treatment. The objective in each was to perform biochemical conversions in artificial structures, with greater speed than nature afforded and with smaller expenditures of money.

Processes moved, therefore, through adaptation of land treatment to artificial sand filtration, contact beds filled with stone, trickling filters, and to activated sludge and its many modifica-tions. In virtually all, the sewage was first settled in large tanks to remove as much of the suspended material as possible so as to subject the resulting liquids to increasingly high-speed transformation on smaller and smaller units of land. This evolution may be quantitatively demonstrated by the fact that, whereas an acre of land in the original land-treatment process would provide for 10,000 gallons of sewage per day, the modern activated-sludge treatment plant accomplishes the same or a similar result on one acre for 6,000,000 gallons of sewage per day.

In the developed countries of the world, therefore, current practices in the treatment of municipal sewage are predominantly either by the trickling-filter method or by the activated-sludge process. In the United States, in 1954, the sewage of approximately 95,000,000 urban people was collected, and that of some 60,000,000 was processed to some degree of purification. In general, the treatment was accomplished by an investment cost of from $12.00 to $25.00 per capita and an operation and maintenance cost of from $1.00 to $2.00 per capita per year.

Although it is evident that tremendous strides have been made in the treatment of municipal sewages, it is still true that we must continue the search for better and more economical solutions to two major features of the problem. We are still badly in need of a treatment process which is cheaper than any so far developed for water-carried wastes. Second, the disposal of sludge resulting from such wastes is still unsatisfactory. The complete destruction of such material not only is costly but dissipates a material relatively valuable for soil conditioning. The salvage of this material does not under existing conditions pay for capital investment and operation and maintenance. The fertilizer values of activated sludge, however, are high, and a ready sale for it is sometimes available. In American practice, however, where large amounts of this recovered material reach the market, the price paid for drying and packaging even of activated sludge sharply declines when too much floods the market.

For example, in 1954, at Milwaukee, Wisconsin, the cost of producing a salable and excellent dried activated-sludge fertilizer fell far short of meeting the cost of maintenance and operation of the sludge-drying plant. It met none of the investment cost. In 1955 the price for a somewhat inferior grade of dried sludge, namely, $7.50 per ton, represented in Baltimore, Maryland, about one-half of the capital and maintenance and operation charges on the sludge-drying plant.

The disposal of water-carried sewage, therefore, in most of the Western world entails a public health and a social responsibility. Recovery values, however, are of long-range interest to society for conservation reasons rather than because of economics.

Waste Practices in Under-developed Countries

The comments hitherto presented have dealt exclusively with the disposal of human and industrial wastes in communities of reasonably well-developed countries, for the most part in the Western Hemisphere. In these areas large aggregates of population have made the use of water-carriage sewerage systems and sewage-treatment plants a standard practice.

In these same areas large rural populations have dealt with the problem on a less expensive, less mechanized, and reasonably satisfactory basis by the use of septic tanks and subsurface irrigation. The practices, which have grown up under the more favorable economic circumstances in the Western world, have of course produced better environmental sanitation, even in rural areas where distances between contacts are great and the probabilities of infection correspondingly reduced.

In the rest of the world, however, in what is loosely described as underdeveloped areas, the problem of disposal of human wastes is both difficult and unsolved. The proportion of population, consisting of well over a billion people, living in rural areas is very great and poorly provided with disposal facilities. In the urban and densely populated cities some semblance of water-carriage sewerage facilities is available.

Simple and less-than-perfect methods prevail in all the rural areas. The facilities vary from the most up to date and sanitary for a few to the most medieval ones for most. The outside privy, of the bucket or pit system, in most instances offers the only economical and successful solution. The cost or scarcity of water in relation even to reasonable aggregates of population makes the installation of water-borne sewerage well-nigh impossible.

In the Middle East the field of sanitation is still untilled for the rural sanitarian. Where ministries of health have been especially active or internationally assisted, sanitation projects have been started. Satisfactory latrines have been installed by individuals and sometimes have been well maintained. By and large, however, these have been the exception rather than the rule. Even the elementary precepts in the sanitation code of Moses or of the Koran and the Bible are poorly obeyed. As in many other parts of the world, the safe disposal of human excreta here remains one of the greatest sanitary challenges. The discharges are promiscuously distributed in the field, on the banks of irrigation canals or drains, in the houses, or in the secluded nooks or corners of the village street. The latrine is rare, simply because the ideal or universal and cheap one still remains to be developed or used. General use of human excreta for fertilizer is fairly widespread, relatively uncontrolled, and generally not too effective.

In rural Brazil several types of inexpensive excreta-disposal facilities have been developed: the bored-hole latrine and two types of pit privies. Many of these have been installed, largely through the co-operative enterprises of Brazil and the United States of America. Their continued maintenance remains a problem, and the use of the contents for any well-controlled agricultural purpose is minimal.

In the Philippines surface disposal in rural areas has been found to be most convenient and perhaps most dangerous. The bamboo groves in the back yard provide privacy, the excreta quickly dry up in many seasons of the year, and the odor and fly problems have not been too severe. Under the pressure of the Central Health Department, however, more effective means of waste disposal are gradually being installed in the village and farm areas, particularly in view of the fact that gastrointestinal disease is one of the leading causes of death in infants. The pit-privy type of installation has moved forward slowly, but, where it has become generally used, it, again, has not offered a major agricultural supplement.

In East Pakistan 42,000,000 people subsist mainly on agriculture in an area of approximately 55,000 square miles. The density of population is very high, and many preventable diseases of sewage origin prevail in great numbers. Cholera, typhoid, dysentery, and diarrhea account for 30,000–40,000 deaths a year. Disposal of human excreta is elementary in character and quite unimportant in economic recovery for agricultural use.

More than 85 per cent of India's population lives in innumerable impov-erished villages, all dependent for their existence on farming and agriculture. Neither good water supply nor satisfactory excreta disposal is to be found. The open spaces and the by-lanes are the natural places for excreta deposition. Generally, no recognized means for excreta collection and removal are to be found.

The towns and the smaller cities of India are not much better served. The dry-pail type of latrine is common. The socially outcast scavenger provides for hand removal and the cleaning of these latrines. They are washed in the street drains, and only a small quantity of excreta ever finds its way to any central disposal ground. Where the excreta are actually collected, they are stocked in drums at selected depots and carried to a central ground disposal. In most cases this material is composted with the town refuse, using the familiar "Bangalore Method." This consists primarily of mixtures in trenches three to four feet deep. Here the contents are held for four to six months. Thereafter, low-grade soil-conditioner results, which is applied to the agricultural land. This compost has a market value and is readily salable, but the collection system is eminently unsatisfactory and hygienically dangerous. Many efforts have been made in the past to extend this composting procedure with a more hygienic system of collection, but the sanitarian has a long way to travel before the procedure may be considered acceptable.

Scott (1952) has frequently emphasized the significance of fecal-borne disease in China and has pointed out the importance of controlling these diseases at their source. For this purpose he has offered three alternatives: (1) disposal of the excreta in bored-hole latrines; (2) piping it to central treatment plants (both expensive and wasteful); or (3) composting the excreta so that sanitation aims are achieved and plant foods are conserved for agricultural purposes.

So far large-scale experimentation has been the only effort along any of these lines in prewar China and in scattered areas in Japan. The underlying principles of composting are sound, but the increasing cost of transport of excreta, the hygienic management of composted materials, and the undemonstrated economic values to be attained still offer stumbling blocks to widespread use. As the great metropolitan areas in these countries have developed and spread, the night-soil collection, transportation, and disposal costs have mounted, in some instances to the point of vanishing money return for excreta use on the land.

In recent years the University of California has devoted considerable time to a study of the reclamation of organic wastes by composting. The eternal search for a cheap way not only to convert these organic wastes but to supplement soil fertility has renewed interest in the subject in all parts of the world in recent years. Even where the process has been reasonably well developed, it has been practiced as an art. Its scientific basis and control have not been too well understood. Perhaps the greatest progress in the direction of combining excreta with organic refuse for periods of time sufficiently long to produce a fairly stable humus has been made in England, in the Netherlands, and in recent years in Santa Ana in the Republic of El Salvador in Central America. Here the process has been successful, for the control has been careful and accurate. Important contributions on a field scale have come from the operations at the University of California; Dannevirke, New Zealand; Ficksburg, South Africa; Dumfriesshire, Scotland; and the Netherlands.

Interest in composting, of course, has persisted over the centuries, as in China and India, where the resultant preservation of soil fertility has been significant. The mixtures have covered sewage sludge and sewage screenings, municipal refuse, street and market refuse, stable manure, night soil, and straw. Yet at this writing, although interest is again high, a sound and economical composting procedure is still unavailable to meet reasonable public health and fiscal requirements. The search will undoubtedly go on, because the process remains one of the most promising possibilities for sewage reclamation.

WASTE WATER AND RECLAMATION UTILIZATION

The search for an economic recovery of human waste products has been paralleled by efforts to obtain the general acceptance of the concept of waste water as a true water resource. For many years workers have insisted upon viewing sewage wastes as potential material for irrigating land, for the recharge of subterranean aquifers, or for industrial re-use. Many examples of successful applications for each of these purposes are to be found in the United States and to a limited degree in other countries of the world. Obviously, these practices have been developed most rapidly in arid and semiarid areas. This accounts for the fact that in California alone some 350,000 acre-feet per year of sewage-plant effluents from private and public institutions and municipalities have been applied to the soil for agricultural purposes or for underground-water recharge. The extension of these uses will undoubtedly occur as time goes on because of the economic value of such application and because of the increasing pressure for water conservation.

In the United States some nine industries now make use of effluents from municipal sewage-treatment plants, with important economic benefits. Such effluents are used for cooling water, for process water, for irrigation and boiler-feed water, and for combined process and cooling water.

Perhaps the largest installation of this type is at the Bethlehem Steel Company plant at Sparrows Point, Maryland, near Baltimore. The plant manufactures rod, wire, tin plate, rails, pig iron, nails, pipe, ships, and miscellaneous steel products. It employs between 25,000 and 30,000 people and uses vast quantities of fresh, brackish, and salt water for various purposes, ranging from drinking to the quenching of coke. Since 1942 this plant has been using the processed-treated effluents of sewage of some 950,000 people in the city of Baltimore. In 1955 it used virtually the entire flow of sewage from this great city, after the sewage had passed through the municipal sewage-treatment plant and had been further processed for industrial plant purposes. This re-use of treated sewage will soon represent approximately 150,000,000 gallons per day, perhaps the largest amount of water-carried sewage re-used in any one place in the world.

The processes used for the above purposes are neither complex nor hazardous. The activity has been successfully managed for over twelve years and has resulted in major economic and sanitary advantages to both the city of Baltimore and the Bethlehem Steel Company. It offers a fruitful example to many parts of the world of the recycling of waste water for conservation and economic values.

REFUSE DISPOSAL

The accumulation and disposal of rubbish, garbage, small dead animals, street dirt, weeds, and other evidences of community living has been one of the major problems of society over the ages. In this, as in the field of human wastes, the search has been perennial and persistent for a process which would salvage valuable materials and would have economic validity.

The differences in practice in various countries of the world are striking. In England, where salvaged materials, such as glass, metal, and fats, are potentially significant, much is recovered from these types of municipal wastes through central salvage stations. Many of these plants grew to importance during and after World War II. In the United States, where labor costs are high, salvage for waste materials generally is not practiced, and the recapture of metals, glass, and fertilizer values has not been too favorable from an economic standpoint.

The disposal of refuse, therefore, has moved from an earlier so-called "reduction" process to high-temperature destruction at 1,200°–1,600° F. The emphasis on reduction resulted from the desire to produce grease and low-grade fertilizer. Reduction caused great sanitary difficulties with the disposal of gaseous, liquid, and solid wastes. The by-products brought highly fluctuating prices on the open market, years of prosperity being followed by years of virtually no sales. Construction costs were high, and operating problems were numerous and costly.

It was not long, therefore, before most American cities in the mid-twentieth century were driven to high-temperature destruction, because of lower capital investment, easier operation, and more satisfactory hygienic disposal. As even these costs rose, however, many municipalities turned to the controlled sanitary fill, encouraged by the added prospect of recovery of wasteland.

This method was and is widely practiced and has reclaimed many areas for park and recreational purposes. Operating costs per ton of material are a fraction of those entailed in high-temperature destruction—some 50 to 60 cents per ton compared with $2.50 to

$3.00 per ton for the latter. Unfortunately, areas within economic transportation distance of the production of refuse which can serve for sanitary fill purposes are becoming fewer in number and extent in the great metropolitan areas of this and other countries.

For the major cities, composting techniques at this writing have not been widely accepted. The requirements of land, the excessive costs of haul, the difficulties of true composting control methods to avoid nuisance, and the problem of finding adequate markets for ultimate product have all militated against the widespread adoption of this procedure. It is still true, however, that many people are attracted to the method and will continue to pursue its development, at least experimentally. The next decades may see wider application of composting.

In spite of the efforts of the past, it must be admitted that no satisfactory method has so far appeared for handling and disposal of refuse which meets the joint requirements of sanitation, of conservation, and of economy in costs. In this field, as in others, the day of balance between destruction of wastes and re-use or salvage will probably dawn as the resources of each country become relatively more and more limited. It is perhaps axiomatic that conservation is most often the child of necessity, at least where re-use and recovery of human and community wastes are concerned.

REFERENCES

ANONYMOUS
    1930 *London Cleansing.* (Command Paper, Report of Departmental Committee Appointed by the Ministry of Health.) London: H.M. Stationery Office.
    1951 *Present Economic and Technical Status of Water Reclamation from Sewage and Industrial Wastes.* (University of California, Institute of Engineering Research, Series 37, Issue 4.) Berkeley: University of California Press. 24 pp.
    1953 "Working Papers." (Expert Committee on Environmental Sanitation, World Health Organization, Third Session, Geneva, 27–31 July.) Not available to public. (Mimeographed.)

ELIASSEN, ROLF
    1942 "War Conditions Favor Landfill Refuse Disposal," *Engineering News-Record,* CXXVIII, No. 23, 72–74.

FAIR, GORDON MASKEW, and GEYER, JOHN CHARLES
    1954 *Water Supply and Waste Water Disposal.* New York: John Wiley & Sons. 973 pp.

FRANCIS, T. P.
    1931 *Modern Sewage Treatment.* London: Contractors' Record, Ltd. 322 pp.

FULLER, GEORGE W., and McCLINTOCK, JAMES R.
    1926 *Solving Sewage Problems.* New York: McGraw-Hill Book Co. 548 pp.

GUTTERIDGE, HAL
    1952 "Refuse-Sewage Composting—Engineering Aspects," *Journal and Transactions of the Society of Engineers,* XLIII, No. 3, 135–61. Westminster.

IMHOFF, KARL, and FAIR, GORDON MASKEW
    1940 *Sewage Treatment.* London: Chapman & Hall, Ltd.; New York: John Wiley & Sons. 370 pp.

MARTIN, ARTHUR J.
    1927 *The Activated Sludge Process.* London: Macdonald & Evans. 415 pp.

METCALF, LEONARD, and EDDY, HARRISON P.
    1930 *Sewage and Sewage Disposal.* New York: McGraw-Hill Book Co. 783 pp.

RICER, E. G. (in charge)
    1941 *Survey of Landfill Characteristics —New York City.* (Sanitary Engineering Research Laboratory, New York University.) New York: New York City Department of Sanitation. 90 pp.

SCOTT, JAMES C.
    1952 *Health and Education in China.* London: Faber & Faber, Ltd. 279 pp.

STONE, RALPH, and GARBER, WILLIAM F.
  1951   *Sewage Reclamation by Spreading Basin Infiltration.* (American Society of Civil Engineers, Proceedings Separate No. 87.) New York: American Society of Civil Engineers. 20 pp.

VAN VUREN, J. P. T.
  1949   *Soil Fertility and Sewage.* London: Faber & Faber, Ltd. 236 pp.

VEATCH, N. T.; WILCOX, L. V.; WOLMAN, ABEL; and POWELL, S. T.
  1948   "Reclamation of Sewage Effluents," *Sewage Works Journal,* XX, No. 1, 3-95.

WEAVER, LEO, and KEAGY, DONALD M.
  1952   *The Sanitary Landfill Method of Refuse Disposal in Northern States.* (U.S. Public Health Service, Federal Security Agency, Publication No. 226.) Washington, D.C.: Government Printing Office. 31 pp.

WILSON, H.
  1944   "Some Risks of the Transmission of Disease during the Treatment, Disposal and Utilization of Sewage, Sewage Effluent and Sewage Sludge," *Journal and Proceedings of the (British) Institute of Sewage Purification,* pp. 214-38.

WOLMAN, ABEL
  1924   "Hygienic Aspects of Sewage Sludge as Fertilizer," *Engineering News-Record,* XCII, No. 5, 198-202.

Sanitation Practices and Disease Control in Extending and Improving Areas for Human Habitation

A. LESLIE BANKS* and J. A. HISLOP†

INTRODUCTION

The subject of man's rôle in changing the face of the earth deals with one of the most important problems confronting the world today, and it is with some considerable anxiety, and a due sense of the responsibilities involved, that we have approached our task of discussing the influence of disease and disease control in this context.

In order that there should be no mis-understanding as to the manner in which we have interpreted our title, it will be advisable at the outset to define the terms involved. By "sanitation" is meant the adoption or control of any measures pertaining to, or connected with, the improvement of the health of mankind or relating to the preservation of health. In other words, we have accepted the Latin definition of *sanitas*, i.e., health of body and mind.

Regarding the word "disease," we do not propose to be bound by the ancient meaning of lack of ease, or its later interpretation of departure from the clinical norms of bodily or mental health, but rather to accept the World Health Organization definition of health as "a state of complete physical, mental and social well-being and not merely the absence of disease or infirmity" (World Health Organization, 1946), and to deem disease as the antithesis of this concept of health.

Similarly, in discussing areas for human habitation, we have not limited ourselves to the great cities or industrial communities, nor should our remarks be taken to refer to continents and countries, but rather to the individual and his family wherever they may be found. It may be advisable at the outset to make clear our belief that it is in small units of civilisation, for example, the local neighbourhood in the town and the village in the rural area, that

* Dr. Banks, who is a Fellow of the Royal College of Physicians, London, is also a barrister-at-law and a member of the Honourable Society of Lincoln's Inn. He is Professor of Human Ecology in the University of Cambridge and Head of that Department. His interests in the field of health and welfare include membership of the World Health Organization Advisory Panel on Medical Care. His published works include *Social Aspects of Disease*, 1953, and a number of papers on medico-social subjects. He edited *The Development of Tropical and Sub-tropical Countries*, 1954.

† Dr. Hislop is Assistant Director of Research in the Department of Human Ecology in the University of Cambridge. He is a barrister-at-law and a member of the Royal College of Physicians of Edinburgh and was engaged in active clinical practice for a number of years before joining the staff of the Department of Human Ecology in 1950. Since that time he has directed research projects concerned with the social aspects of disease, including a survey of rheumatic disease in rural areas and a comprehensive investigation into medical care with particular reference to maternity services, mental health, the chronic sick, and specialist services.

the problems under discussion may best be studied.

Man's interest in maintaining his health and that of his family is a subject which has exercised the minds of the leaders in each succeeding civilisation. A study of folklore in all countries reveals many instances of attempts, sometimes pathetic and sometimes brutal, to drive out disease, whether by means of charms, witchcraft, talismans, or trephining. The earliest medical code known was devised by Hammurabi with the clear intention of improving the practice of medicine and discouraging the careless and over-ambitious surgeon, and the Edwin Smith, Ebers, and other papyri contain many hundreds of remedies against disease still recognisable today.

It was in ancient Greece, however, that our modern pattern of disease became more clearly evident and where its study by careful observation and deduction was undertaken. As might be expected, the emphasis in the ancient world was on cure or palliation rather than the prevention of disease, and indeed it may have been considered impious to examine too closely the causes of disease, for this might provoke further the wrath of the gods who had inflicted it.

An exception was the Mosaic code, which provided simple instruction for preserving the health of nomadic and of semi-nomadic agricultural communities. It was not, however, until the growth of the Roman Republic that the ancient clinical and preventive knowledge was combined as the resources of the community grew. It is unfortunate that with the decline and fall of the Roman Empire this wisdom, collected and practised over a thousand years, became forgotten and was not recalled for fifteen hundred years.

Little is known about health and welfare conditions in Europe, or indeed in the world, for the six hundred years following the fall of Rome, but it is not long after that before we begin to find ample evidence of the influence of the three spectres of war, famine, and disease. It is said, for example, that between A.D. 970 and 1100 there were sixty famine years in France alone, and one-third of the population of Paris died of starvation in 1418 (Sand, 1952, p. 149 n.). Venice, by reason presumably of its commerce with the East, had the unenviable history of sixty-three epidemics of plague in six hundred years (*ibid.*, p. 151). In 1493 we have the first recognition of the great pox, syphilis, in Europe. By medieval times the pattern of disease which we are now making such desperate efforts to alter had clamped down on the world. Infant mortality, for example, was so heavy that in England in 1550 the expectation of life from birth was eight and a half years, and in Geneva in the same year it was four years and nine months. Indeed, the average expectation of life from birth never exceeded nineteen years in Britain until some one hundred and fifty years ago.

It is no exaggeration to say that by the eighteenth century the great killing diseases had reached their peak throughout the world—a peak which in many countries has developed into a plateau. The infectious diseases of infancy, including the dreaded infantile diarrhoea, and the great killers, tuberculosis, syphilis, and malaria, combined with the pandemic diseases of cholera, plague, and typhus to make life brief and uncertain. Parasitic infestations were the rule, rather than the exception, throughout all classes of society. It is small wonder that with this appalling background the general level of ignorance was high, and that few attempts were made to stem the overwhelming tide of disease.

It is true that quarantine had been introduced in Venice as early as 1377 and was subsequently adopted by other countries. Some towns and city states also made attempts, from time to time, to improve their sanitary environment and the health and well-being of their inhabitants, but these attempts seem to have depended almost entirely upon the efforts of one or two men and were not sustained for long periods. Looking back over these troubled times, it seems clear that the main defect in the attempts to control disease was the absence of continuity of effort, quite apart from the lack of special knowledge. Once again one is forced to the conclusion that it is useless to promulgate laws unless the means to enforce them are available, a state of affairs which still prevails in many parts of the world.

From the sixteenth century onwards the voyages of discovery, and the acquisition of overseas possessions by a number of European countries, led to increasing wealth and the organised development of industries such as wool, iron, coal, printing, and glass, which called for more labour in the towns. The inventions of the eighteenth century set mankind working at a fearful pace. Furthermore, having left the country for the town, there was no return, and the mass of people were at the mercy of fluctuations in world markets over which they had as little control as their ancestors had over the elements. Worse still, it was soon found that women and children could tend machines as well as or better than men, and it was not long before the exploitation of female and child labour developed to such an extent as to endanger the future health of entire nations.

DISEASE CONTROL IN TEMPERATE CLIMATES

The beginnings of our present methods of disease control date back only about two hundred and fifty years. In England, for example, the writings of Sir William Petty (1690, 1691) and others, and the statistical researches of John Graunt (1662) into the London Bills of Mortality, demonstrated that the effects of disease could be measured in economic terms. The Great Plague of London, according to Petty, cost the country some seven million pounds by reason of the lives lost, and Graunt was able to demonstrate, *inter alia,* the high mortality in infancy and especially of male children.

Here it is worth noting the factors which influenced then, and still do, the efforts to control disease. They are three in number: fear, altruism, and economic needs. The reason for fear may vary. Formerly it was inspired by the great pandemic diseases of plague and cholera, and lately it has changed to other diseases and their effects on society. Altruism is as old as man himself, for it forms the basis of all the ancient religious teachings on charity to the poor and suffering. Economic expansion is a more modern factor, but one which now dominates the other two, whether the search be for labour, new markets, or for rare minerals or oil.

It will be advisable to consider at this stage the methods by which measures for disease control have been carried out. First came voluntary effort, next local government effort, then legislation on a national basis, and finally international action. In some countries the stage of local government action has been omitted, so that we have a picture, not of the growth of health services from below, but of their imposition from above—a most undesirable state of affairs.

A term much in use in Britain some eighty to ninety years ago was "sanitary science," which dealt with the principles by which health was to be maintained and disease prevented. There was a general belief that all that was needed was to improve the physical environment, and there was little understanding of the other environmental components, biological and social, to which we now devote so much attention. While it was understood that pure air, adequate water supplies free from contamination, the safe disposal of waste products, and a dust-free working environment were necessary to prevent disease, lack of knowledge, particularly in the bacteriological and pathological fields, prevented further developments in this direction. The study of the social environment, in particular, belongs rather to this century than to the last.

It was also fashionable, when scientific boundaries appeared to be more clear cut than they do at the present time, for many human ailments to be ascribed to hereditary influences. The rheumatic diathesis was thought to account for many of the problems of rheumatism, and similar considerations applied to tuberculosis and a number of other diseases. The environmentalists, on the other hand, held that the influence of the environment was all-important. Today it is recognised that both influences are at work, and if more attention is paid to the environment it is because this offers a promising short-term prospect of improvement, whereas genetical change is a long-term matter.

It is, however, on the interplay between inherited strengths and weaknesses and a faulty or sound environment that a true picture of the causes of disease may often be found. If the tubercle bacillus can be removed from the environment by eliminating the human carrier, and by providing tubercle-free milk, then any inherited tendency to this disease ceases to be of importance. In his struggle against disease man seeks, therefore, firstly to build up his natural powers of resistance, secondly artificially to enhance these, and thirdly to destroy the causes of disease in his surroundings. In the field of acquired immunity there have been truly remarkable advances. For many years

Jenner's discovery in the prevention of smallpox was the only noteworthy contribution, whereas today it is possible to protect against nearly all the great infections, including vaccination with B.C.G. against tuberculosis, so much so that the traveller to foreign countries may find himself in sympathy with a pincushion.

It is in the realm of the antibiotics and insecticides that the most dramatic means of controlling the biological environment have been evolved, and it is no exaggeration to say that the discovery of penicillin and related substances has revolutionised the control of disease in many parts of the world.

In many Western countries the killing diseases of childhood and early adult life have receded in importance far enough to reveal other conditions, such as certain virus diseases, cancer, the degenerative diseases, and the so-called "stress" diseases, which have hitherto been obscured by the great mass of infections and the early deaths from these. Already it is possible to see the transition in emphasis from the physical and biological to the social environment, for many current "medical" problems are now recognised to be medico-social or, indeed, socio-medical in character. The word "social" is not easy to define. It derives from the Latin *socius*, "a company," and the old definitions relate it to society, men living in society, or to the public as an aggregate body. More popularly, we might consider it as relating to man himself, with all his faults and virtues. Certainly, from the health and welfare point of view, there is a multitude of mental and emotional factors to be considered in connection with the extension and improvement of urban areas for human habitation, for the whole field of mental health must be explored here in addition to that of physical disease.

It is in our highly urbanised communities that the causes of mental ill-health and emotional unrest are particularly to be found. Here disease in its more ancient meaning no longer applies, for mental unhappiness turns on matters such as faulty human relations in industry, inadequate education, financial crises, and the threats of war, in addition to the inability of the individual to adjust to the environment in which he finds himself at a given moment. Now the remedy must be sought anew, and it is in the field of family welfare, preventive psychiatry, fitting the job to the man rather than the man to the job, and in a sound educational pyramid that the prevention and cure of these conditions must be sought. Such diseases, for example, as peptic ulceration, coronary thrombosis, and certain types of eczema, cannot be dealt with only by means of specific medical remedies, for they require detailed investigation into the social circumstances which have produced them, and in a highly industrialised community these may be complex.

In simple nomadic or agricultural communities the problem of communal living was solved many thousands of years ago. We are thus confronted with a picture of two worlds. The wealthy industrialised countries have built up an elaborate structure of health and welfare services and have taken steps to protect their members from all those conditions against which remedies are available. They have even learnt to limit their numbers, so that we now have societies composed of small family units, perhaps with an average of two or less children, whose physical health is so good that infant mortality has fallen to a small fraction of that which prevailed a hundred years ago, and in which the chances of survival to mature adult life are excellent. In such countries the causes of death which prevailed a hundred years ago, and which still prevail in many parts of the world, no longer predominate. Infection has given

place to cancer as the major cause of death, closely followed by the degenerative diseases of the cardiovascular system. Such communities show, as would be expected, a decreasing number of children under sixteen and a high proportion of adults, with an increasing number of old people (cf. Fig. 156 and Tables 28 and 29 for the changing age structure of the population in England and Wales [Benjamin, 1954]). So far so good, but some communities, for example, the United States of America and Great Britain, have also had to make provision of nearly 50 per cent of their hospital accommodation for mental patients, and the prevention of mental ill-health assumes even greater importance with increasing age, for almost one-quarter of all patients in those mental hospitals are aged sixty-five years and over (Ministry of Health, 1953, pp. 121 ff.).

DISEASE AND DISEASE CONTROL WITH PARTICULAR REFERENCE TO THE TROPICS

Turning now to other parts of the world, an extraordinarily interesting but confused pattern is to be found, varying from the florid manifestations of disease which were to be seen in Europe in medieval times to the equally dramatic results of attempting to apply the whole armamentarium of prevention and cure to communities which may not be ready for this. In countries where birth rates and death rates are high, and the expectation of life is short, it is usually the physical environment which bears most harshly on the people.

When such communities are brought into contact with modern advances the result may sometimes be unfortunate for them. In a collection of villages recently seen by one of us (A. L. B.) in Asia an irrigation scheme had been undertaken, with well-constructed canals suitably furnished with booster pumps, so that what had hitherto been a dry and harsh plain could now be converted into a green and fertile land. Unfortunately, the water snail had followed the waterways, carrying the parasites of bilharzia with it, so that this area, hitherto free, was now so heavily infested that people were leaving in search of more healthy lands.

and environmental sanitation measures applied on a wholesale scale. It may not be irrelevant here to pause and consider what are some of the problems in the field of disease control in tropical countries which either remain to be solved or are, in fact, being created by the solution of other problems.

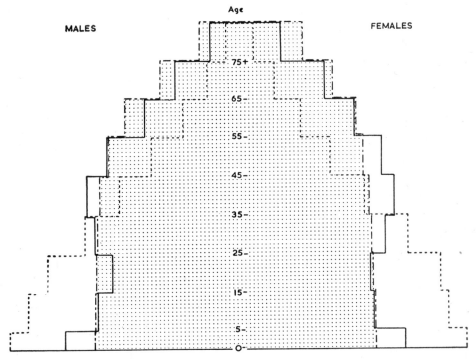

FIG. 156.—The changing age structure of the population in England and Wales. The area of the block for each age group represents the proportion of the total population in that age group.

Throughout the world there is, at the present time, a process going on whereby the full weight of modern preventive measures is being applied to the elimination of disease. International teams, subsidised by the combined resources of many nations, can move into an area and so treat it that malaria is stamped out in a few months. Children in whole countries can be immunised with B.C.G.

Study of the environmental factors affecting health, or predisposing to disease in tropical countries, is fruitful of results, and much progress has been made in recent years. It is now recognised, for example, that the level of nutrition plays a fundamental part in determining matters so apparently unrelated as resistance to infectious disease and the number of stillbirths in a community. Faulty housing, and especially the aggregation of slums in the great industrial cities, has been known to be associated with epidemic disease for many centuries, but it is only within recent years that overcrowding, as measured by the number of persons per room, has been recognised as an important factor in spreading infection, and this may occur as readily in the village as in the city, and in a technologically under-developed country, as well as a highly industrialised one.

Water, "good or bad," has governed

TABLE 28

POPULATION OF ENGLAND AND WALES
(In Thousands)

Source	Year	Total Population of All Ages	Persons Aged 65 or Over	
			No.	Per Cent of Total
Census........	1841	15,914	706	4.4
Census........	1861	20,066	932	4.6
Census........	1881	25,974	1,189	4.6
Census........	1901	32,528	1,518	4.7
Census........	1921	37,887	2,291	6.0
Census........	1931	39,952	2,963	7.4
Census........	1951	43,745	4,789	10.9
Projection*....	1973	46,175	6,745	14.6
	1993	46,382	7,444	16.0
Life table†.....	1901	....	....	9.7
	1953	....	....	14.0

British Crown copyright. Reproduced by permission of the Controller of Her Britannic Majesty's Stationery Office.

* Assumptions: Death rates declining over the next twenty-five years; at ages under forty-five to about one-half of their present values; at ages over forty-five progressively smaller reductions with advancing age; no further reduction after twenty-five years. Annual births averaging 640,000 during the first twenty-five years and declining during the ensuing fifteen years to about 600,000 at the end of the period. Migration, nil.

† Assuming a constant annual number of births subject to the sex ratio at birth and the mortality at all ages experienced in 1901 and 1953, respectively.

TABLE 29

POPULATION OF ENGLAND AND WALES BY AGES, PER 10,000 AT ALL AGES,
1901, 1911, 1921, 1931, 1939, 1951, AND 1973

Age (l.b.d.)	1901 Census	1911 Census	1921 Census	1931 Census	1939 Midyear	1951 Census*	1973 Projection
0–........	1,143	1,069	877	749	690	850	684
5–........	2,099	1,995	1,895	1,635	1,415	1,375	1,319
15–........	1,958	1,805	1,756	1,734	1,592	1,283	1,396
25–........	1,616	1,651	1,520	1,605	1,671	1,446	1,397
35–........	1,228	1,344	1,411	1,368	1,465	1,538	1,208
45–........	892	978	1,167	1,235	1,244	1,369	1,335
55–........	597	637	769	932	1,026	1,045	1,200
65–........	331	377	434	535	643	742	964
75–........	121	126	151	182	225	309	423
85 and over.	15	18	20	21	29	43	73
All ages....	10,000	10,000	10,000	10,000	10,000	10,000	10,000

British Crown copyright. Reproduced by permission of the Controller of Her Britannic Majesty's Stationery Office.
* One per cent sample.

the choice of settlements from the most ancient times, but, whereas quantity has always been regarded as essential for purposes of cleanliness, irrigation of crops, and the raising of cattle, it is only within the past one hundred years that quality, as measured by chemical and bacteriological purity, has been recognised as essential to the prevention of disease.

More recently still has come the recognition that the freedom from disease of a community depends in large measure on its social and cultural pattern, and that a well-organised and enlightened administration can, over a period of years, so raise the general living standards that improvements in health follow from this cause alone. In other words, the control of disease requires both sustained effort on the part of the people, and their leaders, in addition to special medical knowledge.

These general comments are particularly true of the control of the so-called "tropical" diseases. So called, because many of them were at one time widespread throughout the world. Indeed, it is necessary to recognise at the outset that the great killing diseases, pneumonia, tuberculosis, and syphilis, operate as malignantly in tropical countries as ever they did in Europe. On the other hand certain diseases, such as yaws, leishmaniasis, fungus infections of the skin and internal organs, leprosy, and filariasis are found predominantly in hot countries, and especially in the humid tropics, where the conditions are most favourable to the development of the causal organisms and the vectors, especially insects, by which many of them are spread.

In tropical countries also may be found the extremes of malnutrition, as manifested by conditions such as kwashiorkor, beri-beri, pellagra, and similar diseases due to vitamin and other deficiencies in the diet. Clearly there is here some relationship between disease and the poverty of tropical soils and the plants and animals reared on them.

When discussing environment and disease, it is necessary to distinguish between the social and cultural and the climatic environment, for, as noted above, many "tropical" diseases were formerly more widespread than they now are. Malaria, plague, typhus, yellow fever, leprosy, amoebic and bacillary dysentery, and infestation of the intestinal canal with worms, have all been known to occur widely throughout the world, and, with the exception of yellow fever, all these diseases have occurred in a country as far to the north as Great Britain. It is important to remember that many of them declined in importance in such countries long before their causes were known. Plague never recurred on a large scale in England after 1665, the "ague" finally disappeared some fifty years ago from the eastern Fens in England, and leprosy in Europe received a mortal wound after the Black Death in medieval times. It was the improvement in social conditions, rather than the application of medical knowledge, which caused their disappearance.

The diseases currently associated with the tropics are themselves undergoing changes in incidence and extent more rapidly than is commonly realised. The opening-up of communications by air, land, and sea, new methods of cultivation of land, and the extension of irrigation canals have all tended to cause a widening of spread of some diseases hitherto localised, while the recent introduction of massive methods of control have altered the natural rhythm of others.

It is still said, and with truth, that malaria is the most important single disease in the world, for it has the power to disable as well as to kill, and the mosquitoes bearing the parasitic protozoa may readily avail themselves of modern methods of transport to carry the disease, or more virulent forms of it, to areas hitherto free. Measures of control, on the other hand, by means of screening, attacking the breeding places of mosquitoes, the use of D.D.T. and other insecticides, and of modern drugs to destroy the parasites circulating in the human blood stream, have been so efficacious that the date of the first effective attack on malaria can sometimes be shown accurately by the sharp fall in the death rates for that year. That is particularly well seen in islands such as Ceylon, where the death rate in 1947 fell from 22 to 14 per thousand. The story of malaria control, however, is by no means complete as yet, for each continent poses different problems. Control in tropical Africa, for example, requires different methods, social, cultural, and even biological, from the forest areas of South America. Assuming, for the moment, that the full control of malaria which is theoretically possible was complete, we should still be faced with the further complication of rapid increases in population made possible by success in dealing with this one disease.

The mosquito conveys not only the plasmodium of malaria to man, but also the virus of yellow fever, and the minute worms causing filariasis, so that its destruction will affect these diseases.

Insect vectors are also responsible for conveying to man the viruses of dengue and sandfly fever, the rickettsia of the typhus group of fevers, the plague bacillus, and the trypanosomes causing African sleeping sickness. All these diseases are now controllable by one means or another, by attacking the vector, or the causal organism, or by creating an artificial immunity in the host. But the application of these methods, the supervision of the results of control, the remote effects in changing the lives of the people concerned—all these require corresponding improvements in other fields of human activity

if the advances are to be of lasting benefit.

In countries with the highest standards of hygiene, disasters are not uncommon. It is only a few years since an outbreak of amoebic dysentery occurred in Chicago, and the Croydon typhoid epidemic in England in 1937 is still fresh in the memory of many people. Water and food supplies may be protected, and flies and other insect vectors destroyed, but the human carrier is less easily dealt with.

Much has been said, in derogation or praise, since Malthus propounded his views on population. The ancient enemies of war, pestilence, and famine have changed in order of precedence, so that war is no longer necessarily the bringer of disease. Indeed, the medical discoveries made during, or as a result of, the First and Second World Wars have been of great benefit to mankind. It is, however, in the suppression of the small "tribal" wars that modern governments have been most successful, with incalculable benefits to human health, and especially in reducing the epidemic invaders which follow, such as typhus, smallpox, cholera, and dysentery.

Similarly, the development of a tropical country by extension of roads, railways, and exchange of goods leads inevitably to a rise in social standards which, as noted earlier, plays, over a long period of time, a notable part in causing the decline of disease. One is tempted to add canals to the above list, but the spread of bilharzia by means of the fresh-water snail along such waterways can be a formidable new cause of disease.

Bilharzia, or schistosomiasis, is caused by small worm-like parasites which live in the blood vessels (Mozley, 1951, 1952, 1953), and it has been estimated that 114,000,000 people were suffering from this disease in 1947 (Stoll, 1947). Perhaps its most common characteristic is the weakness which it causes in the victim, whose ability to work is thereby impaired, and this accounts for much of the apparent laziness to be found in heavily infested areas. In causing lethargy, it resembles hookworm disease, or ankylostomiasis. Hookworm larvae require a constant temperature of not less than 70° F. for a minimum of five days, together with moisture, to reach their optimum development, and therefore dwellers in the humid tropics are particularly susceptible. Hookworm disease ranges, however, from 36° N. to 30° S. of the Equator and is capable of affecting about one-half the inhabitants of the world (Price, 1939).

The incidence of these diseases, bilharzia and hookworm, depends much on social and cultural factors, and they are, therefore, good examples of the wider problems to be faced in the attack on tropical diseases. Density of population, sex, age, sanitary habits, nutrition, and the general standards of life, are all of great importance. Hookworm, for example, which formerly showed heavy infestations in the south-eastern United States, may also affect the southern shores of the Gulf of Mexico, Central America, the northern parts of South America, the Brazilian coast and tableland, most of the West Indies, Equatorial Africa, parts of the Malay Peninsula and Siam, some of the South Sea islands, some limited areas in China, and the north-eastern coast of Australia. In essence its prevalence or absence is dictated by such fundamental measures as supervision of water supplies, the wearing of shoes, adequate latrines, sanitary habits, and the avoidance of malnutrition. When the people of Puerto Rico were treated intensively for this disease, it was noted that the efficiency of the labourers increased by more than 60 per cent. As a result of intensive campaigns the International Health Board were able to report, in 1926, that the disease had almost disappeared from the United States. It is

therefore controllable, and so also is bilharzia.

Similarly malaria, although primarily a "geographical" disease, the incidence of which is determined by temperature, rainfall, and in some parts of the world by the presence of Tertiary limestone basins, is influenced very greatly by standards of living, and especially by housing and nutrition.

When considering disease control in tropical areas, it is also important to pay adequate attention to the adverse effects, over prolonged periods, of hot and humid climates on mental efficiency. Here it must be said that our knowledge of the relationship between climate and psychology is incomplete, as regards both indigenous peoples and expatriates. The latter, in particular, may be exposed to many causes of stress in addition to the unfamiliar environment. The fact that they do not "belong," the use of unsuitable diet and clothing, and the abuse of alcohol must be included among these. The introduction of good sanitation, together with refrigeration of food supplies and air-conditioning of buildings, are rendering many of the former "white man's graves" healthy for both adults and children. Indeed, the problem for the latter is becoming one of educational rather than health facilities.

The humid tropics, in particular, offer rich rewards for development, for there may be found lumber, fruits, oils, and spices, in addition to fossil fuels and rare metals. The story of the conquest of tropical diseases dates back over the past eighty years. First came the discovery of the cause and method of transmission of tropical elephantiasis by Patrick Manson in 1878. Then the demonstration by Alphonse Laveran of malaria parasites in blood in 1880 followed by the painstaking work of Ronald Ross, and the epoch-making strides in the elucidation of yellow fever by Walter Reed, Gorgas, Finlay, and Noguchi. Then came the discovery of try-panosomes, and the relation of leish-mania and sandflies to kala-azar and oriental sore; the link between the trematodes of schistosomiasis and the fresh-water snail, and the bacterial re-searches into the dysenteries and rickettsial diseases.

There remain to be discovered the causes of a number of rickettsial and virus diseases, but, in general, it may be said that we are well into the second stage of disease control, viz., the appli-cation of specific measures of preven-tion, immunisation, and therapy. The yellow fever vaccine, the specific drugs for the treatment of malaria, the various vermifuges, and more recently the anti-biotic substances used for attacking yaws, tropical ulcer, amoebiasis, and the rickettsial diseases, together with the sulphonamides for bacillary dysentery, make an impressive list.

We are now witnessing, throughout the world, the third phase of attack. It is clear that the ills of temperate cli-mates, both physical and mental, to-gether with the relatively small but virulent group of diseases peculiar to the tropics, depend in large measure on the relation between man and his en-vironment. The ecological forces at work are numerous, and include social, economic, and demographic factors. Put more simply, the basis of much of the disease in the world is poverty, igno-rance, and malnutrition.

Large-scale drainage and engineering projects, as in the Tennessee Valley, can do much to improve and extend areas for human habitation, but there is still need to improve the primitive sanitation and housing in villages throughout the world, and particularly in those areas where human excreta must be used as fertilisers for the soil. Reference has al-ready been made to the low fertility of tropical soils and the resulting deficien-cies in animal protein, minerals, and vitamins, and it is here, perhaps, that the greatest contribution to health has yet to be made, by improving diet and nutrition. It is not going to be easy to do so, for a race is already developing between the increase in numbers of people and the availability of food sup-plies. Already India, Java, Puerto Rico, and other areas are showing only too clearly the results of over-population. Wholesale application of disease con-trol methods and enlightened sanitation practices require a stable administra-tive background. This in turn depends for its success on reliable statistics, a sound economy, trained personnel, and the education of the people in the way to live healthy lives.

THE FUTURE

Retaining our earlier distinction be-tween highly urbanised and less well-developed communities, it should be noted that the former have still a num-ber of unsolved problems, for example, in the field of virus infections, where influenza can play havoc, particularly among the elderly. Poliomyelitis can strike terror as deep as did cholera a hundred years ago, and, when the acute stage of the epidemic passes, we may be left with a heavy load of cripples as a result. Even in the province of en-vironmental sanitation such communi-ties still face many problems, for rivers are now heavily polluted with sewage and are the vehicles by which wastes are removed from the factories. Pollu-tion of waterways by radio-active sub-stances poses a problem to which there is as yet no answer. People living in large urban communities are at risk from outbreaks of food poisoning on a scale unknown to their ancestors, while "smog" is a new and hideous word which has rapidly become as familiar in London as it is in Pennsylvania and Los Angeles. In such communities also new and exotic topics arise for discussion. Should euthanasia be practised on the mental defective, the incurable, and the aged? Is it justifiable to begin life by means of artificial insemination, or to terminate it by therapeutic abortion as soon as it has started? In addition to these and kindred subjects, man in such communities has learnt the most terrible of all secrets, namely, how to destroy the individuality and separate will of his fellow man by psychological means, or to change the whole personality of an individual by operations such as prefrontal leucotomy. Above all, there is the great new problem of the preservation of the mental health of the people.

In the less-developed communities the problems are not so complex, but are equally urgent in their need to be solved. Many such communities are knit together by ancient traditions and customs which require that the head of the family shall have many children; that those children shall be set to work at an early age; that daughters should make good marriages and embark at the earliest possible age on the endless succession of pregnancies that beset their mothers; and that the sons should keep their father in his old age. Such communities are conditioned to a short and harsh life, but they have succeeded over the centuries in making it a reasonably happy one. How far is there justification for disrupting this? To rid such a country suddenly of its traditional burden of disease means that death rates fall with dramatic rapidity, while birth rates remain high, and may even rise, because of the increasing numbers of children living to adult life and because of the increase in fertility of the adults. Immediately there becomes apparent the fresh problem of whether it is better to die of disease or survive to die of starvation later.

If this were the only problem, the outlook is not so unsatisfactory as the pessimists would have one believe, for it is then a matter of growing enough food to keep pace with the increasing numbers. Unfortunately, it is not so simple as this, for such countries are not merely subjected to the battery of health measures, but are also expected, and are trying, to initiate all the other welfare and economic developments which the highly developed countries have taken several hundreds of years to achieve. Birth control has been suggested as, at least, a partial solution to this problem, but there are serious practical difficulties in introducing this into technologically under-developed countries, quite apart from conflicting religious and cultural beliefs.

Whether money comes from within or from without, the governments of such countries are trying anxiously to introduce not only additional health and welfare services but also education, transport, roads, and agricultural development on a vast scale. It might be asked what such considerations have to do with the subject of this paper, and the short answer is that it is impossible to consider sanitation practices and disease control in extending and improving areas for human habitation without at the same time taking into account these other factors.

What, then, are the basic needs for the future? First and foremost is the need for more adequate information. We do not know the true population of many communities in the world, and, when it comes to analysing the mortality and morbidity statistics, we can safely assume that we need to modify by plus or minus 50 per cent some of the current figures. Secondly, we do not know enough about men's reactions to a sudden transition from disease to health, and in particular we have no guide as to what happens to populations suddenly subjected to a dramatic increase in numbers. Thirdly, while we can control many physical diseases, we have as yet insufficient knowledge of the components which make for mental health and stability. What, for example, is required to keep an agricultural community happy and contented on the land, and what can be done to stop the drift from such communities to the towns? We do not know, and until we have more adequate information by means of censuses, surveys, and long-term studies, we are not justified in pressing too hard for radical changes. We must subject ourselves to some searching enquiries. Why do we wish to bring about these changes and for whose benefit are they to be wrought?

Perhaps the most important subject in the world as a whole is that of food production, and here again our knowledge of soil fertility, particularly in tropical and sub-tropical countries, is pitiably inadequate. Nor do we know what are the critical populations for a given area or how to estimate these. We do know that success in one field may endanger another, and that the development, for example, of an industrial community tends to denude the associated agricultural communities by attracting labour from them. There is a need also to relate projects for development, including those of health and welfare, to the cultural background of the community involved, and here again our ignorance is great.

Where, then, does one look for guidance in the process of extending and improving areas for human habitation? And what principles can be followed? Those countries in which the changes outlined in this paper began earliest have been forced to do three things to ensure that their plans would be successful. First they had to build up their economic resources so that they could in fact afford the new developments. Next they had to make the machinery to apply health measures, by the creation of stable systems of local and central government. Then they endeavoured to educate their peoples in the fundamentals of healthy living, using that term in its widest sense.

In less well-developed countries these things have sometimes to be done from above because of the absence of stable local government, or from outside by international agencies, and they also have to be done in conjunction with all the other activities of the country. Unless the provision of adequate food keeps pace with the increasing numbers of those kept alive by health measures, disaster follows. Unless the people in rural communities can be kept happy, healthy, and contented, disaster follows. And unless a country can be sure of continuity of effort in these fields, disaster follows. To encourage sanitation practices and disease control for a short time by external effort, and then to walk out and leave a country to its own resources, is as dangerous as distributing dried milk to infants until such time as the mothers lose the habit of breast feeding and then to withdraw the supplies.

The power to extend and improve areas for human habitation by means of sanitation practices and disease control is almost unlimited. It is in its application that there is a risk of failure, mainly because of man's own impatience. The desire to press on and get results within the space of a few years is almost overwhelming, but the temptation should be resisted until such time as we have more adequate knowledge, both of man himself and of his environmental resources. To ensure that we have this knowledge much research is required, and this must be undertaken, not in the great cities or countries or continents, but at the village and family level. The ancient motto "Festina lente" is now seldom heard, but it rests upon a sure foundation.

Above all, one consideration must never be lost to sight. No matter what steps are taken to ease the lot of mankind, they will be of no avail unless they lead to and preserve the happiness of the people.

REFERENCES

ANONYMOUS
  1953 *Report of the Great Britain Ministry of Health,* Part II: *On the State of the Public Health.* 2 vols. London: H.M. Stationery Office.

BANKS, A. LESLIE (ed.)
  1954 *The Development of Tropical and Sub-tropical Countries.* London: Edward Arnold, Ltd. 217 pp.

BENJAMIN, B.
  1954 "The Aging Population," *Monthly Bulletin of the Ministry of Health and the Public Health Laboratory Service,* XIII, 214–16.

CHADWICK, EDWIN
  1842 *Report to H.M.'s Principal Secretary of State for the Home Department from the Poor Law Commissioners, on an Inquiry into the Sanitary Conditions of the Labouring Population of Great Britain: With Appendices.* London: W. Clowes & Sons (for H.M. Stationery Office). 279 pp.

CORWIN, E. H. L. (ed.)
  1949 *Ecology of Health.* New York: Commonwealth Fund. 196 pp.

GOUROU, PIERRE
  1953 *The Tropical World.* London: Longmans, Green & Co. 156 pp.

GRAUNT, JOHN
  1662 *Natural and Political Observations Mentioned in a Following Index, and Made upon the Bills of Mortality.* London: Tho. Roycroft (for John Martin). 85 pp.

LILIENTHAL, DAVID E.
  1944 *TVA: Democracy on the March.* New York: Harper & Bros. 248 pp.

LOGAN, JOHN A.
  1953 *The Sardinian Project.* Baltimore: Johns Hopkins Press. 415 pp.

MOZLEY, ALAN
  1951 *The Snail Hosts of Bilharzia in Africa.* London: H. K. Lewis. 78 pp.

  1952 *Molluscicides.* London: H. K. Lewis. 87 pp.

  1953 *A Background for the Prevention of Bilharzia.* London: H. K. Lewis. 71 pp.

PETTY, SIR WILLIAM
  1690 *Political Arithmetick.* London: Printed for Robert Clavel and Hen. Mortlock. 117 pp.

  1691 *Political Anatomy of Ireland.* London: Printed for D. Brown and W. Rogers. 24 pp.

PRICE, A. GRENFELL
  1939 *White Settlers in the Tropics.* (Special Publication No. 23.) New York: American Geographical Society. 311 pp.

SAND, RENÉ
  1952 *The Advance to Social Medicine.* London: Staples Press. 655 pp.

SIMMONS, JAMES STEVENS (ed.)
  1949 *Public Health in the World Today.* Cambridge, Mass.: Harvard University Press. 332 pp.

STOLL, N. R.
  1947 "This Wormy World," *Journal of Parasitology,* XXXIII, 1–18.

WORLD HEALTH ORGANIZATION
  1946 "Preamble," p. 11 in *Final Acts of the International Health Conference.* New York: United Nations. 53 pp.

  1954 "International Sanitary Regulations, Two Years' Experience," *Chronicle of the World Health Organization,* VIII, No. 9, 269–75.

  1955a "Kwashiorkor in Central America," *ibid.,* IX, No. 1, 20–23.

  1955b "Malaria, a World Problem," *ibid.,* Nos. 2 and 3, pp. 33–100.

For disease control in specific areas see appropriate papers published by the World Health Organization.

Effects of Fission Material on Air, Soil, and Living Species

JOHN C. BUGHER[*]

Radioactivity is a characteristic of matter in transmutation. Most of the transitions from one elemental state to another are attended by the emission of energy. Not only our own existence but also our knowledge of the limitless expanses of the universe are dependent on the complex nuclear phenomena which are accompanied by the radiation of energy. We exist in the warmth of one of the lesser thermonuclear reactors of the universe—the sun. We learn something of the expanse and structure of the comparatively modest galaxy of which our solar system is an inconspicuous component through radiation emitted by nuclear reactions centuries past. Their history is expressed not only by visible and invisible light but also by much longer wave lengths of the radiofrequency spectrum.

The earth, born in exceedingly complex transmutations of matter, is a radioactive mass. To its own nuclear reactions there are added the extremely energetic cosmic rays from outer space, which, in the aggregate, give rise to considerable quantities of unstable elements in the earth's atmosphere and crust. The spontaneously radioactive elemental series of uranium,

thorium, and actinium pervade the earth's crust everywhere, so that no portion of our material environment is free from members of these radioactive series. It is estimated that there are 10^{15} tons of natural uranium in the earth's crust and that there are 10^{10} tons of natural uranium in all the oceans. Even larger amounts of thorium occur, with the average concentration in soils being 12 parts per million by weight, or twice that of natural uranium. Associated with these parent-elements are all their daughter-products resulting from radioactive decay, so that the average surface soil contains 1 gram of radium per square mile for each foot of depth. All the waters of the earth and all the organisms that abound on the land and in the sea thus inevitably contain small amounts of radium. The average amount occurring naturally in the human body is 1.59×10^{-10} grams.

Natural potassium, of which vast quantities occur, has a radioactive isotope, K^{40}, the activity of which is appreciable. K^{40} constitutes 0.011 per cent of the total potassium. The average activity of surface soil 1 foot in depth is such that approximately a million disintegrations of K^{40} atoms occur per minute per square foot. This is slightly less than ½ microcurie. The water of the ocean contains approximately ⅓ microcurie of K^{40} per cubic meter, and it has been estimated that there are approxi-

[*] Dr. Bugher at the time of the Symposium was Director of the Division of Biology and Medicine, United States Atomic Energy Commission, Washington, D.C. He is now Director for Medical Education and Public Health, The Rockefeller Foundation, New York.

mately 5×10^{11} curies of K^{40} in all the oceans. At the other extreme of magnitude the human body contains an average of 27 milligrams of this radioactive isotope, which is equivalent to 0.23 microcurie.

Another important naturally occurring radioactive element is carbon-14, which is formed almost *in toto* by the action of cosmic rays on the nitrogen of the atmosphere. C^{14} constitutes a constant fraction of all carbon which is part of the active world pool in the proportion of 1 atom of C^{14} to 8×10^{11} atoms of C^{12}. It is estimated that there are 96 tons of radioactive carbon in nature.

An additional and remarkable radioactive element which occurs naturally is tritium, the mass 3 isotope of hydrogen. Tritium is also a product of cosmic-ray action on nitrogen and exists in the form of tritium water. As a consequence of this, the air masses that are most remote from the oceans yield the highest concentrations of tritium water in their rainfall. Thus, we find approximately six times as much tritium in comparison with hydrogen in rainfall over inland areas as may be found in rain falling over the seas. The total amount naturally occurring has been estimated at slightly more than 1 kilogram, all but about 10 grams of which is to be found in the oceans.

To the radiations emitted by these naturally occurring elements must be added an approximately equal amount due to cosmic rays. Until the advent of nuclear fission initiated by man, the environmental radioactivity was derived entirely from these sources. Even nuclear fission may be regarded as simply the acceleration of reactions which in one form or another proceed naturally in the parent-substances. The significant alterations which man has introduced into the world are a very great acceleration in time in the processes of radioactive decay and in the changing of the proportions of the resulting radioactive elemental products, with, in some instances, the introduction of forms unrecognizable in nature.

THE FISSION PROCESS

At the risk of repeating matters already familiar, may I call attention to certain fundamental aspects of nuclear fission that have important bearing upon the biological problems presented by the atomic era into which we have so recently entered. We recognize three elements which may undergo prompt fission upon capture of thermal neutrons. They are uranium-235, uranium-238, and plutonium-239. Only the first of these occurs naturally; the other two must be prepared by neutron bombardment from thorium-232 and uranium-238, respectively. In addition, natural U^{238} may undergo fission from fast neutrons; that is, neutrons whose energies are 1 million electron volts or more.

A distinctive feature of the fission reaction is its asymmetry (Figs. 157–159). Pairs of fragments are formed, and, because of the frequency distributions of the masses, the large number of elements forms a bimodal frequency distribution with the maxima in the neighborhoods of masses 95 and 140. In terms of atoms, therefore, the largest classes of radioactive elements have masses in the two regions mentioned. Thus 3.2 per cent of the atoms formed will have mass 95, in the case of U^{235}, while only 0.005 per cent will have mass 117.

A second important characteristic of these products of fission is that the immediate fractions are, for the most part, highly unstable isotopes and proceed to decay at greatly varying rates into isotopes of other elements, in themselves frequently radioactive (Figs. 160–161). It is most instructive to consider some of these chains. For example, the sequence of elements of mass 90 prob-

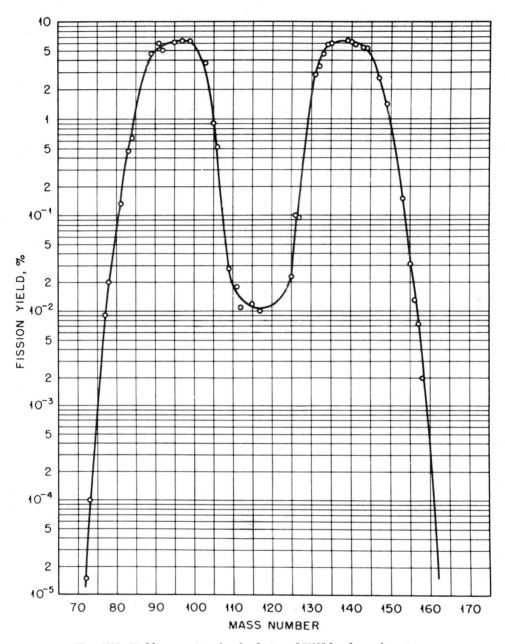

FIG. 157.—Yield-mass curve for the fission of U²³⁵ by thermal neutrons

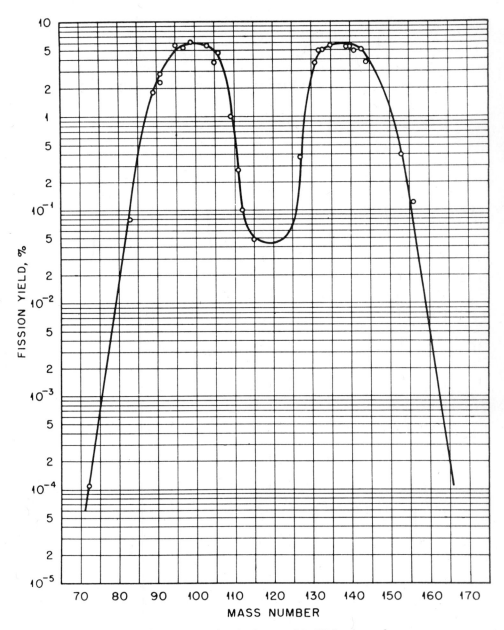

FIG. 158.—Yield-mass curve for the fission of Pu^{239} by thermal neutrons

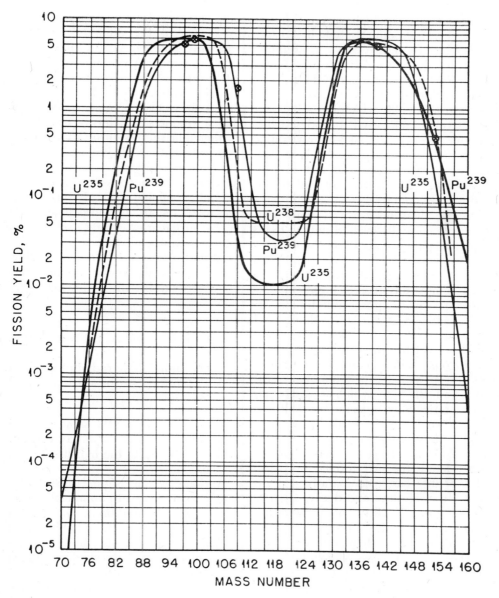

FIG. 159.—Comparison of the yield-mass curves for the fission of U[235], U[238], and Pu[239]

ably starts with a series which might be considered a part of the arsenic-selenium species but which very quickly is evident as a bromine isotope of 4.5 seconds half-life. This decays to krypton-90, a gas having a half-life of 33 seconds. Kr^{90} in turn decays by beta emission to rubidium-90, and this very shortly to strontium-90, which has a half-life of 20 years. Sr^{90}, itself a modest beta-emitter, decays to a 64.6-hour yttrium-90, which emits a powerful beta ray, and becomes zirconium-90, a stable element which comprises over half of the natural zirconium.[1]

In this chain we see transitions from elements normally in solid state to those that are gaseous at all ordinary temperatures and, further, those which revert to other elements and are solid in their compounds even at high temperatures. There are appreciable time intervals between these transitions, and there may be very marked differences with respect to time constants between analogous chains. Thus, for the mass 89 series, Kr^{89} has a 2.6-minute half-life, and Rb^{89}, to which it decays, is characterized by a 15-minute half-life. The 89 masses exist in the gaseous or vapor phase for a much longer time than do those of mass 90 series. On the other hand, the Sr^{89} formed by decay of the Rb^{89} has a comparatively short half-life of 55 days and decays by beta emission to Y^{89}. All the naturally occurring yttrium has, in all probability, been formed by this particular mode.

The fission process which is fundamental to the release of atomic energy, whether in nuclear weapons or in reactors for power and other purposes, is thus attended by a highly complex but entirely predictable production of a large number of radioactive elements. Because of the distributional character-

1. The most recent and precise determination of the half-life of Y^{90} yields 64.60 ± 0.43 hours, as reported by Chatham-Strode and Kinderman, *Physical Review*, March 1, 1954.

istics which have been mentioned, these elements vary greatly in their proportions. Further, fractionation may occur, by reason of the differences in time constants and physical characteristics of the component elements in the disintegration chains. For our purposes, we can assume these fissionable elements to yield the same spectrum of fission products and thus be able to say further that the fission of approximately 3×10^{24} atoms of U^{235}, or 1 kilogram of element, will yield a mass of mixed radioactive elements whose activity at 1 hour, assuming that all the fissions are simultaneous, is approximately 6.0×10^3 megacuries. While each isotope in this complex mixture will decay exponentially, the mixture as a whole shows a dependable decay, which may be described by the following equation:

$$A = A_0 t^{-1.2} ,$$

where t is time and A_0 is the activity at unit time.

Each individual radioisotope will decay according to the relationship

$$A = A_0 e^{-\lambda t} ,$$

where A_0 and t have the same meaning as before, and λ is the decay constant which is related to the half-life T by $T = 0.623/\lambda$.

As long as the original mixture has not been subjected to appreciable fractionation and alterations, the general formula given is quite reliable. When specific radioelements, however, become of primary interest, the exponential formula must be used.

The great variation in the rates of radioactive decay of specific isotopes in the fission-products mixture results in a constantly changing situation. The proportion of total radioactivity contributed by any one isotope rises to a maximum, after which it diminishes as that particular isotope decays at a more rapid rate than the mixture as a whole. Eventually, all the activities will be

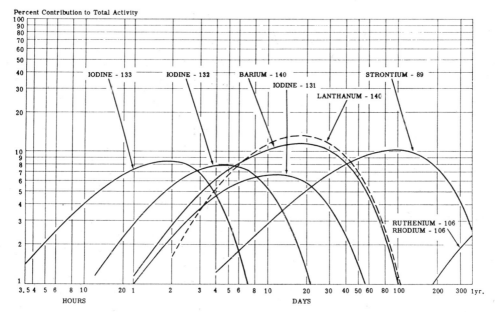

FIG. 160.—Relative activities (in hours and days) of nuclide products of simultaneous slow neutron fissions of U^{235}.

FIG. 161.—Relative activities (in years) of nuclide products of simultaneous slow neutron fission of U^{235}.

associated with the few fission-product elements that have long half-lives.

It is readily shown that, in a normal mixture of fission products, each radioisotope makes its maximal proportional contribution to the total radioactivity at a time that is 1.4 times its half-life. This time is also the average life of the isotope.

The energy released by 1 kilogram of any of these elements undergoing fission is approximately 8.4×10^{20} ergs, or 2.3×10^7 kilowatt-hours. It is also equivalent to 20,000 tons of TNT. It thus becomes a matter of simple arithmetic to compute the inevitable results in the way of fission-product formation from the release of any given quantity of energy through the fission process. These materials, subjected to radioactive decay with time, mentioned before, become in some degree a part of the natural environment. Their diffusion and presentation to the earth's surface may be rapid in the case of airborne material or very slow where the substances are maintained in firm containment. Time is a relentless factor, and in the course of 100 years or so nearly all the atoms will have decayed to stable natural elements.

In addition to fission products, interaction between energetic neutrons and atmospheric nitrogen in the case of nuclear explosions may produce a certain amount of C^{14} and tritium. The first isotope has a long half-life of about 5,600 years. The maximum amount of C^{14} produced by fission of 1 kilogram of U^{235} or similar material in an explosion in air is about ½ ounce. A large thermonuclear weapon would produce correspondingly much more C^{14}. The actual production is certain to be less than the calculated amounts, so that, in relation to the 192,000 pounds of C^{14} known to exist, the failure to measure any increase in natural C^{14} is understandable. Since, however, the amount of natural tritium is quite

small, it has been relatively easy to demonstrate increased tritium in rainfall over the United States and other areas following large thermonuclear detonations. The tritium half-life being comparatively short (10.7 years), the only radioactive product from nuclear explosions of really long-time characteristics is C^{14}, and the amount formed is inappreciable in comparison with the naturally occurring pool of this isotope.

These radioactive products, created by natural processes under human control, may thus be presented to the three great ecological compartments: the atmosphere, the land, and the oceans. These, of course, interact, but it will serve our convenience to consider them separately for a moment.

ATMOSPHERE

Particulate and gaseous material ejected into the atmosphere either achieves ultimate diffusion throughout the air mass or is brought to the surface of the earth by gravitation. The time factors are determined by the physical characteristics of the material. The fission products of an atomic explosion tend to be associated more or less indiscriminately with all the resulting particles. Their return to earth depends on the particle size and the height to which the material was lifted at the time of the explosion. The influence of these factors on time of descent is further modified with respect to location of fall by wind directions and velocities. Coarse particles, which result when explosions are on or near the surface of the earth, fall out relatively quickly, while very fine particles may remain suspended aloft for such a prolonged time that radioactive decay is largely completed before they reach the surface of the earth. Large explosions, detonated high in the air, result in fine particles which may be carried high into the stratosphere. Under such conditions there is little or no significant local fall-out but, instead, a diffusion throughout the atmosphere and a slow deposition over wide areas of the globe.

The descent of particulate material is mediated by gravity and vertical turbulence. Close to the earth, usually below 20,000 feet, descent may be accelerated by rain or snow. This is a scavenging action and, while spectacular at times, does not affect the total amount of material which descends. That which is air-borne has comparatively little biologic implication, although, where considerable amounts are present, the gamma-radiation field created may be hazardous. An atomic cloud for the first hour or so after its formation would be dangerous to living things if they were to remain in it an appreciable time. Similarly, in the presence of heavy fall-out there may be a heavy field of gamma radiation established by radiation from material in the air being added to that on the ground. In both of these situations, however, inhalation of the air by man or animals is relatively unimportant. This fact is often incredible to those who think of the lungs only in relation to inhaled air. Most of the actual exposure to the lungs comes not from the material inhaled but from the large volume of air and suspended particles surrounding the individual and from which gamma radiation is emitted to penetrate the entire body.

Substantially, then, the radioactive contamination of the atmosphere by fission products is important as a mechanism for their transport but is not directly a source of biological concern.

LAND

The radioactive materials presented to the land either by fall-out from the atmosphere or by direct outflow from centers of nuclear industry differ widely in their biological consequences. Again time is a most important factor. Within the first days and weeks after detonation or controlled nuclear fission, the iodine fraction which results from radioactive decay of isotopes of tellurium may be prominent. The amounts of iodine, because of their position in the mass-frequency curve, are considerable. They are all, however, of short half-life and do not persist in the environment. Physiologically, radioiodine behaves as does ordinary iodine in that it is concentrated in the thyroid gland and is readily absorbed from the intestinal tract. During the Castle series of tests in the Pacific, which began on March 1, 1954, it was relatively easy to detect measurable amounts of iodine-131 in thyroids of cattle and in urine from both grazing animals and man. The total dose to the thyroid from the combined radiation was estimated at less than 1.5 roentgens equivalent. Approximately 2,000 roentgens equivalent to the thyroid are required to produce detectable changes in that gland and about 50,000 to produce partial destruction and hypothyroidism.

During the same period a group of Marshall Island residents were exposed to a serious fall-out, resulting in 175 roentgens total body exposure of gamma radiation. In addition, they acquired sufficient internally absorbed iodine to add an additional 170 roentgens equivalent exposure to the thyroid gland. None of the subsequent clinical symptomatology was attributable to thyroid exposure. In these cases symptomatology was due almost entirely to the combined effects of depression of bone marrow and severe exposure of the skin from adherent fall-out material. The iodine uptake of the Marshall Islands people involved close to the accident was of magnitude several orders greater than that experienced by people elsewhere.

Although easily detectable, entry of iodine into the environment is in general of minor consequence, owing to its short half-life. The only concentration of iodine of which we have knowledge is found in living forms having a thyroid function. No significant entry of the material into plant metabolism has yet been demonstrated.

Many of the other radionuclids of the mixed, fission-product system are either chemically identical with, or closely related to, constituents of the soil. Chemical characteristics of soil, together with its finely divided state, account for the very efficient adsorption of nearly all fission products. Thus, in a fall-out area, even after a year's exposure to rain and wind, about 80 per cent of the total radioactive material is found in the top 1 inch of soil. Ion transport is slow, and migration of radioactive material takes place at a very retarded rate. Flow of water over and through such soils does not remove radioactivity, and rivers flowing from a heavily contaminated land carry surprisingly little radioactive material leached from soil.

It becomes more apparent as studies progress that various classes of radioisotopes enter into exchanges with existing complexes of soil, becoming more or less bound. Strontium isotopes, for example, resemble calcium in their behavior and, entering into slightly disassociated complexes, become partly unavailable to plants.

In the time scale with which we are concerned, only certain radioelements seem to be of any importance. None by reason of its radioactivity has any known direct effect on plants, and the chief interest lies in the mechanism by which important isotopes may reach man by way of predominant food chains. To be important in this system, a given isotope must be capable of entering into the physiology of the growing plant and of accumulating in the portion used as food. It must be available to the animal consuming plant material as food. Further, after entry into the human or animal body, the isotope must be retained in a physiologically critical structure. And, lastly, its radioactive half-life must be sufficiently long to produce appreciable radiation injury to tissue.

The one element outstanding by reason of its exhibition of all these characteristics is strontium, and, because of its long radioactive half-life, Sr^{90} is presently regarded as the most significant one by many orders of magnitude. Cesium is not generally readily taken up by ordinary forage plants but may be absorbed almost selectively by the coconut palm. However, on ingestion by man, cesium becomes distributed throughout the muscle tissue and is rapidly excreted, unlike the Sr^{90} component.

Nuclear fission is the only known source of Sr^{90}, and it may be presumed that all detectable Sr^{90} has been the result of test operations with nuclear explosions. The release to the environment of Sr^{90} containing waste has been otherwise insignificant. The present average contamination of United States soil by Sr^{90} is 1×10^{-4} microcuries (220 dpm [disintegrations per minute]) per square foot, or 2–3 milicuries per square mile. It is about 1/240 of the soil's normal radium content and about 1/1,600 the amount estimated to be required to approach the maximum permissible body burden of 1 microcurie.

The most important food chain involving Sr^{90} is soil, forage, crops, grazing cattle, milk, and man. Further, although Sr^{90} mimics calcium, there is in each biological transition a discrimination against strontium in favor of calcium. If we express the amount of Sr^{90} in relation to the available calcium from the same material,[2] data such as shown in Table 30 result. This table gives the amounts determined by analysis for the various components in a food chain in the Chicago area in

2. The Sunshine Unit (S.U.) employed here is defined as $1 \times 10^{-6} \mu c$ Sr^{90} per gram of calcium.

October, 1953. The table is self-explanatory, except for the units pertaining to soil, where the relationship is that between the total Sr^{90} and the total available calcium in the top 6 inches of soil.

A second branch of the food chain probably existed in this instance in the direct contamination of alfalfa by fallout. In this case, radioactive material would not be subjected to passage through soil and root systems. This probably accounts for the rather poor correlation between soil values and

may be considered reasonably typical of the midwestern United States until the spring of 1955.

The Chicago soil data show that Sr^{90} activity is retained near the surface for several years. The resampling in 1954 demonstrated that 80 per cent of the total Sr^{90} activity was still found in the top 2 inches of soil.

Further evidence that Sr^{90} is retained by soil is revealed by comparison between rain and tap-water activity. In 33 rain and 25 tap-water samples for

TABLE 30

SUMMARY OF SR^{90} ANALYSES OF CHICAGO DAIRY AREA

Soil (dpm/ft^2)	S.U. in Top 6 Inches	Alfalfa S.U.	Milk S.U.	Stillborn S.U.	Rib of Growing Child S.U.
312	6.2	8.5	1.4	0.13	0.7

TABLE 31*

SR^{90} ANALYSES OF PASTURE AREAS

LOCATION	SUNSHINE UNITS		
	Soil (0-2 Inches)	Vegetation	Bone
Robinson farm, Logan, Utah	1.2 ± 0.1	$10\ \ \pm0.8$	4.4 ± 0.2
College pasture, Logan, Utah.......	1.1 ± 0.1	$6.3\ \ \pm0.7$	1.7 ± 0.2
Native range, Tifton, Ga..........	$31\ \ \pm2.7$	$30\ \ \pm1.7$	7.0 ± 0.3
Improved pasture, Tifton, Ga.......	$11\ \ \pm0.5$	$3.9\ \ \pm0.8$	2.7 ± 0.2
Raleigh, N.C.....................	8.6 ± 0.4	$26\ \ \pm0.5$	2.1 ± 0.2
New Brunswick, N.J..............	7.7 ± 0.3	$9.1\ \ \pm0.4$	2.7 ± 0.2
Ithaca, N.Y.....................	3.5 ± 0.1	0.15 ± 0.07	2.4 ± 0.2

Source: Atomic Energy Commission, Division of Biology and Medicine.

those of alfalfa grown on that soil. The human-bone values were determined from autopsies and surgical material in Chicago, where the persons presumably had obtained all or most of their milk and milk products from the farm areas sampled. The apparent discrimination against strontium in relation to calcium in successive stages of the food chain has been a consistent finding.

Repeat samples of soil from these same areas in 1954 showed a 10 per cent increase in soil activity, and milk analyses in Chicago as well as in New York revealed a practically constant level into the spring of 1955. These data for the October, 1953, samples

Sr^{90} in the New York area between July, 1953, and February, 1955, the rain averaged 13 dpm per gallon of Sr^{90}, while tap water averaged 0.5 dpm per gallon. The New York water supply is not subjected to treatment, and differences here may be attributed to adsorption by the soil of surface and percolating waters on their way to reservoirs.

Further data are available on the soil, vegetation, and animal-bone chain of Sr^{90} uptake by pasture lands at various places in the United States. These data are shown in Table 31, which gives the value of Sr^{90} in the top 2 inches of soil, in the forage growing in the fields, and in the skeletons of cattle and sheep that grazed thereon. There was here good evidence of direct uptake of Sr^{90} from leaf-surface adsorption.

From the widespread dissemination of mixed fission products, it is evident that minute amounts of Sr^{90} inevitably become part of our ecological situation. The radioactivities of this material are small in comparison with the activities of natural substances, but the chemistry is such that precise measurements down to a level of 1 dpm of Sr^{90} may be made. While the studies which have been mentioned originated through concern to prevent hazards to health as a result of testing of weapons, the system itself has proved to be of great value in extending our knowledge of meteorology and of the broad movements of particulate materials in plants and animals.

OCEAN

Most of the particulates transported in the atmosphere inevitably fall into the sea. Where surface detonations are conducted on islands, a large fraction of the total fission products descends locally into the sea. Additional increments come from land areas through drainage outflow from fall-out areas or from centers of atomic industry. Additions to the total sea activity from disposal of radioactive wastes have been insignificant until the present, but the depths of the ocean may be utilized in the future for large-scale disposal.

The studies of radioactive contamination in the ocean have returned valuable dividends in the form of substantially increased knowledge concerning ocean currents, turbulence and depth of mixing, and the interaction of plankton and larger living species. Marine food chains may be both massive and rapidly transited. Specific elemental affinities may be prominent, so that actual concentration of particular isotopes may occur, especially in the case of phytoplankton.

Our knowledge of the movement of the waters of the western Pacific has been enlarged by the voyage of the Japanese scientific vessel "Shunkotsu Maru" in 1954 and the more recent oceanographic expedition of the United States Coast Guard vessel "Taney," approximately a year after the Castle series. In substance, many measurements of water samples showed that the equatorial current flowing westward from the Marshall Islands is subject to appreciable dispersion horizontally by what appear to be large eddies. Radioactivity could be detected in depth to 600 meters, the maximum depth of which the sampling equipment was capable. The peak values were of the order of 100 dpm per liter, with approximately 0.5 per cent of the total activity being due to Sr^{90}.

These studies showed that radioactivity could be followed for a year after the tests, and it was estimated that the water in question would pass Japan in the summer of 1955. With careful technical work, it was anticipated that radioactivity would still be detectable and that it would be possible to follow this ocean-water movement northward past the Aleutians.

Of especial interest have been the analytical results with plankton. In general, the gross activity of plankton as taken in routine hauls was about a thousand times that of water when compared in terms of wet weight. It appears that examination of plankton is a most exquisite test for the presence of fission products in water. Fish that subsist on plankton, as might be expected, showed a corresponding activity in the intestinal contents but a much lower level in their tissues. Preliminary analysis failed to show that strontium was taken up selectively.

Experiments of the Fish and Wildlife Station at Beaufort, North Carolina, have disclosed that various species of marine phytoplankton are highly discriminating with respect to strontium. Of nine species, only one accumulated appreciable amounts of Sr^{90}. The remainder showed a marked preference for Y^{90}. Throughout the experiment accumulation of Sr^{90} was directly proportional to the total amount present in sea water. Accumulation was also related to the degree of metabolic activity of the cells.

Ordinarily, mixing of surface waters tends to be limited to the zone above the thermocline. At various stations studied by the "Taney," there seemed to be no evidence of such limitation. Part of the downward descent may have been due to the settling of insoluble particles having a density greater than that of sea water. However, in view of the apparent inconsistency between these observations and the earlier conclusions based on tritium analysis, it seems evident that further study is needed, especially in the higher latitudes, before we can be certain about the relation of the thermocline to the depth of surface mixing.

The movements of water in the great depths of the oceans are largely a matter of speculation. If it is reliably true that the rate of change is small and that the turnover time is to be measured in hundreds of years, then deep-sea disposal of radioactive wastes is an obviously desirable procedure. However, a pronounced and rapidly upwelling of deep water would render hazardous such disposal through bringing to the zone of biological production appreciable concentrations of radioactive materials. Deep-sea experiments with megacurie amounts of crude fission products as tracers are very much needed and are entirely practicable.

All these matters are important because of the likelihood that the enormous productivity of the ocean will be increasingly drawn upon for human needs during the next century. The biologic cycling of individual radioisotopes, with the operation of selective concentration, tends to offset in part the effect of dilution. In contrast to the rapidity of atmospheric mixing, it is evident that the ocean approaches equilibrium of solutes at a very slow rate and even then involves chiefly surface waters.

In view of these matters, it seems evident that we need to divert some of our scientific preoccupation with land-locked problems and to apply a steadily increasing effort to the advancement of knowledge of marine biology.

INTERACTION

Discussion of fission-product contamination of our world as though the earth existed in clearly separate ecological compartments of atmosphere, land, and ocean has served our immediate convenience, but it falls far short of a complete analysis of the situation. There is always complex interaction between components of these compartments. While water moves from the oceans to land by way of the atmosphere, there is a constant flow of organic material by way of water connections. To the tonnage due to marine industries, there is the vast return from movements typified by spawning salmon, by which highly significant amounts of precious trace elements may be returned to a deficient watershed.

The concentration of isotopes such as Sr^{90} in marine plankton has apparently little parallel on land, although the growing larvae of some species of mosquitoes appear capable of appreciably concentrating this particular isotope. The two systems differ markedly, however, in that plankton is the basis for the utilization of solar energy in ocean areas and is the foundation of all important food chains therein. Terrestrial insects, as important as they are ecologically, do not perform a similar function.

The ultimate effects on man of the radioactive contamination of his environment have had prolonged and detailed discussion, and there probably is little that we can add to what has been said. In general, there is little uncertainty about the major problems of heavy radioactive contamination resulting from major atomic warfare or in areas of local fall-out from test explosions conducted on the ground. The problems are simply those of survival from exposure to the whole body by gamma radiation to which may be added a variable but always potentially dangerous exposure to fall-out material which adheres to the skin. The chief source of reliable information on these matters has been the careful medical studies on the 287 Marshall Island and Task Force people accidentally exposed from the test detonation of March 1, 1954. The first year of follow-up results of these people were given in full at a recent annual session of the American Medical Association. Findings, taken with long-term studies of survivors of the wartime attacks on Hiroshima and Nagasaki, showed that the immediate problem is that of minimizing gamma exposure and, subsequently, of giving good nursing care for the whole body gamma effects and local skin injury that may result from combined gamma and beta radiations. Comparatively, medical problems resulting from ingestion and inhalation were insignificant. The threat to life and survival was from the two factors mentioned.

With respect to the exposures to large populations remote from the test sites, we have no method of measurement sufficiently precise to demonstrate any physiological effect, although the physical methods are adequate to determine the magnitude of exposure and to analyze its components. Since we know that the total exposures from all tests are much less than that from background radiation, the problem is essentially that of evaluating the effects of the natural background. Despite much speculation, we simply do not know even approximately the biological import of the natural radioactivity about us. It is an interesting conclusion, pointed out recently (1955) by Dr. Libby, of the Atomic Energy Commission, that the congregation of people in an assembly must increase the total gamma-radiation exposure from K^{40} contained in their own bodies by about 2 milliroentgens per year—an appreciable fraction of the average human exposure in the United States of 15 milliroentgens from fall-out material during the year 1954.

The greater concern with the genetic consequences of low-level exposure has found expression in a considerable variety of opinion. The most authoritative and thoughtful statement on this matter has been made to the Commission by the Advisory Committee for Biology and Medicine of the Atomic Energy Commission. This statement is as follows:

In its recent meetings the Advisory Committee for Biology and Medicine has carefully reviewed the state of our knowledge concerning the genetic effects of ionizing radiation with particular reference to the problem in relation to radioactive fall-out from atomic weapons. The following statement, in which we all concur, represents our best analysis of the problem and our considered opinions based on all of the evidence which has been collected.

Genetic Considerations of Atomic Weapons Tests

One of the important tasks of the Division of Biology and Medicine of the U.S. Atomic Energy Commission has been the safeguarding of the public against the effects of atomic radiation. The Advisory Committee for Biology and Medicine, consisting of independent scientists from various institutions throughout the country, share this concern.

The ability of radiation to change the genes, the hereditary material of mankind, has been a topic of much public discussion. In view of the widely contrasting opinions which have been voiced, the Advisory Committee wishes to point out the following facts and estimates.

1. The AEC from its inception has supported a large number of studies on animals and plants in order to increase knowledge on the genetic effects of radiation, particularly on mammals. These studies, conducted in numerous universities and research institutes, have been freely published in the scientific literature. The AEC has also supported the extensive investigation carried out, under the auspices of the National Academy of Sciences, on the survivors of Hiroshima and Nagasaki and the children born to them.

2. Experiments on animals and plants and observations on man show that mutations occur spontaneously at all times. Most of these mutations act unfavorably on the development, growth or well-being of individuals. The spontaneously mutated genes have accumulated in large numbers in all human populations. Their presence accounts to a considerable extent for the fact that at least one percent of all new-born exhibit developmental abnormalities, most of them to a very slight degree but some in a more serious way.

3. Irradiation of animals and plants adds to the number of more or less detrimental mutations. Human genes must be considered as being equally subject to the mutagenic effect of radiation. Indeed, a considerable fraction of the so-called spontaneous mutations of man are probably caused by the natural background irradiation from cosmic rays, soil and food.

4. The radiation produced by fall-out from atomic weapons tests as well as from present and future peaceful applications of nuclear energy will result in additional mutations in human genes. The number of these cannot be estimated accurately at this time. At the current rate of irradiation from fall-out, among the four million children born each year in the United States, perhaps from a hundred to several thousand may carry as a result of this irradiation a mutated gene. At most, a small percentage of these genes will produce any noticeable effect in the first generation. Only slowly, over hundreds of years, will the majority of these radiation-induced genes become apparent, in a few individuals at a time, usually by causing a less than normal development or functioning of the person concerned. It will be impossible to identify these individuals among the large number of similar ones, affected by genes already present in the population due to accumulated spontaneous mutations.

5. No measurable increase in defective individuals will be observable at any time as the result of current weapons' tests, since the few radiation-induced defectives will not change measurably the number of about 40,000 defectives who will occur spontaneously among the four million births of each year in the United States. It may be pointed out that no significant change in the percentage of malformed children has been observed among those conceived after the war whose parents had been exposed to the atomic bombs in Hiroshima and Nagasaki.

6. The foregoing conclusions apply only to the genetic effects of weapons' tests carried out at the present level and of foreseeable peacetime uses of atomic energy. The genetic effects of a generalized nuclear war would be one of many catastrophic consequences of such a disaster.

> G. Failla, *Chairman*
> Shields Warren, *Vice-Chairman*
> C. H. Burnett, *Member*
> S. T. Cantril, *Member*
> E. A. Doisy, *Member*
> Curt Stern, *Member*

May 12, 1955

In the present state of knowledge of radiation genetics it seems evident that part of the pace of evolution is attributable to mutations induced by environmental radiation. A large increase in this radiation should be attended by a corresponding increase in the rate at which ill-adapted species would improve their position. The betterment of the species with respect to a previously adverse environment would presumably be achieved at a very large cost in terms of individuals, since only rarely would the mutations occurring lead in the direction of better adaptation and selective advantage. Consequently, it may be presumed that an increase in the constant level of radiation exposure might be to the evolutionary advantage of the species, where the cost of such adaptation does not need to be measured in terms of pathologic individuals. For man, we see no such benefit, but the modification of races of plants and animals through radiation-induced mutations may be turned to man's economic or material advantage in various ways.

We can say categorically that the Sr^{90} component of the environmental contamination does not present a genetic problem because of its localization in the skeleton remote from the gonads and because of the limited range in tissue of its beta radiation. The possible effects of Sr^{90} are thus upon bone marrow or upon the structure of bone itself. Very large doses may produce an acute anemia in animals, but these are magnitudes that could not be acquired under any environmental situation which can be visualized at present. It is presumed that the most important effect of Sr^{90} accumulation in the skeleton would be to incite the formation of malignant tumors of bone, or bone sarcoma. Actually, no such instances in man have been known, and such knowledge as we have has been derived from animal experiments with high levels of Sr^{89} and Sr^{90} deposition. At the present time our accepted permissible limit for Sr^{90} is 1 microcurie, continuously maintained in the skeleton. There is a factor of safety here of at least 10, and probably much larger, since the figure has been established chiefly by comparison with radium.

The considerations that apply to weapons-testing become even more consequential when large reactors for power and other purposes come into existence. There is no absolute zero of safety in these matters, and it must be accepted, with reactors as well as with weapons-testing, that there is some degree of hazard, small though it may be. The operation of a reactor at full power over a year's time results in the accumulation of large amounts of fission products which, because of the decay of those of shorter half-life, have become greatly enriched in those of long persistence. A serious reactor accident, therefore, may result in heavy local contamination whose long-term characteristics may be equivalent to those of the surface burst of a large bomb.

In connection with the radiation levels attained where there is a constant increment of radioactive material to the environment, it should be recalled that under these circumstances an equilibrium is reached between the constantly added radioactivity and the influences of radioactive decay. If we increase the rate at which the contaminating material is added to the environment, we merely shift to a new equilibrium level. In neither case is there a continuous build-up. We have estimated that an entire Castle series could be detonated every year and that the Sr^{90} level resulting would be increased only by a factor of 10 over its present value.

SUMMARY

The significance of a low level of radioactive contamination of the environment must be evaluated in terms of the natural radioactivity. At the low levels presently existing, remote from sites of atomic tests, it seems highly improbable that any biologic effect can be demonstrated. These levels of contamination, however, can be accurately measured by present-day techniques, and continuous monitoring of the environment can be maintained.

Greatly increased levels of contamination, such as might result from general atomic war, would unquestionably lead to serious biologic complications, along with other aspects of a transcendent catastrophe. Similar problems could arise in the neighborhood of a large reactor involved in a destructive accident, but, in the latter case, the areas contaminated would be relatively small and capable of adequate management.

Probably the most significant aspect of the presently existing very low levels of contamination is that unique elements occur which act as very sensitive tracers. Although no directly measur-

able increase in our long-term background has resulted, the characteristic radionuclids, such as Sr^{90}, may be separated and quantitatively measured. Using this contamination as a tracer system, we should be able to advance our knowledge of large-scale phenomena involving the atmosphere and the oceans especially. Thus, the existence of these traces of radioactive substances should lead to a substantial expansion of the knowledge necessary to our successful utilization of nuclear energy for large-scale power production.

REFERENCES

AYERS, H. E.
1954 *Control of Radon and Its Daughters in Mines by Ventilation.* (AECU-2858, March 15.) Washington, D.C.: Public Health Service. 23 pp.

BALE, WILLIAM F.
1951 "Hazards Associated with Radon and Thoron." (Memorandum to AEC files, March 14.)

BOND, V. P.; CONRAD, R. A.; CRONKITE, E. P.; FARR, R. S.; and SHULMAN, N. R.
1955 "Response of Human Beings Accidentally Exposed to Significant Fall-Out Radiation." (Paper presented at the meeting in Atlantic City of the Scientific Assembly Section on Military Medicine of the American Medical Association, June 8.) Bethesda, Md.: Naval Medical Research Institute; San Francisco, Calif.: United States Naval Radiological Laboratory. 19 pp. (Mimeographed.)

BUCHER, JOHN C.
1954 "Medical Effects of Atomic Blasts." (Address before the Seventh Congress of Industrial Medicine, Houston, Texas, September 25.)

COWAN, FREDERICK P.
1952 "Everyday Radiation," *Physics Today*, V, No. 10, 10–16.

EISENBUD, MERRIL, and HARLEY, JOHN H.
1953 "Radioactive Dust from Nuclear Detonations," *Science*, CXVII, No. 3033, 141–47.
1955 "Radioactive Fall-out in the United States," *Science*, CXXI, No. 3150, 677–80.

EVANS, ROBLEY D.
1954 *Physical, Biological and Administrative Problems Associated with the Transportation of Radioactive Substances.* (Nuclear Science Series Preliminary Report No. 11, NP-3824.) Washington, D.C.: National Academy of Sciences–National Research Council. 69 pp.

FITCH, WILLIAM EDWARD
1927 *Mineral Waters of the United States and American Spas.* Philadelphia: Lea & Febiger. 799 pp.

FÖYN, E.; KARLIK, B.; PETTERSSON, H.; and RONA, E.
1939 *Kungliga Vetenskapsvitterhets–Samhällees Handlingar*, VI, No. 12, 38–43.

HURSH, JOHN B.
1953 *The Radium Content of Public Water Supplies.* (Atomic Energy Project, University of Rochester, Report No. 257.) Rochester, N.Y.: University of Rochester Press. 28 pp.

HURSH, JOHN B., and GATES, A. A.
1950 *The Radium Content of the Body for Individuals with No Known Occupational Exposure.* (University of Rochester School of Medicine and Dentistry Report No. 119.) Rochester, N.Y.: University of Rochester Press. 39 pp.

JOINT COMMITTEE ON ATOMIC ENERGY
1955a *AEC-FCDA Relations: Hearing before Subcommittee on Security of the Joint Committee on Atomic Energy, March 24, 1955.* (84th Cong.,

1st sess.) Washington, D.C.: Government Printing Office. 57 pp.

1955b *Health and Safety Problems and Weather Effects Associated with Atomic Explosions: Hearing before the Joint Committee on Atomic Energy, April 15, 1955.* (84th Cong., 1st sess.) Washington, D.C.: Government Printing Office. 63 pp.

KURODA, K., and NAKANISHI, M.
1942 "On the Radon Content of the Mineral Springs of Masutomi," *Bulletin of the Chemistry Society of Japan,* XVII, No. 11, 489–90.

LAWRENCE, JOHN H., and HAMILTON, JOSEPH G. (eds.)
1951 *Advances in Biological and Medical Physics,* Vol. II. New York: Academic Press, Inc. 348 pp.

LIBBY, WILLARD F.
1955 "Radioactive Fall-Out." (Address before the University of Chicago Alumni Association, June 3.) Washington, D.C.: Atomic Energy Commission. 15 pp. (Mimeographed.)

LOVE, S. K.
1950 "The Natural Radioactivity of Water" (Paper presented at the Symposium on Radioactive Waste Problems and Treatment, Division of Water, Sewage and Sanitation Chemistry, Chicago, September 7), *Industrial and Engineering Chemistry,* XLIII, 1541–44.

MORGAN, KARL Z.
1951a "Maximum Permissible Concentration of Radon in the Air." (Unpublished memorandum to AEC files, October 4.)
1951b "Standards of Radiological Protection and Control," pp. 176–209 in *The Role of Engineering in Nuclear Energy Development (Third Oak Ridge Summer Symposium, Aug. 27–Sept. 7, 1951).* Oak Ridge, Tenn.: Oak Ridge National Laboratory and Institute of Nuclear Studies.

OHLINGER, L. A.
1950 "Engineering Aspects of Nuclear Reactors," *Nucleonics,* VI, No. 3, 46–57.

SHIMOKATA, K.
1942 *Journal of the Chemistry Society of Japan,* LXIII, 1109–13.

SODDY, F.
1932 *The Interpretation of the Atom.* London: John Murray; New York: G. P. Putnam's Sons. 355 pp.

TOBIAS, C. A.
1951 "Radiation Hazards in High Altitude Aviation," *Medical and Health Physics Quarterly Report,* April–June, pp. 44–45. Radiation Laboratory, University of California.

UNITED STATES ATOMIC ENERGY COMMISSION
1950 *The Effects of Atomic Weapons.* Washington, D.C.: Government Printing Office (for Los Alamos Scientific Laboratory). 457 pp.

Urban-Industrial Demands upon the Land

Urban-Industrial Demands upon the Land

Man's Selective Attack on Ores and Minerals

DONALD H. McLAUGHLIN[*]

MAN AS A GEOLOGIC AGENT

In addition to possessing characteristics that will make him a remarkably fine index fossil, man through his works has attained a geological significance that is altogether out of proportion to the shortness of the period in which he has been the dominant form of life on the globe or to the length of time he is likely to survive if some current trends persist. As a geologic agent, man has already made a notable mark on the earth and left rather a distinctive record, for he has been peculiarly active in a number of ways that have had no counterpart in any other age in the history of the planet.

One of his most sharply directed efforts in this capacity has been his attack on those relatively scarce geologic bodies known as ore deposits. With remarkable selectivity he has sought for these local concentrations of specific elements wherever he has been able to reach them in the crust of the earth, and for the past few centuries he has been most energetically digging them out as promptly as he could find them.

This procedure, in a geologic sense at least, has been a most sudden one, for it did not attain any importance whatever until the current industrial civilization developed. It is really less than a couple of hundred years old, and yet it has become a phenomenon that is one of the unique features of the age.

The bulk of the raw materials needed for the machines and tools and for the structures, chemicals, and power, without which modern industry and the life it supports could not survive, comes from ore or mineral deposits or from organic accumulations formed in the remote past. In a very real sense they are a geologic heritage, which we are spending freely and enjoying thoroughly, and without which human life on earth would have necessarily been organized on a very different and less elaborate basis. Once gone, these accumulations of metallic and other useful minerals cannot be replaced in any period of time significant to the human race. The destruction of these rare and valuable deposits and the dissipation of the elements contained in them are geologic changes of truly profound character which can be attributed almost entirely to man's very special and increasing need under current conditions for the materials obtained from them.

Metals and minerals are the "vitamins" of modern industry, as the Na-

* Dr. McLaughlin is President of the Homestake Mining Company, of San Francisco, California, and Lead, South Dakota. He was formerly professor of mining geology at Harvard University (1925–41) and professor of mining engineering and dean of the College of Engineering at the University of California, Berkeley (1941–43). He is a regent of the University of California, a member and past president of the American Institute of Mining and Metallurgical Engineers, and a member of the National Science Board, National Science Foundation. His publications include: "Geology and Physiography of the Peruvian Cordillera, Departments of Lima and Junín," 1924; "Geological Factors in the Valuation of Mines," 1939; and "Gold, Our Most Strategic Mineral," 1950.

tional City Bank of New York put it recently. Some, such as copper, lead, zinc, and aluminum, as well as steel, are needed in huge tonnages, whereas others are required only in very small amounts for some special function. Germanium is a critical element in transistors, which are revolutionizing communications, but only a minute fraction of an ounce is needed in each instrument. In contrast, wire and cable consumed nearly 800,000 tons of copper in 1954. Without alloy steels, dependent on elements such as nickel, manganese, chromium, molybdenum, and vanadium, modern engines and soaring structures would be impossible. And another metal—gold—serves us well in another very special capacity by providing some measure of international support to the depreciating paper dollar.

To meet the insistent and growing demand for these essential metals and minerals, the whole world is being searched for the deposits from which they are derived. Whenever found, these restricted geologic bodies are being exploited with ever increasing skill and on scales that are becoming grander and grander. The consumption of these basic resources has now become so great—and is expanding at such a rate—that their adequacy in relation to the mounting requirements must be most carefully reviewed in any serious appraisal of means by which the multiplying masses of human beings in all parts of the earth will be able to support themselves. It is most surely a factor that has to be taken into account in any forecast of the course that competent and ambitious nations or races are likely to take in the centuries ahead.

The distribution of ores and minerals has had a profound effect on the migration of peoples and on the settlement of particular lands. It has been a dominant element in the growth of states in which possession or content of such deposits has led to the creation of vast industrial enterprises. Exploitation of these resources has resulted in new patterns of life in many old regions, and their exhaustion in some places has forced adjustments of a far-reaching sort that at times have had disturbing consequences.

NATURE OF ORE DEPOSITS

Ore deposits are an end product of long-continued geological processes of concentration by which some element or group of elements has been accumulated in a restricted environment and left there in far greater local abundance than is common elsewhere in the crust of the earth.

The means by which such concentrations have been brought about are many and varied. The actual processes are the ordinary ones of geology, but their effectiveness as agents of concentration has been determined by the specific physical and chemical characteristics of each element and its compounds and by the environment in which they functioned. They range from processes as diverse as the washing of resistant minerals from sands and gravels by streams and waves to the condensation of sulfur from the vapors of a volcano. They include processes of rock decay as well as the segregation of elements from crystallizing melts of the many sorts from which igneous rocks are formed.

With the single exception of magnesium obtained from sea water, the metals we need are derived from these end products of processes of concentration. In a sense, they are geologic freaks, for they nearly always have required an unusual combination of circumstances for their initial gathering, for their transportation and deposition in a specific place, and for their preservation and distribution in places where men can find and reach them.

As geologic bodies, ore deposits are

generally small and uncommon. Aluminum, iron, and magnesium alone occur in rocklike masses with high enough content to serve as sources of these metals, if we were willing to meet the high cost in human effort, materials, and power required to recover them. But if we had to depend on such very low-grade materials—abundant but most expensive to treat—the price of the metals derived from them would be so high that their uses would have to be severely restricted except in the case of magnesium extracted from sea water. As it is, the ore deposits that provide the large tonnages of aluminum and iron to meet the world's growing needs are not exceptions to the rule. They, too, are geologic concentrates and represent the end products of processes that have raised the content of these metals to levels that make it possible to recover them at reasonable cost.

A simple example of a geologic process of concentration is afforded by the lateritic ores of iron and aluminum, whose origin is now well established. Three conditions which led to the formation of these ores were (1) the occurrence of a rock with aluminum or iron content somewhat above the average; (2) exposure to long-continued weathering under appropriate tropical conditions, resulting in thorough decay of the rock exposed at the surface, with leaching and removal of silica and other elements and with enrichment in iron or aluminum as the resistant oxides of aluminum or iron accumulate in the residual surface layer; and (3) the preservation of gentle land surfaces on which these extensive scablike crusts accumulated. The concentration may be of the order of four- or fivefold, not very large, but critical in its bearing on costs of recovery.

In contrast to these bulky elements are the much less abundant ones such as copper, lead, zinc, and practically all the many other metals used in industry. They occur in no common rocks in sufficient quantity to offer any hope whatever of successful commercial recovery. In every case the deposits from which they are derived represent concentrations of much greater magnitude. In relation to the content of such metal in ordinary rocks, they usually represent a concentration of more than a hundred fold. Such deposits may be the result of segregation of heavy immissible components of a melt—comparable to the separation of a matte from a slag in smelting—or the collection of an early mineral that has separated from such material. Under other conditions the rarer elements might have been gathered in residual volatile fluids and carried upward by them from the hot depths of the earth to be deposited as the solutions dropped their loads successively upon cooling or upon coming into contact with more chemically reactive rocks. Concentrations of similar order may also have been brought about simply by migrating solutions that derived their load of metals by leaching of rock masses under one set of conditions and deposited it elsewhere in some restricted locus where an environment that induced precipitation or reaction was encountered.

Apart from these deposits, there is no source in the common or even in unusual rocks that can be tapped for these metals.

It is far from the purpose of this paper, however, to discuss the origin of ore deposits. The subject was introduced merely to emphasize our dependence on them and to point out their unique character as geologic bodies, being as they are the end products of geologic processes of concentration that have gathered specific elements—many of them extremely rare and very sparsely distributed in the earth's crust—and have deposited them in one form or another in special environments, where they have been preserved and left within man's limited reach from the surface of the earth.

The best clues as to the places where ore deposits are likely to exist are to be derived from knowledge of the migration of elements in the superficial parts of the crust of the earth and from the reasons for their accumulation in specific environments. In other words, understanding of the way ores are formed is the best approach to the problem of discovering them.

In organic deposits, such as coal, where stratigraphy and structure provide reliable guides, or in large targets, such as oil pools, where relationships both to source and to reservoir rocks can be recognized and where structures on a major scale influence collection of the petroleum in traps, the geologic approach—and essentially the genetic geologic approach—has achieved its greatest success.

Metalliferous ores or deposits of useful non-organic materials present far more complex problems. Each element has to be studied separately, for the processes that tended to concentrate it here or dissipate it there were determined by its own distinctive chemical and physical properties and by the ways these determined a specific response under the various geologic conditions and in a particular environment. The student of ore deposits or the practicing exploration geologist or engineer, therefore, is faced with far more complicated problems than his colleague who is concerned with coal or oil. He still is justified in believing that his best approach is through geologic knowledge bearing on the origin of the deposits he seeks; but he is likely to be searching for a body with qualities comparable to Cleopatra's—at least as far as its infinite variety is concerned—rather than one that conforms faithfully to simple rules.

Within specific mineral districts, or even provinces, where local characteristics can be established, geology has served the practical ends of exploration most successfully. In the search for ores in the complex of sediments and intrusives at Morococha in Peru (Graton and Burrell, 1935), in the block of intricately faulted granitic rock at Butte, Montana (Sales and Meyer, 1949), in the involved folds of the ancient rocks of the Black Hills of South Dakota (McLaughlin, 1933), and in many other active mining districts, mapping of pertinent geologic and mineralogic data and structures has served most useful ends, particularly when interpreted in the light of genetic theories. Broader geologic principles also provide essential guidance for correct thinking, but they rarely give the close direction to actual efforts to find ore that is desired and needed.

The older geological methods usually can be effectively supplemented by the more recently developed geophysical and geochemical techniques, whereby an ore may be located directly by observation of an anomaly caused by it in a physical field of one sort or another—such as, for example, irregularities in the earth's magnetic field caused by a deposit of magnetite—or indirectly by using anomalies or other physical or chemical data as a means of determining the distribution of rocks and trace elements or minerals and of deciphering structures that have a known or suspected relationship to ore.

Successes can be recorded for these and other devices used to guide exploration—as well as for the sharp eye of the prospector or the reckless drilling of the wildcatter—but the fact remains that the deposits that have been found thus far probably amount to only a small percentage of the total quantity of ore within range of man's skill in mining and boring.

As the empty parts of the world are reduced, however, as is happening very rapidly in this age of the airplane, the rate of chance discovery is surely slowing down. Exploration will become more scientific and more technical, and even with better guidance and better instrumentation it is bound to become more costly. But it is a bold man who predicts that nothing remains to be found, even in regions that have been worked over with considerable skill.

ADVANCING TECHNIQUES OF EXPLOITATION

So far our industrial civilization has been developed in an age of abundance, particularly in the United States. An amazing, rapid succession of mineral districts of first rank in the world was found as the westward exploration of the continent progressed. Then, a half-century or so later, as the richer ores were running out, deposits of far lower grade but with even greater gross value were profitably exploited as the base of immense enterprises by application of new methods of mining and by concentration on scales that dwarfed any such activities in the past. The technical record is a most brilliant one, and it deserves to stand high among the achievements that made the nation powerful by vastly increasing its effective mineral resources.

By lowering the grade of ore that could be profitably mined and beneficiated, the technical advances that occurred in the first decade of this century enormously enlarged the potential ore reserves of the world. Achievements of this sort, however, are possible only where the specific element occurs in bodies that are susceptible to such treatment. The porphyry-copper deposits were the first outstanding example. The successful concentration of the taconite ores of iron in the Lake Superior region is a more recent one. In the case of copper, the technical skills developed in the handling of the low-grade ores on a large scale reduced the cost of the metal in spite of the smaller content of metal recovered per ton. In the case of the taconites, the additional beneficiation is likely to result in costs that will exceed those for iron derived from the higher-grade pits —but will still provide a furnace feed at a competitive price and will vastly extend the life of mining in the Mesabi region.

Again the properties of each metal determine the nature of ore bodies from which it will be won. At one extreme, we have small erratic deposits, so difficult to find or to work economically that the supply at best falls far short of the potential demand. Prices necessarily remain high, and uses are restricted. Such is the situation with regard to beryllium. At the other extreme, a metal may be so widely distributed in relatively lower concentrations that immense tonnages might be added to reserves of available ore by a substantial increase in its price, as may be illustrated by uranium, or by reduction in costs per ton of mining and treatment, as happened in the case of copper.

EFFECTS OF SCARCITIES

Periods of scarcities of long or short duration are certain to occur for a specific metal or mineral as the demand fluctuates and as old mines are depleted. The immediate effect of scarcities in a free-enterprise system is to raise the price of the material concerned. In the case of metals, this would at once lower the grade of ore that is profitable to mine and thereby extend the life of old operations and stimulate the development of new ones. Substantial tonnages of such marginal ore exist in the case of practically all the common metals. Even a modest price rise stimulates exploration, enlargement of plants, and increased production. If the response is too enthusiastic, an oversupply is likely to be created, whereupon the balance is restored fairly promptly by a fall in price and the closing-down of operations where costs are high.

A marked rise—say, a doubling or trebling of the price of a metal—could have most spectacular results. Far more money would be risked in exploration and new developments, and it is a certainty that the available reserves in the case of nearly every metal or mineral—on a planetary basis at least—would be very greatly increased and the evil date of drastic scarcities postponed beyond the foreseeable historic future.

Furthermore, under such conditions, the higher price would enforce economies in use. Specific metals or minerals would be employed solely where their qualities gave them unique value. Under these circumstances it is a certainty that technical management, in its effort to reduce costs, would develop and use substitutes to whatever degree prices and the need dictated. (In the last war, for example, the Germans were not long in replacing brass cartridge cases with entirely satisfactory cases made of steel; and on this continent the scarcity of mercury was much relieved by the substitution of lead azides as fulminates.) The result of such changes would certainly be economies in the use of a specific metal or mineral, leading possibly to extreme reduction in quantities used in some cases. In other instances, the irreducible minimum might still be large, where the metal had unique properties for which a substitute could not be found and even an extremely high cost would not be a serious deterrent, as could well be the case in certain of the alloy metals.

The profound effect of price upon supply and demand for metals and minerals was emphasized in a recent paper by Just (1955). As an example, he cited manganese, which at the current price of about four cents per pound is scarce enough to warrant special effort to build up a national stockpile for the protection of the steel industry, in which it is an essential material, and to provide subsidies to stimulate development of domestic enterprises. If the price were increased to one dollar per pound, Just asserts with reason that the world's commercial deposits would be multiplied tenfold through making it possible to mine and treat certain enormous deposits that are hopelessly low grade at the present price. Specifications for use would probably be made less exacting, more effort to obtain the desired results in the steel industry with less manganese would undoubtedly be made, and as much as three-quarters of the manganese now wasted might be recovered. The combined effect, according to Just, could conceivably make the manganese supply go a hundred times as far as under present conditions. The final cost to users of steel with the suggested increase in price would not be prohibitive—and the time of shortages would be pushed far enough into the future to curb the fears even of a geologist.

In 1952 the President's Materials Policy Commission submitted a report, now commonly called the "Paley Report," in which a lengthy compilation of statistics on ore reserves and rates of consumption were presented, the situation discussed at length, and conclusions drawn with regard to future shortages and their dates of arrival. Predictions were based mostly on straight-line projections of present rates, with inadequate allowances for the effect of price rises as scarcities developed. The difficulty, if not the impossibility, of consolidating so many uncertain variables in a curve makes such projections of rather limited validity, for at best they are hardly more than an indication of what might be expected if current conditions (exploration rates and returns, scales of production, uses and consumption, etc.) all continued without much change.

This assumption, however, is an unreal one. About the best that can be said is that each metal and each type of ore or mineral deposit must be studied individually, and the prospective outcome of exploration on district, province, and world scales appraised. The balance between supply and demand, future prices, advances in technology, and a number of other variables, partly dependent and partly independent, would also have to be assessed before even a tentative guess could be made.

All in all, it seems to me to lead to the conclusion that, although ore supply or supply of mineral raw materials may well be a most worrisome consideration for an individual district and for the enterprises based on it, or in some cases for a nation or even for a province, the time of scarcities that would be painfully acute on a worldwide basis is probably long postponed. So long, in fact, that predictions with regard to what the activities of the human race are likely to be when the shortages eventually develop are rather futile, especially in these days when those high priests of the present age—the physicists—continue to surprise us by their revelations and the engineers by the promptness and ingenuity with which they take advantage of the new ideas of the scientists for useful purposes.

DISTRIBUTION OF ORE DEPOSITS

Although only a geologist is likely to regard the exploitation of the planet's ore deposits as a very short-lived affair, statesmen and others who think in units of time longer than decades may well find that inadequacy of the accessible supply of mineral raw materials is an acutely serious matter to their particular country and creates problems that must be solved with enlightened self-interest if trouble is to be avoided. This situation, however, is to be attributed to the uneven division of such resources among nations rather than to impending scarcities on a world-wide scale.

Ore deposits are generally distributed in patterns that reflect the geologic history of regions. To the extent that the geographic features are determined by the geology, they will exhibit a relationship to them as well. Belts, such as the Cordillera of the two Americas, obviously have closely related geologic and geographic characteristics; and the ore deposits, associated genetically with specific geologic events, exhibit striking geographic habits that have led to the recognition of such regions as metallogenetic provinces. Basically, however, the control is geologic.

These trends in distribution of ore deposits or mineral districts are likely to exhibit a perverse independence of the lines established by political geographers. The great iron-ore deposits of Western Europe lie along the troubled zone of contact between the Germanic people and the French, and the actual border in most periods has caused uneconomic separation of essential industrial activities. Prior to the last war, the German-Polish border cut through the lead–zinc-bearing region of Silesia, which did little to promote good relations in that uneasy region; and the nickel deposit of Petsamo, developed in Finland by the International Nickel Company of Canada just prior to the war, was one factor that pulled the current Russian frontier toward the west.

Certain regions are richly endowed, while others are hopelessly barren, and no amount of effort or wishful thinking will change this fact (McLaughlin,

1945). Metalliferous provinces cut across many lines important in human history. Countries, unlike men in a much-quoted political phrase, are not created equal but must be accepted as they are. To obtain the ores and minerals that industry demands, men have to go to the places where these deposits exist. And the value under a system of free enterprise that is placed on the distinctive products of particular lands is a powerful magnet that draws to these regions persons who are capable of exploiting such resources. This is bound to lead to excursions across lines established by distribution of races or across boundaries set up in response to economic forces of an age that is long past. Migrations of this sort will inevitably occur in a world in which industrial nations will pay well for the minerals they must have to survive, and the disturbances thus caused to preexisting patterns of living must be taken into account in any serious effort to preserve international stability.

The need for minerals on the part of any moderately developed industrial nation is so great that no country, not even the United States or Russia, is any longer self-sufficient. Some countries are truly "have-nots" as far as their minerals are concerned. Every major industrial country is a "need-more."

As successive scientific discoveries were applied to technical ends, one metal after another became critically needed—copper, as electricity was employed on a world-wide scale; nickel, tungsten, chromium, and other alloy metals, as steels had to meet more and more exacting demands in machines, structures, and tools; aluminum and magnesium and now titanium, as aircraft advanced in design—and so on, until the consumption of metals reached levels that no nation could match from its own geological endowment. First, the countries with limited resources had to obtain ores from abroad. Belgium, where the famous mines of the Moresnet district had played an important part in the development of the zinc industry, was able to maintain its position as a zinc producer only by obtaining ores from abroad for its smelters. Britain long ago outran its meager resources in copper and tin, though its Swansea smelters continued to struggle along with a fair success by importing ores. The Empire of course helped England maintain its position, but, as far as domestic supplies were concerned, Great Britain in the last few decades must be regarded as a land nearly depleted of all ores except iron and dependent on water-borne supplies even for much of that. In spite of the unusually bountiful natural endowment the United States enjoys, our immense industrial development has transformed us from a country with an exportable surplus of most metals and minerals to one in which our consumption of nearly every important mineral exceeds our own substantial domestic production.

Under these conditions, isolation or the assumption of self-sufficiency becomes an absurd concept. It could be entertained only if we were willing to curtail our industry, reduce our consumption of raw materials, and revert to a much simpler form of life. Even if there were any inclination to do thus (which there certainly is not), the necessity of supporting the present immense population would rule it out. Our current output of metals and minerals could undoubtedly be increased by substantially higher prices, which might be achieved through tariffs, subsidies, bonuses, or other forms of special consideration. But this would only result in higher prices for all we manufacture, inevitable loss of markets in the growing international competition, and economic suicide.

The uneven distribution of ores and minerals—uneven geologically and geographically in a basic sense and still more uneven in relation to the vast difference in industrial needs—makes international trade a necessity and perhaps more than any other factor will promote the sort of understanding between nations that to my way of thinking offers more hope than any other influence for preserving peace—namely, the recognition of each other's needs and of the ways they can be met to mutual advantage.

There is nothing new in the export of technical skill across borders. For centuries the more highly developed industrial nations have undertaken mining enterprises in countries far removed from their own. In the last fifty years the most conspicuous of our activities have been the American copper mines developed in Chile and Peru and the many base-metal enterprises in Mexico. Bauxite ores from New Guinea and Surinam, iron ores from Venezuela, and chromite from the Rhodesias are more recent examples. In the deserts of Chile and Peru, in the high Andean Plateau, and in the tropical forests of Venezuela and other countries of the Caribbean, new centers of population have been created, and towns and even cities have been built up through the winning of new wealth from the mines and auxiliary activities. In connection with these mining undertakings, railroads have been built, power provided, standards of living raised, and new means of support supplied beyond anything known in the past. In each of these cases, private enterprise provided the money, machinery, and technical skill that developed these immense undertakings to the mutual advantage of the countries in which the investments were made and in the end to the investor. Such transactions have long set a pattern that is well understood by businessmen of international stature and that behind the scenes commands more respect than the strange giveaway schemes of more recent years.

SUPERFICIAL EFFECTS OF MINING

Except in the case of those deposits that were formed by processes of weathering or recent sedimentation and are themselves actually part of or close to the more superficial layer of the earth, mining has created few scars. The removal of lateritic deposits (the ores of iron and aluminum, previously mentioned), covering rather extensive areas in various countries usually to depths of not more than tens of feet, involves of course complete obliteration of the original surface; but, as such ores are rarely if ever in regions of good soils, no damage of any importance results, unless the actual consumption of a valuable mineral resource could be so considered by some ultraconservationist.

The mining of placer deposits (i.e., gravels and sands in which a resistant mineral such as gold or cassiterite has been concentrated) may in some cases result in the virtual destruction of valuable alluvial soils where such deposits occur in valleys and particularly where they are mined on a large scale by dredging. The gold alluvial deposits on the margin of the Sacramento Valley in California are a well-known example. Even in this rather extreme case, however, the limited extent of these deposits will make the actual loss of valuable land relatively small and far less than that resulting from the spreading blight of housing projects in response to the rapidly expanding population.

Dredging in other regions, particularly in the tin fields of Malaya or the gold fields of New Guinea, where only dense jungle growth is removed, causes no loss whatever, and the slight debit if any against the mining operations hardly deserves mention.

A most conspicuous disturbance of the surface occurs in the course of mining of the porphyry-copper deposits and of the iron ores of the Mesabi in immense open pits. None of these deposits, however, is situated in a region where the surface is of more than nominal value. Even from an aesthetic standpoint, the result is not distasteful, for the terraced walls resulting from the removal of the ore in successive benches have a peculiar beauty of their own. Indeed, the great man-made pit at Bingham Canyon in Utah very properly excites high admiration, as do many other similar workings on somewhat smaller scale. Surely no damage of any sort can be charged against these notable mines that have added metals and minerals worth billions of dollars to the world's stock.

The mining of deeper deposits causes little or no marks on the surface except dumps of waste rock or tailings from the mills. The headframes and buildings for the plant not uncommonly have considerable architectural merit, with their truly appropriate functional designs. The dumps may be conspicuous, as they are on the Witwatersrand in the Transvaal, where some 60,000,-000 tons per year of siliceous gold ore are broken, ground to a pulp, and stacked in huge piles after the gold is extracted. There they bring an interesting element of relief, standing high above eucalyptus groves, to an otherwise rather monotonous and unproductive landscape.

All in all, the losses to soils, to forests, or to streams resulting from mining operations in all fairness must be regarded as negligible, even if considered in their entire gross effect, and utterly insignificant in relation to the values made available by the enterprises themselves.

Indirect damage to a region, such as stripping of forests to provide fuel for power or for mine timber, was not uncommon in the earlier days of mining

in many American districts, particularly in the West, when survival in remote places with primitive facilities for transportation was possible only if such procedures were employed. They have, however, disappeared completely in modern practice, and most of the larger organizations in the industry have played an important part in promoting orderly forestry practices in the regions that serve their needs. Indeed, the first contract for carefully controlled cutting of timber in a national forest was granted to the Homestake Mining Company in the Black Hills of South Dakota, and the good practices established in that region have long served as an excellent example of wise utilization of forest resources.

SUMMARY

From even as cursory a review of the problem as is presented in this paper, it seems reasonable to list the following conclusions:

1. The intensive exploitation of mineral resources at the current rate will result in their exhaustion in a period of time that is very short in a geological sense.

2. The depletion of such resources already creates serious problems for certain nations.

3. The consumption of metals and minerals on the part of the major industrial powers has exceeded the supplies available from the domestic sources of any one of them, even the United States.

4. Scarcities could be relieved or almost indefinitely postponed, except possibly in the case of a few metals and minerals, by a rise in prices, which would inevitably result in more intensive exploration for ores, in enlargement of plants and building of new ones, and in economies in use; such increases in price could if necessary be

substantial without seriously disturbing the industrial economy.

5. Even though the exploitation of mineral resources causes the dissipation of an irreplaceable geologic heritage, accumulated over a vast extent of time, it is being accomplished with little or no serious damage to the surface of the earth as a habitat for man and has made and is making a wealth of metals and mineral products available for use without which the present industrial civilization would be impossible.

6. In spite of shortages that may be very disturbing to restricted national economies, the time before serious scarcities will occur for the earth as a whole is still so far in the future that adjustments and adaptations to the slowly changing conditions can probably be made without creating drastic dislocations.

REFERENCES

BATEMAN, A. M.
1949 "America's Stake in World Mineral Resources," *Mining Engineering*, I, 23–27.
1950 *Economic Mineral Deposits*. 2d ed. New York: John Wiley & Sons. 916 pp.

GRATON, L. C., and BURRELL, H. C.
1935 "Copper Resources of the World," *XVI Geological Congress, Washington, D.C.*, II, 527–44.

JUST, EVAN
1955 "Minerals for the Future," *Science*, CXXII, No. 3164, 317.

LEITH, C. K.; FURNESS, J. W.; and LEWIS, C.
1943 *World Minerals and World Peace*. Washington, D.C.: Brookings Institution. 253 pp.

LINDGREN, WALDEMAR
1933 *Mineral Deposits*. 4th ed. New York: McGraw-Hill Book Co. 930 pp.

McKINSTRY, H. E.
1948 *Mining Geology*. New York: Prentice-Hall, Inc. 680 pp.

McLAUGHLIN, D. H.
1933 "Geologic Work at the Homestead Mine, Lead, S.D.," pp. 722–29 of chap. xii in FINCH, J. W., *et al.* (eds.), *Ore Deposits of the Western United States* (Lindgren Volume). New York: American Institute of Mining and Metallurgical Engineers. 797 pp.
1945 "The Wasting Ores of a Small Planet," *American Journal of Science* (Daly Volume), CCXLIII-A, 467–78.

1952 "The Exploitation of Mineral Resources," pp. 527–40 in LOHR, LENOX R. (ed.), *Centennial of Engineering, 1852–1952*. Chicago: Museum of Science and Industry, Centennial of Engineering, Inc. 1,179 pp.

McLAUGHLIN, D. H., and SALES, R. H.
1933 "Utilization of Geology of Mining Company," pp. 683–729 of chap. xii in FINCH, J. W., *et al.* (eds.), *Ore Deposits of the Western United States* (Lindgren Volume). New York: American Institute of Mining and Metallurgical Engineers. 797 pp.

PARSONS, A. B.
1933 *The Porphyry Coppers*. New York: American Institute of Mining and Metallurgical Engineers. 581 pp.

PRESIDENT'S MATERIALS POLICY COMMISSION
1952 *Resources for Freedom*, Vol. I: *Foundations for Growth and Security;* Vol. II: *The Outlook for Key Commodities;* Vol. III: *The Outlook for Energy Sources;* Vol. IV: *The Promise of Technology;* Vol. V: *Selected Reports to the Commission*. Washington, D.C.: Government Printing Office.

RICKARD, T. A.
1932 *Man and Metals*. 2 vols. New York: McGraw-Hill Book Co. 1,601 pp.

SALES, R. H., and MEYER, C.
1949 "Preliminary Study of the Vein Formation, Butte, Montana," *Economic Geology*, XLIV, 465–84.

The Role of Transportation and the Bases for Interaction[1]

EDWARD L. ULLMAN[*]

Few forces have been more influential in modifying the earth than transportation, yet transportation itself is a result of other forces. Nor have the main results of transportation been the mere scratches of transport construction on the surface of the earth. Such traces, important locally and changing as we shall see, are really significant even on the habitable portions of the globe.

In order to define the role of transportation on the earth's surface, it is instructive to broaden the concept of transportation to the French *circulation,* which includes all movement and communication. Circulation, then, is basic to spatial interaction and thus to the geographic term "situation." Situation refers to the effects of phenomena in one area on another area. Specific processes relevant to situation include diffusion, centralization, migration, or transportation. Situation contrasts with

* Dr. Ullman is Professor of Geography at the University of Washington, Seattle. Formerly he was associate professor of regional planning at Harvard University and during part of the war served as director of the Joint Army-Navy Intelligence Studies. He has been a member of the Council of the American Council of Learned Societies. His publications include "A Theory of Location for Cities," 1941; "Rivers as Regional Bonds: The Columbia-Snake Example," 1951; and "Amenities as a Factor in Regional Growth," 1954.

1. Acknowledgment is gratefully made to the Office of Naval Research for support of research for this paper.

"site," which refers to local, underlying areal conditions, such as type of soil correlated with type of agriculture. Site thus might be conceived as a vertical relationship; situation, as a horizontal one.

As early as 1890 Mackinder noted this dualism: "The chief distinction in political geography seems to be founded on the facts that man travels and man settles."

An example of alternate interpretation based, respectively, on site and on situation is provided by the age-old puzzle of assigning reasons for the growth of particular civilizations in particular places. Thus Toynbee, in his challenge-and-response theory, uses a site concept with a new twist—the challenging effect of a relatively poor environment. Gourou (1949), in reviewing this concept, poses the following query: Does the substitution of the effects of an unfavorable environment for the effects of a favorable one represent progress over previous interpretations based on environmental determinism? He poses as an alternate possibility a situation concept—the rise of civilizations in favored corridors for interaction, so that contact with other civilizations and contrasting ideas was facilitated, as in parts of Europe. Without going into the merits of either explanation, we would hold that undoubtedly site, situation, and other factors as well are all involved in any total understanding.

Basic to this process of interaction is

the ease or difficulty of movement and communication. A host of authors justifiably, though perhaps not too critically, attest to the overwhelming importance of transportation and communication. With considerable logic, many scholars regard the early stages of the industrial revolution to be more properly labeled as the "transportation revolution" (Taylor, 1951).

Economists and others have recognized through the ages that, in general, trade and improvements in transportation to facilitate it raise the standard of living of all parties concerned, although not necessarily equally. Thus Cammann writes (1951, p. 96) that Samuel Turner reported from his mission to Tibet in 1783 as follows:

Necessity had developed a commerce that was only languidly conducted by a naturally lazy people. He felt, however, that once the Tibetans had become acquainted with the pleasures of luxury and the profits of commerce, they would be roused from their apathy and would feel the need for a higher standard of living.

SOME EFFECTS OF IMPROVED TRANSPORTATION

Improvement in transportation and circulation has produced two contrasting and contradictory results: (1) In many cases it has made the world and its peoples more alike, since they are enabled to share ideas, products, and services; this aspect has been stressed most by social scholars and undoubtedly is of great importance. (2) Simultaneously, in many cases it has made areas more unlike, since each region has been enabled to specialize in activities it can do best, whether based on factors of production related to land, labor, capital, or simply economies of scale.

This latter has been emphasized by numerous students of transportation and economics and would appear to be the more important factor in the physical modification of the earth by man. Let us consider it in more detail.

Effect on Areal Specialization

Areal specialization promoted by improved transportation has resulted, in part, in the creation of large, monolithic, particularized production areas tied to distant markets. The wheat belts, corn belts, and truck areas in agriculture and the specialized manufacturing belts in industry have become the characteristic land-use features of the modern commercial world. This has produced a pattern drastically different from that of earlier subsistence economies, with little or no transportation, or even from the spatial economy envisaged in 1826 by von Thünen in his famous *Der isolierte Staat* as concentric rings of land use around a central-city market, their intensity being dictated by transport costs (see Fig. 76, p. 254).

The chief change that transport improvement has wrought is in the scale of areal differentiation. Within the large specialized agricultural areas, for example, there is less subregional differentiation now than formerly, inasmuch as a wide range of subsistence or locally transportable crops need not be grown.

Some features of von Thünen's rings persist. Location near market is still important, as witness, for example, Bogue's (1949) studies on dominance and subdominance, wherein he shows that in the United States counties near metropolises tend to have denser population and greater development than counties farther out. This is due in part to easier access and in part, I am sure, to the fact that cities tend to be located near the middle of productive areas, in line with the "central-place" theory (Christaller, 1935; Ullman, 1941). Bogue also notes that development tends to be greater in sectors along the main connecting transport lines, as would be expected and as is confirmed for most of the world by a mere glance at population maps.

The extraordinary development of steam navigation and steam railroads in the nineteenth century especially precipitated a drastic rearrangement of settlement patterns in much of the world (see Malin, pp. 356–57 above). Wheat-growers in many parts of Europe were forced out of business by overseas competition. New England farmers abandoned their hill farms, particularly from the 1830's on, and moved to the superior farm lands of the Middle West or to new manufacturing opportunities in the cities. In much of New England the rural areas became among the least populous in America, the fields reverted to woodland, and only the indestructible stone walls remained as reminders that the land had once been farmed.

Conversely, in some cases transportation has enabled the natural environment to be "corrected." In France, for example, the construction of railroads permitted lime to be transported cheaply to poor fields and thus increased agricultural yields (Fromont, 1948, pp. 66–69). Fertilizer of course is now widely transported around many parts of the world and is a feature of modern agriculture.

Specialization, made possible by transportation, has also produced some of the evils associated with one-crop farming and excessive specialization. However, it seems reasonable to assume that such specialization, on balance, is probably more beneficial "ecologically" than harmful. Steep slopes or other poor areas near markets, for example, no longer need be farmed. The forest is taking over such areas throughout the northeastern United States, as Klimm (1954) has shown.

Effect on Cities

Cities, the principal seats of population in the Western world, have long been intimately related to transportation. Their very existence on a large scale was made possible by the development of means to transport farm surplus to them. It was of course necessary that there first be a farm surplus, as Adam Smith (1937, p. 357) and others have noted (Sombart, 1916, pp. 130–31). This has been contingent on improvement in farming technique, a process still going on, as witness the declining number of farmers in much of the world. The specific city-building factor, however, is not the mere focusing of routes on a city but rather the transferring of goods from one form of transportation to another—a break in bulk as between land and water (Cooley, 1894; Harris and Ullman, 1945). Where goods must be handled, storage or further processing tends to develop.

Cities have long recognized their dependence on transportation and have sought to improve their connections. It has been standard practice for cities to subsidize transport routes to or through them. Some cities even built their own lines, for example, Cincinnati, which still owns the Cincinnati, New Orleans, and Texas Pacific, connecting the city with the South and now leased to the Southern Railway. Much of the historical geography of the eastern seaboard of the United States since independence is related to the struggles of the principal ports to gain access to the interior.

In newer parts of the country the railroads in many cases preceded extensive settlement and virtually created cities; on the other hand, some of them failed to touch major centers because of the multiplicity of competing lines. A somewhat chaotic geography is the result. In New England the rail pattern developed somewhat more rationally without a multiplicity of competing lines. Here the urban centers had been already established; the larger cities were able to put up more money than the smaller ones and thus obtained rail routes to reinforce their dominance (Kirkland, 1948). In many parts of Europe, also, the dominance of political capitals was strengthened by rail construction.

Effect of Freight Rates

The rate practices of transportation are often said to produce an artificial, "unnatural" economic geography. To a degree this may well be true in many specialized cases. A well-established practice, for example, is to charge less than total-cost rates (sufficiently high to cover out-of-pocket or variable costs) for low-value commodities which cannot afford to pay high costs and to recoup the difference on higher-value commodities. In consequence, low-value, bulk commodities tend to be moved longer distances, and higher-value commodities shorter distances, than might otherwise be the case (Penrose, 1952).

How much the monopolistic rate practices cited by Penrose actually affect major flows in the United States is difficult to determine. The largest-volume haul of one commodity in the United States, for example, is coal from West Virginia and Virginia to the Middle West and the eastern seaboard (see Fig. 166, p. 874). The three principal coal-carriers (Norfolk and Western, Chesapeake and Ohio, and Virginian) obtain the overwhelming bulk of their revenue from this one commodity. It is likely, therefore, that their rates do cover total costs, since these three roads are the most profitable railroads in the United States (Lambie, 1954).

A generalized hypothesis that I would like to advance concerning the effect of freight rates is that they often tend to accentuate and perpetuate initial differences between areas. Most freight traffic, at least in the United States, moves on so-called "commodity rates" specifically established from point of origin to point of destination. Low rates are granted on volume movements, which specialization tends to foster. Thus new areas or small producers may find it difficult to compete initially. Alexander found (1944) that the fertile, cash-grain area of central Illinois had low rail rates per mile to principal markets for its chief product —corn—and high rates on cattle, whereas rates in the less fertile cattle-producing area of western Illinois were reversed—low on cattle and high on corn. The rate structure thus tends to accentuate and perpetuate areal specialization based on natural conditions.

Much work remains to be done on interpreting the multiplicity of freight rates in meaningful geographical terms. Previous research has been concerned largely with regulatory or pricing aspects. Through new research the proposed generalization can be tested, and others may well emerge.

Effects of New and Varied Mediums of Transport

Improvements in transportation have tended to promote concentration and long hauls and thus to change the scale of the earth's regions. Rate structures, including former "basing-point" systems, work in the same direction, as do the relatively low ton-mile rates applied to carloads, trainloads, and shiploads and on long hauls. This contributes to the growth of large cities, to large and more distant production areas, and to the elimination or reduction of, for example, small ports and some small producing areas.

Certain more recent developments, however, may be working in the opposite direction, namely, the use of the automobile in transportation and the telephone in communication, both of which are pre-eminently short-distance connectors. One of the main effects of the automobile is to provide uniform transport service throughout an area and thus to open all of it to interaction. In American cities the automobile has had the spectacular effect of opening up interstices between former transport "spokes" on the periphery of cities and thus has increased the area available for urban settlement far more than the distance to work. Thus, if the radius of a city doubles during growth, the maximum length of journey to the center of the city also doubles, but the area available for settlement increases fourfold. Areas tributary to cities have become similarly accessible, and the spacing of cities thus has been made more regular. We are still adjusting to the effects of this revolutionary, universal transport medium.

Forms of transportation differ in their ability to overcome terrain and other features of the environment. When draft animals were used, forage was all-important, and routes were selected for good grazing conditions. The first railroad in South Africa, from Cape Town across the arid Cape Flats, was laid out partly because there was no forage for animals along this barren stretch (Goodfellow, 1931). To give but one more of possible examples, of all the forms of land transportation, if canals be excluded, railroads are the most sensitive to grades; hence the choice among alternative routes is more restricted for a railroad line than it is for a highway.

Developments in transportation have changed the impact on man of features of the natural environment. A mountain range is not the same phenomenon to canalboats, steam locomotives, diesel engines, automobiles, trucks, jeeps, horses, yaks, pipelines, electric wires, airplanes, and radios. Advances in construction technology have also drastically altered the effects of terrain. Early railroads, built by men and animals, avoided extensive excavation and substituted curves or steep grades. The revolutionary improvement in earth-moving equipment in recent years has drastically cut excavation costs, in spite of great increases in labor and other costs. As a result, railroads and highways are realigning their routes; they are creating new and bolder marks on the earth's surface.

General Effects of Transportation Changes and the Effort Devoted to Movement

Interaction in the modern world has been enormously increased by improvements in transportation. The great trade routes of the past were mere trickles compared to today's volume flows. Bulk movements of raw materials even remotely comparable to the shipments which come daily to a modern steel plant were unknown. Each area of concentrated settlement, therefore, had to produce most of its own fuel, food, and other necessities, and trade was restricted largely to luxury items that could stand the high cost of shipment. To be sure, the relative cheapness of transportation by water permitted a certain amount of crop specialization even in sailing-ship days, as witness the dependence of Athens on the wheat-lands of what is now the Ukraine and the dependence of Rome on grain shipped by sea from Egypt and other parts of North Africa. The partial dependence of Great Britain on specialized producing areas overseas also began before the development of modern forms of transportation. As just one example, the introduction of superior English ships into the Mediterranean in the fifteenth century in part made feasible winter navigation even in that inland sea (Braudel, 1949).

Transportation consumes an important part of the world's energy. In a modern industrial country like the United States, I estimate that about 20 per cent of the labor force is directly or indirectly employed in the operation, servicing, manufacturing, and selling of transportation and communication facilities. In a primitive society, equipped with little or no machinery, the daily output of energy is also great, as each person laboriously moves things from place to place within a small area. But the volume and distance of movement are small; the scale and range of spatial relations are likewise small.

It may be that the energy devoted to transport in primitive societies is as great as in modern ones, even though movement is negligible. Specialists in transportation operation or manufacture are few, and much movement is dependent on part-time efforts of others. For example, on the northern China plain in the 1930's great distances were not traversed by carts, in part because the farmers who provided the service were loath to leave their farms untended for more than three or four days (Yang, 1944). Even in the United States farmers not long ago had to devote much energy to local hauls, as the following statement of an Iowa farmer indicates (Moe and Taylor, quoted in Atherton, 1954, pp. 238–39):

> Years ago to haul hogs to market, I had to get the help of five of my neighbors. In 6 wagons we would carry 30 hogs. We went 5½ miles to the railroad stop in Irwin. I had to buy a meal for the men and myself. Generally it cost me about 50 cents apiece. Those men ate a real meal, not a lunch. That's $3. To put the 6 teams in the livery barn cost $1.20. Because I had the men come and help me, I had to go and help them, which meant 5 days of work off the farm for myself and my team. The cash cost alone was $4.50. Today, I can hire a trucker to take 25 or 30 hogs to Harlan, more than twice as far, for only $2.50. He can get them there and be back in 2 hours. And I don't have to spend any time off the farm.

THE BASES FOR TRANSPORTATION AND INTERACTION

Transport is seldom improved without a demand. Many immigrants came to the United States before the steam-boat was perfected, and settlers began to push across the Appalachians before the Erie Canal or the railroads were built (Healy, 1947). Improvements in transportation alone, although important, were not as a rule responsible for the whole of increased interaction between places. What, then, are the conditions under which interaction develops? The following three-factor system is proposed for explanation.

1. *Complementarity.*—It has been asserted that circulation or interaction is a result of areal differentiation. To a degree this is true, but mere differentiation does not produce interchange. Numerous different areas in the world have no connection with each other.

In order for two areas to interact, there must be a demand in one and a supply in the other. Thus an automobile industry in one area would use the tires produced in another but not the buggy whips produced in still another. Specific complementarity is required before interchange takes place.

So important is complementarity that relatively low-value bulk products move all over the world, usually utilizing, it is true, relatively cheap water transport for most of the haul. Some cheap products in the distant interior of continents, however, also move long distances. Thus, when the steel mills were built in Chicago, they reached out as far as West Virginia to get suitable supplies of coking coal, in spite of the fact that the distance was more than five hundred miles by land transport and that the coal was of relatively low value.

Complementarity is a function both of natural and cultural areal differentiation and of areal differentiation based simply on the operation of economies of scale (Ohlin, 1933). One large plant may be so much more economical than several smaller ones that it can afford to import raw materials and ship finished products great distances, such as specialized logging equipment from Washington to forest areas of the South. In this case the similarity of the two regions in other respects provides the market and encourages the interaction. This, however, is generally insufficient to affect significantly total interaction, because specialized products dominate the total trade of many regions. Thus total shipments from Washington to the southern states are low because of the dominance of forest products in each (Figs. 162–163). On the other hand, flows of animals and products from Iowa to the complementary Industrial Belt and California are heavy, even though these are far away (Figs. 164–165).

An example of similarity producing complementarity is provided by the overseas Chinese, who furnish a significant market for the export handicrafts and other products of the mother-country (Herman, 1954). The same occurs with Italians and other transplanted nationals. Perhaps we could generalize and say that similar cultures in different natural environments tend to promote interchange.

2. *Intervening opportunity.*—Complementarity, however, generates interchange between two areas only if no intervening source of supply is available. Thus, sixty years ago, few forest products moved from the Pacific Northwest to the markets of the interior Northeast, primarily because the Great Lakes area provided an intervening source. Florida attracts more amenity migrants from the Northeast than does more distant California. It is probable that many fewer people go from New Haven to Philadelphia than would be the case if there were no New York City in between. This, presumably, is a manifestation of Stouffer's law of intervening opportunity (1940), a fundamental determinant of spatial interaction.

Under certain circumstances inter-vening opportunity might ultimately help to create interaction between distant complementary areas by making construction of intermediate transport routes profitable and thus paying part of the cost of constructing a route to the more distant source. On a small scale this occurs with logging railroads: a line is extended bit by bit as timber nearer the mill is exhausted, whereas, if the line had had to be constructed over the long distance initially, it might never have been built. On a larger and more complex scale this is what happens in transcontinental railroads—every effort is made to develop way business, and, as this business develops, it contributes to some of the fixed costs for long-distance interchange.

3. *Transferability.*—A final factor required in an interaction system is transferability or distance, measured in real terms of transfer and time costs. If the distance between market and supply is too great and too costly to overcome, interaction will not take place in spite of perfect complementarity and lack of intervening opportunity. Alternate goods will be substituted where possible; for instance, bricks will be used instead of wood.

Thus we might consider that the factor of *intervening opportunity* results in a *substitution of areas* and that the factor of *transferability* results in a *substitution of products.*

It is a mistake to assume that every place in the world is linked equally with every other place in the world. Distance and intervening opportunity drastically trim the relative quantity of such dramatic, long-distance relationships which international trade enthusiasts like to emphasize. Great Britain and the United States provide contrasting examples. To reach enough complementary sources, Britain must trade with the world. The United States, on the other hand, has enough complementary areas within its own borders

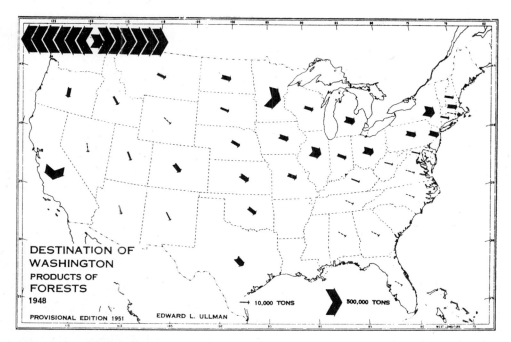

FIG. 162.—Destination, by states, of forest products shipped by rail from Washington, 1948. Width of arrows is proportionate to volume. Arrows within Washington represent intrastate movements. (Tons are short tons of 2,000 pounds).

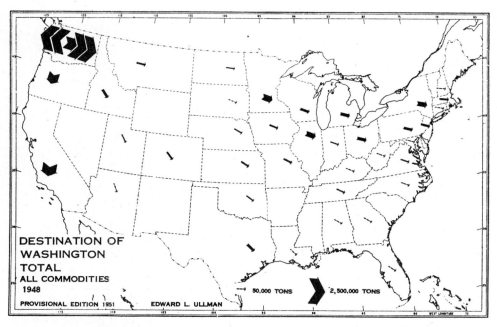

FIG. 163.—Destination, by states, of total commodities shipped by rail from Washington, 1948. Note scale of arrows is one-fifth that on Fig. 162. (Tons are short tons of 2,000 pounds.)

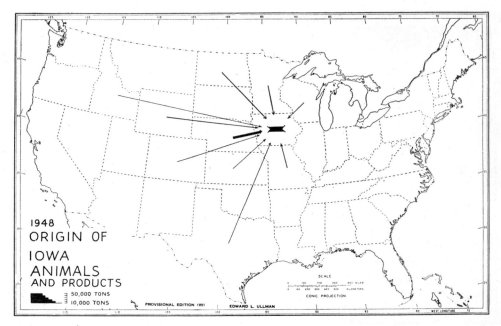

FIG. 164.—Origin, by states, of animals and products shipped by rail into Iowa, 1948. Width of lines is proportionate to volume on Figs. 164 and 165. (Tons are short tons of 2,000 pounds.)

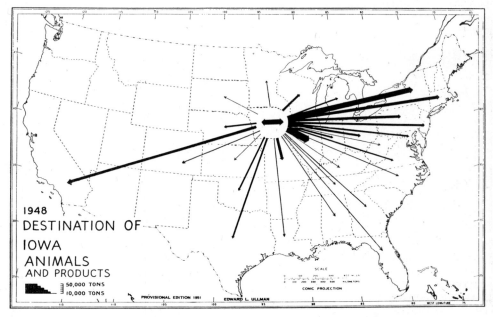

FIG. 165.—Destination, by states, of animals and products shipped by rail from Iowa, 1948. Source of data for Figs. 162 and 165 is Interstate Commerce Commission's 1 per cent sample of rail traffic reported in *Carload Waybill Analyses* (Washington, D.C., 1948) (statements: 4838, October, 1948; 492, January, 1949; 498, March, 1949; 4920, June, 1949). (Tons are short tons of 2,000 pounds.)

to account for the overwhelming bulk of its trade. Much of the remainder comes from Canada and the near-by Caribbean, although some of course comes from the farthest reaches of the world, and more will probably follow as the United States exhausts its own raw materials.

To sum up, a system explaining material interaction can be based on three factors: (1) *complementarity*—a function of areal differentiation promoting spatial interaction; (2) *intervening opportunity* (or intervening complementarity) between two regions or places; and (3) *transferability* measured in real terms, including cost and time of transport and effect of improvement in facilities.

The system proposed applies primarily to interaction based on physical movement, principally of goods but also to a large extent of people. It does not apply to spread of ideas or to most other types of communication, except as they accompany the flow of goods or people, which admittedly is often the case. Intervening opportunity, for example, would seem to facilitate rather than check the spread of ideas. Similarity of two regions also probably would facilitate the spread of ideas more than difference or complementarity, although the latter would be important in some cases.

An empirical formula often employed to describe interaction is a gravity model which states that interaction between two places is directly proportionate to the product of the populations (or some other measures of volume) and inversely proportionate to the distance (or distance to some exponent) apart of the two areas. This measure is often written P_1P_2/d, where P is population place and d is the distance apart of the two places. This model, however, is useless in describing many interactions, because it assumes perfect or near-perfect complementarity, a condi-

tion which seldom obtains for physical flows. Some form of the model (with d modified by some exponent, n) apparently does come close to describing many interchanges, even for goods in a few cases, but apparently primarily for more or less universal, undifferentiated types of flow such as migration of some people or telephone calls between cities. It has been developed by Zipf (e.g., 1949), Stewart (e.g., 1947), Dodd (e.g., 1950), and others (Cavanaugh, 1950).

The three-factor system of complementarity, intervening opportunity, and distance, however, will cover, I believe, any case of material interaction of goods or people. The system should be kept in mind by investigators lest they be led astray by assigning exclusive weight to only one of the factors in attempting to explain past interaction or in predicting interaction under changed conditions.

Traffic versus Facilities as Generators of Interchange

Examples of erroneous single-factor explanations are numerous. One type concerns the role of traffic versus that of facilities as promoters of interchange, as has been noted earlier. Thus New York City was the largest port in the United States before the Erie Canal was built (Albion, 1939), and its size plus some settlement in the West made feasible construction of the Erie Canal, just as the opening of the canal had the effect later of drastically cutting real distance and enormously facilitating interchange and the growth of New York. Likewise, the great voyages of discovery were made in large part to tap the growing traffic between the Orient and Europe. Between these two centers were no significant intervening opportunities, although some were discovered as the routes were developed.

A more detailed example is provided by the opening of the St. Gotthard Pass across the Swiss Alps in the thirteenth century (Gilliard, 1929). According to an earlier, ingenious interpretation by the German historian Aloys Schulte, in 1900, it was the invention and construction of a suspension chain bridge along the vertical walls of the gorges of Schoellenen that opened up this best of all passes and produced a flood of traffic through Switzerland. Thus it was not William Tell who won independence for Switzerland but an unknown blacksmith who built the chain bridge which opened Switzerland to the currents of freedom from the south and the trade to support many people. Twenty-five years later careful research by scholars indicated that, (1) before the hanging bridge was built, the precipitous gorge actually had been by-passed without too great difficulty via a longer route through Oberalp; (2) hanging bridges of the type noted were in reality common in the Alps by the thirteenth century; (3) the key bridge was not really the one credited but rather another farther downstream, which had been built of stone masonry by an unknown mason, requiring much more effort and capital than a mere suspension bridge; and, finally, and most important, (4) this key bridge and the rest of the route were not built until traffic was sufficient to pay for them! The traffic was generated by increased activity in the complementary regions of Flanders and the Rhineland, on the one hand, and the upper Po Valley, on the other hand, between which were few intervening complementary sources. Thus we must conclude that traffic was equally, if not more, instrumental in creating the route than was construction of the route.

A still different type of erroneous single-factor analysis concerns the role of certain features of the natural environment in promoting or retarding interchange. Mountain ranges, for example, are commonly thought of as barriers to interchange, but in many cases their barrier quality may be more than compensated for by the differentiation or complementarity which they produce. Thus climate, in many instances, differs on two sides of a mountain range; this difference may create interchange. More directly, the mountains themselves may be so different as to generate interaction, as in the case of transhumance—the moving of animals from lowland winter pastures to mountain summer pastures. Even more important in the modern world is the production of minerals in mountains associated with folding, faulting, uncovering of subsurface deposits by stream erosion, or other occurrences. The central Appalachians thus provide enormous quantities of coal, producing the largest single commodity flow in America. The Colorado Rockies, because of minerals, at one time had a denser network of rail lines than neighboring plains areas, in spite of formidable difficulties of penetration.

Potential Interaction

An example of the second reason for using the system—to predict or understand potential interaction under changed conditions—is provided by Portland, Maine, and Canada. At the end of the nineteenth century Portland was known as the winter outlet for Canada because it was the nearest ice-free port. The Grand Trunk Railroad built a line down from Canada to the city and also extensive docks at Portland. Canadian wheat was shipped out in quantity. Then Canada decided to keep the wheat flows within its borders and diverted the trade to the more distant, ice-free ocean ports of St. John and Halifax in the Maritime Provinces of Canada. Portland declined. Recently two changes have occurred. First, during World War II a pipeline for gasoline was constructed from Portland to Montreal to save long tanker trips from the Caribbean and Gulf of Mexico to Montreal through submarine-infested waters and to insure a year-round supply when the St. Lawrence River was frozen in winter. This gave Portland a shot in the arm and resulted in construction of large tank farms.

The second change can be illustrated by a story. In the summer of 1950, on a Sunday night, I stood on the international border between Derby Line, Vermont, and Rock Island, Quebec, and marveled at the constant stream of automobiles returning to Canada. I asked the customs inspector the reason, and he replied, "Ninety per cent of the cars are bound for Quebec City and are coming from Old Orchard Beach, Maine." Old Orchard Beach is near Portland and is the ocean beach nearest to parts of eastern Canada, just as Portland is the nearest ocean port. The Dominion government in this case could hardly force tourists to drive a whole extra day to reach the Maritimes (once the Canadian economy had enough dollars). Thus (1) Portland's potential complementarity reasserted itself; (2) no intervening opportunity (ocean beach) occurs between Portland and Quebec; and (3) the distance is short enough so that it can be driven in a long week end. Presumably if the distance were much greater, residents of Quebec would confine their swimming to the bathtub and use sun lamps. Needless to say, the underlying changes permitting both interactions were the invention and development of the automobile and, in conjunction with the tourist movement, increased leisure and higher standard of living, both fundamental trends, especially in Anglo-America.

A similar example, but one in the nature of a prediction, is the reasonable expectation by Professor Folke Kristensson of the Stockholm School of Economics that, as living standards rise in Sweden, Swedish diet will change, as the American diet has, and more fresh fruits and vegetables will be consumed the year round. This will result in increased interaction between Sweden and the nearest complementary sources—Italy, southern France, North Africa, etc.—just as occurred between the northeastern United States and Florida and California, today a fundamental feature of the American interaction pattern.

In fact, it is difficult to conceive of any changes—technical, political, social, or economic—which do not have some effect on interaction patterns and concomitantly on man's modification of the earth.

TRANSPORTATION PATTERN OF THE UNITED STATES

The results of the forces noted above are summed up by Figure 166, which shows traffic flow on American and Canadian railroads.[2] The map is based on prewar data but on this scale is essentially correct today. Only lines carrying more than 1,000,000 net tons of freight per year are shown; these lines represent about 90 per cent of the American rail traffic measured in ton-miles. Highways are not shown, but their inclusion would hardly change the pattern, since highways even today carry only about 15 per cent of the ton-miles as compared to the railroads' more than 50 per cent, and the highways generally parallel the railways.

2. This map, based on private data collected by H. H. Copeland and Sons, has never been published before. It and numerous detailed origin and destination maps will be included in a forthcoming monograph on "American Commodity Flow and Rail Traffic." Additional analysis and maps for three states are in an article published in *Die Erde* (Ullman, 1955). Other maps showing facilities and more detailed analysis have been published (Ullman, 1949, 1951).

RAILWAY TRAFFIC

ON LINES OF CLASS ONE RAILWAYS
HAULING OVER 1,000,000 NET TONS
PER MILE PER YEAR
ADJUSTED TO 1929 TRAFFIC LEVELS

FIG. 166.—Traffic flow on United States and Canadian railroads. Figures are for late 1930's, adjusted to previous high level of 1929. (Prepared from data copyrighted by H. H. Copeland and Sons, New York; Canadian lines added and map adapted by Edward L. Ullman.)

Cross-Grain Pattern of American Transportation

Note the cross-grain pattern of the flows in the United States and Canada in Figure 166. Relief generally runs north-south, but traffic more generally moves east-west. Where possible, the railroads use *dioric* streams or gaps crossing some of the grain of the country, such as the Columbia, New, Kanahwa, Potomac, Susquehanna, Juniata, and, especially, Mohawk rivers (Ullman, 1951). Only the latter cuts entirely across the Appalachians, yet traffic through its gap via the New York Central, while heavy, is less than on the Pennsylvania or other lines which climb over the mountains. This cross-grain alignment of America is perhaps the major modification of the American earth due to transport. Transport connections are a more real feature of the geography of an area from a human-interaction viewpoint than is terrain. The inland waterways flow map (Fig. 167), depicting less than 5 per cent of total United States traffic, reveals a pattern geared more to the grain of the country. Prior to the opening of the Erie Canal in 1825 and the railroads thereafter, the American Middle West shipped goods south via the Mississippi and thence via coastal ships around to New York and other eastern seaboard ports (Taylor, 1951). The existence of this traffic spurred construction of the transappalachian lines and linked the East with the heart of America.

TRANSPORTATION AND THE AMERICAN INDUSTRIAL BELT COMPARED TO EUROPE

The other major feature which emerges from this pattern is the focusing of the transport net on the Industrial Belt and on contiguous productive farm land (Fig. 168). The Industrial Belt, because of its marked dominance in America, naturally has the greatest volume of transportation; it also aligns the routes of the rest of the country, since it is the great market. Raw materials are shipped to it, and finished products are shipped out; as a result, traffic going into the belt is two or three times heavier than the return flows of lighter-weight, higher-value finished products. Note this phenomenon in Figures 164 and 165 (p. 870), where Iowa receives more animals and products from the West but ships more of them to the East, a standard feature of the United States pattern. The only other market area of even close intensity is the southern half of California, but it is tiny in comparison with the main belt (Harris, 1954). It is growing rapidly and affecting shipments; the only animals and products (mainly pork products) shipped west from Iowa in volume are, logically, to California, in spite of the great distance.

The Industrial Belt in one sense represents man's major modification of the American earth. It has its counterpart in Western Europe, the other heart of the world, and to a lesser extent in Russia, with other minor areas around the world. The American Industrial Belt, like Western Europe, is strongly dependent on coal which is in or adjacent to it and which furnishes the chief traffic to the railroads. Iron ore is also accessible in both cases in the United States, because cheap Great Lakes water transport is used to bring it to the belt. The heavy density of short lines on the northwestern end of Lake Superior (Fig. 166) shows the rail haul of this ore from the Mesabi Range to Lake Superior for transshipment.

A new and vital resource which the Industrial Belt has in only negligible quantities is petroleum-natural gas, already the major source of energy in the United States. Fortunately for the Industrial Belt, oil is cheaply transported by pipeline or tanker, and gas by pipe;

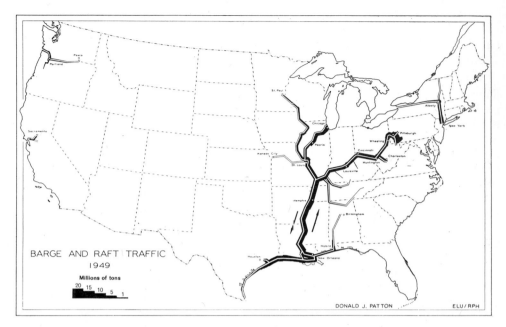

FIG. 167.—Traffic flow on United States inland waterways, 1949. (Donald J. Patton from Corps of Engineers data and field investigations.)

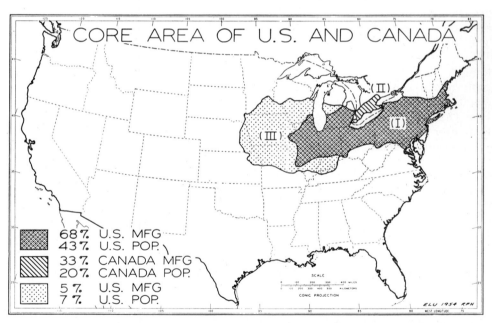

FIG. 168.—Core area of the United States and Canada. Additional data for these regions: Area I: 7.7 per cent U.S. area; 52 per cent U.S. income; 70 per cent of persons listed in *Who's Who*. Area III: 6.9 per cent U.S. area; 7.3 per cent U.S. income. Areas I and III combined: 14.6 per cent U.S. area; 50.3 per cent U.S. population; 59 per cent U.S. income; 73.3 per cent U.S. industrial employment. Area II: 0.4 per cent area of Canada; 19.8 per cent population; and 33 per cent Canadian industrial employment. Areas I and II combined percentage of U.S. and Canada: area 3.7; population 41.2; industrial employment 65.9. Areas I, II, and III combined percentage of U.S. and Canada: area 6.9; population 47.7; industrial employment 70.8.

as a result, the 1,000–1,500-mile distance from the southwestern fields is no major handicap. This movement by pipeline and tanker has become an important feature of the American traffic pattern. Already natural-gas lines cover more route miles than railroads. Western Europe is in a parallel situation; it has little or no petroleum, but petroleum is available in the Middle East only slightly farther away than the American supplies are from the United States belt. Cheap tanker transport is employed, but natural gas as yet cannot be piped across conflicting political jurisdictions to Western Europe. This is a handicap; the market and supply are obviously both large, and the distance is not excessive. Will this strong complementarity triumph over the poor transferability resulting from political fragmentation, or will political barriers continue to prevent the substitution of the new fuel for the old?

CONCLUSION

The major modification of the earth by transport is the creation of large specialized agricultural and industrial areas, although improvement of transport has also created some uniformities. The major change has been in the scale of regional differentiation.

Transport improvement alone does not develop the increased interaction so characteristic of much of the modern world. Rather, a three-factor system of complementarity, intervening opportunity, and transferability (or distance) is suggested as a basis for explaining material interaction. The process of interaction links only certain areas, often in a quite specialized way, and leaves other areas relatively untouched. Bases for interaction with many hitherto relatively untouched areas, however, are growing, along with depletion of resources near markets, use of new ones

by a changing technology, and extensions and improvements in transportation.

Some results of interaction processes are shown in (1) the predominantly cross-grain alignment of the United States and (2) the focusing of flows on the Industrial Belt, a phenomenon repeated somewhat in Western Europe and to a lesser extent in other parts of the world.

The study of interaction provides a fruitful field for investigation of the modification of the earth by man. It is evident even in the natural world (Whitaker, 1932), although it is the result of a quite different process probably requiring other explanations for sophisticated understanding. In the border zone between the natural and cultural worlds, as in the origin and diffusion of domesticated plants and animals, interaction is a rewarding field for investigation (e.g., Sauer, 1952).

In the cultural world interaction appears to be a topic of growing interest in many disciplines, although different labels may be attached to it. In economics, the term "linkages" is commonly employed (Social Science Research Council, 1954). In sociology, interaction is extensively investigated, although it is often defined somewhat more narrowly and specifically. In political science, study of interaction patterns has been termed "one of the two basic ways to describe and explain international politics," the other being a decision-making approach (Snyder, in Deutsch, 1953). In history and other fields, the diffusion of ideas and their effects has been treated often and is considered by some to be a major unifying thesis (Highet, 1954). In geography and in understanding man's modification of the earth, interaction is implicit. A goal of this paper has been to make it more explicit.

REFERENCES

ABRAMOVITZ, MOSES
1955 "The Economic Characteristics of Railroads and the Problem of Economic Development," *Far Eastern Quarterly*, XIV, No. 2, 169–78.

ALBION, ROBERT
1939 *The Rise of New York Port*. New York: Charles Scribner's Sons. 485 pp.

ALEXANDER, JOHN
1944 "Freight Rates as a Geographic Factor in Illinois," *Economic Geography*, XX, 25–30.

ATHERTON, LEWIS
1954 *Main Street on the Middle Border*. Bloomington: Indiana University Press. 423 pp.

BOGGS, S. W.
1941 "Mapping the Changing World: Suggested Developments in Maps," *Annals of the Association of American Geographers*, XXXI, 119–28.

BOGUE, DONALD J.
1949 *The Structure of the Metropolitan Community: A Study of Dominance and Subdominance*. (Contributions of the Institute for Human Adjustment, Social Science Research Project, University of Michigan.) Ann Arbor: University of Michigan Press. 210 pp.

BRAUDEL, FERNAND
1949 *La Mediterranée et le monde mediterranéen à l'époque de Philippe II*. Paris: Librairie Armand Colin. 1,160 pp.

CAMMANN, SCHUYLER
1951 *Trade through the Himalayas*. Princeton, N.J.: Princeton University Press. 186 pp.

CAPOT-REY, R.
1946 *Géographie de la circulation sur les continents*. Paris: Gallimard. 297 pp.

CAVANAUGH, JOSEPH A.
1950 "Formulation, Analysis and Testing of the Interactance Hypotheses," *American Sociological Review*, XV, 763–66.

CHRISTALLER, WALTER
1935 *Die zentralen Orte in Süddeutschland*. Jena: Gustav Fischer. 331 pp.

COOLEY, C. H.
1894 *The Theory of Transportation*. ("Publications of the American Economic Association," Vol. IX.) 148 pp.

CROWE, P. R.
1938 "On Progress in Geography," *Scottish Geographical Magazine*, LIV, 1–19.

DAGGETT, STUART
1955 *Principles of Inland Transportation*. 4th ed. New York: Harper & Bros. 788 pp.

DAGGETT, STUART, and CARTER, JOHN P.
1947 *The Structure of Transcontinental Railroad Rates*. Berkeley: University of California Press. 165 pp.

DEUTSCH, KARL W.
1953 *Political Community at the International Level: Problems of Definition and Measurement*. (Introduction by RICHARD C. SNYDER.) ("Organizational Behavioral Section, Foreign Policy Analysis Project," Series No. 2.) Princeton, N.J.: Princeton University. 71 pp.

DODD, S. C.
1950 "The Interactance Hypothesis: A Gravity Model Fitting Physical Masses and Human Behavior," *American Sociological Review*, XV, 245–56.

FEBVRE, LUCIEN, and DEMANGEON, ALBERT
1931 *Le Rhin*. Strasbourg: La Société Générale Alsacienne du Banque, Imprimerie Strasbourgeoise. 307 pp.

FROMONT, PIERRE
1948 "Les Chemins de fer et l'agriculture," *L'Année Ferroviare, 1948*, pp. 63–96. Paris: Librairie Plon.

GILLIARD, CHARLES
1929 "L'Ouverture du Gothard," *Annales d'histoire économique et sociale*, I, 177–82.

GOODFELLOW, D. M.
1931 *A Modern Economic History of South Africa*. London: G. Routledge & Sons. 267 pp.

GOUROU, PIERRE
1949 "Civilisations et malchance géographique," *Annales, économies, sociétés, civilisations*, October–December, pp. 445–50.

HARRIS, CHAUNCY D.
1954 "The Market as a Factor in the Localization of Industry in the United States," *Annals of the Association of*

American Geographers, XLIV, No. 4, 315–48.

HARRIS, CHAUNCY D., and ULLMAN, EDWARD L.
1945 "The Nature of Cities," *Annals of the American Academy of Political and Social Science*, CCXLII, 7–17.

HARTSHORNE, RICHARD
1939 *The Nature of Geography*. Lancaster, Pa.: Association of American Geographers. 482 pp.

HEALY, KENT R.
1940 *The Economics of Transportation in America*. New York: Ronald Press Co. 575 pp.
1947 "Transportation as a Factor in Economic Growth," *Journal of Economic History*, VII, 72–88.

HERMAN, THEODORE
1954 "An Analysis of China's Export Handicraft Industries to 1930." (Ph.D. dissertation, University of Washington, Seattle.)

HIGHET, GILBERT
1954 *The Migration of Ideas*. New York: Oxford University Press. 85 pp.

HUNTER, LOUIS C.
1934 "Studies in Economic History of the Ohio Valley," *Smith College Studies in History*, XIX, Nos. 1–2, 1–32.

KIRKLAND, EDWARD C.
1948 *Men, Cities and Transportation*. 2 vols. Cambridge, Mass.: Harvard University Press. 528+499 pp.

KLIMM, LESTER E.
1954 "The Empty Areas of the Northeastern United States," *Geographical Review*, XLIV, No. 3, 325–45.

KOHL, J. G.
1850 *Der Verkehr und die Ansiedlungen der Menschen in ihrer Abhängigkeit von der Gestaltung der Erdoberfläche*. 2d ed. Leipzig: Arnold. 602 pp.

LAMBIE, JOSEPH T.
1954 *From Mine to Market: A History of Coal Transportation on the Norfolk and Western Railway*. New York: New York University Press. 380 pp.

MACKINDER, H. J.
1890 "The Physical Basis of Political Geography," *Scottish Geographical Magazine*, VI, 78–84.

MAYER, HAROLD M.
1954 "Great Lakes–Overseas: An Expanding Trade Route," *Economic Geography*, XXX, No. 2, 117–43.

OHLIN, BERTIL
1933 *Interregional and International Trade*. Cambridge, Mass.: Harvard University Press. 617 pp.

OUREN, TORE, and SØMME, AXEL
1949 *Trends in Inter-war Trade and Shipping*. ("Norwegian University School of Business, Geographical Series," Publication No. 5.) Bergen. 72 pp.

PENROSE, E. F.
1952 "The Place of Transport in Economic and Political Geography," *Transport and Communications Review*, V, No. 2, 1–8. New York: United Nations.

PLATT, R. S.
1949 "Reconnaissance in Dynamic Regional Geography: Tierra del Fuego," *Revista geografica*, V–VIII, 3–22. Rio de Janeiro.

SAUER, CARL O.
1952 *Agricultural Origins and Dispersals*. (Bowman Memorial Lectures, Series Two.) New York: American Geographical Society. 110 pp.

SCHEU, ERWIN
1924 *Deutschland's wirtschaftsgeographische Harmonie*. Breslau: F. Hirt. 175 pp.

SESTINI, ALDO
1952 "L'Organizzazione umana dello spazio terrestre," *Rivista geografica italiana*, LIX, 73–92.

SIEGFRIED, ANDRÉ
1940 *Suez and Panama*. Trans. from the French by H. H. and DORIS HENNING. New York: Harcourt, Brace & Co. 400 pp.

SMITH, ADAM
1937 *The Wealth of Nations*. New York: Modern Library. 976 pp. (1st ed., 1776–79.)

SOCIAL SCIENCE RESEARCH COUNCIL
1954 *Interregional Linkages: Proceedings of the Western Committee on Regional Economic Analysis*. Berkeley, Calif.

SOMBART, WERNER
1916 *Der moderne Kapitalismus*. 2 vols. 2d rev. ed. Munich and Leipzig: Duncker & Humblot. 919+1,229 pp.

STEWART, J. Q.
  1947 "Empirical Mathematical Rules concerning the Distribution and Equilibrium of Population," *Geographical Review*, XXXVII, 461–85.

STOUFFER, SAMUEL
  1940 "Intervening Opportunities: A Theory Relating Mobility to Distances," *American Sociological Review*, XV, 845–67.

TAYLOR, GEORGE ROGERS
  1951 *The Transportation Revolution.* New York: Rinehart & Co. 490 pp.

THÜNEN, J. H. VON
  1910 *Der isolierte Staat in Beziehung auf Landwirtschaft und Nationalökonomie.* Jena: Gustav Fischer. 678 pp. (1st ed., 1826.)

ULLMAN, EDWARD L.
  1941 "A Theory of Location for Cities," *American Journal of Sociology*, XLVI, No. 6, 853–64.
  1949 "The Railroad Pattern of the United States," *Geographical Review*, XXXIX, No. 2, 242–56.
  1950 *United States Railroads: Classified According to Capacity and Relative Importance.* (Map.) New York: Simmons Boardman Pub. Corp.

  1951 "Rivers as Regional Bonds: The Columbia-Snake Example," *Geographical Review*, XLI, 210–25.
  1954 "Transportation Geography," pp. 147 and 310–32 in JAMES, PRESTON E., and JONES, CLARENCE F. (eds.), *American Geography: Inventory and Prospect.* Syracuse, N.Y.: Syracuse University Press. 590 pp.
  1955 "Die wirtschaftliche Verflechtung verschiedener Regionen der USA betrachtet am Güteraustausch Connecticuts, Iowas und Washingtons mit den anderen Staaten," *Die Erde*, Heft 2, pp. 129–64.

WHITAKER, J. R.
  1932 "Regional Interdependence," *Journal of Geography*, XXXI, 164–65.

YANG CHING-KUN
  1944 *A North China Local Market Economy.* New York: International Secretariat, Institute of Pacific Relations. 41 pp.

ZIPF, G. K.
  1949 *Human Behavior and the Principle of Least Effort.* Cambridge, Mass.: Addison-Wesley. 573 pp.

The Pressure of Residential-Industrial Land Use

CHAUNCY D. HARRIS[*]

We stand today in the midst of a gigantic and pervasive revolution, the urbanization of the world. This revolution has not yet spent its full force. It is in a phase of rapid upswing.

Cities are not, however, exclusively a modern phenomenon. The beginnings of life in permanent village settlements may have occurred in Mesopotamia nearly seven millenniums ago, as suggested by the excavations of Braidwood at Jarmo (1952, p. 31). Cities arose soon thereafter with the development of a specialized social and economic organization, a high density of agricultural population, and greater security. Babylon and Nineveh in Mesopotamia and Thebes and Memphis in Egypt became powerful centers, with palace, temple, and market place. Cities were the core of Greek civilization and of the Hellenistic world. The far-flung Roman Empire was the creation of a city. The population of ancient imperial Rome may have approached 700,-000, a size not again equaled in Europe until the nineteenth century.

Non-European cities surpassed those of Europe until quite recently. During the Middle Ages the cities of China far exceeded in population those of the Western world. According to unpublished estimates of Edward A. Kracke, two-score Chinese cities probably had populations of more than 100,000 each in the later Sung dynasty (A.D. 1127–1279); Hangchow, the capital, is calculated to have contained about 900,-000 persons within the city wall and 600,000 more in adjacent areas, for a total of 1,500,000. London, the largest city in England, and one of the largest in Europe, had only about 35,000 inhabitants a century later. Marco Polo found Rome and Venice small compared with the Chinese cities he had seen during the Mongol dynasty. Mexico City at the time of its conquest by Cortez may have been larger than any European city of the time. The great cities of India also doubtless outstripped those of Europe (Crane, 1955, pp. 468–69).

The proliferation of gigantic cities and their dominating economic role, however, are particularly characteristic of the mechanized, industrialized, commercialized, specialized, interdependent Western world—the child of the industrial revolution. Modern cities are the most stupendous of man's cultural artifacts. They rise high into the sky and sprawl over thousands of square miles, effacing visible relics of the natural landscape or of agricultural land use. Furthermore, by the activities, in-

* Dr. Harris is Professor of Geography at the University of Chicago and Dean of the Division of the Social Sciences. In 1946–48 he served as secretary of the Association of American Geographers. His publications include: "A Functional Classification of Cities in the United States," 1943; "The Geography of Manufacturing," 1954; and "The Market as a Factor in the Localization of Industry in the United States," 1954.

881

ventions, and products of cities, man's utilization of the earth has been utterly transformed. Indeed, "the beginning of what is distinctively modern in our civilization is best signalized by the growth of great cities" (Wirth, 1938, p. 1).

Although the amount of land currently needed for cities represents but a tiny fraction of the total surface of the earth, the demands are mounting rapidly. In this paper we select for treatment three topics: (1) In view of the expanding need for agricultural and forest products, can further encroachments of urban building on farm, forest, and wild landscape be justified? (2) How efficient is the city in the utilization of resources? (3) What are the present and potential total urban land needs?

URBAN EXPANSION AT THE EXPENSE OF OTHER LAND USES: GOOD OR BAD?

Protests against the waste of good agricultural land by cities have been widely proclaimed. Many have felt that the natural fertility of the soil is its most precious resource—one that should not be sacrificed to demands merely for sites on which to place houses or factories. Urban buildings cover the soil and prevent the utilization of its direct food-producing potentialities.

The French geographer Brunhes classified houses and routeways as unproductive use of the soil (1925, pp. 99–282).

A discussant at the recent American Mid-Century Conference on Resources said:

We should classify our lands, designating the lands that are most suitable for farming on a statewide basis, and then take measures to protect that land to reserve it for future farm uses. There are millions of acres that are less desirable for farming that can be used for residential and industrial purposes. But because the farm land is usually level and has roads and utilities, it is more

easily developed and goes first [Jarrett, 1954, p. 32].

In Britain the Scott Report recommended that

land which is included in one of the categories of good land should not be alienated from its present use unless it can be clearly shown that it is on balance in the national interest [with any proposed change from agricultural land bearing the onus of proof]. . . . We strongly recommend that new satellite towns, housing estates, garden cities and suburbs be sited wherever practicable away from the better farm lands. . . . As far as possible tracts of good soil in the neighbourhood of towns and villages should be kept . . . and . . . allotment holders should have security of tenure instead of the liability of being displaced by housing developments [Great Britain, Ministry of Works and Planning, 1942, pp. 86, 72, 96].

The Scott Report deplores that

sites for [urban] development have been chosen from the point of view of the usual factors affecting location, for instance, accessibility of road and rail transport, availability of public utility services and suitability of land for building purposes, and since the development value of a site far exceeds its value as agricultural land . . . there has been nothing to hinder the developer from taking his choice. It is often the best agricultural land . . . which is most suitable and least expensive from the building point of view. Having regard to the profits arising out of the sale of land for factory or housing development, it is hardly surprising that landowners and farmers . . . should have been unable to hold out against the pressures of builders [*ibid.*, p. 28].

We need to bear in mind, however, that the purpose of conserving resources is to promote the highest human welfare in the long run. Admittedly, human welfare is complex and difficult to measure. Yet, other things being equal, the higher the standard of living, the greater the welfare of man. But standard of living ultimately depends on the productivity of human labor. Man is the greatest resource of all, and we need to exercise a jealous concern for the most appropriate utilization of this resource. Probably the most flagrant waste of resources in the world today is the serious rural underemployment associated with surplus farm population in many lands.

We should not overstress the value of preserving physical materials at the expense of human effort. The story is told of workers on an estate who spent much of their time sorting old nails and straightening them. "Laudable conservation of iron," some may say, but the same amount of labor applied in mines, smelters, and nail factories would have produced more and better nails and a much higher standard of living for everyone concerned.

In assessing the relative value of alternative land uses, we should think in terms of total useful output in relation to total input, not merely in terms of physical quantities (Knight, 1935, p. 43). We need some method of making benefit-cost calculations in comparing uses of land for agriculture or for industry or for housing. The price which various activities are able to pay for the land constitutes the best single measure of the comparative value of the land for the different uses, but this measure is imperfect and inadequate. It is imperfect because institutional factors often affect the market price. It is inadequate because ends not expressed through the exchange relationship may be socially significant. For example, Britain may decide, wisely or unwisely, as a matter of public policy, to maintain a high degree of self-sufficiency in food in case of war and a shortage of shipping. Social costs and benefits affecting persons other than the user of the land should also come into the picture. The potentialities for very high land values are, of course, much greater in connection with intensive urban land uses than for extensive agricultural ones.

S. R. Dennison points out in his dissent from the Scott Report (Great Britain, Ministry of Works and Planning, 1942, p. 118) that fertility is not the only quality of land which gives it usefulness. The value of even agricultural land is partly determined by other factors such as proximity to market. The usefulness of a piece of land may be much higher for industry than for agriculture. Just to make this clear, suppose the factory in question is a fertilizer plant, an agricultural machinery works, or a chemical plant producing insecticides. The manufactured goods may make possible an increase in agricultural production on other lands a thousand times as great as the crops that could have been grown on the plant site itself. Or take another case— the use of agricultural land for an oil well. The petroleum produced through the well, if utilized for farm power in tractors, may release thousands of acres of productive land that otherwise would have to be used to grow feed for the draft horses necessary to do the same work.

The opening of the semiarid grasslands to wheat production, a remarkable advance in resource utilization and one of the major agricultural achievements of all time, depended on industrial products: the railroad for the transport of grain long distances to market and of supplies to the farm; well-drilling equipment to reach deep sources of underground water; roller mills capable of crushing hard wheat; the steel plow to break up the tough sod; agricultural machinery to make possible extensive farming with high returns per farm worker notwithstanding the low yields per acre; cheap ocean transport by steamship; and the industrial market in Western Europe for commercial grain. These products of industrialization and urbanization underlay a revolutionary increase in food production and testify that agri-

cultural output does not depend solely on the natural fertility of the soil.

American agricultural production has
been doubled in the last fifty years, not
primarily by adding new land, but by
a series of advances, many of which depended on industrialization: the expanding utilization of machinery in
many farm operations, the development
of improved insecticides and pesticides,
the replacement of farm-produced
horsepower by non-farm inanimate
power, and the increased use of fertilizer. The role of land as a factor in
agricultural production is declining as
the importance of non-farm urban-produced factors increases. Studies of land
use should emphasize total productivity
of agriculture and other activities, not
merely such items as the amount of
land occupied or the small patches lost
by farming to other activities.

The specter of Malthus rises not in
densely populated urbanized industrialized countries but in non-urbanized
ones. If they are to improve the diet,
increase the standard of living, and
raise the levels of health and sanitation,
underdeveloped areas need a whole
transformation of production through
urbanization and industrialization.

But what about housing? Should
good agricultural land be given up for
housing? It may be argued that, if there
be only a small plot of paddy land
suitable for rice production but abundant adjacent upland, maximum production would be obtained by locating
the farmhouse off the paddy field. But
suppose that rich corn land extended
unbroken over a tract of several thousand square miles, as in central Illinois,
should the farmers be forced to com-
mute from outside the area in order to
preserve all land for corn production?
By allocating a small corner of the farm
to a homestead, the farmer saves effort,
which, applied to the remaining land,
results in higher total output than if he
spent a large part of his time traveling

between field and home. Land for urban housing, as for a farm homestead,
is valuable for many qualities but especially for its potentialities for saving
time and effort in the journey to work.
Accessibility is the key. The use of land
for urban housing, by saving human
energy, may contribute far more to the
net of valued outputs over valued inputs than would use of the same land
for agriculture.

In Britain the expansion of housing
onto agricultural land has been widely
publicized and legally restricted. For a
time after World War II building licenses for houses in certain rural areas
of Great Britain were denied to individuals who could not demonstrate a
connection with agriculture. Yet a
study by Vince (1952, pp. 74–76) indicates that in many British rural areas
the density of population is too low to
provide minimum social amenities. He
therefore raises the question whether
elements of the non-farm population
should not be attracted to rural areas
in order to help support amenities and
thereby make rural life attractive
enough to discourage further rural depopulation. The argument, then, is
really for the diversion of some agricultural land for residential uses in order
to prevent erosion of the rural human
resources. But does such land utilization for non-farm purposes differ in
essence from urban residential occupance? In the Manufacturing Belt of
the United States, especially in southern Michigan, industrial urban workers
are diffused, by use of the automobile,
throughout vast rural areas and occupy widely separated dwellings set
among and on farms.

If any particular bit of urban building could be sited with equal cost of
construction and with equal convenience and desirability on poor as on
good agricultural land, even a moderate
difference in land cost should divert the
construction to the cheaper but equally

suitable land. But the question is whether other land is really equally suitable for urban purposes. The arbitrary reservation of *all* good land for agriculture could result only in a lower standard of living through decreased efficiency in the performance of urban functions.

Some types of urban land use are incredibly more intensive than agricultural use. For example, on a piece of land about equal in area to a good-sized farm, 200 acres, just south of Times Square in New York City, 150,-000 workers are engaged in the women's clothing industry. The population supported by work in this tract is about the same size as the rural farm population of the entire state of Kansas.

Perhaps we should recall at this point that man's material prosperity has always been associated with altering the landscape. The return of the land to a wild or natural landscape, if that were possible, would deny to man the material foundation on which advanced cultures can be built and thus would condemn him to an uncivilized existence. Cities transform the landscape more drastically than other types of land use, but they also have greater potentialities for maximizing the productivity of the human resource.

EFFICIENCY OF CITIES IN THE UTILIZATION OF RESOURCES: THE ECONOMIC BASIS FOR URBANIZATION

The city is the most efficient instrument yet devised by man for utilizing resources in most types of production, distribution, and consumption. The most eloquent testimonial to its effectiveness is its very growth. As Florence points out (1955, p. 88), "On the assumption of the survival of the fittest, their prevalence constitutes a prima facie case for the economic advantages of a metropolis and metropolitan cities." Florence outlines the major economic efficiencies of cities: efficiency in production is favored by low cost of assembly, low cost of distribution, economies of scale through large plants or massing of small plants, and economies of combining the factors of production, three of which—labor, capital, and management—are more easily secured in urban concentrations. Efficiency in the urban pattern of income is indicated by stabilization of income through alternative opportunities for employment, by increasing income per head, and by greater equalities in income. The key factors as noted by Harold M. Mayer (comment in R. M. Fisher, 1955, p. 150) are accessibility through the focusing of transport on cities and variety through the massing of resources and facilities. The metropolis, in its variety, affords a wider selection of economic opportunities to the individual than any other form of human settlement; an individual has his choice of many types of work without changing his residence or of many types of housing without changing his job (Mayer, 1955, pp. 215–16). The employer similarly has a wide choice and can expand, contract, or alter his activities with maximum flexibility. Such flexibility facilitates more productive use of human and other resources. The city is also a center of intellectual contacts stimulating cross-fertilization of ideas, recognition of opportunities, and facilities for research—all conducive to progress in increasing future productivity.

Edgar M. Hoover (in Greer, 1942, pp. 1–5) predicts that the course of technology and social organization will more and more favor large metropolitan centers. Among the developments he foresees are improved long-distance transportation, reduction of the urban and rural industrial wage differentials, search for security and diversity of metropolitan employment, construction of large plants to utilize existing metropolitan facilities, services, and labor supply, and the cumulative effect of metropolitan growth. Paul Samuelson (*ibid.*, pp. 6–17) notes that rising prosperity results in ever higher proportions of total income being spent on products of cities rather than of farms. He further asserts not only that unemployment is greater in rural areas than in cities (though often disguised) but that during depressions the per capita income falls more sharply in rural areas than in urban ones.

URBAN LAND NEEDS: HOW MUCH?

The total urban requirement for space is a function of two major variables: (1) total urban population and (2) urban density of population, that is, the intensity with which space is utilized for residential, industrial, and similar uses.

Urban Population

The number of city dwellers depends in part on the total population. The number of people in the world has multiplied by ten times in the last two thousand years. It took about seventeen centuries of this period for the population to double. Then with the great population explosion of European overseas expansion and the industrial revolution the population multiplied by another five times in only three centuries.

With the population explosion came rapid urbanization; cities have mushroomed particularly in the last century and a half. In 1800 only London approached a million population. Today eighty-two cities, nearly equally divided among Europe, Asia, and the Americas, have more than a million inhabitants each. In the last one hundred and fifty years the number of people living in cities of more than 100,000 population has multiplied by more than twenty times—from 15.6 million in 1800 to 313.7 million in 1950 (Davis, 1955, pp. 433–34). The proportion of the world population living in such cities rose from 2 per cent to 13 per cent. In the United States in this same period the total urban population increased from 0.3 to 96.5 million, and the proportion from 6 to 64 per cent.

In most industrialized or commercialized countries more than half the population lives in cities, whether in industrial states, such as Britain or Germany; countries with balanced economies, such as France; new countries with commercial agriculture, such as Australia, New Zealand, Cuba, or Argentina; or oriental countries with new industrialization, such as Japan. The world-wide distribution of large cities and the high proportion of the total population living in them are phenomena of modern industrial society. Many countries are on the threshold of urbanization, and a powerful further upsurge of population in cities may be confidently predicted.

Density of Population within Cities

The national average density of population within urban areas is of the same order of magnitude for such diverse lands as the United States, Japan, England and Wales, and Germany—about 5,500 persons per square mile. According to the 1950 United States census, the average density of population for the 157 metropolitan urbanized areas was 5,438 per square mile. Figures from the 1940 Japanese census for the 208 larger Japanese cities (*shi*) in boundaries as of 1943 indicated an average density of 5,500 persons per square mile. Long-urbanized England and Wales on the eve of World War II had 41 million people occupying some 4.1 million acres for urban, residential, and industrial purposes, at an average density of about 6,400 persons per square mile (Great Britain, Ministry of Works and Planning, 1942, p. 2). The 1951 census of the German Federal Republic recorded an average density of population in all cities (*Stadtkreise*) of 4,988 persons per square mile in spite of heavy World War II destruction. There are differences in the coverage of the figures, of course, since the German and Japanese data are based entirely on political boundaries and those for the United States and for England and Wales include built-up areas outside the major cities. These differences are more in form than in substance. The particular American census invention of measuring the built-up urbanized area outside city limits was called for by the widespread disparity between political units and functional units—a disparity that does not particularly characterize Japanese and German cities. In any case the near-uniformity of the average urban density figures in four different industrial countries in two major culture areas appears quite significant. We shall return to this figure later, but first we need to note that it is merely an average and masks a wide range of variations among cities, within any given city, and in time.

Urban densities vary among the cities within each country, depending on size of city and other factors. In the United States urban densities reach as high, for example, as 25,000 persons per square mile. The world's largest cities, however, whether American, European, or Asiatic, have similar densities; these densities for giant cities are about five times as high as national average urban densities. Within the city limits, New York City had a density of 25,000 persons per square mile in 1950; Paris, 27,000 in 1936; London, 28,600 in 1951 (county of London); and Tokyo, 30,-000 in 1940.

City averages mask wide variations within each urban area. In Chicago in 1950 the community area with the highest density ran four times as high as for the city as a whole, and two small census tracts ran over 100,000 per square mile, or seven times as high. In London in 1951 the highest density in a metropolitan borough (Paddington) was about twice as high, and in a tiny area, three times as high, as for the county of London as a whole. In Tokyo maximum densities run up to 240,000 per square mile, or eight times as high as the city average (Kiuchi, 1951, p. 355).

London is a good example of declining densities. World War II sharply accelerated the trend. Thus in 1921 the ward of Northeast St. George in East Stepney Metropolitan Borough had a density of 180,000 persons per square mile; by 1931 it had declined to 150,-000. As a result of damage during World War II in all the densely populated London wards, none had a density of more than 90,000 in 1951. The county of London reached its maximum density of population in 1901 (39,000 per square mile) and has been declining since. The City of London, the ancient core of the metropolis, has had a declining density for a century and a half from the time of the first national census in 1801. From 120,000 persons per square mile in 1801, the figure fell to 4,000 in 1951. From 1801 to 1851 the decline was spotty and slight, but since 1851 the density of population has dropped steeply each decade.

If the suburban trend persists, as is almost certain, the residential requirements per capita may sharply increase. Factors leading to suburbanization are many, but perhaps the most important are the desire for more (or cheaper) space and for lower expenses generally. These lower expenses are usually accompanied, of course, by lesser governmental services, whether of roads, water, sewage, police, libraries, schools, or fire protection. The density of population declines sharply outward from the city to the suburbs. Throop (1948, p. 87) found in Portland, Oregon, that the density of dwelling units in the inner suburban zone was only a fifth as high as in the city proper and in the outer suburban fringe only a fifteenth as high.

Urban densities are affected by technology in many ways. Perhaps the most obvious is by transportation. As long as people had to walk, they were forced to live at high residential densities within a few miles of places of work. With the coming of horse-drawn vehicles, railroads, streetcars, bicycles, private cars, and busses, the ability of people to remove themselves ever farther from places of work has been augmented. The result has been a growth in the demand for low-density residential land as individuals are willing to travel farther in order to obtain more living space. The transport potentialities of the automobile make possible new lines of residential development with greater flexibility in location and also greater demand for space. The telephone and other means of rapid communication also make possible a wider range of choices among locations.

Perhaps we should consider not what average urban densities are but what desirable urban densities ought to be. But we simply do not know what densities are most efficient or desirable. Desirable densities may very well differ sharply according to types of culture, economic status, and family structure. Oriental and occidental ways of life might make for contrasts in optimum densities. Luxury flats for wealthy families who go elsewhere for recreation pose quite different problems from low-cost housing for economically disadvantaged groups who must find recreation on the site. Desirable densities for unmarried single workers, for married families with young children, or for retired couples are not necessarily the same.

Such meager studies as exist indicate that either undue dispersion or excessive concentration results in higher costs. The disadvantages of high urban densities have been cited often: lack of light, open air, open play space, adequate parking facilities, and privacy and the presence of noise, dirt, smoke, and traffic hazards and congestion. Low densities in the sprawling fringes are excessively expensive to service. High public costs are particularly involved in premature subdivisions with thousands of unused lots wholly or partially served with urban facilities.

Ludlow (1953, pp. 120–98) has pointed out that further investigations are needed of at least three different aspects of urban efficiency:

1. *The cost of construction and operation of building types at alternative densities.*—The costs of building do not appear to differ greatly in various types of construction, whether of private houses, row houses, two-flats, walk-up apartments, or elevator apartments. Land cost is the critical element in the determination of the types of buildings and therefore of density of population.

2. *The cost of providing public services at various densities.*—Account needs to be taken of the cost of streets, parks and playgrounds, schools, fire and police protection, sanitation and refuse disposal, transportation facilities, and water, sewage, electricity, gas, and telephone service.

3. *Total cost of transportation at various densities, both capital and operation cost of movement of goods and of people.*—The concept of movement includes raw materials for and products of factories, goods and customers for commercial enterprises, workers for all types, journeys to schools for children, and recreation for the entire family. Fatigue and peak-load characteristics of commuting are also considerations. The terminal costs, whether of loading platforms for trucks or of parking facilities for private passenger cars, need to be taken into account.

These cost factors need to be offset

by the quality of the various densities with respect to light, ventilation, family privacy, and space for outdoor recreation. But, since most redevelopment schemes or planned housing projects are in large cities, they are built for densities much above the national urban averages.

Total Urban Land Requirements

Data on the land actually occupied by cities are available for the United States. The core of the problem of urban expansion in this country is in the metropolitan diffusions—the 157 metropolitan complexes which include cities of more than 50,000 population and the adjacent urbanized areas. These areas contained in 1950 about 70 million people, almost half the total population of the country. They occupied an area of 12,733 square miles (about 8 million acres), or less than one-half of 1 per cent of the land surface of the United States. If the entire population of the United States were clustered in such urban agglomerations at comparable densities, the total land requirement for residential, industrial, and similar land uses would be less than 30,000 square miles, or under 1 per cent of the land surface of the country.

No comprehensive world-wide data are available on the total land surface actually occupied for residential and industrial purposes or of the total land within cities at the present time. But, if all the people in the world lived in cities at an urban density of 5,500 persons per square mile, the 2.5 billion people would occupy only about 450,-000 square miles, or less than 1 per cent of the land surface of the globe.

Supposing that the population of the world were to multiply by another five times (as it has in the last three centuries), the total population could still be housed on less than 5 per cent of the land surface of the globe. If such

an increased population were to agglomerate at densities characteristic of the large cities, however, the population could still be crowded into only 1 per cent of the land surface. With technological advances, such as the automobile, individuals are able to escape from extreme crowding and flee to suburban areas; such a flight increases the urban land needs per capita. What the trends of land-use density under oriental conditions will be is not now clear.

Since the current total residential, industrial, and other urban land needs of mankind amount to only a fraction of 1 per cent of the land surface, it is obvious that neither the present nor potential total land pressures of urban agglomerations are critical. Special problems, however, may arise in connection with (1) the type of urban expansion into rural areas and (2) the pressure of urban land use in certain areas of high urbanization and sharply limited agricultural land, such as Japan, Britain, and California.

Urban land use suffers many types of maladies. One of the compelling problems is blight. Such areas typically have high tax delinquency; they impair taxable values in adjacent areas and require high costs of police, fire, and health protection. They are an economic drain on the rest of the city. Another problem is premature subdivision and overexpansion (Wehrwein, 1942, p. 223). A third problem concerns urban fringes. Suburban invasion of good farm land may result in breaking up good farming units and raising taxes for roads and other services to such an extent as to make farming unprofitable; at the same time the density of suburban infiltration may be too low to support the streets, sidewalks, water and sewage service, and other urban facilities demanded by the suburban dwellers. More attention may need to be devoted to the problems of zoning metropolitan areas to encourage a more orderly and economical transfer of land from agricultural to residential use.

The threat to *local* agricultural production in Japan and Britain is indicated by the figure that in Japan the area within city boundaries equals a fifth of the total cultivated land and by the statement of Stamp (1948, p. 437) that the need for additional urban land in Britain exceeds the total amount of first-class agricultural land in the entire country.

ENVOI

The role of cities as centers of cultural and economic change transcends their role in space competition with agriculture (Hoselitz, 1953, 1955). Industrialization and urbanization augment the power lever of man; his puny physical arm is extended a hundred fold in its ability to transform the surface of the earth. The tools by which he cuts off the great forests, churns up the soil, or gouges minerals out of the rocks are urban-produced.

Possibly more important than the artifacts of the city itself are urban-engendered attitudes. The urban way of life is penetrating rural areas through improved means of communication and transportation; many rural folk are becoming urbanized "in place." Urban-centered markets in industrial countries are the centers of organization for much of the world's economy. The rational, interdependent, market economy which underlies Western economic development stands in contrast to the tradition-bound subsistence peasant way of life. To a certain extent man loses contact with nature; his sense of close affinity with the earth as his home is numbed. He becomes social-conscious instead of nature-conscious.

Should cities be blamed or praised for making possible the high standards of living of industrial society? These standards make voracious demands on natural resources. They sustain the market for the tens of millions of tons of iron ore that flow into blast furnaces and thence into new automobiles, for the incredible quantities of forest trees that go into newsprint, and for the many metals that go into television sets. Furthermore, urbanization occasions greater pressures on agricultural resources by the improvement of diets in industrialized countries.

REFERENCES

ADAMS, THOMAS
    1936 *Outline of Town and City Planning: A Review of Past Efforts and Modern Aims.* New York: Russell Sage Foundation. 368 pp.

ANDREWS, RICHARD B.
    1942 "Elements in the Urban Fringe Pattern," *Journal of Land and Public Utility Economics,* XVIII, No. 2, 169–83.

ASCHMAN, FREDERICK T.
    1949 "Dead Land: Chronically Tax Delinquent Land in Cook County, Illinois," *Land Economics,* XXV, No. 3, 240–45.

BARTHOLOMEW, HARLAND
    1932 *Urban Land Use.* Cambridge, Mass.: Harvard University Press. 174 pp.

BOGUE, DONALD J.
    1949 *The Structure of the Metropolitan Community: A Study of Dominance and Subdominance.* (Contributions of the Institute for Human Adjustment, Social Science Research Project, University of Michigan.) Ann Arbor: University of Michigan Press. 210 pp.
    1953 *Population Growth in Standard Metropolitan Areas, 1900–1950: With an Explanatory Analysis of Urbanized Areas.* (Housing and Home Finance Agency, Division of Housing Research.) Washington, D.C.: Government Printing Office. 76 pp.
    1955 "Urbanism in the United States, 1950," *American Journal of Sociology,* LX, No. 5, 471–86.

BOGUE, DONALD J. (ed.)
1953 *Needed Urban and Metropolitan Research.* ("Scripps Foundation Studies in Population Distribution," No. 7.) Oxford, Ohio: Scripps Foundation for Research in Population Problems, Miami University. 88 pp.

BRAIDWOOD, ROBERT J.
1952 *The Near East and the Foundations for Civilization.* (Condon Lectures.) Eugene, Ore.: Oregon State System of Higher Education. 43 pp.

BREESE, GERALD W.
1949 *The Daytime Population of the Central Business District of Chicago, with Particular Reference to the Factor of Transportation.* Chicago: University of Chicago Press. 267 pp.

BRUNHES, JEAN
1925 *La Géographie humaine.* 3d ed. Paris: Felix Alcan. 974 pp. (Trans. from the French by T. C. LE COMPTE: *Human Geography.* Chicago: Rand McNally & Co., 1920. 648 pp. Rev. ed., 1953.)

CARPENTER, NILES
1932 *The Sociology of City Life.* New York: Longmans, Green & Co. 502 pp.

CHABOT, GEORGES
1948 *Les Villes: Aperçu de géographie humaine.* Paris: Armand Colin. 224 pp.

COLBY, CHARLES C.
1933 "Centrifugal and Centripetal Forces in Urban Geography," *Annals of the Association of American Geographers,* XXIII, No. 1, 1–20.

CORNICK, PHILIP H.
1938 *A Report to the State Planning Council of New York on the Problems Created by the Premature Subdivision of Urban Land in Selected Metropolitan Districts in the State of New York.* Albany, N.Y.: Division of State Planning. 346 pp.

CRANE, ROBERT I.
1955 "Urbanism in India," *American Journal of Sociology,* LX, No. 5, 463–70.

DAVIS, KINGSLEY
1955 "The Origin and Growth of Urbanization in the World," *American Journal of Sociology,* LX, No. 5, 429–37.

DEMANGEON, ALBERT
1947 *Problèmes de géographie hu-*
maine. 3d ed. Paris: Armand Colin. 405 pp.

DENNISON, S. R.
1939 *The Location of Industry and the Depressed Areas.* London: Oxford University Press. 216 pp.

DICKINSON, ROBERT E.
1947 *City, Region, and Regionalism: A Geographical Contribution to Human Ecology.* London: Kegan Paul, Trench, Trubner & Co. 327 pp.
1951 *The West European City: A Geographical Interpretation.* London: Routledge & Kegan Paul. 580 pp.

DORAU, HERBERT B., and HINMAN, ALBERT G.
1928 *Urban Land Economics.* New York: Macmillan Co. 570 pp.

ELY, RICHARD T., and WEHRWEIN, GEORGE S.
1940 *Land Economics.* New York: Macmillan Co. 512 pp.

ERICKSEN, E. GORDON
1954 *Urban Behavior.* New York: Macmillan Co. 482 pp.

FISHER, ERNEST M. and ROBERT M.
1954 *Urban Real Estate.* New York: Henry Holt & Co. 502 pp.

FISHER, ROBERT M. (ed.)
1955 *The Metropolis in Modern Life.* ("Columbia University Bicentennial Conference Series.") New York: Doubleday & Co. 401 pp.

FLORENCE, P. SARGANT
1955 "Economic Efficiency in the Metropolis," pp. 85–124 (chap. vi) in FISHER, ROBERT M. (ed.), *The Metropolis in Modern Life.* New York: Doubleday & Co. 401 pp.

GEORGE, PIERRE
1952 *La Ville: La Fait urbain à travers le monde.* Paris: Presses Universitaires de France. 399 pp.

GILBERT, E. W.
1936 "The Human Geography of Roman Britain," pp. 30–87 (chap. ii) in DARBY, H. C. (ed.), *An Historical Geography of England before 1800.* Cambridge: Cambridge University Press. 566 pp.

GILMORE, HARLAN W.
1953 *Transportation and the Growth of Cities.* Glencoe, Ill.: Free Press. 170 pp.

GINSBURG, NORTON S.
1955 "The Great City in Southeast Asia," *American Journal of Sociology,* LX, No. 5, 455–62.

GIST, NOEL P., and HALBERT, L. A.
1946 *Urban Society.* 2d ed. New York: Thomas Y. Crowell Co. 629 pp.

GREAT BRITAIN, MINISTRY OF WORKS AND PLANNING
1942 *Report of the Committee on Land Utilisation in Rural Areas.* (The Scott Report.) (Command Paper No. 6378.) London: H. M. Stationery Office. 138 pp.

GREER, GUY (ed.)
1942 *The Problems of the Cities and Towns: Report of the Conference on Urbanism, Harvard University, March 5–6, 1942.* 116 pp.

HAIG, ROBERT M., and McCREA, ROSWELL C.
1927 *Major Economic Factors in Metropolitan Growth and Arrangement: A Study of Trends and Tendencies in the Economic Activities within the Region of New York and Its Environs.* ("Regional Survey," Vol. I.) New York: Regional Plan of New York and Its Environs. 111 pp.

HALLENBECK, WILBUR C.
1951 *American Urban Communities.* New York: Harper & Bros. 617 pp.

HARRIS, CHAUNCY D.
1943a "A Functional Classification of Cities in the United States," *Geographical Review,* XXXIII, No. 1, 86–99.
1943b "Suburbs," *American Journal of Sociology,* XLIX, No. 1, 1–13.
1954a "The Geography of Manufacturing," pp. 292–308 (chap. xii) in JAMES, PRESTON E., and JONES, CLARENCE F. (eds.), *American Geography: Inventory and Prospect.* Syracuse, N.Y.: Syracuse University Press. 590 pp.
1954b "The Market as a Factor in the Localization of Industry in the United States," *Annals of the Association of American Geographers,* XLIV, No. 4, 315–48.

HARRIS, CHAUNCY D., and ULLMAN, EDWARD L.
1945 "The Nature of Cities," *Annals of the American Academy of Political and Social Science,* CCXLII, 7–17.

HATT, PAUL K., and REISS, ALBERT J.
1951 *Reader in Urban Sociology.* Glencoe, Ill.: Free Press. 714 pp.

HAWLEY, AMOS H.
1950 *Human Ecology: A Theory of Community Structure.* New York: Prentice-Hall, Inc. 456 pp.

HOOVER, EDGAR M.
1948 *The Location of Economic Activity.* New York: McGraw-Hill Book Co. 310 pp.

HOSELITZ, BERT F.
1953 "The Role of Cities in the Economic Growth of Underdeveloped Areas," *Journal of Political Economy,* LXI, No. 3, 195–208.
1955 "The City, the Factory, and Economic Growth," *American Economic Review,* XLV, No. 2, 166–84.

HOYT, HOMER
1939 *The Structure and Growth of Residential Neighborhoods in American Cities.* Washington, D.C.: Government Printing Office. 178 pp.

HURD, RICHARD M.
1924 *Principles of City Land Values.* 4th ed. New York: Record and Guide. 159 pp.

ISARD, WALTER
1951 "Distance Inputs and the Space-Economy," *Quarterly Journal of Economics,* LXV, 181–98, 373–99.

JAFFE, A. J.
1951 *Summary of the Proceedings of the University Seminar on Population Held at Columbia University, 1950–51, and Devoted to the Topic of Urbanism.* New York: Columbia University, Bureau of Applied Social Research. 62 pp.

JARRETT, H. (ed.)
1954 "Urban Land," pp. 27–42 in *The Nation Looks at Its Resources.* (Mid-Century Conference on Resources for the Future.) Washington, D.C.: Resources for the Future, Inc. 418 pp.

JEFFERSON, MARK
1931 "The Distribution of the World's City Folk: A Study in Comparative Civilization," *Geographical Review,* XXI, No. 3, 446–65.
1939 "The Law of the Primate City,"

Geographical Review, XXIX, No. 2, 226–32.

KIUCHI, SHINZO
1951 *Urban Geography: The Structure and Development of Urban Areas and Their Hinterlands.* Tokyo: Kokon-Shoin. 435 pp. (In Japanese.)

KNIGHT, FRANK HYNEMAN
1935 *The Ethics of Competition and Other Essays.* London: George Allen & Unwin. 363 pp.

LIEPMANN, KATE K.
1944 *The Journey to Work, Its Significance for Industrial and Community Life.* London: Kegan Paul, Trench, Trubner & Co. 199 pp.

LÖSCH, AUGUST
1954 *The Economics of Location.* New Haven, Conn.: Yale University Press. 520 pp.

LUDLOW, WILLIAM H.
1953 "Urban Densities and Their Cost: An Exploration into the Economics of Population Densities and Urban Patterns," pp. 101–220 (Part II) in WOODBURY, COLEMAN (ed.), *Urban Redevelopment: Problems and Practices.* Chicago: University of Chicago Press. 525 pp.

McMICHAEL, STANLEY, and BINGHAM, ROBERT F.
1928 *City Growth Essentials.* Cleveland: Stanley McMichael Publishing Organization. 430 pp.

MARTIN, WALTER T.
1953 *The Rural-Urban Fringe: A Study of Adjustment to Residence Location.* Eugene, Ore.: University of Oregon Press. 109 pp.

MAYER, HAROLD M.
1945 "Moving People and Goods in Tomorrow's Cities," *Annals of the American Academy of Political and Social Science,* CCXLII, 116–28.
1954 "Urban Geography," pp. 142–66 (chap. vi) in JAMES, PRESTON E., and JONES, CLARENCE F. (eds.), *American Geography: Inventory and Prospect.* Syracuse, N.Y.: Syracuse University Press. 590 pp.
1955 "Current and Prospective Population Trends—Some Real Estate Implications," *Appraisal Journal,* XXIII, No. 2, 212–24.

MECKING, LUDWIG
1949 *Die Entwicklung der Gross-Städte in Hauptländern der Industrie.* ("Planung, Schriftenreihe für Landesplanung und Städtebau," Series II.) Hamburg: Heinrich Ellermann. 102 pp.

MITCHELL, ROBERT B. (ed.)
1945 "Building the Future City," *Annals of the American Academy of Political and Social Science,* CCXLII, 1–162.

MITCHELL, ROBERT B., and RAPKIN, CHESTER
1954 *Urban Traffic: A Function of Land Use.* New York: Columbia University Press. 226 pp.

MUMFORD, LEWIS
1938 *The Culture of Cities.* New York: Harcourt, Brace & Co. 552 pp.

NATIONAL RESOURCES COMMITTEE
1937 *Our Cities: Their Role in the National Economy.* Washington, D.C.: Government Printing Office. 87 pp.
1939a *Structure of the American Economy,* Part I: *Basic Characteristics.* Washington, D.C.: Government Printing Office. 396 pp.
1939b *Urban Planning and Land Policies.* ("Committee on Urbanism, Supplementary Report," Vol. II.) Washington, D.C.: Government Printing Office. 366 pp.

NATIONAL RESOURCES PLANNING BOARD
1943 *Industrial Location and National Resources.* Washington, D.C.: Government Printing Office. 360 pp.

NEW JERSEY PLANNING BOARD
1941 *Premature Land Subdivision, a Luxury.* Trenton, N.J.: New Jersey State Planning Board. 58 pp.

POLITICAL AND ECONOMIC PLANNING (P.E.P.)
1939 *Report on the Location of Industry: A Survey of Present Trends in Great Britain Affecting Industrial Location and Regional Economic Development, with Proposals for Future Policy.* London: Political and Economic Planning. 314 pp.

PRESIDENT'S MATERIALS POLICY COMMISSION
1952 *Resources for Freedom.* 5 vols.

Washington, D.C.: Government Printing Office.

QUEEN, STUART A., and CARPENTER, DAVID B.
1953   *The American City.* New York: McGraw-Hill Book Co. 383 pp.

QUINN, JAMES A.
1950   *Urban Ecology.* New York: Prentice-Hall, Inc. 561 pp.

RATCLIFF, RICHARD U.
1949   *Urban Land Economics.* New York: McGraw-Hill Book Co. 533 pp.
1955   "Efficiency and the Location of Urban Activities," pp. 125–48 (chap. vii) in FISHER, ROBERT M. (ed.), *The Metropolis in Modern Life.* New York: Doubleday & Co. 401 pp.

RIEMER, SVEND
1952   *The Modern City: An Introduction to Urban Sociology.* New York: Prentice-Hall, Inc. 477 pp.

RODWIN, LLOYD
1945   "Garden Cities and the Metropolis," *Journal of Land and Public Utility Economics,* XXI, No. 3, 268–81.

SCHULTZ, J. H.
1952   *Stadtforschung und Stadtplanung.* ("Veröffentlichungen der Akademie für Raumforschung und Landesplanung," Vol. XXIII.) Bremen: Walter Dorn Verlag. 186 pp.

SMAILES, A. E.
1953   *The Geography of Towns.* London: Hutchinson's University Library. 166 pp.

SMITH, T. LYNN, and McMAHAN, C. A.
1951   *The Sociology of Urban Life: A Textbook with Readings.* New York: Dryden Press. 831 pp.

SORRE, MAX
1948–52   *Les Fondements de la géographie humaine,* Vol. II: *Les Fondements techniques;* Vol. III: *L'Habitat.* Paris: Armand Colin. 608+499 pp.

STAMP, L. DUDLEY
1948   *The Land of Britain, Its Use and Misuse.* London: Longmans, Green & Co. 507 pp.

TAYLOR, GRIFFITH
1949   *Urban Geography: A Study of Site, Evolution, Pattern and Classification in Villages, Towns and Cities.* London: Methuen & Co. 493 pp.

THROOP, VINCENT M.
1948   *The Suburban Zone of Metropolitan Portland, Oregon.* (Ph.D. dissertation, Department of Geography, University of Chicago.) Chicago: Privately printed. 244 pp.

UNITED NATIONS
1950–53   *Proceedings of the Scientific Conference on the Conservation and Utilization of Resources, Lake Success, New York, 17 August–6 September 1949.* 8 vols. New York: United Nations.
1953   *Urban Land, Problems and Policies.* (Housing and Town and Country Planning Bulletin No. 7.) New York: United Nations. 182 pp.

VAN CLEEF, EUGENE
1937   *Trade Centers and Trade Routes.* New York: D. Appleton–Century Co. 307 pp.

VINCE, S. W. E.
1952   "Reflections on the Structure and Distribution of Rural Population in England and Wales, 1921–31," *Institute of British Geographers, Transactions and Papers,* No. 18, pp. 53–76.

WEHRWEIN, GEORGE S.
1942   "The Rural-Urban Fringe," *Economic Geography,* XVIII, No. 3, 217–28.

WEIMER, ARTHUR M., and HOYT, HOMER
1954   *Principles of Real Estate.* 3d ed. New York: Ronald Press Co. 618 pp.

WIRTH, LOUIS
1938   "Urbanism as a Way of Life," *American Journal of Sociology,* XLIV, No. 1, 1–24.

WOODBURY, COLEMAN, and CLIFFE, FRANK
1953   "Industrial Location and Urban Redevelopment," pp. 103–288 (Part III) in WOODBURY, COLEMAN (ed.), *The Future of Cities and Urban Redevelopment.* Chicago: University of Chicago Press. 764 pp.

WOYTINSKY, W. S. and E. S.
1953   *World Population and Production: Trends and Outlook.* New York: Twentieth Century Fund. 1,268 pp.

WRIGLEY, ROBERT L., JR.
1947 "Organized Industrial Districts with Special Reference to the Chicago Area," *Journal of Land and Public Utility Economics*, XXIII, No. 2, 180–98.

ZIMMERMANN, ERICH W.
1951 *World Resources and Industries: A Functional Appraisal of the Availability of Agricultural and Industrial Materials*. Rev. ed. New York: Harper & Bros. 832 pp.

Recreational Land Use

ARTUR GLIKSON*

* Mr. Glikson is an architect, Head of the Planning Department of the Housing Division, Ministry of Labor of Israel, and Senior (Guest) Lecturer on National and Regional Planning at the Israel Institute of Technology in Haifa. His works include: *Report on Regional Planning and Development in the Netherlands,* 1951, and *Regional Planning and Development,* 1955.

ORIGINS OF THE RECREATIONAL MOVEMENT

A general survey of the origins of the problem of recreational land use reveals the following relevant stages of development of many industrialized countries during the last century or so:

1. Large numbers of peasants and peasants' sons gave up their ancient relationship to the soil and village, leaving their rural environment to concentrate in towns and seek employment in industries and services. Overnight, small urban or rural settlements grew enormously, both in area and in density of habitations, so that huge tracts of the surrounding landscape underwent urbanization. This expansion of urban political and economic power into the countryside and urban methods of production and commerce led first to a growing economic utilization of rural resources and later to a gradual deterioration of the rural and indigenous landscape by deforestation, mechanization of agriculture, parcellation, introduction of monocultures, faulty methods of cultivation, mining, and construction of industrial and power plants. Soil erosion, disturbance of the water cycles, and loss of fertility and of beauty of landscape are among the well-known symptoms of a man-made land disease.

2. The still increasing urban population, compressed in quarters where unhealthy conditions prevailed, remote from the open country, began to sense what it had lost and raised a demand for temporary environmental compensation. The rural and indigenous environment became for the urbanite a recreational environment. The peasant sons still wished to return to the country for a holiday. Gradually the need for recreational facilities to maintain the health and efficiency of the urban population became recognized. However, during the period of urban expansion the original cultural landscape had been largely defaced and turned into the "steppe of culture"—as the Dutch call the new rural pattern. Only isolated parts—often spots of economic decay—had kept their original rural character.

3. Pressure of vacationers on the remaining rural and indigenous places and on newly established resorts became violent. This very pressure destroyed these places as true resources for restful recreation. In the attempt to escape overcrowding and noise and to rediscover landscape, holiday-makers were driven ever farther away from the cities. Gradually, social and medical demands for recreational areas for the inhabitants of big cities became incompatible with the physical limitations of, or distance to, recreational land. The recreational movement of the population was hampered, and, as the crisis

became obvious, there originated the problem of recreational land use.

The recreational movement should be considered as belonging to the wider contemporary phenomenon of population movement to and from the big centers—of spatial contraction and expansion of resources and commodities, of people and ideas. The most obvious and well known of these phenomena is the tremendous concentration of population and produce from the most distant regions in metropolitan and other big-city centers. In the dynamics of city life the demand for recreation represents a reaction against the psychophysical complexity of life introduced by centralization and industrialization and reveals a tendency to reverse the prevailing spatial relations. It is an attempt to balance the centripetal concentration by centrifugal diffusion—by a temporary escape back to the places of natural and historic origin of the people: to the indigenous and rural landscape, the hamlet, the little town bypassed by modern development—in the hope of restoring, of "recreating," health, energy, and mental equilibrium.

We have little evidence of specifically recreational land use and facilities for preindustrial periods, because they represented a wholly integrated and therefore unrecognizable ingredient of environment. Private gardens and orchards, large public squares, the well, the streets, and the near-by surrounding rural landscape, all in the context of but moderate housing density generally, provided for the recreational needs of the medieval citizen. In ancient health resorts, such as Bath in England, Tiberias in Israel, and Epidaurus in Argolis, people were not directly seeking relaxation and change but rather the healing qualities of air, water, and places. In comparison with our century, any recreational movement of former times was composed of a mere trickle of population, "confined to well-to-do folk

and beset with difficulties of communication" (Abercrombie and Matthew, 1949, p. 141).

The appearance of a demand for recreation is evidence of the loss of environmental integrity. When residences become mass dwelling machines and factories become poisoned prisons, the "natural life" becomes an ideal. The ugliness of the places we pass through during daily life stimulates a yearning for purified beauty during a period of rest. "Natural" and "beautiful" become notions attaching to a part-time recreational existence. To compensate for these irritations, a new specialized function becomes a social need of city life and therefore the destiny of special extra-urban areas of forests, riverbanks, mountains, beaches, memorable places, as well as resorts: *recreation,* promising all pleasure, play, and adventure in a concentrated spatial and temporal dosage.

Recreation is not, however, confined to outdoor holiday-making, though this is at present its most conspicuous part. To understand recreational needs, let us for a moment consider recreation as a biological need, an ingredient of the rhythm of life: effort—relaxation, toil—leisure, routine—adventure. It has its place, then, in the life-maintaining functions in the same way as exhaling is necessary to the physical maintenance of life at any moment. The most important means to achieve recreation in this sense is considered to be a change of environment—we are inclined to say *any* change, the more radical the better. Whereas townsmen migrate to the open country and to the seaside, the farmer looks for recreation in the city. As a counterbalance to the daily way of life, people may search for recreation either in solitude or in crowded centers of amusement, either in closed space or in open squares. Because of this variety of individual demand for recreation, we include in any enumeration of recreational facilities establishments as different as a coffee-house and a park, a swimming pool and a historical site, a pleasure garden and a whole river system with its fishing and boating facilities, a holiday resort and a wildlife reservation.

The motives driving man to search for recreation in change of environment have not been sufficiently clarified. In many cases it is possible to explain recreation as an attempt to return to lost environmental values and ways of life. Among the most desired targets of such recreational return is the primitive life of hunting and berry-gathering—primitive in food, shelter, clothing, habitat—whereas people may content themselves also with rediscovering the indigenous environment in solitude.

It is also possible to assume that there exists in man a biological urge to employ his ability to change his environment. This ability, characterizing animal life generally, is even more the achievement of man, who can adapt himself artificially to varying environments; it is especially exhibited by urban man. But he has often little chance to exercise that ability in the daily run of life. The trend to move about reappears, then, as a recreational need. For we find recreation in just what we had to forego in daily life. To come in touch with different types of environment belongs probably in the same category of desires as the physical demand for a variegated nutrition and the psychic demand for variegated social contacts.

It might be possible to see a parallel between the motives behind recreational mobility and those behind nomadism. With the pastoral nomad, it is the low grade of fertility and carrying capacity reached by land after a period of pasturing which compels him to travel in search of unexploited regions. Similarly, a modern urbanite could be considered to be "undernourished" in respect to

environment. The recreational movement, therefore, is a proof of the interrelation between man and his physical environment. We detect the importance of environmental variety as a resource of human life because we miss it, especially in our time characterized by the low quality of our artificial urban environment.

The need for recreation varies with the individual; it obviously depends on personal versatility as well as on the quality of his daily environment. To consider recreation as a human need in past, present, and future, we shall have to make a clear distinction between the normal demands for change of environment on the part of members of healthy communities and the abnormal recreational insatiability of modern men living compressed in cities which are not planned to the human scale and which time and again compel attempts to escape.

THE RECREATIONAL CRISIS

Land Requirements of Recreation

Recreation by change of environment is a need felt in all the temporal frameworks of life: times during the day, the day itself, the week, the yearly seasons, and lifetimes. Though individual variations are huge, the life of man may be considered to be intersected by periods of recreation (or the desire for such periods) which help to revitalize the cycle of life, to maintain its rhythm by confronting man with change—different environment and food, association with different people or substantial isolation from society, different occupation, and a different feeling of progress of time.

In our civilization each of these types of time periods can be related in a general way to types of spatial frameworks which provide for the needed recreation of man: the family house, which has to serve recreational needs during parts of the day; the public gardens, squares, playgrounds, amusement and cultural centers, which provide for the daily and some of the weekly recreational needs; the city surroundings—with their parks, forests, rivers—where recreation will be sought by many on week ends; and the region in which one's city is situated, in which it should be possible to stroll about during different seasons of the year. Obviously, this series of time-space correlations with types of recreation can be further elaborated; for example, the generally assumed. In an average European home planned for a family of four to five persons (about 85 square meters) at least a third of the built-up area may be considered to serve indoor recreation during parts of the day: leisure within the family circle after a day of work, play, or solitude in reading, writing, or meditating. During parts of the year recreation will also be pursued on additional private areas, such as ter-

KITCHEN YARD —— KITCHEN

DINING

LIVING

BATHRM

W.C.

SON

DAUGHTER

PARENTS

○ INDIVIDUAL RECREATIONAL USE
☆ COMMON RECREATIONAL USE

0 1 2 3 4 5 METERS

FIG. 169.—Recreational use of house and garden. The recreational problem generally has to be approached first by providing in the house the necessary recreational space for the individual and family.

"migratory periods" of youths and adults, striving to escape any environmental frame or to turn the whole of the earth into their recreational framework.

In town and country considerable tracts of land have already been reserved exclusively for recreational purposes, and ever more are being demanded. For certain countries the amount of space needed per person for recreation can be calculated on an empirical basis. These amounts are much larger than is races, courtyards, or directly accessible gardens, which in numerous quarters take up 40–50 per cent of the total land requirement of the neighborhood (Fig. 169).

Calculating the land areas needed per family, according to British standards, for public parks, squares, playing fields, and cultural and amusement centers, we again meet the proportion of approximately one-third (about 110 square meters) of the total land requirement of a neighborhood (Abercrombie, 1945, p. 114). The importance of such areas for physical health has often been emphasized. They are also socially essential; besides the bonds formed in an urban society by work and trading, these urban recreational areas are the places where community bonds are formed during leisure time. But in the space allotted to recreation it must

United States, Austria, Holland, and Israel, we would say that the similarities in the different countries are more striking than the differences. The amount of urban land needed per inhabitant is tending to become uniform throughout the world, and it is possible to assume that equality of recreational needs, wherever these needs are recognized, is

Fig. 170.—Recreational land-use planning in a neighborhood, Giv'at Olga, coastal area of Israel. Recreational areas of a neighborhood should constitute an integrated system of lanes and parks, situated so as to confront the urban inhabitant during the different functions of daily life. Green areas should contain segregated pathways as well as meeting grounds and through-lanes.

be possible as well to find spots for solitude and rest.

Summing up, the land required for such a recreational program within a well-planned neighborhood amounts to more than 70 per cent of its total area. In comparison, the land needs for the "utilitarian" functions of working, shopping, circulating, hygiene, education, etc., are very small. Though this figure varies for countries such as England, the

the most important factor making for the uniformity (Fig. 170).

No attempt has been made to measure the land requirement of modern townsmen for recreation on week ends or during monthly or yearly holidays. The larger the scale, the more intricate the calculation becomes. Such measurement would depend strongly, for example, on local climatic conditions, which might "compress" the yearly holiday

period into a very few weeks of expected reasonable weather; on topographical and geographical conditions;
on movability of urban population; on
means of transportation; and on local
custom.

The existence of great recreational
pressure on land surrounding the metropolitan concentrations of population is
well known, but no standards of land
needs have been established. A hint
comes from the Netherlands. In this
densely populated and most intensively
used land, natural areas amount to only
0.056 hectare per inhabitant (Buskens,
1951). That the Dutch complain of a
definite lack of areas for week-end and
holiday recreation within their country
is an indication that the amount of
recreational land has become insufficient for the needs of the population.
In the United States the area of national parks, state parks, and national
forests amounts to 0.6 hectare per inhabitant (American Society of Landscape Architects, 1954). And even that
amount is, in the opinion of many
American conservationists and landscape architects, wholly inadequate.

But are such figures of any real help
in the calculation of regional needs?
The safest assumption seems to be that
the amount of land needed is very
large. Surveys of demand vis-à-vis availability indicate that the need is still
rising sharply. The present tendency
seems to be toward a rapid increase
in leisure hours and toward extending
facilities and recreational areas accordingly. With the increase in population
and the still growing congestion of
cities, it seems that each new urban
generation exhibits a stronger urge for
recreation. On the other hand, motorization and construction of roads and
airfields are making ever larger parts
of the continents accessible for vacationers. To comply under these conditions with the theoretical needs for
recreational facilities, huge districts—in-

deed, the whole of the regions surrounding large cities or even whole countries
of high-population density—would have
to be turned into recreational areas.

We may conclude that it has become
impossible to provide sufficient land in
the vicinity of most centers of population to serve exclusively for week-
enders and holidayers. At the same
time there is no way of suppressing the
recreational movement into the countryside. Evidently, therefore, the quantitative aspect of the question of recreational land use on a regional scale
cannot be seriously considered before
going more deeply into its qualitative
aspects: the motives for, and the means
of, pressure of urban population on
extra-urban land for recreation.

Recreational Pressures

The provision of recreational space
in the house, the town, the region, and
the country is essential for the harmonious conduct of urban life; it leads
to a proper dimension of cells in which
individual, family, and social life can
take place, but it leads also to the securing of organic relations and harmonious transitions among these different
levels of human association—the creation of a spatial rhythm of life. The
daily, weekly, and yearly frameworks
of recreation indeed exist in the strongest dependence on one another. Only
if all of them can be provided for can
the rhythm of individual and social life
be satisfactorily maintained. The lack
or inefficiency of one of them creates
a direct pressure on the other. A slum
is characterized not only by lack of
space and obsoleteness of flats or houses
but also by hordes of children and
adults escaping their dwellings and filling streets, courtyards, and gardens
whenever the weather permits. Since
they do not meet in properly dimen-
sioned squares or gardens but, instead,
are compressed in narrow streets or
yards, the nearness of one to another

stimulates friction, quarrels, and hate among the fellow-sufferers—proof of the fact that man, even urban man, needs a certain quantity of land under his feet.

A slum quarter, therefore, requires larger public gardens and squares, more public facilities of all kinds, than a healthy quarter; but, of course, every administrator and planner rightly prefers to invest money in the demolition of slum quarters and in their replacement with better houses rather than in the consolidation of slums by the establishment of public facilities. We know today that town planning depends on and begins with the planning of the basic cells of community life—the dwellings.

In many cases, however, town planning also ends with provision for houses and minimal amenities within a street or neighborhood. The towns of our century have inherited an immeasurable volume of incompatibilities—social, aesthetic, technical, and educational. With a very few exceptions our larger towns suffer from a huge deficiency in land areas for daily recreation, and none of the metropolitan centers meets the theoretical requirements for urban recreational land. We have to understand that this fact is the cause not only of poorly functioning towns but also of the heavy pressure of "land-hungry" urbanites on the rural countryside—for "Glasgow is a good place to get out of" (Abercrombie and Matthew, 1949, p. 130).

Similar to the process whereby erosion and floods result from the loss of absorptive capacity of the small particles of soil, the recreational movement on the country is the result of the obsolescence of urban dwellings and the lack of recreational land within the town. The recreation-searching masses turn into a "flood wave." We can assume that in many countries it is only that large portions of the population cannot afford a holiday far from the city which has preserved up to this time large tracts of landscape from final defacement and destruction.

On the one hand, our civilization requires ever larger areas of recreational land, but, on the other hand, we are making the landscape ever more uniform and limiting its restful and beautiful parts by maximum exploitation of resources. The violent result is the invasion by townspeople into the rural surroundings of the city on fine week ends and holidays. Here a new conflict of interest between farmer and townsman has originated; the farmer looks upon the holiday-makers as pests—damaging crops, destroying fences, disturbing the cattle, burning the forests, and soiling the countryside. Indeed, a recreational area after withdrawal by its visitors is a wretched sight. But the townsman, on his side, considers the farmer an egoistic tyrant who meets his visitor grudgingly and tries to prevent his short week-end enjoyment.

The better the economic condition of the average town dweller, the greater becomes the problem of recreational invasion of the countryside. Eventually, the growing numbers of holiday-makers begin to constitute a nuisance not only for the country folk but also for one another. Trying to return for a holiday to primitive conditions of life, people meet or "surprise" one another instead of finding solitude. Overcrowding prevails, just as within the city. Recreation here, like the trip from home to the countryside and back, is a nuisance, often more strenuous than the daily toil. Every big city knows those spots in its vicinity where recreation means only a change from an honestly artificial urban environment to a specially manufactured "natural environment"— a change from the difficulties of daily life to the difficulties of Sunday recreation.

For a large part of the population,

recreation is spoiled when it does not offer them a chance to escape from one another. Even in the United States, with its comparatively large areas of wilderness, a conflict is evident between the desire to put at the disposal of urbanites better recreational facilities and larger areas of land and the desire to preserve the natural countryside in its original state to make possible its solitary enjoyment by individuals and small groups (Feiss, 1950). The more artificial the urban environment, the larger the demand for compensation in indigenous landscape. But the most beautiful spots in a region are often kept a secret, because advertisement of them would mean their certain destruction by an influx of visitors.

The problem of recreational "inundation" of the countryside has to be tackled first of all inside the town by securing for the townsman the minimum measure of land he needs. A large part of his recreational needs thus would be met in his immediate environment, and the urge to leave the cities would be normalized. The whole character of outdoor recreation would be changed from one of flight from the city to one of harmonious movement of townspeople meeting their regional environment. But any such change for the better to be expected from town planning and development would not reduce the radius of travel for urban holiday-makers or restore the inaccessibility of rural and indigenous landscape. The same motives of social welfare which would encourage a community to enlarge its own recreational facilities would also induce it to prolong the yearly vacation of the average citizen and improve his chances of using that time for recreation outside the cities. In looking for a solution to the recreational problem, our main concern must be with regional development and regional design. We cannot expect a return to past conditions, and

we are therefore compelled to turn our thoughts and energies to the comprehensively planned reconstruction of town and landscape as well as to the change of attitude toward environment.

METHODS OF APPROACH TO RECREATIONAL PLANNING

The beginnings of land-use planning for recreation lay with those romantic lovers of nature who demanded the preservation of indigenous or rural landscape in the name of God, the nation, or nature in general. Their approach was defensive, and their fight actually was for the salvation of this or that natural area and animal species from the impact of techniques and industry and thus for its artificial separation from the landscape of modern civilization. For them the destruction of indigenous landscape was an indictment against our civilization, an offense against the wholeness of life.

We feel that theirs was a righteous cause; the rational arguments which they used to defend nature, however, were less convincing to businessmen and politicians. Investment in recreational facilities is by no means a good business proposition if such facilities are not intended for mass recreation. Nor could an expectation of greater man-hour production as the direct outcome of the influence of landscape on human health and vitality be substantiated. Arguments concerning the loss of income of local hotels, gas stations, and other small businesses were employed as a last attempt to preserve the integrity of the landscape (American Society of Landscape Architects, 1952), but expectations of short-term profits through exploitation of land for lumbering, mining, and power generation always proved much more attractive.

The truth might be that for conservationists the very existence of wild nature is the real issue. By advocating the part-time use of landscape as an amenity, they tried to influence a utilitarian society to co-operate in the realization of their lofty ideal.

Given the existence of such mercenary interests, it should be considered a most fortunate achievement that conservation societies and outstanding individuals have succeeded in many countries in preserving limited areas of wilderness as nature reserves or national parks. Even in these the fight for preservation against industrial or agricultural interests, on the one hand, and against invasion by holiday-makers, on the other hand, has to be vigilantly pursued. It is no wonder, therefore, that pessimism is widespread among nature preservation societies (Clarke, 1946–47). They understand that stretches of wilderness are becoming museum pieces—exhibits to show the coming generations what they have lost. The rate of deterioration of landscape is still much faster than that of preservation, and the prospects of accomplishing by preservation a finer environment are indeterminate.

But, while the fight of the conservationists is directed against certain basic symptoms of environmental change, it does not touch on the man-land relationship as a whole, on comprehensive environmental reconstruction. Positive goals of environmental health have to replace the defensive actions of conservators. As Patrick Geddes wrote in his *Cities in Evolution* (1949, p. 51), "The case for the conservation of nature must be stated more seriously . . . not merely begged for on all grounds of amenity, of recreation, and repose, sound though these are, but insisted upon."

Out of the theoretical development of, and the still very limited practical experience in, regional and town planning, the most important conclusion to be drawn with respect to planning for recreation is the need for comprehensiveness. Land-use planning for recreation should be comprehensive in the geographical sense. For practicability, the interdependent recreational facilities of the house, the town, and the region have to be equally considered and provided for. The problem of recreational pressure on the countryside cannot be solved without providing first for the necessary recreational areas and facilities within the town. The same is true of planning for public open spaces in the town and the planning of individual houses and flats. On the other hand, the most efficiently planned town, containing a full quota of recreational facilities, is still a beautiful prison if its regional surroundings do not offer the town dweller an attractive and accessible environment. Ample recreational facilities should confront man in all the different spatial frameworks through which he moves; the problem cannot be partly solved, because the very compression of recreational land use into an insufficient framework negates the possibility of recreation.

Planning for recreation in regions and towns should be comprehensive also in the functional sense. As far as possible, the environment planned for functions such as working, trading, circulating, and dwelling should be recreational as well as utilitarian. To be effective, recreation has to be found casually in the factory at the hour of rest, on the way home, and at home. Vigilance with respect to the availability of recreational facilities should not be limited to a few zones or to the center of a city but should encompass the whole city—its houses, gardens, squares, and streets, providing at one place nooks for individual seclusion and elsewhere for excitement and pleasure in a social context. Recreation would thus represent one of the elements composing habitability.

To the numerous extant formulations of the aim of planning we would, then, add another: Planning aims at perpetuating recreation in all environmental frameworks. This implies that recreation should be part and parcel of the function of all land use and not only the destiny of specific chosen areas of land. It belongs to the planning program to turn town and country as a whole into a functional and aesthetically enjoyable environment.

When recreation is considered a part-time function of man, necessitating a specially treated, segregated environment, there occurs an awkward contradiction in the act of planning for recreation: the more one plans explicitly for recreation, especially on the regional scale, the less satisfactory the result. There are several reasons for this difficulty. A planned natural or historic environment in holiday resorts cannot fulfil the longing of many vacationers to return to the lost rural or indigenous landscape. Neither nature nor history can be "designed." Attempts to do so have led only to the fabrication of ridiculous junk—ornamental "prettification" in a money-making atmosphere—but not to any true environmental quality. Also, such planning assumes on the part of contemporary men a sort of contentedness with the existence of "utilitarian" land areas, the inferior environment of everyday, for which, it is further assumed, part-time compensation can be had by recourse to a complementary artificial recreational environment. The dual existence of discrete ugly and beautified environment is thus perpetuated; it becomes the confirmation of the rupture between daily life and the good life, which is one of the marks of our big cities—the confirmation of a dualism which ought to be eliminated by planning.

Whereas the planning of separate zones for industry, through-traffic, and residence, as practiced today, seems to be in many cases a reasonable method, recreational zoning, as it is often proposed, may miss the very meaning of recreation: it is precisely the specialization of functions which upsets the equilibrium of man in the modern city and which should be balanced by variety—variety which recreation should provide. To become a true source of recreation, the whole of our regional surroundings has to be turned into an environment which provides for nourishment, occupation, interest, enjoyment, and health at the same time. Planning for recreation should be enlarged from compensatory or defensive zoning to planning for comprehensive purposes of higher environmental quality everywhere.

Summing up this short survey of the planning problems of the present recreational crisis, we present two statements:

a) It is impossible to provide for the theoretically needed amount of land for outdoor regional recreation if it is intended to be exclusively recreational land. Given the increase in world population, first call on land rests with food production, power generation, and industry—especially in the immediate surroundings of large population centers. Recreation, therefore, would have to be confined to the remaining "useless" wastelands, coastal and mountainous areas, or preserved stretches of indigenous landscape, wherever these happened to be located, and for as long as no economic importance was ascribed to them.

b) It is, however, not even desirable to develop a specific recreational environment on the regional scale for the part-time use of inhabitants of the large cities. Visiting such an environment may be a matter of social or erotic interest, of fashion or prestige, but it does not represent a true source of physical and psychological enrichment and renewal. The reason lies in the inevitable overcrowding, which, together with recreational specialization, should be considered as contrary to the essential recreational needs of metropolitan inhabitants. From the point of view of quality of recreation, we have to search for areas of basically functional importance —areas of indigenous nature, agriculture, fishing, pasturing, lumbering, etc. —where recreation would represent one of multiple uses for such land.

Our conclusion, therefore, is that the crisis of recreational land use can be solved only by opening up for recreational use the whole of a region. Nowhere should recreation be an exclusive function of an area; a landscape should be useful and beautiful at the same time—a resource of life and of its renewal.

But is it possible to expect the recreational need for rest and beauty to become the instigator of such a general reconstruction of landscape and environment?

RECONSTRUCTION OF LANDSCAPE

There is an intrinsic conformity of aesthetic and functional qualities of an environment, and in this conformity lie all prospects for recreational improvement. To be precise: not all functions create environmental beauty, nor is all environmental beauty functional; but quality creates conformity between them. This was most probably sensed by those nature-lovers who maintained that disfigurement of landscape meant also the decline of our civilization and life. But, as long as mechanistic concepts of land as a food-producing substance prevailed, that feeling found no material "nutrient," and aesthetic and recreational values remained widely separate from reality. Today the teaching of ecology, organic agriculture, soil science, and land-capability classifications are making conformity a scientific certainty. Now, indeed, "the case of nature conservation . . . can be insisted upon." The disfigurement of landscape is not merely a symptom but also one of the basic physical causes of cultural decline; it is the effect of a radical

change in the relation of man to land and a new cause of human deterioration as well. It is a source of vital aesthetic and recreational dissatisfaction and at the same time a source of deficiency in quantity and quality of food, water, wood, climate, and habitability of the earth. The recreational crisis is part and parcel of the general crisis of basic resources.

Though industrial developments are closely linked with the rise of the birth rate in many countries, the landscape as transformed by industry is incapable of providing the nourishment for an increased population over a long time. It is a landscape of man-made erosion and of declining fertility—and other ever mounting physical problems. All the emphasis is on maximum crops and high profits within the shortest time and for a price which is to be paid by future generations. The land can be interpreted as being functionally degenerate. To secure a permanent basis of civilization, a further step, one of environmental reconstruction, is needed.

In the shaping of tools, houses, and even cities we have learned the intrinsic relationship of material, function, and form, brought to high expression in handicrafts, architecture, and city design. Now, recent developments in biology have made us understand the natural processes to a degree where we begin to recognize our immediate power over, as well as our final dependence upon, the ecological functions. The outstanding importance of our new biological knowledge lies in the fact that it sets us at the beginning of new enterprises on a larger scale, which may be called "reconstruction of landscape," "regional design," or, as Geddes put it, "geotechnics."[1] This is a scientific enter-

1. That Geddes used the term "geotechnics" is reported by Benton MacKaye in "Geography to Geotechnics," a series that appeared in *The Survey*, October–December, 1950, and April–June, 1951. New York: Survey Associates, Inc.

prise as far as it is the observation and the emulation of nature's rule of return, and an artistic enterprise as far as nature leaves us the freedom, or even incites us, to express our developmental longings in the creation of higher qualities of environment.

The first realization of geotechnics—in the United States especially the Tennessee Valley Authority; in European countries the beginnings of afforestation and agricultural intensification, such as in Israel—as well as of the theory of landscape reconstruction, as developed in the last few years, indicates the changes in the cultural landscape to be expected: an increase in forests and wooded strips, an intensification and variegation of agricultural land use ac-cording to soil capabilities, terracing and strip cultivation, the following of lines of natural contours or soil qualities in the delimitation of parcels and fields, and the bringing to an end of the grid pattern of fields introduced by the land surveyor and the real estate merchant. There emerges a reallotment and redevelopment of whole rural countrysides, as begun in the Netherlands and in other European countries—a far-reaching reorganization of the treeless "food factories" or of the abandoned eroded fields into smaller fields bounded by wildlife strips (Figs. 171–173).

The application of ecological principles of maintenance of soil fertility will lead in different countries to different landscape designs, because such appli-

ROADS
RAILWAY LINES
SEMI-URBAN AREA
VILLAGES
MARSHLAND

1 KILOMETER GRID

Fig. 171.—Existing condition—center of Esdraelon Valley, Israel. The lack of forests, wadies cutting deep into the land, marshland, and parcellation in long narrow strips are the symptoms of a landscape which is in a stage of functional and aesthetic deterioration. Intensification of agricultural land use and settlement and afforestation are leading to a gradual improvement of the landscape, i.e., greater fertility and habitability.

cation will be based on research into regional soil conditions and capabilities and human conditions. For many regions we can imagine as the result the creation of a pattern of freely curved wooded strips, traversing the plains in many directions, widening here and there into woods, running along streams and rivulets, and eventually connecting merous planners have observed that in land-use planning on the regional scale recreation is always among the objectives "obtained . . . as collateral benefits" (Blanchard, 1950). Game preserves would be kept not because of the unceasing endeavors of conservation societies but because "the cover needed for watershed conservation [would be] . . .

ALL AGRIC. USES
LIGHT CONSERV. PRACTICES
TERRACING, ORCHARDS
GRAZING LAND
AFFORESTATION
SEVERE AGR. RESTRICTION
WATER SHED LINE

1 KILOMETER GRID

FIG. 172.—Soil-capability survey—center of Esdraelon Valley, Israel. The soil-capability classification, combined with the physiographic survey of a region, is the key to the planning of a new and better pattern of landscape.

with the mountainous hinterland, where they would gain in width and finally merge into forests. The shady pathways, the rivers, and the forests of wildlife, for which people in many countries long, would again come to life—not because we should be ready to pay for recreation but because we should be obeying the scientifically recognized rules and preconditions for our permanent settlement and nourishment. Nu- restored to the drainage channel and hillsides" (Leopold, quoted in Graham, 1944, p. 170). A beautiful recreational landscape, as Sharp (1950, p. 67) has pointed out, "arose out of activities that were undertaken primarily for other motives, rather than that it was deliberately created for itself."

We can imagine also an increase in planting along roads and trenches to avoid soil erosion and the planting of green belts around villages and cities to absorb the urban floodwaters, to minimize the range of influence of urban dust and smoke, and to create a harmonious transition of great recreational value from town to country. Green strips may converge on the cities and even penetrate into them. Here certain new trends of town planning, which sent a memorial which the townsman erects in the heart of his city to remind him of the lost natural landscape. It is a condensed artificial landscape in which a large variety of plants, as well as rocks and water, often represents the natural landscape "in a nutshell." In many new towns, however, a new way of designing planted areas has

FIG. 173.—Landscape plan for center of Esdraelon Valley, Israel. The reconstruction of landscape can never restore the original untouched quality of land. It leads, by the application of ecological principles of land use, to a harmonious pattern of recreational and useful areas: wooded strips, lakes, terraces, and forests, with intensively cultivated fields and villages and towns in between.

have already found expression in several countries, conform entirely with the large geotechnical principles of reconstruction. In former centuries the formally arranged private garden symbolized in a way the conquest and taming of nature by man. The free design of public gardens during recent decades has been the next step and may repre- appeared; these designs admit, without much artificial treatment, a wedgelike penetration of the surrounding landscape into the center of the city. In this way an extensive net of green pathways subdivides the town in a natural way into the residential neighborhood units; it represents the most attractive and convenient route of communication among places of work, homes, shopping centers, and friends, and it joins with sports fields, playgrounds, and schools. Here recreation has been truly integrated into the whole of the functions of urban life, and there is no longer a need for obtrusively specialized recreational facilities (Fig. 174).

as the mutuality of social and biotic life. The human communities of such a region can be strengthened only through the enhancement of its biotic communities. Its biological improvement, however, involves its aesthetic and recreational improvement.

Man has changed his landscape time

Fig. 174.—The new town of Beer-Sheva, Israel. The new town of Beer-Sheva numbers 20,000 inhabitants to date. Though the development of amenity is necessarily slow, the plan secures the future integration of the town with its regional environment as well as ample recreational facilities within the town.

The new town no longer represents an isolated fortress, as in past centuries, or an agglomeration of houses alienated from its regional surroundings, as in the nineteenth century, but a regionally integrated nucleus of the landscape, from which open freely the channels which connect its center with the region and through which its lifeblood streams in and out. The function this pattern fosters and expresses may be interpreted

and again. But all large-scale landscape design has been based on functional rather than aesthetic foundations. It may be expected that both "useful" and "useless" landscape will gain, by the new reconstruction of landscape, much of that "indigenous" character which is so valuable for recreation (MacKaye, 1928, pp. 138 and 169). But what does that indigenous character signify in this context? It would be superficial to explain it merely as a return to a primitive past. "Indigenous" should be interpreted, as MacKaye has, as a quality of past, present, and future. As appeared in a recent memorandum of the (British) Soil Association, "The primitive environment was better, not because it was primitive, but because the rule of the natural biological cycle prevailed" (Anonymous, 1955, p. 77). In the same way recreation would be better, not as an attempt to return to the past, but as a way to eternally desirable values. The indigenous character of landscape which may result from application of scientific methods would be a confirmation of the quality of our work of reconstruction. That landscape would be a realization of our aspirations toward health and wholeness.

REALIZATION OF RECREATION

We began this essay by searching man for his needs and the landscape for its recreational resources; we found man's needs to be rising at the same time that the recreational landscape is deteriorating; only comprehensive regional reconstruction can restore the true sources of recreation. Now we have to look for the human resources for this tremendous enterprise which may be described as *recreation of environment*. Our problem has become reversed, and it is no longer possible to separate "recreation by environment" from "recreation of environment." Indeed, the very term "recreation" hints at this ambiguity: recreation means the revitalization of man's life by whatever circumstances, but it means also the restoration of life in man's biotic and physical environment. Recreating and being recreated—both are included in the original meaning of recreation, and, indeed, only in this double sense can it be realized.

We have dealt with the problem of recreation for the most part skeptically.

As long as we are satisfied with *expecting* recreation from the environment, there is much room for skepticism. Hope begins when we deal with recreation in its active as well as its passive aspects. Such recreation loses the character of temporary compensation; it becomes a positive act of observing, enriching one's experience, widening one's interests, participating in the activities of communities, and developing receptivity for environmental qualities.

In our time we often meet the tendency to identify recreation with certain ways of behavior in free nature and in foreign places—a sort of planned emotionality and permanent enthusiasm. When we speak of "active" recreation, we aim not at the instigation of any such recreational enthusiasm but at positive purposes of recreation. Active recreation may become the voluntary preparation of the urban inhabitant for the geotechnical renewal of his region; it may be the first step—reconnaissance —in the long-overdue fight against soil erosion, declining fertility, and landscape devastation, aiming at the qualitative and quantitative enhancement of food-growing areas as much as of the habitability in town and country. This sort of recreation would serve the progress of regional survey of towns and country. As conceived by Geddes (1949, p. 157), it would renew our acquaintance with our regions, "rationalise our own experience," and prepare us for its planned change by widening our factual knowledge as well as educating us to a synoptic planning attitude; it would become "regional survey for regional service" (Boardman, 1944, p. 187).

Wherever attempts at land reconstruction have been made, it has emerged clearly that this is a multipurpose enterprise, involving agriculture, water supply, power production, industry, transportation, and population movement and geared to residential as well as recreational purposes. To be successful, such an enterprise has to be undertaken by collaborating parties of different interests. The rural forces alone are in our time unable to accomplish the task. Urban scientific and technical achievements have to be fully applied to the country to bring about afforestation, dam-building, terracing, drainage, planting, reallotment of land, and construction. If repair of the man-land relationship were to become the essential content of recreation, the recreational return of the urban inhabitant to the land would mean the beginning of mutuality of urban and rural land-use interests and of co-operation in planned regional reconstruction.

We can now summarize by forecasting three stages of environmental development beyond those set forth at the outset—though these represent no certainties but only postulates:

4. Urban man should realize that, when he conquered the countryside and created towns, he at the same time lost important environmental values. Forced thereby to search for his own recreation,

he returns to the country. The more that industry and cities expand, the greater is the demand for recreation—but the greater also are the chances to realize recreation in its double sense by combined economic rehabilitation, social re-education, and physical reconstruction.

5. In the reconstruction of landscape, co-operation between town and country and among professions would re-create a fertile and habitable environment. It would be the greatest enterprise of planned environmental change since Neolithic times and the best act of social creation we can imagine. With the help of science, man reconstructs nature in its own image, which is at the same time his own best image.

6. Acting toward these purposes, man would rediscover the land as an inexhaustible resource of human recreation; making such discoveries, he would at the same time regain confidence in his own creative capabilities. Recreation would then become means and ends in one—and the earth, a better habitation.

REFERENCES

ABERCROMBIE, PATRICK
1945 *Greater London Plan.* London: H.M. Stationery Office. 221 pp. (In this work important beginnings have been made to calculate the land needs of modern urban inhabitants.)

ABERCROMBIE, SIR PATRICK, and MATTHEW, ROBERT H.
1949 *The Clyde Valley Regional Plan, 1946.* Edinburgh: H.M. Stationery Office. 395 pp. (Chapter iii, "Open Space and Recreation," pp. 129–58, deals with the regional problems of recreation of the Clyde Valley and helps to clarify the problem of recreational land use generally.)

AMERICAN SOCIETY OF LANDSCAPE ARCHITECTS
1952 "Selected 1951 ASLA Committee Reports: Public Roads, Controlled Access Highways, Parkways," *Land-scape Architecture,* XLII, No. 2, 57–77.
1954 "Selected 1953 ASLA Committee Reports: National and State Parks and Forests," *ibid.,* XLIV, 136–37.

ANONYMOUS
1955 "The Dental Health of Children" (memorandum to the British Dental Association from the Soil Association), *Mother Earth,* VIII, No. 1, 75–80. London.

BENTHEM, R. J.
1952 "The Development of Rural Landscape in the Netherlands," *Journal of the Institute of Landscape Architects,* No. 25, pp. 2–9. London.
1949 "Report of Documentation on Reconstruction of the Landscape in the Netherlands." (Unpublished lecture.) 4 pp. (In Benthem's articles as well as in his practical work the idea of the

reconstruction of the cultural landscape of a densely populated country comes to a clear expression; it means improvement as a multipurpose enterprise, comprehending useful and recreational functions.)

BLANCHARD, R. W.
1950 "Master Land Use Plan for Crooked Creek Reservoir," *Landscape Architecture*, XXXVII, 140–41.

BOARDMAN, PHILIP
1944 *Patrick Geddes, Maker of the Future*. Chapel Hill: University of North Carolina Press. 504 pp. (The life-story of the great biologist, geographer, educator, and planner is at the same time a forecast of the science of renewal of man—work and environment.)

BUSKENS, W. H. M.
1951 "Recreatie als Vraagstuk van Ruimtelijke Ordening," *Natuur en Landschap*, Vijfde Jaargang, pp. 21–29. Amsterdam.

CLARKE, GILMORE D.
1946–47 "A Challenge to the Landscape Architect," *Landscape Architecture*, XXXVII, 140–41.

FEISS, CARL
1950 "National Park and Monument Planning in the United States," *Town Planning Review*, XXI, No. 1, 40–56.

GEDDES, SIR PATRICK
1949 *Cities in Evolution*. 2d ed. London: William & Norgate. 241 pp. (This book is the only publication of Geddes' numerous scripts on comprehensive planning. The more one penetrates into Geddes' ideas and formulations, the wider appear the horizons of the future in thought and action.)

GRAHAM, EDWARD H.
1944 *Natural Principles of Land Use*. New York: Oxford University Press. 274 pp. (In this scientific work the importance of our new biological knowledge for a comprehensive change of the landscape becomes obvious.)

JACKS, G. V., and WHYTE, R. O.
1944 *The Rape of the Earth*. London: Faber & Faber. 313 pp.

LEOPOLD, ALDO
1949 *A Sand County Almanac*. New York: Oxford University Press. 226 pp.

1953 *Round River*. Ed. LUNA LEOPOLD. New York: Oxford University Press. 173 pp. (Leopold's nature descriptions are of a lyric beauty. They reveal a deep longing for recreation of man in nature's eternal ecological cycles. His philosophical and ethical conclusions represent the most essential and concise appeal to man as a "biotic citizen.")

MACKAYE, BENTON
1928 *The New Exploration: A Philosophy of Regional Planning*. New York: Harcourt, Brace & Co. 235 pp.

1950 "Dam Site vs. Norm Site," *Scientific Monthly*, LXXXI, No. 4, 241–47. (MacKaye's ideas of indigenous landscape, rural and city life, the flow of population and commodities, habitability, and active and passive recreation constitute most essential building stones of regional planning.)

MEARS, SIR FRANK C.
1948 *Forth and Tweed: Regional Plan for Central and South Eastern Scotland*. Edinburgh and London: Morrison & Gibb, Ltd. 180 pp. (The chapter on "Recreation and Amenity," Part V, pp. 141–49, hints at the true extent of the problem.)

MUMFORD, LEWIS
1938 *The Culture of Cities*. London: Secker & Warburg. 530 pp. (The true importance of these interpretations of past and present environmental culture is revealed by the fact that they constitute a continous stimulation for thought, criticism, design, and action.)

NIXON, H. CLARENCE
1945 *The Tennessee Valley, a Recreation Domain*. (Papers of the Institute of Research and Training in the Social Sciences, Vanderbilt University.) Nashville, Tenn.: Vanderbilt University. 22 pp.

RAINER, ROLAND
1947 *Die Behausungsfrage*. Vienna: Gallusverlag. 120 pp. (This book reveals in a very simple and convincing manner the quantitative and qualitative aspects of urban land use.)

SHARP, THOMAS
    1950 "Planning Responsibility of the Landscape Architect in Britain," *Landscape Architecture,* XL, No. 2, 67–72.

TAUT, BRUNO
    1920 *Die Auflösung der Städte oder die Erde, eine gute Wohnung.* Hagen: Folkwang Verlag. 82 pp. (More than half of this book written by an architect consists of fanciful sketches of a reconstructed earth as a good habitation; the other half is an interesting collection of quotations from Kropotkin, Walt Whitman, Fuhrmann, Scheerbart, Oppenheimer, Tolstoi, and others—all on the subject of improvement of life and environment.)

UNITED STATES DEPARTMENT OF THE INTERIOR, NATIONAL PARK SERVICE
    1943 *Recreational Resources of the Denison Dam and Reservoir Project, Texas and Oklahoma.* Washington, D.C.: Government Printing Office. 98 pp.

WRENCH, G. T.
    1946 *Reconstruction by Way of the Soil.* London: Faber & Faber. 262 pp. (In this stimulating collection of Dr. Wrench's works, the agricultural, political, and economic problems of many countries are treated at different historic periods. The problem of quality of land use clearly emerges as the central problem of all civilizations.)

Symposium Discussion: Process

Symposium Discussion: Process

Changes in Physical Phenomena

The Changing Levels of Land and Sea

Man's Debt to the Sea

Waters of the Land and Development of Watersheds

Climatic Change

Mineral Resources and Energy Control

Dr. ALAN BATEMAN, in introducing this session as Chairman, thought that most members of the group were convinced that man *has* effected changes on the face of the earth. Now it was time to turn to a consideration of the processes by means of which some of the changes have taken place—processes that are going on today and have gone on in the past. The present subject deals more with the realm of earth science, and we must not overlook, as Russell brings out in his chapter, that forces entirely independent of man not only exist but, coincident with man's activities, have been active in producing changes on the surface of the earth.

Discussions of change, THOMAS brought out, usually do not start with definitions of change. From what "Garden of Eden" or "Golden Age" are changes to be measured? For example, we speak of "overgrazing." Grazing is the function of an animal; the term "overgrazing" is used to describe the ill effects of grazing upon plants, and thus it is the function of a plant. Use of the term implies certain standards. Similarly, in using the term "geologic normal of erosion," we have to tell what the normal is before telling what the changes in erosion have been. Natural changes are occurring; the changes brought about by man are to be measured from a moving base. Often, as in the cases of erosion, of rising of sea level, and of shifting stream channels, it has been man's interest to institute changes that counteract those made by nature—the changes man hopes to cause are simply to preserve the status quo. The determination of changes due to man's efforts is rendered difficult in that the effect of natural forces must be assessed to give a base from which to measure man's changes, and natural forces are, in many instances, not static but in movement.

THE CHANGING LEVELS OF LAND AND SEA

The measurable quantity of man's efforts, so far as changing the sea is concerned, is very low. Both inland processes and oceanic or marine processes affect the coast line. The contact of sea and land has been a great tension zone over all periods of time. DAVIS cited the accumulating evidence—in peat profiles, in mangrove swamps, on tidal gauges, in different sedimentary deposits—of the postglacial, or Recent, rise of sea level. And what is going to happen to New York or Miami when the sea level rises—say, 20 feet—higher than it is at present?

917

Several scholars cited evidence for rising sea level along the coasts of northwestern Europe. DARBY mentioned the rise along the eastern coast of England of 5–6 feet since Roman times—approximately a foot every three hundred years. The implications of this are obvious for intensifying the difficulties of draining the marshes of the English Fenland. After the fifth century A.D. the agricultural activities of the Romans in England, as revealed on aerial photographs, ceased comparatively suddenly. This may have been due, in part, to a lack of organization during the confusion of the period, but it also must have been due to physical changes. PFEIFER cited the man-made hills of the German marshes, where excavation has revealed successive additions on which houses were built. GOUROU referred to the rocky coast of French Brittany along which the rising of sea level, termed "Dunkerquian rising," has been measured in places where it could not possibly be confused with subsidence of land due to contraction of peat soils under cultivation.

SAUER remarked that some speakers referred to sinking of the land, while others spoke of rising of the sea, even using the terms alternatively. The dilemma is that sinking of the land and rising of the sea are not the same process.

DARWIN asked whether we now have enough knowledge to know the maximum sea level that could be reached. Floating ice would not enter into the calculations; only melted land ice would add to the volume of the sea. DAVIS replied that the highest known terrace in Florida is about 280 feet. The assumption is that almost all ice was melted during an interglacial period. BOULDING calculated the rise of ocean level to be 300 feet, basing his calculations upon the assumption that the average depth of ice over Greenland and Antarctica is 10,000 feet. BATEMAN

added that depths of 11,500 feet for Greenland ice were recorded by a 1954 expedition made by Dr. Richard F. Flint, which indicated a greater quantity of ice than had been anticipated. The bottom of the ice is actually below sea level. BARTLETT, in writing, pointed out that the effect of melting ice in Antarctica and Greenland would be partially offset by isostasy as well as by the shift of weight caused by the deposition of eroded materials into the sea.

LANDSBERG thought it unlikely that there had ever been a melting of the Antarctic icecap since the early Pleistocene. Even in the so-called "interglacials" it remained intact, so that the estimates are likely to be maximized. Also, if the earth's atmosphere is heated, more water is going to be stored in the atmosphere. SAUER agreed that there never had been complete deglaciation during the Pleistocene and would put the possible rise at something like 100 feet.

It was brought out by THORNTHWAITE that oceanographers have found sea levels to change regularly twice a year, with the peak for September and October being higher than that for March. While the change in level is not great, the amount of water involved is enormous. It is temporarily stored on the land. More water is in the soil and underground in the spring than at other times of the year. The difference in the peaks is due to there being less land in the Southern Hemisphere, where the seasons are reversed. As summer comes on, evapotranspiration increases, and the moisture in the soil and on the land diminishes.

SCARLOTT added the footnote that one reason for the rising sea level is sediment washing from the land into the sea. Since man in recent millenniums has been a factor in increasing the rate of erosion, he too should share some small blame for the rising sea.

The question of the changing base level (sea level) is important as a demonstration of how slowly knowledge acquired in one field extends into others in which it would be useful. SAUER pointed up how, for years, earth science has been well aware of the significance, if not the magnitude, of the swings of world-wide sea level connected with the locking-up and unlocking of water in successive phases of glaciation and deglaciation. Daly introduced this knowledge to a part of the American public in his *Mobile Earth;* yet even in the narrower range of the profession its indications were not sufficiently regarded. The famous system of erosion-cycle hypotheses by William Morris Davis in considerable measure broke down because it was based upon base levels of duration such as have not existed in the world almost certainly for several million years. We are still dealing with a lag in knowledge, extending far beyond the geomorphologist, in the unawareness of the world-wide swings (except for isostasy in the higher latitudes) of sea level in this critical question of where land meets sea. A great deal of archeology and of some early history is not realistic because it is unaware that present alluvial valleys were eroding during glacial stages and filling during interglacial stages. This is applicable to most of the valleys entering the seas throughout the world and has been precisely demonstrated by Russell and his associates in Louisiana for the Mississippi River system. A further point they have added is that great alluvial systems are themselves in constant process of deforming and depressing the earth's crust, and in these slowly sinking areas, within which so much history of mankind has transpired, records of the past are being buried more and more deeply.

HUZAYYIN added that there is a similar problem in the Nile. Changing base level was not the only factor, for in the lower Nile Valley there are eight terraces or so, while during the pluvial period the oscillations of the sea could not have exceeded perhaps four phases. Climatic changes also could have affected the cycle of erosion and deposition in the lower Nile Valley. With more abundant water during a pluvial phase, the river would spread higher and more widely, and more abundant deposition would result; with a phase of less pluviosity, the waters limited to a smaller bed would erode. Also, river capture in the Abyssinian highlands would add to the volume of waters and to the material growth of the lower Nile. Erosion and deposition occur simultaneously along different parts of the river course. Today the Nile is depositing in northern and middle Egypt and is eroding in Nubia; this is why the great Aswân Dam has not been silted.

MAN'S DEBT TO THE SEA

DAVIS was inclined to regard man's civilized activities as having originated along the sea. The evidence for this, such as coastal shell mounds, has been mostly lost through the encroachment of the sea over the land. JONES, in writing, observed that The Dalles on the Columbia River supported one of the densest, most prosperous, and definitely localized Indian populations, as did the Northwest Coast, and he added that fishing may well have preceded agriculture as a "civilizing factor" in human history.

KLIMM noted that a great deal of attention has been paid to the sea as a source of food and wondered whether the generalization were true that, after the agricultural stage is reached, man turns to the sea only as a last resort. The hypothesis is that, if man can make a living from agriculture, he is reluctant to go to sea, where the same amount of effort and risk will return less to him. If it were demonstrated that labor input applied to the sea yields less in the way of food or other economic return than labor input in agriculture under anything like favorable conditions, then we would have some perspective on the possibility and probability of man's making any major change in the sea as a resource base. Do we have to await a period of agricultural exhaustion or overcrowding before it will pay man to put his economic effort into the sea?

MURPHY remarked that, though today we may see it as a sort of last resort, he doubted that primitive man in coastal regions turned to ocean waters for a substantial part of his proteins for any reason other than preference. We must consider taste and choice as much as relative labor and availability. He recalled reading that the shell heaps between Maine and Florida contain a greater bulk of bivalves than have been consumed by Europeans since their settlement in North America, despite the fact that our daily take is now in thousands of barrels.

PFEIFER pointed out that peoples have developed and adapted whole ways of life around the activity of fishing. It is not easy to assume that these will easily be changed over or abandoned in accordance with more efficient technological processes developed elsewhere in the world. Even where fishing is not used as a means of livelihood, there is great inclination to continue it as a sport. Reporting on his work among fishing people of Maritime Canada, CLARK concluded that a very large number simply prefer to fish and thereby get a meager living from the sea, even though it would be more profitable for them to farm. They realize this; it has been demonstrated to them; yet essential conservatism or love for the sea keeps them on a lower standard of living. SAUER added that the island Caribs, as commented upon by early observers, knew farming but

that they preferred to go out in boats. Again, almost all the late prehistoric shell mounds of southern Louisiana are associated with agricultural populations, who, like the Cajuns of today, simply like to go shrimping and oystering.

MUMFORD asked whether Klimm had restricted his concept of the economics of fishing too much to ocean fishing, whereas a great deal of fishing during the development of civilizations was done from the rivers, inland fishing being a standard way to eke out income. Almost the earliest guild on record was a fishing guild in the town of Ulm. HEICHELHEIM brought out that, while evidence from the Greeks and Romans indicates ocean fishing to be post-Homeric, ancient oriental economies early developed careful organizations—such as the fishing guilds in Sumer—for lake and river fishing. While we have not the least evidence that the persons drafted into fishing did so with pleasure, nevertheless there are people who love the sea and prefer it to agriculture. HUZAYYIN added that fish always were an important part of the food supply in Egypt. Neolithic peoples around the lake at Faiyûm combined agriculture with fishing, principally for catfish. Also, in the bas-reliefs of the tomb of Ti of the Sixth Dynasty of the Old Kingdom, a large variety of fresh-water fish are to be found.

SPOEHR considered the history of man's cultivation of the sea as somewhat in the category of hunting—one part of the search for protein food. Population densities today on certain atolls of the Pacific are computed as 1,200 per square mile of land area, yet this high density is misleading as regards food supply, for these populations could not survive without the inclusion of the sea as part of their resource base. The question arises whether man has ever been able to cultivate the sea in the same way as he has been able to raise protein through the domestication of animals; the fishponds or fish "farms" of Hawaii and of southern and eastern Asia would be examples of this sort of activity. SCHAEFER related the intensity of fishing to ease of living. Tremendous shell mounds remaining along the sea indicate the ease with which a rich variety of shellfish was obtained from the sea. By comparison, shell residues in the Hudson River Valley indicate that man used the few barely edible shellfish only when other types of food were unavailable. If we look at the product of activity in terms of food, the conclusion is that it is far easier and much more effective to use land for obtaining food for the greatest number of people. On the other hand, new technological developments are likely to provide easier ways of procuring more attractive materials from the sea.

Growth in the sea is not separate from growth on the land. ALBRECHT emphasized that sea life struggles to obtain its protein just as the fisherman struggles to get his. And it is only by erosion and the movement of decomposed rock into the sea that life there survives. There is a linkage, then, between climate, physical changes on the earth, and fishermen. In addition, man goes back to the sea for iodine and other essentials to make up for shortages in harvests from the land. "I am pleading," ALBRECHT added, "for the consideration of agriculture, but not its flattery. I don't believe you want to flatter agriculture so much as to believe that it can feed us so efficiently that we won't go back to the sea."

GALDSTON developed further Albrecht's point on the biological evaluation of fish protein. Excluding the shellfish, modern nutritional studies indicate that fish proteins are of inferior quality when compared to meats and even to some vegetable compounds. Experiments show that carnivorous animals fed on fish do not thrive. There may thus be a biological basis for the use of the term "fish-eater" as a disparaging epithet. The nutritional effect in human development is reflected in the marked contrasts between some vegetarian and some meat-eating groups in India. EVANS, however, pointed out the energy noted among those African peoples who had easy access to a fish supply, there being a very marked difference in quality in tropical Africa between those living on the rivers and those living away from them.

WATERS OF THE LAND AND DEVELOPMENT OF WATERSHEDS

The changes which man has made in the water economy of the earth can be either permanent or temporary, as with other non-renewable resources. LEOPOLD considered the mining of ground water actually to be semipermanent, but permanent relative to man, since the time span of recharge is very long. The greatest effects of man, however, are those changes which initiate a chain reaction, such as the building of large dams on large river systems. In the United States, for example, present plans look forward to a complete change in river systems. Dams already designed for the Missouri River will, if built, transform the valley into practically one continuous lake. There will come a time, be it a hundred or five hundred years, when a series of essentially level silt beds will be formed, and interesting changes in physiography and in the operation of the water economy will result from this sedimentation. First, riparian vegetation associated with the relatively high water table in these sediments will completely change the evapotranspiration losses. Second, there will be, as is so in the case of Lake Mead, an actual, though small, subsidence due to the weight of water behind the dams. It is not impossible that, when the entire Missouri

River Valley is one continuous lake, the subsidence effect will considerably change the base level of tributaries, which, in turn, will account in part for changes in the longitudinal profiles of all tributaries to the main river. Third, another effect is on tributaries: under natural conditions the occurrence of a flood peak on the main river is more or less directly related to flood peaks on the tributaries. However, when water is stored behind a dam, the flood peak of the main river is eliminated, while the undammed tributary when it comes to peak will be graded to a new level—that of the controlled water level of the main river. Such an upset of base levels due to control of the flood hydrograph of main stream versus tributary has caused important changes in erosion and sedimentation of many tributaries throughout the West, where the main stream has been subject to control by large structures and the tributaries have not. Fourth, recent research has indicated that, in general, a flood plain is built by a river to such a level that overflow occurs approximately once a year. In LEOPOLD's opinion, this is the diagnostic characteristic of flood plains. When the frequency of flooding is changed by control of the flood hydrograph, the same physical relationships that operated originally to form the flood plain will rebuild it in accord with the new frequency of flooding. Fifth, there is the effect of channel storage, which is going to be quite different from that at present, when water is able to flow over a very much greater width of valley. Thus, quite apart from economic or social factors, there are many hydrologic reasons why the construction of a series of dams on a long river system has many ramifications.

BURKE then asked Leopold for his opinion on what is basically wrong with the kind of watershed development that has taken place to date in the United States. Briefly, LEOPOLD replied

that the conservation program lacks basic understanding of hydrologic interrelationships as, for example, between upstream engineering and upstream land management. As things now stand, conservation, in the broadest sense, is carrying on its back an engineering program that cannot in itself be justified except locally.

Making the Missouri River a series of lakes with the sediment in the bottom would, ALBRECHT asserted, be an agricultural disaster. Those tributaries to the Missouri have a gradient as the crow flies of from 6½ to 7½ feet per mile. As the stream courses go, then, gradients are about 4 feet per mile. They come eastward from the highland, an area of low rainfall and relatively unweathered rock, and deliver and deposit sediment in the Missouri River, which has a gradient of less than a foot per mile. The Missouri River does not run at flood amounts all the time; and, even when the river becomes a trickle, the winds continue. Blowing from the southwest across that elbow of the Missouri River eastward from Kansas City, the winds have a maximum opportunity to pick up sediment, later to be deposited as so-called "loessal soil" at a rate of 1,000 pounds per acre per year over northern Missouri, Iowa, and Illinois, and are an integral part of the cycle of annual renewal of fertility in those cultivated areas of higher rainfall. We lose sight of the biological aspects of the situation because the technological aspects of building big dams look so wonderful, but man's engineering ambition to push the world around with a bulldozer is seriously disturbing when this biological performance is completely upset.

It was brought out by BARTLETT, in writing, that the late Professor Hobbes discovered present-day conditions in Greenland which explained how the great Pleistocene loess deposits of the Middle West south of the great ice sheets had been formed. The streams emerging in summer from under the central Greenland icecap carried in suspension great quantities of rock flour which were deposited on the coastal plain. When this fine material dried, it had no coherence and blew away in quantity, to settle in layers and drifts wherever there was vegetation enough to break the force of the wind. Fixation of this wind-blown dust by vegetation, to form loess, seems to have been a postglacial phenomenon of great magnitude in Iowa and other grassland states. With removal of the protecting vegetation, by the turning-under of sod, the erosional cycle recurred, and this might easily have been caused by overgrazing and too frequent fires, as well as by plowing. Since geologists regularly recognize that certain great geological deposits consist of wind-blown dust, it seems useless to labor the question of whether dust storms are a new phenomenon or not. Of course they are not. Still, it is interesting to know where the dust of present-day storms comes from.

BOULDING asked about the effect of proposed dams on the delta of the Mississippi and whether there was anything in the story that the effect of Hoover Dam will be to eliminate the Imperial Valley in California as a result of seaward erosion of the Colorado River Delta at the head of the Gulf of California. LEOPOLD thought the answer to be unknown. It is difficult to understand what happens even immediately below each individual dam. For example, the flood problem created at Needles, California, as a result of building Boulder Dam and the complete elimination of floods in the lower Colorado River were completely unforeseen. Degradation by the clear water released from the dam took place in the channel immediately below the dam; the resulting aggradation at Needles now causes the relatively low water volumes

released to become local floods. Not enough is known about river mechanics and related subjects to be able to forecast even local events, let alone questions of the future.

SMITH cited the example of the upper Rio Grande Valley, which, in part, is a series of filled mountain valleys. Between the ridges, water has brought down loose material and filled the valleys from side to side for many miles with soft, meal-like earth. When white men appeared on this surface, grass was growing higher than a horse and covered the valley from end to end and side to side. Floods mashed down the grass, rushed over it, but did not cut the land. White man's sheep and cattle ate the grass; streams cut the great mass of valley fill into channels; and the valley became a series of canyons. At Albuquerque, on the Rio Grande, the bottom of the river behind the dikes is higher than the town's main street.

BANKS was concerned about developments in the United States, because such huge projects will be copied blindly in other parts of the world. He asked who owns and controls these vast masses of water which either are being moved or are about to be moved. THOMAS answered that, according to the Constitution, all rights not committed to the federal government are reserved to the states. The Constitution declares commerce to be a matter for federal control. Navigation being a part of commerce, the federal government can control the navigable waters, including, according to court interpretation, the non-navigable tributaries of navigable streams. In addition, the "public welfare" clause of the Constitution permits the federal government to have an interest in waters in any locality, provided it has general rather than local concern. However, the working arrangement has been that each state has been pre-eminent in allocating rights within its area. For interstate waters, such as the Colorado or Mississippi rivers, the federal government has a very important obligation in navigation and flood control, but individual uses of water nearly always come under state jurisdiction. In general, water rights in the western states have been decided by supreme courts of the individual states. Only in cases of interstate interests, such as Arizona versus California or Nebraska versus Wyoming, have water cases reached the United States Supreme Court.

Competition for water exists in many parts of the world. BARTLETT, in writing, referred to the great disruption in the agricultural economy of the older settled areas of northwestern Argentina, caused by the diversion and utilization of water that formerly flowed into the region. Rivers there do not have sufficient volume to reach the sea but disappear into great alkaline and saline marshes. The northwestward movement of population, with its demand for irrigation, has deprived the earlier centers of sufficient water supply. Thus it can be seen that a chain reaction can result from tampering with one aspect of the hydrologic cycle. Water has a continuous movement through a number of interrelated stages: precipitation onto the surface, adsorption into the soil, runoff over the land, movement downward into ground-water reservoirs, and lateral movement underground. THOMAS related an experience that stressed the need for further information on ground water. In 1951 Kansas had some very serious floods in the eastern part of the state; the years 1952–54 were the three driest consecutive years on record. The state asked for some soul-searching on the matter of water supply and control, and a report was prepared. Characteristic has been the development of flood-control reservoirs in the eastern part of the state and, elsewhere, the formation of watershed associations for conserva-

tion by upstream engineering. These watershed developments were based not upon knowledge of quantities of water that could be placed in the soil but upon public interest which led to group organization. Engineers have quantitative information (chiefly present precipitation and runoff) on surface water but are handicapped by lack of information in estimating the quantity of water that may be held underground.

BURKE cited a small-scale example of disaster based upon insufficient knowledge. A realty operator in coastal Connecticut began to erect some 480 houses in a square-mile area. After putting up some 80 houses, he wanted to know why individual wells for each home were running dry. When the land was purchased, there had been no accurate information on the availability of ground-water supplies. The watershed association simply did not have information on ground water. The need for such information seems vital, particularly in view of the industrial use being made of large amounts of water today in congested areas.

MUMFORD, on the other hand, brought up the matter of the disuse of local water supplies. In urban areas there is a tendency to depend upon a centralized supply and to forget the enormous amount of ground water that was originally available in urban areas but now is left to run off underground without further use. This was discovered during a water famine in New York City, when certain astute owners dug wells under their buildings and used for industrial needs water that had been a nuisance up to that time. The question, then, is how far it would be useful to bring local supplies of water into co-operation again rather than to reach out farther and farther into the countryside for centralized supplies.

THOMAS, in writing, replied that

many cities that once depended upon wells for water supply have been forced to develop other sources more capable of supplying their needs as population and water requirements increased. New York City depended entirely on wells, with increasingly unsatisfactory results, until its population reached 200,000 in 1830.

Today, of the forty-one cities in the United States with populations greater than 250,000, only Houston and San Antonio, in Texas, and Memphis, Tennessee, obtain their municipal supplies from ground water. It is evident that pipe lines and stream channels are far superior to aquifers for transmission of hundreds of millions of gallons of water a day to points of concentrated demand. In cities that develop a new source of water after a long period of overdraft on ground-water supplies, an early effect of cessation of pumping is to permit replenishment of the depleted resource. In Brooklyn, New York, for example, overdraft had caused intrusion of sea water in the 1930's, but this problem was solved by reduction of pumping from wells. As Mumford suggests, several cities now have underground reservoirs, including some that have been heavily depleted in the past, which could be tapped for additional water supplies. Wells could be developed for emergency use by the city in periods of peak demand or for use by those who require water of uniform temperature or quality. Also, ground-water reservoirs in metropolitan areas are likely to become of increasing importance in the current trend toward dispersal of population and industries, because most ground-water reservoirs are at their best when called upon to supply water to widely dispersed wells. CLARK asked Mumford about the progress being made in re-use of water in urban systems (i.e., reclaiming water from sewage, from storm drains, etc.) and whether the re-use of water from

such sources promises any solution for the problem. MUMFORD felt that such sources were only partial solutions because of the increasing water famine to be expected from the extension of air-conditioning. Even with a re-use of water, by pumping an air-conditioning system, the draft on local supplies is tremendous.

SAUER interjected to remark that Californians are beginning to wonder whether in their pumping they are no longer dealing with recharge but are tapping geologic (Pleistocene) water. With regard to the mining of water, THOMAS pointed out that public opinion as found in court decisions is not in accord with conservation principles. In many states water is not considered differently from copper ore or other non-renewable resources. Where the mining of water is actually under way, it is unlikely that there will be any stoppage through state regulation, either by an administrative officer or by court decision, unless there is an alternate source of supply available.

Examples of ground-water competition in North Africa were supplied by HUZAYYIN. At some of the oases in the Libyan Desert, deep wells simply draw water from adjacent wells and, rather than enable the expansion of the cultivated area, deprive other wells of their source of water. In Algeria new companies, established to create oases of cultivated date palms and using modern methods for obtaining underground water, killed off the older oases of poor people subsisting on old palm trees around the smaller, shallower wells.

The civilizations of Egypt, India, and China were all extremely water-conscious and active in water control long before the existence of modern European nations or of the industrial revolution. WITTFOGEL redressed the balance of the discussion by pointing up that in China, which prior to the eighteenth century had more written literature than the whole of the West, there existed a water classic, the *Shui Ching*, an account of the country's rivers and canals. In hydraulic civilizations man not only manipulates water; he makes rivers and lakes. The agronomist F. H. King estimated the miles of man-managed watercourses in the Far East and perhaps in China alone at fully 200,000 (*Farmers of Forty Centuries*, 1927, p. 98). King estimated that these watercourses would be greater in number of miles than forty canals across the United States from east to west and sixty from north to south. Even on the modest levels of ancient Indian civilization in North America, such as Hohokam in Arizona, men had created impressive irrigation canals.

WITTFOGEL foresaw revolutionary changes in the arid parts of the world, such as southwestern United States and the Sahara, when new developments of power enable salt to be removed from sea water and the resulting fresh water to be brought cheaply to the land.

CLIMATIC CHANGE

EVANS thought it important to keep in view the very critical question of change of climate. While he would go a long way with Sauer in thinking that environmental changes can be independent of climate, the very discovery by the Irish naturalist Dr. Lloyd Krager of the Atlantic phase, or postglacial climatic optimum, was based upon marine forms and therefore was independent of vegetation changes that might have been induced by man. Climatic change during the time since subsistence economies came into being must be taken into account.

Within recent years and only within recent months, SEARS added, there has been a piling-up of tangible evidence of definite climatic change that has affected human cultural activities. This evidence is substantiated in wonderful fashion by carbon-14 dates. For example, the Atlantic period, that moist period around 3000 B.C. (five thousand years ago), shows up very definitely in records from areas as widely separate as Connecticut and the valley of Mexico. Evidence from a variety of sources indicates that, at the present time, the regions which are now quite arid have been undergoing a period of increased hazard, with very little margin of safety so far as water supply is concerned.

Coming from an area where climatic fluctuations are more significant than they are in some other parts of the world, HUZAYYIN also hoped that increased attention would be given to climatic change. He would rather proceed from the known to the unknown; to learn especially about unusual present-day climates. Studies of unusual drought years or unusual storms will give clearer ideas of what happened in the past during long phases of drought or of pluvial activity.

WISSMANN felt that Central Asia could not be discussed without dealing with the question of change of climate. Knowledge of this for Inner Asia is only at the beginning, though on the whole it appears that during the Ice Age there was a great shift of temperature but not a great change in moisture. A colder climate makes the available moisture more effective for plant growth, since less is lost through evaporation.

The unique historical records of China were referred to by WITTFOGEL, who pointed out that since the Shang dynasty there has been for over three thousand years an uninterrupted flow of written records which included details on climate, droughts, and floods, because such facts were of great interest to China's great agro-managerial bureaucracy. Of thirteen thousand examined oracle texts of the Shang dynasty (1766–1122 B.C.), three hundred indicated specific reactions to climate which could be placed into the various months; the indications were that by 1400 B.C. it was slightly warmer and more humid than previously.

STRAHLER raised the question of whether man *can* change climate. He wondered if Albrecht (pp. 654–57) was not overenthusiastic in attributing fundamental changes in climate to man's treatment of soils, specifically the development of drought as a result of soil tillage and reduction of vegetative cover. STRAHLER had the impression that Albrecht was saying that, by raising the temperature of the air close to the ground as a result of exposure of the soil, man has actually brought about climatic change which somehow affects air masses and the interaction of fronts and cyclonic disturbances, with the result that he has created his own deserts. On the other hand, Thornthwaite, in his chapter (pp. 567–69), discounted this very old theory. What man does with the land surface will not change climate appreciably. Resolution of these conflicting statements was not attempted, although EGLER, in writing, mentioned an aspect of the interrelations of vegetation and climate. The influence of deforestation on increasing aridity in temperate regions has been the subject of study and of speculation for several centuries. Of the designed research on this subject—in Russia, in western Europe, in North America—no definitive results have yet been obtainable. In EGLER's opinion, the situation in the tropics is fundamentally different and is well deserving of careful research and unprejudiced interpretation. Because of high temperatures in the tropics, the total *range* of insolation, evaporation, transpiration, vapor-pressure deficits, and related phenomena is much greater than in temperate regions. In the tropics conditions of light, temperature, and moisture between dense forested areas and barren wastes can be extremely different. This situation is expressed in a variety of statements that have appeared in the literature, the significance of which EGLER did not believe had been realized. For example, small low islands in the Pacific are known to have borne dense scrub or forest which has been totally destroyed following the introduction and increase of rabbits, pigs, or goats. Small sandy islands of this type are reported to have "split" a rainstorm as it approached from the ocean. Actually, it is probably extreme radiation from the barren sands that evaporates the rain before it strikes the land. On the high islands, clouds passing obliquely over valleys and ridges tend to persist over forested coves and forest plantations but evaporate over anthropically induced savannas and grasslands. In the French West Indies it has been observed that rain will fall on the forest on each side of a roadway but not on the roadway itself, presumably because of the dryness and radiation over this roadway. Laymen visiting the tropics are astonished at the extreme shade and dank coolness within the forest in contrast to the dry, scorching sunlight of adjacent cleared land. In short, regardless of what influence vegetation may be shown to have, or not to have, on regional climate in temperate regions, it was EGLER's opinion that the situation in the tropics is worthy of additional research that may possibly have a very important bearing on the practical management of these lands.

MINERAL RESOURCES AND ENERGY CONTROL

In introducing the subject of metals and minerals, Chairman BATEMAN recalled their importance in classical civilizations. In the country near Colchis, the people dug gravels in which were found particles of placer gold. These gravels were shoveled into a hollowed log lined with sheepskins. Water was admitted at one end of the log, and, as it ran over the gravels, it carried away the lighter material, leaving behind the heavier gold particles. The sheepskins were removed and shaken to remove the gold, but the fine particles adhered to the fleeces, which were hung on trees to dry. Thus, in the story of the "Golden Fleece," Jason and his Argonauts represent the first "gold rush" recorded in the literature. More importantly, the silver mines of Laurium upheld the grandeur of Greece; the decline of Greece coincided with the decline of the mines of Laurium.

HEICHELHEIM brought out that more numerous than the mines which went out of use because of the depletion of their minerals were cases where a lowering in the price of the mineral made working a mine unprofitable, even though much of the ore remained undisturbed. When Alexander conquered an enormous part of the world, the silver price, which had been a hundred and twenty times that of the same unit of copper, fell in value by half. Immediately afterward, the famous silver mines of Laurium were practically discontinued, and silver coinage in Athens stopped. The Romans, through their conquests of the eastern Mediterranean, so disturbed the caravan roads and production that, between 190 and 180 B.C. or so, the silver price again rose to a hundred and twenty times the same unit of copper. Immediately, the mines of Laurium began to be reworked, and the second Athenian coinage issue was begun, lasting until the silver price broke again in the first century B.C. Today these mines are used for lead, and some silver has remained.

An important conclusion of Ayres's chapter is that United States production of petroleum will reach a peak at approximately 1965 and world production at approximately 1985, after which production will begin to decline (cf. p. 379). BATEMAN, in writing, could not agree with these conclusions or with the charts upon which they were based, particularly that of a world production peak in 1985. A statistical conclusion is generally based upon available statistical data, and premises, in turn, are based upon the estimates of others. Ayres's estimate of domestic peak production in 1965 is based upon a probable curve that uses a figure of potential (not proved) United States reserves of 90 billion barrels. This is an older figure still used by statisticians but not generally believed by geologists who have followed petroleum-discovery developments in recent years. The offshore drilling in the Gulf of Mexico, for example, has made a great difference in estimation of potential reserves and geological thinking. Ayres states (p. 376): "We have drilled about 150,000 wells in this country." Actually there have been about 450,000 wells drilled, and the information available from the 450,000 wells is much greater than that from the older figure of 150,000. Ayres also states (p. 376) that the current rate of drilling is about 10,000 wells a year, whereas the current rate is between 40,000 and 45,000 wells per year. In 1954 some 13,000 purely exploratory holes alone were drilled. Despite heavy consumption, *proved* oil reserves have risen from 24 billion to over 30 billion barrels in the last four years and are still increasing. These data indicate a greatly accelerated rate of discovery and the building-up of potential reserves and an increasing fund of geological knowledge regarding petroleum, which, in turn, suggests that the period of domestic peak production will extend far beyond 1965.

Similarly, the world production peak in all likelihood will be extended well beyond 1985. Our geologic knowledge is far from complete in areas outside the United States. What knowledge there is indicates vast potential reserves, particularly in the Middle East, where some 250 wells, with an average daily production of 5,000 barrels of oil, may be contrasted to the United States, with around 450,000 wells averaging about 13 barrels per day. Large areas geologically suitable to contain oil have not yet been explored.

The need of modern industry for minerals and fuel has profound international implications. BATEMAN emphasized that extraction of mineral resources in countries in which there is abundance and demand for them by countries in which minerals are deficient means the continuance of international relations. Dependent upon mineral resources from distant areas, the United States cannot become isolationist. JONES took up one aspect of man's role in changing the face of the earth which the symposium had not discussed, that is, man's division of the world into independent political units.

Though not the whole story, energy is a key factor in the political power of states; but all kinds of energy are not commensurable or completely substitutable. Curiously, nuclear energy may make possible, for better or, more likely, for worse, the dreams of some of the aeronautical enthusiasts such as Douhet, Mitchell, and de Seversky. When applied to propulsion of aircraft, nuclear energy will bring realization of unlimited range and virtually unlimited destructive power. The hope is that the availability of the means will turn this politically divided world into a world of mutually respectful polecats. Were the world a unit, as a scientific meeting of this sort tends to consider it, we could expect science to supply energy where and when needed; but, in reality, ours is a world in apparently permanent conflict, and we cannot wait for laissez faire discoveries.

Changes in Biological Communities

Factors Affecting Population Growth

The Ecology of Disease

The Shift from Balance or Equilibrium in the Newer Ecology

The Direction of Change

Dr. MARSTON BATES, Chairman, prefaced the discussion with introductory remarks about the difficulties of keeping "Process" separate from "Retrospect" and "Prospect." He expressed his desire to interpret "changes in biological communities" to mean man in relation to ecological processes. With the introduction of the word "ecology," he defined his concepts of what the term implies. He preferred the term "natural history," in order that man might be seen in relationship with the processes of nature, and thought of ecology as "skin-out" biology, a descriptive term to delimit its area of interest. The skin is something observable and serves as a convenient boundary to separate skin-out from skin-in biology. By viewing ecology in this manner, we can segregate a constellation of subjects which are primarily concerned with internal functioning from those which are primarily concerned with organisms as wholes, even though there is really no way of cutting the interconnected web of relationships into pieces that are terribly logical.

The basic units of skin-out biology are of three sorts: the individual, the population, and the community. Though the individual is perhaps the nearest to an objective category among the three, even individuals blend when a time dimension is added; this renders the study of the individual meaningful only in a rather limited way. When we study individuals over time, the web of interrelationships producing new individuals is recognized. The emergence of the unit of study called "population" is one of the most significant aspects of skin-out biology. Biologically, populations can be defined as aggregates of similar items that conform to some particular definition. The concept of population coincides in part with the concept of species. The biological species is now commonly defined as a population of organisms that actually do or have the potential to interbreed with one another, separated from other similar populations by reproductive barriers of one sort or another. The word "population," used for the species as a whole, can also be used for parts of the species— for populations within political units or for those of particular age groups. But, in the broad sense of population as species, it is found that different populations are related to one another to make up what is called the "biotic community."

In biology a community (or "biocenose") means an aggregation of populations which have some sort of relationship to each other—such as a food relationship. A human community, in the biological sense, then, would comprise an aggregate of individuals of the species *Homo sapiens* together with dogs, cats, cows, cockroaches, mice, and other animal forms, and the neighboring tributary areas for plant food, etc.

BATES interpreted the problem of changes in biological communities to be the problem of changes in population relationships. Thus we should view man as a population or a series of populations in a biotic community or in a series of biotic communities. However, rather than to attempt to look at the broad biological community, he preferred to begin the discussion by considering the question of the process of population dynamics of the human species, for example, the relation between human densities and disease and disease control.

FACTORS AFFECTING POPULATION GROWTH

JANAKI AMMAL presented the problem of India's rise in population. Over the sixty-year period 1891–1951, India's population increased by 122 million, though in 1891 the figures included the area of present-day Pakistan, and it is to be questioned how accurate the census was. Upon analysis, it is found that between 1891 and 1920 the increase in population was only 12 million; from 1921 to 1930, 27.4 million; from 1931 to 1940, 37.3 million; and from 1940 to 1951, 44.1 million. The question is, then, what effect such rises in population are going to have on world resources, on India itself, on the health of the world, and on the ecology of humanity, because today, when the population of India is compared with the rest of the world, one out of every seven persons on the face of the earth comes from India. JANAKI AMMAL asked for comment on the direction in which a remedy might lie and expressed her willingness to answer any questions on difficulties that India might have in putting into action any remedy proposed.

BROWN opened discussion on the problem of the growth of Indian population by repeating a remark of the demographer Chandrasekaran, who said that the rate of population growth during the decades 1921–31, 1931–41, and 1941–51, in his view, could not be explained on the basis of any real change in village life, such as in public health techniques or education, for to the best of his knowledge the people in the villages today live essentially as they did many, many decades ago. Why, then, the remarkable rise since the early 1920's? After talking with a number of people in India, it seemed to BROWN quite likely that there have been three major contributing factors to the growth of India's population: absence of famine conditions, construction of a railroad system, and the whims of climate.

Of course, India has suffered famine after famine. There has been constant malnutrition, and on an average of every five to ten years the climatic conditions become rough in a particular area, widen, and lead to a recognized famine. Every fifty to one hundred years or so, things "gang up," and famines become fantastically large.

As early as 1819 or so, the ancient Indian irrigation system was reconstructed to allow a major extension of irrigation. The really major factor, however, in accounting for the growth of India's population followed the famine of 1880, when a railroad system was instituted, which today extends to the point where the service in the whole subcontinent has a mile of railroad for every 25 square miles of land. The extension of the railroad system was significant, for it meant that, when there was a famine in a particular area, food could be taken from other regions into the area of famine. That in itself, by making possible the movement of food, contributed enormously to the reduction of disease.

The importance of transportation in India in the over-all famine picture may be indicated by the example of the great Bengal famine of 1943. When we read the many papers which were written about the Bengal famine, it seems rather clear that there was an ample supply of food (relative to what Indians are used to eating) and that the main causes of the famine appear to have been a transportation tie-up and administrative bungling in connection with transportation. At the time there was a war on, which effectively hindered the movement and distribution of food from other areas of India.

TABLE 32*

DROUGHTS, FLOODS, AND DEATH RATES
FOR INDIA PER DECADE, 1891–1949

Decade	Number of Droughts	Number of Floods	Death Rate per Thousand
1891–1900...	19	30	44
1901–10.....	19	11	43
1911–20.....	42	25	49
1921–30.....	5	11	36
1931–40.....	5	16	31
1941–49.....	5	17	27

* From *Indian Census Report of 1951* (New Delhi, 1953).

The other factor, which probably has nothing important to do with man's intentional activity, however, is the whim of climate. Throughout all India there are floods here and droughts there, floods in one part and a drought in another part. These catastrophes bring about conditions of famine or near-famine. The record over the years is exceedingly interesting, as shown by Table 32.

Several were moved to comment on the figures in the table. Some were concerned over drought rates, others were skeptical of the rates given for floods, and still others questioned the figures for the death rates. With regard to the figures for drought, LANDSBERG warned against accepting the rates given as anything but a figment of somebody's imagination. Citing a study made of rainfall changes in India over the last sixty years, he added that in the last thirty years the total rainfall has gone down rather than up, as the table would seem to indicate to some extent. BROWN commented that he had also been curious about that, but the question was not one of mean rainfall. In India, where the monsoon is depended upon, rain either is or is not there. Apparently, from the point of view of reported drought areas, Table 32 is reasonably accurate. JANAKI AMMAL made the point that, according to statesmen who have been in charge of revenue areas and drought-recording, the census of each province has a definite relation to the income derived from the land; therefore, she felt that the figures in Table 32 were reliable.

Though not questioning the figures given in the table, THOMAS commented that "drought" and "flood" are words in common usage, not quantitatively defined. A single drought over extensive areas may be far more depressing as far as the country is concerned than one which is broken up into several areas and recorded as several droughts scattered over several small areas.

BROWN turned to the whole question of fertility as another aspect of Indian population growth. When it comes to decreasing fertility, economists and sociologists have said that the growth of urbanization must be awaited, and, indeed, the experience of the West certainly indicates that. However, a recent study, made at the Gokhal Institute and sponsored in part by the Rockefeller Foundation, of the fertility in the Poona area, where it was possible to compare the fertility in the rural region with that in the urban area, showed that there is not the slightest visible indication of a drop in fertility in Indian urban areas. Concerning the spread of family-limitation techniques, BROWN mentioned the study made in the Bangalore area and also in New Delhi of the success of the application of the rhythm method. This study showed rather clearly that the rhythm method could not be applied by all the people or even by a substantially large fraction of them all the time. As for the use of chemical means in family-limitation techniques, Lady Rama Rau's organization, after spending large sums of money and a fantastic amount of effort in the village of Badlapur, succeeded in persuading twenty-five women from a total population of three thousand to use a form of biologically effective tablet, but even the twenty-five have not used it in what could be called a consistent manner. BROWN expressed a pessimistic view that family-limitation techniques might spread rapidly in India.

A good part of the resistance to methods of family limitation lies, of course, in the whole cultural pattern. A look at the reasons given for not using contraceptives shows high on the list a concern over not having a child for support in one's old age. To persuade somebody not to have children is the same as asking a Westerner to tear up his insurance and annuities.

SMITH questioned Brown's comment that the railroad system in India was the cure to famine, because of the observation that every organization eventually increases up to the limit of its food supply. Egypt illumines this observation. Egypt is in a very acute situation. It is a place to watch because it is a nicely walled-in experiment, with the Nile Valley on one side and the desert on the other. Egypt shows a decline in the death rate, a decline in droughts, and a decline in floods—and it has railroads. And, as Brown had said, the birth rate remains effective. An official report of the Egyptian cabinet revealed that between 1929 and 1953 or 1954, the average intake of food by the people of Egypt had gone down 25 per cent. This condition is a very tragic and acute illustration of what lies ahead if the population of the United States, India, Egypt, or any place continues to increase. Are there any examples of a large body of population with a good food supply over a long period of time which has not approached the limit of that food supply? BATES offered Australia, but OSBORN characterized Australia as a country where the population is tending to come up to its food supply and where their exports are threatened. GALDSTON suggested the Scandinavian countries; Germany and Belgium also were cited as examples. HUZAYYIN explained that the drop of 25 per cent in intake of food by the people of Egypt, as mentioned by Smith, represented only food products *within* Egypt. Imported food was not included in the figures. Although an agricultural country, Egypt imports from 20 to 30 million pounds of food per year.

GOUROU, in writing, called into question the values of death rates as given in Table 32. Though they are *vraisemblables*, they are not very valuable. In fact, it is impossible to give values other than hypothetical ones for the death rate in 1891–1900. Comparisons between two estimates, each being distant from reality by several per cent, are not convincing. THOMPSON also felt that the figures given on death rates in Table 32 should not be taken too seriously. To show this, he projected birth rates as they would be if the death-rate figures as given in the table were correct. If the death rate in the decade 1891–1900 is correct, then the birth rate was about 45 per thousand. In the decade 1901–10 the population showed a rate of increase about 9 per cent; the birth rate then would have been about 52 per thousand. During the next decade, from 1911 to 1920, there was no increase in the birth rate to speak of. That was the decade of the great influenza epidemic in which eight million died in about three or four months, according to the smallest estimates. If the death rate for the decade 1921–30 is correct, the birth rate must have fallen to a bit over 50 per thousand. In the decade 1931–40 the birth rate dropped to 43 or 44 per thousand; and in the last decade, 1941–49, the birth rate was down to 40 per thousand. Therefore, it can be seen that the decrease in the birth rate as projected from the figures given for the death rate in Table 32 reveals the fact that accurate figures for the death rate in India are unknown. THOMPSON added that the figures could not be considered as evidence of a falling birth rate and that he did not believe that the birth rate in India had fallen.

Commenting further on the relation between urbanization and a decline in death rates, THOMPSON did not think that the relation need be accepted as a universal rule. Though he was doubtful about the ability to reduce the birth rate very rapidly in all underdeveloped countries, certain changes in contraceptive practices are on the way, and it is possible that there might be a very marked decline in the birth rate in a comparatively short time if there were a contraceptive which was absolutely certain, which was free, which people might obtain, and which was simple to use. Nevertheless, whether it is better economic conditions, better medical practices, or whatever that is responsible for the decline, it is the *change* in the death rate that has been the important thing in the great development of world population growth during the last two centuries. The birth rate among nearly all peoples has been high enough to produce a very large increase of population with what would be called only a moderate death rate, comparable to that of 1900 in the United States. If a birth rate is in the neighborhood of 40–45 per thousand, the death rate could

be lowered under favorable conditions to 15 or 16 per thousand within two, three, or four decades.

NORTHROP made the point of an Indian economist that there is no evidence from the study of other societies that population is ever cut down by birth-control propaganda or education; rather, reduction is taken care of by industrialization. This is quite a different thing from the move to cities from villages; the heart of the matter centers in the ethics of social organization of the people involved. In cultures that have not emerged with the law-of-contract, abstract ethic for organizing communities, everything tends to be family-centered. Filial piety is the top social virtue in Chinese culture, in Hindu culture, and in most of the so-called "primitive" societies. As was noted by Brown, this puts a premium on having children to take care of one in one's old age.

What happens when industrialization comes in? Technical education is necessary to operate an industrial society. This means sending the young sons and daughters to universities. They meet, and they mate on intellectual grounds. This breaks them loose from filial piety, the marriages no longer being arranged by the families, as they were in a family-centered ethical society. Then, in order to carry on the skills of a technological industrial society, they have to get advanced degrees. When they see that they cannot get for their children the same kind of education they have had if they produce large families, the law-of-status society with family-centered ethics is automatically broken. Here is where just the bringing-in of technology, of Western ways of thinking about these matters, may serve to check population growth in the long run. This is the reason why the study made in the Poona area, which Brown mentioned, that showed no difference in birth rates between the village and the city does not prove very much unless changes are seen in family habits—whether the children have been captured by a new way of relating themselves in marriage, have related themselves socially to a law-of-contract constitution, and have acquired technological skills.

THE ECOLOGY OF DISEASE

GALDSTON advanced the point that a growth of population can be derived from two principal sources—one an absolute increment and the other an increment from survival. In the United States, recent increments in population, discounting immigration, derive from survival. This is an important factor to bear in mind. The life-expectancy in the United States at birth during the last half-century has increased by some eighteen to twenty-odd years, but the increase is relatively meaningless as far as the total health of the total population is concerned, for, at forty-five and above, life-expectancy is increased by little more than a year or two. This has an enormous bearing upon the ecological picture as far as the composition of the community, its medical and custodial services, and as far as its consumption and production are concerned. Unless the importance of the change in the ecological picture is appreciated and unless the disease problem is viewed as an ecological problem rather than as a specific disease causality with specific treatment, medicine will be retarded.

To illustrate how the increment from survival has changed the composition of communities, GALDSTON compared the distribution of diseases and the deaths resulting in 1900 with the mortalities of 1950. In 1900 the dominant diseases were tuberculosis, pneumonia, the infant diarrheas, typhoid fever, scarlet fever, and diphtheria. Now, the principal ills are cancer, heart disease and hypertension, as well as neurological disturbances. The interesting thing about the two groups of diseases is that

they cannot really be compared. In the case of tuberculosis, the average life-expectancy of the tubercular individual in 1900 ranged from three to five years. Pneumonia, typhoid fever, the diseases of children, scarlet fever, etc., claimed their victims in short order. Today, though a heart-disease victim may die suddenly, generally he has anywhere from five to ten years of relative disability before death, and the cancer patient also may have from one to five years of so-called "survival." Thus, the death categories of the 1900's were quick exits, whereas those of today are disabilities drawn out over a decade or more. Modern medicine to a large extent has substituted mortality for morbidity; and this longer survival rate has serious consequences—political, economic, social, and cultural. The spectrum of population distribution in most communities has been freighted away from the early and productive decades into the older ones, where people are more likely to become dependent and require support by others. What to do with the aged of a community has become a very acute problem. They no longer are contained with three-family homesteads to perform useful service. Twenty-five per cent of new admissions to state institutions are of older people who suffer from depressive states resulting from social disorientation and dislocation, not because they are so arteriosclerotic as to be unable to carry on. We have to, after all, orient ourselves to ecology —an ecology which in the last analysis must have a human, if not humanitarian, implication. The orientation point must be taken more or less from human needs. Unless medicine really becomes other than merely the treatment of disease, and unless doctors treat the individual in the aim of helping him to fill effectively his destiny, populations are going to be exhausted long before mineral or water resources or anything else are exhausted.

With regard to the influence of modern medicine as a factor in the upsurge of population, BANKS pointed to the inherent urge to survive in man, which has three major things militating against it: war, pestilence, and famine. When great pestilences are studied to see what happened, it will be found that some of them in certain parts of the world disappeared of their own accord, though modern medicine can claim to be directly responsible for the disappearance of others.

Plague disappeared in Britain before even the cause of it was known; it never came back after 1665. It was not known that it was the rat or the rat flea, although the rat was suspected; certainly nothing was known about plague but its symptoms. The reason for its disappearance was a function of improving social conditions in its widest sense—the replacement of old brush floors by carpets, brought by expanding trade, which made it less easy for the rat to hide in floors, and the erection of stone buildings instead of wood and thatch buildings, etc., after the Great Fire of London. Malaria died out in England only in the last fifty years, and, again, nobody knew why. Steps were not taken, and the English did not even know its cause, but it died out.

A turn to the other side of the list shows that modern medicine has made it possible to stamp out directly a great number of diseases: the parasitic diseases, the septic infections, and the insect vectors of disease. Therefore, we cannot just generalize about causes for the decline of disease; we must take the specific disease, the part of the world in which it occurs, and the conditions in that part of the world. But the decline of pestilence, as a result of the operation of other factors, has made possible large population increases and population pressures, though it is doubtful whether that is the whole story. Is there a biological phenomenon at work? Birth rates in many countries remain

high or are rising because of the increased numbers surviving to adult life and because of the increased health of adults in maturity. Some of the drop in the death rate can be traced directly to the control of disease. For example, in looking at the death rate year by year in Ceylon, the year when malaria control was effective can be picked out, because the death rate drops by about half in the year 1947.

As for fertility, the British Royal Commission on Population supported the comment made that there certainly has been no decline of fertility in the population of England. There has been a most dramatic decline in the size of family over the last seventy years, but fertility is unchanged.

As a penultimate paradox, so to speak, improvement of living conditions is primarily not a medical matter but a function of good government in its widest sense—the access of wealth and its proper use, proper distribution of resources, and the like in a country.

GALDSTON offered the idea of modern medicine that disease is largely a product of deprivation, not primarily of parasites. The best illustration is provided by the fact that, concomitantly with the deprivation of food among Poles and Jews, the incidence of tuberculosis rose more acutely among the depressed Jews. Also, in England, many neurotic reactions which were present in peacetime disappeared when the Englishman had something else to occupy him. It is deprivation that renders invalid the generalization that public health is really the resultant of good government. Good government has power, but good government cannot really provide those things which have a natural limit. When that limit is approached, we suffer deprivations, and disease becomes inevitable.

BANKS explained that what he meant by a solution to the problems of overpopulation and food supply was a function of good government, not public health at all. He thought the stabilization of population or the reduction of births to be a function of improving social conditions, quite apart from any contraceptive technique. This takes very much longer; in England it took seventy years. It may take India, or any other country, one hundred years.

OSBORN expressed more concern over the increase in population in the United States than in that of India because of the future of the United States as a place that can continue to serve the world as a whole. How effectively can the United States cope with world conditions if there are going to be, as present prognostications indicate, 250 to 300 million people in the United States, with their tremendous demands for raw materials, social amenities, and education?

GLIKSON, in referring to the theory of Malthus and the Neo-Malthusians of the relation of population increase to land resources, spoke of the improvement needed in the development of resources in a country as overpopulated as India. To provide decent livelihoods for such a large population, there is still much room for the development of the basic economic needs. Improvement must be oriented first of all toward development of resources and not toward decrease or control of birth.

A second comment was on the theory of De Castro that the low quality or the lack of proteins in foods seems to be responsible for the increase of population. GLIKSON could not accept the theory, but he did feel that, as long as people are economically destitute, they cannot really be presented with demands for birth control; only when their standard of living is raised can they be approached as people who are responsible for the coming generation in the social community.

Then a number of questions were asked regarding the possible effects on

health of the unprecedented interference with natural processes now occurring over large areas of the world. For example, to what extent is the balance of nature being affected in the wholesale destruction of insects? What will be the long-term effects of the extensive use of antibiotics? How will the disease patterns of a population be influenced by the intense efforts now being made to raise the standards of environmental sanitation and of hygiene in general? And how important is the contamination of the air, soil, and water caused by the increased use of atomic energy?

ANDERSON agreed with the remarks by the biologist Dr. H. J. Muller, as reported in the *New York Times*, that the increase of atomic radiation had reached a point where it had a predictable quantitative increase in the percentage of human children that will be born as misfits. ANDERSON did not know of any geneticist working in this field who did not agree. Debate is not over the fact of change but over the differences in percentage of effect. MURPHY felt that, without discounting the effects of radiation, the latest information differed from that of Muller and his colleagues. The total effect of radiation to date, outside the centers of explosion, is less per capita than exposure to a single X-ray. So far as can be judged from human data and from experimental work on animals of much less length of life, the scare aspect has been somewhat overdone.

BATES interjected to say that, though he was particularly fascinated by the ecology of disease, he was hesitant to continue discussion about it, since it would lead back into the problem of the population spiral. However, diseases are a very curious part of the human habitat; the way diseases have disappeared without our knowing it makes study of them very important. He then called on Hitchcock to speak about the work on the distribution of disease by the American Geographical Society.

HITCHCOCK described the program of the Society to map those diseases which are able to be mapped on a world-wide basis. Under the direction of Dr. Jacques May, seventeen maps related to various aspects of disease and disease vectors will have been prepared by the end of 1955. A text on the epidemiology of various diseases is also in preparation, containing information on certain aspects which cannot be shown on a map, such as the mysterious disappearance of malaria. This project shows the importance of thinking in terms of maps and the value of using them as an aid to discover distributions which otherwise might remain unnoticed.

THE SHIFT FROM BALANCE OR EQUILIBRIUM IN THE NEWER ECOLOGY

By alluding to the idea that man lives always in a subclimax sort of state—in one that is arrested in its ordinary line of succession—BATES returned the discussion to the community, the nature of the human habitat in relation to climax, and man's interference with nature.

EGLER regarded climax as equilibrium, a steady state, a balance. However, everyone agrees that change is universal—that there are trends and tendencies offered in certain directions. The peneplain of the geologist is an excellent example of a concept of a theoretical end stage, but no geologist would say that the entire world was going to be reduced to a peneplain. It is hoped that ecologists also do not consider the end stage of an ecosystem to be the best stage. For example, Mettler's Woods, near New Brunswick, New Jersey, has been referred to as a virgin forest but should not be considered as an ideal forest. But it is necessary for man to alter the balance of nature, and thus the word "balance" means a dynamic balance.

To show the general implications of man's alterations of nature, EGLER referred to the increasing amount of land in the United States which is being required for roadsides, railroad rights of way, pipe lines, telephone lines, etc. Transportation and communication are integral parts of the economy, but their total demands for land are not often considered in their true importance. Charles Morrow Wilson, the writer on agricultural subjects, has said that the acreage in roadsides of the United States not including other rights of way is equal to the size of the state of Georgia, the largest state east of the Mississippi. And roadsides and other means of communication are going to be increased. What is to be done with that land? It must be managed, manipulated, and kept down from the final end stage.

Wildlife management, taking into account another huge amount of land in the United States, aims to divert the tendency of nature to go off in another direction. In forestry, efforts are made toward changing the tendency of nature to proceed to climax. Forestry may possibly be on the verge of a revolution in regard to the use of chemicals, which would have a selective effect upon species, destroying undesirable ones but not harming those desirable. Within a decade aerial sprays probably will be in common use as a reforestation procedure. In commenting upon Egler's alarm at the amount of land required for transportation, HARRIS posed the question whether total productivity would not decrease if land were taken out of transportation. EGLER replied that he mentioned the amount of land going into transportation only as an example of land being changed and added that he was alarmed only that certain forces in the United States have perverted public pressure to use land in a manner which he felt was unwise.

GRAHAM felt that soil erosion represented perhaps a heavier impact upon the face of the earth than any other single process and has been due very largely perhaps to the disturbance of vegetation. We could take a very baleful point of view with respect to the disturbance of vegetation and the resulting problems it has created, such as soil erosion, but there is at man's disposal the tremendous power for re-creation that exists in natural communities of plants, whether disturbed by man or not. Plant communities do not regress or deteriorate as such, for, as soon as a disturbance caused by man is relaxed, the plant community has a tendency to reconstitute itself. This process of re-creation occurs not only in the grassland of western North America (as mentioned by Graham in his chapter) but also in the forests of eastern North America. A new experiment in the Egyptian desert likewise shows this kind of recovery, even where land has been grazed for thousands of years. The positive force in plant communities, if used wisely, enables man to develop and maintain the productive capacity of the land.

CURTIS, in writing, brought out that the categorical definition of ecology as the study of organisms in relation to their environment suffers from the weakness of excessive broadness. A more useful operational definition might be as follows: Ecology is the study of material and energy changes in biotic communities. This definition involves the comparison of efficiency of different communities in space and changes in efficiency in time as communities develop. It also includes the study of the organization of structures through which energy and materials flow and of the methods whereby that organization is maintained. This operational definition is in itself very broad and results in confinement of the attention of some ecologists to the investigation of community organization (what organisms, how many, how big, how arranged in space) and how communities are related to each other. Other ecologists study populations of single organisms and the environmental limits within which they reach levels of efficiency sufficient to gain and maintain a place in the community. The contribution of ecology to the symposium theme is largely to be made in showing the effect of man on natural communities. This effect can be understood only when the behavior of non-exploited communities is known, and this knowledge is only partly complete, owing to the size of the task, the lack of time, and the lack of support.

Several speakers have indicated that fires occurred on the grassland, that the grassland community was adapted to fire, that the fires were set both by men and by lightning, and that the man-induced fires probably caused the grassland to expand into the forest, since the forest recovered when fires were stopped. To the ecologist, such facts are interesting, but the real question is not, "Did one community replace another under the influence of fire?" but, rather, "What changes in material and energy transfer are affected by such a fire replacement?" Only when answers to questions like these are known can a value judgment be made as to whether replacements are good or bad. When the ecologist has learned enough about the internal workings of communities and especially about their ways of maintaining themselves in a non-deteriorating condition, he should then be able to offer advice on how man can substitute artificial communities for natural ones and still prevent degradation.

In adding to Curtis' ideas, TUKEY said that, when commercial economies (through conservation movements, conferences, etc.) become also subsistence economies, in the large, by returning to the soil enough nitrogen and minerals to balance that removed in crops, it will be natural to regard forest and field as yet another kind of factory—a factory to which raw materials are brought and from which finished products are transported. At that time the relative roles of various kinds of factories as (1) incorporators of energy, (2) synthesizers of proteins and other building-block materials, and (3) builders and blenders of tastes and textures will be carefully reconsidered. When it is known more clearly what is wanted from such factories, then, provided power (nuclear, solar, or other new forms) is available at low enough cost, there will be a strong tendency to shift at least part of the production off the land. How soon such a shift can become possible is unclear. (If the human race is transient enough, this knowledge may never be had.) But if and when this stage is reached, the ecological relation of *Homo sapiens* to the land may alter substantially.

BATES interpreted Curtis' remarks and those of other conservationists and ecologists to mean that man exists in a state of disequilibrium, and necessarily so, and asked whether anyone would explore the generalization.

BOULDING thought a useful conceptual framework to express the relation of man to his biological environment was a succession of short-run equilibriums. What is encouraging is that man is a parasite and that parasitic relationships are rather stable; it is mutually co-operative or mutually competitive relationships that are so unstable. However, when we look at the process of change in time as a whole, the factor which differentiates an equilibrium with man in it from a system without

man is man himself—the problem-solving animal. When man's consciousness enters the evolutionary framework, it means essentially that the organism which is dealt with is no longer the individual; it is the whole network of communications. That part of the human race which is in communication is a single organ in a way that no simple biological community is. This, in a sense, is the key to human history. The problem is: Under what circumstances does a problem-solving communications network go wrong? Historically, under processes which Boulding had called "vicious dynamics," the communications network occasionally has gone wrong. An arms race is a good example, in that it is a process in which the attempt to gain security on the part of each results in insecurity for all. A situation is possible in which the solution of a problem for one part of an ecosystem creates worse problems for other parts. We can never get a system in which all parts go from bad to better. Even when things as a whole are going from bad to better, some parts of the system are going from bad to worse. The attempt to create subsystems in which all parts go from bad to better can easily create a situation in which the whole system goes from bad to worse. SEIDENBERG felt that man deserved a nobler description than that given by Boulding—a problem-solving animal. He thought man should be called a "problem-raising animal."

Returning to the notion of balance or equilibrium in nature, DAVIS brought out that constant shifts of control prevent dynamic stability. Equilibrium will never become static. Man may be called the agent of shifting, but that is about all that he is. Every seasonal condition of the surface of the earth, now, as well as throughout the Pleistocene, represents shifts of control. We cannot evaluate whether a condition is becoming better or worse, because the dynamics of the whole universe are open to shifts. BATES interjected to ask Davis whether ecologists do not have to isolate factors. One of the difficulties of ecology is that it lacks the use of experimental methods. DAVIS replied that he imagined that the nearest thing to the experimental method in nature is to find something in it that is stable long enough for a person to live and understand it. THORNTHWAITE illustrated Davis' point with a parable of the play *Green Pastures,* in which "de Lawd," who is the principal character, ranges the earth, passing out five-cent cigars, organizing fish fries, and passing miracles. The miracles are necessary because "de Lawd" sees things wrong with the world. But one miracle immediately makes two or three other things wrong, and so, consequently, he always has to go on passing miracles.

GALDSTON compared the concept of equilibrium in ecology with the concept of homeostasis in medicine. The principle of homeostasis has recently been challenged, because, like the idea of ecology pictured as static, homeostasis was conceived of as static. No human being is ever in constant homeostasis. Homeostasis is but a base line for subsequent disequilibrium.

EGLER felt that much of traditional ecology is pretty well "on the skids"— going out—and it would be rather hard to find a strong and powerfully convinced, evangelistic ecologist, even though there are some who are thoroughly grounded in the old "plant succession to climax." There seem to be no good lines of evidence, for example, to indicate that the United States was in a state of virgin climax at the time of entry of the white man, who, in fact, arrived at an unstable moment. The past is not necessarily an indication of what the future will bring.

GLACKEN was convinced that the idea of nature and its history and the ideas of Egler and others lay at the basis of

much of the thinking regarding human society and the natural environment. The curious thing is that the newer expressions, such as disequilibrium, do not appear in the ecological literature. Perhaps this accounts for the basis for some misunderstandings of ecology. He asked for comment on his observation. BATES replied that, just as physiology books were preoccupied with homeostasis and economics books with equilibrium, so was there little of these newer ideas of constant change in the ecological literature.

THE DIRECTION OF CHANGE

BROWN introduced the point that what he sees happening all about is that man is more and more living in a completely artificial world. This began when man first made a tool. We can imagine the process accelerating during the years ahead to the stage where essentially the whole continent is covered with concrete and where everyone's life is based on controlled climate, on growing mutations of cows that are just globs of protoplasm lying down while they are milked. Already there are wingless chickens. He asked the ecologists what they visualized from the point of view of process. Do they visualize a world in which man lives as a part of nature, and, if so, how does he live as a part of nature? OSBORN answered that, though he was not an ecologist, he had one observation to make —until there were alternatives, the resources and processes of nature would have to be used as best they could be. A completely artificial environment is quite a long way off. Everybody who thinks about the use and development of natural resources realizes that the physical world is constantly and rapidly changing. When time came for a cement-paved America, irrespective of its social charm, the economists would say, "Well, what kind of a life is it, and is it worth the price?"—because, for instance, water would theoretically have to come from the oceans. Resource conservationists hope that natural tools or processes will continue to be used as effectively as possible. With regard to food supply, each country ought to do the best it can to protect a given agricultural base, until other sources of food can be obtained. It is theoretical to say that algae can be used as food until some proved practical way of producing them can be found, regardless of whether they should be desirable as food.

Tax thought that no one should make the choice of what kind of world everybody else ought to live in. What must be found is a way to open the eyes of everyone in some kind of general communication fashion: by conferences leading to books, by the books of others, and by any means available, so that whatever mistakes occur are those made after discussion rather than after action of what some people think of as selfish interests and others think of as inevitable trends which cannot be stopped, which none want, but which just come. The issue for technicians when asked to help is to make clear the consequences and to offer the help that is asked for under the circumstances. Beyond that one cannot go in the making of value judgments for other people. This probably is one of the reasons why conservationists have a strong feeling that, until the answers are really known, a judgment should not be made that will affect posterity and that will be irreversible.

As an example of the sort of thing where ignorance destroys things, Tax asked Murphy to relate his story about an oyster bed. Murphy described a proposal of some twenty years ago to build a bridge across the Lynnhaven River at Norfolk, Virginia. A retired biologist, upon hearing of the plans to build the bridge, wrote to the newspapers, published diagrams of the river, and insisted in many communications that the bridge at the point proposed would be the end of the Lynnhaven oyster beds in the estuary of the river. No more attention was paid to him than to Cassandra. He was asked by everybody, "What do you know about building a bridge?" He replied, "I don't." The bridge was built, and the oyster beds were buried under some 20 feet of silt. Oystermen say that the Lynnhaven oyster now is nothing but a traditional name.

Tukey provided an example of a wise use of a resource by mentioning the case of a fishery in an inland river or lake. To obtain the maximum take of fish, the fishery clearly should be operated with the fish population rather noticeably below the level that it is when the fishery is undisturbed. Therefore, when more is known quantitatively about other processes, ecologists will tell us that nature should be altered, but only by a certain amount.

Recognizing that man is only one element in the whole ecological community, Glikson felt that it is not so much the increase in numbers of population which is dangerous as it is the lowering of the quality of man which appears with increase in numbers. Mass culture, for instance, about which so much is said, is perhaps one of the consequences of the tremendous increase of population. Others are loss of community coherence, loss of human happiness, and loss of values for life and the fact that mass man becomes so easily the victim of cheap propaganda. Glikson reported his meeting in Holland with an ecologist in which their talk was about soil conservation and organic agriculture. The ecologist pointed out that two things are implied when we speak of soil conservation—the necessity to conserve natural resources and retain the health of the soil and the desire for a higher quality of man.

Conservation of resources and soil can be demanded, but the quality of man is something about which very little can be said.

LANDSBERG, in pondering the question of the scale of magnitude in biological communities and in thinking of the changes that have occurred in geological history, wondered whether an analogy could be drawn. At one time or another the earth has been populated by other biological communities living in other kinds of environment provided by nature. It is entirely possible that the earth will revert to the Tertiary type of conditions, in which man as now constituted would be very uncomfortable. When things come to final stages, everything goes in an explosive type of fashion. Is the world at such a point now? With the present armaments race and other things, mentioned by Boulding, considerable changes in the biological environment could be made on very short notice, and it might well be that man is just going to be an index fossil for the Recent geological age.

Techniques of Learning: Their Limitations and Fit

Phenomena and Definitions: Two Approaches

Classification and Measurement

Learning of Techniques: The Human Element

In opening the session, Dr. EDGAR ANDERSON, as Chairman, recognized that all the participants had come together because of their interest in interdisciplinary matters. He thought it might be profitable with experienced representatives of so many different disciplines present to attempt an examination of the methodology of working between two fields or among three, four, or five fields. Interdisciplinary thought and research is something which cannot be forced very much; with money it can be tried, but the most effective results have been such completely unexpected developments as the recent interdisciplinary studies of carbon-14. Forcing implies a knowing in advance of how things are going to fit.

In the Preface to a volume on mathematical methods in evolution Sir Ronald Fisher remarked that biologists and mathematicians use their imaginations in different ways and gave this illustration: Sex is one of the main studies of biology. But the first thing a mathematician would say about the problem would be, "Let me see, you always have two sexes. Sometimes you have just one, but usually you have two, never more. But what would be the consequences of three sexes, four sexes, five sexes, and up to n sexes?" Thus, one of the main mathematical techniques—one

of the ways mathematicians use their imagination—is to consider what did not happen. Biologists and natural historians seldom use their minds in this way, but it is a good way to use them. What are the things that do not happen? In an elementary course ANDERSON said that he sets his students to studying three plants common around St. Louis. The students then are asked: Where are the plants? Where are they not? Why are they where they are? Why are they not where they are not?

PHENOMENA AND DEFINITIONS

TWO APPROACHES

In the humanities, people seem to begin with definitions; in the most purely biological of the biological sciences, people seem to begin with phenomena. To be sure, ANDERSON stated, definitions and phenomena are used in both branches of knowledge. Perhaps the interest in definitions is one of the legacies from Scholasticism, while those who have learned to use the taxonomic method work in chaos but have a very good time of it. The thing to do now is to think reflectively about the advantages and disadvantages of each. What are the disadvantages of not paying enough attention to definitions? How do we use definitions? From our viewpoint are there any dangers in definitions? Do we see nothing but good in

944

them? As one who has had to struggle with both definitions and chaos, Darling was called upon to open the discussion.

DARLING called ecology the most undisciplined of the sciences—a new band wagon upon which a good many naturalists have jumped. The name does sound better than calling our week-end sport "bird-watching." Ecology, according to the classical ecologists, is defined as the science of organisms in relation to their environment and of the interrelationships of organisms and societies among themselves. This is a splendid definition; it is only its interpretation that begins to be troublesome. Human ecology has been defined as social medicine; Professor Banks of Cambridge, the first professor of human ecology in England, was an epidemiologist to begin with. Geographers, of course, are ecologists in their own way. Then there are sociologists who call one aspect of their field "human ecology." Rightly, there should be no difference at all between social anthropology and human ecology, yet the former is insufficiently concerned with the phenomena of the organic environment and the development of societies in relation to their environment. But there is not a "human" ecology or a "plant" ecology or an "animal" ecology. There is only one ecology. The problems that an ecologist might tackle in the human field lean toward social behavior and land use; this is really social anthropology, but with this much more added: a sense of history and of process and a recognition of the importance of dealing with the organic environment.

As a human geographer, GOUROU, in writing, felt that his view of the relation between *men* and environment was somewhat different from that of Darling. The relations between *man* and environment are of interest but of limited interest. More important are the relations between *men* and environment. As Sauer has said, man is a domesticated animal, and it is impossible to understand the relations between *men* and environment if an importance of first rank is not given to the techniques of production and the systems of organization of space. From this first principle we conclude that "ecology" (physical ecology) is a dangerous word to apply to human things, because the position of *men* in the environment is not exactly the same as the position of animals and vegetation.

1. Men violently modify the environment. What is, or, more precisely, when does there exist, a "natural environment" for *men*? It is necessary for human geographers to have a sound knowledge of the physical elements of the landscape, but that is not exactly ecology.

2. *Men*, groups of men, are tied together by techniques of production and of organization of space, and their view of the environment is conditioned by their organized system of techniques (in other words, their civilization). Their view of the environment is, in large part, a subjective one. Thus each civilization has its particular view of ecology. For geography, men and environment are interdependent and inseparable.

JONES, in writing, pointed out that the discussion at this symposium had made clear that separation of "natural" and "social" sciences, which survives in part because of the traditional organization of American universities, is nonexistent and should be discarded. Plant ecologists have had to consider social man as a major factor to explain what they have found. They have had to give up trying to imagine what the plant cover might be if man did not exist. But it is even more necessary that social scientists give up the imaginary world in which "nature" does not exist or is simply the economist's abstract "land." Though it is risky to employ the concepts of another science, perhaps "human ecology" can be clarified by the concepts of economics and their evolution. Classical economics divided the factors of production into *land, labor,* and *capital. Land* was regarded as an essentially inert, static factor. Modern civilization is converting *land* into a part of *capital.* That is, *land* (or "nature") is now being looked upon as part of the productive equipment, and, like any other equipment, it requires *maintenance.* "Nature" is no longer capable of automatic maintenance at the pace of output now required. This *merging* of the concepts of land and capital is where the "human ecologist" comes in.

It seemed to NORTHROP that definition is the scientific method for handling concepts so that they convey the meanings intended. The Aristotelian concept of a definition—species, genus, etc.—began the science of natural-history biology. Definition was not limited to the humanities. But ANDERSON pointed out that the humanists had gone one way and the biologists another. If biology and the humanities are to come together, it seems necessary to understand how those of either side use their imaginations. When putting together different sciences studying the relations between man and the earth, a problem is encountered, NORTHROP felt, in that all the different sciences have introduced certain concepts to account for their particular phenomena. First, it is necessary to become clear about the technical definitions of the phenomena as approached with the conceptual apparatus of each of the sciences and, second, to find a means of putting these different conceptual systems together. This is where difficulties in any interdisciplinary conference arise, which are further complicated if different cultures are represented. Each technical scientist's definition of the words he has used has to be brought out into the open;

then a common terminology with which to speak with precision must be found. In ecology there is a prodigious number of variables, but what are the key ones? What does the ecologist do when he studies the relationships between man and environment that is different from what an economist does, a historian does, or a geologist does? What are the ecologist's operational definitions?

On the virtues and limitations of definitions, SEIDENBERG, in writing, considered the following logical point to be pertinent. Any definition involves other terms. The precision of the definition will come to depend upon the exact limitations, explicit or implicit, inherent in the terms used. But this in turn exacts a continuation of the process of definition. Theoretically, this is an *ad infinitum* process of chasing one definition after another in an endless chain of definitions. The ultimate dilemma is a circularity of expression from which there is no escape. How this semantic trap is broken is well known and understood, but its solution depends in each instance upon the nature of the discipline involved. Nevertheless, its solution depends finally upon some intuitively perceived common ground of agreement which is axiomatically accepted.

For ANDERSON a good biological definition was a description of a phenomenon approached as a limit. For example, genetics did very brilliantly long before it knew what a gene was, or knew the word, for Mendel discovered the main principles without knowing that his hypothetical unit was in the chromosomes. In taxonomy, also, no one can define a species yet. But this matter of operational definitions seems extremely important. JONES thought that the best operational definition of an operational definition appeared in the *American Scientist* some time ago. It asked for the definition of "cake." If we wanted to find a categorical definition, we would look in the dictionary; for an operational definition we would look in a cookbook. As ALPERT, in writing, later pointed out, the phenomenon "cake" was what, in fact, the baker baked, which may differ from the model or aspiration.

DARWIN also expressed an admiration for definitions but not for a motive that he regarded as very exalting. The function of definition is to save a lazy man the trouble of thinking. When we started going to school, we were given horrid little questions about three boys sharing seventeen apples, etc. And, if we were innocent, we tried all the figures and finally found the answer. Later we were taught algebra and then realized that there was a general system. But algebra has no function except to save us a lot of thought. Now the same thing probably applies to taxonomy. We cannot think about every insect, so we generalize. The great virtue is that it is a lazy operation.

DAVIS felt that scientists, in trying to be pragmatists, had a common fault. Operational definitions are useful as means to an end, but a true scientist should not have any end at all. He preferred to study phenomena whether they were useful or not and whether his definition was useful or not to someone else.

The operational definition is of such extraordinary utility in science that STEINBACH believed that he did not see how we can get along without it. The most beautiful example in biology comes from genetics, in which the gene was originally defined as "a hypothetical thing which if present would account for the result." Then mutation was invented, and its definition became "a presumed change in a hypothetical substance which, if it took place, would account for the result." Operational definitions merely are statements with which we can work. Usually they are

dignified by calling them "hypotheses" or "hypothetical constructs."

WITTFOGEL, in writing, thought that, if definitions are attempts to describe our concepts, then obviously we have occupied ourselves with definitions since childhood. Man perceives phenomena analytically (conceptually), and he clarifies and stabilizes his concepts by defining them. Definitions as verbally fixed concepts are both the result of previous experiment (and thought) and the tools for handling new experiences. A scholar who takes his work seriously also takes his tools seriously; and thus there is a moral aspect to definitions. A conscientious scholar will establish (and change) his definitions with care and will endeavor to be consistent in their use. And he will ask others to understand his arguments in terms of his definitions, just as he will likewise treat the ideas of others. Many scholarly writings would be clearer and many discussions less heated and more productive if those concerned were more consistently aware of the technical and moral issues underlying their efforts.

The discussion of definitions and phenomena was concluded by ANDERSON's praise of definitions, despite his self-characterization as a person to whom definitions do not come easily and who is impressed with the study of phenomena.

CLASSIFICATION AND MEASUREMENT

ANDERSON contrasted the differences of natural history and exact science by the taxonomic method and the method of pointer readings. One of the great things that has happened in biology in the last two decades has been the introduction of pointer reading. Claude Bernard was one of the first to see clearly the advantage of isolating out of a big, fuzzy problem a factor that could be measured—temperatures, dry weights, lengths, radiation, etc. What are the advantages and disadvantages of these two kinds of work?

BLUMENSTOCK related the results of his experience in following a broad problem that led to discussions with physical scientists as well as with humanists. He found that some people immediately go to epistemological matters, while others speak of the limitations of their data. For example, a physicist speaking about relaxation phenomena in gases immediately gave some idea of the accuracy of the measurements which form the basis for being able to say within known degrees of probability what happens in a few microseconds in a gas undergoing relaxation. His next contribution was of the time dimension of the system and then the objective—what he was trying to arrive at—how it fitted in with the mechanic aspect of quantum theory, etc. What the physicist told about was the "size of the net with which he catches fish"—the spatial and temporal dimensions and the system in which it was imbedded. By contrast, a historian took a long time to get around to telling anything about limitations. It did not occur to him to make clear that the evidence was limited, say, to five manuscripts. The limitations of the data have to be pried out of social scientists and humanists by asking the question. An awareness of the limitations of data seems to be more in the mode of thinking of physical and biological scientists. At the heart of the problem of interdisciplinary research is communication, that is, making clear to one another (1) the limitations of the data, (2) the dimensions, and (3) the scheme into which the data fit.

THOMAS, in writing, brought out that, although scientists are generally well aware of the degrees of accuracy of data in their specialized fields, and therefore of the limitations that should apply in the use and interpretation of those data, these same scientists are likely to be less inhibited in the use of data from fields other than their own. In particular, the integrators of information from a wide variety of specialized fields may draw conclusions that the originators of that information would consider highly speculative. A few examples might be drawn from statements made in this symposium concerning water. Huzayyin (p. 403) mentioned that water levels in wells in a certain region had declined 6 feet, and this was offered as an indication of the effect of deforestation in the past several centuries. However, greater changes than this have resulted in many regions solely from changes of climate. If the water table was at reasonably shallow depth below the land surface, many species of trees could draw upon ground water for their supply, and the water level in wells might have been lower than had the deforestation not occurred. Curtis (p. 727) correlated reduction in forest cover in Wisconsin with decrease in total length of perennial streams draining the area, using data collected in 1935. Hydrologists quickly recognize that year as one following a series of drought years and would not choose 1935 for evidence of the effects of man on water resources because of the difficulty of discriminating such effects from the natural effects of drought.

Being called upon by the Chairman to speak about the relation between mathematics and the topics discussed so far in the symposium, TUKEY began by saying that mathematics per se did not seem to be a tool that was ready to be used. There is clearly a place for some quantitative thinking; some fields are at a place where statistics may help a little, but mathematics for a mathematician means more of a formal abstract structure and its uses. This point of view was elaborated in terms of four deficiencies in so far as the symposium discussion was concerned.

First, it seemed to TUKEY that there has been a rather consistent failure to treat the systems discussed as components in larger systems. For example, there is no reason to be surprised at the notion of Western civilization of an expanding economy. When things are changing in the world, whichever group thinks in terms of an expanding economy is likely to be the one that expands for the moment. Another example is the tendency to look at short time periods in and for themselves rather than to relate them to longer periods, with more consideration for trends, back-and-forth swings, and catastrophes.

The second failure has been that of not attempting to use the same sort of concept at different scales in a way that the physicist, for example, uses the same concepts to discuss both the very large and the very small. How much of the contrast between subsistence and commercial economies is a matter of scale? Some fairly large sections of the world today ought to be compared to the small group and the subsistence economy. Are there not some concepts useful at both scales? Another question is: What are the different time scales involved, and how many early family or village groups destroyed the soil and disappeared in a small area before other groups learned how to maintain a balance in the biological situation and stay in existence? Did the discussion about the retreat of villages and population decline in fourteenth-century Europe mean that man at that stage of sociological and technological development had reached an ecological climax?

Third, there has been a failure to study the balance of forces as such. At this point there must be some quantitative thought. Malin (p. 413) brought out two examples of grass fires set by lightning, saying that there was no need of further multiplying examples. For his immediate purposes this was true. His two cited examples thoroughly and irretrievably destroyed the previously expressed view that there were no authentic records of such fires. In the long run, however, the collection and *quantitative* study of *many more* such examples might teach us about the frequency of lightning-induced grass fires and the relation of this frequency to climate. Then we might be able to make much better judgments of the importance of Indian fires in the North American grassland.

A fourth deficiency has been the failure to make effective use of closely related but distinct concepts. The physical scientist seems to have done this rather well; in thermodynamics, there are not only heat and temperature but also various kinds of free energies that are appropriate for dealing with various problems. Why, for example, should there be only one definition or concept of the difference between a city and a village? Why not a half-dozen which are mutually related? But, when one is chosen for use, the reasons for that choice are understood.

ANDERSON concluded on the subject of reflective thinking. One thing he has tried to induce in his graduate students is productive laziness. Generally speaking, he thought most graduate students and productive scholars to be too busy. A very brilliant young man had come to him; he worked very hard; he was always doing something. Like so many of us, he had this inherited feeling that, if one is happy and having a good time, it is not quite right. Rather, one should not enjoy one's self. One is paid to be miserable about his lifework; the easy thing is not the thing to do. One summer he presented a list of all the things he was going to do in a field study. Anderson crossed out the list with a blue pencil and wrote to him as follows:

These are all very good ideas, but I've got something else that is very much more important. Every time you get where there is one of these populations of plants, find a large, flat rock, in the shade if necessary; sit down upon it for at least fifteen minutes by your wrist watch; and do not try to think about your clematises. Just think what a nice day it is, how pretty the flowers are, and the blue sky. Think how lucky you are to be doing this kind of work when the rest of the world is doing all the awful things they do not want to do. Just let your mind alone. Now I am not joking. Please do this, by the clock if necessary.

About three weeks later he replied:

DEAR DR. ANDERSON:

I got your letter, and I thought you must be joking. But you were so earnest about it that I finally went and did it. Now it is probably just coincidence, but, when I got up from the rocks the first time and started down across the hillside, I noticed. . . .

He had found the key to his problem the first time he tried it.

Then there is the tragic case of the student who has since become one of the ablest young professors of biology of his generation. He has found out something terribly important—people in the next century are going to remember it, ANDERSON was sure—but it was not in the main line of what he thought he ought to be studying, and this biologist has kept himself so busy with details that he does not know the importance of his own incidental findings.

In teaching his students how to look at a corn plant, ANDERSON said that he had urged that they lie down in a corn-field and get an ant's-eye view of the corn. It looks very different when one is lying down. Different boys in different years gave virtually the same answer: that they would feel self-conscious and funny lying down in a cornfield just to look at a plant. And this is a reflection of the peculiar habits we have inherited in our civilization that keep us from doing natural and interesting things. Since then these students have become successful corn-breeders. Anderson has been in their dusty fields and has found

marks that indicated someone had been lying down there. They had done it, but not in front of him.

* * *

LEARNING OF TECHNIQUES

THE HUMAN ELEMENT

The second half of this discussion session was chaired by Dr. SOL TAX, who pointed out the ambiguity of the title. In addition to the problem of how scientists go about learning of environmental phenomena and processes, there is also the matter, very relevant to the symposium theme, of how people in different cultures learn to treat nature differently. Certainly, an important part of the process of man's changing the face of the earth is what he does and why he does it, whether intentional and unintentional. Understanding how man comes to have the views he does about nature—about what is right or fit—and how he might come to change his views seems critical as the basis for discussion of "Prospect." Three themes from the particularly large subject appear particularly relevant. One theme is the notion of historical progress. To what sorts of prophecies can we apply the concept of progress? It is true that we *do* control more energy now than we did a century ago or than we did a million years ago. We *can* talk about progress with respect to the measurable, cumulative aspects of culture, such as knowledge, science, technology, etc. For there is a single scale able to be measured, and we can talk about progress along a scale without indicating any value judgment as to whether it is good or bad.

On the other hand, there are non-cumulative aspects of culture which we all recognize. One aspect is social organization—the way society is organized, its patterns of interpersonal behavior, etc. It becomes very difficult to talk about progress except with reference to the wider and wider integration of society. We can speak of different kinds of social structures, of integrations of people, or of modes of behaving in interpersonal relations, but it is more difficult to talk about whether they are better and better—the quality of the integration of society. Other noncumulative aspects of culture are its aesthetic and religious parts and the whole problem of values. Obviously, with reference to what man has done to nature, we can speak of progress only in terms of the cumulative aspects of culture.

A second theme for discussion is the conservatism of people. It does not matter whether we think about individuals or of a society or a cultural group, because, more or less, one is related to the other. With people or culture, distinctions in conservatism must be made. We can talk about conservatism with respect to some things but not with respect to other things. This question of conservatism is somewhat like using the word "superstition" to refer to *other* people's beliefs. Conservatism, on the whole, probably amounts to the things that other people do not want to do that we want them to do. That is, the idea of conservatism exists not in people but in the attitudes of others toward them. The American Indians may here be used as an example, because these tribes are supposed to be conservative as compared to the progressive whites. Yet, when we consider that all the Indian tribes populated America within a limited time, very quickly adapting to a thousand different environments and readapting as they moved around, and making many refinements in their ecological adjustments, it is very hard to think of them as being unchangeable or difficult to change.

The third theme for discussion is the integration of culture. The general notion is that there is an integrated whole and that everything readjusts when a change takes place. Thus, with a change in one part of a culture, all sorts of unforeseen consequences can be expected in the rest of the culture. Anthropologists frequently are accused of being very conservative in this respect, saying: "Don't change anything; don't touch it. You cannot know all the changes that will occur. Unpredictable changes will occur that, being unforeseen, may also be undesirable; therefore, go easy." But there is a real question for discussion as to how valid this attitude is. Are all the parts of any culture so interrelated that, if one part were touched anywhere, everything else would change?

Whichever of these three themes we think of—historical progress, the conservatism of people, or the integration of culture—we are involved in change in people and culture. The main thing to remember about change, when dealing with human beings, is that man is a valuing animal. He wants things, yet the things that he wants frequently involve doing things that he does not want to do. Man always has to make choices and decisions. This is what political scientists these days call the "decision-making process." If we want to see why people change or why they will not change, we have to see why they make the decisions that they do. Man may not consciously think out either to do something or not do something or to do one thing as opposed to another. Every human culture, as well as every individual, consists of conflicting values. Human culture is such that we find it difficult to weigh the values. Frequently we do not know the kind of decision we are going to make until we make it. After the choice is made, we can in retrospect look back and ask why it was done as it was.

The frustration that most people express when they ask why people behave the way they do—it is always somebody else, not themselves, of course—results from a lack of understanding that people cannot be taught or influenced without first learning what it is that they basically want to do. Now, what people want to do, remember, need not be conscious, but, nevertheless, it is they, not we, who decide what they want to do. The only way that purposeful culture change, or planning, can be done effectively and not be self-defeating occurs when people determine their own futures.

The point is that people make their own decisions on the basis of their own values rather than on the basis of the values that someone else wants to impose. Generally speaking, we discover that force does not really work in the long run. We have had enough experience in colonial and other situations to know that for a while it appears as though we can impose, but in the long run, somehow or other, the people bounce back and do what they want.

However, this does not mean that people are hard to change. It is only that they are hard to change in the way that someone wants to change them. They would not be hard to change in a direction that they wanted to go themselves. This is particularly true in cross-cultural situations. Hard as it is, it is much easier for us to have our children do what we want, or to have the farmers in our own country do what we want, because we at least share the same general values. But, when we deal with other cultures, we find it is a real impediment, because we do not understand what it is that other cultures want. As a matter of fact, we cannot simply ask them, for consciously they do not know what they want themselves. Remember that there are a lot of conflicts within cultures. In order for people to change and for their own leaders or for anybody outside to help them to change, the first prerequisite is to learn what they want.

A personal incident illustrates a dra-matic instance. Among the North American Indians there is a native religion whose ceremonial centers around a little cactus known as the *peyote*. Now the peyote is frequently thought of by white folks as a narcotic or a drug. It has a bad name. Missionaries are always objecting to it, partly because the native Indian church has become very successful, more Indians joining the native church than the missionary churches. At any rate, although the federal government has taken this little cactus plant off the narcotics list, some states have passed laws prohibiting its sale. The Indian church is always in danger; it could not go on without that little sacrament, peyote, which is chewed during ceremonies.

It happened that the annual convention of the national church, attended by Indians from all the different tribes, was held in Iowa, where Tax had been working with a local group of Indians. Because of this contact or association, he was invited to come to the national convention. It was to be a four-day convention, starting with ordinary meetings and discussion of policy and to end on Saturday night with a ceremony, at which a large tepee is erected, and all sit around a ceremonial fire. This latter is a beautiful, impressive, and elaborate ceremony that lasts all night. Although Tax had only a week's notice, it occurred to him that if a documentary film of the whole thing were made, including the political aspects of the meeting and ending with the ritual itself, there would exist a public relations instrument and a defense of this as a legitimate church. It could then come under our laws of freedom of religion and not be considered as a wicked cult.

There was but a week's time and no money to make a color-and-sound film. The prospect of organizing such a thing was rather appalling, but fortunately a young movie-maker at the

University of Chicago helped in all technical matters. In addition, the Extension Division of the State University of Iowa was able to furnish a sound truck, a crew, and the supplies, so that all technical problems were solved surprisingly easily and quickly. Arrangements were completed in Iowa City the day before the convention was to start. There had not been any time to ask any Indians of the church whether they wanted a movie made, so the motion-picture people in Iowa City were told that the whole crew should be prepared to come to the meeting only after a telephone call that the project had been explained to, and had the approval of, the Indians.

Tax and his associates were excited and enthusiastic at the prospect, for he thought it would not be too much trouble to convince the Indians that this was a very good idea. Since many tribes were represented, all speeches had to be in English; thus Tax could both speak and understand the deliberations without any trouble.

On Thursday, the first day of the meeting, Tax explained carefully and at length the possible importance to the church of the film and the unusual good fortune that had made this possible at no cost. There were questions and discussions at the meeting, and there was a night to sleep on it. He was optimistic. The next morning the discussion resumed, and again he made explanations and answered questions. He promised that they would help to edit the film and that they would have to give approval before it would be used in any way; the project was entirely up to them. Then followed a very interesting session, with speech after speech—some in favor of making the film and some against it. It became clear that everybody thoroughly understood that this film, perhaps to be shown as evidence in court, could some day establish theirs as a legitimate reli-

gion, with peyote as a sacrament that they felt it to be. Otherwise the church seemed to them in danger.

The rub came in the prospect of filming their sacred ceremony. The ritual itself would be inevitably disturbed by technical problems, but, perhaps more important, they could not picture themselves engaged in the very personal matter of prayer in front of a camera. As one after another expressed his views, pro and con, the tension heightened. To defile a single ritual to save the church became the stated issue, and none tried to avoid it. Not a person argued that perhaps the church was not in as great danger as they thought; neither was there any suggestion of distrust of Tax. They seemed to accept the dilemma as posed as though they were acting out a Greek tragedy. As he sat in front of the room, together with the president of the church, and as he listened with fascination to the speeches, gradually the realization came that they were choosing their integrity over their existence. Although these were the more politically oriented members of the church, they could not sacrifice a longed-for and a sacred night of prayer. When everyone had spoken, the president rose and said that, if the others wished to have the movie made, he had no objections; but then he begged to be excused from the ceremony. Of course, this ended any possibility for making the movie; the sense of the meeting was clear.

When it was over, the realization seemed to come to the Indians that Tax must be hurt. For all his unselfish intentions, high hopes, and hard work, his reward had been a clear rebuff. They had suffered through their dilemma and had made the painful choice that should have relieved their tension, but now they realized that their peace with themselves had been bought at Tax's expense. And so they began painful speeches to make amends. But, as their decision was being made, it had been understood that what had been proposed was akin to asking a man to deliver his wife to a lecherous creditor to save the family from ruin. Tax then rose to speak and with genuine sincerity apologized for having brought so painful an issue to them. He had meant to be a friend but had hurt them. He agreed with their decision, and it would be a poor friend, indeed, that would resent their deciding an issue for their own good simply because it was not decided the way someone else should want it.

This story illustrates the impossibility of planning for people instead of having them plan for themselves. Of course, in the case cited Tax had not done any damage. In most cases we are not so fortunate to have a clear decision. What happens is that people do only half of what we wish. Then, of course, we become disappointed; nothing has come out right, and the people get blamed for not doing an obviously sensible thing. For example, there was one plan—a beautiful plan costing a million dollars—which was presented by the federal government to a group of five hundred Indians in Iowa. It was to do all kinds of things: straighten the river, this, that, and the other thing. The government people could never understand why the Indians turned the plan down "cold." They had no notion as to why the Indians turned it down, but they thought it to be just another example of how hopeless the Indians are.

But there is no other way to discover what people want and the directions in which they will change except by the hard way of having them make their own choices from these very conflicting values that nobody can predict. And this is what was meant when Tax said that people are not conservative at all. They are willing to go in a direction, but it has to be their own. They only

appear conservative when they will not do what we think is only sensible, but no one can possibly weigh the choices that another person or another community has to make.

The conflict of values in decision-making places a limit on historical progress. It puts a limit on the things that people are willing to do in the way of technological advances. Values get in the way of "obviously rational" goals and have always gotten in the way. What happens to civilizations is but the same process on the long time scale. On the short time scale the question is posed as to whether a culture is an integrated whole. It is clear that culture is integrated but not in the mechanistic sense that permits an outsider adequately to judge the "fit" of a new item or to predict the ways in which changes in one part will affect other parts. A culture is, rather, integrated by the acts of selection by the people themselves after struggling through their value conflicts. The very act of choosing resolves the value conflict publicly, so that, for this particular purpose, one value is given precedence over another, and the society at large knows that this has been done.

Only the people involved can actually do that. Such is the difficulty in studying humans and in asking them to do things.

Smith asked whether Tax had ever had an audience with the people who are going out to save the world through Point 4. Tax replied that not only are there differing philosophies involved but also there are practical difficulties of application. To contact intimately the hundreds of thousands of villages in India is very difficult. This is so not only for us of another culture; even the elite, in a country like India which wants to change the villages, are only somewhat better able than we to predict what it is the villager wants to do. But at least they have a little bit more right to help the people make mistakes than we have.

Even within the small confines of Great Britain there is exactly the same problem, DARLING commented. The Highlander does not have a primitive culture; he is white in the skin and has a vote, and it is not considered proper to study him anthropologically. These people are treated administratively in exactly the same way as are the Britishers in one of the new satellite towns.

"Gaeldom" (which was DARLING's term for the culture) is based primarily on subsistence. On the western seaboard it is up against a very harsh environment. DARLING said that he saw very strong resemblances between Gaeldom and the culture of the Hopis in Arizona, who also are in one of the fringe environments for human life. In the old days the Gaels had an extremely conserving type of husbandry. But, as soon as it was cut across with the ideas of the dominant southern Scots, eastern Scots, and the English, that attitude of conservation, which was very much based on identification with the environment, was lost. The terrible acts of non-conservation which take place once the surface has been broken are quite extraordinary. The Highlanders are devastating their own environment, and they have no feeling for it. To investigate the failure or breakdown of a culture would be a very proper anthropological study. There must be much more of this in some of the Micronesian and Melanesian cultures.

But, as regards teaching people, Western man has the notion that he has only to demonstrate how much better some scheme is than that being practiced and that then the people will follow. Well, they do not. They never will follow an example because of the cultural pressure to avoid becoming different. Create one's self different within one's culture, and one is in trouble. In a simple culture, to become different is to lose identification; one is in a bad spot. And the Gael knows that quite well. He keeps quiet. We show him the advantages of a certain type of husbandry, and he agrees entirely with us. And we say he is as two-faced as he can be, because he agrees with us and then behind our back does nothing about it. Well, he does agree with us that to do what we suggest is a better thing; but he does not agree with us that it would be a better thing for him within his society.

Tax, as a good man of science, had not been hurt by the end of the experience that he related; he had merely accepted the situation. But so many of us coming with enthusiasm to suggest changes to native cultures are hurt when our changes are not accepted. Because we are as vain as peacocks, we identify ourselves with the thing that we are putting over; we like to think that we are the bringers—that we are the big men. If they take it from us and they accept it, we identify ourselves with their success.

Well, this is an absolutely untenable position. In all this kind of thing there is no such thing as reward. Our culture tends too much to desire rewards. There is no reward. If we go to work on a culture and do what we think is right, giving our whole heart, then we must be prepared to be crucified, and we must not object; we must accept that fact. We do not say, "What on earth have you done to us?" And we do not turn away and say, "Those people are worth nothing; we can do nothing with them." This is part of the job. We are pushing something forward; but, if it is not accepted, we retire. In Tax's case he had the whole thing laid before him in a remarkable fashion. So few of us ever have that opportunity because of the matter of language; we are so often not in on the decision-making process, and our methods of communication are so rarely theirs.

Just as Spoehr had prompted Darling to speak, so OSBORN urged Gregg to recall his valuable experiences in transposing methods from the United States to those of other cultures. GREGG said that he had made it a rather regular rule not to go to a country unless invited. Being very realistic, he recognized that sometimes there were certain groups in the country that were responsible for the invitation and that it may not have been an entirely unanimous affair, but at least his rule prevented his going where he would be universally turned out or unwelcome. He also had come to the conclusion that it was not morally justified to attempt to improve somebody else simply because, from his set of standards, it would be an improvement. The experience of Tax did not cover the whole picture for the reason that Tax had had the grace not to expect to be thanked for his offer to make a motion picture of the holy rite. But a great many people who go to "improve the heathen" not only are furious if they are frustrated in that effort but are extremely annoyed that they were not thanked for coming. As GREGG put it:

If I were going to do something to other people which I think is good for them, it is my obligation to be extremely grateful to them if they accept what I think is good for them, and not the other way around. This view changes our existence pretty substantially. We have to have full concurrence from the recipient of our largesse or kindliness of spirit. We have to have full concurrence on the standards before we can get a rod from shore on real co-operation and real help.

We must realize all the time that, if people of another culture let us do what we think is good, we owe them the debt, and not the other way around. One corollary of this is extremely important for any work among cultures other than our own. It is a profound emotional experience to be among the minority. A bit of evidence in the United States in that direction is that white doctors who best deal with Negro physicians in our American colleges are those who have had the experience of being in the minority either in the Near East or in the Far East and know what it feels like. They can handle the minority of our Negroes far more wisely, far more modestly, and far more skilfully, with immense sympathy and identification for the minority.

In his closing remarks GREGG related a statement that Thomas Nixon Carver once made. There are remarks that teachers make which are "howitzer" remarks, in the sense that some of them go over our head at the time. It occurred in the spring of 1910 during an afternoon lecture, and Gregg more or less woke up to hear Carver say something that applies to America as of the present day. He said:

Gentlemen, anyone could essay to write a record of the human race in terms of its survival of adversity. And there has been adversity in three principal forms: epidemic disease, war, and inadequate nutrition up to the point of famine. Now, gentlemen, medicine has made enough headway, so that we do not have to be afraid of as many epidemic diseases as was the case a hundred years ago. Transportation and communication have made enough headway, so that, aside from the almost incontrollably large populations of China and India, no river valley in western Europe need fear famine, because food can be transported on credit relatively cheaply. I do not think that the time of warfare as a serious form of adversity has passed [then Carver took off his glasses and looked over the class], but I do suspect that many of you young gentlemen may live to see a time for which neither by tradition nor experience are we particularly well prepared, because the struggle of the future is going to be who will survive prosperity, not adversity. We have had a long racial experience on surviving adversity, but what do we know about surviving prosperity?

This relates to intercultural relationships, for if we cannot go with the utmost self-abnegation and complete modesty to cultures other than our own, we will save a good deal more than boat fare by staying at home.

HUZAYYIN was so deeply moved by these sagacious exposés of Gregg, Tax, and Darling that he sought to add a footnote to convey a tradition found in the East. Tax had spoken about the impact of culture on a horizontal basis —the modern American attempting to influence the Indian—but in a lateral way, since the same generation is involved. Those in the East have a different problem, because more often than not there is a living past, and the impact has to percolate down. Sometimes in certain communities more than one cultural generation coexists even in material things. The notion of conservatism has been very badly understood. It may be thought that the peasant community is usually conservative, but this is a very superfluous and superficial mental attitude toward the peasant, which, as Tax had said, is really based on a misunderstanding.

For example, the Egyptian peasant, as portrayed in the textbooks, especially of the West, is conservative; he lives just as his forefathers used to live generations ago. But in reality this notion has no basis whatsoever. In the material aspect of life the peasant may use a hoe which in its form goes back to prehistoric types; use a plow which originated in Egypt in the Eighth Dynasty, about the end of the Old Kingdom; use the Archimedes screw as a way of lifting water, a technique which was introduced in the Greco-Roman period; and use at the very same time an American truck. All are in coexistence. In the spiritual aspect of life the peasant has his ancient Egyptian traditions and customs, manners, and rituals. When Christianity came, it was adopted; when Islam came, it was adopted; and a good many of the ideas have coexisted right through history. Even today the Egyptian peasant's conception of Islam finds harmony with his idea of Christianity and with some of the good things which have persisted from the early pharaonic period. The peasant has been able officially to change his religion two or three times and not suffer any complexes as a result of it. There is really no conservatism. Studies by the Institute of Sociology at Alexandria University of response by communities to the change of material culture found that, on the whole, institutions which spring from the environment itself are difficult to change. Institutions borrowed from the outside are relatively easy to change, but the original local institutions evolving in the Egyptian's own environment do not preclude the introduction from the outside world of either the prehistoric hoe or the American tractor. There is no prejudice about it. The more we learn about manners and customs and ways of living and see how people behave toward change, the more we will begin to change our own attitudes about the ability of communities to change.

Particularly in Egypt, HUZAYYIN stated, the people are trying to adapt new methods from the West while at the same time endeavoring very hard not to obliterate their own pattern—to preserve what is good in their tradition and take what they feel to be good from the Western mode of life. They do not want, in the history of humanity as a whole, to have fragile superstructures—to have a two- or three-storied house built in the East and then have a Western story built on top, with no link whatsoever with what is below.

This would not stand; the wind would blow it away. It is essential to try to integrate the various successive stages of civilization and of culture. The West, to HUZAYYIN's mind, has suffered a great deal from the fact that the pattern of social structure in the industrial-revolution phase of modern Europe was not properly linked with the earlier understructure, part of which was borrowed from the East. Christianity came from the East; the West still feels the conflict, in that the Christian spirit and attitude have not been properly fused and linked with the new social systems of the West brought about as a result of the industrial revolution.

The West in its contact with the East is not simply making a lateral contact in the twentieth century. It is contacting all at once a good many centuries of human evolution, all of which are part of the human story.

TAX added, in summary, that the consensus of the session seemed to be that a substantial part of the learning has to be done by those who would do the teaching of techniques to others. It is the teachers who could be less conservative by realizing that progress is not something that can be handed out like lollipops and thereby produce gratitude. People or cultures change all the time, but new elements such as techniques have to be integrated with old values. This can be done only by the people themselves.

We seem to learn from this session that persons who are involved in community-development programs should create in their minds a device: In any situation where they are tempted to say, "These people are conservative," a bell should ring. Then the sentence should be re-formed: "I am ignorant about what these people want." This is especially needful where great cultural differences exist.

Part III
Prospect

Limits of Man and the Earth

Limits of Man and the Earth

The Time Scale in Human Affairs

SIR CHARLES G. DARWIN, F.R.S.[*]

The purpose of the present note is not so much to contribute any facts of knowledge as to suggest a point of view. There are many things which are each of them so familiar to us that we never group them together and notice that there is a general principle underlying them. Yet a generalization may illuminate a whole subject, and this it may do even though it is mainly by providing a name for the common characteristic of the group. It is the aim of this note to present such a generalization in the hope that it may be useful to others, as in fact it has been useful to the author.

In the course of various conversations I have heard the late Lord Rutherford say that most of the problems presented to us by nature could be defeated by experiment but that there was one thing which would always defeat us, and this was *time*. If a process takes a long time, and if no device can be found for shortening the time, the experimental method will fail. Rutherford was thinking mainly of experiments in physics, but the point seems worth generalizing in a wider field.

Man is now as never before trying to take advantage of his rapidly growing knowledge of the nature of things in order to make all sorts of plans for the control and the future development of the world. For this purpose he is guided mainly by the general method of science, that is to say, experiments and inductions from the experiments; and it is a particular difficulty in the application of this method that I am going to discuss. Much of the experiment is concerned with inanimate nature and with the lower types of living matter, and we know no absolute reason why the planning derived from it should not be successful; there is even a hope that sometimes it may be so. But sooner or later the planners run into the necessity of making plans about humanity itself, and at this stage things obviously become much more difficult. The most fundamental difficulty in planning about humanity is that the plans must then be subjective instead of objective. This entirely alters their character; it is a tremendous subject calling for deep and difficult consideration, but it is not the point I want to discuss here. Often the plans proposed for the treatment of man are formed from the results of experiments on animals or other things by regarding him as an example of these things; but, even though such work can be regarded quite objectively, it may still run into a special difficulty not found in other experiments. The difficulty is related to the time scale, and, to make clear what I mean by the time scale, I must glance at the general subject of scientific experiment.

LABORATORY EXPERIMENTS

In most experiments of an engineering type a model of the object to be studied is made on a reduced scale. For

* Dr. Darwin was Tait Professor of Natural Philosophy in the University of Edinburgh (1922–36) and director of the National Physical Laboratory (1938–49). He is the author of *The New Conception of Matter*, 1931, and *The Next Million Years*, 1952, as well as of papers in mathematical physics.

example, suppose that a ship is to be built of 800-foot length which is to go at 25 knots; then a model will be made of 20-foot length, and this will be towed in a model basin. The speed at which it is to be towed is not the 25 knots that the ship is to have; the speed must be altered in scale too, and in the present case it would be about 4 knots. This speed is fixed by a principle laid down by Froude, the first man to study these matters, and there is a number, called the Froude number, associated with the size and the speed, that links the ship with the model. So too in the design of an airplane which is to fly at some given speed a reduced model is made for test in a wind tunnel, and here again there is a change of wind speed appropriate for the test. In this case things are made more difficult, because the wind should blow faster the smaller the model; the appropriate speed is determined not by the Froude number but by another one, the Reynolds number. This number dictates that, if the model is half the size of the plane, the speed in the tunnel (if the tunnel is not pressurized) should be twice the speed of real flight; and I may say that one of the most formidable difficulties in airplane design is that it is seldom possible to get a high enough wind in the wind tunnel without running into a lot of other troubles I have not mentioned. In spite of such difficulties the broad principles are well understood, and they signify that a great deal can be got out of experiments with models but that it is usually necessary to alter the speed in the model experiment, that is to say, to alter the time scale as well as the size scale.

In the experiments I have described so far the time scale is affected only through changes of speed, and these changes may be attainable. However, some of the things we want to study depend not on speed but on time itself, and then everything becomes much more difficult. I may take an imaginary example. Until recently, at any rate, we did not know how to convert ordinary carbon into diamonds, but I am going to suppose that by our theoretical studies we had reached the conclusion that, if a supply of carbon were encased under some specified high temperature and pressure with suitable catalysts for not less than two hundred years, then on opening the case at the end of that time it would be found to contain a large diamond. It seems rather unlikely that anyone would undertake such an experiment. He would probably have no confidence that the experiment would be kept going steadily for two hundred years by his successors, and he would also probably have insufficient interest in a result that he could not possibly survive to verify for himself.

Turning now to biological experiments, there is one great difference, because the size of things is fixed by nature; we cannot make a little model of a horse and run it at a reduced speed according to its Froude number with a view to improving the breed of race horses. But sometimes something can be done. One of the outstanding contributions to the science of genetics was Morgan's choice of the right animal for his experiments. Up to that time Mendelian researches had made use mostly of plants or animals which could produce only two or three generations a year. It was Morgan's genius that saw that the time scale was the enemy and that it could be defeated by working with an animal, the *Drosophila* fruit fly, which produces a new generation every two or three weeks. In consequence we now know a great deal about chromosomes, and we can apply much of what we have learned from the fruit fly to other animals or plants. This has of course been a tremendous achievement, but it cannot be expected that everything about a human being can be inferred from an animal as different as *Drosophila*. We must do some of our work nearer home, and then at once we run again into the difficulty of the time scale. So, in working out the scientific methods aimed at controlling the future destiny of man, we must have very close regard to the formidable difficulties presented against our efforts to cheat the time scale.

HUMAN EXPERIMENTS

I can most quickly make my main point by a rather fanciful exaggeration. Imagine that both knowledge and operational techniques had so developed that it was possible for the "genetic surgeon" to take the germ cell of any animal, dissect out from it bits of a chromosome which were known to contain deleterious genes, and replace them by other more beneficent ones. Imagine further that we knew all about the chromosomes of humanity, so that we could locate in a human germ cell all those genes which are going to determine the qualities of the developed man. It is most unlikely that anything like this will ever be done, but there is nothing absolutely impossible about it as far as we know. With all this knowledge and technique in his mind, one of the leading genetic surgeons decides it is time to get to work on improving humanity and that he will do so by producing a really great man. He considers that he knows and can get all the necessary chromosome ingredients to produce an embryo which will develop into whatever may be his ideal: Shakespeare, Newton, Napoleon, or—let us be broadminded, since we cannot foresee the political tastes of the surgeon—perhaps Marx. The surgeon then sets to work to compound a germ cell which he has good reason to believe has exactly the constitution that Shakespeare's had. But now comes the trouble of the time factor. It will be forty years or so before the germ cell will have devel-

oped into the Shakespeare who will be recognized and universally acclaimed as a great poet. It is unlikely that the surgeon would have developed his full skill until he was himself about forty, and thus by the time he can verify the result of his labors he will be on the retired list; very probably he will be dead or showing the signs of senility. However that may be, he will surely be in no condition to profit from his experiment and make a new and improved Shakespeare.

Thus an essential feature in such biological experiments of man on man is that no individual would be able to take advantage of the results of his own experiments. This is because there is a definite time scale in human affairs—the length of the human life, with its various stages of development—birth, growth, adulthood, and senility—and the experimenter is inevitably going at the same rate through the same stages as the objects of his experiments. Thus such experiments are condemned to be different in quality from others in the sense that no one can *himself* hope to put into practice anything that he learns for his experiments.

I have of course much oversimplified things. Thus I have spoken as though the surgeon were living in isolation, capable of profiting by his own past experiences but by no one else's. In fact, of course, there are hardly any experiments like this one, in which the surgeon would do his work and then have to wait inactively for forty years for the result. Almost always progress consists in making small steps, in each of which the worker is being helped by the advice and the criticism of other scientists. This evidently softens the sharpness of the time scale but does not fully remove its effects. The advisers and critics are themselves also subject to the conditioning of their own time scales, and, though some of them may be twenty or thirty years younger than the surgeon, there will never be more difference than that between them. Thus the time scale is to be regarded not as a period measured by the exact length of a human life but rather as a continuous variable. Gradual changes will be occurring all the time, but the rate at which those changes occur is still to be measured on a scale of magnitude corresponding to the length of an adult human life, that is to say, forty or fifty years.

The effect of time scale does pervade the conditions of human life to a surprising degree. I noted one of its effects in a most unexpected place. A few years ago there appeared an excellent book called *Elephant Bill,* by J. H. Williams (Hart Davis, 1950), which gives an account, not romanticized in any way, of the relations of the elephant-keepers in Burma to their charges. The point comes out that the domesticated elephant, because his life is as long as a man's, is unlike any other domesticated animal. A man may get very fond of a horse, but the horse will die after ten or fifteen years, so that the man will have several such horses during his life. But the elephant lives for seventy years—as long as his mahout—and so their relation is quite different. They are not like master and slave, but instead they become friends—or at worst they are like master and one of those old family retainers whose lifelong devotion often becomes such an affliction to his master. It seems rather likely that it is not its exceptional intelligence that distinguishes the elephant among domesticated animals as much as it is the equality of the elephant's and the man's time scales.

There are of course many problems about man of the first importance which are not subject to the human time scale; for instance, this is true of much medical work on the cure of diseases. This is because for ordinary diseases it is not the human time scale that

counts but rather the time scale of the bacteria causing the sickness, and this scale is measured in days, not in tens of years. But there are diseases of a different kind, such as cancer, for which the human time scale would seem appropriate, because they especially attack old age; whether this idea would be of any value in the actual case of cancer research must be doubtful. In the same general connection there arises the extremely interesting question of what mechanism determines the rate of the process of aging. What kind of clock can be imagined which should tell the human body that it is to run down after about seventy years? The normal rhythms of the human body, such as the heartbeat, or the twenty-four hours of waking and sleeping, seem much too short for it to be any cumulation of their effects that can be held responsible. However, this is a question for the physiologist, and the fact of aging has simply to be accepted for the purposes of the present argument.

Returning to the example of the genetic surgeon, there is, to borrow a metaphor from aeronautics, a sort of "sound barrier" in human affairs at seventy years, or rather it would be more accurate to say at about forty years of active adult life. In any field of science an experiment taking ten years may be twice as difficult as one taking five years; one demanding twenty years may be twice as difficult as one demanding ten; but in the study of humanity one requiring forty years will be immensely more than twice as difficult as one requiring twenty. It is necessary to remember that, though the old saying, "Practice makes perfect," may be true, yet it is incomplete. There is no benefit from practice unless the practicer can see the results of each of his attempts; the observations made by a deputy are of little use. An experiment concerned with a whole human life necessarily takes a lifetime, and therefore the experimenter can *himself* never get the practice which would enable him to improve his methods.

It is a very proper question, then, to consider whether methods might be devised which would penetrate the "sound barrier." This requires that the target must be something *objective* which will be acceptable to everybody without making any call on the personal experience of the individual. As an example from another field, take the case of the race horse. Though a man may control the breeding of four or five generations of horses during his lifetime, it is not in fact his continuity in this personal action that has really improved the breed. The improvement has come from the simple fact that certain horses do win races, a purely objective standard that has got to be accepted by all trainers and breeders. This objective standard passes on the experience of each of them to his successors without any difficulty from the human time scale. Similarly, in a dairy herd the actual yield of milk is an objective standard that can be accepted by anybody, and therefore the human time scale need not be the limiting factor in improving the breed of dairy cows.

Could human affairs be so arranged that similar purely objective standards would mitigate the difficulties of the human time scale? The prospect does not seem very encouraging in any of the really important things, because it implies objective standards of human values which will be acceptable over several generations of mankind, and all past experience suggests that human values vary enormously from one generation to another. There are, it is true, many simple matters where such standards could be applied; for example, the high jumper will always have the height records of the past to compete against, so that in such matters we could be independent of the human time scale. But such things do not seem very important. The important qualities of man are those of the intellect, and it is much harder to see how there could be objective standards for the highest levels of these that could be carried through the generations, so as really to control the continuous development of humanity in some constant direction. The nearest thing to the test of the race horse that we have is the test of the student by examinations in the university. Setting aside the point that anyone who has conducted such examinations knows how unsatisfactory they usually are, the parallel is bad. The *final* aim of the race horse is to win races, while the student's examination is not a final aim at all but merely a test to indicate his probable intellectual capacity. His final test is the success of his performance in later life, and for that no absolute objective standard can be set. So for his really important qualities man can never hope to become independent of the human time scale.

FUTURE APPLICATIONS

The main purpose of this note has been to bring out the importance of the idea of time scales in general and of the exceptional relation that we must inevitably have with our own time scale. Once this is accepted, the application to individual cases becomes really rather obvious, and it need only be lightly touched on. A natural first question is to ask how far past history reveals the effect. There is the obvious fact that most people are unwilling to change their habits, so that ways of life, roughly speaking, never change faster than at a rate measured in human generations. In the prescientific age this was certainly true, because then developments always depended on some form of craftsmanship, and each craftsman was concerned to preserve the mysteries of his craft and prevent any changes in it. It might make an interesting study for the historian of past cultures to see whether, even in the most revolutionary periods, things did not really conform rather exactly to the human time scale.

In the scientific age the same thing remains true of the things that can be classified as crafts. For instance, schools of painting seem to last roughly a generation, and the changes of style are usually brought about by the revolt of the young artists against the old, which illustrates an effect of the time scale. But it is by no means true that the human time scale has been the controlling influence in a great many of the recent developments of technology, even in cases where progress has chanced to be at a rate which was roughly the same. For example, it did happen to take about a generation for the telephone, from its first invention, to come into really wide use; this was not because of the distaste of the old-fashioned for the innovation but because of the enormous elaboration of the techniques required. The technologist is not a conservative like the craftsman, and he is always trying to cheat the human time scale and to accelerate the rate of change. Often he succeeds; for instance, it was hardly ten years between the first experiments on television and the provision of a full television service in London in 1937. But there still remain many things in which the scientist cannot hope to defeat the human time scale—for example, in agricultural science. Agriculture is inevitably a craft as well as a science, and it will be the time scale of the craftsman-farmer and not of the technologist-scientist which will finally control the widespread adoption of new discoveries in agriculture. No matter what wonderful things may be found out in the way of food production, it can be regarded as nearly certain that it must take two or three generations at least before the innovations can play any serious part in world history.

One of the crafts that certainly still survives is politics. Most people tend to form their political opinions between the ages of twenty and thirty, but high political rank is rarely reached before the age of fifty, so that there is practically always a lag of thirty years between the growth of political opinion and its execution; this is often attributed by reformers to the wicked stupidity of politicians, whereas in fact it is really an almost mechanical result of the human time scale.

One of the most interesting points about the human time scale is that there is now occurring a real change in its length. This is to be attributed to the wonderful new developments of medical science. In the old days the average human life was perhaps fifty years, after leaving out of account the enormous infantile mortality of those times. That is to say, adult life lasted about a generation. Now it is more like a generation and a half or even two generations. This is an important aspect of a problem which we often hear discussed, the problem of our aging population, but it is taken from a rather unusual angle. The lengthening of the human time scale from thirty to fifty years makes a real alteration in the character of human life. It is still too early to know what the actual consequences will be, but it may be conjectured that changes in world conditions will tend to be slowed down by it. In so far as man continues to be master of his fate, it will be the grandfather more than the father who will decide what is to happen, and this may go some way toward canceling the effects of the present increasing rate of scientific discovery.

Finally, I will touch on what must be regarded as the central problem for mankind—as I think for all time, but certainly for the coming century. It is the menace of world overpopulation. All sorts of proposals are being made for improving agriculture so as to meet the menace and for improving birth control so as to prevent it. It is quite evident that both these matters are intimately related to the human time scale. Thus, whatever may be done in discovering how to make the soil more fertile, it is simply out of the question that the hundreds of millions of farmers in the world could learn it; to get these improvements, a single generation is an irreducible minimum, and a space of three generations is a much more reasonable expectation. Very similar considerations apply even more forcibly for the other side of the account, the restraint of population increase. So we ought to take warning that, however alive the experts may be to the menac-

ing condition of the world, it is effectively certain that these things will continue with their present trends for nearly a century; this is so quite apart from other threats of disaster, such as the approaching exhaustion of some of the world's mineral resources. A consciousness of all this is most sobering, but it should be in the mind of everyone who is laying plans to mitigate the menace. It has to be recognized that developments in human history have a sort of momentum, so that, when they are changing in some direction, they will tend, in a manner dictated by the human time scale, to go on changing further in the same direction. This consideration must play an important part in any attempts we may make to recast the role of man when he is engaged in changing the face of the earth.

The Spiral of Population

WARREN S. THOMPSON*

Historically we know comparatively little about the changes in the numbers of mankind in the different parts of the world in the past. Even today there is much uncertainty regarding the numbers of people living in most of Africa and some parts of Asia and Latin America and, hence, regarding the changes that may have taken place in their numbers during the last century or century and a half (Anonymous, 1949——). Thus we do not *know* whether China, in the area now governed by the Communists, contains the 582 million plus (Anonymous, 1955) which they have recently announced as the result of their first "census," or the 450–75 million quite commonly claimed during the last three or four decades, or the still smaller number indicated by certain earlier

studies like that of Rockhill (1905) and in the critical examination of Chinese data by Willcox (1940, pp. 511–40). Hence, even today, we must recognize that there may be an error of 100 million or more in any estimate of world population and that the pattern of growth of certain countries in recent decades, or even during the past century or more, cannot be described with any assurance.

However, this is not the place to discuss the reasons supporting the belief in a particular amount of growth in any given population for which reliable data are lacking. It will be more useful to survey the relatively recent changes in population about which we do have useful knowledge, although not always so reliable as could be desired, and to note as well as we are able the social and economic conditions associated with these demographic changes. In this way we may be able to arrive at a reasonably good understanding of the dynamics of the changes in the size of different populations since about 1800. This should enable us to evaluate more accurately the probable changes in the numbers of people in the different parts of the world during the next few decades.

In the first place, it may be noted that every change in man's techniques of production and every change in social organization which affected his ability to co-operate with his fellow-men carried in themselves possibilities of population change. If such changes in-

---

* Dr. Thompson was Director of the Scripps Foundation for Research in Population Problems at Miami University from its establishment in 1922 until his retirement in 1953. He is now Director Emeritus. His publications include: *Population: A Study in Malthusianism*, 1915; *Danger Spots in World Population*, 1929; *Population Problems*, 1930 (1st ed.) and 1953 (4th ed.); *Population and Peace in the Pacific*, 1946; *Plenty of People*, 1948 (rev. ed.); *The Growth and Changes in California's Population*, 1955; and many articles on various aspects of population. He has acted as consultant on various population matters to several governmental agencies, the Bureau of the Census, the Natural Resources Planning Board, and SCAP in Japan. He has been president of the Population Association of America, vice-president of the International Union for the Scientific Study of Population, and vice-president of the American Association for the Advancement of Science.

creased man's ability to use his labor effectively, they favored an increase in his numbers as long as he accepted a subsistence, or near-subsistence, level of living as his inevitable lot. Periods of peace, of widespread commerce, and of general prosperity have long been recognized as favorable to the increase in man's numbers. If, on the other hand, these changes reduced the effectiveness with which man applied his labor to getting a living, they probably not only prevented any appreciable growth in numbers but often led to a decrease (Gibbon, 1880, III, pp. 262–63; Beloch, 1886). Thus the domestication of animals and plants and improvements in the cultivation of crops obviously favored an increase in population. Likewise the invention of a social order in which greater division of labor became possible, or one in which the co-operation of larger numbers of men to a common end was developed, tended to make life easier and to raise numbers. Many other inventions (using this term in its broadest sense) also increased man's ability to support larger numbers, but there must also have been many times, such as in the Dark Ages, when man lost his techniques and/or the organization needed to make them effective and thus also lost his ability to support as large a population as had existed in the past (Lot, 1953, pp. 55–85).

It is also of importance to realize that, even though a more efficient social organization and improved methods of production have always made possible the support of a larger population at any given level of living, they have not always led to this result. Many incidental and accidental factors have also affected the growth of population at particular times and in particular places. Famines and epidemics have always been unpredictable. The cultural patterns which had much to do with determining the birth rates of peoples did not necessarily change as rapidly as the techniques of production, nor did many of the practices which largely determined the level of infant mortality, and thereby had a strong influence on the survival rate, change simultaneously with changes in techniques. It is highly probable, however, that the cultural factors which have operated in the past to determine the level of the birth rate have been of far less importance in effecting differences in rates of growth between groups than those social, economic, and natural conditions which determined the death rate. What we know about population growth during the nineteenth century tends to confirm this view.

Throughout much the larger part of the past few thousand years the most important factors determining the death rate may be summed up in three words: disease, hunger (including famine), and war. Malthus called these the *positive* checks to population growth and thought of them as *hardships*. But these factors have never operated independently of the organization of society, although, in the absence of knowledge of the cause of disease and because hunger was almost always present, with actual famine a frequently recurring phenomenon, it must have seemed to most men in past ages, when they thought about such matters, that a high death rate—about as high as the birth rate—was as natural as the rising of the sun and that just as little could be done to change the level of the one as the rhythm of the other.

This extremely brief statement of some of the general factors associated with the changes in the size of populations will have to suffice as an introduction to the description of population changes since about 1800, to which most of our attention will be directed.

Very little is known about the size of the population of the world as a whole in 1800. At that time only a few European countries had actually taken censuses, and outside of Europe exact data were even more meager, the census of the United States being almost unique.

The two estimates of world population in 1800 which are most commonly used today, because they are considered the best available, are those by Walter F. Willcox (919 million) and by A. M. Carr-Saunders (906 million). It will be noted that there are comparatively small differences between these two world estimates. When broken down by continents, the differences between them for the populations of Europe and Asia were also negligible, but the differences for Africa and Latin America, for which data were very

scanty, were somewhat larger. The estimate of Carr-Saunders for the world's population by 1850 exceeded that of Willcox by 80 million, all but 5 million of which was in Asia. This difference will be referred to later.

Adjusting these estimates of Willcox and Carr-Saunders for 1900 to make them comparable with the estimates of the United Nations for 1920 and later years, as has been done by the Division of Population of the United Nations in Table 33, makes it appear that the population of the world approximately doubled between 1800 and 1920—a period of a hundred and twenty years. It may also be noted in passing that these two estimates varied more proportion-

TABLE 33

ESTIMATES OF WORLD POPULATION BY REGIONS, 1650–1950

SERIES OF ESTI-MATES AND DATE	ESTIMATED POPULATION (IN MILLIONS)							
	World Total	Africa	Northern America*	Latin America†	Asia (Excluding U.S.S.R.)‡	Europe and Asiatic U.S.S.R.‡	Oceania	Area of European Settlement§
Willcox' estimates:‖								
1650............	470	100	1	7	257	103	2	113
1750............	694	100	1	10	437	144	2	157
1800............	919	100	6	23	595	193	2	224
1850............	1,091	100	26	33	656	274	2	335
1900............	1,571	141	81	63	857	423	6	573
Carr-Saunders' estimates:#								
1650............	545	100	1	12	327	103	2	118
1750............	728	95	1	11	475	144	2	158
1800............	906	90	6	19	597	192	2	219
1850............	1,171	95	26	33	741	274	2	335
1900............	1,608	120	81	63	915	423	6	573
United Nations' estimates:**								
1920............	1,834	136	115	92	997	485	9	701
1930............	2,008	155	134	110	1,069	530	10	784
1940............	2,216	177	144	132	1,173	579	11	866
1950............	2,406	199	166	162	1,272	594	13	935

* United States, Canada, Alaska, St. Pierre, and Miquelon.

† Central and South America and Caribbean Islands.

‡ Estimates for Asia and Europe in Willcox's and Carr-Saunders' series have been adjusted so as to include the population of the Asiatic U.S.S.R. with that of Europe rather than Asia. For this purpose, the following approximate estimates of the population of the Asiatic U.S.S.R. were used: 1650, 3 million; 1750, 4 million; 1800, 5 million; 1850, 8 million; 1900, 22 million.

§ Includes northern America, Latin America, Europe and the Asiatic U.S.S.R., and Oceania.

‖ Willcox (1940, p. 45). Estimates for America have been divided between northern America and Latin America by means of detailed figures presented *ibid.*, pp. 37–44.

Carr-Saunders (1936, p. 42).

** United Nations, *Demographic Yearbook, 1949–50* (1950), p. 10; and United Nations, "The Past and Future Growth of World Population . . ." (1951), Table II; the 1940 figures are unpublished estimates of the United Nations.

ally for the world, and particularly for Asia, as they were extended backward to a time when all population data were extremely fragmentary and any estimates were necessarily only guesses based on what appeared to the estimator as the most reasonable interpretation of the scanty and uncertain data available. Thus, according to the estimates of Willcox, the increase in world population during the hundred and fifty years between 1650 and 1800 was about 95 per cent, while Carr-Saunders placed it at about 66 per cent. In any event, it is quite generally believed today that the population of the world was twice as great in 1920 as in 1800 and that almost two-thirds as many people as lived in the world in 1800 have been added to it since 1920.

In considering population growth since 1800 in somewhat more detail, it will be convenient and instructive to divide the period 1800–1950 into two subperiods: (1) the nineteenth century (1800–1900) and (2) the first half of the twentieth century (1900–1950).

The most significant difference in the rates of growth shown in the estimates of Willcox and Carr-Saunders for the nineteenth century is in the growth of Asia's population. A second but less important difference is in Africa's population growth during this century. As regards population changes in Africa, Willcox accepted a round 100 million in 1800 and made no change in this figure for 1850, but for 1900 he used the figure 141 million, indicating his belief that a rather large increase had taken place between 1850 and 1900. Carr-Saunders, on the other hand, allotted Africa only 90 million in 1800, raised it to 95 million in 1850, but to only 120 million in 1900. Thus Willcox's estimate for Africa in 1900 was 21 million, or about one-sixth higher than that of Carr-Saunders. The United Nations statistical services were apparently disposed to accept an approximate

average of these two figures, because they gave the population of Africa as 136 million in 1920.

The most important difference between these two estimates, as has been said, was in the population of Asia in 1900. Whereas both had accepted a figure of approximately 600 million in 1800, Willcox arrived at an estimate of only 857 million in 1900, while Carr-Saunders estimated Asia's population at 915 million. (Both of these figures exclude the population in U.S.S.R. territory from that of Asia.) This difference, amounting to 58 million, is due chiefly to the fact that Willcox did not believe the available data justified the acceptance of a fairly steady growth of population in China during the nineteenth century, whereas Carr-Saunders did. The writer, who has given some attention to the problem of China's population, is disposed to agree with Willcox on this point. But the facts were, and still are, so unreliable for China, for certain other parts of Asia, and for much of Africa that it is not surprising there should be rather wide differences in the estimates of their populations by careful students trying to make sense of the data available.

Using these estimates as they stand in Table 33, the population of Africa increased by only about 40 per cent between 1800 and 1900 according to Willcox and by about 33 per cent according to Carr-Saunders, while the population of Asia increased by about 44 per cent according to Willcox and by about 53 per cent according to Carr-Saunders. On the other hand, the population of Europe, regarding which there was no significant difference in these estimates, increased by approximately 119 per cent, while that of the Americas increased by 396 per cent according to Willcox and by 476 per cent according to Carr-Saunders. Moreover, the entire "area of European settlement" increased by about 158 per cent. Even allowing for considerable errors in estimates, there can be no reasonable doubt that during the nineteenth century the population of European origin increased at least three times as fast as that having its origin in other continents and may very well have increased four times as fast. This fact of differential increase among the continents and different peoples is one of the most significant events of our time in helping to understand the dynamics of modern population change, as will be pointed out in more detail below.

Since 1900 the population of the world has increased about 50 per cent, while that of Europe (including that of the U.S.S.R. in Asia) has increased only about 40 per cent, but that of the "area of European settlement" has increased about 63 per cent. The increase in Asia (excluding the U.S.S.R.) was about 48 per cent if the United Nations' estimate for 1950 uses Willcox's estimate for 1900 as the base but only by about 39 per cent if Carr-Saunders' estimate for 1900 is made the base. In any event, it is reasonably certain that since 1900 the differential between the rate of growth of population in Europe and Asia has largely disappeared and may possibly have been reversed (almost certainly if the estimates of Communist China are accepted) and that only the "area of European settlement" outside of Europe still has a somewhat higher rate of growth than Asia and Africa. The differentials in growth in different areas and the changes taking place in these differentials will be discussed in some detail, because any assessment of the probable future course of population growth must rest on what we know of the dynamics of the changes that have taken place during relatively recent times.

There can be no reasonable doubt that the most significant change taking place around 1800 in the operation of the factors which determined the change in the relative size of populations in the different parts of the world was the reduction of the death rate in the Western world. The evidence for this statement will be presented below. But a simple calculation will show that a doubling of the world's population in a hundred and twenty years must have been a very unusual event during the Christian Era.

If it is assumed that the total population of the world was only 100 million at the beginning of the Christian Era and that it doubled in each one hundred and twenty years, it would have grown by A.D. 480 to about the level it actually attained in 1900, and by A.D. 600 it would have been one-half larger than it is today. (Beloch, 1886, has shown that the population of the Roman Empire alone may well have been 50–60 million at the death of Augustus.)

Actually, the doubling period for the population of the world from the time of Christ to A.D. 1800 must have been five hundred to seven hundred years or more rather than the one hundred and twenty years about which we can be fairly certain since 1800. It would appear highly probable that the pattern of population growth throughout human history prior to the eighteenth or nineteenth centuries consisted of a succession of periods of increase or decrease interspersed with periods of little or no change in national and local populations and with no consistent trend in world population over long periods of time. That is to say, the changes in the size of the population of China, or of India, or of the whole of Europe during any particular time (e.g., 200 B.C. to A.D. 200) had no significant relation to one another or to those taking place in the world as a whole. A particular period of time during which India may have suffered so severely from epidemics, famine, and war that its population declined for several consecutive decades, or even for a century or more, may have witnessed a large increase in China's population. Moreover, the Black Death of Europe in the fourteenth century, although it probably came to Europe from the Far East, may not have caused an equal degree of devastation in the latter region, just as it is reasonably certain that the world-wide influenza epidemic of 1918–19 wrought far less havoc in the West, where it seems to have originated, than in India, whither it was carried. The point of chief interest is that the changes in the dynamic factors which determined the growth or decline of population have, until quite recently, been more or less local in their incidence.

Furthermore, we now know with reasonable certainty that the growth or decline in the population of a given area was in the past determined primarily by the degree of hardship under which the people lived, that is, by their death rate. Few peoples have ever had birth rates so low that they would not have had a fairly high and steady rate of increase if their death rates had been only moderately high according to nineteenth-century European standards. Throughout most of human history the death rates of most peoples must have been almost as high as, and often even higher than, their high birth rates, and the changes in the numbers of most peoples must have followed a wavelike pattern. Almost certainly there was never any relatively large and long-continued excess of births over deaths over a large part of the world such as appears probable in several large areas since about 1650 and appears almost certain since about 1750 or 1800. There probably have been times in the history of particular peoples or empires when there were rather large and prolonged periods of population growth. Such a period of growth appears to have taken place in

China for some time after 1650, during a period under the Manchus of prolonged peace and improving husbandry (Ta Chen, 1946), and in the Roman Empire from about the time of Augustus until about A.D. 200, also a period of peace and of the spread of a more efficient agriculture and industry. There is no evidence, however, that such periods witnessed prolonged population growth throughout the world, although it does appear probable that the growth of population in Europe between 1650 and 1750 (recovery from the Thirty Years' War and the beginning of an agricultural revolution) coincided with the fairly rapid growth of population in China just noted and that both arose from essentially the same causes, although there was no direct relation between growth in these two areas.

Fortunately we have considerable evidence regarding the cause of relatively rapid and steady population growth in several countries since 1750 and especially since 1800. This evidence relates chiefly to countries in Western and Northern Europe,[1] but there is no good reason to believe that it is not equally valid for much of the remainder of Europe and the areas settled by western and northern Europeans. It may also be valid for other areas, but the evidence is not conclusive. The chief factor in effecting a rather rapid growth of population in Europe during this period, as already noted, was the mild relaxation of those hardships which determined the level of the death rate—what Malthus called the positive checks to population

1. The statistical yearbooks of Sweden, Norway, Finland, and Denmark contain data on births, deaths, and natural increase in those countries since 1750 (Sweden and Finland) and since 1800 (Norway and Denmark). The statistical annuals of France also contain data for the period since 1800. These are all official publications, and any volume will contain data for earlier years as well as current data.

growth. The chief of these positive checks, as already noted, have always been hunger (including famine and malnutrition) and disease, although at times war became a check of major importance. But, when war was a major check, it was generally because it enhanced the hardships arising from hunger and disease rather than because of the actual slaughter of people.

The mild relaxation of the positive checks was itself due chiefly to the increased productivity of man's labor, arising from the improvement in agriculture in the first instance and later from the improved industrial techniques constituting the industrial revolution. During the latter part of the seventeenth century and much of the eighteenth there were very significant improvements in tillage practices, in the introduction and wider use of greater-yielding crops, and in animal breeding. This advance in agricultural productivity now appears small in comparison with what was achieved during the nineteenth century and thus far in the twentieth, but it was sufficient to support a considerably larger number of people having a better, a more abundant, and a more certain food supply. As the industrial revolution gathered momentum, it not only produced better tools and implements to aid in further agricultural advance but made possible the more efficient use of labor in providing all other types of goods and services. It made possible the reconstruction of the filthy and deadly medieval cities; it provided better transportation, so that local shortages of food were less apt to result in serious famines; and it drew into more productive non-agricultural tasks the surplus of people from the land, so that there was less underemployment in agriculture.

On the whole, the increase in simple cleanliness which accompanied the mild relaxation of the pressure of people for the necessities of life probably did as much to reduce the death rate as the improvement in per capita consumption in the century from about 1750 to 1850. It is little wonder that our grandmothers and great-grandmothers were fond of saying that "cleanliness is next to godliness."

There is clear evidence in the vital statistics of the Scandinavian countries that, long before smallpox vaccination became general (Jenner's discovery was established by 1798 but was only slowly put into practice) and a century before the role of bacteria in causing contagious diseases (as shown in Pasteur's work) was widely known, the death rate was declining slowly, while there is no indication of any definite decline in the birth rate until some decades later. In England and Wales satisfactory vital statistics came much later than in the Scandinavian countries, but, when the first census was taken (1801), it was believed by all those especially interested in population changes that there had been a relatively rapid growth in numbers during the latter half of the eighteenth century, and this growth was attributed to the improvement in the means of subsistence and to the betterment of the physical environment in the cities as well as in the country villages. When vital statistics first became available for all of England and Wales in 1838, they showed a significantly higher birth rate than death rate and continued to do so for over three-quarters of a century. For the first two or three decades of the nation-wide registration of births and deaths an increase in the birth rate was noted, but some of the most careful students attribute this increase to a more complete registration of births rather than to an actual increase in the rate (Farr, 1885, p. 89). The most significant facts shown by the first half-century of English vital statistics are the rather steady but slow decline in the death rate and the negligible change in the birth rate until about 1880. In England it would appear that the rather widespread but slow improvement in living conditions which had been taking place since about 1750 had no appreciable effect on the birth rate until after the famous trial, in 1878, of Bradlaugh and Besant for the dissemination of birth-control information.

It is not possible to go into more detail here regarding the population changes in other western European countries during the nineteenth century, but it can be said in general that, with a partial exception in the case of France, the improvement in living conditions which was taking place resulted in a decline in the death rate some decades before there was any significant change in the birth rate, with the result that population grew fairly rapidly and far more steadily than in any known past.

In the New World and particularly in North America after the early days of settlement, the excess of births over deaths, as shown by the increase in population, was so great that there could be no doubt of a significant decline in the death rate due to the relative abundance of land and the consequent ease of securing a sufficiency of the necessities of life, or of a significant rise in the birth rate, or of both of these changes. It was literally true that, where good land was available cheaply, or even free, "every mouth was accompanied by a pair of hands to feed it." For several generations the migrants to the New World and their descendants increased in numbers so rapidly that there is reason to believe they had significantly higher birth rates than the people in the countries from which they came (Thompson and Whelpton, 1933, chaps. vii, viii, ix). If there was a substantial increase in the birth rate among the people settling in the New World, it was probably due chiefly to the marriage earlier than was customary in Europe of a larger proportion of the women. In 1751 Benjamin Franklin wrote: "For People increase in Proportion to the Number of Marriages, and that is greater in Proportion to the Ease and Convenience of supporting a Family. When Families can be easily supported, more Persons marry, and earlier in Life." He was certain that this was what was happening in the North American colonies (1907, III, 63–73).

In any event, there probably was no period, from the time when the first European settlements became firmly established until after 1860, when the natural increase in North America was less than 2.5 per cent per annum; most of the time it was probably nearer 3 per cent.

What the experience of the Western world as regards population growth during the nineteenth century has shown us can be summed up briefly in three statements: (1) When improvements in the processes of production led to somewhat enlarged per capita consumption, or when there was an abundance of new and fertile land available, thus easing the positive checks, the death rate declined, and most of this decline (before 1900) occurred in spite of an almost total lack of knowledge regarding the nature of disease and the methods for its control. (2) The increase in per capita consumption had little or no effect on the birth rate for several decades after the death rate began to decline (in the case of England and Wales, almost certainly somewhat more than a century). (3) Although the relaxation of the hardships determining the death rate was not entirely confined to Western and Northern Europe and the areas settled by people from these areas, these peoples profited most by the improvement in level of living, as will be noted in a moment, because many circumstances led to an unprecedentedly rapid economic development among them.

Two points encouraging this rapid economic development in the West will be emphasized here: (*a*) The European peoples, through actual settlement, were able to exploit vast areas of new land and, through extension of the colonial system, were able to intensify the exploitation of other large areas. In either case, for all practical purposes the area and the resources of Western Europe were very rapidly and greatly increased during the nineteenth century. (*b*) The industrial revolution, which may be defined as the application of science to production, proceeded so rapidly in this larger resource area that per capita production grew steadily, in spite of the unusually steady and rapid population increase.

The net effect of the large decline in the death rate during the nineteenth century in the area of European settlement, coupled with a relatively small decline in the birth rate, was that, by 1900, Europe itself (including Asiatic U.S.S.R.) contained over 26 per cent of the world's population as compared with about 21 per cent in 1800, while the whole area of European settlement grew from about 24 per cent of the total to about 36 per cent in the same period of time—a proportional increase of about one-half, in which emigration from Europe played a significant role.

On the other hand, the proportion of the world's people living in Asia declined from about 65 per cent in 1800 to about 55 or 57 per cent in 1900, depending on whether the estimate of Willcox or Carr-Saunders is used. Thus the best information available indicates that a relatively large part of the total increase of population in the world during the nineteenth century took place in those areas in which much new and fertile land came into use at that time and in which the new techniques of production, arising from the application of science to economic activities, replaced the older traditional patterns of work. These economic changes in turn led to a steady decline in the death rate throughout the nineteenth century, thus inducing a rapid growth in numbers, since, until near the end of the century, there was only a rather small decline in the birth rate in many of these Western countries. France alone of the Western countries had so reduced its birth rate fairly early in the nineteenth century and at the same time failed to reduce its death rate as fast as most of the others; therefore, it had a comparatively small natural increase during a considerable portion of this period. In spite of the reduction of the death rate in the area of European settlement during the nineteenth century, death rates of 16–18 per thousand were considered quite good in most of the more advanced Western countries in 1900, whereas in 1800 death rates of ten to fifteen points higher were the rule rather than the exception. On the other hand, the earlier death rates of 1800 still prevailed in most other parts of the world in 1900.

It is of course purely arbitrary to select any particular date and say that a marked change took place at that time in the factors affecting the growth of population in the world as a whole or in any given portion of it. However, around 1900—a decade or two in either direction, depending on conditions in particular areas—such significant changes in birth rates and death rates became manifest that it is worthwhile to note these in some detail. In the first place, although the bacterial cause of many contagious and infectious diseases had been discovered some years earlier, it was not until after 1900 that these discoveries were put into practical use on a large scale and began to exert a profound influence on the death rate. Furthermore, about the time the control of such diseases as diphtheria, tuberculosis, and diarrhea and enteritis in young children, and of several other deadly contagious and infectious diseases, had become so secure that they no longer took nearly as heavy a toll of life in the more advanced countries as they had before 1900, the discovery of the sulfa drugs and of antibiotics and the use of DDT for the extermination of the anopheles mosquito gave a new impetus to the control of the death rate. In addition, there was no letup, but rather a more rapid increase, in the development of better methods of production in both agriculture and other industries, so that the level of living continued to rise in much of the West.

The effect of the great medical advances in Western countries since 1900 plus the continued improvement of living conditions among the poorer portions of their populations may be shown clearly by a few figures. In the period 1898–1902 Denmark had a death rate of 16.0 per thousand; for the years 1950–52 it was 9.0. For England and Wales the decline was from 17.4 to 11.8; for Sweden, from 16.2 to 9.8. Thus, about the time that it would have been reasonable to expect a slower decline in the death rate due to the further improvement in economic conditions, science took over, and the death rate in the more advanced Western countries fell almost as much proportionally between 1900 and 1950 as it did between 1800 and 1900, although in absolute amount it was less in most of them.

It was also around 1900, with a variation of a decade or two in either direction, that the decline in the birth rates in many Western countries became more clearly marked. But, in spite of this decline in the birth rate, there was no large decline in the excess of births over deaths in most European countries until after World War I. The period 1908–12 to 1918–22 saw a decline in natural increase in Denmark from 14.1 to 11.3 per thousand. It had been 13.7 and 11.5 in the two decades preceding 1908–12 and still lower twenty years earlier. In England and Wales the natural increase was 11.9–11.0 in the period 1888–1912, which was only two or three points below that in the period from 1858–62 to 1878–82, but it fell to 7.2 in the period 1918–22. Much the same pattern is found in Germany, Sweden, most of the countries of Western Europe, and, with some lag in time, in those of southern Europe.

Even before 1900, improved methods of production began to have an effect on the death rates in certain portions of the other continents outside the area of European settlement. Thus the beginning of industrialization in Japan in the 1870's was accompanied by a fairly slow but steady decline in the death rate, so that the population had begun to grow at a modest but steady rate by 1900. Since 1900 it has grown more rapidly and quite steadily, except during World War II, owing chiefly to the continued decline in the death rate. The decline in the birth rate in the two decades before World War II was of much the same magnitude as the decline in the death rate.

In some of the colonial areas the establishment of peace and the encouragement of better agriculture and the better organization of famine relief also reduced the death rate somewhat and thus led to a steadier but slow growth of population. Thus, under the rule of Japan, population grew slowly in both Korea and Formosa until about 1920. After that it grew rapidly. Under Dutch rule, bringing peace and a better economy, it appears that the population of Java began to increase fairly steadily by the end of the first quarter of the nineteenth century and continued to do so up to World War II. In the Philippines there can be no doubt of the relatively rapid growth of population from the time of the American occupation up to the present time. In India and Pakistan, which have the largest populations of any country that has actually counted its people, the increase in population in the thirty years 1871–1901 was only from about 255 million to about 285 million, or about 11–12 per cent, nearly all of which took place in the decade 1881–91, there being two decades in which it was almost stationary (Davis, 1951). Their populations again grew fairly rapidly during the first decade of this century but were practically stationary in the decade 1911–21. Since 1921 there has been a steady and fairly rapid increase comparable to that in many European countries during the nineteenth century, and their populations (combined) had grown to 432 million by 1951.[2] This growth in India and Pakistan, as far as can be told, has all been achieved through the reduction of the death rate, since there is no clear evidence of any decline in the birth rate. Thus for none of these non-European peoples regarding whose recent growth we have even a modest amount of evidence does the birth rate appear to have changed appreciably, except in Japan since about 1930 and especially since 1951. In this respect the pattern of population growth in these underdeveloped areas appears to be following that of the Europeans of a century ago in its general outline. The scanty information we do possess seems to indicate, however, that the birth rates of most of these non-European peoples are now higher than those of the Europeans in 1800 and that their death rates are falling faster than those of Europeans in the early days of the industrial revolution. That their death rates should fall faster is not hard to understand, since it is relatively easy and cheap to carry out health programs today which will rapidly reduce death rates even among

2. See United Nations, *Demographic Yearbook, 1953*, Table 1, p. 75.

peoples having very low levels of living. As regards birth rates, which are an integral part of the general cultural pattern, the change (reduction) does not appear to come until the entire social system begins an adaptation to a new pattern of life arising from a better level of living based on the modernization of their economic activities. This is what the West experienced with population growth during the last one hundred and fifty years. If the history of population growth among the European peoples since 1800 should repeat itself among the non-Europeans during the ensuing one hundred and fifty years, the population of Africa and Asia, in 1950 numbering approximately 1,470 million, could be expected to increase to more than 5,900 million by A.D. 2100, and the total population of the world could be expected to pass 7,200 million before that time.

Among the underdeveloped peoples there appear to us to be two possible variations from the path of economic and social development followed by the Western peoples which may so affect their growth during the next several decades that the above figures will have no meaning: (1) The increase in the productivity of labor may proceed more slowly than it has in the West (to be discussed somewhat more fully below), thus preventing the easing of the positive checks (death rate) to population growth, to the same extent as in the West, over a relatively long period of time. This would mean that the actual lack of the necessities of life would continue to keep their death rates high in spite of modern medicine and health work. Except for this contingency a more rapid decline in the death rate in these areas than took place in Europe during the nineteenth century can be expected. (2) The spread of the voluntary control of the birth rate at a much faster pace than took place in Europe before World War I would reduce the natural increase in a shorter time and thus lessen the number of additional persons to be provided with the necessities of life year by year. The opposite of the first of these variations (i.e., a more rapid increase in the productivity of labor) may take place, but, when all is considered, this seems to us rather unlikely; the opposite of the second (i.e., the slower spread of the voluntary control of births) seems more likely. If both of these opposites were to become actualities, the above calculations for growth would be far too small.

At this point it may be well to give concrete examples of the possibilities of lowering the death rate today under fairly favorable conditions. In Japan the death rate in pre–World War II days was 17–18 per thousand. In the latter days of the war and in early occupation days it rose to about 29, but for the entire year of 1946 it had again fallen to the prewar level (17.6). By 1949 it had been brought down to 11.6, and the preliminary figure for 1954 is 9.0. Thus it had been cut in half between 1946 and 1954, most of the decline taking place in the period 1946–50. This is a very remarkable demographic phenomenon and proves what well-planned health work backed up by modern medical achievements can do in a few years' time if the necessities for even a rather low level of living are available.

The experience of Ceylon in wiping out malaria had an almost equally startling effect in reducing the death rate. The average death rate in Ceylon in 1945–46 was about 21 per thousand. In the period 1949–52 it averaged only a little over 12—a reduction of about 40 per cent. As a result of these health improvements in both Japan and Ceylon, the rate of natural increase rose to heights it had never before attained. In Japan the continuation of the natural increase of 1947–49 would have led to the doubling of the population in about forty years, and in Ceylon the present natural increase would double the population in twenty-five years.

Let us now enumerate and consider briefly the changes in death rates and birth rates which seem most likely to take place in the next few decades, especially in the underdeveloped areas of the world.

In the first place, we should realize that, even if our knowledge of the factors effecting population changes in the West during the last one hundred and fifty years were entirely adequate, it could not serve as an infallible guide in projecting the growth of world population, or even that of any given nation, during the next few decades. The chief reason why we must use our knowledge of recent population growth in the world with caution in trying to look ahead is the simple fact that the conditions which were closely associated with certain population changes in any particular group in the past can never repeat themselves precisely in the experience of another people, or group of peoples, or even in the same people, at a different time. Again, close association of conditions is not a proof of causal relationship. Besides, even though the circumstances associated with past population changes may appear to be very much the same among certain peoples today, we know very well that these circumstances are found in a different cultural setting and will not result in exactly the same type of population changes as has been observed in the past, even if the observed relationship is causal. This is not to say that knowledge of past population changes is useless, but it is to say that we must be cautious in the use we make of our knowledge of past population changes in trying to foresee future changes. Such knowledge can be only suggestive of probable future changes.

I presume the chief questions regarding future growth of population to which most students of population are most anxious to find useful answers may be phrased somewhat as follows: How long will it take the peoples living in underdeveloped countries to pass through the period of population change corresponding to that which the western European peoples, and those in the areas settled by them, have passed through since about 1750–1800? How much are the populations in these underdeveloped lands likely to grow before they attain a relative stability, or at least a low rate of increase, based on low birth rates and low death rates rather than a low rate of growth based on high birth rates and death rates nearly as high? Another very practical question may be regarded as an essential part of the above: What chance is there that during this transition period these underdeveloped peoples can enjoy a rising level of living such as that which took place among the Western peoples during their demographic transition and which appears to have been an essential factor among them in developing effective motives for birth control?

It is evident at once that such questions implicitly make several important assumptions. But the chief assumption involved in both questions is that the modernization of the economy in any underdeveloped area will result, in the course of a few decades, in such an improvement in the level of living in this area and in such changes in the organization of society that much the same motives for the voluntary control of the birth rate will come to prevail in it as now prevail in much of the West.

In our opinion this broad assumption is open to serious question. We cannot be certain that the modernization of their economies will result as quickly in the growth of motives leading to the effective control of the birth rate as it did in the West after 1800, for the underdeveloped areas are undertaking the modernization of their economies with a cultural heritage greatly different from that of the Europeans of 1800. There can be no assurance that cultural development in the two cases will follow the same pattern as regards control of the birth rate. The development of Japan suggests that industrialization in the underdeveloped areas of today may lead to many of the same changes as regards reproduction as it did in the West, but it certainly does not prove that this will be the case.

In the second place, it is far from certain that the modernization of the economy of the underdeveloped peoples of today can be accomplished with the same speed as in the West, in spite of the fact that we now know how to increase the tempo of economic development *if all conditions are favorable*. We are saying, in effect, that there are many reasons to believe that the underdeveloped peoples of today, in their efforts to modernize their economies, will labor under many handicaps which did not exist for the Europeans of 1800, not the least of which are, for many of them, a large and relatively dense population and a lack of new lands available for exploitation.

We cannot, because of these and many other uncertainties, be positive that the peoples in the underdeveloped countries will pass through a demographic transition similar to that of the Western peoples. However, most students of such problems believe that they will. How long it will take them to make this transition can be only guessed at. Modern means of communication might be expected to shorten the time within which knowledge of how to modernize their economies can be conveyed to them and can be put to practical use and also to reduce the time it will take to make known the fact that it is feasible to control the birth rate. Furthermore, it seems probable that science can be relied upon to find surer, simpler, and cheaper means of birth control than are now known anywhere. All this would indicate that the time needed to pass from an uncontrolled birth rate (or one largely uncontrolled) to a controlled birth rate might be considerably shortened and need not depend as much upon a substantial rise in the level of living as was the case in the West.

On the other hand, we cannot know how these peoples, whose cultural heritage is so much different from Western peoples, will react to the control of the birth rate. The "cake of custom," of which their reproductive life is an integral part, may be very hard to break, although many people in these lands do not think this will be especially difficult. Again it is possible that the breaking of the cake of custom as regards productive processes, which is demanded for success in effecting both an agricultural and an industrial revolution, will be a much slower process than in the West. If this should prove to be the case, it is highly probable that the continuance of low levels of living would make for the continuance of high birth rates and death rates, that is, for the continuance of the existing patterns of reproduction, in spite of increasing knowledge of the close relation between a high birth rate and a higher level of welfare. We are not predicting this; we are merely saying that it is another of the imponderables encountered in trying to assess the probability of population changes in the world in the near future.

Another important matter which must be taken into account when we think of population change in the underdeveloped lands is the scarcity of new areas open to them for exploitation as compared with those available to Europeans in 1800. In addition, many of these underdeveloped areas are not endowed with the abundance of mineral and water resources found in the West. These differences in available resources may make the economic improvement in living conditions much slower than that of the Western peoples even in spite of the availability of much better techniques for their use. This, coupled with the fact that the death rates in these underdeveloped areas may be reduced much faster than those of the West, may discourage the belief in the effectiveness of man's efforts to bring about a progressively more abundant economy such as was never felt by the Western peoples during their demographic transition.

To offset this possibility of relatively slow economic development, we know that the application of science to the processes of production in the future is likely to accomplish results in enlarging production which were scarcely dreamed of a few years ago. How soon these underdeveloped areas can adopt these new techniques we do not know, and we cannot know until trial has been made. If this trial is made and if it is as successful as the most optimistic believe it will be during the next few decades, another question is certain to become of much importance. Will the leaders of these peoples interpret this rapid economic advance as meaning there is no need to give consideration to the reduction of the birth rate and therefore turn to the encouragement of a high birth rate and the expansion of their political power, as is happening in the U.S.S.R. and in China?

We might continue for many pages the enumeration of considerations which would seem to favor a rather rapid and easy transition of the peoples in the underdeveloped areas of the world from their present poverty-stricken conditions and the hardships associated with high death rates and high birth rates to the relatively easy conditions of life in the most developed areas of the West, where both birth rates and death rates are low. Likewise, we could cite an equally impressive array of considerations seeming to indicate the like-lihood of a relatively slow transition in the underdeveloped areas which would be accompanied by much hardship and suffering, because the constant increase in numbers would consume practically all the increased product likely to be made available by improved processes of production. Such a course of development would prevent any substantial improvement in the level of living in the foreseeable future. Much has been written on these matters recently, and the conclusions arrived at have often been diametrically opposed.

On the one hand, a consideration of the evidence has led some students to make statements to the effect that, no matter how great the increase of population may be in coming years, the development of science and the ingenuity of man in applying it to the production of goods to supply his needs will prevent any pressure of population on the necessities of life. On the other hand, more of the men who have given this matter much thought conclude that the increase in numbers in the underdeveloped areas will be so great in the foreseeable future that no reasonably probable increase in the efficiency of labor can prevent growing hardship and a rise in their death rates, unless these people learn to reduce their birth rates even more rapidly than occurred in the West during the demographic transition there. We, personally, incline to the latter view. Since we cannot at this time go into the detail needed to support this view, only general conclusions regarding the probable pattern of growth during the next two or three decades are presented in the form of several brief and much too dogmatic statements.

The Western peoples as a whole have passed the period of their most rapid growth, although they are still growing fairly rapidly by the standards of what constituted rapid growth a cen-tury ago, and seem likely to continue to grow significantly, but probably more slowly, for at least two or three decades. Since there are still considerable differences in the rates of growth of different Western peoples, probably owing to the different stages of economic and social development they have attained, these differences seem likely to persist for some time. The peoples in eastern Europe and in the Americas will probably continue to grow more rapidly than those in Western and Central Europe for at least two or three decades. However, the people of European origin are quite likely to become a slowly declining proportion of the world's population, although their proportional decline may not be so rapid as is sometimes thought.

In spite of the high birth rates among the underdeveloped peoples, they will not soon attain the high rate growth which the increased control over their death rates, made possible by the use of the medical knowledge at man's disposal today, leads many people to expect. The most basic consideration leading us to this belief is our assessment of the difficulties standing in the way of increasing agricultural and industrial production among the underdeveloped peoples. We find it hard to believe that over-all production of the necessities of life can be increased at a rate of 2 per cent or more a year in most of these countries during the next two or three decades. Until this is done, we do not see how they can support a much larger rate of growth than they now have. Even in the United States, where conditions have been most favorable to a rapid increase in over-all production, the average annual increase for the last fifty years is generally estimated at about 3 per cent. It does not seem reasonable to us to believe that such a rate of growth in production can be attained in the near future in these underdeveloped areas, and any rate of

3 per cent or less will certainly mean that nearly all the increase will be absorbed in the support of the more rapid increase in population, which can easily be achieved by a well-planned health program in almost any underdeveloped area. Witness what has happened recently in Ceylon as described above. Another important factor increasing the difficulty of raising production rapidly in these underdeveloped areas is the meagerness of new lands and of mineral resources available to them as compared with those available to the Europeans of 1800.

The cultural obstacles standing in the way of the rapid spread of the voluntary control of population growth (chiefly by contraception) are very formidable. Hence, even though means of contraception which are sure, are simple, are cheap, and are not injurious to health may soon become available, their use may not become so widespread during the next two or three decades as would seem necessary to insure a rapid rise in the level of living which, in turn, would do more to encourage the rapid adoption of contraception than would any other change.

As a consequence of these beliefs, we expect the underdeveloped peoples of the world to attain only slowly a significantly greater degree of freedom from the positive check (hardship) to population growth which now is the chief factor in keeping their rate of growth at 1.0–1.5 per cent per year on the average. Hence, although we believe that these underdeveloped peoples are likely to grow at a somewhat faster rate in the near future than are the peoples of European origin, we do not believe that they are likely to increase at as rapid a rate over a long period of time as the latter did during the nineteenth century. Thus, it will be seen, we believe that the growth of underdeveloped peoples of the world still depends more largely on the rate at which their means of subsistence can be increased than upon the improvement of health conditions made possible by modern science. The *positive* checks to population growth are, even yet, the effective checks to the upward spiral of population growth in that part of the world's people who have not yet made the transition from high and largely uncontrolled birth rates and death rates to low and controlled birth rates and death rates.

REFERENCES

ANONYMOUS
1949—— *Demographic Yearbook.* New York: United Nations. (Each annual volume contains one or more articles on special subjects as well as annual demographic data for the world.)
1955 *The Population of Communist China.* (Series P-90, No. 6.) Washington, D.C.: United States Bureau of the Census.

BELOCH, JULIUS
1886 *Die Bevölkerung der griechisch-römischen Welt.* Leipzig: Duncker & Humblot. 520 pp.

CARR-SAUNDERS, A. M.
1936 *World Population: Past Growth and Present Trends.* Oxford: Clarendon Press. 336 pp.

DAVIS, KINGSLEY
1951 *The Population of India and Pakistan.* Princeton: Princeton University Press. 263 pp.

FARR, WILLIAM
1885 *Vital Statistics.* London: Office of the Sanitary Institute. 563 pp.

FRANKLIN, BENJAMIN
1907 "Observations concerning the Increase of Mankind, Peopling of Countries, etc.," pp. 63–73 in SMYTH, ALBERT HENRY (ed.), *The Writings of Benjamin Franklin, Collected (with a Life and Introduction),* Vol. III. 8 vols. New York: Macmillan Co.

GIBBON, EDWARD
1880 *The Decline and Fall of the*

Roman Empire. 8 vols. London: J. Murray.

LOT, FERDINAND
   1953   *The End of the Ancient World and the Beginnings of the Middle Ages.* New York: Barnes & Noble. 454 pp.

ROCKHILL, W. W.
   1905   "An Inquiry into the Population of China," *Annual Report of the Smithsonian Institution for 1904*, pp. 659–76. Washington, D.C.: Government Printing Office.

TA CHEN
   1946   *Population in Modern China.* Chicago: University of Chicago Press. 126 pp.

THOMPSON, WARREN S., and WHELPTON, P. K.
   1933   *Population Trends in the United States.* New York: McGraw-Hill Book Co. 415 pp.

WILLCOX, WALTER F.
   1940   *Studies in American Demography.* Ithaca, N.Y.: Cornell University Press. 556 pp.

Possible Limits of Raw-Material Consumption

SAMUEL H. ORDWAY, JR.*

Whether there may be any unbreakable upper limits to the continuing growth of our economy, we do not pretend to know, but it must be part of our task to examine such apparent limits as present themselves.—PRESIDENT'S MATERIALS POLICY COMMISSION, *Resources for Freedom* (1952).

This paper does not seek to analyze the availability, present or prospective, of particular raw materials. This already has been done effectively by the President's Materials Policy Commission, and some of its findings, summarized below, constitute basic information from which the arguments herein stem. This information leads to presentation of a theory of the limit of growth. The possibility of avoiding, in the United States, arrival at such limit by imports and technological discovery is minimized. The remainder of the paper is addressed to possible ways by which our prosperity may be sustained. It is suggested that, for the next few decades at least, there will be increased prosperity and plenty. In the same period there will continue to be decreases in the hours men have to work, accompanied by an abundance of leisure for many. These factors of plenty and leisure can lead to individual and group activity which can develop new national awareness and discipline and a needed ethic for an age of conservation.

BASIC INFORMATION

British Political and Economic Planning (PEP), in a draft report dated January, 1955, excerpted and summarized relevant findings from the President's Materials Policy Commission's report (1952) most succinctly as follows:

There is a Materials Problem of considerable severity affecting the United States and the industrialized nations of Western Europe. Unless the problem is effectively met, the long range security and economic growth of this and other free nations will be seriously impaired. The Commission's report is primarily concerned with the United States problem, which cannot, however, be isolated from the rest of the free world problem.

The basic reason for the problem is soaring demand. This country took out of

* Mr. Ordway is Executive Vice-President of The Conservation Foundation and was chairman (1954) of the Natural Resources Council of America and a member of the Conservation Advisory Committee to the Secretary of Interior. Trained as a lawyer, he engaged in active practice in New York from 1924 to 1935; thereafter he served as a member of the New York City, and later the United States, Civil Service Commission; and was president of the National Civil Service League and of the City Club of New York. He served in various capacities in the Executive Office of the Secretary of the Navy in World War II, with the rank of captain in the Naval Reserve, and following the war wrote the official wartime *History of the Navy's Civilian Personnel and Industrial Relations*. His publications in the field of conservation include: *A Conservation Handbook*, 1949, and *Resources and the American Dream*, 1953.

the ground two-and-one-half times more bituminous coal in 1950 than in 1900; three times more copper, four times more zinc, thirty times more crude oil. *The quantity of most metals and mineral fuels used in the United States since the first World War exceeds the total used throughout the entire world in all of history preceding 1914.* Although almost all materials are in heavily increasing demand, the hard core of the materials problem is minerals.

In 1950, the United States consumed 2.7 billion tons of materials of all kinds—metallic ores, non-metallic minerals, agricultural materials, construction materials, and fuels—or about 36,000 pounds for every man, woman and child in the country. With less than 10 per cent of the free world population, and only 8 per cent of its area, the United States consumed more than half of 1950's supply of such fundamental materials as petroleum, rubber, iron ore, manganese and zinc.

War would alter the patterns of materials demand and supply in swift and drastic ways; yet if permanent peace should prevail, and *all the nations of the world should acquire the same standard of living as our own, the resulting world need for materials would be six times present consumption.* In considering materials at long range, therefore, we have roughly the same problems to face and actions to pursue, war or no war.

For the last hundred years, the United States' total output of all goods and services (the Gross National Product, or GNP) has increased at the average rate of 3 per cent a year, compounded. Such a rate means an approximate doubling every twenty-five years (which would mean a nineteen-fold increase in a full century). As of 1950, the GNP was approximately $283 billion. In considering the next quarter century the Commission has made no assumption more radical than that the GNP will continue to increase at the same 3 per cent rate compounded every year, which is the average of the last century, all booms and depressions included. This would mean a GNP in the middle of the 1970's of about $566 billion, measured in dollars of 1950 purchasing power. The Commission has also assumed, after consultation with the Bureau of the Census, that population will increase to 193 million by 1975, and the working force to 82 million, compared to the 1950 figures of 151 million and 62 million. It has also assumed a shortening work week, but that man-hour productivity will continue to rise somewhat more than in the recent past. But even these conservative assumptions bring the United States up against some very hard problems of maintaining materials supply, for natural resources, whatever else they may be doing, are not expanding at compound rates.

Absolute shortages are not the threat in the materials problem. We need not expect we will some day wake up to discover we have run out of materials and that economic activity has come to an end. *The threat of the materials problem lies in insidiously rising costs* which can undermine our rising standard of living, impair the dynamic quality of American capitalism, and weaken the economic foundations of national security. These costs are not just dollar costs, but what economists refer to as *real costs*—meaning the hours of human work and the amounts of capital required to bring a pound of industrial material or a unit of energy into useful form. Over most of the 20th century these real costs of materials have been declining, and this decline has helped our living standards to rise. But there is now reason to suspect that this decline has been slowed, that in some cases it has been stopped, and in others reversed. The central challenge of the materials problem is therefore to meet our expanding demands with expanding supplies while averting a rise in real costs per unit.

In materials, there is always a tendency for real costs to rise because invariably people use their richest resources first and turn to the leaner supplies only when they have to. What is of concern today is that the combination of soaring demand and shrinking resources creates a set of upward cost pressures much more difficult to overcome than any in the past. In the United States there are no longer large mineral deposits in the West waiting to be stumbled upon and scooped up with picks and shovels; nor are there any longer vast forest tracts to be discovered. We can always scratch harder and harder for materials, but declining or even lagging productivity in the raw materials industries will rob economic gains made elsewhere. The ailment of rising real costs is all the more serious because it does not give dramatic warning of its onset; it creeps upon its victim so slowly that it is hard to tell when the attack began.

In recent years, the general inflation has struck with special force at many materials, causing their prices to rise more than the price structure as a whole. Some materials prices are high today because demand has temporarily outrun supply; here we can expect the situation to adjust itself. But in other cases the problem is more enduring than this, and reflects a basic change of supply conditions and costs. It would be wishful, for example, to expect lumber prices to settle back to their pre-1940 price relationships. We are running up against a physical limitation in the supply of timber, set by the size and growth rates of our forests, and cost relief through easy expansion is not to be expected. For such metals as copper, lead, and zinc, United States discovery is falling in relation to demand, and prices reflect the increasing pressure against limited resources.

Although the GNP can be expected to double between now and 1975, the total materials input necessary for this will *not* double, but perhaps rise only 50 to 60 per cent. Demand for materials will rise most unevenly, sometimes increasing one-quarter or less, sometimes rising fourfold or more. Among the major classifications, something like this might be expected in the United States (1975 compared to 1950):

Demand for minerals as a whole, including metals, fuels and non-metallics, will rise *most*—about 90 per cent, or almost double.

Demand for all agricultural products will rise about 40 per cent.

Demand for industrial water will increase roughly 170 per cent.

Taking these classifications one by one shows wide ranges and various problems within each. There can be plenty of room for argument as to how high demand for this or that will really rise, but the central fact is: *demand for everything can be expected to rise substantially.* These projections, which look high today, may look low tomorrow.

The above figures apply to the United States alone. For the rest of the free world the projections made by the commission are necessarily much rougher, but they suggest that demand in other free nations, building as it will on a smaller base, will be even larger in its percentage increase than United States demand, and that the United States, although its total of materials consumption will increase greatly, will probably consume a somewhat smaller share of the free world's total supply.

Demand for iron, copper, lead and zinc might rise only 40 to 50 per cent over the next quarter century, but other increases might be: fluorspar, threefold; bauxite for aluminum, fourfold; magnesium, eighteen to twenty fold (the largest projected increase for any material).

Industrial water, which used to be had for the taking in most of the country except the arid parts of the West, now shows a growing shortage problem, because modern industry uses it in such vast quantities. About 18 barrels of water are needed in refining a barrel of oil, and more than 250 tons of water must go to make a ton of steel or a ton of sulfate wood pulp. During World War II plans for at least 300 industrial or military establishments had to be abandoned or modified because of inadequate water supplies, and an already serious problem may be much sharper by 1975.

All of the above facts are symptoms of the same condition: the United States is outgrowing its present usable domestic resource base. This condition has been a long time in the making, but it was not until the 1940's that we completed the change from being a raw materials *surplus* nation to being a raw materials *deficit* nation. Whereas at the start of the century we produced some 15 per cent more raw materials than we consumed (excluding food), by mid-century we were consuming 10 per cent more materials than we produced. This is a peacetime situation, and the trend seems firmly established.

With the nation facing such situations the Commission draws a sharp distinction between being alarmist, which it is not, and seriously concerned, which it is. The nation cannot assume that "everything will be all right if we just leave things alone"; the forces causing the materials problem will increase, not diminish. We must become conscious of the existence of the materials problem and guide ourselves by its seriousness in every way possible [1955, chap. iii, pp. 2–6].

THEORY OF THE LIMIT OF GROWTH

It is our opinion that the President's Materials Policy Commission, while concerned, is not sufficiently concerned by the implications of its findings. It is obvious that we shall not come to the end of any of our raw materials suddenly and without warning, but it is submitted that continuing consumption each year of more raw materials essential to industrial expansion than the earth and man together re-create will bring us some day to a limit of growth. We have been living, and we are still living, on resource capital as well as income to make possible continuing industrial expansion and higher levels of living for ever more people.

This part of the thesis has been developed by the author of this paper in the following terms:

None of us can doubt that population densities have sharply increased in many parts of the world, that many people are undernourished and that there are today growing shortages of strategic and necessary materials in some places much of the time. None of us can doubt that technology has found new sources of raw material and new products to substitute for old, to our great betterment as well as to our woe. No one seems to have examined carefully enough the causes responsible for our current fantastic consumption of raw materials—causes which are more significant than population growth or preparation for war. No one has assumed to analyze the basic philosophy, indeed religion, of modern man, that makes us what we are: a race working, struggling, inventing, fighting, living *to create an ever higher level of living for all mankind*. That is our great inspiration, our almost universal goal, and it may turn out to be our great illusion.

This aspiration for an ever higher level of living has become the obsession of mankind. It is an expression of the democratic aim toward greater equality; it is the dictator's justification for a five-year plan; it is a tangible fulfillment of the spiritual aim of the church to better the poor as well as the rich; it becomes the internationalist's formula for relieving the pressures which "have not" people exert on wealthier nations, and a major means of preventing war. If we keep on raising the standard of living, want will be satisfied. To most of us today an ever higher level of living is the very meaning of human progress.

To laymen, human progress must have tangible expression. It means more and better food, clothing, and housing, better health and longer life, greater leisure (often confused with the idea of freedom) and more security, accompanied, of course, by less physical effort.

In the United States we have steadily moved to attain these things. Despite occasional setbacks and depressions, production has increased miraculously in all areas almost year by year; wages have risen, working hours decreased, investment income and corporate profits have mounted. Industry has been able to plow back millions and millions of dollars into new plants and new equipment. This is expansion, economic growth, the realization of a dream.

Economists substantiate these obvious evidences of economic growth. Industrialists boast of industrial expansion. Despite Malthus and the fact of population growth, our aim, our goal, our aspiration, our way of life is being fulfilled. We are achieving an ever higher level of living.

For this end, and this ideology, Americans have worked harder than they have worked for any other article of faith. Our modern religion is growth. But at what cost, material and spiritual, to the nation?

The President's Materials Policy Commission affirms, as right, our American faith in the principle of growth, because "it seems preferable to any opposite, which to us implies stagnation and decay" [Ordway, 1953, pp. 5–8].

An ever higher level of living for an ever expanding population has been brought about primarily by increased industrial and agricultural production. Expanding industry has converted raw materials into more useful products. It has produced in the last thirty years the most remarkable tools that man has ever known—tools which help find and extract more raw materials and refine them more economically into time and labor-saving devices. Industry also produces machines and tools and fertilizers which help increase the growth of living things. This enables us now to feed and clothe more people at lower cost. Our laboratories, directly and indirectly supported by industry, have found substitutes for scarce materials, and new chemicals and drugs that cure ills heretofore incurable, and save and prolong life. Industry thus increases wealth, health, and leisure.

At the same time the growth of industrial production has increased consumption of raw materials out of all proportion to our increase in population—although it is population growth which continues to arouse concern in neo-Malthusians. The population of the United States has exactly doubled in the last fifty years and neo-Malthusians still insist that mankind will eat itself out of house and home within foreseeable time, particularly if the birth rates not only here but in underdeveloped countries in the rest of the world follow their current upward patterns and death rates, due to improved medical care and longer life, continue to decline. William Vogt [1948] says: "It is obvious that fifty years hence the world cannot support three billion people at any but coolie standards—for most of them. One third of an acre cannot decently feed a man, let alone clothe him and make possible control of the hydrologic cycle." It is this threat which the cornucopian scientists believe new discovery and new technology can offset; but what has not been discussed at length in the literature, or adequately analyzed in conservation forums,

is the fact that continuing and increasing consumption of raw materials due to economic expansion is proportionally far greater than the population rise.

While the number of persons in the United States doubled in fifty years, the production of all minerals increased 8 times; the consumption of power increased 11 times; the consumption of paper and paperboard increased 14 times over the same period. The use of some raw materials more and more exceeds domestic production with the result that we are increasingly dependent upon foreign imports to supply our higher level of living.

At the same time, despite technological advances in farming, our gross farm product is not increasing currently as fast as our population. This is a rich land. Nevertheless, since 1945 our food production has increased 50 per cent less than our population. And manufacture each year is using more and more organic products from the land.

While food in the United States is not scarce, many of our inorganic resources are scarce. Thirty-three separate minerals are presently on the critical list. Millions of dollars a year are being spent to speed the search for new deposits and to find substitutes (other raw materials) for them. No one doubts that there is a limit to the supply of these raw materials we are consuming so fast in the earth, sea, and air. There is doubt as to the extent of undiscovered supplies . . . there is doubt as to the extent of discoverable substitutes . . . and there is doubt about the time in which we shall reduce the supply to a point where rising costs will curtail use. Yet, to the satisfaction of all who have faith in an ever higher level of living, increasing use of our natural resources goes steadily on. Both industry and population continue to grow. The resource base grows less.

Much of the wealth produced by industry today is reinvested in expansion—to the extent of more than twenty billion dollars per year! One company alone last year paid out in dividends 34 million dollars, but withheld 623 millions of its earnings for new equipment and expansion. Few of us appreciate the extent to which continuing expansion makes further inroads, quantitatively and qualitatively, on the productivity of the earth [*ibid.*, pp. 10–15].

Increasing pressure on renewable resources also affects adversely productivity of the land itself, unless extraordinary and expensive techniques are used to restore and increase its productivity—techniques which are often not known by, and frequently beyond the means of, smaller owners who eke their living from the earth. One *Yearbook of Agriculture* [1938] stated: "Fifty million acres of farm land have already been abandoned by farmers because they are no longer productive, and 30,000,000 acres more are in process of abandonment." Year by year, productive acreage per person is declining.

There is little unexploited land left in the United States. As lands are exhausted and abandoned (further increasing the new acreage needed) more and more farmers enter industry. Urban and industrial pressures continue to grow.

Not alone in terms of food, but also in terms of industrial production, shortage of agricultural land is a limiting factor. Approximately one half of the raw material used by business and industry is organic in origin. Automobiles are made of animal and vegetable, as well as of mineral, products.

Reports of technicians to the Materials Policy Commission emphasize the growing industrial drain on agricultural products and the fact that the problem is worldwide. They predict a 17 per cent increase in *industrial* consumption of cotton and wool by 1975. They also anticipate a 34 per cent increase in *industrial* requirements for wood, which exceeds the output considered probable at that time by 39 per cent. The shortage of wood predicted for the United States will not be prevented, the report states, by imports from other parts of the world. Even with free trade, and full Soviet participation in meeting estimated 1979 import needs of the present free world, the gap in 1979 between such requirements and available supply would still remain far from closed [*ibid.*, pp. 21–23].

The theory of the limit of growth is based on two premises:

Levels of human living are constantly rising with mounting use of natural resources.

Despite technological progress we are spending each year more resource capital than is created.

The theory follows:

If this cycle continues long enough, basic resources will come into such short supply that rising costs will make their use in additional production unprofitable, industrial expansion will cease, and we shall have reached the limit of growth.

Despite reductions in prices of many finished products caused by increased production, raw materials—food, wood, water, and minerals—are becoming dearer. The limit of expansion will not be reached until raw materials have become so scarce that the industrial product can no longer be sold at a profit.

This is not a matter of temporary boom and depression, or artificially stimulated high or low prices, or overstocking which commonly causes ups and downs in industrial production—sometimes with drastic temporary effect on the economy. This is a matter of expanding industry, approaching maximum profitable use of its resource base, and finally overreaching that maximum at a time when (unless we are prepared) it is too late to alter values voluntarily, willingly abandon the dream of higher levels of living, and peacefully adapt our thinking and our ideals to another very different way of life. This kind of enforced, unexpected reversal of a faith, this end of an expanding industrial civilization, could be the end of the culture we know.

That kind of end may well overtake us, despite all our apparent wealth, unless a new philosophy of conservation, by which we reorient our views of the Good Life and many of our values, becomes generally accepted within a reasonable time [*ibid.*, pp. 31–35].

LIMITATIONS ON IMPORTS

Some people believe that, as shortages of raw materials develop in the United States, we will be able to supply our needs from the rest of the world. British Political and Economic Planning (PEP) comments on this as follows:

One of the encouraging developments of recent years has been the growth of a world conscience demanding a steady approach to equality of economic opportunity for all countries. Increasing technical assistance and grants are being given for this purpose.

It is argued that the purchase of minerals from underdeveloped countries is one of the best ways of enabling those countries to import the machinery and other equipment they need for development, and that therefore the heavy purchases of minerals by the developed countries are a major advantage to the underdeveloped countries. This is true in the short run; the exchange of minerals for machinery and plant must be generally a pure gain to the underdeveloped countries who almost universally welcome such trade.

But if we look ahead for two generations the position is a very different one. There is plenty of iron looking a very long way ahead. On the other hand, copper will be exhausted in about 50 years; lead, zinc and tin before 1980. And the supply of other important minerals is likely to be exhausted before the year 2000.

The Paley report does not consider the effect of the demand by the U.S.A. and the other highly-developed countries of the world on the underdeveloped countries. The developed countries, including a quarter of the population of the world, consumed in 1950 about 95 per cent of the minerals, whereas the underdeveloped countries, including three-quarters of the population of the world, consumed about 5 per cent. In total, the developed countries consumed nearly twenty times as much as the underdeveloped countries. Per caput they consumed nearly a hundred times as much.

In 1954 the population of the United States increased by three million; that of India increased by five million. The consumption of iron by the three million Americans would be at 1950 rates 100 times as much as that of the five million

Indians and about 40 per cent more than the consumption of the total population of India, which is 350 millions.

The industrial revolution began in Europe about 200 years ago and has been carried on at an accelerating pace in the New World. Japan joined in vigorously towards the end of last century, and the U.S.S.R. after the Revolution. They had the advantage of a highly-developed technology and no shortage of materials, with the result that they developed their industry as fast or faster than the Western world. Some of the South American countries have already made considerable progress.

The underdeveloped countries are hoping to begin their development shortly; India is perhaps the only one that has made a substantial beginning. Most of them are not likely to get far in the next generation or even two generations; by that time very serious difficulties as regards metals and other materials may well have arisen. The difficulties in their way will undoubtedly be very much greater than those hitherto experienced.

The Paley report estimates that if the rest of the non-communist world achieved the present American materials standard, the world consumption of minerals would be multiplied by six. It is quite obvious that to supply such standards would mean an impossible demand on the world's mineral resources.

The scientific optimists argue, firstly, that reserves may be much greater than is now realised; and secondly, that technology has performed such wonders that there are no limits to what it may achieve. In fact, this easy optimism is dangerous nonsense. The essentials of the position are a balance of rates: the rate of production of alternatives or substitutes for each mineral must equal or exceed the rate of consumption of available reserves. Technology has achieved great triumphs and will, if all goes well, certainly achieve greater triumphs, but it would be irresponsible folly to count, for instance, on technology producing adequate alternatives for lead, zinc and tin before the existing supplies are exhausted or become excessively expensive, which must occur at some date; it may be about 1980 [1955, chap. iii, pp. 7–8].

It does not seem likely that imports or "technology" will be the means of keeping us from ultimately reaching the limit of growth.

CAN PROSPERITY BE SUSTAINED?

Now what can be done in the next few decades (from three to seven) to prevent our economy from overreaching this possible limit of growth? However complex the physical, economic, and social factors involved, the answer to this question is stark as it is simple. The only way to avoid reaching that limit some day is eventually to cease to consume more resources each year than nature and man together create.

As our scientists and technicians, and those of us who lag in applying their discoveries, deliver on cornucopian promises to find substitutes and synthesize new raw materials from earth, sea, and air, there will be more annual increment available for annual use. So far, unfortunately, annual increase in consumption has continued to rise faster than any such increment, while the resource base continues to decline. To the extent that consumption continues to exceed creation in the decades ahead, the budget will continue to be unbalanced. If we are to eliminate annual deficits, we shall have to reduce annual consumption until annual consumption no longer exceeds annual creation.

This is obviously not a matter that can be exactly defined in terms of particular resource creation and expenditure. Had we been of a conserving mind a hundred years ago, we might have reduced the use of marble for building, because marble was running out. We now use building materials then unknown.

But the fact that we lack inventories, which would be partially meaningless if we had them, and the fact that the several resources we use and are using up may not be requisite to future progress in various fields of our endeavor does not mean that we have a never ending storehouse of materials of plenty. The fact that we have many funds to draw on and that we constantly shift, to support our prosperity, from one fund to another does not mean that we can keep on forever drawing over-all more than is replaced. It is not only the part of prudence to reduce consumption of raw materials which are becoming scarce; it is a law of life itself. If we do not do so voluntarily and gradually, we shall be forced to do so ultimately against our wills, and with a very upsetting loss of the freedom of initiative— with involuntary reversal of our "American Dream" of prosperity for all.

This solution—voluntary reduction of consumption either general or selective —is simple enough to state. It may even be that America would prosper more if it succeeded in disciplining itself to get along with less. But the idea is so foreign to our society, to our industrial planners and managers and their stockholders—including both labor and consumer as well as tycoon—that voluntary reduction is not likely to be realized in an era of prosperity unless something quite revolutionary happens to our philosophy, our conscience, and our current faith.

It is the purpose of the remainder of this paper to consider various factors which in the next few decades might substantially change the thinking and the faith of our people and make possible sustained prosperity on what Stanley Cain, in a speech in 1954, called a "dynamic equilibrium."

We Are Entering an Era of Abundant Prosperity

The next few decades, at least in the United States, is likely to be a period of unprecedented marshaling and utilization of our remaining resource capital. Regardless of what may seem to some of us to be prudent and wise in the way of reducing consumption, the present temper of our spirit and our faith is such that we shall continue to expand, to produce, and to prosper. Even without restraint, our essential resources will not be exhausted during the lives of most of us living today.

Let us start with an appraisal of our soil situation. How serious is the loss of these thousands of tons of topsoil by erosion each year? How serious is the depletion of soil nutrients and continuing damage to the structure of the soil itself? How long can this continue before we shall find ourselves unable to produce the foodstuffs and the fibers we shall need to keep on raising the level of living of our people, whose numbers are increasing by nearly three million additional souls each year?

The United States Soil Conservation Service reports that each year we are losing by water and wind erosion three billion tons of "solid material" from the land surface of the United States. It adds that no less than two hundred million acres of cropland have already lost approximately half of their topsoil. More worn-out farmlands are being abandoned to the states. Over five million acres of such farmland have already been abandoned in New York alone. In the United States there are approximately eighty million acres of land—still being farmed by a half-million operators—said to be so meager that it would pay the states to help these operators transfer to some better occupations and to reforest the old farms. Each year new roads, airports, factories, and factory communities are taking over about two million additional acres of potentially productive land. In addition, the present rate of population increase will require, to maintain present dietary levels, the full product of an additional seven and one-half million acres of cropland each year.

This continuing trend is certainly serious in its long-term implications, for there is comparatively little additional land to be reclaimed. Even the most optimistic plans of the Bureau of Reclamation contemplate the reclamation of only six million acres of new irrigated cropland by 1975. If reclaimed today, this would supply enough food for new mouths alone for only three years. It seems probable that unless some miracle occurs far more wonderful than the increase in production per acre over the last fifty years, or unless we derive new food supplies from the air or sea, we are going to be bankrupt in our food account in another hundred years.

However, we have surpluses now, and for the next three to seven decades we should still have enough to keep us well fed. Productivity per acre on our good land will continue to increase, for our farmers have only begun to apply the knowledge that exists. And today a full 90 per cent of our food comes from the best 50 per cent of our farmland. The poorer 50 per cent, which will probably have to be retired soon, provides a very small part of our total supply today. Carskadon and Modley state (1949, p. 94) that, if under pressure we really want to extend ourselves, we can crop more than an additional one hundred million acres—one-third more than now—by plowing our pastures, by clearing unproductive woodlands, and by draining and irrigating. In short, we can still put more pressure on our land. "We could then boost our food production totals half as much again. This gives us some idea of the power of America to bring forth food from our soil." To be sure, to do this could finally mine the land of its productive power. But, unless we attempt to feed the rest of the world, it does give us assurance that we *can* produce plenty of food in the coming decades—a time in which we shall be facing, and, we hope, solving, the problem of our long-term future.

So much for soil for the short run. Turning to forests, we see a slightly less pleasant picture. We will certainly be short of saw timber in the next seventy years, even if every last tall tree on accessible land is cut. It will be after that time that our current replanting programs, commenced in the name of conservation, will begin to produce fully mature saw timber—and then only if we are willing and can afford to let it grow to maturity. Even so, the situation is not desperate. We are using less wood for construction purposes all the time—more plastic, glass, aluminum, concrete, and brick. We are more and more using small trees, quickly replaced, in the form of plywood and veneer, and we are beginning to use hardwood in place of soft. Pulp for paper and plastic is already being produced commercially from hardwood.

A substantial part of our presently existing forest resource is in farm wood lots, and these we, as a nation, have only begun to nurture and use commercially. Good management of small forest holdings is difficult to achieve, because most of them are an integral part of lands used primarily for farm and grazing purposes. The truck farmer, or even the wheat farmer, is concerned with annual plowing, planting, and harvesting of crops and with marketing; he may use his wood for fenceposts or firewood, but he also lets his cattle graze over young forest growth; and he is frequently persuaded by an itinerant sawmill operator to sell all his trees at one fell swoop for ready cash at a tenth of their true worth. Substantial wood lots are often clean-cut and not replanted. As of 1954 our farm wood lots, tremendously important in the aggregate, made up 57 per cent of all our remaining timber, yet they are the least well managed of all woodland

holdings. They are thought of as minor appendages by farmowners and are treated as such. A proper expenditure in training for conservation management of farm wood lots can do much to help us through the lean period.

Granted a modicum of thrift, salvage of current waste, extension of fire protection and pest control, and full utilization of known substitutes, we should have enough wood to last through the year 2000. We shall not be like those of our contemporaries in India, who have now to burn dung for cooking and for warmth instead of using it to restore the fertility of the earth.

Water is another matter. Water is the one essential resource without which we should have no production from our soil, no forests, no industry, no animals, no beauty—no life at all on earth. Most of the time, in one place or another, man is either suffering from floods, exerting all his effort to get rid of excess water to avoid disaster, or suffering from drought, exerting his skill and knowledge to tap new sources, bring water from far away, make rain, or somehow tide over his thirsty crops and his thirsty industrial processes until more rains come. Only three-tenths of 1 per cent of all the rain that falls on earth is available when and where needed for man's use. Total runoff is twenty-six hundred times the total withdrawal for use.

Man's demand for and consumption of water is increasing each year out of all proportion to population growth. Not only do we use more water all the time for agricultural and domestic purposes but industrial demands are ever more exorbitant. Much water used in industry can be re-used after purification, recooling, or other processing at large expense, but the greater part of it cannot be economically used again. And industry is constantly expanding. It appears now that in many places we may be shorter of available water than of any other essential resource to enable us to continue our economic expansion in the decades just ahead.

Nevertheless, these increasing shortages of water will not stop prosperity in the next sixty years. There are ways of storing underground, as well as on the surface, more of the water that now runs off, and ways of reducing waste. Industry and federal and state governments are gradually becoming aware of this threat to progress, and their geologists, engineers, agronomists, and hydrologists are combining to make more fresh water available in quantity in many places to meet the imperative needs of agriculture and industry. This is costly in the beginning, but it will be done.

The problem of storing vast quantities of flood waters which now course wasted and threatening down our inland rivers from the melting snows and rains of spring cannot be solved by expensive engineering alone. Millions of dollars are already programed for upstream development as well as for construction of multiple-purpose mainstem dams.

The United States government has recently appropriated two million dollars for research on methods of converting salt and brackish waters to usable freshness. Five or six different processes for doing this have been developed; all require some form of heat and power, and the cost of the delivered product today exceeds economic feasibility. But costs of conversion are coming down, and the value of available fresh water is going up. Conversion processes at a price, if necessary, will help take care of expansion in the decades ahead.

Rain-making, by artificially seeding clouds under suitable meteorological conditions, is still a controversial subject. There is a lack of adequate climatological, meteorological, and other data needed to ascertain whether, where, and how storms can be controlled to produce more or less precipitation in any one place, particularly without causing unnatural flood or drought somewhere else. If enough data can be collected and the problem of meteorological controls solved, we may in the coming decades see the end of water shortages.

While sufficient fresh water to assure prosperity ahead is not everywhere available today, we know that more than enough water falls on the United States each year to meet our every need and can be made available at a price, just as sweet water can be converted from the ocean at a price if necessary. The evidence is that adequate fresh water will be available to us in the next sixty years as we curtail waste and pollution and develop new programs of conversion, storage, and delivery. This does not mean that in the distant future we may not go the way of previous civilizations—of Babylon and Tyre and Sidon—which denuded their lands, neglected their water sources, and became arid deserts. It means that we shall have time yet, in the age ahead, to avert such catastrophe—if we will.

Power we shall have in plenty. There are still huge untapped sources of hydroelectric power in the upper reaches of the Missouri, Columbia, and Colorado rivers, if we should be foolish enough to insist on tapping them at the expense of other greater values, including wilderness and recreation. Several variant sources of power known today may turn out to be less costly than the more remote hydroelectric storage projects we now have planned. For we have found of late that the cost of big dams is greater than we knew, because we failed to include as part of the cost public losses from the inundation of productive valleys, evaporation, siltation, and loss of million-dollar fisheries.

Power from lignite, which is available in some areas in large quantities, has already been produced at a cost per kilowatt hour, after sale of by-products, considerably less than that of more remote hydroelectric power. Progress in the development of power from atomic fission for peacetime uses has been remarkable. While comparable prices are not yet available, we know we can have atomic-powered machines and plants of many kinds and that we may thus be spared additional hydroelectric dams on our great rivers. Progress has also been made in harnessing solar energy, though not yet at competitive cost, and the experiment of harnessing the Quoddy tides has been revived. At any rate, whatever the cheapest source, there will be ample power for this golden-age-to-be.

The condition of our metal supplies for the near future is also related to cost—in this case cost of extraction and refinement. We shall run out of high-grade ores, particularly iron, lead, and zinc, in the years immediately ahead. But we can turn to lower-grade ores to meet industrial needs, particularly as methods of extraction and use become more economical and as the salvage of used metals is stepped up. Our copper should last another forty years, and it is probable that we shall stockpile a large part of our production of this and of other scarce metals as we increase and seek to maintain, as long as possible, imports from abroad.

It does produce an uneasy feeling to contemplate the rapid rate of exhaustion of some of the world's important mineral supplies. There will be gradual curtailment of the use of many presently essential minerals. Ultimately, unless adequate substitutes are found, we shall have no more to use. It is difficult to predict exactly when the pinch will really come or when the rate of our industrial expansion will be forced to slow down because of short-ages of raw materials. But it will not be tomorrow.

In summary, it does seem certain that for the next sixty years, no matter how profligate we continue to be, we shall have enough natural wealth at our disposal in one form or another to feed ourselves and most of the man-made machines and laboratory processes upon which present prosperity depends. We shall have time and wealth to face up to the problem of how to save prosperity.

We Are Entering a Period of Abundant Leisure

Until very recent times man applied his own efforts, aided only by other animals, fire, flowing water, and his handmade tools, to produce a livelihood from the earth. Today manpower is less and less needed to deliver the wonders derived from the earth's wealth to man's use. For almost a half-century great mechanical excavators, harvesters, and machine tools have been helping to ease the work of man. Today giant computers and almost automatic factories are beginning literally to perform man's work for him. Powered by ample, low-cost electricity, mineral fuels, and even atomic and solar energy, these will produce far greater wealth in far less time than ever could be done before.

In this mechanistic century, even before the creation of man's incredible new automatic tools of production and the development and use of feedback circuits, man-hours of labor were declining while output of wealth per man-hour and take-home pay increased. There are many variables in computing man-hours and output. Economists and statisticians differ in detail on the record, but all agree on the actuality of the trend. Let us examine the trend before the rise of automation.

One important study of America's resources, made in 1947 by the Twentieth Century Fund, reports (p. 695) that in 1850 the average human work-week in industry was 68.0 hours; in 1890 it was 58.0; in 1910 it was 53.0; in 1920 it was 48.0; in 1940 it was 41.7; and, by current report, in 1950 it was 39.0.

A 1953 study by W. and S. Woytinsky on world population and production reports that the average work-week in the United States declined from seventy-two hours in 1850 to forty hours in 1950. Over the last century, they tell us, average hours per week worked in the United States declined nearly 50 per cent; for the world as a whole they declined slightly more than 30 per cent. The average decline per decade from 1850 to 1940 was three hours, but from 1910 to 1950 the decline was four hours per decade. If we project this rate of decline forward five more decades, we would have the twenty-hour week. This trend has occurred without benefit of automation, which has enjoyed limited industrial application only in the last five years.

This reduction in the average number of hours per week worked in industry has been accompanied by continuously increased productivity. In the last fifteen years, since 1939, output per factory in the United States has increased 37 per cent. Average hourly pay per week has increased 170 per cent. In 1940, before the war, the value of our factory output averaged 74 cents per man-hour. Despite and because of retooling and postwar readjustments, the factory output in 1950 averaged 87.5 cents in 1940 prices. Our yearly consumer income *per capita* in 1932 was $610. In 1950 it was $1,140. This includes every man, woman, and child. Income per *family unit*, which was $2,050 in 1932, had increased in constant dollars to $3,420 in 1950. This includes farm families as well as the families of industrial workers. It measures

increased national prosperity despite the decline in hours worked.

Have man-hours decreased on farms as well as in factories? There are still no regular or fixed hours of work for the man who cultivates the land or husbands domesticated animals. But the trend in total number of man-hours worked per unit of production is down even more than in industry. In 1870, 53 per cent of the total United States labor force worked in agriculture. In 1952 only 10 per cent worked in agriculture. Between 1900 and 1950 agricultural production increased 80 per cent. Mechanization, plus better farming practices on more acres, development and use of better seed and fertilizer, and improved animal and plant genetics are causes. As recently as 1920 there were 11.5 million gainful workers in agriculture, 25 million horses, and 200,000 tractors. In 1940 there were about 9 million gainful workers, 14 million horses, and 1.5 million tractors. By 1950 there were less than 7 million workers, 7.5 million horses, and 3.5 million tractors. The important point is that, with constantly decreasing man-hours and horse-hours worked on our farms, the farm product and the farmers' income have increased along with the product and income of industrial workers.

On the basis of increasing use on the farm and in industry of modern machines and tools with which most of us are now familiar, at least by photograph and description, it is evident that the trend in hours per week worked, as production increases in the decades ahead, should continue downward. The individual worker will have more and more free time to suffer or to enjoy as his earnings continue to grow.

Now let us look at the miraculous new labor-saving devices just coming into use and try to understand how they work—what there is incorporated in them that is so radically different from and more effective than anything we have had before. Perhaps the simplest and clearest assembly of "non-technical" descriptions of these new wonders is contained in a special issue of *Scientific American* devoted exclusively to this subject in September, 1952. This was followed by innumerable scientific and technical treatises in engineering and electronics publications.

"*Automation*" is the word used to describe the employment of automatic machines in industrial production—machines operated by machinery instead of men—to perform one function or a great number of complex functions faster and more accurately than human beings, regardless of numbers, have ever been able to perform them. An increasing number of automatic machines utilize feedback circuits, electrical or mechanical, to achieve and control high production speeds.

Feedback uses the *output* of a machine to control the *intake* and, therefore, the speed and functioning of the machine itself or any number of its parts. James Watt is credited with designing for his steam engine a novel device, the first mechanical "*governor*," to maintain a relatively constant speed for that engine regardless of its work-load without manually advancing or retarding the throttle; as the revolutions slowed down, the throttle automatically advanced, and, as the revolutions speeded up, the throttle automatically retarded. This is a simple and probably the first example of mechanical use of the feedback principle. Today the principle is applied electrically by coupling a generator to the drive motor and to a magnetic brake. As the motor speeds up, the voltage from the generator increases, the brake tightens, and the motor slows down—and vice versa. A point of equilibrium can thus

be automatically reached and maintained regardless of load variations.

What has been needed to make various manufacturing processes, operating instruments, and complex computing machinery automatic is some way to compensate for variables—for internal and external environmental changes. Such internal automatic control is now possible.

There are still limitations to the industrialists' dream of a completely automatic factory manned only by button-pushers and a few trouble-shooter repairmen. But, as more and more of the processes of production become automatic, the dream comes closer and closer to attainment. The limitations are less in perfection of the machines than in the human "programing" which must be perfected before the machines can be set to turn out their product.

What is the meaning of this in terms of time and leisure for Americans in the next few decades? First of all, it is clear that industry is going to proceed with automation just about as fast as it can prepare to use it—that is, master the programing aspects of its use. Already the proportion of annual investment in new equipment which is going to automatic controls has begun to sky-rocket. From 1948 to 1954 total expenditures for plant and equipment increased about 12 per cent. During the same time expenditures for automatic control devices increased 100 per cent. That this is profitable investment is shown by the fact that there is in industry today a steadily decreasing ratio of fixed investment per unit of output and an accelerating decrease in man-hours per unit of output.

This does not mean that there will be mass unemployment. There will be as many or more jobs as there are today, but they will require fewer hours of work from each worker each week. The drudgery-type jobs will gradually diminish. Leontief says (1952) that man has already "all but ceased to be a lifter and mover and [has] become primarily a starter and stopper, a setter and assembler and repairer. With the introduction of self-controlled machinery, his direct participation in the process of production will be narrowed even further." This will mean retraining and upgrading of the labor force, a task which we found not overly difficult during the shortage of skilled tradesmen in World War II. The task is eased by the increasing emphasis, whether good or bad, on vocational training in our high schools and the ever increasing attendance at our technical colleges and graduate schools. Skilled workers, clerks, and professional personnel already make up 42 per cent of our working population. Since product is increasing out of proportion to capital outlay, the business community would be foolish indeed to reduce take-home pay of so large a part of its consuming market while its profits are mounting, even though this may mean a drastic increase in hourly wages.

Indeed, Stuart Chase points out (1954, p. 10) the advantage to industry in providing more leisure time without decreased earnings. "The industrial worker," he says, "must have time to practice the arts of consumption if inventories are to be cleared. Abundant leisure will provide added employment in the trades which supply the means and materials of recreation."

If wages stay up and profits remain high, as they can well do so long as raw materials are available at reasonable prices, it is not likely that there will be produced more than our mounting population will consume. Sumner Slichter, the Harvard economist, bears this out when he says (1954): "Fears that demand cannot be expected to rise rapidly enough to provide sufficient jobs are

out of date," and he adds that through industrial research for promotion "the demand for goods can be made to grow as rapidly as our capacity to produce goods."

The point of all this is not that everyone of us will have less paid work to do in the years ahead. The evidence is that there will be more jobs, as production rises, requiring less time and less effort of each worker per unit of production. But, regardless of whether additional jobs do keep pace with reduced labor requirements, individuals will work shorter and shorter periods of time each week. Some may be engaged for only four hours a day in a five-day week. Others may work eight hours a day for only two and a half days a week. But very many will have one hundred and thirty to one hundred and fifty free hours a week to concern themselves, if they will, with the problem of assuring that the leisure, pleasure, and plenty which they enjoy can continue to exist in times beyond their own.

Leisure and Plenty Can Change Our Faith and Dream

Leisure and plenty in the next decades will expose the people of America, as never before in this industrial age, to variant ways of life. People will be engaging in individual activities of many sorts for which there was not enough time before. They may well begin with simple new hobbies, home crafts and arts, and lead into extended work for improvement of the home environment and, later, the community environment. There will be time for new forms of recreation, much of it outdoors, introducing many urban dwellers for the first time to the land, the mountains, and the sea. This will bring them into closer contact with nature and natural resources and will help to develop growing awareness of resource depletion. The problem will be to channel the opportunity for awareness to the grand account of ultimate survival.

In good times there is willing mass acceptance of things as they are. We shall have to help cultivate individual awareness of the eternal importance of man's relationship to the earth and its resources; we shall have to find leadership to induce action to hold the prosperity we have. The motive cannot be material alone. We must be concerned with the future of the spirit as well as with the future of the machine. It is not we but generations unborn who must concern us. What we shall need is cultivation of a new ethic in and for this age of leisure.

It should become more feasible to acquire such an ethic as we achieve the leisure that will give us time to recognize the need. With leisure, after the first burst of relaxation, will come contemplation born of a kind of restlessness, the will not to be idle, and with it a will to find meaning in life. This, in time, will produce the kind of attention to nature and natural things "in which man begins to see how worthy of veneration they really are."

Given all the leisure in the world, Americans would not long be inactive. As Stuart Chase says (1954, p. 10): "A man must have something to do, preferably something he can believe in, if he is to keep sane. His whole nervous system is geared to survival activity."

And Josef Pieper, one of the religious philosophers who has analyzed this problem, says also that opportunity for leisure is not enough to make leisure fruitful. He asserts (1952), after Plato, that leisure must become "a festive companionship with the Gods" and be, as Aquinas phrased it, "at once a sacrifice and a sacrament."

This is rather a heady way of putting it, but it is clear enough that man is going to need an ethic for his con-

science and his discipline in the wise pursuit of leisure. The trouble with the proposals of Plato and Aquinas today is that we Americans are likely to prefer "overtime work at overtime pay" on the dreariest belt line to constant celebration of a sacrament.

Obviously an ethic implies faith in something—"something a man can believe in"—something important enough to change his use of leisure from routine conformity and make of it a worthwhile and therefore satisfying—festive, if you will—contribution toward the realization of a purpose. This is what we greatly need. Stuart Chase gives us a clue to this modern faith when he refers to man's inherent need for "survival activity." In both the Greek and the Latin derivations of our word "leisure," *skole* and *schola,* the meaning is "work, discipline, activity." It is possible that *activity* for survival—of resources, of prosperity, of the race—can become the purpose of the age ahead. It is unthinkable that as a nation we should bask idly in our new luxury of machines and leisure or that we should "eat, drink, and be merry, for tomorrow we die," while we leave to succeeding generations of baskers the knowledge that men are coming closer all the time to the day when they will have consumed the earth's remaining resources, made barren the land, and ended survival opportunity forever.

An ethic for our new age of leisure, as we see it develop, can be based upon a clear-cut survival activity: effort to develop such an understanding of our relationship to the natural world and its resources that we find a way not only to enjoy plenty through leisure but help to create it; to create more than we consume so that we do not ultimately come, after a few more decades, to the end of prosperity.

Of course not everyone will have a hundred and thirty hours a week of leisure, but more and more of us are going to have more and more free time. We can waste it as a nation or we can use it to preserve our wealth and pleasure for succeeding generations. If we do not do the latter, the future looks dreary indeed. How can this diverse nation find its way to the fashion or the faith or the ethic which will save the world? It can do so only through individual and group activity in the impending golden age.

By what processes can we find, amid leisure, pleasure, and plenty, the *will* to devote supreme effort to the sustenance of natural resources? Walt Whitman wrote: "Perhaps, indeed, the efforts of the true poets, founders, religions, literatures of all ages, have been and ever will be essentially the same—to bring people back through their persistent strayings and sickly abstractions to the original concrete"—which he defines, in the words of Marcus Aurelius, as "a living and enthusiastic sympathy with nature."

Human experience has shown that man will always work and fight for the survival of his family, home, community, state, and even civilization whenever he is aware of grave danger and of the kind of effort required of him. If men recognize today the danger ahead from continuing overconsumption of resources and basic lack of human sympathy with nature, they will seek remedies. There is evidence already that they are beginning to comprehend. Leisure will advance that comprehension as more and more free time is devoted to the improvement of local environment, even without distant vision. Vision is expansive. As sympathy and comprehension grow locally, more and more men will begin to organize and work on the grand scale, using leisure "in sympathy with nature" to turn the tide of resource destruction.

This will not be any sentimental return to the nineteenth century's nostalgia for a "Blue Flower," or flight from reality to ivory towers of the Romantic Age. This will be a hardheaded, hardworking alliance of men with both nature and science to engineer a solution for survival. It will mean a new application of man's old will to serve himself and others too.

Whitman's concept of "sympathy with nature" sounds vague and philosophical, but it is basic and can be highly practical. Its importance is attested by ageless re-emphasis in the literature of history, religion, and art of all races as a main truth of existence. Yet the concept has never before been connected so directly with impending destruction of prosperity and life itself. A feeling for nature has always existed in man; his will to prosper as well as to survive has always existed—but the relation of that feeling and will to the increasing decline of world resources has not been significant in the past. It is evidently significant now.

But, even though men come to comprehend its significance, the concept will remain inchoate unless the resultant feeling for nature and our will to survive are translated into truly common motive, thought, and action. A turn of the tide will be attained only when those who are not poets, dreamers, mystics, or reformers choose to devote time and effort to this human service above all other.

Let us consider the kinds of human service from which we shall have to choose. For ages we have conceived that the most worthy human service for those with leisure is charity. Charity has assumed many forms. Today amateur "social service" is no longer sufficient. In addition to time, the tithe which men once were expected to give to help the poor is now exacted through taxation and goes to provide slum clearance, modern housing, health clinics, employment service, job insurance, old age benefits, playfields, beaches, and swimming pools. We the people have accepted the view that social service is a public responsibility to be administered by those professionally trained. Accordingly, leisure-time social service has turned more and more in the direction of study and participation in educational and civic enterprises. There is still time given to fund-raising for private charity and church, but personal participation in useful, unpaid activity is increasingly related to the development of group pressures to improve parent-school relationships, town and district planning, development of recreational facilities, and encouragement of better governmental practice in the handling of health, housing, delinquency, and community resources. In short, welfare endeavor is directed to environmental rather than individual relief. This is an encouraging trend.

At the same time there is excessive concern over personal security—job insurance, old age and disability pensions, and governmental protection in crowded communities which no longer expect the individual to protect himself. But it is becoming apparent that security is decreased rather than increased by dependence on machines. Judge Learned Hand has said that the new devices of science, industry, and government have their perils: "They lull men into the belief that because they are severally less subject to violence, they are more safe; because they are more steadily fed and clothed, they are more secure from want. . . . Our security has actually diminished as our demands have become more exacting. Our comforts we purchase at the cost of a softer fiber, a feebler will and an infantile suggestibility." A new respect for environment will make both government and machines seem less important.

The will to serve continues to exist and will grow, with added leisure, along new lines. This will to serve is the will to do. It is in our inheritance and has long been in our blood as a people to do what has to be done, and what we cannot do alone, through group effort. Barn-raising, the husking bee, the quilting party, building the frontier church, the western trek, the underground railroad—are all examples of realization of individual needs and aims through group action. As a people we will still do, in groups, what needs to be done when we recognize the need.

This will to group service is the greatest asset we shall have in the age of leisure. As we become increasingly aware of dwindling natural resources, we will join more and more in local and national efforts to balance the creation and consumption of raw materials. This will not be a sterile or lonely use of leisure, for it will bring us into contact with sentient citizens of all kinds —landowners, scientists, civic leaders, and technicians who know the land and the pressures on it and on our security—in what may be the greatest of all charities: the improvement of environment in relation to life for the present and future betterment of all living things.

There are many ways we may use our leisure through existing local and national groups, most of which are constantly seeking more working members and which are striving to help America meet the resource problem at home and throughout the world. There are associations made up of citizens interested in particular subject matter such as farming, forests, range management, sports fishing, or reclamation. There are watershed associations and soil-conservation districts, conservation workshops of all kinds for laymen and teachers, park associations, recreation associations, wildlife study clubs, and a host of local and federated women's organizations, garden clubs, and voters' leagues which have conservation committees to study, plan, and lead action programs.

The Mid-Century Conference on Resources for the Future (1954) emphasized "the paramount importance of people working together, as individuals and as groups, to formulate and attain objectives in the resource field. . . . The interplay of many interests and forces will determine how well the country's resources are used and how long some of them will last."

Resource study committees have been appointed by the United States Chamber of Commerce, the National Association of Manufacturers, the American Bankers Association, and the Congress of Industrial Organizations. Labor and industry both have a large stake in resources for the future. The storm warnings are out, and people with leisure as well as people with responsibility for industry and government are recognizing the need to devote more of their time and thought to resource problems.

There is opportunity for all and need for all who have leisure time to give and the will to serve the land they love as active members of hundreds of educational group endeavors. For this sort of creative and satisfying pursuit there will never be too much leisure.

Today a nation cannot win a military war simply by hiring professional soldiers and sending them to fight at the front. All the people have to pitch in together on land, on sea, and in the air—fighting, producing equipment and supplies, and sustaining the home economy through mass effort. So the large task of trying to balance resource supply and consumption for future survival of prosperity is going to require the whole vigor of our people, each working in his own small area on a thousand varied fronts. Fortunately we still have time and the means to do this job. Leisure, pleasure, plenty, and the will to serve will help us do it.

This implies a change of thought, a renunciation of false gods, shibboleths, prejudices, customs—a changed way of life. But our life will be changed, willy-nilly, by leisure. At last we shall have time to face up to issues of human fertility, resource consumption and creation, and the building of an ethic which will cause man to choose to use his time and his will to conserve all that is best in his environment. We shall have time also to participate in developing the patterns of governmental, business, and educational policy related to resources and their use—patterns which will be ever changing in the decades ahead as we direct our force toward conservation of the resource base.

Currently developing patterns in education can help abundantly in the decades ahead. Granting that no man should be considered educated to meet the problems of this age without a minimum of knowledge about the earth's resource and population trends, without comprehending the relation of life to its environment and the interdependence of all matter, we are confronted with the practical question of how our schools and colleges can manage to supply this considerable information and comprehension within existing limits of time, curriculum, and facilities.

With all the other vital problems in the world today—the new applications of science, the international conflict for resources and ideologies, the overwhelming issue of peace, international organization, the four freedoms, the constructive use of atomic energy, and dozens more—why ask education when or how it is going to begin to teach values and conservation? The answer is clear. These other "vital" issues it is already teaching in manifold disciplines; indeed, it is pointing most of its emphasis in all "general studies" toward these recognized majors. Yet there continues to be an almost complete lack of awareness of the related underlying importance of population control and resource depletion and what they mean in terms of international conflict, the issues of peace, freedom and prosperity, or the growth of communism in the world of tomorrow. This is itself a matter of values in education. It is clear that demography and ecology can be and are going to have to be integrated with these other modern majors as educational essentials. We, as citizens who participate on school boards and in parent-teacher associations, who pay for the schooling of our children against tomorrow, are able to get these things taught when we will.

These uses of leisure are all essential to the struggle that lies ahead. But they are only beginnings—conditioners, so to speak—for the acceptance of an ethic which will enable us to accomplish the ultimate, essential goal.

Conditioning we may achieve. But in the end the only way to consume less raw material is by reducing individual and industrial consumption. If we are not to lower our living standards, we shall have to reduce the number of consumers. It is apparent that will take a very long time indeed, because we have as yet no natural control of human fertility and because we are still prolonging life-expectancies and want to keep on doing so. The alternative is to cut back industrial consumption even though that does reduce the level of living. But could this be done, either voluntarily or by government rationing in an industrial nation such as ours, without causing economic depression and unemployment sufficiently prolonged to bring about stagnation and decay?

This is a problem our economists and sociologists need to study. Life was not apparently intolerable, even among the masses, before internal combustion engines were known to man. The first such engine was developed about a hundred years ago. The first oil well was drilled as recently as 1857. Our first electric utility plant was constructed in the 1880's. Now our entire way of enterprise and life seems to be dependent on machines and power. Life might be harder once again, but it might still be good—tomorrow—with fewer machines and gadgets.

That life may be quite tolerable with levels of living less advanced is suggested by the statistics on suicides set forth by Louis Dublin (1933): Suicides in the United States increased from 10 per hundred thousand population in 1900 to 18.8 per hundred thousand in 1932. In rural Ireland in 1928 the suicide rate was 3.2 per hundred thousand, and in urban England it was 12.5. Suicides among the colored people of Alabama, 1925–29, were 1.8 per hundred thousand, while among the whites of Alabama, with a considerably higher level of living, they were 8.4; among all citizens in New York State and in California the rates were 15.7 and 26.3, respectively. It seems, indeed, that, the higher the level of living, the less tolerable life is.

If initiated soon, and carefully planned, industrial cutbacks could be made gradually. In wartime we survived very substantial cutbacks in production of consumers' goods. Reduction in the use of some materials might have to be more drastic and occur faster than reduction in the use of others. And the duration of the period of retraction would depend on the speed with which substitutes are developed and productivity stepped up, as our scientists deliver on their promises. Of course there would be some measure of business recession which would be painful. All tightening of the belt, all reducing of expenditure, to meet a lowering income is painful.

But since, today, nature, man, and science are not reproducing nearly as much of some materials as they consume, and are not likely to do so while our industrial civilization continues to expand, retraction is bound to occur sometime; it can occur gradually by plan, or it will occur ultimately by force of circumstance. Short of a miracle, we are going to suffer this pain eventually, and the sooner we begin balancing the budget, by plan, the less acute the pain should be. By early diagnosis and treatment we may be able to prevent what otherwise could be a mortal process. This is not a happy thought, but it is a necessary conclusion. We are coming to a crisis that will require of this and future generations conviction, courage, new values, and a new ethic to resolve.

Sixty years is a short space of time in which to change our values, to regain a faith in nature, to preserve the sources of our prosperity, and to build an ethic for survival. It is hard, indeed, in prosperity, to see that what we have may not survive. Yet the prospect of leisure is propitious. For with leisure more of us are likely to turn to nature and become more aware of the state of our resources and the fact that they are the true source of prosperity and satisfaction.

The will to conserve resources will not come from early warnings of the imminent danger of losing them, for those who cry "danger" will be written off as "prophets of doom and gloom." It will rise, if it rises at all, from a much stronger and better compulsion than danger. It will rise from a resurrected understanding and appreciation of life and an affection for the things that are fundamental—from spiritual adjustments we shall have time to acquire with leisure. It will rise largely from the very love of what we have and a growing desire to pass on to the future the things we love.

Faith is something not always constant and not necessarily always good. We have today extraordinary faith in the virtue of progress. But, as we attain

progress, we find that some of its by-products are more gratifying than satisfying. If we can resurrect a more natural faith in things of the earth and of the spirit, we shall gradually become less eager to indulge in waste and idleness made possible by progress and more concerned with preserving the sources of prosperity. We shall drift further and further from reliance on what machines can do to give us gratification and turn more and more to what we and nature, working together, can do to succor prosperity of the earth and of the human spirit. For these are dependent one on the other.

Survival may be the by-product of love of creation, not love of exploitation. We have worked for economic prosperity, and we needed it. Now that prosperity is reaching maturity at last, we could well transfer our faith to conservation.

But how? It is apparent that man needs a new ethic for his conscience and his discipline in the wise pursuit of leisure. Such an ethic would need to be so appealing and compelling that it would cause us as a people not only to divert our use of leisure from routine acceptance of waste and idleness but also to channel it into individual and group activity to preserve material and spiritual prosperity. It has been suggested that we shall need leadership to translate such an ethic into a way of life that will create more than we consume, so that we do not ultimately come, after a few more decades, to the end of prosperity.

In leisure, as men tire of idling, some of their free-time activities will certainly be directed to human service. More than a few of us will recognize that the salvation of prosperity is the most compelling human service of our time. Conservation discipline and action to save prosperity is idealistic; it is creative; it deals in practice with the sciences; it is modern; it is ethical. But does it provide spiritual and emotional overtones essential to a faith?

Conservation, Paul Sears has said, is an attitude as well as a concept and a cause. The attitude is that of harmony between man and the life-forces of the earth—forces greater than man but of which man is a part and in which he does play both a destructive and a constructive part. The concept is that man's part should be constructive. The cause is nothing less than the survival of prosperity on earth. The way is through establishment of a *continuing* relationship between man and his environment, establishment of understanding and discipline by which there is consumed each year less raw material taken from earth, sea, and air than nature and man together create.

Thus conservation is both profound and virtuous, for it serves the well-being of all of life as well as man's need for material prosperity. Concept, cause, way, profundity, and virtue— here are the makings of an ethic.

Conservation for prosperity appeals to logic also. It is practical as well as creative and constructive. It is co-operative and convivial as well as ubiquitous. It is consonant with the "joining" instinct and the "do-good" instinct, and it is respectable. It is educational, social, and political as well as scientific. It benefits the poor and debases no one. It links respect for the primitive with respect for the sophisticated; love of nature with love of the machine. It would build, not wreck. It would save, not destroy. It lifts man's thought beyond himself.

What more can man ask of an ethic? Where else will he find so much? Such an ethic offers purpose and meaning for modern life. It provides temporal faith in material salvation compatible with spiritual faith in the salvation of the soul.

This sense of the importance of conservation, this goal of balancing the resource budget, this dedication to survival of prosperity and ultimately of mankind, is something that can be understood and accepted universally—and lived by in the decades ahead. It is clear that circumstances make such acceptance possible. If accepted by even a few leaders in an age of leisure, more and more people will embark on individual and group activities and practices that will increase their comprehension of environment and bring new purpose to their lives. This will increase their readiness to accept and in turn express the ethic, and the mass of men may ultimately follow; for the enterprise will be good, the practice bearable, and the faith satisfying. There will be new purpose in life, and gradually, in practice, the budget will be balanced.

With such an ethic there would be fewer unexpected children and fewer unneeded luxuries; gadgets would be made to last longer; there would be less waste. There would be increased productivity, less erosion and destruction of soil, less escape of valuable water, better forestry, more wildlife habitat, wiser husbandry of all resources. The bases of prosperity could be preserved.

Once citizens in the age of leisure begin to apply their time and energy to social activities that develop awareness, to business activities that renounce overconsumption of resources, and to development of political and educational policies that increase productivity, we shall be on the way to stability. Once citizens take active interest in these practices and active part in policy determination and execution, our dream will begin to be remade. Then we can be done with this ridiculous insistence upon industrial expansion and with all unnecessary production. Our goal will become industrial stability. Our civilization, so called, will have matured.

We have talked about a coming

golden age—an age of plenty and an age of leisure. If we wisely use our senses and our courage, our spirit and our faith, our resources and our leisure, it will be better known to history as the "age of conservation"—an age which embraced an ethic and a discipline that saved prosperity.

REFERENCES

CARSKADON, THOMAS R., and MODLEY, RUDOLF
1949 *Measure of a Nation.* New York: Twentieth Century Fund. 101 pp.

CHASE, STUART
1954 "Forty, Thirty, or Five Hours a Week," *New York Times Magazine,* May 30, p. 10.

DEWHURST, J. FREDERIC, AND ASSOCIATES
1947 *America's Needs and Resources.* New York: Twentieth Century Fund. 812 pp.

DUBLIN, LOUIS
1933 *To Be or Not To Be.* New York: Smith & Haas, Inc. 443 pp.

FLANAGAN, DENNIS (ed.)
1952 "Automatic Control Issue," *Scientific American,* Vol. CLXXXVII, No. 3. 196 pp.

LEONTIEF, WASSILY
1952 "Machines and Man," *Scientific American,* CLXXXVII, No. 3, 150–60.

ORDWAY, SAMUEL H., JR.
1953 *Resources and the American Dream.* New York: Ronald Press Co. 55 pp.

PIEPER, JOSEF
1952 *Leisure, the Basis of Culture.* Trans. from the German by ALEXANDER DRU. New York: Pantheon Books. 169 pp.

POLITICAL AND ECONOMIC PLANNING
1955 "World Population and Resources." London. (Mimeographed.)

PRESIDENT'S MATERIALS POLICY COMMISSION
1952 *Resources for Freedom,* Vol. I: *Foundations for Growth and Security;* Vol. II: *The Outlook for Key Commodities;* Vol. III: *The Outlook for Energy Sources;* Vol. IV: *The Promise of Technology;* Vol. V: *Selected Reports to the Commission.* Washington, D.C.: Government Printing Office.

SLICHTER, SUMNER
1954 "The Prospects Are Bright," *Atlantic Monthly,* CXCIII, No. 6, 31–44.

UNITED STATES DEPARTMENT OF AGRICULTURE
1938 *Soils and Men: Yearbook of Agriculture, 1938.* Washington, D.C.: Government Printing Office. 1,232 pp.
1946 *Our American Land.* (Soil Conservation Service Miscellaneous Publication No. 596.) Washington, D.C.: Government Printing Office. 31 pp.

VOGT, WILLIAM
1948 *The Road to Survival.* New York: William Sloane Associates. 335 pp.

WHITMAN, WALT
N.d. *Prose Works.* Philadelphia: David McKay Co. 476 pp.

WOYTINSKY, W. and S.
1953 *World Population and Production: Trends and Outlook.* New York: Twentieth Century Fund. 1,268 pp.

Limitations to Energy Use

CHARLES A. SCARLOTT*

If the title of this paper were to be taken literally, it would be a very short paper indeed. In fact, it could be reduced to one word: *cost*. The real limitations to energy use are not the absolute amounts of the various fuels in existence but the economics of making energy available from the sources where and when found and in forms suitable for use. It is a question of how much pains we are willing to take and how much ingenuity we can muster to the task.

AMPLE ENERGY—AT A PRICE

The earth is possessed of ample stores of fuels and of energy in other forms. Techniques for their capture, storage, transportation, and conversion as needed are known. If we were to lift the restriction of price, or if we were to become considerably more

* Mr. Scarlott, since 1954, has been Manager of Technical Information Services in the Public Relations Department of the Stanford Research Institute, Menlo Park, California. He began his career as a junior engineer with the Mountain States Telephone and Telegraph Company in Phoenix, Arizona. In 1926 he joined the Westinghouse Electric Corporation, Pittsburgh, Pennsylvania, as a technical editor. For thirteen years he was managing editor of the *Electric Journal*. In 1941 he established the company's major engineering publication, the *Westinghouse Engineer*, and was its editor for fourteen years. He is the co-author of several technical books, including *Fundamentals of Radio*, 1944; *Electronics for Industry* (with W. I. Bendz), 1949; and *Energy Sources: The Wealth of the World* (with Eugene Ayres), 1952.

clever in mining, the seams of coal threading the underground strata could alone carry the burden of man's energy requirements—as well as provide a large part of his chemicals—for thousands of years. The coal is there. The difficulties attendant to bringing it to the surface from great depths, from thin veins, or from badly faulted or tilted seams, or because of poor quality, reduce the net amount that will finally be recovered to a small fraction of the gross.

To a much lesser extent the same is true for petroleum and natural gas. How much of these deluxe fuels could be produced if money were no object is an open question. It is also an academic one. In any case, both the practically and the technically recoverable petroleum and gas are substantially less in terms of British thermal units (Btu.'s) than the solid fossil fuel that will eventually be actually surfaced.

The tonnages of oil presently locked in shale and in tar sands are almost astronomical. Even now the recovery of oil from shale borders on the economically feasible. If the allowable price could be doubled or recovery techniques improved, the inventory of potential oil from shale would be substantial. Virtually nothing has been done about tar sands. The deposits are extremely large. But the economic difficulties are also large—so much so that tar sands remain virtually unknown both in extent and as to technical feasibility of fuel recovery from them.

1010

The world also has lots of peat. However, as long as cheaper Btu.'s can be obtained in more convenient form in other ways, peat bogs will not be much disturbed except for certain local uses.

The new star in the fuel firmament—fissionable materials—is still of uncertain size. However, the successes of discovery already attained under the incentive of a guaranteed market and an artificial but moderately high price show that uranium ores will be forthcoming in much larger amounts than was believed possible five years ago. If we were willing to double or triple the ante for uranium ore, the quantities brought to market would rise in even greater proportion. Hundreds of spoil banks from old mining operations and many phosphate-fertilizer operations would become uranium sources. Carry the price high enough, and virtually every back yard as well as the ocean would become fissionable-fuel sources.

Mr. Jesse C. Johnson, director of the United States Atomic Energy Commission's Division of Raw Materials, summarized the situation of the uranium-ore reserve in 1955 as follows:

Areas of the Free World now in production or under development have uranium resources in the moderate cost category (less that $12 per pound for uranium in a concentrate) that may be between one and two million tons. Considering the limited amount of exploration, there are possibilities of much greater tonnage. Certainly the economic reserves would be greatly increased if uranium cost up to $30 per pound could be considered. If the permissible cost is increased to $50 a pound, vast low-grade deposits, such as shale and phosphate deposits, would become sources of production. Available resources could then be measured in terms of many millions of tons of uranium.

In addition to the non-renewable energy resources, some are sustained. The strength of the winds, the weight of the tides, and the temperature differences of the oceans contain, in the aggregate, great funds of energy. Since each has been tapped on occasion, we know it can be done technically. A few possible installations to function on these continuing energy sources are competitive, or close to being competitive, for special situations. However, the world will become extremely desperate for Btu.'s before any of these will provide more than token amounts to the energy bank.

Finally, we have the sun. Daily the earth is bathed in energy many thousands of times more than man, for all his voracious energy appetite, has found use for. Indeed, this resource—renewed every sunrise—appeals to many students of the energy situation as the ultimate bulwark against eventual energy starvation. Such belief, coupled with certain encouraging developments in radiant-energy capture, lies behind the resurgence of interest in solar energy.

Thus, if man runs out of energy, it will not be because the various wells of energy have dried up. The limitations are those of the pains man is willing to take to draw it out and his cleverness in doing so.

NEWCOMERS TO THE ENERGY TABLE

There are, however, several other limitations to energy use I wish to offer for your contemplation. These are certain factors not commonly thought of as affecting energy use. I wish in this discourse to be selective rather than comprehensive.

Inventories of economically recoverable energy reserves have been adequately set forth elsewhere. Further repetition until new data are available is pointless. The rates of population increase and the demands placed on energy resources by man's rising standard of living have been well summarized by others (Putnam, 1953). To have some numbers as guides, let us take present annual consumption of fuels in the United States as about 500 million tons of coal, nearly 3 billion barrels of petroleum, and 10 trillion cubic feet of gas.

Rising energy use is generally accounted for by man's propensity for physical comforts—houses that are warmer in winter and cooler in summer; automobiles with power steering, air conditioning, power-operated windows and seats, and rolling on soft, low-pressure tires; and the eminently desirable trend, though costly in energy, to do the work of the world with machine instead of muscle. It is of little point for me to repeat these obvious items of increasing direct energy use.

But there are other trends often overlooked in terms of their energy significance. I shall address myself to these.

Iron Ore

Some of the diners crowding in for seats at the energy table are without invitation. It has been man's habit to serve himself the choicest resources first. This has its justifications. It also has its consequences.

We are, for example, witnessing a major, and energy-significant, shift in the source of iron. The deposits of soft red ore that have for decades been scooped by immense shovels from the gigantic open pits of the Mesabi Range in Minnesota, and used with little or no enriching treatment, are nearing their end. The steel industry is already in transition to using a concentrate won from flint-hard rock called taconite. Much of this taconite is so hard that it defies the toughest bits. The rock is wrested from its bed by dynamite placed in holes formed by jets of flame of 4,500° F. moving 6,000 feet per second, created by burning kerosene and oxygen under pressure. The boulder-size taconite rocks must then be crushed and milled to the size of face powder, and the iron particles sepa-

rated magnetically. By heat and the addition of carbon (i.e., fuel) the concentrate must finally be re-formed into manageable lumps. Each of these steps consumes large amounts of energy.

A ton of direct-shipping ore scooped from the dwindling Mesabi pits is ready, with no or only simple mechanical enrichment, for shipment to the blast furnaces and represents an energy investment of less than 5 kilowatt-hours (kw-h.) per ton. Taconite concentrate of equivalent iron content contains about 75 kw-h. of electric energy plus the fuel used in processing. The total energy content of blast-furnace feed of taconite origin comes to something like thirty-five times more than for the ores concentrated and softened by nature in the past several million years.

Many other minerals display this same pattern of rising energy use—copper, for example. A few decades ago ore containing less than several per cent copper was ignored as worthless. Now, big open pits are operating on rock containing about 18 pounds of copper per ton (0.9 per cent). This is possible, of course, because of the facility with which mountains of material can be handled by machinery—petroleum-consuming machinery.

The light metals—aluminum, magnesium, and more recently titanium—are taking larger places in the industrial economy. Each of these metals comes only with a high energy investment—a requirement established by nature, not by lack of man's ingenuity.

Synthetic Rubber

Other newcomers in our industrial economy are more subtle in their impositions on the energy supply. World War II forced the Western world to an independence of the hevea tree for rubber. Under the pressure of necessity, chemists learned how to produce it synthetically, using ingredients that have their origin in fossil fuels. Thus, in making rubber instead of growing it, another burden has been shifted from the sunshine of today to the sunshine stored in past millenniums.

Consumption of synthetic rubber in the United States is now running about two-thirds of a million tons annually. To produce this much synthetic rubber requires nearly a half-million tons of petroleum products. While probably no one begrudges synthetic rubber except the rubber-tree plantation owners and workers, it does represent—in the United States alone—about 100 million gallons of petroleum per year that we do not have to drive trains, airplanes, and automobiles, to build roads, or to heat homes.

Latex-base paints have rocketed to great popularity. Even these, in their small way, have energy implications. In 1954 the people of America spread nearly 50 million gallons of latex paint. To make this paint required about 10,000 tons, or nearly 3,000,000 gallons, of raw material that came from oil wells. Insignificant in the national total, yes. But it combines with many similar little-observed developments to become a limitation to energy use.

Man-made Fibers

Another tree has figured in the shift from the energy of today's sunshine to that of Paleozoic times. This is the mulberry tree, the traditional origin of silk, long cherished by women for the luxury feel it gave to stockings and other garments. The silkworm has been largely displaced by the mechanical spinnerette that continuously extrudes the fabulous filament known as nylon. The 300 million pounds of nylon currently produced yearly comes not from the ceaseless mastication of leaves by the silkworm but from prosaic lumps of coal or smelly crude oil. Gracing each nylon-encased feminine leg are at least 750 Btu.'s of energy in raw materials

alone. But let no man say it is not worth it.

The ladies wear out about 600 million pairs of nylons each year. If all the raw materials for hose and other nylon products were to come from coal (some is now derived from petroleum and farm wastes), the annual production of nylon would require 300,000 tons of coal.

Nylon was but the first of a large family of man-made fibers having their origin in fossil fuels instead of growing things, Dacron, Orlon, Dynel, Acrilan, Saran, and others have become familiar household textile names. Production of these man-made fibers in the United States (excluding the rayons and acetates, which originate in animal or plant fibers) amounts to about 200,000 tons annually and is increasing.

Plastics

On almost every bathroom shelf and in almost every kitchen is something new—the squeezable bottle. This flexible, unbreakable bottle that has captured our fancy and much of the market for cosmetic containers and other uses is made of polyethylene. It is only one of the new developments in plastics that is based almost entirely on crude oil and natural gas. Last year the United States consumed over 100,000 tons of polyethylene, which called for some 100 million gallons of petroleum products.

Looking at the plastics industry as a whole, we see that the numbers are becoming very large. About a million tons of plastics are currently being produced in the United States annually. That represents a take of nearly that much tonnage from the fossil-fuel reserves.

At the automobile shows and occasionally on the highways we have admired the sleek lines of the plastic-bodied sports car. We fondly envision the day when a dented fender on a new car will be less of a tragedy. However, we may not have thought—and quite possibly should not think—of the Fiberglas plastic body in terms of the oil bank account. Just suppose, however, that the day arrives when a significant number of the automobiles have them. Each 100,000 plastic-bodied cars will mean about 3,000,000 fewer gallons of fuel with which to run them.

Detergents

For centuries man has freed his clothes of soil with soap made from animal greases or tallow or from vegetable oils. The last decade, however, has seen this time-honored practice upset by the development of detergents. These have had phenomenal acceptance. Starting from almost nothing in 1944, United States production of detergents has grown to about a million tons per year. As a consequence, tallow in the United States is on the technologically unemployed list to the extent of about a billion pounds yearly, with the figure still rising. Detergents—it hardly need be stated—are made from chemicals originating in petroleum products.

The list could be continued. But these suffice to suggest the many new seats being occupied at the energy table as scientists continue to learn to synthesize materials better than nature currently grows them.

More Roads

Other trends also qualify as new or increased users of energy. Seldom are they thought of in terms of their energy implication.

Take roads. The United States Congress is considering a program for an enormously expanded road-building program. The request is for an additional $25 billion of federal money to be spent over the next ten years. This sum combines with other federal road-building funds and those provided by state, county, and city governments to make a total of $101 billion.

With congestion mounting daily on the highways, most of us are prone to say that this new order of magnitude of road-building comes not a bit too soon. It is interesting, however, to measure the cost in terms of energy as well as dollars.

From past experience, and averaged over the country as a whole, we can expect that, in the execution of a $100-billion road program, the earth-moving and road-building machinery and other equipment will consume the stupendous total of 15 billion gallons of gasoline, oil, and grease. This is at the rate of 1,500 million gallons per year—which is to be compared with the total present United States annual consumption of motor fuel of 50,000 million gallons.

Also to build that $100 billion worth of roads we must order 1,250 million barrels of cement and 30 billion tons of bituminous aggregates. To manufacture these 1,250 million barrels of cement will require 30 billion kw-h. of electric energy and the equivalent of 9 billion gallons of petroleum in direct heat energy.

This road-building program does not, of course, represent either all or the end of the job. It is recognized as simply an attempt to catch up with the needs of the voracious energy-consuming machine, the automobile. After 1965 even larger expenditures of dollars—and energy—will be called for.

These several facets of our expanding economy that have little-suspected influence on the energy situation are by no means all. They are only illustrative. Each by itself is small when measured against the total direct energy consumption. They are presented here not as disquieting evidence of pending energy shortage but to help complete the picture of our future energy requirements.

It is not suggested that we should

shut down any man-made fiber plants or synthetic-rubber factories or curtail the road-building program because they are eating into our fossil-fuel reserves. Certainly that will not happen. But these facts do point to the growing need to adopt that other alternative to ease the pending limitation to energy use—increase the energy supply.

LIMITATIONS TO SOLAR ENERGY USE

Concepts like those just discussed make many observers believe it is prudent to intensify our efforts to utilize directly a portion of the tremendous shower of radiant energy from the sun. Encouragement for this belief comes from comparatively recent developments in the laboratory, which suggest that practical ways of harnessing solar energy for some purposes may not be distant. These include developments in solid-state physics, of which the silicon solar battery is a well-publicized example. Forced culture of low-order plants, such as algae, offers prospect that further development will make it a practical source of fuel as well as food. The photosynthesis reaction is still a mystery in spite of extensive studies of it. However, both organic and inorganic photosynthesis reactions will probably be mastered without plant or animal aid and will become practical on large scales.

Man has been working at solar-energy utilization a long time. The ancients produced their salt by drying up ponds of brine. In spite of advanced technology, we are not doing much better than this today. There are reasons for this poor showing, of course.

The Mechanism of Solar Energy

To understand the problems attendant to solar-energy use—limitations, if you will—it is well to observe the basic mechanisms by which the sun's radiant energy can be converted into useful forms.

In dealing with solar radiation, we are concerned with energy "bundles" or photons of fixed, discrete sizes. Those at the ultraviolet end of the solar spectrum are much more energetic than those in the visible band, which in turn contain more energy than those in the infrared or heat region. The important fact is that each photon is a fixed amount; it cannot be cut in half, or two cannot be added together to do the work of one. Solar-energy capture becomes, then, a matter of learning the different ways individual molecules of matter react under the impact of these solar photons of different size. In fact, solar-energy uses can be catalogued and separately examined in those ways.

It is convenient to start with the simplest responses of the molecule to sun-radiated photons and continue on through the more complex. When radiant-energy photons strike some molecules, they are altered only in their direction of motion. They are reflected. This is the mirror effect. As far as the molecule is concerned the result is—nothing. The molecule is in no way changed.

Mirrors and lenses are not, of themselves, solar-energy devices, but they can be joined with a second-type response to wave motion to produce stoves and furnaces, as will be mentioned.

The Flat-Plate Collector

The simplest—and by far the most common—active participation of the molecule in transformation of light photons to usable energy is the conversion of light to heat. The molecule is set into some form of motion by the solar photon. This can be vibration, spin, or translation. However, as the molecule returns to rest, it releases its energy in at least two and usually several smaller photons of energy. These are in the infrared or heat region. The energy is thus degraded into smaller size units. The direction of light-energy conversion is always downhill.

This mechanism of setting molecules in motion by light-energy photons provides the simplest and, at present, most useful solar-energy device susceptible to man's control. It is the principle of the greenhouse. It is also the principle of the flat-plate collector now receiving increased attention. Basically this consists simply of a base of some good radiant-energy absorber, an air space, and one or more covers of transparent glass or plastic. Some fluid—air, water, or other liquid—is pumped through the space between absorber and cover, picking up heat en route.

The flat-plate collector is a simple structure. It requires no maintenance, has long life, is simple to construct, and can recover a large proportion of the incident radiation. Practical considerations dictate that it be set in a fixed position and not turn with the sun. Its principal limitations are that it produces heat only when the sun shines and that its output is heat at a low level. In practical collectors the temperature created in the fluid does not exceed the ambient by more than 300° F. This is because the expenditure for materials to prevent excessive heat losses at higher temperatures becomes prohibitive.

The need here, if this limitation is to be lessened, is primarily an engineering one. To reduce the heat lost by conduction at the sides and bottom, materials are needed that are both better heat insulators and are cheaper. Heat lost above the absorber can be materially cut down—particularly on windy days—by increasing the number of dead air spaces, that is, the number of layers of transparent material. The practical number of layers is determined by cost and by the light-transmission coefficient of the material. The need is for a transparent material of lower cost and higher light-transmission factor. These

are two areas in which further engineering development is needed. The standing rewards for success are high.

Heat from the flat-plate collector can be used for several purposes. The one most likely to have early extensive use is house-heating. This is of utmost consequence, because house-heating accounts for one-fourth to one-third of the total energy consumption. Any appreciable reduction in the load imposed by comfort heating on the stored fuels' reserves is of first-order importance.

A number of houses heated all or in part—sometimes even cooled—by flat-plate collectors have been erected. The heat from the collector, usually built as a portion of the south wall or roof of the house, is stored by circulating air (or a liquid) through it and into a reservoir of water, stones, or chemicals from which the heat can be withdrawn as needed. Water or stones are cheap enough. The problem with them is bulk. For localities where heat must be stored for several days in the absence of the sun, or where the heating load is severe, the volume (and hence cost of installation) is high.

Use of chemicals that conveniently melt in the range of 85°–110° F. offers a large reduction in storage volume by virtue of the high heat storage resulting from the latent heat of fusion. There are several such chemicals. Sodium sulfate, or Glauber's salt, is the best known.

The limitation of salts for heat storage is—again—their higher cost and the fact that most of them are two-phase chemicals. They tend to separate gradually with recurring cycles of melting and freezing. Periodic agitation is required.

A cheaper, single-phase compound with a low-temperature fusing point is urgently needed. If anyone knows of one, please step forward, for the solar-energy engineers are looking for you.

The warmed fluid from a flat-plate

collector can be used to operate a heat engine. Many ingenious ones have been devised, some of them in ancient times. Almost none has endured. The cost or complexity is too great, or the net output of the device hovered just above the zero point. However, a few solar-operated pumps are now being marketed. They are practical where the water being pumped is relatively cold, fuel is scarce, and sunshine abundant.

The weakness of the low-level heat engines is their low efficiency. To begin with, any heat engine has a ceiling efficiency fixed by that of the familiar Carnot cycle. With small differences between inlet and outlet temperatures this sets a pretty low ceiling on even a perfect engine. For example, if a flat-plate collector provides to the engine a fluid that is 250° warmer than the fluid used in the condensing portion of the engine cycle, the maximum possible efficiency would be 32 per cent.

This is not too serious. Because solar energy is free, to double this—or, more properly, to double the power—requires only that the flat-plate collector be doubled in size and the engine made larger. The real limitation, however, is that engines operating at low heat levels are not efficient even within the boundaries set by their theoretical maximums.

A vast amount of research and engineering development has gone into perfecting the high-temperature engine, such as the internal combustion machines and steam and gas turbines. Relatively little has been expended on improving low-temperature engines. This is another area in which engineering effort could profitably be spent.

It is natural that we should look hopefully to "free" solar energy, as provided by devices operating on the flat-plate collector principle, for relief from water shortages that daily are growing more critical. If the sea water available in abundance could be freed of salt, many of these shortages would be resolved. Distillation has always cost too much in energy, except under special circumstances where the need for water is acute.

Frankly, the prospect that solar energy will provide the answer to the water problem is slim. And for the same old reason—cost. Solar energy is too diffuse, and the Btu. investment to boil water is too high, for presently known systems to be practical. For any solar still to operate on a large scale will probably require some means for partial recovery of the heat released on the condensation portion of the cycle. Such a mechanism obviously adds complexity and cost. Whether further development can ease this limitation is not known. The odds against it appear to be long.

Solar stills will be used to a limited extent where fuel is costly, water is urgently needed, and sunshine is abundant. The solar still to produce drinking water for aviators adrift at sea is an example.

Solar Stoves and Furnaces

The principle of photon reflection and the principle of conversion of photons to infrared photons underlie two other solar-energy devices—the solar stove and the solar furnace.

Several varieties of stoves have been demonstrated. A simple solar stove is being manufactured for sale at about fifteen dollars in fuel-poor but sun-rich India. The limitation to its use is that the Indians cannot afford a stove so expensive. A solar oven, designed by Maria Telkes, of New York University and consultant on solar energy to the Stanford Research Institute, has four flat mirrors that direct the sun's rays into an oven. A temperature of about 350° F. is achieved.

A few solar furnaces are in operation. The Consolidated-Vultee Aircraft Company in San Diego uses one with a 10-

foot mirror for metallurgical research. Professor Felix Trombé, of France, has one furnace with a mirror 40 feet across and has several smaller solar furnaces. With them he produces refractory ceramics such as fused quartz and titanium dioxide on a commercial basis. He is building four smaller, mirror-type furnaces for experimental use. A furnace of different design with an aluminum reflector 27½ feet across was built by the government of Algeria to produce fertilizer by fixation of atmospheric nitrogen.

Solar furnaces are relatively efficient, converting upward of 70 per cent of the total incident radiation into usable heat. Temperatures above 7,000° F. have been obtained. The solar furnace provides a readily controllable means of obtaining extremely high temperatures and is a useful tool for several applications. However, it produces heat only when the sun shines and only while the mirror is focused directly on the sun. The initial cost is comparatively high. The solar furnace seems destined to be a special-purpose tool, not a general producer of power.

This about sums up what is being accomplished by devices that convert solar radiation to heat. One thing is conspicuously missing: a large-scale producer of power. If the sun is to be the source of substantial amounts of power, in contrast to heat, we must look to some other way of using the photons.

Light Storage

En route to examination of potentially more important solar-power devices we should mention only in passing a third type of response of a molecule to light energy. This is the disturbance of the satellite electrons from their normal orbits. When the molecules of certain substances receive light energy, some of the electrons spinning within the atoms are boosted into orbits more distant from the nucleus.

Eventually—in a time that may be as short as a millionth of a second or as long as several hours—the electrons fall back into their original orbits. They almost never return in a single jump. They do it in a succession of steps. At each step a photon of energy, smaller than the original, is emitted. Thus the color of the light emitted differs from the incident light. This is phosphorescence.

Phosphorescence is an interesting way of storing light energy briefly. While it has some limited applications, it is not regarded as having any prospect as a major energy device.

Photoelectricity

Potentially of much greater significance is a fourth way of operating on the molecule with solar energy. When the atoms of certain molecules are hit hard enough, some of their electrons are jolted entirely out of their orbits and away from the parent-atom. Once out in the open, they create an electric potential that establishes electron flow in a connecting circuit and load. This is the principle of the photographer's exposure meter. Although it is an extremely useful device, it is inefficient. It converts only about two-tenths of 1 per cent of the received light into electric energy.

A much more attractive photoelectric power source is the silicon solar battery, such as has been demonstrated by Bell Telephone Laboratories. The announced efficiency is 12 per cent, but improvement can be expected. However, the silicon cell has a ceiling efficiency of about 22 per cent. This is because most solar photons (those in the infrared) are too weak to dislodge electrons from the silicon surface. Much of the sun's radiation is simply wasted as heat or is reflected. Also, a precise amount of energy is required to lift an electron away from its normal orbit around a molecule nucleus. Surplus energy is spent needlessly accelerating the electron and does not contribute to the power output. The energy left over from one photon cannot be used partially to dislodge another electron. Hence, not all the energy of the more energetic photons toward the violet end of the spectrum can be used.

An efficiency of some 15 per cent can be eventually expected for a practical silicon battery. That is pretty good. It is a direct conversion device without moving parts and requires no attention. Indeed, the performance of the present silicon battery is good enough for the device to be practical for many purposes where small amounts of energy are adequate and where continuity is not essential.

Further research on the principle of photoelectricity is definitely worth while. Materials other than silicon may be found that are less costly or even more efficient converters of solar to electric energy—preferably both.

Photosynthesis

We come now to the final way by which molecules can react under photon attack. In the discussion thus far the molecular structure has remained aloof. The molecule can be set in motion to give heat, or the orbital electrons can be disturbed to provide brief energy storage or a direct current, but in all these the chemical structure has not been altered.

Molecular changes can, however, be affected by radiant energy. Indeed, these are the sources of man's sustenance—both food and oxygen. This is the photosynthesis reaction. Chlorophyll manages to utilize radiant energy to force the reaction of water and carbon dioxide to carbohydrates and oxygen. How chlorophyll performs this reaction, which requires 112 kilocalories, with photons having only one-third or one-half that amount of energy, is not known. Scientists in many laboratories

are working hard to find out. Their eventual success is highly probable. That new knowledge should hasten solar-energy utilization on a large scale.

However, it does not seem likely that we can look to land-plant photosynthesis as a major energy source. Photosynthesis, for all its importance, is not an efficient converter of sunlight into chemical energy. Most scientists believe that it is in the neighborhood of 25 per cent. Even that is utilization of the total light falling on the plant and is achieved only under the best laboratory conditions. In the fields and forests the conversion is much less, considering that the energy in the infrared spectrum (about half the total) is not used at all, that much of the energy falls on bare ground between the plants, and that the growing season is only a portion of the year. The conversion for even the best plants, such as sugar beets, is about 2 per cent. Most farm crops use no more than one-half of 1 per cent of the light that falls on the field.

If we are to augment our energy sources by photosynthesis, it seems that we can do better by turning to the simple plant forms, such as algae, that thrive in water. In particular, the green unicellular algae *Chlorella* has commanded much research attention and offers considerable prospect of producing both food and fuel.

This technique has much to recommend it. *Chlorella* can be grown in a water solution continuously. The proportions of carbohydrate, protein, and fat in the end product can be varied widely. If *Chlorella* could be grown in large quantities with the same yield as in laboratory culture, the result would be 20 tons of protein and 3 tons of fat per acre per year, which far exceeds that achieved with land plants. This would be an efficiency of nearly 20 per cent.

No one, however, has succeeded in

doing this. There are many unsolved problems, such as the proper turbulence of the water containing the algae (sunlight is too strong for continuous exposure of algae), the most suitable temperature for algae, the optimum carbon dioxide supply, the development of disease-free strains of *Chlorella*, etc.

Inorganic Photosynthesis

Perhaps we can learn how to cause molecular changes with radiant energy on a large scale without plant or animal aid and with much better total utilization of that energy than is achieved by nature. Herein, many believe, lies the great hope of practical solar power devices. But, as yet, all are a good distance from success.

Of particular fascination is the possibility of breaking up water into its constituent hydrogen and oxygen for later recombination for energy recovery. Several reactions by which water is dissociated by radiant energy into oxygen and hydrogen are known. Dr. L. J. Heidt, at the Massachusetts Institute of Technology, has been experimenting for several years with the chemical decomposition of water containing ceric perchlorate and perchloric acid by ultraviolet light. This reaction, however, does not seem to lend itself to general use as a means of capturing solar energy, because it employs only the more energetic portion of the radiant spectrum.

Scientists of the Stanford Research Institute are studying a different reaction for dissociating water. In this reaction a solution containing water, an inorganic chemical, and a small amount of chlorophyll as catalyst is exposed to sunlight. The products of the reaction, again, are oxygen and hydrogen. This reaction is attractive because, in theory, it can use almost all the visible spectrum of sunlight. It is too early to state whether success will be achieved.

Use of solar energy to effect the rupture of water molecules is promising, and major research effort is justified. Water is readily available as raw material. If oxygen and hydrogen can be inexpensively and efficiently produced, the troublesome problem of energy storage is solved. Hydrogen could be conveniently stored as a gas for recovery of the energy-burning, releasing heat and forming water. The temperature of burning oxygen and hydrogen is extremely high—too high for presently known heat engines. Effective utilization of these temperatures in a heat engine to produce mechanical or electric energy would entail further research and engineering effort.

However, there is prospect of recovering the energy directly as electricity without going through the wasteful heat cycle or the use of moving machinery. Experimental cells for doing this have been built. In one, the Bacon cell, hydrogen and oxygen are introduced through porous walls inclosing a liquid electrolyte. Therein they recombine to form water and electric current without producing significant amounts of heat. Extremely high efficiencies of these small, laboratory cells—from 50 to 65 per cent—are reported.

Solar Energy Is Attractive but Elusive

Thus, we see that solar energy has its limitations too. However, the rewards for success are so great, and recent advances in solar-energy technology are so sufficiently encouraging, that it is receiving vastly increased attention. Of special significance in this direction was the World Symposium on Applied Solar Energy held in Phoenix, Arizona, during November, 1955. This unique symposium brought together the solar-energy scientists with the engineers, industrialists, and businessmen whose talents are required to effect the transition of laboratory developments to salable devices. If ways can be found to utilize a significant proportion of solar energy, the limitation on our use of energy would be substantially relieved—but not eliminated.

THE H-BOMB IN HARNESS?

We should also not overlook another possibility—a possibility of such immense potentiality that, if realized, all our notions of energy use or shortages will have to be revised. This is the possibility that the nuclear-fusion reaction can be made a controlled energy source.

The amounts of energy such a reaction would make possible are almost incomprehensible. Theory states that the heat in the interreaction of heavy water (deuterium to helium) in a gallon of ordinary water is about 20,000 kw-h.—if the reaction can be managed outside the bomb. A bathtub of water would offer 6,000,000 kw-h. A cubic mile of sea water on the same fanciful basis and on the assumption of 10 per cent over-all efficiency would yield 2 million billion kw-h. As a comparison yardstick, the electric power plants of the United States in 1954 generated 410 billion kw-h.

Fusion makes for fascinating—and challenging—speculation. Whether or when fusion power plants will become a reality is not known. The problems are tremendously formidable. It is unwise to assume that the substantial limitations to energy use immediately before us will be dispelled by the development of controlled fusion.

The facts about our energy resources are sobering. The rapidity with which we are finding ways of spending that energy, often without realizing it, is shocking. The problems attendant on tapping unused reservoirs of energy are discouraging. Just the same, no one should say that man's standard of living is likely to toboggan for lack of energy—cheap energy. This optimism comes not from a blind faith in the scientist and engineer but, instead, from an infinite confidence, supported by a long record of the past, that man's ingenuity is equal to the task.

REFERENCES

AYRES, EUGENE
    1953a "U.S. Oil Outlook: How Coal Fits In," *Coal Age*, LVIII, No. 8, 70–73.
    1953b "Liquid Fuels in America," *Petroleum Refiner*, XXXII, No. 8, 90–95.

AYRES, EUGENE, and SCARLOTT, CHARLES A.
    1952 *Energy Sources: The Wealth of the World*. New York: McGraw-Hill Book Co. 344 pp.

CHAPMAN, SYDNEY
    1941 "The Sun and the Ionosphere (The Thirty-Second Kelvin Lecture Presented before the Institution of Electrical Engineers, London, May 8, 1941)," *Journal of the Institution of Electrical Engineers*, Vol. LXXXVIII, Part I.

DAVIS, E. W.
    1950 *Beneficiation of Magnetic Taconite*. (Bulletin of the Mines Experiment Station, University of Minnesota.) 15 pp.

HAND, I. F.
    1953 "Distribution of Solar Energy over the United States," *Heating and Ventilating*, L, No. 7, 73–75.

MACNEW, THOMAS
    1953 "The Challenge of Plastics," *Automotive Industries*, CIX, No. 6, 42–49.

MILNER, HAROLD W.
    1955 "Some Problems in Large-Scale Culture of Algae," *Scientific Monthly*, LXXX, No. 1, 15–21.

PATTERSON, IAN D.
    1954 "How Synthetic Rubbers Affect You," *Rubber World*, November, pp. 218–24.

PUTNAM, PALMER C.
    1953 *Energy in the Future*. New York: D. Van Nostrand Co. 556 pp.

SCARLOTT, CHARLES A.
  1951 "Copper—Problems and Prospects," *Westinghouse Engineer*, XI, No. 3, 74–80.
  1952a "Man-made Fibers—Revolution in Textiles," *ibid.*, XII, No. 3, 82–89.
  1952b "Rise of Titanium," *ibid.*, No. 4, pp. 114–17.
  1954 "Iron Ore—the Hard Way," *ibid.*, XIV, No. 4, 130–34.
  1955 *We Turn to the Sun.* Menlo Park, Calif.: Stanford Research Institute. 16 pp.

SUMAN, JOHN R.
  1953 "Perspective on the World Oil Picture," pp. 63–67 in *Proceedings of the American Petroleum Institute.* New York: American Petroleum Institute. 1,080 pp.

Technological Denudation

HARRISON BROWN*

* Dr. Brown is Professor of Geochemistry at the California Institute of Technology, Pasadena, California. His works include *The Challenge of Man's Future,* 1954.

MACHINE CIVILIZATION

A modern industrial society is characterized by the production of enormous quantities of goods which, for various reasons, people want to own. In order to produce these goods, raw materials are needed. Machines are needed to transform the raw materials into other machines, into secondary materials, and into finished products. Machines are needed to transport the diverse materials and goods which flow through the complex network of mines, factories, farms, and cities. Energy is needed to power the machines which extract, produce, and transport. The continuation of these operations is ultimately dependent upon the extraction of materials from the earth, the atmosphere, and the oceans.

In order to produce the multiplicity of goods consumed by society, we mine iron ore, convert it into pig iron, and then mill it into steel. We produce copper, lead, zinc, aluminum, and a variety of metals from their ores and blend and shape them to suit our needs. We mine phosphate rock, fix the nitrogen of the atmosphere, evaporate sea water, and quarry rock. We transport vast quantities of sand, gravel and clay; manufacture cement; and mine sulfur, gypsum, and pyrites. For every person who lives in a highly industrialized society, many tons of material must be moved, mined, and processed each year.

From the time that coal was first linked to iron, the per capita flow of goods in the industrialized part of the world has steadily increased; associated with that increasing flow we see an increasing per capita demand for raw materials. By 1950 the yearly per capita demand for steel in the United States had reached 1,260 pounds; demand for copper had reached 23 pounds; demand for stone, sand, and gravel had reached 7,300 pounds; and demand for cement had reached 520 pounds. In order to power the industrial network, energy demands had risen to the equivalent of over 8 tons of coal per person per year. It must be stressed that these per capita demands are still rising.[1]

In addition to the rise in per capita demands, we must consider the fact that machine civilization is spreading throughout the world. The Soviet Union and Japan are the most recent additions to the roster of industrialized nations, and enormous efforts aimed at industrialization are now being made by India and China. Further, the human population of the world is increasing rapidly and is apparently destined to continue to increase for some time in the future.

When we attempt to assess the prospects with respect to both the supply and the demand of raw materials on a

[1] See the report of the President's Materials Policy Commission (1952) for a detailed discussion of current needs in the United States.

world-wide basis, we must inquire into several important aspects of the over-all problem: (1) How large might per capita demands for raw materials become? (2) How rapidly might machine civilization spread over the world? (3) How large is the human population likely to become? (4) How large is the potential source of raw materials?

THE IRON AND STEEL CYCLE

Steel is the most widely used metal in our society, in part because of the relatively high abundance of iron ore in the earth, in part because of the relative ease with which metallic iron can be extracted, and in part because of the useful physical properties of the alloys of the metal. From an examination of the path of iron through the industrial network, we can obtain a useful picture of some of the present trends in industrial society, and we will be able to assess some of the more important limits placed by nature upon man's operations.

In order to produce a ton of metallic iron within the framework of our existing practices, approximately 1¾ tons of high-grade iron ore, nearly a ton of coke, and nearly a half-ton of limestone are required.[2] Energy is required to mine the iron ore and limestone, to produce the coke, and to bring the ingredients together. The greater proportion of the resultant pig iron is channeled into steel production, the balance being used for the fabrication of a variety of cast-iron products. The output of the steel furnaces is shaped into a variety of finished products; about 25 per cent of the steel ends up as scrap, which is recycled, and about 10 per cent is lost in the processing. The shaping into finished products and the recycling again require expenditure of energy.

The finished steel is sold to manu-

facturers, who fabricate a diversity of machines and products. During the course of this fabrication there are certain irrecoverable losses, and a substantial fraction of the steel ends up as scrap, which is recycled through the steel mills.

Manufactured steel articles have finite lifetimes. Machines become obsolete. Wear, corrosion, accident, and loss constantly take their tolls. Some abandoned items are sold for scrap and recycled through the steel mills. Others are discarded and permitted to disintegrate, never to be recovered. Present evidence indicates that, on the average, about twenty years will elapse from the time an object is manufactured until it is returned to the steel mill as scrap.

The annual irrecoverable losses of metallic iron depend upon the amount of steel in use, upon the mean lifetime of steel products, and upon the rate of increase of the amount of steel in use. It seems likely that annual irrecoverable losses, other than those involved in steel production, amount to about 1 per cent of the amount in use and that losses involved in steel production amount to about one-eighth of the total annual production of ingots and castings.

It has been estimated that, of the 2 billion tons of pig iron produced in the United States between 1870 and 1950, nearly 40 per cent has been lost as a result of the various processes discussed above. The balance, corresponding to about 1.3 billion tons, represents the total amount of steel in use in 1950 in the United States—the railway tracks, girders, automobiles, nails, screws, etc. This corresponds to about 8 tons of steel in use per person.[3] Between 1947

---

2. Zimmerman (1951) provides a detailed description of the steel industry.

3. This estimate was given by the author (1954). *Steel Facts,* published by the American Iron and Steel Institute, gave an estimate of 7.3 tons per person in 1948. According to the same organization's *The Picture Story of Steel* (1952), an estimated 10 tons of steel ore are in use per person.

and 1952 the total amount of steel in use in the United States increased by an average of about 3.4 per cent per annum, an annual rate which is greater than the rate of population growth. This average growth rate corresponds to a doubling of the amount of steel in use every twenty years.

In 1951 pig-iron production in the United States amounted to 70 million tons and steel production (ingots and castings) to 105 million tons.[4] Thus, losses of iron in steel production amounted to about 13 million tons, and other irrecoverable losses amounted to about 12 million tons. As a result, 25 million of the 70 million tons of new pig iron were used to replace losses, and the balance of 45 million tons represents the net increase in the total amount of steel in use during that year. This corresponds to an increase of 0.28 ton per person per year. By 1975 the per capita amount of steel in use might well amount to 15 tons per person.

LOSS OF METALS IN USE

The patterns for the cycling of most metals are similar to the pattern for iron, although the amounts in use and the proportions lost irrecoverably each year vary greatly from metal to metal. For example, out of every 100 pounds of lead consumed each year in the United States, 24 pounds are used in gasoline, in paints, and in diverse other uses where the element is dispersed, never to be recovered.[5] Annual gold losses, on the other hand, are very small. The proportion of copper lost irretrievably each year is intermediate between these extreme examples.

The proportion of a metal which is lost irrecoverably will depend upon the amount of effort and energy which

4. Most statistics concerning metal production can be found in the *Minerals Yearbook* (United States Bureau of Mines, 1952).

5. See the report of the President's Materials Policy Commission (1952).

must be expended to prevent loss relative to the amount of effort and energy which must be expended to obtain new metal from the ore. In principle, losses of metals in use and in cycling can be greatly decreased, but only at the cost of greater energy expenditure per unit of output. Thus, in the long run, efforts to decrease metal losses in use and in cycling result in greater consumption of coal and petroleum. Our operations are in effect limited not only by the first law of thermodynamics but by the second law as well, and the best we can do is to balance the value of the metal which is lost against the value of the energy and effort which would be required to prevent the loss. In any event, losses can never be entirely eliminated, with the result that there will be a continuing demand for new metal for as long a time as industrial society exists. Even were the time to arrive when all nations of the world were highly industrialized, and when world populations and per capita quantities of metals in use were stabilized, demands for new metal would be substantial and would be determined in effect by the energy expenditure required to obtain new metal relative to the energy expenditure required to prevent the loss of old.

PER CAPITA QUANTITY OF METALS IN USE

We have seen that there are about 8 tons of steel in use per person in the United States. This "steel inventory," together with the inventories of other metals in use in our society, is required for the maintenance of our existing per capita flow of goods. The per capita quantities of metals in use are increasing with time, and, as we shall see, they are destined to increase in the future to levels considerably above those of the present.

Almost all major increases in per capita consumption of goods fall initially into the "luxury" classification, but, as time goes on and as society adjusts itself to the new situation and indeed becomes dependent upon it, the increased consumption becomes a "necessity." Again and again we have seen this transformation take place in the United States—the automobile, the telephone, and the electric light were all initially luxuries, yet they made certain things possible which had not been possible before. And, as society took advantage of these new possibilities, slowly but relentlessly the automobile, the telephone, and the electric light became necessities. A part of this transformation has resulted from a progressive change in our definition of "necessity." But even were we to define a necessity specifically and narrowly as something which is necessary for the avoidance of premature death, a surprisingly large fraction of both modern production and consumption would qualify for the "necessity" classification. The automobile, the telephone, and the electric light, for example, have all played major roles in increasing average life-expectancy, and, were we suddenly to be deprived of the use of these devices, there would be little doubt that mortality would increase substantially.

Thus, solely on the basis of our seemingly infinite capacity to accept new products and then to become dependent upon them, it seems likely that the per capita quantities of metals in use will increase in the future—and, indeed, may increase to levels far above those which exist today. But, quite apart from this aspect of the problem, the per capita quantities of metals in use would increase in the future even were we to attempt to maintain only the existing per capita flow of goods. The quantities must increase for the reason that, as time goes by, new metal must be obtained from progressively leaner ores, fuels must be obtained from deposits which are progressively more difficult

to mine, and more equipment will be required for the handling and processing.

In the eighteenth century, ores that averaged less than 13 per cent copper were considered impracticable. By 1900 the average grade of copper ores being processed was about 5 per cent. By 1951 the average grade of ore being handled had dropped to 0.9 per cent, and ores containing as little as 0.6 per cent copper were being processed. Although copper consumption is much smaller than that of iron, it is necessary, in order to obtain the copper, to handle a quantity of copper ore each year which is equal to the total amount of iron ore produced in the United States annually.

As the grades of various metal ores fall, the amounts of equipment required for mining and extraction and the energy requirements per unit of output will increase. In turn, as we drill more and more deeply for our oil, and as we shift over to oil shales, coal hydrogenation, and atomic energy, more and more equipment will be required per unit of energy output.[6] These additional requirements for equipment will in turn result in greater per capita quantities of metals in use. Thus, while the amount of steel in use in the United States now corresponds to about 8 tons per person and might reach 15 tons per person by 1975, it might eventually reach much higher values when we look at the picture from a long-range point of view, possibly reaching 100 tons per person or more in the United States, in the absence of a major world catastrophe, by the end of another century.

SPREAD OF INDUSTRIALIZATION

Although the pig-iron production of the world has fluctuated as the result

6. See the discussion by Ayres and Scarlott (1952) concerning energy losses.

of war and economic depression, the general trend has been exponentially upward. Between 1885 and 1915 the United States pig-iron production doubled every twelve years.[7] Since 1935 production has been doubling every ten years. During the period 1924–41 Japan succeeded in doubling pig-iron production every five years. A five-year doubling time was achieved in the U.S.S.R. between 1926 and 1936. Soviet recovery and expansion, following the low production of 1942, have apparently progressed with a doubling time of about four years. Steel production was started in India shortly after the turn of the century, and since 1924 production of pig-iron has been increasing, with a doubling time of twenty-six years. It is likely that production will soon be accelerated and will increase at least another threefold during the next decade.[8] With the continued spread of industrialization, consumption of other metals has increased with equal rapidity.

It is the declared intention of Asian leaders to stimulate the industrialization of their countries to levels which approach existing Western levels. Whether or not they are able to accomplish this will depend upon a variety of factors: resources, population, rate of capital formation, rate of population growth, extent of help from the outside, etc. However, for the purpose of our discussion, let us assume that India is able to carry out successfully an industrialization program and that it is able to double its consumption of metals every ten years—a rate somewhat less than that achieved by the U.S.S.R. and Japan for rather lengthy periods. Starting with a pig-iron production of 1.8 million tons in 1951, production would reach 10 million tons by 1976 and 100 million tons by 2009. By 2021 production would reach 235 million tons, and a total of 1,400 million tons of pig iron would have been produced since 1951. By that time the population of India will almost certainly have doubled once again, and, when we take into account the losses of iron in use and in the steel cycle, the amount of steel in use would correspond to about a ton per person—a value considerably lower than the 8 tons per person in use in the United States at the present time.

Were pig-iron production to double every ten years, coal production would probably do likewise and might reach 4,000 million tons annually by 2021. By that time, 27,000 million tons of coal would have been removed from the ground, an amount approximately equal to the estimated reserves of all grades of coal *in situ* in India down to a depth of 2,000 feet (excluding lignite). The amount actually susceptible to mechanized mining operations may be only a small fraction of this.[9]

India possesses some of the richest and most extensive iron-ore deposits in the world, and, in the absence of exports either of the ore or of pig iron, its reserves would probably permit India to build up an amount of iron in use equivalent to existing Western per capita levels. With a doubling time of ten years nearly a century would be required. However, it might well turn out to be necessary for India to export pig iron or iron ore in order to help finance the considerable capital outlay which would be required for such an industrial development.[10] In such an eventuality it might be necessary for India to utilize low-grade deposits in

7. *Minerals Yearbook* (1952).

8. This estimate is based upon discussions with members of the Indian Planning Commission.

9. This estimate is based upon discussions with members of the Geological Survey of India.

10. There is at present considerable responsible discussion in India concerning the possibility of exporting iron ore.

order to approach existing Western levels of industrialization.

On the basis of considerations such as those outlined above, the industrialization of India would necessarily follow a pattern markedly different from the pattern observed thus far in the history of industrialization. India's existing resources would enable it to obtain a reasonable start toward industrialization; but, long before existing Western levels of productivity could be achieved, supplies of metallurgical coal would have disappeared, and India would be forced to produce pig iron by utilizing low-grade coals, perhaps by the sponge-iron process or by a process similar to the Swedish electrometal process. Again, long before existing Western levels are achieved, coal itself will be in very short supply, and pig iron will have to be produced by utilizing some other energy source, quite possibly atomic energy. Again, it is quite possible that, before India achieves existing Western levels of production, it will be forced to utilize ores of lower grade. This would create still greater needs for energy and for metals.

When we examine India's long-range requirements for other metals, we encounter similar difficulties. Local high-grade deposits of most ores are completely inadequate sources of metals in the quantities which are required. Clearly, the industrialization of India will require either the importation of huge quantities of metals, many of which are becoming scarce elsewhere in the world, or the satisfying of the demand internally by the extraction of the needed metals from very low-grade deposits, utilizing processes which are at present undeveloped but nevertheless conceivable.

There are those who maintain that areas such as India will not attempt to emulate the industrialized West with its high per capita level of productivity. Persons subscribing to this view maintain that the average Indian or Chinese does not desire large quantities of material possessions—that he desires only to live at a consumption level where life is not quite so difficult as at present. He would be happy, it is maintained, with an adequate food supply and adequate clothing, medical care, schooling, and housing—but divorced from the luxuries to which we have become accustomed in the West. Proponents of this general view believe that the bulk of Western productivity is aimed at the production of luxuries and that the production of life's necessities would require relatively little industrialization.

However, most persons, both Asian and non-Asian, agree that one of the better features of industrial civilization is that it has increased the length of the average human life-span, and most persons believe that each human being should have the right to live out that normal life-span. Indeed, the desire to live for as long a time as possible is one of the strongest of human desires and one which has contributed substantially to the formulation of existing development efforts.

When we enumerate all the facilities which are necessary in order to make it possible for the average person to live for a span of seventy years or thereabouts, we find that the list is surprisingly long. First, we require adequate food production, and this in turn requires irrigation and fertilizers. Elaborate transportation facilities are required to insure adequate distribution of fertilizers and food and to insure distribution of raw materials to the fertilizer factories. Construction of fertilizer factories, hospitals, and plants for the production of antibiotics requires steel, concrete, power, and a variety of raw materials. And, indeed, when we carry to completion our list of essentials which are necessary in order to permit the average man to avoid premature death, we find that we are not far removed from the per capita flow of goods which exists in the West today. To be sure, it is not necessary to have 8 tons of steel in use for every person, but it would be very difficult to get by with fewer than 1 or 2 tons.

Thus we see that the underdeveloped areas of the world are enormous potential consumers of the earth's resources. It is of course possible that war, political difficulties, social upheavals, or technological barriers will effectively prevent the industrialization of these areas. But if industrialization continues to spread over the surface of our globe, as seems likely, there will be consumption of resources on a scale difficult even for Americans to imagine.

AVAILABLE RAW MATERIALS

It is clear that, as material desires and needs increase, as more and more areas become industrialized, and as the population of the earth increases further, ever greater demands will be placed upon the earth's mineral resources. Although only a small fraction of the world is at present industrialized, we have already been confronted with diminishing concentrations of needed elements. And whereas man once found abundant high-grade ores at the surface of the earth, he must now frequently follow seams deep underground. The time must inevitably come when ores as such no longer exist, and machine civilization, if it survives, will feed on the leanest of substances—the rocks which make up the surface of our planet, the waters of the seas, and the gases of the atmosphere.

As time goes by, we will see mineral grades diminish, but with each step downward in grade there will be an enormous step upward in tonnage. As grades move downward, increasing emphasis will be placed upon the isolation of by-products and co-products, and

eventually we may reach the time when as many as twenty to thirty products are obtained from a single rock-mining operation. As grade goes down, energy costs per unit of output will of course go up; but, given adequate supplies of energy, it will be possible for industry to be fed for a very long time from the leanest of substances.

One hundred tons of average igneous rock contain, in addition to other useful elements, 16,000 pounds of aluminum, 10,000 pounds of iron, 1,200 pounds of titanium, 180 pounds of manganese, 70 pounds of chromium, 40 pounds of nickel, 30 pounds of vanadium, 20 pounds of copper, 10 pounds of tungsten, and 4 pounds of lead.[11] Given adequate supplies of energy, these elements could be extracted from the rock, and it appears likely that the rock itself contains the requisite amount of energy in the form of uranium and thorium.

One ton of average granite contains about 4 grams of uranium and about 12 grams of thorium. The energy content of this amount of uranium and thorium, assuming nuclear breeding, is equivalent to the energy released on burning approximately 50 tons of coal. It seems likely that the actual processing of the rock can be accomplished at an energy expenditure considerably smaller than 50 tons of coal, with the result that it seems possible to obtain a net profit from average rock and at the same time obtain a variety of metals which are essential to the operation of an industrial society.

There are large beds of rocks of various types which are intermediate in richness between existing low-grade ores and the average rocks discussed above. Before man processes average rock on a large scale, he will process higher-than-average rock. He will isolate iron from taconites, aluminum from anorthosites and clays, produce sulfuric

11. See Rankama and Sahama (1950).

acid from calcium sulfate, and isolate copper, tin, lead, nickel, and germanium from a variety of very low-grade deposits. But, eventually, man will learn to process ordinary rock, and, with practically infinite amounts of this lowest common denominator available, he will be able to build and power his machines for a very long time.

THE LONG VIEW

In the absence of a world catastrophe it seems highly likely that machine civilization either will spread rapidly over the surface of the earth, eventually to become stabilized, or will prove to be but a transient "Golden Age" in human history, destined eventually to disappear, much as biological species have disappeared in the past as the result of changing environment and the diminishing availability of the substances upon which the species have fed. If there is a world catastrophe, or if civilization regresses to an agrarian existence, technological denudation will be halted. However, let us assume for the purpose of discussion that industrialization spreads during the course of the next century to India, to the rest of Southeast Asia, to China, to Africa, and to South America. Let us assume further that world population continues to rise and that per capita demands for goods in existing industrialized areas continue to increase. Clearly in such an eventuality denudation will take place on a scale which is difficult for us to comprehend.

Let us now examine some of the patterns of consumption of raw materials which might be expected, during the decades and centuries to come, on the basis of these assumptions. In order to do this, we must let our imaginations run free and recognize that almost anything is possible from the technological point of view which does not violate the fundamental physical and biological laws which govern our world.

As time goes by, and the earth's resources of fossil fuels are consumed and deposits of high-grade ores are exhausted, we will approach asymptotically the condition wherein machine civilization is fed entirely by the processing of lowest common denominators —air, sea water, ordinary rock, and sunlight. By this time, population densities will have risen to the point where a great deal of water will be distilled from the sea for agricultural and industrial purposes, and most food will be grown by using artificial fertilizers. Metals such as iron, aluminum, titanium, manganese, copper, tungsten, and lead will be obtained from rock, which raw material will also provide the major source of phosphorus. The waters of the seas will provide magnesium, chlorine, bromine, iodine, and sulfur. Energy will be provided by the uranium and thorium of rocks, by the rays of the sun, and conceivably by controlled thermonuclear reactions utilizing deuterium extracted from the oceans. Liquid fuels and the whole complex of organic chemicals and plastics will be produced from the carbon of limestone, utilizing either atomic energy or controlled photosynthesis— probably both.

Let us assume that, by the time this point is reached, the technological complexities of extracting the necessary raw materials and of producing and transporting the requisite finished products necessitate that about 100 tons of iron and other metals be in use for every person alive. Under this circumstance the bulk of the necessary metals could be obtained under steady-state conditions by processing something on the order of 50 tons of rock per person per year. An amount of energy would be available from the rock which, depending upon the efficiency of extraction, might amount to the equivalent of about 1,000 tons of coal per person. Making due allowance for the efficiency of utilization of atomic energy under circumstances where nuclear "breeding" must be accomplished, at least this amount of energy will probably be necessary for powering the diverse extractive and manufacturing operations and for the processing of the sea water.

The total rate of denudation in this hypothetical world of the future will depend upon the level of population which has been reached by that time. On the basis of what we now know concerning the rates at which population growth can be slowed down, it is difficult to see how the population of the world can be stabilized at a level of much less than 7 billion (again, in the absence of a world catastrophe). On the basis of what we know about the potentialities of technology, a population of perhaps 100 billion could be supported, although, even with the high level of technology described above, the task of supporting this number might prove to be extremely difficult. For the purpose of our discussion let us assume that world population reaches a level intermediate between these two extremes—about 30 billion, corresponding to a twelve-fold increase over the existing population level.

A population of 30 billion persons would consume rock at a rate of about 1,500 billion tons per year. If we were to assume that all the land areas of the world were available for such processing, then, on the average, man would "eat" his way downward at a rate of 3.3 millimeters per year, or over 3 meters per millennium. This figure gives us some idea of the denudation rates which might be approached in the centuries ahead. And it gives us an idea of the powers for denudation which lie in mankind's hands.

The approach to the condition described above is, for obvious reasons, difficult to put in time perspective. However, certain probable patterns of future raw-material consumption emerge which can be discussed.

If we assume that pig-iron production outside the industrialized West doubles every decade, we can expect that, by the turn of the next century, a substantial fraction of the world will depend upon low-grade iron ore such as taconite. As supplies of metallurgical coal dwindle, an ever increasing fraction of our iron will be produced by utilizing processes which minimize or avoid the use of coke.

As supplies of bauxite dwindle, the aluminum industry will shift over to the processing of anorthosites and clays. Consumption of magnesium will increase, in part due to the ready availability of the element in sea water.

As supplies of elemental sulfur dwindle, increasing quantities of sulfuric acid will be manufactured from pyrites. As pyrites in turn disappear, sulfuric acid will be manufactured from calcium sulfate. These developments in turn will result in increasing emphasis being placed on the utilization of nitric and hydrochloric acids in chemical processing.

As the higher-grade deposits of the minor metals such as copper, lead, zinc, tin, germanium, and nickel dwindle, increasing emphasis will be placed upon the processing of low-grade deposits and upon the isolation of by-products and co-products. The mining industries as we know them today will gradually be transformed into enormous chemical industries.

As petroleum and oil shales dwindle, liquid fuels will be produced by coal hydrogenation. As coal in turn dwindles, its use will be confined to premium functions such as the production of chemicals.

These various changes, from one type of technology to another and from one type of raw material to another, will take place irregularly in the various regions of the world. Anorthosites will be processed in one region, while bauxite is still being processed in another. The use of atomic energy will become widespread in some regions, while others are still obtaining their energy from coal. But, gradually, the leveling effects of denudation will result in convergence of techniques and of raw materials—and mineral resources as we now know them will cease to play a major role in world economy and politics.

REFERENCES

AMERICAN IRON AND STEEL INSTITUTE
1948   *Steel Facts.* 8 pp. (Issued bi-monthly.)

ANONYMOUS
1952   *The Picture Story of Steel.* New York: American Iron and Steel Institute. 57 pp.

AYRES, EUGENE, and SCARLOTT, CHARLES A.
1952   *Energy Sources: The Wealth of the World.* New York: McGraw-Hill Book Co. 344 pp.

BROWN, HARRISON
1954   *The Challenge of Man's Future.* New York: Viking Press. 290 pp.

LASKY, S. G.
1945   "The Concept of Oil Reserves," *Mining and Metallurgy,* XXVI, 471–74.
1950   "How Tonnage and Grade Relations Help Predict Ore Reserves," *Engineering and Mining Journal,* CLI, No. 4, 81–85.
1951   "Mineral Industry Futures Can Be Predicted," *ibid.,* CLII, No. 8, 60–64.

PRESIDENT'S MATERIALS POLICY COMMISSION
1952   *Resources for Freedom,* Vol. I: *Foundations for Growth and Security;* Vol. II: *The Outlook for Key Commodities;* Vol. III: *The Outlook for Energy Sources;* Vol. IV: *The Promise of Technology;* Vol. V: *Selected Reports to the Commission.* Washington, D.C.: Government Printing Office.

RANKAMA, KALERVO, and SAHAMA, TH. G.
1950   *Geochemistry.* Chicago: University of Chicago Press. 912 pp.

UNITED STATES BUREAU OF MINES
1952   *Minerals Yearbook.* 3 vols. Washington, D.C.: Government Printing Office. (Issued annually.)

WOYTINSKY, W. and S.
1953   *World Population and Production: Trends and Outlook.* New York: Twentieth Century Fund. 1,268 pp.

ZIMMERMANN, ERICH W.
1951   *World Resources and Industries.* Rev. ed. New York: Harper & Bros. 832 pp.

The Role of Man

The Role of Man

Influence of Man upon Nature—the Russian View: A Case Study

ALBERT E. BURKE*

Several historical writers of the late nineteenth and early twentieth centuries considered the Slavic peoples of eastern Europe to have been one of the more important historical and geographical influences on the practical development of ideas in science which took place in Atlantic Europe after the seventeenth century (Sarolea, 1916; Kluchevsky, 1911–32; Wallace, 1877). The role, in this development, of the East Europeans who moved eastward to populate the forests and grassland margin of the great Russian plain was that of a "buffer" between the peoples of eastern Asia and the peoples of the small European peninsula in the west. Their geographical situation placed them close to, and in several places athwart, the main land routes of migration between east and west that lie north of the mountain rim[1] which separates present-day Russia from the coun-

tries of the Middle East. South of that mountain rim, centered on present-day Turkey, the Byzantine Empire performed a similar function in blocking the main land routes of migration from southeast to northwest. Together, the peoples of Byzantium and the peoples of early Russia formed a physical as well as a cultural axis, a buffer zone which acted for several hundred years to slow down or absorb westward-moving peoples from the east and southeast. For this reason, Europe—particularly Atlantic Europe—was left largely to its own devices, which were gradually worked into the tools and inventions that led ultimately to the industrial revolution. This gradual development of practical ideas in science took place among European peoples who were largely spared the disruptive impacts of non-European cultural invasions.

England, where the industrial revolution began, had a "defense in depth" against such invasion. The East European peoples and the Byzantine peoples comprised an "outer defensive rim," while the peninsula of Europe and the English Channel formed an inner protective belt. The people of England were favored by geographical conditions and by historical circumstance to be able to devote the greatest part of their energies to trade and commerce, on the one hand, and to the development of ideas in science, on the other. Spared the disruptive influence of non-

---

* Mr. Burke is Lecturer in Geography and Director of Graduate Studies in the Conservation Program at Yale University, New Haven, Connecticut. As the son of an American engineer employed in the U.S.S.R. after World War I, he lived and went to school for a number of years in the Soviet Union. His academic interests have been in geography, ecology, conservation, and education. For the last three years he has presented a weekly half-hour television program, entitled "This Is Your World," over WNHC-TV, New Haven, Connecticut.

1. The mountain rim made up of the Caucasus, Elburz, Hindu Kush, Pamir, and Tien Shan ranges.

European culture invasion, the British people worked those scientific ideas into the most disruptive physical and cultural force in human history.

The tools and inventions of the industrial revolution transformed the lives of most European peoples soon after their introduction into European affairs but have only within recent years reached out to affect the lives of the Slavic peoples, whose geographical and historical role on Europe's "outer rim" helped to make the development of those tools and inventions possible in the first place. The industrial revolution has been in process of disrupting the lives of Russia's people for somewhat less than a hundred years. It is in process of transforming the ways of life of people in many other places now. No other force in our lives is responsible to the same degree for the unrest and turmoil in the world today. No other force in human history has given man the power that he now commands to change the face of the earth. No other group of people is more determined to use that power to change the face of its part of the earth—a very large part—than the descendants of those early peoples along the northern part of Europe's outer rim—the Russians.

In his book *Russia in Flux*, Sir John Maynard suggested (1948, pp. 14–15) that one of the most important ideas brought into the lives of the Russian people by the Bolsheviks when they assumed control in Russia in 1917 was the idea that science gave creative powers. This concept, Sir John believed, was the essence of the New Russia, and it stemmed originally from the writings of Karl Marx. As interpreted by the Bolsheviks, Marx seemed to say that man was not bound to a pitilessly revolving wheel of fate but could contribute to the making of his own history—through the powers of science. This was a concept suited to

the needs of the hard core of Russian revolutionaries who were determined to transform a backward, agricultural Russian empire into a balanced industrial-agricultural nation in the shortest possible time. It was the kind of hope, or faith, needed to motivate the Russian people to fight against the severe physical limitations which affect literally the whole of Russia—limitations not entirely understood by the casual observer of the Russian scene.

Cressey (1949, p. 335) has stated succinctly and well the "too much" or "too little" aspect of Russian geography. Northern Russia is too cold and wet, southern Russia is too dry and hot, and eastern Russia is too high and cold and dry to be worked easily for the production of the quantity and variety of agricultural and industrial raw materials needed by a modern, balanced, agricultural-industrial state. More effort and energy must be expended to wrest industrial raw materials from a frozen landscape in Siberia than from resource bases in the Ruhr Valley or the mines in our states of Illinois and Kentucky. More effort and energy must be expended to wrest agricultural raw materials from a land base affected by a strong continental climate and unprotected by any significant geographical barriers in the north from the influence of the Arctic than are needed to grow the foodstuffs and industrial crops taken off the farmlands of Europe or the United States. The need for a strong faith in man's ability to overcome such limitations explains in large part the heavy emphasis on the place of science in Soviet affairs from the outset of the Soviet regime. Science in the U.S.S.R. is considered to be a weapon for use in "transforming nature." This purpose was clearly expressed in what was called the "Great Plan for the Transformation of Nature" announced by the Soviet press late in 1948.[2] The essence

2. *Pravda*, October 24, 1948.

of this plan was to change the face of the Russian earth, but its roots go deeper into Russian history than the last thirty-eight years of Soviet emphasis on science.

The tools and inventions of the industrial revolution reached Russia long after they had disrupted and transformed the ways of life, and landscapes, of peoples in Europe. About two hundred years before the Bolshevik seizure of power in 1917, Peter the Great, personally and with great diligence, tried to import the newly developing industrial bases of national and international power from western Europe and to establish them in Russia. To do this, he spent two years traveling through Germany, Holland, and England, working as a common laborer in shipyards, studying the factory system, conversing with learned men of science, and gathering models of machines as well as scientific literature. His efforts were not successful because he tried to superimpose the more advanced material standards of western Europe on a fixed, feudal agricultural base which had already been discarded in England and was on the way out in much of the rest of Europe. Not until Russia's defeat in the Crimean War a hundred and fifty years after the time of Peter the Great did the full effect of this measure of Russia's retarded development, its feudal system, become clear. The industrial revolution had produced a new power base in the world through the practical development and use of ideas in science. Russia did not have that base. Alexander II, who ruled at that time, acted to establish the new base of power in Russia by introducing the reforms which abolished feudalism in that country in 1861. This was the point in time when the industrial revolution entered the body of Russian life by disrupting the near-subsistence economy of the peasant. A money economy was introduced by requiring the peasant

village community to buy land from the landed aristocracy. Alexander hoped that the need to acquire money for payment of land would force the Russian peasant to produce agricultural surpluses which would require more modern methods of farming and which would produce a reserve of capital to be used by the aristocracy in establishing and expanding a Russian industrial base. It was a well-conceived idea; as carried out, though, it was tragically inadequate to the need of that time.

However, Alexander's reforms did bring about significant changes in the Russian landscape. Urban centers immediately began to expand as displaced farm labor moved to the cities. Farming areas expanded, too, as a railroad network was established linking the main agricultural districts to domestic and to world markets. The extractive industries boomed as industrial bases were established in the Ukraine and central Russia. The industrial revolution began the process of transforming the ways of life and landscapes of Russia's people more than fifty years before the Bolsheviks came to power to intensify that process. The roots of present-day Soviet plans to change the face of Russian earth go deep into Russian history. The need to do so goes deep into Russia's future.

Few concepts developed in western Europe have been castigated by Soviet scientists as thoroughly as that of Thomas Malthus and those of other European and American writers who suggest that man must operate within a framework of specific, though changing and fairly broad, limitations at all times (Semenov and Popov, 1950). The Malthusian concept, published in 1798, suggests a close relationship between the size of populations of living organisms and the means for their subsistence. The concept that there is a need to maintain a balance in nature, in which man recognizes limitations imposed by his natural environment beyond which it is not wise to go at a given moment in time, crosses the grain of Soviet purpose to use science as a means of mastering all environmental limitations. Subsequent to the publication of Malthus' idea, more than a hundred years of great undreamed-of economic expansion pushed it into the background of scientific thinking in those parts of the world affected by the industrial revolution. Recent events the world over, however, in places where populations are pushing the limits of their food and other resource supplies, have once more brought the ideas expressed by Malthus into focus. Russia itself is one of those places, despite the vehement denials of Soviet cornucopians.

To a degree that most Americans cannot quite understand, a healthy industrial economy rests heavily on a healthy agricultural base. America has been so graciously endowed with vast tracts of fertile lands, and has been so fortunate in not having to overcome established traditions of land use during its agricultural development, that the full significance of land problems—in Russia or any place else—simply has not been grasped by us. Considerable emphasis has been placed on several important similarities which exist in the agricultural histories of the American and Russian peoples by writers who point out the movement of each group from a forested base to grasslands and finally into desert and mountain country. The movement in North America, which dominated agricultural development in what is now the United States, was westward from the humid forested hearth in which the original colonies were located. Russia expanded primarily to the east, from the humid forested hearth of early Muscovy. However great the similarity of landscapes into which both peoples moved as they grew into land empires, the land-use systems laid down in each place were not alike.

America's growth was not accompanied by the imposition of a land-use pattern which was intended to integrate the whole of the expanding state into an already established agricultural system—such as that which operated in Russia during that country's feudal period. While there were areas in the United States in which elements of the feudal system did operate, as in the southern colonies and in later time the group of states included in the southern Confederacy of the mid-nineteenth century, nevertheless it was the northern farmer whose influence was greatest in the evolution of American agriculture. This influence in the United States resulted in an emphasis upon individual property rights in land, and it was supported by the homestead system through which the American "public domain" passed into the hands of a largely independent farm population. The face of the American earth in the United States shows the effect of this land-use pattern in the widely distributed homesteads of our farmlands. Each farmer lives on the land he owns or works.

The face of the Russian earth presents a very different aspect, reflecting the evolution of a land-use system rooted in large part in the historical experience of the Russian people. Geography and history combined to affect the development of Russian society on the great Russian plain in ways that placed the farming population of that country in village communities, not in individual homes on individual farmsteads. The Soviet Russian collective-farm and state-farm system today is essentially superimposed upon this early village community pattern in which the farmers live together in a central place and work the farmlands which are laid out around the central place. This land-use system is not uniquely or distinctly Russian. It operated in Europe at one time, and vestiges of this system still remain there. It operates today in much of the rest of the world. The reasons for its presence in Russia, however, and its strength as an element of present-day Soviet society are relatively unique and distinctive.

Conflict with other societies and the problems presented by the physical environment are a part of the backgrounds of human beings throughout the world. The Slavs on the great Russian plain reacted to the stimulus of their particular physical and cultural problems by banding together into communal groups to overcome them. These communal groups operated under conditions that have been described for other peoples in other places as those of a system of archaic communism (Hourwich, 1892, p. 19). On the Russian plain this early communal organization served best to meet the periodic impact of cultural invaders from east and west, on the one hand, and to wrest a livelihood, on the other, from a land base with severe environmental limitations. Unlike the gray-brown podzolic soils of the early northern and middle colonies in North America, which are the most naturally fertile and productive of the world's pedalferic soils, the much less fertile and less productive podzolic soils of early Muscovy were easily "worked out" in most places and necessitated a form of shifting agriculture. The particular combination of geographical and historical circumstances involved made a settled existence for the early Russians hazardous and the establishment of a firm Russian government difficult. The first firm government of national character appears in Russia with the crowning of the first great prince of all the Russias in 1462. At this point in time, when grants in land were given to loyal servitors of the great prince, the basis for Russian feudalism which tied the communal groups to the land was established. As indicated earlier,

Russian feudalism lasted into the mid-nineteenth century, incorporating, as it expanded eastward, new lands and new peoples into an existent agricultural system. The land-use pattern which developed during that time had too much cultural momentum to break down in the relatively short period between the end of feudalism in 1861 and the establishment of Soviet power in 1917. The Bolsheviks in 1928 acted to perpetuate this deeply rooted Russian land-use system by making it the basis for a collectivized agriculture. Thus the face of Russian earth presents a very different aspect of human occupance and activity from the face of American earth, whatever similarities may otherwise exist in the agricultural histories of both places.

Today's collectivized agricultural system in Russia has increased agricultural production over all but not at a rate to keep pace with the expanding needs of a rapidly growing human population. Population pressure on Russian farmlands has been an important factor in that country's land problems since the middle of the nineteenth century. As a region of extensive agriculture, with a lower carrying capacity than exists on the farmlands of the rest of Europe, where a more intensive agriculture is practiced, Russia's agricultural means of subsistence to support its growing population is one of its more serious present problems. The increasing pressure of growing populations on their agricultural means of subsistence and other resource supplies also confronts more than two-thirds of the agricultural world around the "Western" industrial nations.

The American people have not known this kind of problem and do not understand it. More than anything else, this lack of awareness of the meaning of land problems in the lives of the largely agricultural world around us is at the root of our current troubles in international affairs. The Russians are more closely attuned to the problems of peoples in that agricultural world because of their own agricultural difficulties, which are severe. Russia's physical disadvantage in this respect has been manipulated to its political advantage on the ideological "front" in the nature of its drive for the support and loyalties of land-poor and land-hungry peoples throughout the world. However, in the long run, this ideolog-

is great. Russia's status as a world power depends upon the degree to which success in changing the face of its earth is possible.

The "Great Plan for the Transformation of Nature," mentioned previously, was planned to attack the land problem and thus expand the means of subsistence being put under pressure at the moment by the rapidly expanding Soviet population. In December, 1953, it was announced that many parts of

Fig. 175.—The Russian agricultural wedge

ical advantage is not enough. Raw materials feed the expanding industrial capacities of all industrial societies. Roughly half the raw materials consumed in our manufacturing industries in the United States come from our farmlands (Ordway, 1953, p. 22). Comparable statistics for the Soviet Union's manufacturing process are not available, but there is no reason to assume that Russian farmlands are less important in this respect than our own. Russia's need to overcome its land problems

this plan had been discontinued. However, its importance for our consideration lies in an analysis of the problems the plan was originally designed to overcome as well as of the methods to be used in overcoming them which are reflected in landscape change. The Soviet Union's best agricultural lands (Fig. 175) are situated in a fairly narrow triangular wedge on the great Russian plain in the western half of the country. The broad base of this wedge lies in the west, with the apex in the east roughly at that point where the Yenisei River pours out of the Siberian upland. The bulk of the Soviet Union's political, social, and economic activities are centered in that agricultural wedge, and all these activities are subject to physical hazards not encountered in other parts of the industrialized world.

The northern part of the Siberian upland, in the eastern half of Russia, has been called the world's "weather factory." Air-mass movements originating here affect the weather of North Americans and Europeans most of each year. During the winter months a heavy mass of cold air descends on the Siberian upland as a result of the extreme cooling of the land. It spreads out at the surface in all directions to affect all parts of the Asian land mass in varying degree, but that part of it moving westward undergoes some changes which have a strong influence on human activities on the great Russian plain (Balzak *et al.*, 1952). There are no significant barriers between the agricultural wedge on the plain and the Arctic Ocean. A cross-section of the Russian plain from north to south will show a gradual rise in the elevation of the land mass from the shores of the Arctic Ocean to a low east-west divide about midway between the northern and southern limits of the country and a fall to the south. In the eastern part of western Russia this fall continues to points well below sea level in the central Asian depression which includes the Caspian Sea.

North winds from the Arctic move across this barrier-free landscape to penetrate deeply into the country. These north winds join forces with the flow of bitterly cold air off the Siberian upland; together they act to blanket the Russian plain. I lived in the city of Kharkov during the winter of the year 1931 and can remember a siege of cold waves which lowered temperatures there to —30° F.—cold waves which kept temperatures near freezing that

year until about the first week of May. If for any reason this blanket of cold air lasts too long in the spring, or sets in too early in the fall, many agricultural districts on the plain are affected adversely, for the growing season is shortened critically. Any loss today of harvestable crops can be a serious blow to the Soviet economy, which needs to support a population of about 210 million persons.

The combination of Arctic winds from the north and the flow of air from the Siberian upland also creates on the Russian plain what are known as *burani*. These are strong surface winds which act to remove the winter snow cover from open fields, thus reducing the reserve of soil moisture available for crops during the planting period the following spring. The evaporative power of these winds during the winter months is particularly effective in removing moisture from the soil in the absence of a protective snow cover. Many experimental methods have been undertaken to ameliorate this problem (Kovda, 1952, p. 27).

The winter climatic hazards in the agricultural picture are matched by the problem of periodic drought during the growing season and by the movement of hot, dry winds called *suxovei* from the arid lands of south-central Russia into the forest-steppe and black-earth districts of the western and central parts of the country. According to Russian agricultural records, there were thirty-four such years of drought and dry winds in the eighteenth century and forty of them during the nineteenth century, an average of approximately one year of drought every two or three years (*ibid.*, p. 23). The dry, summer *suxovei* are similar to the hot winds from the desert interior of California, which are known locally as "Santa Anas" and have a high evaporative effect. Attempts to cut down the effects of these winds on Russian farmlands go back more than a century in the Ukraine and were supported strongly in the writings of Russian soil scientists, such as Williams, Doku-chaev, Kostichev, Vysotskii, and others on behalf of afforestation projects.

The "Great Plan for the Transforma-tion of Nature," announced in 1948, of the *suxovei* and so mitigate their ef-fect on the grain-producing regions (Fig. 176). A thick network of collec-tive-farm and state-farm forest strips were to be established as well, which would cover about 15 million acres but would protect up to 300 million acres of farmland, some of which would be

Fig. 176.—Shelter-belt network: Dokuchaev Experiment Station, Stony Steppe, Voronesh Re-gion, U.S.S.R. (From *USSR in Construction*, 1949, Issue 3, p. 1.)

was basically a huge afforestation proj-ect and was described as "a fifteen-year plan for changing the natural condi-tions of the steppe and forest-steppe regions of western Russia" (*ibid.*, p. 30). According to the plan, eight state forest belts were to be established along the flood lands and watersheds of the major rivers. It was hoped and be-lieved that these vegetation barriers would act to slow down the movement placed under crops for the first time (Fig. 177). At the same time a specific pattern of grassland crop rotations was to be introduced to better the condition of farmland soils, along with the con-struction of 44,000 ponds and reservoirs for storage purposes and to meet local irrigation needs. The farmed areas be-tween the tree belts would be protected against the loss of winter snow cover due to the *burani* as well as against the

Fig. 177.—Location of the projected state shelter belts and field windbreaks, U.S.S.R. (From *USSR in Construction*, 1949, Issue 3.)

effects of the summer *suxovei*, thus contributing to greater reserves of moisture
in the soil each year to meet plant needs
and so provide bigger and better harvests for a rapidly expanding Soviet
population.

Implicit in this plan was the idea that
man can control climate. Not only was
it expected that the planting of trees
and shrubs, by altering the microclimate in the protected areas, would protect Russian farmlands against the severe physical hazards but it was also
believed that the macroclimate of the
affected regions in the western part of
the Russian plain would be changed
significantly by the artificial creation of
tree belts as planned. The consensus at
the moment is that such speculation is
largely nonsense. Meteorologists and
climatologists are pretty much agreed
that climate produces vegetation and
that vegetation does not affect the climate significantly. However, there are
dissenting points of view on this matter, particularly among those scientific workers who point out that our
knowledge is inadequate about ground-
water characteristics and their effect on
plant life and about evapotranspiration
rates for different kinds of trees and
plants and their effect on local climates
(Zon, 1927). Then, too, there are others
who suggest that the full extent of
man's activities in the past in creating
artificially cleared landscapes and the
effect of this carried into the present
period are not well known either
(Sauer, 1952, pp. 12–18). The latter
point of view is supported by the Russian geographer Kotelnikov (1950, pp.
150–53), who states his belief that the
original character of any landscape is
altered for very long periods of time, if
not permanently, by human activity.
He stresses the fact that, were all human activity in any given area to end
suddenly, all the elements of nature in
that area would not revert to an "original" state and could not "by themselves." Kotelnikov sees the "Great Plan

for the Transformation of Nature" as
a means of restoring nature to former
levels of productivity through the careful and sensible use of the scientific
method and in this way getting nature
to work better to satisfy man's needs.

Two important factors in the possible
success or failure of this effort to alter
Russian agricultural landscapes are the
nature of the area involved and its importance in the Soviet economy. The
afforestation project was intended to
protect a large part of Russia's good-
to-excellent farmlands located in the
"forest steppe" (Fig. 178). This is a region, located south of the mixed and
coniferous forest zone of northern and
central Russia, which in the past was
covered by fairly heavy stands of trees
in many places. With the expansion of
the Russian state into this vegetational
zone, practically all of this natural tree
cover was removed in order to prepare
the land for farming. Whether or not
an area once in trees could again be
planted to trees and be made to maintain them—restoring nature to a former
level of productivity as visualized by
Kotelnikov—was of considerable importance in the tree-belt plan.

A similar afforestation project in the
United States in 1934 undertook to
plant approximately 30,220 tree belts
along the hundredth meridian. Almost
18,600 miles of such belts on our farmlands in that region were eventually established, but the results were not generally successful except in local places.
Much work remains to be done to analyze specifically the effects of our shelter-belt plantings upon agriculture in
that part of North America. The area
involved in the United States encompassed that part of American farmlands
in the vicinity of the 20-inch rainfall
line, which is generally considered to
be the line beyond which agriculture
either cannot be carried on without irrigation or is considered to be a hazardous undertaking (Fig. 179). It is also
in the general vicinity of the line sep-

Fig. 178.—Landscape zones of the U.S.S.R.

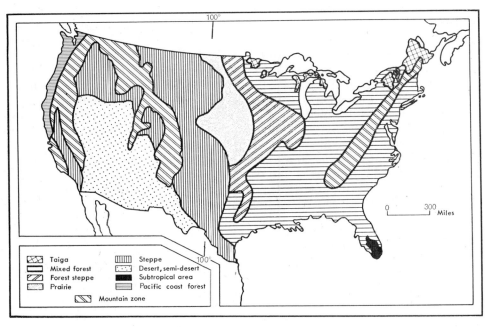

Fig. 179.—Landscape zones of the United States

arating the short-grass and tall-grass country and is not considered to be a part of the forested area of the country. This region along the hundredth meridian does not include the bulk of this nation's best producing farmlands; but the area encompassed by the Soviet Union's afforestation project does include a large part of Russia's best farmlands.

These are very important and significant differences, too often ignored. The differences which exist underscore a greater Russian need to make the shelter-belt program succeed in the Soviet Union, where a similar effort might not be considered worth the time or expense in other parts of the world. In the years immediately preceding World War II, when the population of the Soviet Union numbered about 175 million persons, that country harvested crops on about 338 million acres of farmland. During the same period the United States, with a smaller population numbering about 130 million persons, harvested crops from 343 million acres of farmland. The amounts of cropland in production have not changed appreciably in either place since that time, though population growth has been great in both countries. With a larger population dependent upon a smaller and more severely restricted agricultural base than exists in the United States, the Soviet Union is striving to overtake and surpass America as a leading world power. The serious nature of the Russian problem—its greater need to stabilize and expand its agricultural situation as was contemplated in the plan to establish tree belts—is clear.

Whatever the ultimate effect of the plan may have been, a progress report issued in 1951 indicated that at that time more than 5,000,000 acres had been planted with trees and shrubs, more than 13,000 reservoirs and ponds were completed, and 350 forest-protection stations had been organized and were served by specially assigned, skilled personnel. Survival rates were not listed to indicate how many of the trees and shrubs planted since the start of the project remained alive in 1951. The record of other afforestation experiments of similar nature carried on in various parts of Russia since 1931 indicates a survival rate of about 20 per cent under roughly similar conditions (Krylov *et al.*, 1948, pp. 199–220). Despite this inauspicious prospect, there is no doubt that the effort to bring about this colossal transformation of the Russian landscape was stressed and that part of the plan was accomplished, prior to December, 1953, to meet Russia's immediate need for a stabilized as well as an expanded agricultural base.

Soon after the explosion of Russia's first atomic bomb in September, 1949, the Soviet Union's chief delegate to the United Nations, in a speech before the General Assembly of that body, stated that atomic power would be used to "move aside mountains" and to "change the courses of rivers" in the peaceful development of the Russian economy. The motivation for this speech was an article which appeared in a geological journal published in 1949 by the Academy of Sciences in the USSR outlining a plan for the displacement of fresh water from rivers in the Russian north to the central Asian desert territories in the south. This was to be a gigantic effort to reclaim the arid lands in the south and at the same time provide fresh water to stop the fall in the level of the Caspian Sea, which had been particularly noticeable in recent years (Obruchev, 1949, pp. 230–33).

The plan was considered to be feasible by the Russians because of the lay of the land mentioned earlier in describing the cross-section from the Arctic through to the central Asian depression. The upland ridge, or divide, extending east-west through the center of Russia's great plain and lowland region west of the Yenisei River is responsible for the north-south drainage pattern in the western half of the country (Fig. 180). One of the flattest unbroken landscapes on earth exists north of this continental divide in the area between the Ural Mountains and the Siberian upland. Across this terrain, with a fall of only 298 feet in 1,864 miles (a drop of less than 2 inches per mile), the Ob-Irtysh river system drains northward to

water into the rivers, which then proceed to flood large areas of this flat land surface until such time as the ice dam breaks. At that time this great reserve of fresh water—needed so badly in Russia's agricultural districts in the southern and western regions of the country —is lost as it enters the Arctic Ocean.

The Ob-Irtysh lowland is a part of the earth's crust which underwent subsidence sometime during pre-Jurassic

FIG. 180.—Drainage network of the U.S.S.R.

the Arctic Ocean (Nuttonson, 1950). The direction of flow is such that freezing of the mouth of the Ob occurs with the onset of cold weather before the main body of water in the rivers to the south is affected, which causes an annual pile-up of fresh water behind an ice dam. This winter condition, however, is little more than a prelude to the deluge of waters from the south which begins with the spring thaw. Melting snows and the early spring rains falling on a largely frozen, impermeable land surface pour great quantities of fresh

time (Edelstien, 1926). During the first half of the Tertiary period this lowland was covered by a sea which drained through a break in the upland ridge rimming the lowland in the south in the vicinity of the headwaters of the Tobol River. The essence of this water displacement scheme, envisaged by a Soviet technician named Davidov, was to dam and drain parts of the flooded Ob-Irtysh lowland through this ancient channel which once fed a much larger Aral Sea. This would provide the water needed to expand agricultural activities in the central Asian depression and at the same time supplement the water taken for irrigation purposes from the Volga River. The Volga is the main source of water for the Caspian Sea, and the fall in level of that water body has been attributed to the great drain on the Volga's water as that river passes through Russia's farmlands. Water from the Ob-Irtysh river system would replace this loss. Parts of this plan, as in the case of the "Great Plan for the Transformation of Nature," have been undertaken and in part completed. The grand scale of this latter project also was reduced in scope in December, 1953. The important aspect of both plans, however, is the expressed conviction that man can dominate nature.

This conviction is passed on forcefully in the educational system of the Soviet Union, in which a devotion to science, technology, and machinery is stressed. From the start of the drive to build an industrial power, the Soviet schools have performed a very important role in teaching what was considered to be the correct point of view about land use in Russia. In 1928, at the outset of the first of the several five-year plans which have raised Russia from an eighth-rate industrial power to a point where that country is now second in industrial production only to the United States, the slogan "Technique Decides Everything" shaped the emphasis on Soviet education (Johnson, 1952). This emphasis was expressed clearly in a textbook published in the U.S.S.R. in 1929 for school children from twelve to fourteen years of age. It was called "The Great Plan" and referred to the meaning of the first five-year plan which was begun in October, 1928 (Ilin, 1929). Page 2 of this textbook states in part:

On the banks of a large river great cliffs are being broken into bits while great machines like prehistoric monsters lumber clumsily up and down a gigantic ladder carved out of a mountain. A river appears where none existed before, many kilometers long. A swamp is suddenly transformed into a broad lake. On the steppe, where only feather grass and red top grew, thousands of acres of wheat now wave in the breeze. Steel masts rise over the whole country; each mast has four legs and many arms and each arm grasps metal wires. Through these wires runs a current, the power and might of rivers and of waterfalls, of coal beds and peat swamps. This is the five-year plan.

Chapter iv of this book goes on to say:

We must discover and conquer the country in which we live. It is a tremendous country, but not yet entirely ours. Our steppe will truly become ours only when we come with columns of tractors and plows to break the thousand-year-old virgin soil. On a far-flung front we must wage war. We must burrow into the earth, break rocks, dig mines, construct houses. We must take from the earth. . . .

This emphasis upon the need to wage constant war against nature, to dominate the physical world around man, to control it, was expressed in a basic textbook for children. It is matched on a higher level, in science, by the often-quoted statement of the Russian plant scientist Ivan Michurin to the effect that "we can expect no favors from Nature; our job is to take them." To make it possible for Soviet man to subdue nature, the Soviet educational system has emphasized and provided the necessary techniques. The drive to subdue nature is an essential part of the Soviet economy.

In a report delivered at the Eighteenth All Union Conference of the Communist Party of the Soviet Union on February 18, 1941, N. Voznesensky, one-time head of the State Planning Commission, after reviewing the accomplishments of the Soviet economy, described and discussed its goals. Briefly stated, they are:

1. The national economy of the U.S.S.R. . . . implies first and foremost a constant and steady growth in all branches of that economy.
2. It further implies a steady increase in Socialist accumulation.
3. It further implies a steady rise in the material standard of the working people, an increase in their consumption.

As described by Voznesensky, the Soviet economic ideal is that of a constantly expanding economy which provides for a steady increase in the accumulation of material wealth and a progressively higher standard of living for its people. Whatever political label may be attached to this economic purpose, it cannot be realized without an adequate resource base and an adequate development of that resource base.

In contrast to its agricultural situation, the Soviet Union's industrial base is strong. A considerable part of Russia has not yet been adequately mapped geologically, but that country is already almost self-contained in the minerals required by industry. This favorable mineral situation is to a considerable extent the result of the post–World War II expansion of Soviet power, which has included the countries of eastern Europe, China, North Korea, and North Viet-Nam in the Communist bloc. From these countries are derived those mineral items which were in short supply in Russia before World War II (Bateman, 1952). The need to supply these items has resulted in an expansion of the extractive industries' base in the newly created Soviet states which is closely related to the establishment of heavy industry in each place. This emphasis is in line with the basically similar development that took place in Russia during the several five-year plans which have resulted in striking changes of cultural landscape in that country. Older cities and towns in Russia grew quickly under the stimulus of industrialization, and new rural and urban centers have been created where the need existed. Moscow, for example, increased in population from 1,800,000 in 1913 to 5,100,000 by 1950. Similarly, the city of Kharkov in the Ukraine jumped from 250,000 persons to almost 850,000 during the same period. Gorki, an important automotive center in west-central Russia, has grown about six times its size of 1913. Stalino, in the industrial center of the Ukraine, expanded ten times. Cultural landscapes in the Soviet world show the effects of widespread urbanization as the disruption of the formerly dominant agricultural economies of most of that part of the world goes on.

Considered over all, the resources available to the Soviet Union of States and to Russia in particular are not favorably distributed. There is no real equivalent in the Soviet Union today for its major industrial centers to compare with the favorable juxtaposition of resource items that exists in many parts of the United States. The bulk of Russian coal supplies, for example, are located east of the Ural Mountains, while the major supplies of its good iron ores are located west of that mountain range. Distances are great, and the long hauls required to bring industrial minerals and related resources together explain the critical role of the railroads in Russian industry. It also explains the location of new cities and towns which have been created across the length and breadth of Russia in the Soviet period.

The resource base of the United States, well favored by nature in the quantity, quality, and variety of materials as well as the accessibility of those materials, has made the realization of the economic goals stated by Voznesensky in 1941 possible for the American people. The attempt to realize this goal in the U.S.S.R. has required not only greater effort to obtain the necessary materials from a less-favored Russian resource base but has resulted, as well, in different economic institutions to make this possible. One such institution is the Soviet State Planning Commission, which spearheads what the Russians have described as the "war against nature on a far-flung front." All activities devoted to an expansion of the Soviet economy—whether this involves the opening of new farmland, the building of new cities and hydroelectric installations, the establishment of shelter belts, or the number of can-openers and hairpins available to the Russian public—are affected by the operation of this government agency. It mobilizes and directs the nation's entire resources, physical as well as cultural, to the end that the limitations hindering Soviet development into a great power will be overcome. The results of this drive in Russian life are already evident in the changes that have been made in the natural landscape to support a balanced agricultural-industrial state. There is little doubt that greater changes are in the offing as the Soviet Union, dedicated to the idea that science gives creative powers, tries to narrow the gap between its basis for natural and international power and those that exist in Europe and America.

REFERENCES

BALZAK, S. S.; VASYUTIN, V. F.; and FEIGIN, Y. G.
  1952 *Economic Geography of the USSR.* New York: Macmillan Co. 620 pp.
BATEMAN, A. M.
  1952 "Our Future Dependence on Foreign Minerals," *Annals of the American Academy of Political and Social Science,* CCLXXXI, 25–32.
CRESSEY, GEORGE
  1949 "USSR: The Geographic Base for Agricultural Planning," *Land Economics,* XXV, No. 4, 334–36.
EDELSTIEN, A. S.
  1926 "Geologicheskii Ocherk Zapad-no-Sibirskoi Ravnini" ("Geological Sketch of the West-Siberian Plain"), *Journal of the All Union Geographical Society,* No. 5, pp. 1–75. Leningrad.
HOURWICH, J. A.
  1892 *The Economics of the Russian Village.* ("Columbia Studies in Economics, History, and Public Law," Vol. II.) New York: Columbia College. 182 pp.
ILIN, M.
  1929 *Velikii Plan* ("The Great Plan"). Moscow: Government Publication. 162 pp.
JOHNSON, W. H. E.
  1952 "Education in the Soviet Union," pp. 384–413 in MOEHLMAN, A. H., and ROUCEK, J. S. (eds.), *Comparative Education.* New York: Dryden Press. 630 pp.
KLUCHEVSKY, V. O.
  1911–32 *History of Russia.* 5 vols. London: J. M. Dent.
KOTELNIKOV, V. L.
  1950 "Ob Izmenenii Geographicheskoi Sredi Selskoxoziaistvennoi Deyatel-nostiv Cheloveka" ("Changes of Geographical Environment through Agricultural Activities of Man"), *Journal of the All Union Geographical Society,* Vol. LXXXII, No. 2. Leningrad.
KOVDA, V. A.
  1952 *Velikii Plan Preobrazovania Prirodi* ("Great Plan for the Transformation of Nature"). Moscow: Academy of Sciences of the USSR. 110 pp.
KRYLOV, A. V.; EITINGEN, G.; and DEMIDOV, S. F.
  1948 *Podëm Kulturi Sotsialisticheskovo Zemledeliya* ("Raising Crops of Socialist Agriculture"). Moscow: Government Publication. 328 pp.
MAYNARD, SIR JOHN
  1948 *Russia in Flux.* New York: Macmillan Co. 564 pp.
NUTTONSON, M. Y.
  1950 *Agricultural Climatology of Siberia, Natural Belts, and Agro-climatic Analogues in North America.*

(Study No. 13.) Washington, D.C.: American Institute of Crop Ecology. 64 pp.

OBRUCHEV, V. O.
1949 Discussion in *Journal of the Academy of Sciences Geological Series,* No. 6 (November), pp. 230–33. Moscow.

ORDWAY, SAMUEL H., JR.
1953 *Resources and the American Dream.* New York: Ronald Press. 55 pp.

SAROLEA, CHARLES
1916 *Europe's Debt to Russia.* London: William Heineman. 250 pp.

SAUER, CARL O.
1952 *Agricultural Origins and Dispersals.* (Bowman Memorial Lectures, Series Two.) New York: American Geographical Society. 110 pp.

SEMENOV, Y. N., and POPOV, A. Y.
1950 "Maltuzianskie Teorii na Sluzhbe Anglo-Americanskovo Imperializma" ("The Malthusian Theory in the Service of Anglo-American Imperialism"), *Questions of Philosophy,* I, 245. Moscow.

VOEIKOV (WOEIKOF), A. I.
1949 *Vozdeistvie Cheloveka na Prirodu* ("The Effect of Man on Nature"). Moscow: Government Publication of Geographical Literature. 255 pp.

VOZNESENSKY, N.
1941 "Results of 1940" and "Economic Plan for 1941," pp. 21–51 in *USSR Speaks for Itself.* London: Lawrence & Wishart, Ltd. 359 pp.

WALLACE, D. MACKENZIE
1877 *Russia.* New York: Henry Holt & Co. 788 pp.

ZON, RAPHAEL
1927 *Forests and Water in the Light of Scientific Investigation.* (United States Department of Agriculture, Forest Service.) Washington, D.C.: Government Printing Office. 35 pp.

Man's Relation to the Earth in Its Bearing on His Aesthetic, Ethical, and Legal Values[1]

F. S. C. NORTHROP[*]

Contemporary man is at once the creator and the captive of a technological civilization. Its instruments have related him to the earth in a new way. This new way has reflected back upon man himself, forming and altering his values. Of what do these modifications of the humanity of man consist? This, I take it, is our question.

Put more concretely, the question is: What effect has man's role in changing the face of the earth had on his aesthetic sensitivity and creativity, his ethical and legal standards for ordering his relations to his fellow-men, his emotive relation to nature itself and to its creation, and his moral standards for determining whether his tools are used for good or for bad ends? The last factor suggests that the answer which the evidence and its analysis permit us to give to this question may well determine whether man remains the master or becomes the slave and perhaps even the murdered victim of his tools.

In selecting and analyzing the relevant evidence, what method are we to use? Clearly the method chosen will determine the character of the answer. It is important, therefore, that we allow the nature of the question to guide us to the relevant data for answering it. Our question implies two things: first, that man's relation to nature is different in a technological civilization from what it is in a non-technological one; second, that his cultural values differ correspondingly. Our first task, therefore, becomes that of finding the criterion which distinguishes a technological from a non-technological civilization. Having done this, we can then turn to the respective values of each.

THE DIFFERENCE BETWEEN A TECHNOLOGICAL AND A NON-TECHNOLOGICAL CIVILIZATION

Finding this difference is not easy. The difficulty becomes evident when one asks: Do not all men have tools, at least the tools of their natural hands

* Professor Northrop is Sterling Professor of Philosophy and Law at Yale University, New Haven, Connecticut. He is a member of the American Philosophical Association (Eastern Division) and was its president in 1952; of the American Association for the Advancement of Science and formerly vice-president, Section L, on the History and Philosophy of Science; and of the East-West Conference on Philosophy in 1939 and 1949; and he is currently advisory editor of *Philosophy East and West*. In 1953 he received the Freedom House—Willkie Memorial Building Award presented by the American Political Science Association for *The Taming of the Nations*. His publications include: *The Meeting of East and West*, 1946, and *The Taming of the Nations: A Study of the Cultural Bases of International Policy*, 1952. He was editor of *Ideological Differences and World Order*, 1949.

1. The author is gratefully indebted to the Wenner-Gren Foundation for Anthropological Research for grants which have made this study possible.

and of natural objects, and hence are not all civilizations technological civilizations? An affirmative answer to this question would mean that the difference confronting us is merely one of quantitative degree or complexity and not a difference in kind. Then the point at which one draws the line between a technological and a non-technological society would be purely arbitrary. But, if so, why did the passage from the one civilization to the other result in a change in men's mentality and values? Why, when the instruments and legal norms of a technological civilization enter Africa and Southeast Asia, do the natives there feel that they are confronted with something baffling which they do not understand and which to them seems destructive of all values? These reactions could hardly occur if the difference between a non-technological and a technological civilization were merely one of complexity.

How is the suggested difference in kind to be found? Our question indicates the way. When it refers to a technological civilization, it clearly means one in which mechanical, chemical, electrical, and the recently born communication engineering play a dominant role. From where does this type of toolmaking come?

Its source clearly is in physical chemistry and in physics. More specifically these engineering sciences derive from the mathematical acoustics of Democritus, the mathematical-physical chemistry of Willard Gibbs, the mathematical mechanics of Newton, Einstein, and Schroedinger, and the mathematical electromagnetics of Maxwell, Lorentz, and Planck.

These sciences are unique. Their basic elementary scientific objects and relations are not directly observable. Instead, they are axiomatically constructed entities and relations whose existence is verified only indirectly by way of experiments which confirm their

deductive consequences. Professor Einstein tells us (1934) that this way of knowing nature arose with the ancient Greeks and adds that the person who has not been thrilled by Euclid does not understand contemporary mathematical physics. Chiang Monlin, former vice-chancellor of Peking National University, tells us also (1947) that the ancient Greeks discovered a unique way of knowing nature and of relating man to nature. After being trained in the way of knowing man and nature of a Confucian, Chinese non-technological civilization, he came, as a young man, to the University of California at Berkeley, where for the first time he was introduced to the abstract concepts of Greek philosophy and of Greek mathematical physics. He adds that he felt quite at home mentally in the Western, natural history, descriptive sciences of botany and zoölogy but that in Greek philosophy and in deductively formulated mathematical physics he found himself confronted with something completely foreign to his classical Chinese mind. Students of the history of mathematics (Cohen and Drabkin, 1948) confirm also that, while many people previous to the ancient Greeks had discovered isolated propositions of Euclid, such as the Pythagorean theorem, it was the Greeks who first grasped the idea of proving these otherwise isolated findings by deducing them rigorously from a very small number of axiomatically constructed entities and relations and then using this way of thinking and knowing to understand man and nature empirically.

Here we come upon the difference in kind which distinguishes a technological civilization from a non-technological one. The nature to which a non-technological civilization relates man is completely exhausted by immediately apprehended, or by purely inductively sensed, entities and relations. Its scientific objects are defined in terms of directly sensed properties. As noted above by Chiang Monlin, such science exists in non-technological societies. It is the science of the purely descriptive, natural history type. Natural history biology, with its species and genera, is an example. Aristotle's physics, in which the terrestrial scientific object "water" was defined in terms of the sensed qualities "wet" and "cold," is another example. Early atomic theories of the Charvakian materialists and the Vaiseshika dualists of India are similar examples. The Chinese natural history paintings of birds and bamboo are another instance (Sowerby, 1940). Such science is strong descriptively but weak predictively. It is also weak in the tools which it generates. This occurs because, deriving its tools from sensed objects and materials, it obtains only such tools as come from modifying and manipulating such objects and materials (Singer *et al.*, 1954, chaps. v, vi, xx–xxv).

The science of a technological civilization takes this natural history type of knowledge merely as its data. It does not suppose that adequate knowledge of man or of nature has been obtained until the gross sensed objects and their described relations can be deduced from a very small number of unobservable, more elementary, axiomatically constructed objects and relations such as electrons, electromagnetic waves, and their mathematical laws. From the axiomatically constructed postulates of the deductively formulated theory, which designates such elementary particles and their relations, theorems can be logically deduced. These theoretically deduced theorems specify the possibility of new tools—tools quite different from anything one would come upon merely by moving sensed materials about.

The atomic bomb is an example. It was not discovered by engineers moving sensed materials about, after the manner in which the tools of a non-technological civilization arise. If we had depended for it upon engineers alone working inductively and pragmatically, it would never have come into being. The idea of the possibility of releasing atomic energy came not from an engineer, or even from an experimental physicist, but from a very theoretical one—Albert Einstein—and the mass-energy equation of his special theory of relativity. This equation is not a relation which can be sensed. Instead, it is a theorem deduced from the very abstract and shockingly novel, axiomatically constructed postulates of Einstein's indirectly, and experimentally, verified special theory of relativity. The latter theory was discovered or introduced not in order to make a new tool but in order to clear up a theoretical difficulty in the foundations of modern mechanics and electromagnetics which was revealed by the Michelson-Morely experiment in 1885.

It is in this difference between tools made out of scientific objects of the purely inductively manipulated, immediately sensed type and tools derived from scientific objects and relations of the axiomatically constructed and deductively formulated type that the difference in kind between a non-technological and a technological civilization consists. Furthermore, it is in the difference in meanings and materials and their forms provided by immediately apprehended and immediately sensed man and nature as compared with the meanings, materials, and forms provided by axiomatically constructed, deductively conceived man and nature, with its more elementary and universal scientific objects and relations, that the difference in kind between the aesthetic, ethical, and legal values of a non-technological civilization and those of a technological one has its basis.

CULTURAL VALUES OF A NON-TECHNO-LOGICAL CIVILIZATION

We must put ourselves within the way of knowing one's self and nature from which the cultural values of a non-technological civilization derive. To this end, let us suppose that we know nothing about mathematical physics and its contemporary, unimaginable and unsensed, axiomatically constructed, scientific objects and equations. Let us try to imagine also that we have no concepts of the regular solids of Euclid's geometry or of Newtonian linear, infinitely extended time, or even of matter itself. Let us try, in other words, to approach nature and ourselves afresh, in a radically empirical and purely inductive manner. What do we immediately apprehend?

Must we not describe nature somewhat as follows: It is a vast, spread-out, going-on-ness, vague and indeterminate at its outer fringes, ablaze with diverse colors, and issuing forth manifold sounds, fragrances, and flavors. This initial evidence of sounds, vivid colors, flavors, and fragrances is of considerable relevance to our major question. Such entities are essentially aesthetic, at bottom indescribable and hence ineffable, the stuff of which art is made, especially impressionistic art in which the proportions of Euclid's geometry and the perspectives of geometrical optics are not present. We would expect, therefore, that so-called "primitive man," or man in a non-technological society, would have considerable aesthetic sensitivity and that his paintings would not embody the techniques of perspective and of three-dimensional geometrical proportions of classical Western sculpture and painting. The anthropologists who have studied him (Thompson, 1945; Mead, 1940) and the artists who have examined his paintings or music (Adam, 1940; Barrett and Kenyon, 1947; McPhee, 1946)

tell us that in these judgments we are correct.

We have described our initial all-embracing experience as one from which sounds issue forth. Would it not be likely that we would be impressed more by the sounds issuing forth to us than from those issuing forth from us? This would be especially true if these sounds were those of the rolling thunder of the Himalayas. Then we might well speak, as do the early authors of the Hindu Vedic hymns, of the Maruts shouting their noisy terror at us from the sky (Müller, 1891, p. 81).

Furthermore, since we would experience the particular instance first and come only long afterward to the class of all similar particular instances, would it not be scientifically correct for us to describe the particular instance with a proper name? Non-proper names are appropriate only for abstract classes of particular things, when the particularity of each is neglected and their similarity only is seized upon. But this means that early man was not unscientific and guilty of a spurious anthropomorphism, as many of his observers have supposed, when he described particular events with proper names. Proper names are the only accurate scientific names for describing individual events or things.

Actually, however, in our initial experience and description we have not yet arrived at the concept of a thing, least of all at the concept of a persisting, substantial thing. We sense the terrifying shout of the thunder. It does not, however, last. Thus, although it is a particular which is appropriately described with a proper name, it is a perishing particular, succeeded by different perishing aesthetic qualities or particulars. From this sensed sequence of perishing aesthetic particulars, we arrive at our first concept of time. This is sensed time. Each particular sensed sound, fragrance, or flavor comes into being and goes out of being to be replaced by its successor.

This sensed succession of perpetually created, perpetually perishing particulars is quite different from the mathematical time of Newton or Einstein's physics, with which the people in a technological civilization order their daily lives. The latter, theoretically constructed time, is an infinitely extending series which does not return upon itself. The sensed time given in a sequence of perpetually perishing sensed particulars does return on itself as the following sensed facts make clear. There is the sensed brightness which comes into being at dawn, reaches its highest intensity at high noon, and perishes at dusk. It is succeeded by the sensed darkness which begins with a minimum degree of intensity, reaches its maximum intensity at midnight, and perishes at dawn. This cycle has continued as long as men have sensed nature. Within the sensed darkness there appears another cyclical sequence of perishing images. This cycle is composed of the two-dimensional, yellowish crescent called the new moon. It perishes and in a succeeding creation of darkness is succeeded by the two-dimensional, yellowish image called the quarter-moon, which in turn, in a later sensed particular darkness, is succeeded by the half-moon, and so on through the full moon and receding quarter-moon until the new crescent appears. Thus it is that the monthly cycle of perishing particulars is known (Singer *et al.*, 1954, p. 114).

These cycles can be counted just as the cycles of day and night can be counted. In this manner an aesthetic and qualitative astronomy becomes quantitative, and the inductive concept of number arises. This inductive concept of number is, however, sensed number. It is not the axiomatically constructed concept of number of the

Greek and of modern technological society.

Similarly, the sequence of brightness in the cycle of days and nights is also differentiated with localized two-dimensional images. The most important of these is the two-dimensional, localized image called the sun. It appears first at dawn as a very thin, two-dimensional segment. This perishes and is succeeded by a thin portion of a bright, yellow patch which is circular on one side and rectilinear on the other. This perishes and is succeeded immediately by a larger circle, then a still larger circle, and finally a fully rounded, two-dimensional, intensely bright, yellowish patch. Concomitantly, the differentiation between earth and sky becomes evident. The intense, round, yellowish patch called the sun vanishes at one point in the sky and appears at a higher point. This goes on until high noon, when the cycle is reversed. In the next brightness of the following morning the sequence of images called the sun appears at a different point on the horizon. This point varies in successive diurnal and monthly cycles. Similarly, it also comes back on itself. This sensed cycle is called the year. This cycle also can be counted, and the number can be related to the sensed number of monthly cycles and the sensed number of daily cycles.

Within the daily, monthly, and yearly succession of brightnesses, there are other sensed colors than those of the sun. There are the vivid greens of the initial growth of sensed plants, the golden yellows of their mature growth, the reddish browns of their decline, and the dull blacks and grays of their death, succeeded again by the vivid greens of the following spring.

All these directly sensed cyclical changes man feels within himself. He notes his introspected moods changing with these colorful cyclical sequences of the seasons. He notes also, for himself as for other animals and plants, that there is birth, youth, maturity, the fall of life, and its winter, or death, succeeded again by a new birth. And so, through the generations of the sensed biological family, the human cycle goes on as part and parcel of the interconnected, numerically countable cycles of nature.

Knowing himself and everything else thus in terms of emotively felt and immediately sensed aesthetic qualities, it never occurs to non-technological man to separate the aesthetic and emotive beauty of everything from the things themselves, after the manner of a technological civilization. Nor does it ever occur to him to think of himself as outside of nature or as an exploiter of nature. The earth is "Mother Earth." Are not her materials and the forests and other plants and animals which arise out of her, like himself, fellow-members of an interconnected set of cycles? Taking this for granted, the concept of the good, common to Confucian, Buddhist, Hindu, Indonesian, and all other nontechnological societies, arises—the concept of the good for man as immersion within, aesthetic sensitivity to, and harmony with nature.

Each immediately sensed thing has one other characteristic. It is a temporarily created and perishing particular. It comes into being only by its predecessor's dying. It dies that its successor can come into being. When at dusk the brightness which is day dies, the darkness which is night is born. When at dawn the darkness of night dies, the brightness of day is born. So it is with every sensed thing that is determinate and finite. Determinate, finite human beings are no exception to this rule. The doctrine of transmigration is nothing but the thesis that the cycle of sensed perishing particulars goes on for man as for other things. This doctrine does not mean that man persists as an eternal, determinate substance. Restricting one's

knowledge thus to immediacy, one does not come upon the concept of substance. All that one finds is a succession of perishing particulars which return upon themselves cyclically.

The sensed fact that nothing comes into being without the death of its predecessor and that nothing goes out of being without its successor coming into being, the early native Indonesians expressed as the principle of the cosmic equilibrium. This principle affirms that nothing is ever received except as something else is taken away. To violate this principle is to be immoral in a non-technological civilization. This is why the early Indonesians and their present descendants do not feel that they can cut down a virgin forest to gain land for cultivation unless they express sympathy, through a ceremony, for the death of what they destroy and accept the trust of creating faithfully that which is new to replace the old. To exploit nature, taking from it while giving nothing back in return, is to act immorally. Similarly, when the young Indonesian takes a bride, he or his family must make a gift of a very considerable amount in return. The Dutch interpreted this as the purchase of a bride and outlawed it as slavery, thereby showing that they were looking at the values and social norms of a nontechnological society from the conceptual standpoint and mentality of a technological one. The so-called "payment" of the groom for the bride is, from the standpoint of the native Indonesian, a moral requirement. Failure to give something in return for what is taken would be to violate the cosmic balance; it would be to act immorally.

This conception of man as immersed in the cyclical sequence of nature shows in the aesthetic values of a nontechnological society. Instead of starting with the musical theme and countertheme, which move linearly toward their resolution in a climax, after the practice of Western music, the tonal sequences in the music of a non-technological society are cyclical in character. There are melody and rhythm but no harmony and counterpoint. Also, the music is not recorded or controlled by meticulous, mathematically ordered scales. Instead, it is mastered and directed wholly by ear and transmitted from generation to generation in this way. The standard with respect to which the notes of the melody are measured and ordered is also different. This standard in Hindu music is called the "drone" (Ranade, 1951; Tagore, 1879). The drone is a continuous background. It is against this constant background that the differentiated sounds of the melody rise and fall and succeed one another in time cyclically.

The drone also symbolizes something immediately experienced. We described our initial experience of nature as "a vast, spread-out, going-on-ness, . . . ablaze with diverse colors, and issuing forth manifold sounds, fragrances, and flavors." The drone expresses both the dynamism of the going-on-ness and the relatively undifferentiated character of the vast spread-out-ness. It symbolizes, therefore, the infinite timelessness out of which each sensed particular thing, including sensed particular man himself, arises and to which it returns at death.

Early in this century William James attempted (1923, 1928) to bring scientific and philosophic discourse back to radically empirical immediacy. In doing this, he noted that it is only the portion which is at the focus of attention that is sharply differentiated into the determinate colors, sounds, fragrances, flavors, and feelings; the periphery of immediacy is vague, formless, undifferentiated, and indeterminate, one portion of it being no different from another. James suggested also that it is from this undifferentiated, indeterminate periphery that religious

experience arises. This periphery is both the subject of consciousness and its object. But, being indeterminate and undifferentiated, there is nothing in it to distinguish subject from object. Thus it is both subject and object and neither subject nor object. These are the defining properties of what the Hindus call the "divine" or "true self," "Brahma" or "Atman," and the Buddhists call "nirvana." It is also the factor in immediate experience with which the divine is identified in all non-technological societies. At this point the radical empiricism of William James and the radical empiricism of a non-technological society become identical.

This all-embracing, indeterminate consciousness within which the sensed differentiations come and go in cyclical sequence is called by Hindus the "chit consciousness" to distinguish it from the differentiated, sensuous consciousness (Northrop, 1946; Woodroffe, 1929, chap. xiv). Both types of consciousness give immediately apprehended objects. One does not, however, sense the undifferentiated or chit consciousness, since sensing always involves a distinction between the sensing percipient and the sensed object. One can sense only differentiated qualities within the chit consciousness; one cannot sense the chit consciousness itself. In the case of the chit consciousness, to apprehend it is to be it; hence, being undifferentiated, there is no distinction between subject and object in the knowing of it.

The Hindus and Buddhists of a non-technological society call the cyclical sequence of perpetually born and perpetually perishing particulars the "law of karma." This is the concept of causality in a non-technological society. The transmigration of sensed souls is a special case of it. Salvation comes for man, however, only by escaping the karma cycle. This occurs when man realizes that he is the timeless chit consciousness within which the perishing particulars of the karma cycle come and go. To realize this is to be able to accept with equanimity the death of one's sensed self in the karma cycle.

The drone of Hindu music is the minimally differentiated expression of the all-embracing, infinite formlessness and dynamism which the Hindu terms "Brahma" or "Atman." The measure of the differentiated sounds, in their cyclical temporal successions, against the continuous drone expresses the tension between the temporal and the eternal, the finite and the infinite, in man and in things for people in a non-technological civilization.

Its legal norms are of two types. One type derives from the all-embracing formlessness of things within which the conflicting, differentiated, sensed creatures come and go. Since all sensed objects are relative to perceivers, only the all-embracing formlessness is common to all men. Hence only it can provide an absolute norm for a common law. In a concrete, sensed dispute each participant's experience of that dispute is relative to him. Ethical and legal codes, therefore, which are defined in terms of sensed objects cannot give a common law, since sensed objects are one thing for one perceiver and another thing for another. How then is anything common going to be found for settling social disputes in a non-technological society?

The basic answer is that it can be found in the sole factor in immediate experience which is common to disputants—namely, in the all-embracing, immediately felt formlessness within which the relativistic objects of each particular disputant's experience come and go. This formlessness, precisely because it is a formlessness, cannot be expressed in codes. It has to be immediately experienced to be known. It is to be found, moreover, pragmatically, as the Buddha teaches, in the "middle way" between the conflicting claims arising from the relativistic sensed ex-

periences of the disputants (Warren, 1906). Mediation is the method of finding this middle way (Northrop, 1952). Consequently, as Confucius emphasizes, the moral man does not indulge in litigation. He does not settle disputes by resort to codes. Also, no dispute is settled until both parties, working through a mediator, are satisfied (Liu, 1947). Expressed in musical terms, the moral man looks to the drone rather than to any determinate ordering of the melody for the solution of his intrapersonal legal and social problems.

There are, however, certain sensed objects and relationships which seem, to most people in a non-technological society, to exist, the same for all perceivers. At this point their epistemology shifts from radical empiricism to naïve realism. These realistic, sensed objects and relationships are the biological objects and their heredity of a natural history, descriptive biology. One basic rule governs their sequence through time. No child exists without parents. From this scientific law of sensed biological human life, there arises the basic, determinate, ethical rule and legal norm of a non-technological society—the tie of the family and the priority of the family to the individual. In Confucianism this is called "filial piety." Objectively, it appears as the patriarchal or matriarchal joint family (Hsien Chin Hu, 1948). From this natural history, biological science of man, there arises the social ethics and codified law of what Sir Henry S. Maine (1908, p. 151) called the "law of status."

In such a society men are not equal before the law. Daughters do not inherit equally with sons, nor do the younger sons inherit equally with the eldest son. Nor are people of a different family or a different heredity stock, or tribe, treated with the same moral rules that one uses for the members of one's own family or of one's own tribe.

Having based one's social ethics and

law in this manner on the sensed objects of natural history biology, the sensed color of the skin of people becomes important ethically. Consequently, the idea that a good society has nothing to do with differences in color of skin is foreign to the ethics of a non-technological society. In classical Hinduism, for example, the word for caste is the word for color. Furthermore, in the Hindu *Laws of Manu* the penalty for the same crime differs, if the offender is of one caste, from what it would be if he belonged to a different caste (Müller, 1886). The classical Chinese called all other people "barbarians." The ancient Hebrews, Greeks, and Romans, in the ethics of their patriarchal law of status, judged similarly.

Since the family has a head, so the groups of families in the tribe and the nation tend to have a head. Hence, the political ethics of a non-technological society is hierarchical and monarchical. The codes of a law of status express these familial, tribal, hierarchical, and regal relationships in common-sense terms.

It is to be remembered, however, that in non-technological societies the ethics of the law of status is combined with the ethics of the law of mediation. Moreover, the former is usually regarded as a second best, to be followed only in the middle stage of life when the family is being bred and nurtured. Before this "householder stage," as the Hindus call it (Müller, 1886, pp. 75–128), and afterward, the ethics of mediation, of the musical drone, and of the all-embracing formlessness take over.

Considered by itself, apart from the ethics of the law of status, the ethics of mediation is democratic rather than hierarchical and regal. This is the case because the chit-nirvana consciousness, being undifferentiated, is the same in all men. Actually, however, even in the Buddhist society of Burma or Thailand, in which there is no hierarchical ordering of the patriarchal families according to caste, there is nevertheless a king. This is achieved in Buddhist Burma and Thailand by combining the raj, the law of status codes, and the literary epics of Hinduism with Buddhism (Prince Dhani, 1947; Le May, 1938; Lingat, 1950; Müller, 1886). It is this combination of the hierarchical ethics of the family of a naïvely realistic, natural history, biological science and the ethics of equality and mediation of a radically empirical science that gives a non-technological civilization its codified law of status, expressed in common-sense terms, with its legal and hierarchical social values combined with a basic theory of the ultimate or true self which is egalitarian and democratic (Banerjea, 1954; Osgood, 1951).

CULTURAL VALUES OF A TECHNOLOGICAL CIVILIZATION

We have already come upon these values by way of contrast in connection with the values of a non-technological society. We noted also (pp. 1052–54) that the differentiating character of a technological society is that, in it, man knows himself and nature in terms of the unsensed, indirectly verified, axiomatically constructed entities and relations of mathematical physics. This frees scientific objects and their relations from sensed properties, thereby giving determinate public meanings the same for all men. It also frees ethical and legal norms from the necessity of being expressed in terms of the sensed qualities. This frees moral and legal man from a definition of his ethical values in terms of the color of his skin and the biological stock of his family or his tribe. Forthwith, the law of status is replaced by the law of contract. Thereby, meaning is given for the thesis that moral, legal, and political man is not family or tribal man but universal man.

This ethics of the law of contract

generates a completely new ethics of inheritance in which inheritance rights are equal for all offspring regardless of sex or differences in age. It gives rise also to a new philosophy of education —that of equal opportunity for all. It also generates a completely new concept of the basis of political and moral obligation.

In the social ethics of a law of status of a non-technological society, the sanction for the legal codes is in the fact of one's birth within the family and in the status relationship of one's family within the tribe or the nation. The authority for such a law and the obligations to abide by it have nothing to do with the consent of those who were born into it. As Sir Robert Filmer pointed out in his *Patriarcha* (Laslett, 1949), the younger sons have never given their consent to the inheritance of the family manor house and the entire family estate by the eldest son; nor have the patriarchical families lower in the social hierarchy ever given their consent to the privileged social positions and governmental powers enjoyed by the patriarchal families near the top of the hierarchy and the royal families at the top.

In the ethics of a law of contract of a technological society, consent, however, is of the essence. Such a law, being axiomatically constructed and hence hypothetical, has no validity, obviously, unless those to whom it is applied give their consent. This is precisely why it is called the law of contract. In a contract, nothing is binding unless the parties to the contract have consented to accept it. Furthermore, with respect to consent, and hence with respect to the obligation to obey any law of contract, all men are born free and equal. It is in this legal and contractual sense of the authority of a law resting upon consent, and not in the biological sense, that the Declaration of Independence speaks the truth when it asserts that "all men are created equal." The frequent attempts, therefore, to discredit the Declaration of Independence by pointing to the biological, psychological, and economic inequalities of men at the time of their birth is quite beside the point. Such criticism confuses the epistemological and natural history scientific basis of the ethics of the law of status of a non-technological society with the different epistemological and scientific basis of the ethics of the law of contract of a technological civilization.

The epistemology of the axiomatically constructed, scientific knowledge of a technological society has one other cultural consequence. Being deductively formulated, it defines inductively sensed, different classes of things in terms of a single class of common, elementary, scientific objects. This is but another way of saying that it replaces ethical groups of men, defined in terms of differences in color of skin or of familial and tribal heredity, with the universal moral man of the law of contract.

The very prevalent notion, therefore, that technological society has destroyed human values is quite erroneous. Through the law of contract, which entails the definition of moral authority in terms of consent rather than in terms of family or tribal status, it generates the ethics and politics of democracy. Furthermore, not merely its technological instruments and their capacity to lift the standard of living of the masses but also its democratic ethics of its law of contract have captured the imaginations and the loyalty of the masses of men even in non-technological societies. This is why they are demanding today that they be treated equally before the law in education and politics regardless of their color of skin. When they demand this, they are rejecting the familial, hierarchical, and regal ethics of their own traditional law of status.

An equally significant shift occurs in aesthetic values with the transition from a non-technological to a technological society. The standard for measuring the sequence of musical sounds in the music of a non-technological society has been noted to be the drone. The music of a technological society drops the drone as its standard. In its place it puts the ratios of the deductively formulated, mathematical acoustics of the Greek Pythagoreans and Democritus. But these relations for ordering the sounds of the melody are not sensed. They are intellectually grasped, axiomatically constructed relations. Furthermore, mathematical physics works with an infinitely extending, linear theory of time instead of with the sensed cyclical theory of time. This automatically frees the music of a technological society, not merely from the drone, but also from a cyclical, temporal ordering of the melody.

But if this melodic ordering is to be an order rather than a chaos, some relation must govern it. The ratios and uniform, axiomatically constructed, flow of time defines this ordering. With such intellectual ordering, harmony and counterpoint as well as melody can enter in. For all this, however, there must be a precise, musical scale. Otherwise, again, there would be no standard, and the simultaneous ordering of sounds in harmony and counterpoint would become chaotic, as would also the uniform, temporal ordering of sound in melody. Such a music no longer describes cyclical sequences of perishing particulars against the tension created by the all-embracing, dynamic formlessness of the drone. Instead, the sensuous materials are subjected to a mathematically formal and intellectually prescribed logos of proportion and perfection. Thus it is that there arises in a technological society a new concept of the beautiful.

This more formal intellectual concept of the beautiful appeared first in the music of ancient Greece. It actualized new formal potentialities of itself with Palestrina and came to some of its richest formal fulfilments in Bach and in Beethoven.

The parallel transformation of aesthetic values appears in painting. For all its virtues, the painting of a non-technological society, when seen from the standpoint of classical Western art, is flat. Once, however, the artist grasps the intellectual, three-dimensional, mathematical proportions of the axiomatically constructed Greek geometry of solids, the flat type of painting starts moving into the round. Thence arises Greek sculpture, with a beautiful sense of geometrical proportion, but with its lack of emotive, dynamic beauty, when viewed from the standpoint of the art of the oriental, all-embracing, ineffable, infinite formlessness. With the coming of axiomatically constructed geometrical optics, the logos of the perspective combines with the logos of the regular solids to generate the painting of the giants of the Renaissance—Leonardo, Raphael, and Michelangelo. This, again, is an intellectually guided aesthetic of the beautiful.

It is interesting to note that, when with Berkeley and Hume modern thinking returned to the epistemology of radical empiricism of a non-technological society, concomitantly, impressionistic painting arises in which blurred, vivid, sensuous differentiations become the subject matter of the painter, and the axiomatically guided, mathematical laws of perspective and of solid geometry drop out of his technique. The music of Debussy is a corresponding development in the aesthetics of modern Western music.

It is to be remembered, however, that for a period of over a thousand years, following the decline of the mathematical physics of Pythagoras, Democritus, Eudoxus, and Plato, Aristotle's physics dominated the Islamic and the Western world. This physics is partially a mathematical physicist's physics, since Aristotle had an axiomatically constructed geometry and astronomy. In his physics of terrestrial objects, however, he reverted to the epistemology of naïve realism, defining the physical and chemical elements in terms of their sensed qualities. Water, as previously noted, was defined as anything which one senses as wet and cold. This gave Aristotle's ethics and politics a law-of-contract form with a law-of-status terrestrial content.

The consequence was that the law of contract, as initially formulated by the Stoic Romans and accepted down to modern times, was in considerable part filled in with law-of-status content. This law-of-status content of a law of contract still dominates Roman Catholic and Episcopal thinking as formulated in Aristotelian epistemological and metaphysical terms by St. Thomas and by Thomas Hooker. This type of law of contract with law-of-status content went into the South through the First Families of Virginia, as Laslett has recently demonstrated (1949, pp. 1–43).

It was not, therefore, until Galileo and Newton returned Western physical science to an axiomatically constructed physics of terrestrial as well as astronomical objects that it was possible for Western man to have, for the first time, a law-of-contract ethics with a law-of-contract content. This happened when Jefferson, in writing the Declaration of Independence and insisting upon the Bill of Rights of the American Constitution, followed Locke's theory of natural law and the physics of Newton rather than Hooker, St. Thomas, and Aristotle.

Immediately, a technological society burst forth with new vigor and new moral content. Also, the patriarchal, hierarchical, and regal values of a non-technological society were replaced in the content of the law of contract by the egalitarian and democratic values of a purely technological society. Locke and Newton had replaced Hooker, St. Thomas, and Aristotle in the specification of the content of the ethics of a law of contract. This is what Jefferson meant when he wrote that Bacon, Locke, and Newton were his gods and affirmed that the United States was creating a political society which is unique in the history of the world (Dewey, 1940, pp. 61–62; Koch and Peden, 1944, p. 609).

The axiomatically constructed terrestrial and celestial physics of Galileo and Newton has been replaced, however, by that of Einstein, Planck, Schroedinger, and Dirac. The former physics, while axiomatically constructed, was one, like that of the Greeks, which could be imaginatively envisaged in terms of geometrical models. This is not true of the theory of relativity or of quantum mechanics. Nature as known through contemporary, axiomatically constructed, indirectly verified, deductively formulated theory not only cannot be sensed; it cannot even be imagined. The aesthetic implications of this characteristic of our contemporary technological society are already upon us. Both art and architecture have been released not merely from geometrical optics and its laws of perspectives but also from the geometrical models of Euclid's regular solids. The result in the realms of aesthetics is abstractionism and functionalism in both painting and architecture. Houses and business buildings need no longer be rigidly rectangular. The roofs of public buildings do not have to be spherical domes modeled on the circles and spheres of Euclid. Music can break loose from the restriction of ratios. Giedion, Frank Lloyd Wright, and Le Corbusier; Orozco, Picasso, and Kandinski are already here (Giedion,

1954). With them also have come the tools and the unprecedented high standard of living of a technological society. By means of the deeper understanding of nature and the more powerful instruments which axiomatically constructed knowledge gives man, the work of the world and even its most difficult mental calculations are being lifted from the shoulders and the brains of men. Thus to moral, legal, and political equality is being added the possibility of economic equality.

But with these aesthetic, ethical, legal, economic, and even religious values of a technological society, rooted as they are in the logos of an axiomatically constructed, intellectually known relatedness, there has also come a price and a problem. The basing of human relations on the hypothetically constructed constitutions of the law of contract has opened up the possibility of more than one constitution and the actuality of incompatible constitutions. In this, as well as in the conflict between the values of technological and non-technological societies, the ideological problems and conflicts of the contemporary world find their origin and their basis. It is of the essence of a contractually constructed constitution that it defines a social and ethical utopia. Utopias tend to turn themselves into crusades. When these crusades of a technological society become armed with its instrument, the atomic bomb, the possibilities are appalling. This is why the members of technological societies are filled today with both high hopes and deep fears. To understand the source of these fears is to discover the way to construct an international law which will give mankind the values of a technological society without its dangers (Northrop, 1952, 1954).

There is a second price which one pays for a technological civilization. Its traditional fault arises from the tendency to take the emotively moving, immediately sensed, radically empirical man and world, ablaze with aesthetic fragrances, colors, and sounds as a bare starting point, to be dismissed as mere appearance when the axiomatically constructed, scientific objects and their relations are obtained and the ethics of its democratic law of contract is constitutionally formulated. This has created a modern man who has become so absorbed by the intellectual imagination, its technological tools, and its abstract legal codes that he is starved emotionally and with respect to aesthetic immediacy. Out of this half-man has come the crowds of people housed in the rigidly, rectangularly ordered streets and dull, gray buildings and slums of our huge cities. No one with aesthetic sensitivity to the immediacy of things and to the emotions within himself could ever have created or have tolerated such a thing. This is the aesthetic and emotive paradox of a technological society. Need one wonder that such a modern man, for all his abstract art, democratic laws, and effective tools, is a frustrated, even often a schizophrenic, individual?

But the ethics and aesthetics of a non-technological society have their paradox also. Notwithstanding the affection of its folk for trees and all other creatures of "Mother Earth," its people, owing to their emphasis on family values, tend to produce more people than their instruments or their natural resources enable them to provide for. The consequence is, notwithstanding their affection for trees, that they eat the green twigs of the trees in order to live. In this way China has become denuded of its forests, and the rich top soil of its "Mother Earth" has been washed into the sea. The result is, not merely that millions upon millions of its trees have been destroyed, never to be replaced, thereby violating the cosmic equilibrium, but also that millions of its people die each year by starvation. The story of the non-technological civilization of India is similar. Owing to prolific breeding and for want of food, its people have turned hundreds of thousands of square miles of its once-forested or food-producing territory, extending from south of the Ganges Valley to the southern portion of the peninsula, into almost a desert. Egypt, where the situation and the cure are even more hopeless, tells the same story. This is the paradox of the ethics and the tools of a non-technological civilization.

The resolution of both paradoxes would seem to be clear. To this resolution, moreover, the analysis of the philosophy of contemporary mathematical physics is now taking careful thinkers in our contemporary technological society. A full account of knowing in even mathematical physics reveals the irreducibility and the ultimacy of both the aesthetically immediate, with its all-embracing formlessness, and the axiomatically constructed (Margenau, 1950; Northrop, 1947). Clearly, it is by specifying the relation between these two components of complete human knowledge, supplementing the one with the other, that the paradoxes of the traditional technological and the traditional non-technological civilizations are to be resolved.

Whitehead has worked out in great detail one way in which this can be done (Northrop and Gross, 1953). The writer has sketched another (Northrop, 1946, pp. 436–78). Contemporary sociological jurisprudence (Ehrlich, 1936) demonstrates also that an effective law for the contemporary world must root itself in the living beliefs, practices, and values of its non-technological as well as its technological societies (Northrop, 1952). Recently, the artist Rudolf Ray, born and reared in the technological society of the West, has discovered the art of the all-embracing formlessness of a non-technological society. The scientific, philosophical, legal, and aesthetic insights necessary to reconcile and preserve both types of civilization appear, therefore, to be at hand.

REFERENCES

ADAM, L.
 1940 *Primitive Art.* Harmondsworth, Middlesex: Pelican Books (published by Allen Lane). 160 pp.

ANONYMOUS
 · 1952 *A Catalogue of Recorded Classical and Traditional Indian Music.* Paris: UNESCO. 236 pp.

BANERJEA, AKSHAYA KUMAR
 1954 "The Contribution of Saivism to the Spiritual Culture of India," *Bulletin of the Ramakrishna Mission Institute of Culture,* V, No. 10, 227–34. Calcutta.

BARRETT, CHARLES L., and KENYON, A. S.
 1947 *Australian Aboriginal Art.* Melbourne: National Museum of Victoria. 39 pp.

CHIANG MONLIN
 1947 *Tides from the West.* New Haven, Conn.: Yale University Press. 282 pp.

COHEN, MORRIS R., and DRABKIN, I. E.
 1948 *A Source Book in Greek Science.* New York: McGraw-Hill Book Co. 579 pp.

DEWEY, JOHN (ed.)
 1940 *The Living Thoughts of Thomas Jefferson.* New York: Longmans, Green & Co. 173 pp.

DHANI, PRINCE
 1947 "The Old Siamese Conception of the Monarchy," *Journal of the Siam Society,* XXXVI, Part II, 91–106. Bangkok.

EHRLICH, EUGEN
 1936 *Fundamental Principles of the Sociology of Law.* Cambridge, Mass.: Harvard University Press. 541 pp.

EINSTEIN, ALBERT
1934   *The World as I See It.* New York: Covici-Friede. 290 pp.

FERNÁNDEZ, JUSTINO
1942   *José Clemente Orozco: Forma e idea.* Mexico, D.F.: Libreria de Porrua Hnos. y Cia. 209 pp.

GANDHI, M. K.
1948   *Gandhi's Autobiography.* Washington, D.C.: Public Affairs Press. 640 pp.

GIEDION, SIGFRIED
1954   *Space, Time and Architecture.* 3d ed. Cambridge, Mass.: Harvard University Press. 778 pp.

HU HSIEN CHIN
1948   *The Common Descent Group in China and Its Functions.* ("Viking Fund Publications in Anthropology," No. 10.) New York: Viking Fund, Inc. 204 pp.

HUGHES, E. R.
1942   *Chinese Philosophy in Classical Times.* London: J. M. Dent & Sons, Ltd. 336 pp.

JAMES, WILLIAM
1923   *The Principles of Psychology.* 2 vols. New York: Henry Holt & Co. 689+704 pp.
1928   *The Varieties of Religious Experience.* New York: Longmans, Green & Co. 534 pp.

KOCH, ADRIENNE, and PEDEN, WILLIAM
1944   *The Life and Selected Writings of Thomas Jefferson.* New York: Modern Library. 730 pp.

LASLETT, PETER (ed.)
1949   *Patriarcha and Other Political Works of Sir Robert Filmer.* Oxford: Basil Blackwell. 326 pp.

LE MAY, REGINALD
1938   *A Concise History of Buddhist Art in Siam.* Cambridge: Cambridge University Press. 165 pp. (plus plates).

LIN YUTANG
1938   *The Wisdom of Confucius.* New York: Modern Library. 290 pp.
1939   *My Country and My People.* Enlarged ed. New York: John Day Co. 440 pp.

LINGAT, R.
1950   "Evolution of the Conception of Law in Burma and Siam," *Journal of the Siam Society,* XXXVIII, Part I, 9–31. Bangkok.

LIU, FRANCIS S.
1947   "Some Observations on Judges, Lawyers and Court Administration in China," *National Reconstruction Journal,* VII, No. 4, 3–16. New York.

MCPHEE, COLIN
1946   *A House in Bali.* New York: John Day Co. 234 pp. (plus plates).

MAINE, SIR HENRY S.
1908   *Ancient Law.* Cheap ed. London: John Murray. 370 pp.

MARGENAU, HENRY
1950   *The Nature of Physical Reality.* New York: McGraw-Hill Book Co. 479 pp.

MEAD, MARGARET
1940   "The Arts in Bali," *Yale Review,* XXX, No. 2, 335–47.

MÜLLER, F. MAX
1886   *The Sacred Books of the East,* Vol. XXV: *The Laws of Manu.* Oxford: Clarendon Press. 620 pp.
1891   *The Sacred Books of the East,* Vol. XXXII, *Vedic Hymns,* Part I. Oxford: Clarendon Press. 556 pp.

NORTHROP, F. S. C.
1946   *The Meeting of East and West.* New York: Macmillan Co. 531 pp.
1947   *The Logic of the Sciences and the Humanities.* New York: Macmillan Co. 402 pp.
1952   *The Taming of the Nations.* New York: Macmillan Co. 362 pp.
1954   *European Union and United States Foreign Policy.* New York: Macmillan Co. 230 pp.

NORTHROP, F. S. C., and GROSS, MASON
1953   *Alfred North Whitehead: An Anthology.* New York: Macmillan Co. 928 pp.

OSGOOD, CORNELIUS
1951   *The Koreans and Their Culture.* New York: Ronald Press Co. 387 pp.

RANADE, G. H.
1951   *Hindusthani Music: An Outline of Its Physics and Aesthetics.* 2d ed. revised and enlarged. Poona: G. H. Ranade. 204 pp.

SINGER, CHARLES; HOLMYARD, E. J., and HALL, A. R. (eds.)
1954   *A History of Technology,* Vol. I: *From Early Times to Fall of Ancient Empires.* Oxford: Clarendon Press. 827 pp. (plus 36 plates).

Sirén, Osvald
  1936 *The Chinese on the Art of Painting.* Peiping: Henry Vetch. 261 pp.
Sowerby, Arthur de Carle
  1940 *Nature in Chinese Art.* New York: John Day Co. 203 pp.
Tagore, Sourindro M.
  1879 *A Few Specimens of Indian Songs.* Calcutta: The Author. 113 pp.
Thompson, Laura
  1945 "Logico-aesthetic Integration in Hopi Culture," *American Anthropologist,* LVII, 540–53.

Warren, Henry Clarke
  1906 *Buddhism in Translations.* ("Harvard Oriental Series," Vol. III, ed. Charles Rockwell Lenman.) Cambridge, Mass.: Harvard University Press. 520 pp.
Woodroffe, Sir John
  1929 *Shakti and Shâkta.* 3d ed. Madras: Ganesh & Co. 724 pp.
Woodward, F. L.
  1949 *Some Sayings of the Buddha.* ("World Classics," No. 483.) London: Oxford University Press. 356 pp.

Symposium Discussion: Prospect

Symposium Discussion: Prospect

Limits of the Earth: Materials and Ideas

Soils

Water

Minerals, Fuels, and Energy

Population

On Methods of Dealing with Limitations

What Are *the Future Limits?*

In introducing this session, Dr. Joseph Willits, as Chairman, emphasized how much the topic invited the
widest kind of cross-disciplinary participation. Modern truth is rapidly becoming so much more complex that no
one approach and no one individual
can hope to be adequate to it; the
symposium is both the mood and the
method of pooling various contributions, so that we can succeed in not
being outdistanced by the pace of complexity. Josiah Stamp once put it very
well when he said, "Any truth is many-
sided, even simple truth; but the complex truth of today needs approach by
many different methods and by many
different types of minds before we arrive at even an approximation to the
truth."

In discussing "Prospect," everyone is
eligible to participate; but whoever attempts to advise on future policy,
which is what "Prospect" connotes, neg-
lects any element of the situation to
his peril. Too often it is easy for intellectual folk to jump from the conclusions of their particular piece of truth
into policy-making and to ignore many
relevant elements. Our obligation is
very heavy to make a success of cross-
disciplinary considerations even more
complex than the previous discussions
on the actions of primitive to modern
man and their effects upon physical
and biological processes.

Five topics were suggested for discussion with regard to their limiting
effects: soils, water, oil, energy, and
population. How divergent are our estimates of these resources, and, if so,
why are they divergent? How firm can
our conclusions about limits be? What
are the limits of materials beyond
which we cannot go? When shortages
arise, we must keep in mind (*a*) the
cost-and-price system of a relatively
free market; (*b*) the control and imposition of standards by the state; (*c*) a
thoroughgoing reorganization of value
and perceptual systems and, if they are
to be reorganized, how this will be
done; and (*d*) fundamental research
on the scarcest of all materials—knowledge and intelligence.

SOILS

In discussing the first topic, soils,
Albrecht asked that man's thinking be
related to his physical and chemical
base. The biotic pyramid has man at
the top, animals below him, plants below animals, microbes below plants,
and soil as its basis. In the biological

performance of soil, energy comes from two sources: from within the rock and from the sun outside. Rock, with its propensities to break down and to move from higher elevations to the sea, provides one source of energy, while a synthetic performance that is commonly called "photosynthesis" is derived from the sun.

There are other aspects of soil aside from energy which are often overlooked in discussions of surpluses derived from agriculture. Complex minerals are broken down or simplified to form clays, which are secondary minerals that have the absorptive capacities to hold the fertility elements temporarily. Clay is a temporary jobber to hold nutrients in exchangeable form for plant use. But clay eventually moves on, both bodily and in geological breakdown. The quartz sand that is left contributes nothing, and the hydrogen system is without function. As rock moves toward the sea, it has temporary rest stops, with clay serving to contain dietary arrangements of all the essential fertility elements that feed plants. The ratio of these arrangements determines whether plants can grow.

In the middle United States, for example, the advantageous balance produces a deep soil with organic matter fairly well distributed throughout, and the ratios of calcium, potassium, and magnesium are all properly balanced for legume growth and protein output.

Soil development must be seen as a dynamic procedure. Rock is moved from high elevations and complex mineral forms, is reduced to simplicity, and provides increasing efficiency for plant production. But what are the limits of the soil base to the biotic pyramid?

The reproductive processes of plants and animals have their essential basis in the rich store of fertility reserves in the soil. Protein is required to make reproduction possible, and protein needs a high level of mineral fertility. In the biotic pyramid soil fertility is directly related to microbial nutrition, to plant nutrition, and thereby to animal nutrition. Thus, relating agriculture to the idea of survival, we must try to see what can be done to the soil and then to measure that effect in terms of nutrition for the animal. This can be rather pointedly illustrated in the case of rabbits, which normally are prone to be quite steady in their increase. By experimentally treating the soil which produces their feed, an indifference to reproduction can be created in rabbits in about three weeks. And this occurs before any symptom (change of fur or change in growth rate) manifests itself. What more powerful limit do we have for food production if the animals and plants we grow manifest simultaneously the same results?

This leads to thinking about reproduction as a biochemical operation synthesizing organic substances which, reduced to simpler units, are protein. Protein has the responsibility of carrying life forward. We may be close to synthesizing a protein, but we have yet to create one and to put life into it. The chemist of the gene tells us that it looks as though protein were a straight chain that finally links up into a kind of endoring—the first basic living compound. In any event, we are dealing with a protein molecule that requires tremendous support from the soil in order to be built. But, in exhausting the soil, man has emphasized bulk and thereby increased carbohydrates at the expense of proteins.

A further characteristic of protein is that it has the power to digest other "undisciplined" proteins; in terms of man, this characteristic means that the body has the power to protect itself against disease. Immunity is acquired by inoculation, which is but a successful whip only when the body has the reserve to expand under a stimulus. If we wish to depend more and more on inoculations for immunities, ought we not to make sure that we are not whipping a malnourished horse?

The limit of protein production is not in growth, not in protection, so much as it is in the reproductive process. The crux of this limitation goes back to soils, which must have mixtures of the elements in large enough diversity and supply to grow our protein crops. But the demands of increasing population place a pressure on the available soil resources. Our life-lines are shortening with respect to the supply of complete proteins. It is essential to maintain a supply of balanced amino acids in order that we may grow and reproduce and protect ourselves. The increasing degenerative diseases now recognized have resulted from a breakdown in the protein supply, which has become the limit of the species in the biotic pyramid.

DARLING was concerned with the limited rate of metabolism in any particular habitat. His first point was that, for all practical purposes, we live in a finite world and therefore exist as a part of a biological system. This is so because we are dependent upon photosynthesis, which is a biological phenomenon. The great role of vegetation is to insure photosynthesis. After that, as Albrecht has said, comes protein synthesis, a process of great consequence. Photosynthesis may seem an involved process, depending in large measure on certain fitness of soils, light, and habitat, yet it is relatively simple in comparison to the process of protein synthesis. Albrecht has mentioned protein synthesis from the point of view of soil qualities and ingredients, but, DARLING emphasized, soils not only are chemical entities but are also biological worlds of microscopic organisms. If we accept the premises of the finite world and of the biological system, it is upon protein synthesis that the future of man rests. Yet the extremely complicated systems of protein synthesis are part of still larger systems of energy circulation, which might be termed "ecosystems." An ecosystem is concerned with the circulation and conversion of materials. We do not know the full range of these systems yet. The ecologist apprehends this situation, although he may not yet comprehend it. A hypothetical ecosystem of five thousand species of plants and animals, with full circulation, pulse, and rate, can be bottlenecked in circulation and in the conversion of materials if one, ten, or five hundred species are removed from the complex. For example, Øbergaarde Nielsen, of Denmark, found a millipede to be the only species that was able to tackle a certain kind of plant detritus and to pass it into the circulatory system. Thus a myriapod that seems so insignificant and is not seen by most of us will, when removed from the detritus, block the possibility of a full pulse of energy flow in the ecosystem. Research into ecosystems is the function of the ecologist, who is the physiologist of biotic communities. Fundamental research directed toward increasing comprehension of these biotic communities should continue, as it is the point upon which man depends for his continued inhabitance of the earth.

Based upon his ten years of experience in the Tonkin Delta, GOUROU, in writing, observed that Asian peoples have lived for millenniums on diets that provide only minute quantities of animal proteins and not very large amounts of vegetal protein. Most live in poverty from the products of rice fields. Carbohydrates supply 98 per cent of the calories in their diet; they do not drink milk; eating meat once a month is a maximum; and very few fish are eaten (density of population is so high that the available supply of sea foods produces only low per capita consumption). And yet such people are active, have great fertility, and have built high civilizations.

WATER

THOMAS began his discussion with the oceans, maintaining that for all practical purposes there is no limiting factor on the total amount of water of the earth. It is always possible to demineralize, distil, or otherwise obtain water from the sea at a cost less than that now paid for domestic water in some small towns and not much greater than that for fresh water in many communities. The possibility of obtaining fresh water from saline water exists on ships, on oceanic islands, and from saline springs on the continents; but the limiting factor is energy rather than water.

Ground water in many parts of the world is saline, although it may have a fresh-water skim perhaps a few hundred feet in thickness. The possibilities of using energy for obtaining fresh water are considerable, but, again, the limiting factor is the energy rather than the water. Fresh-water supplies on the continents maintain their source in solar energy and thus depend upon precipitation. In certain instances, some ground water is really fossil precipitation, accumulated in past centuries or, in small part, perhaps dating back hundreds of thousands or millions of years. Thus, we would prefer to claim these water supplies as non-renewable resources. However, we are most interested in renewable resources dependent upon precipitation. But precipitation alone is not satisfactory for plant or animal life; some storage is always necessary. Our living processes require collected water, either ground water or surface water. Storage is a vital factor and in various parts of all continents a limiting factor.

Soils have different storage capabilities. In wet areas annual precipitation is great enough, so that it cannot all be evaporated by the available solar energy. There is, then, an annual surplus of water which flows from a wet region as surface water or goes into the ground and flows as ground water. In some wet areas where there has been enough precipitation for agricultural needs, man has been able through concentrated pumping to deplete the supply of underground water. Pollution, too, has rendered both surface- and groundwater reservoirs unsatisfactory for use in many areas of adequate precipitation.

By contrast, the dry areas, such as deserts, are those places in which solar energy is great enough to evaporate more water than is available from precipitation. It is obvious that dry regions are limited for use by lack of water. But man can use dry areas if he can bring in surpluses from elsewhere. The limit to which desert regions can be developed is dependent upon the amount that man can make available from areas of surplus.

The boundaries of areas wherein average evaporation throughout the year is equal to precipitation shift from year to year. The results are marginal areas—such as our major grasslands, the Great Plains. Man finds difficulty there because of uncertain conditions; as a result he employs for land use an interweaving of techniques from the wet and from the dry lands. In deserts or in wet regions, conditions are rather consistently plus or minus; but in marginal areas we can never be sure. The techniques of dry farming, something of a gamble, are rather characteristic of marginal areas. Man's efforts there in diverting surface water have resulted not in failures but in overwhelming successes. So successful has he been in diverting water and applying it to land that problems of waterlogging and of drainage caused by too much water have resulted. On the other hand, we have found ourselves almost too capable of draining swamps with too much water, for we have lowered the water table and developed troublesome spots around the drained areas.

In the matter of pumping, we have developed a turbine pump to lift water from great depths. This pump has a capability of pulling thousands of acre-feet (or cubic yards) of water out of the ground much faster than it goes in naturally. In Phoenix, Arizona, the problem of surplus water arose twenty years ago because the application of surface water to the land was producing higher and higher water tables. The turbine pump was the answer to that drainage problem, but it succeeded so well that the area is now critically dry, owing to the removal of too much water from the ground. The problem is now to get more water into the ground by artificial recharge.

A project in Arkansas has added water to the ground under the rice prairie. This is a peculiar situation for a humid country where there is plenty of rainfall. But rice, however, requires a relatively impermeable surface. It is possible to pond the water, but that prevents its flowing down into the underground reservoir, which is the main source of water at the top. Natural recharge is inadequate for the reservoir. The problem is to get surface water from large streams into the underground reservoir, so that it can be pumped out for the cultivation of the rice.

In Schaefer's discussion of weather modification there are great possibilities, but behind them all lies the close interrelation among precipitation, soil moisture, ground water, and surface water within streams and reservoirs. When we are successful in changing one, there may be unforeseen modifications in adjacent or related patterns.

MINERALS, FUELS, AND ENERGY

BATEMAN, in writing, called attention to the dependence of industrial nations upon the metals and minerals in the ground. The rise of the leading industrial nations has coincided with the utilization of their mineral resources, chiefly coal and iron. The history of modern industrial development of the West may be read as the conquest of the mineral kingdom, wherein those who hold the purse strings of the mineral resources hold world power. It is startling to realize that under pressure of increasing industrial demands the world has dug and consumed more of its mineral resources within the period embraced by the two World Wars than in all preceding history. No nation, actually, is self-sufficient in all minerals. More than eighty minerals today enter international trade. The U.S.S.R. does stand apart; through supplements from the bloc of its bordering satellite nations, it is essentially self-sufficient for most of the minerals that form the backbone of modern industrial development and is independent of sea-borne mineral imports. The United States cannot support itself industrially; it is deficient in eighteen and lacking in five of the thirty-two most important industrial minerals. The British Commonwealth complements the United States, and together they have practically all the essential mineral ingredients for normal peacetime industrial development and for defense.

AYRES, in writing, could not share the feeling that "power we shall have in plenty," if the inference is that it will be reasonable in price. The following present facts must be faced: (1) Hydroelectric power, in 1930, comprised 30 per cent of United States electric power. Today it is 16 per cent, and the decline has been inexorable in spite of vigorous government promotion. The rate of hydroelectric expansion will be far less than the expected rate of increase in demand. (2) The latest analysis of the United States Geological Survey indicates that only about thirty billion tons of bituminous coal can be produced at or near present costs. If this coal is used only for the generation of electric power and other conventional solid-fuel applications, a peak of coal production can be expected in 1975. After that, coal will be progressively more expensive to mine and to use. (3) The peak of production of United States oil can be expected about 1965; that of world production, about 1985. After 1970, United States importation will be more expensive and more difficult to arrange, because per capita demand of the rest of the world is rising four times as fast as the per capita demand in the United States. (4) Natural-gas peak of production can be expected about 1965. The shortage of gas thereafter cannot be made up by imports from Canada, whose gas reserve is believed to be only about 5 per cent of that of the United States. (5) Shale oil, by 1975, will not amount to more than one-third of the difference between our supply and our demand for liquid fuels. (6) Development of all practicable tidal power sites would provide only a fraction of 1 per cent of our energy demand, and the cost would be high. Large-scale use of solar energy awaits the invention of practical means for its massive storage. (7) The last quarter of this century will find the United States with expensive fuel (solid, liquid, and gas), while some other parts of the world still will have adequate natural petroleum and gas. The United States will be at a competitive disadvantage.

These estimates are predicated on the absence of large-scale nuclear energy at reasonable cost. It is impossible today to have any idea of the cost of nuclear power from a self-supporting industry. The almost-competitive figures given by General Electric are based upon the rejuvenation of fuel being done in government plants at a "fair" price. The Duquesne plant, now building, will cycle about forty million dollars worth of uranium fuel between the power plant and the government-operated plant, making the generation of electric power a by-product of the manufacture of atomic bombs. Nuclear power in Britain is intended to be self-supporting, but reasonable costs can be arrived at only by assigning a value to the plutonium produced from a breeding reactor for use in other nuclear-power plants. Once expansion of the power industry ceased, the cost of power would skyrocket, because there are no outlets for plutonium use except bombs or power plants. The most optimistic of nuclear-power specialists do not anticipate that, regardless of costs, nuclear power will expand at a rate to supply more than 10 per cent of the United States total energy demand by the end of the century.

There will be ample energy for the rest of the century, though costs will rise. It is to be hoped that a method will be devised for the slow release of energy from atomic fusion (as distinguished from fission). Much interesting work has been done with lithium hydride, which involves no critical mass, creates no dangerously radioactive by-products, does not require recycling through a chemical plant, and is five hundred times as abundant as uranium and thorium. Even motorcars might be operated in this way.

For SCARLOTT, a consideration of energy resolved itself into two questions: How much energy do we have in the bank? What is the rate at which we are spending it? By and large, our inventories of fossil fuels are probably adequate, and we can certainly do reasonable planning in this realm. The records of how fast we are consuming energy are fairly good also, and the spread of disagreement is not too great. The only areas of doubt are in the lesser developed countries, but, there, the energy uses are so small as yet that they need not be considered as an appreciable factor. The one large area of disagreement is of how fast we will be using energy in the future. It is quite possible to plot curves of population growth, then to plot the per capita consumption of energy, and thus to discover that the total energy use some fifty to a hundred years from now will be truly staggering.

The more important question to consider is the occurrence of the point at which our demand for energy outstrips our ability to produce it. Does it really matter what the quantities of fossil fuel or natural gas we have in the ground may be if our demands far exceed our ability to produce them?

Let us consider the specific fuels one by one. Oil, for instance, will probably reach a maximum peak of production some time between 1965 and 1975, after which production will decline rather rapidly. This prediction is based on the assumption that ninety billion more barrels will come out of the ground. Even if it were much more, we would not postpone the date of maximum production more than ten or fifteen years, which is a very short span in the life of the country. It appears that we are probably going to be faced with a liquid-fuel shortage around 1975, at least in the United States. In natural gas, using the same line of reasoning, the probability is that we will reach our period of maximum production somewhere between 1985 and 2000. We probably will run into very marked shortages of our high-grade bituminous coking coals by the year 2000, or between 2000 and 2025. Our economy still is based upon steelmaking and ironmaking, which, in turn, depend upon the availability of high-quality, low-volatile bituminous coal suitable for coking. In the event of scarcity, the steel people will have to look to other methods, which most surely will increase the cost.

The question is not the sum total of energy but the costs of the energy units and the ingenuity required for their capture. Beyond the high-quality bituminous coals (currently being wasted for such purposes as house heating, when there is a much greater need in the total social order for other and more specialized purposes), there are also vast quantities of lower-grade coals, on down to the lignites. We often say that, when oil runs out or becomes scarce, we will make liquid fuels from coal or from shale. But both of these technical possibilities encounter serious engineering difficulties as well as rising costs. Fuel can be made from coal only at the expense of one-half of the Btu.'s which are consumed in the process. So, too, can oil be made from shale, but it so happens that great quantities of the shale are located in areas where water is very scarce, and water is quite important in the process of oil extraction. Added to this is the problem of ash disposal, since, to get a usable fuel, 95–98 per cent of the ash is left over from the retorting of the oil shales. Disposal of this material is a serious problem which again bears on cost.

Nuclear energy will be a major energy source in four or five years and will be competitive in cost to energy presently obtained from fossil-fuel stores. Then, too, in running the gamut of energy sources, we must not overlook solar energy. The earth receives from the sun each day some two thousand times more energy than is consumed; as we are threatened with the serious shortage of fossil fuels, the efforts to use solar energy increase. We can look to solar energy to take over a large portion of heat for cooking, for water-pumping, and for comfort heating, on which we now spend about a quarter to a third of our total energy. On large-scale power production from solar energy we are extremely pessimistic, since along with it there is a storage problem. We look to electricity as a continuous flow of energy, but of course solar energy is intermittent. Until the storage problem is solved, electric power from the sun is faced with a twofold handicap.

One thing which should not be ignored is the possibility of energy on a large scale through fusion rather than through fission. We will probably develop large-scale power plants based on the fusion reaction. Should we develop practical controls for the fusion reaction, the energy obtainable would be so great that it would certainly modify all our present concepts of energy consumption and energy needs. Meanwhile, however, we would be foolish to relax our concern for future energy supplies.

In summary, the world has ample fuel stores and energy stores per se. However, there are serious energy shortages ahead of us, and we are faced with consistently rising energy costs inclusive of nuclear and fusion energy.

BUGHER mentioned that his chapter attempted to document what is known of the present radioactive contamination of the world, which has resulted from the past decade of fission activity. The figures presented were based on more than a hundred thousand analyses representing the full-time work of a hundred people for three years. He said that it is almost inevitably true that the generation now being born will derive most of its energy from fission processes, to the point where it will be uneconomic to develop to the full either the coal or the oil reserves. In talking of competitive technology, nuclear power is already competitive in some parts of the world and is underselling thermal power in some situations, even in the United States.

In considering fusion possibilities, we realize that deuterium is one of the abundant elements of the earth and completely inexhaustible as a source of energy. Only two and one-half years ago did we learn for certain that a self-sustaining energy released from deuterium could be achieved. If we had the ability to achieve energy release by deuterium fusion today, the raw material could be considered as without appreciable cost, for the production of heavy water now goes on in terms of tons rather than grams.

THOMAS queried Bugher as to the problem of waste disposal in full-scale, nuclear-energy power development. BUGHER answered that it was not the reactors that occasion difficulty but the residues from chemical processing. The factors of this problem are time, distance, and containment. Such residues must be held in adequate containment for a sufficient time (on the order of a hundred years without disturbance) to allow decay to take place. Two possibilities are attractive: one is the utilization of exhausted oil fields, particularly salt-dome structures known to be tight, and the other is the depths of the ocean, where, if figures on turnover time are correct, we could rely on several hundred years without disturbance. But it is essential that waste products not be released to the environment, or we would certainly get into major population difficulties through genetic disturbance.

POPULATION

THOMPSON attributed the phenomenal increase in population of late to two main causes: the lowering of the death rate and increase of the birth rate and the generally improved sanitary and medical conditions which have eliminated the factor of disease throughout the world. Back in the 1930's we were quite certain that the United States was undergoing a decline in birth rate. We predicted it would slowly continue to approach the death rate, with the result that the rate of natural growth would be comparatively small. But the fact is that since World War II we have continued a birth rate varying between 23.5 and 25 per thousand, with a reduction in the death rate to about 9. We can truly speak of an unexpected explosion of population in the United States.

In the past, most changes have been comparatively slow, because the cultural backgrounds out of which these changes had to take place were different and were changing more slowly than we can change them today. We often speak of the population transition in the Western world which began, roughly, two hundred years ago. It took place in those countries in which economic conditions were such that the death rate was improved long before we knew what the causes of its improvement were. The improvement of living, and probably the cleanliness that accompanied it, was an extremely important factor in cutting the death rate. As a result, there was a tremendous growth of population among a relatively small group of people. (Europeans in 1800 numbered possibly 175–200 million.) Gradually, with industrialization and urbanization, the whole cultural pattern was changed sufficiently to permit reduction of the birth rate to set in. But this, in England, was about a hundred and twenty-five years after the beginning of the industrial revolution. Later, the improvements and application of most modern medical techniques in the control of the various diseases further reduced the death rate.

Birth rates today for many parts of the world are above 40 per thousand. There are death rates as low as 8. As a rule, the two are not combined in the same areas; we have had only partially controlled death rates in places of high birth rates. But more and more it is possible to keep the death rate at a minimal figure of from 10 to 12. Birth rates, however, are of a different order and are subject to quite different types of control. As yet, we see no evidence of the infertility or sterility, mentioned by Albrecht, that arises from lack of protein.

For a long period the increase of food supply was the fundamental limit to increases of population; later, the limits became rather the cultural and political conditions under which people lived. In his recent book, *World Population and World Agriculture,* Sir John

Russell studied the possibility of improvement of agriculture and found that it continually involved cultural and political matters in the acceptance of change. An example of the rapidity of cultural and political conditions to effect changes, both in the matter of food production and in attitudes toward the control of population increase, is set by Japan, which under the prodding of the occupation forces brought its birth rate down from 34 to 20 per thousand and declined its death rate from 29 to 8.9.

The main question, of course, in discussion of population is where we are to find the resources that are going to be demanded as a result of increasing population. We simply do not know how to control many of the variables which affect man's attitudes toward his own reproduction.

GOUROU, in writing, commented upon the demographic revolution in Europe after the seventeenth century. In Picardy, northern France, an accurate examination of the parish registers in some villages and of the recordings of the prices of wheat has shown that (1) a critical equilibrium of population existed between 1630 and 1715, with deaths in some years exceeding births; (2) during this period prices of wheat frequently were very high, an expression of bad harvests and of a situation of scarcity if not of famine, with the worst years for population increase the years of higher prices; and (3) after 1715 population rose continuously, with births in every year exceeding deaths, while the price of wheat was steadier and lacked such high peaks.

GLACKEN, in writing, observed that the relation of world population to world resources had been of considerable interest since the end of the nineteenth century. Albrecht Penck's essay, "Das Hauptproblem der physischen Anthropogeographie," of the mid-1920's stimulated German thinking, and there have been many similar stimuli over the last decade. Estimates of potential world population have varied widely because of (1) differences in calculations of the amount of arable land and (2) differences in standards of living. Obviously, a low estimate of total arable land with a population at the Western European standard of living would result in a far lower potential world figure than a high acreage estimate at an Oriental standard of living.

Several have pointed out that thought on population and resources on a world-wide basis ignores the existence of national states and differences in transportation, production, capital, etc. However, world estimates should not be dismissed cavalierly. Even though the world is divided into different cultures, each of which may be using its environment in different ways for different purposes, it is equally true that problems arising within nation-states have world-wide repercussions. General studies of the earth as a whole keep in mind the dimensions of the problem and the interdependence of all its parts. By emphasizing local units, the world-wide situation too often appears only as an influence on the nation-state that occupies the center of attention.

STEINBACH, in writing, considered *organism* the greatest natural resource and the property of adaptation, change, and progress its greatest virtue. But adaptation and change depend upon a freely available pool of genetic factors. Thus the greatest possible argument for maintaining large populations in man is to produce the genius. Albrecht's plea for animal proteins—or for proteins in general—is valid only within the limits of present-day technical knowledge. There is no reason why man or other animals should not be fed entirely on protein from properly fortified marine algae when enough is known about it. Bugher's point of a new type of energy of unlimited amount, not dependent upon organisms, necessitates an even

closer regard for organisms as a controlling or limiting factor and the need to preserve a large genetic pool—to give mankind its genius and agriculture its hybrid corn.

As a small example of the problem of the human time scale in dealing with man, DARWIN presented a matter of research in eugenics. The Eugenics Society of England had made a considerable study of the criminal classes and then, a little above them, of what we call the "problem families" of humanity, the people who, if left alone, do not get deeply into crime but do create a "slum" from a decent house, and things of that kind. Recently, we have been paying attention to the fact that the really important thing is the other end of the equation, the superior classes of people. We have started a project on what we call "the promising families." The problem is to find an objective manner to discover which among the various families of a country are the really valuable ones, and this is an incomparably more difficult subject than the other. The starting point has been in the schools, beginning with children between the ages of ten and eleven. But this quite convinces us that to start any systematic plan for studying humanity, of any kind, an unavoidable delay is encountered. Student and subject age at the same rate, and this handicap makes the time scale in human affairs such an important subject.

TUKEY suggested that the limitation of the time scale can be broken through. Witness the astronomers, who, to be where they are today in their knowledge, have broken through by a much larger factor than anyone dealing with human problems. Whereas for astronomers a million generations is a short time indeed, we would be in very good shape if we could break through by one hundred generations.

BOULDING, in writing, contributed the following observation: In "classical" Malthusian theory the limiting variable is *per capita food intake.* This leads to the "dismal theorem" that the only things that limit population are starvation and misery; population will grow until people are hungry and miserable enough to stop its growth! It leads further to the "utterly dismal theorem" that any improvement (whether technological or conservational) leads only to *increased* populations living in just the same state of misery as before—that is, assuming no change in the subsistence level itself. The "cheerful" side of the Malthusian system is that, first, the subsistence variable does not have to be food. Even in nature it is usually some other variable, such as living space or "housing," which limits population rather than the food supply. More important, the *level* of subsistence, whatever the subsistence variable, does not have to imply "misery." That is to say, as Malthus himself recognized, "subsistence" is *always* culturally rather than "biologically" determined. The problem, therefore, is to find cultural subsistence levels which are "agreeable," or at least more agreeable than others. A study of the Irish experience since 1846 would be very enlightening in this regard. Generally, for instance, "housing shortages" may be more desirable than "food shortages." Thus the population of domestic cats is limited by a housing shortage (the number of cat-lovers' homes), whereas the population of alley cats is limited mostly by a food shortage. Even better, the development of a "moral niche" may be the most desirable of all —that is, a general willingness to restrict families voluntarily out of a *clear understanding* of the ethical issues involved.

ON METHODS OF DEALING WITH LIMITATIONS

KNIGHT began his discussion, later supplemented in writing, by contrasting the natural sciences and the social sciences. Natural sciences, he said, deal with facts and information to which people generally were fairly hospitable, but social sciences, and particularly economics, tend to remind people of things which they already know but systematically disregard in their own conduct.

In economics, man is dealt with as a rational animal, in terms of his effective or efficient societal behavior. Perhaps there is a degree of rationality in human conduct. Man also is a biological specimen and a physical mechanism to such a degree that we cannot find in the human body any exception to the workings of the laws of physics and chemistry. Yet man is more than these. In all our objectives in social policy aimed toward improvement of society, we find man to be a civilized animal. Perhaps, the difficulty in talking about man is the pluralism found within him —he is a physical mechanism, a biological specimen, a cultural animal, and more or less an intelligent animal. And yet, in discussing man, we cannot ignore the problems of belief and conduct that do not come under the notion of efficiency at all.

No real discussion of social policy can neglect the fact that man is more than an animal with animal needs. Proverbially, he "must live"; but, as Aristotle pointed out, society exists for the sake of living "well," not merely living. Truth, beauty, goodness, and fun have to be provided for. Problems arise because all needs of all individuals come into conflict when all draw upon a common store of means, existing or to be created. The "quality" of human life in its many aspects conflicts with the "quantity," and at some point a balance must be struck, some compromise effected. No truth is more self-evident than that quality and humanness of life depend upon limiting the numbers of people to correspond with the available means of providing for them. The balancing point may be chosen either more or less rationally or left to the forces of nature, which obviously are on the side of quantity, for no "freedom" is more untouchable or difficult to regulate than that of mating and reproduction.

The outline presented by the Chairman provided four main topics for discussing the methods of dealing socially with the limits of the earth: the market-and-price system, political measures, modification of our ends or values, and research.

Taken in reverse order, how can research ever be applied to the crucial values—those which lie beyond mere living? The problem is to define human progress. Logically, we must first know the "given conditions" in nature and human nature, and that knowledge is only vaguely knowable; ascertaining the human and social ideals to be realized is still more difficult. Yet we do the best we can through reflection and patient and tolerant discussion.

The greatest obstacles to the use of intelligence are not ignorance or even error but prejudice and false values. The innate and uniquely romantic character of man leads him to demand easy and pleasant answers to hard problems. Above all, man is impelled to "do something" about his multitudinous discontents (whether rational or irrational) and proceeds to act, well knowing that acting without the knowledge required to act intelligently is far more likely to do harm than good. Man is distinctly the irrational animal. Historically, the conspicuous form of prejudice has been the virtue of believing by faith. Prejudice rather overlaps the categories of error and sin. Animals are held incapable of sin; but men call other men "brutal" and "beastly" for traits like cruelty and obscenity, from which animals are free. Animals sometimes fight but not over the meaning of meaningless words. Man is a social animal but is also distinctively antisocial. An individual belongs to innumerable "societies" but tends to be antisocial—

suspicious or hostile—in relations across the boundaries between them. Man's social nature is largely that of a partisan—a "gangster."

The supreme mystery of man from the evolutionary viewpoint lies in the reversal of the instrumental relation between body and mind. Originally, the brain was merely a biological organ functioning to serve the needs of the organism. Civilized men have made the relation wholly the opposite, the body purely an instrument for producing "desirable experience" or "ideal values" —things without biological meaning and often antibiological. Indeed, the mind is ashamed of having a body; this is kept carefully concealed. But wearing clothes is a small circumstance compared to the mind's dissembling of itself. Man is the deceiver, the liar, the hypocrite of all creation—for the good as well as the bad, just as what is sought for the good life is as often bad as good. The great fact, however, is that some *kind* of life is sought, not just life. It is not life which occasions our shortages—not even the "good" life; but it is the constantly *better* life as measured by increasing use of resources— that is, it is social progress and the equitable distribution of its benefits and its costs or losses—which brings us to the limit of resources.

The problem in changing human values is that men struggle over rights, which are very difficult to discuss objectively. Each would be the judge of his own cause; the result is accusation, recrimination, and appeal to force or settlement by an arbitrator with power to enforce his decisions. Hope lies rather in agreement on "good" law and open-minded, tolerant, and patient administration, all based on faith in the intelligence and reasonableness of human nature.

But what of the choice—the proper balance or compromise—between the market-and-price system and political action? In the present state of the public mind it is the "fashion" to go to an extreme in repudiating the market organization and to resort to political force, with but little rational inquiry into the virtues of the one system or the limited possibilities of the other. Nineteenth-century liberalism, particularly in Britain and America, went to an indefensible extreme in its faith in individualism. This was a reaction against the long centuries of ecclesiastical dictatorship and the following shorter epoch of regimentation under authoritarian monarchical dynasties ruling by divine right. The present counterreaction runs to the opposite extreme—statism. It is surely incumbent on advocates of radical change to consider what powers governments must have if they are to remedy economic injustices, real or supposed, and what such governments are likely to do with power. The basic issue is *freedom*, with its interrelations in economics, politics, and culture and, generally, in thought, expression, and personal intercourse.

A sketch of the principles involved in comparing the market system with political action might begin with the truism that no one really advocates either method to the complete exclusion of the other. In its current meaning "economy" is a fairly close synonym of "efficiency"; it now refers to getting the "best" or "maximum" result from the use of given resources. Economics treats the value judgments of individuals—as expressed in choices actually made in buying and selling goods or services—as final and as facts. But social policy necessarily involves comparison of the wants of individuals in terms of "importance"; this implies superindividual criteria, and this comparison must be made and enforced by an agent representative of society as a whole, that is, the government. Thus any policy is inherently an interference with, or limitation of, individual freedom.

Freedom, to make sense in social re-

lations, has to mean association by mutual consent, that is, with each individual free to choose his associates in terms of maximum advantage to himself but with coercion by duress or fraud excluded. Exchange in the open market is the nearest approach to mutual freedom possible for persons with conflicting interests. Law, voluntarily accepted or enforced, can enter only by way of preventing unfree relations.

In the controversy over the definition of freedom, we see a largely partisan line-up. On the one side are propagandists for business ad lib, who advocate making individual liberty, as expressed in the market, the single final and universal norm. But society is not composed of "individuals" capable of taking the whole responsibility for themselves. A clear majority of any normal population are dependents. The family is the minimum social unit that is at all real. Any society which counts on its continued existence has to accept some responsibility for its weaker members, especially its children.

On the other side of the controversy over the definition of freedom are the propagandists for "justice." But it seems absurd to say that a person is not free to do anything unless he commands all the means, or power, that would be necessary to achieve desired ends—in effect making freedom the right of everyone to do anything he pleases and get anything he wants. Any effective social policy must exercise some control over both the wants and the capacities of its members. This means that freedom must be limited for the sake of other rights and values in so far as these are more important.

Assuming impending shortages, there are still difficult problems in assigning the respective roles of the market system, based upon individual freedom, and of state action, based upon compulsion. Though we assume that state action will be democratic and through law, all law is compulsory and requires enforcement. Enforcement is necessary because law must apply to everyone, and men do not spontaneously or freely agree.

The first threat to free society today lies in the lack of a critical-comparative attitude in viewing the relation between economics and politics; there is also a tendency to irrational rejection of the working of the free market and an appeal to the compulsory power of government. In the same direction away from freedom, but going still farther, is a refusal to face, state, and discuss issues in politics itself and a resort to emotional appeal, trickery, and various psychological techniques of persuasion, all of which are forms of force. What is true is that people who believe in freedom favor the free market. One reason why men appeal from the market to law and the police power of government, and from critical discussion to political "arguments" without intellectual merit, is that critical discussion of objective or social values is terribly difficult. Such an idea is a revolutionary cultural innovation. The problem is utterly different from that of science, where experiment and empirical tests are applicable, for social policy must change society, and its institutions can look forward only to an indefinite future.

The law of nature seems to be, "To him that hath shall be given," since power in any form can always be used to acquire more power. The world of our environment shows no visible concern for our ideals or any norms or standards, no aversions to suffering oppression or cruelty or to ugliness or nastiness. On the other hand, it shows no preference for these things; it is merely indifferent, "inexorable." It is up to man to inject purpose and rationally to turn natural processes to account for good. To do this, men must agree cooperatively on ideals and procedures for their realization. Nature, indeed, shows purposiveness in detail, but, in the large, it seems to cancel out. The spider's web is clearly "designed" to catch flies for the spider to devour; but from the flies' point of view the beneficence appears in a different light. Cooperation is also widespread in nature; but human groups are unified in large part by opposition to other societies. In short, life directed to the realization of enduring values and "progress" toward higher values calls for an organized conspiracy of man against the natural course of events.

History and evolution afford much explanation or "excuse" for man's limited success, so far, in this project. For eons before men appeared there was social life on the mechanistic basis of instinct. In some mysterious way the basis was shifted, in the main, from instinct to socially inherited mores and institutions. But conformity and obedience seem never to have been voluntary or rational; they were "sanctioned" in various ways, especially by fear of punishment by supernatural powers. Then, as mysteriously, gradually in human terms but suddenly in those of human history, men got the idea and aim of reversing the relation, took charge of the process which had produced them, and began to direct history itself toward ideals wholly alien to nature.

In always facing a welter of conflicting values, not merely a clash of self-interests or a simple opposition of "right" and "wrong," we must be critically intelligent. The only general formal rule is the best attainable balance and compromise. To become critically intelligent, man must re-educate himself. This will be a long, laborious, but necessary process if people are to be fitted for life in a free and progressive society. The first requisite is the wish to be objective. The young must be taught that questions are to be answered by reaching agreement through free and critical inquiry, not by repeating inherited dogmas, which are always meaningless without interpretation and enforcement by an authority with plenary power. Discussion calls for modesty, patience, and tolerance, which are not now natural to man. We must learn to attempt only what is possible and then not to expect too much. There is no other way to save civilization, so laboriously and painfully achieved. And we must have faith, but a discriminating faith.

WHAT "ARE" THE FUTURE LIMITS?

Dr. LESTER KLIMM, in chairing the open-discussion portion of the session, pointed out that we must recognize certain assumptions about diversity: diversity in rates of change over time and place as well as diversity in magnitudes. Throughout the symposium discussions there seems to have been a continuing and implicit assumption that American problems were world problems and that all problems were of the same magnitude as those of the United States. However, must we not assume a little variety on the face of the earth and understand not only that the rates of change are different but are also of differing magnitudes?

ORDWAY replied to Willits' suggestion that social scientists may find an inconsistency between the statement that rising prices will gradually limit consumption of resources and the statement that man should now begin voluntarily to cut back on consumption before rising prices force him to do so. But factors of time and human aspiration must be considered. It is not only the part of prudence to reduce consumption of raw materials that are becoming scarce; if this is not now done voluntarily, then gradually we will be forced to do so against our wills, with an upsetting loss of freedom of initiative and with involuntary reversal of our American dream of expanding prosperity for all. Perhaps there is an element of optimism in the belief that prices will accomplish, before it is too late, a balance between resource consumption and resource creation. The ability to be optimistic in the face of disillusionment is a form of escape that may lead to defeat.

In thinking about the future, BROWN thought it absolutely essential that what we would like to see happen be absolutely distinguished from what we think actually will happen. The latter is the present concern. What might a gathering of Paleolithic men have discussed regarding the outlook for resources? What would a group of agriculturalists, meeting prior to the emergence of the agricultural revolution in Western Europe, have said? In the absence of world catastrophe, man is entering upon a new revolution which is bound to have enormous demographic consequences.

Given adequate supplies of energy, water ceases to be a limiting factor, for, as Thomas has remarked, water may be obtained from the sea. Also, are we not on the verge of a revolution in food production, produced by advances in microbiology? BROWN himself in the West Indies had eaten yeast slightly fortified with methionine, which had the amino acid composition distribution of milk and was grown on pure carbohydrate mixed with entirely inorganic mineral nutrients. He had also consumed at the Institute of Food Technology in India a synthetic buttermilk made by growing a particular culture on peanut cake. Similarly with photosynthesis. Growing things in soil is rather inefficient from the standpoint of present yields. Algal research has produced prodigious yields in inorganic nutrient solutions much higher than yields from conventional agriculture.

The main limiting factor today seems to be the rate at which we can produce energy. Our world seems governed, in effect, by the first and second laws of thermodynamics. Thermodynamics tells us what reactions are possible (levels that can be achieved) but nothing about rates (how fast the reactions can take place). As our population increases, our rate of energy consumption will rise, and our energy consumption per capita also is bound to go up. We will have to get used to the idea of greater energy expenditure and to the idea of paying more for it.

But are there limits to our production of energy? BROWN then presented information, previously classified by the Atomic Energy Commission for release at the August, 1955, United Nations meeting in Geneva, on the peaceful uses of atomic energy. His research group at Cal Tech, in the course of measuring the geochemical distribution of uranium in granite, had made an important discovery. Uranium is distributed in granite in such a way that 90 per cent is concentrated in mineral phases that comprise but one-half of 1 per cent of the total weight of the granite. And fully a third of the total uranium and thorium content is so loosely bound within the granite that it can be washed out with slightly acidulated water. Thus, within the framework of existing technology, granite can be processed at a net energy gain equivalent to about 25 tons of coal for every ton of granite processed. Literally, the rocks of the earth's crust are at mankind's disposal as a source of energy.

This will have enormous consequences in the spread of technology, which, in turn, will have enormous consequences on the population that may be supported. A world containing thirty to forty billion people is by no means a wild flight of imagination.

It would seem that the real limiting factors in the kind of world that we are heading for do not lie in phenomena or processes outside of man but reside within him—in purely aesthetic and ethical considerations.

Assuming Brown's premises, OSBORN suggested that consideration be given to what he called "human world strat-egy" and the notion that we should not lose sight of the need for far greater food supplies from whatever process. In the interim of the next century we must encourage and activate as best we can those existing agricultural processes. The necessity arises because, presumably, 60 per cent of the world's people are now devoted to agriculture-utilizing processes that, in light of the world foreseen, will be primitive. We have not yet spoken of the quality of living in a world of a great number of persons. Perhaps we should consider that the values of what we tend to term the "lesser" peoples do have better qualities of living than our own. We should certainly not lose sight of the fact that we do not want to have what we could cruelly call a human anthill on the face of the earth.

GALDSTON related the protein theory, presented by Albrecht, to the human species, which has been adjusting for a million years or so to the world as it is. He suggested that we cannot take the gut, the teeth, the stomach, and the lungs of an organism and of a sudden, i.e., in a hundred years or so, change the nutritional patterns on which their development has been based. It is important to take this evidence into account in planning the development of synthetic foods and artificial products upon which man might subsist in the future. SMITH added that the fundamental psychology of man seems to be that he would rather eat what he pleases than adjust to some new form of living.

SPOEHR brought out that basic to any discussion of what is going to happen in the future is an understanding of the processes of change in our social and cultural systems. The complexity of the human factor must be much better understood before any prediction can be assigned with any degree of probability. The social sciences, for instance, are attempting to understand the major factors that control the rejection or the acceptance of innovations. However, at the present time, the great insight of history has given us only apprehension, not comprehension.

The great difficulty we face is that the investigator, as Sir Charles has so neatly pointed out, is limited by the length of his own life, and this provides him with only partial information and incomplete understanding of the processes of change. Finding that discussion of values tends to become diffuse, SPOEHR recommended Redfield's phrase, "the moral order that governs relations among men." To concern ourselves with moral orders is to translate values into behavior which can be observed, recorded, and compared. It is in this comparison of moral orders that perhaps we find the most promising area of investigation of processes of culture change.

KLIMM, in closing the session, again referred to the differences in the rate of acceptance of culture change in the various parts of the world. The world is not one society with one economy and one means of communication. There is a geography of the rate of change, for there always will be differences between parts of the globe and the rate at which changes will be accepted. Perhaps if we build upon fundamental differences in the rate of accepting social change rather than build upon the differences between one part of the world and another, we would come closer to an approximation of the true picture. It might be a very healthy frame of mind in which to view man's relation to his environment if it were approached with an expectation of diversity!

At the session's close, TAX claimed the floor and read into the record the following poem, composed by BOULD-ING during the course of the discussion:

A CONSERVATIONIST'S LAMENT

The world is finite, resources are scarce,
Things are bad and will be worse.
Coal is burned and gas exploded,
Forests cut and soils eroded.
Wells are dry and air's polluted,
Dust is blowing, trees uprooted.
Oil is going, ores depleted,
Drains receive what is excreted.
Land is sinking, seas are rising,
Man is far too enterprising.
Fire will rage with Man to fan it,
Soon we'll have a plundered planet.
People breed like fertile rabbits,
People have disgusting habits.

Moral:

    The evolutionary plan
    Went astray by evolving Man.

THE TECHNOLOGIST'S REPLY

Man's potential is quite terrific,
You can't go back to the Neolithic.
The cream is there for us to skim it,
Knowledge is power, and the sky's the limit.
Every mouth has hands to feed it,
Food is found when people need it.
All we need is found in granite
Once we have the men to plan it.
Yeast and algae give us meat,
Soil is almost obsolete.
Men can grow to pastures greener
Till all the earth is Pasadena.

Moral:

    Man's a nuisance, Man's a crackpot,
    But only Man can hit the jackpot.

Man's Self-transformation

The Relevance of Total Human Action

The Dominance of Intelligence

The Responsibility of Freedom

Dialogue: Science and Humanities

Dialogue: Western and Non-Western Cultures

Dialogue: Planning and Free Choice

THE RELEVANCE OF TOTAL HUMAN ACTION

Chairman LEWIS MUMFORD introduced the discussion session as that part of the symposium not devoted exclusively to facts and to truth of a scientific order but lying more in the realm of dialectic. As such, it should be conversation, argument, dialogue—an exchange from one person to another, with due acknowledgment of everything that science can give us, but with even greater respect for the human constitution, human desires, human dreams, human purposes, and all those categories usually excluded, for a good purpose, from the method of science. This discussion is to deal with a larger reality than that dealt with by the method of science; it is to include the subjective, the inner, the inaccessible, the individual, and the all-too-complex.

Looking back over the history of species, we see that all animals have been in a process of self-transformation. We do not understand very much about the mechanism, but we know that the result has gone steadily on. In the higher orders there certainly has been an increase of direction, an increase of intelligence, and, finally, in man, an increase of self-consciousness. The change man works upon himself now becomes the equivalent of what nature has been capable of doing over a million years or so.

A question to ask ourselves is: What is the quality and variety of the finished product? Can we get anything in the way of desirable quality? Can we get anything in the way of interesting variety through the mere mechanical multiplication of human beings? Something else enters into our calculations that we have to consider in detail.

As to the method of considering it, we do not leave the world of the natural sciences behind us by any means. To do that would be to repeat the error of Socrates. But neither do we commit ourselves to the opposite bias of Thales: that of concentrating exclusively on the physical world. Rather, we renew and enlarge the tradition of Aristotle, who sought to embrace both man and nature. Speaking in the tradition of Aristotle, we find that the natural sciences that Socrates despised teach man a great deal not only about the earth itself but ultimately about his own constitution. He is a part of nature and participates as a working partner not merely with the trees, rocks, and clouds but with the animals and the plants

1088

and the microscopic organisms. The anthropological sciences extend this knowledge.

On the one hand, then, we renounce the self-centered humanist tradition of regarding the natural world as separated by a great barrier from the world of man. Neither world is conceivable without the other. Once this unity is granted, we have in compensation the privilege of returning to the natural world with knowledge that we have acquired about this more complex creature, man; we may even use "inside knowledge" that we acquire in ways sometimes not open to purely scientific method in interpreting the less complex phenomena in terms of the so far final end product—man himself. As man's own self-knowledge increases, his command of the various aspects of nature increases too.

There is a point that Northrop has added, one originally established by Immanuel Kant, that language, logic, mathematics, and even ethics have entered into the formulation of anything that can be called "natural science." We cannot use the concepts of natural science until concepts themselves—the symbols of language—are invented. Without the tools and methods of the humanities, the natural sciences could not take off from the ground. Intelligence itself is subject to other forms of human creativity. The sciences exist not in a world of their own but in a world made possible by the development of humanistic thought and by the development of man himself as a language-using, idea-communicating, symbol-creating, ideal-projecting, structure-building being.

The sciences very properly deal with that aspect of the future which is revealed in the causal process. Whether nature or man is under observation, they deal with regularities, with uniformities, with things that lend themselves to quantitative and statistical investigation, because they are mass phenomena and exhibit beautifully that kind of order. We necessarily follow that method in order to understand those probabilities, for that kind of reliable predictive knowledge widens our control over the environment.

Necessarily, therefore, we began our discussions of "Prospect" with the limitations imposed by the nature of the earth, the amount of energy available, the possible populations it might contain, and all things about which we have, at least, the beginnings of statistical knowledge and a method of dealing therewith. But, if any tendency that is statistically measurable is extrapolated, the risk is of overrating what is near and known and of ignoring factors that are remote, hidden, or so far unknown. Such statistical predictions will have the very highest degree of probability during the next five minutes, but during the next year, and the next hundred years, and so on, they will have a steadily lessening degree of probability.

On the other hand, there is the future as created and as remolded by autonomous human activity. This is the future for which the causal method is useless as a tool of investigation. It depends upon knowledge of the nature of man; it depends upon an understanding of his purposes and his projections and his ideals or his qualitative reactions. This is the directive and goal-projecting part of the future. If man had only to consider his own desires and needs without respect to the actual nature of things, we would discover that there are almost unlimited numbers of alternatives. Life presents us with an ascending grade of possibilities: the more successful living organisms are, the greater the number of potentialities they disclose. Life itself presents more possibilities than does non-living matter. Living organisms grow, they reproduce, they react, they remember, they learn; and, as they get higher in the scale, they organize, they construct, they anticipate. Just as life in all its forms, and particularly human life, has a much wider range of possibility than unorganized matter, so, similarly, man has possibilities that are not included in purely organic forms: the possibilities that come from his consciousness, from his detachment (by culture) from his original biological nature, from his increasing autonomy and his growing collective desire to steer his own course.

Perhaps the real future is a vector of the probable and the possible, of the objectively allowable and the subjectively desirable—in so far as the latter presses toward action. To understand what the real future is going to be at any moment, it is necessary to understand not only all the probabilities, all the factors in the given situation that will continue through inertia, but also things in the nature of man, the social mutations that are going on, the emergents that are coming forth, and the fresh ideas that are being born which will deflect the statistically probable future toward the actual future. Man's satisfaction with the future depends largely on the ratio of the possible and desirable to the given and inevitable. If he had to submit himself abjectly to life as it was structured in the past without any possibility of altering it, he would lose one of his attributes as a living being.

We are dealing, therefore, with the earth as modified by human action, in its totality, not just by human action in the form of science, technology, economic institutions, but also as modified by religion, by ethical principles, by education, and by art. For example, think of how the natural environment in England was modified by the school of landscape painting that arose in Holland and in England in the seventeenth century. Under the guidance of landscape gardeners these fresh intuitions of naturalism transformed great estates and finally modified an even larger share of the English landscape. All this was the result of fresh aesthetic perceptions that existed at first only in the minds of the seventeenth-century painters and some of the Italian painters ahead of them. So, too, politics, law, and education—all these tend to modify man's own culture and, by altering his nature, his direction, his purpose, his goals, also tend to modify the earth.

The earth as modified by man's total actions is therefore the subject of our discourse, and so we dare to ask ourselves something that we must not ask in terms of a purely scientific methodology: What kind of earth do we want? What kind of men do we want? What forms of life do we want here? This is a point where ideal-projections, which mathematics uses so easily when it is dealing with less complicated things than human society, might be very useful. We might ask ourselves: What are the possibilities for life in a population less than we have now—a population of five hundred million? What are they at two billion? What would they be at five billion? What would they be at sixty billion? Changing one factor in the situation could lead to the creation of a very useful series of abstract utopias which might guide us in the decisions to be made about the population question, although we would certainly require further guidance when we took in a larger sector of human life than reproduction alone.

Then we should ask ourselves: What are the results from the present tendency toward uniformity and standardization, toward a decrease in variety, a decrease in the power of selection? Our institutions today tend to establish our recent technological civilization as a norm. But is it a norm? Is it permanent? Will this suffice for a creature who has such a rich and varied biological and social past as man. Or would he, when faced with some final utopia of the machine, feel about it the way certain primitive tribes in the South Seas have felt about the earlier blessings of that civilization? Would he just sicken and die at the prospect of living under those circumstances? There is the possibility either that we might commit atomic suicide—this has a rather high degree of probability if we continue along our present course—or that we might even have an earlier reaction against our mechanical civilization in the form of boredom. That our highly technological civilization does not tempt a sufficient number of high-school students to study mathematics and physics should give pause. Is this lack of interest to be the weighty brake upon its continued expansion?

Consider the state of mind of a person in the third century A.D. toward the great Roman Empire and all its technological improvements, all its apparatus of learning, all that made it a great civilization. Most Romans would have thought—indeed some actually said—that their civilization would last another thousand years. There is a little third-century dialogue—the *Octavius* of Minucius Félix—between a pagan and a Christian, comparing paganism with the new creed. As we read that dialogue, we see that the pagan has the better of the argument: he is defending Rome, defending the culture of Rome against wicked barbarians, these slavish Christians who would undertake to destroy it. And, as the dialogue approaches the climax, the modern reader would say, "This rational Roman, of course, is on the right side." And just at this moment the pagan falls flat on his face, as it were, because he realizes that the new forces of life are on the side of the Christian, and he is converted to the new creed.

This means that Rome fell, in the minds of the Romans, before it was sacked, long before the barbarian hordes came on. And so our civilization might fall, in the minds of those who

are now supporting it, if the dissatisfactions, the fears, and the frustrations that are visible today continue to mount up. Let the subject for debate then be: "*Resolved,* That it seems impossible to change the direction and impetus of our technological civilization." In opening this session, MUMFORD said that he had followed the method of Thomas Aquinas by first presenting the contrary argument. He believed that the man perhaps best fitted to speak for the affirmative—on the basis of his previous work and thought—was Seidenberg, who in his book *Post-historic Man* carried our present technological civilization to its ultimate ideological and practical conclusions.

THE DOMINANCE OF INTELLIGENCE

SEIDENBERG began the presentation of his point of view by saying that customarily we are not inclined to make serious comments about the future; we feel that modesty requires that we say that we do not know about it. Nonetheless, the future deserves a little more critical thought, if only because it may be said that the future has descended upon us to a degree that is unique in history.

It is doubtful whether in the past man has ever concerned himself so consistently with the future as he does today. One reason perhaps is that, in a civilization or a culture which has attained a certain stability, the future, which is going to be similar to the past, evaporates as a problem. But, in a civilization or culture subject to increasingly rapid change, the future impinges upon us. Perhaps we are approaching some kind of climax. We seem to be going through not a transitional stage but a moment of transformation. We are no longer confined to time, as we were when we spoke of the present or past. We are still on earth, but time is now a free affair.

In approaching the future, we must

take into consideration the length of curve into the past. If our background is only that of a few decades, our estimates of the next decade may be quite wrong; but, if we include as background the trends over several millenniums, the chances are that our predictions may be a little firmer and may carry us for a century or two. Specific, isolated phenomena are a matter for crystal-gazing and prophecy. But beneath phenomena, in the future as in the past, there lies a certain structural quality to life. Therefore we do well to confine ourselves to the more abstract and structural considerations in talking of the future.

Naturally, when we come to the domain of man himself—the most unpredictable of all the phenomena with which science must deal—we become more humble in our predictions. Nonetheless, the effect of intelligence, which perhaps distinguishes man in his function from the animals, has been to make possible a cumulative knowledge which in turn acts as a "fulcrum" for the "lever" of intelligence. If we take a sufficiently long range, we can say that man, owing to his intelligence, has progressively changed outwardly in his mode of life. Anthropologists will bear out the fact that certainly in historic times the intelligence of the individual has not changed perceptibly, and it is perhaps questionable that it will change in the immediate or even long-range future. But intelligence has had the most amazing results and consequences in the manner of life of man. Presumably this will continue to operate in the future as it has in the past.

Technology can be defined as the use of intelligence in respect to the artifacts and living of man. Technology has reached an explosive stage, and the probability that man will continue to maintain and even develop his technology seems fairly certain. The line of intelligence which stems from far back

into the history of mankind can be projected beyond the present moment of technological development.

This symposium principally has asked: What was the role of man in changing the surface of the earth? Now, thanks to this technological factor, we might say: What are the effects of a changing world upon the condition of man? This brings in the whole social point of view with what has gone before.

Percy Bridgman defined science as the application of intelligence. The machine is the result of intelligence, and today, in contrast to the past, intelligence operates unencumbered. We have learned through science to be completely objective in the face of phenomena. We have no preconceived ideas. We simply use intelligence as a method of arriving at our conclusions. Though this be only half the world of thought, science is the half which now to a large extent dominates our effective thinking.

Perhaps the distinction between modern man and past man is that, whereas man in the past had nature as an environment, we of today have a twofold environment. We have nature, but we have with increasing intensity another environment which might be called the "laws of nature." The laws of nature are the result of our scientific appreciation of nature, and we have adjusted ourselves increasingly not to nature directly but to the laws of nature. Formerly, it was the natural scene about us that was our environment.

It is important to observe in respect to those laws of nature that, although we ourselves change them on occasion, as Einstein somewhat amended the laws of Newton, nonetheless they have a tremendous momentum. They are a rock-bottom foundation for our scientific thinking, and, in so far as they are universally accepted, these scientific principles tend to unify the world such as has never happened before. In other words, our secondary environment is a kind of universal environment and in that respect differs directly from nature.

One of the results of technology and perhaps one of the main requirements of technology in order that it might function with the highest degree of efficiency is the matter of predictability. In the ecological equation man seems to be perhaps the least predictable element. In order, therefore, to reach a more stable equilibrium, man will have to subject himself to increasing predictability, and this will in turn result in increased organization. How far that will go no man can say, but perhaps the great problem of the future is the problem of human organization.

Mumford has emphasized the unknown potentialities that may well affect man's further development. In view of man's past history, with all its magnificent examples of self-transcendence, it would seem like a denigration of human nature to question the validity of such an approach and such an attitude toward the possible course of man's future. Plainly, despite the innumerable futures that may seem open to man, he will have in fact but one future. How are we to assess that future? In the face of the profound turmoil of the present world and in view of our deep sense of an impending climax to the whole of our past development, we are perhaps justified, if indeed we are not compelled, to examine once more the whole perspective of our long development, covering not only the historic period but the entire range of our course since we deviated from the biological hierarchy as *Homo sapiens.* The extrapolation from the past upon which alone our predictions concerning the future can rest must be based upon the widest possible view of our own unique development. In this vast perspective the historic phase of

man is seen to be a relatively short, late, explosive phase, the full meaning of which we have not yet clearly comprehended. *Conceivably,* the historic phase as we have known it may thus prove to be a passing phase—a high moment of brilliant efflorescence, of profound conflict, of extraordinary contradictions and unfathomable paradoxes. Indeed, man seems by every sign of the times to be entering upon a wholly new direction in his development. The clear curve that may be plotted for the course of prehistoric man rises abruptly in a series of jagged deviations until, in our day, we have come to ask with more concern than assurance, "Whither mankind?"

The very scope of the problem here indicated demands the most rigid condensation. We may say at once that the influence of intelligence, operative throughout the entire range of man's past development, has at long last resulted in the high technological culture of the Western world. But this attainment is plainly destined to affect the whole of mankind. And though, obviously, it is but one aspect of man's multidimensional nature, it represents the dominant phase of his present condition. More deeply, man has attained through his cumulative knowledge, his scientific advances, and his awareness of his own past a growing sense of consciousness, of deliberate power and command over nature, a dynamic cognizance of his own self in a world of universal laws. If in the remote past he adapted himself to the exigencies of nature along with the rest of the biologic hierarchy, he has at last reversed this status in his present command over nature. Thus he is rapidly adapting his environment to his demands; and, in harnessing the energies of the world, he seems at length to have stepped upon a stage of unbounded and unimagined vistas.

This fair vision of nineteenth-century

progress is open to unsuspected limitations, however. Usually these have been pictured as arising out of the depletion of natural resources—the denudation of the surface of the earth, the exhaustion of fossil fuels, and the loss of irreplaceable metal and mineral resources in the face of an ever expanding human population. There are, of course, countervailing arguments in this equation, based on further advances in technological knowledge, as, for example, in the definite possibilities of improved agriculture and the unplumbed resources of atomic and solar energy. The problem as a whole constitutes what might be termed the "ecological dilemma" of man. Allowing for some grave and perhaps eventually insolvable difficulties with respect to the ultimate availability of certain natural resources, the ecological dilemma of man—viewed in its larger aspects—raises a problem of a totally different nature, however, in regard to its repercussions upon the structure and character of human society. Here we touch upon a phase of the future of man which, dramatically illustrated by his ecological situation, threatens in fact to dominate his entire further development. For the moment, in terms of the argument here pursued, it may prove advisable to state the problem within the confines of its ecological framework. Basically, it may be said that the ecological problem of man, as of all species, arises out of two primary instincts: those of hunger and sex. These are universal instincts, common to the life of each individual. Multiplied as the world is presently constituted by two and one-half billion times, and in the discernible future by perhaps two or three times that number, the problems arising out of these instincts cannot possibly be resolved by them alone. On the contrary, the only solution to their challenge, apart from that which nature imposes blindly, lies with human intelligence. And here we

come upon the great and decisive factor in the further possible development of mankind. For the chaos, the defeat, and the disaster implicit in man's ecological situation can be averted only in the last analysis by his intelligence. Thus his future survival will come to depend upon the deliberate and conscious exercise, on a world-wide scale, of his originally secondary but now dominant psychic component—his faculty of intelligence.

It is worth observing, however, that intelligence does not inevitably lead us wherever we may wish to go but only where, under any given set of circumstances and conditions, we can at best go. Like all else in this conditioned world, intelligence is not a miraculous panacea but merely a method of operation and procedure. In respect to mass problems, it implies an ever greater measure of organized modes of operation. It is not without significance that in the world of contemporary Western man both intelligence and organization have received a kind of uncritical axiomatic acceptance, as though their functioning in human affairs exacted no commensurate price and imposed no commensurate limitations. Actually, their unquestioned acceptance in the world of today represents a historic phenomenon of unprecedented significance for the future condition of mankind. In following the dictates of intelligence, in accepting the vehicle of organized procedures, we are, it is clear, entering upon a profound transformation in the basic structure of human society. The drift toward increased organization in every aspect of life is the direct consequence of a machine technology. Thus modern man is destined to move, irretrievably it would seem, toward a state of increased collectivization under the impact of his technology. In harmony with the predictability of his machine world, he too is approaching a condition of ever more precise and at the same time ever more inclusive predictability. And under the impetus of this trend the individual as such—the source and fountain of man's higher values—will find himself progressively reduced to the status of the common denominator of society as a whole. The ferment of creative self-realization and self-transformation will suffer a gradual decline, and mankind as a whole may thus be subject to a kind of spiritual and psychological denudation in the very process of achieving a secure and permanent niche in the ecological challenge of life.

There are, finally, reasons for believing that history, like evolution in general, follows an irreversible course. Under these circumstances it is conceivable that man may ultimately suffer the loss of that earlier wisdom of his non-technological civilizations which sustained and nourished his higher values and his more intuitive relations to nature. Under the dominance of a rationalistic approach to life and its problems, he may imperceptibly forego the deep inward sources of his spiritual values and, along with them, the indefinable sources of his profoundest aspirations until it is too late. The dichotomy between his intuitive and his rational psychic components, far from being resolved in some higher synthesis, may well become fatefully disrupted in the eclipse of his intuitive faculties and the final dominance of his rational self. Man thus seems destined to approach ever closer to an ultimate condition of relative fixity and permanence—to an unchanging "plateau" existence. However dismal such a fate may seem to us, nourished as we are upon the values of the past, we cannot do other than to continue to respond to the challenge of life *as if* those values were to prevail. Mumford has lightened the stark vistas of the present with courageous hopes in the hidden possibilities of mankind: let us face the

future in all its darkest probabilities with an even greater call upon our courage. Such, it seemed to SEIDENBERG, is our prospect.

It appeared to GLIKSON in a general way that man's historic development is a form of transition toward a stage where man by his intellectual development learns the laws of nature and uses the power he gains by this knowledge to overcome the limitations set by nature. But in an earlier stage, as we know from this and that specific place, man used even better his intellectual potentialities to find his place in the natural cycle of energy.

From the previous stage we see a general transition toward a disorganization of society and toward a certain stage of emergency. Some geographers are of the opinion that in primitive society man enters into a direct connection with his natural environment, whereas in civilized society man enters into relation with his social and economic environment. This idea of a "cushion" between civilization and environment is true and is not true. It is not true in the sense that man never ceases to live on the earth. On the other hand, the "cushion" idea is true in so far as we no longer are conscious that we really live on the earth. We are conscious only that we live in a certain socioeconomic system, but without direct realization of its basis.

GLACKEN commented on Seidenberg's theme that there has been a progressive accumulation of knowledge owing to the application of intelligence, that this is leading us to a greater and greater social organization throughout the world, and that this is more or less inevitable. Perhaps, GLACKEN thought, the future development of mankind does not lie in the universal extension of this social organization. Other non-Western cultures might be far more selective in the future in their borrowings and their adaptations. Perhaps the best illustration of what might happen was the experience the Japanese had at the end of the Tokugawa shogunate— at the Meiji restoration in 1868—when the adaptation and adoption of Western ideas was very selective indeed.

THE RESPONSIBILITY OF FREEDOM

KNIGHT, in writing, thought it worthwhile to follow up a statement by Northrop that "man cannot get away from what he knows." He was quite out of sympathy with the bewailing by modern civilization in its yearning for something in the past that man is supposed to have had but lost and in its looking to the future with gloomy foreboding or prophecy of doom. In no case can the past course of events be reversed, nor would any reasonable person so desire even if it were possible.

In modern times the Western world has certainly made progress at a phenomenal and increasing rate in terms of nearly any namable aspect of cultural values compatible with truth and freedom. The difficulty is that we have experienced so much improvement at a speed so rapid that it has not been fully digested. People have come to expect far too much; they make demands without inquiring as to possibilities or costs and in consequence are more discontented than before. For example, in a few generations the spread of free education has destroyed the former class monopoly of education and has made it intensely competitive. To many of those affected, that naturally means "cutthroat" competition and calls for monopoly as a way to restore "order." But would any reasonable person advocate restoring a small and limited learned caste? How does he think it could be done, as to selection of those to be admitted as members or shut out, and how would the monopoly itself be organized?

In a lifetime of professional effort in a broad sector of social science and

philosophy, KNIGHT asserted that he had reflected a good deal on this much-bruited question of "what is the matter" with man, or the world, or both. One thing we now know and cannot get away from is that the two were not made for each other, or either for the other. Man was not evolved in, or by, or for the kind of environment in which "progress" has placed him in the Western world of today. On the contrary, while man has remained biologically the same, his "habitat," including especially his human relations, has changed in a revolutionary way, inverting many of the most fundamental conditions and values. And this has happened with unexampled suddenness in terms of historical time and in comparison with the conditions prevailing through the long previous existence of this species. And we seem to stand on the threshold of even greater and more rapid change. To think here and now of all the different and contradictory things man is, individually and in the world around, of how he could have got that way and what he may or might become, is to feel overwhelmed with a sense of mystery.

The very first requisite of human social order and its first task is to decide who is to communicate (talk or write) and who is, or are, to give attention. One of the main weaknesses of our technological civilization is that machines and electronics have multiplied the effectiveness of transmission practically to infinity—one person could now speak to or write for the whole race— but have done nothing to increase the capacity of listening (or reading). But there is nothing that could have been done or can be done about that; hence (again) no point in complaining. It also needs emphasis that many kinds of subject matter besides "truth" are involved; fiction of many kinds, poetry, wit and jest, like truth itself, may be "good" or "bad," depending on time, place, and occasion. In fact, most "expression" is more or less figurative. What is needful is to keep the distinctions fairly clear and to apply the appropriate criteria of judgment, which are very different.

Our culture is manifestly in a state of transition, in a new epoch, which it entered with the coming of liberalism, roughly at the time of the "Enlightenment." This ended an intermediate historical "stage," itself relatively short, in which the earlier and much longer period of authoritarianism of "the church" (speaking of Western Europe and its colonies) was replaced by that of "absolute" states. These were not, in general, intentionally more "liberal" than the church had been (i.e., not at all), but their competitive position forced them to tolerate and even to encourage science and scientific technology and trade, for these furnished the sinews of war; but they were also the main ferments of "modernism." The intervening epoch was one of "wars of religion," actually and increasingly, over political, dynastic, and even economic interests in which none of the protagonists wanted or even believed in toleration, not to speak of freedom. Liberalism came when and because it was found impossible for any religion or sect to suppress or exterminate the others, and people got tired of the senseless strife and destruction and turned to other interests. Thus "history" moves in mysterious ways its wonders to perform.

This modernism, we must recall, when fully developed, involved a virtual *Umwertung aller Werte*. First and most important, it established freedom of the mind in place of dogmatism, authoritarianism, and persecution. With this replacement went that of supernaturalism by naturalism and of a pessimistic view of human nature (original sin) with an optimistic view—a faith in human reason and essential goodness.

Such naïveté is hard to imagine, now that we have swung so far back in the opposite direction, but it was real. Further, economic freedoms and rights replaced regimentation by some combination of church and state. Finally, political democracy replaced the divine right of kings (which previously had effectively replaced the divine authority of the priesthood). Democracy came to embody general ideals of equality and betterment, which replaced those of a class or caste society, in which everyone was thought to be providentially called to work out his lot under an eternal and immutable law within the social position into which he was born. Progress would come through rational action, individual and collective, based on advancing knowledge acquired through free and critical inquiry, which would replace belief through faith in a truth and a social order divinely given once and for all in the remote past. In short, man "fell" from ignorance and irresponsibility (except for avoiding the sin of nonconformity and disobedience into which he had "fallen" immediately after creation) into the opposite state. Whether it was really a fall or a rise is the crucial question. The attitude of bewailing it as a fall rests on accepting the poetic principle that "where ignorance is bliss, 'tis folly to be wise." Or, as put by another poet, "men would cast off the burthen, the heavy and the weary weight of this unintelligible world, in favor of living in a pink fog of mysticism." KNIGHT, being a liberal, regarded such sentiments as an expression of the Freudian death urge. But they are fine as poetry, if they make good poetry and are not taken for anything else.

To be more specific about the diagnosis of modern man and culture, KNIGHT found two things in particular "the matter." The first is an essential aspect of the appearance and growth of knowledge. For a dozen centuries, from the fall of classical civilization to the advent of liberalism or modernism, Western man had had *all* the answers. He knew the absolute answer to every question about life and about death and the hereafter. We know, of course, that they were not answers and that he got answers by refusing to ask real questions or to look critically at traditional answers that were handed out by a traditionally established authority—or to look critically at the history or credentials of that authority. The answers and the status of the authority were *enforced;* one who raised any question was assured of eternal torture and of the closest feasible approximation to "hell" in the present world. However, for the most part, the answers satisfied Western man. In contrast, now we know that there is no finally satisfactory answer to any serious question but only "better or worse" answers for the time being and within local and cultural boundaries. The dark-age state of "bliss" for which people yearn was one of complete absence of freedom of the mind. This freedom, basic to all freedom, had prevailed in large measure in classical antiquity but had disappeared with the "triumph of barbarism and religion." On this history we may consult J. B. Bury's little *History of Freedom of Thought* or Lord Acton's essays dealing with the topic.

We also know, it is true, that quite terrible responsibilities are placed on the shoulders of man, and particularly the famous "common man," with this awakening to the knowledge of his ignorance and fallibility by the "unchartered freedom," which many find "tiresome" and long to exchange for life in a pink fog of mysticism. There are indeed many responsibilities—intellectual, economic, and political—involved in living in a social order of freedom, with its concomitants of change and mobility in vast communities and over

the world. It is indeed much harder to live under a law that is indeterminate and constantly changing than under one that is definite and fixed; and it is harder still to exercise collective responsibility for the changes themselves. Still more immediate problems arise from a rapidly changing technology, which at any moment is known only in bits by a myriad of specialists in different branches, whom the plain man must trust for information on nearly any problem that he encounters. Moreover, these authorities do not agree, as he finds if he consults more than one, and he must use his judgment as to which one to follow. All these matters were certainly much simpler in a primitive society or in the Middle Ages—because people were oblivious to facts or fatalistically accepted the ills of life as "the will of God." Modern civilization has chosen (or history has given us) the alternative of recognizing our ills as presenting problems to be faced and of doing what we can do effectively to remove them.

It is historically convenient to date the coming of modernism at the Enlightenment—the period of revolutions in which our nation was born, as was "political economy"—but such a date understates the recency and suddenness with which these conditions which create our current problems have come upon us. Modernism in a stricter sense, especially the democracy of equal suffrage and contemporary technology and business organization, developed gradually through the nineteenth century and at an accelerating pace. The mood of disillusionment, our concern of the moment, is a phenomenon of the present century, particularly of the generation since World War I. It was not at all the mood of the Enlightenment, which was rather the opposite: one of buoyant hope and confidence. At that time, particularly in revolutionary France, men believed that Reason (spelled with a capital *R* and associated with innate moral or sentimental goodness of human nature) was expected to solve human problems if only the "shackles" of tradition and authority could be broken and "freedom" established. However, the aftermath of the revolution, particularly in Europe, and also of the contemporary industrial revolution in England, with the liberation of business enterprise, was the first phase of disillusionment.

To freedom as mere negative liberation, the nineteenth century soon added in the West the positive right of every human being to education, regardless of family or means, at the expense of "society," meaning those members officially deemed most able to bear the burden. This program was rapidly put into effect at tremendous cost, notably in this country. But neither did that lead to any utopia of liberty, fraternity, and equality; in particular it did not allay discontent, which rather increased with the prodigious advance in knowledge. So another "solution" was written off in disillusionment; and the loss of faith in education is perhaps the greatest disappointment of all. Of course this should have been foreseen; for, apart from other limitations, this supposed social panacea must raise the questions of who is to educate and who is to educate the educators and determine the content to be imparted to the supposedly passive and receptive oncoming generation and the methods to be employed. Events have inevitably made education the central social problem, especially as regards information versus indoctrination. This disillusionment would seem to be the final one— or the next-to-final one. The next step would seem to be either disillusionment with discussion as a method and with the whole intellectual approach or else a determined effort to define our problems in terms of facts and possible alternatives and to attack them objec-

tively. In the first eventuality, society will degenerate into chaos and a shambles, unless and until some clique seizes power and restores "order" under a totalitarian regime. There is only too much evidence of this tendency. In economic relations specifically, organized coercion is constantly appealed to for securing "rights," by righting the supposed wrongs of the economy of free exchange. The conspicuous example is "strikes" en masse of wage-workers over any area that "leaders" succeed in organizing to act as a unit, which then hold up socially essential services and coerce society and government as well as employers.

The second of the two things referred to as somehow "the matter" with men or our culture and social order is more specifically economic in its bearings, being a direct result of the success of the economy of free enterprise in achieving its purpose. In our own society, specifically the English-speaking lands and some other regions of Western culture, man's basic wants—his biological needs—have been met to such a degree that people have practically ceased troubling. But, with human nature, nothing *fails* like success. The result is that people simply do not know what to do with themselves, their time, and their powers. Of course, not everyone gets all the "food, clothing, and shelter" he would like to have, but that is a patently false conception of economic wants. Even when we ignore other "goods" which are also economic, it should hardly be necessary to point out that the claims under the three heads named are for a "decent," or "civilized," or specifically in this country an "American" *standard of living*. What is in dispute is not life but a "good" life; and the means to this lie far beyond the biological requirements for life, health, and "physical" comfort. Today, in fact, it is not even the good life but a progressively better life, ever higher standards, and more costly; that is, the demands are for social progress with a "fair" sharing of its benefits and its burdens and the costs of change. The essential "matter" is that, at these "higher" (meaning higher or lower) levels, men literally do not know what they want. Specifically, they do not know what to do with the "economic surplus" which modern technology and business organization have so abundantly provided and can further provide if given the chance. The outstanding case is what to do with "leisure" time. Here we encounter the terms or concepts (the words in quotation marks) which must be defined as the preliminary and hard, but essential, part of a real discussion of our current social-economic problems—the issues on which it is so difficult to secure agreement.

One consequence of modern efficiency is that the economy itself devotes a large and increasing fraction of its energies in competition to persuade people, as consumers and producers, to "want" a wide variety of things that are biologically nonessential in all degrees, often even positively harmful, or that displace things that are really needful biologically. It must be added that it becomes progressively harder and actually impossible to separate "economic" needs in the inclusive sense from others to which economic concepts do not apply, because they do not involve the use of given means to achieve any given end. Human purposes and economic activity move more and more into such fields as "culture" and "sport," where the ends are not given in advance or are relative and inherently social, either common or competitive as the case may be or even both at the same time. They are not concrete "goods and services" specifically wanted by individuals as consumers and produced by individual productive capacity. Cultural progress is a group value,

and its creation is a matter of group exploration. A particularly important problem arises in so far as economic life becomes motivated by competition or rivalry, giving it the character of sport, which is increasingly the case. To that extent the over-all social objective is quite different from that of the players individually or by "sides"; it is not "winning" but having a good game, another concept both necessary and difficult to define. The game must above all be interesting and "fair"; there must be rules which must be obeyed and interpreted usually by an umpire ultimately backed up by the police. Special problems arise in contests between large groups beyond personal acquaintance and face-to-face relations; hence they necessarily act through agents. Sportsmanship is a large element in the ethical ideal of a free society; it calls for an element of generosity but completely excludes "charity."

The problems called "economic" in modern large-scale society must be realistically viewed as combining all these various objectives and are enormously complicated in consequence. For there are both complementarity and conflict among the "ends" or the procedure required to promote them— among freedom, efficiency, progress, and "justice" (this last including both equitable distribution of distributable goods and services and the "fairness" of sport), to all of which must be added "good" social-moral attitudes or "spirit," and with all relative to the ineluctable conditions of civilized life. Discussion in strictly economic terms (taking as given all ends as judged by the acting individuals) goes a long step beyond biology but still covers a small part of the problem. Social action must look to the future, beyond the lives of its members at the time action is taken; it must consider the unborn and the character of the culture that is being created. Many conflicting considerations must be compromised, and no problem is more inescapable than the relation between quantity of life and its quality, beginning with that between resources and numbers of the population. Viewed even in strictly economic terms, no fact is more important than the non-objective or non-specific character of the "real" wants of individuals. What objectivity these have is more aesthetic than biological, though, most fortunately, there is only a limited need for agreement on the former as a requisite for social order and peace, for agreement in taste is notoriously hard to achieve.

Beyond both biological and aesthetic needs or values (and in large part including the latter) men's wants for concrete goods and services are largely "symbolic" of abstract and social values. Especially important are the play interest, the spirit of contest, and that of "work," a negative value to be avoided or minimized. (This finally verges into the quietistic attitude of craving.) The factor of "luck" enters largely, both negatively and positively, into both the efficiency and the game aspects of "economic" association—and more or less into all activity. Curiosity, adventure, even the disposition to gamble, are clearly elements in real human motivation. But these and other elements are foreign to the rational-economic motive analytically defined. In short, in the "economic" life of today, realistically viewed, the goods and services produced and consumed are wanted, in large part, not for any intrinsic quality or satisfying power but as symbols of achievement of deeper general objectives. Especially in point are such abstractions as success, prestige, "winning," being like other people or different from them (cf. "fashion"), keeping up with the neighbors or getting ahead of them, and simply familiarity and novelty or persistence and

change, or security and adventure. To a striking extent these ulterior wants are pairs of opposites in a sort of "polar" relation and inherently require sacrifice of one to the other; hence, again, "compromise" at some vaguely determinate proportion. Above all, men seem innately to want *power* over others or relative to and beyond others. And this power they commonly insist on defining into the freedom they claim as a right. Though rationally defined, freedom in society must be mutual or common, while the power interest is inherently one of conflict (as between persons, in contrast with individual control over "things"). These remarks indicate the complexity of the issues faced by modern society. In its abstract form the problem is still and always that of making "better" laws or rules to govern human association. Presupposed as a matter of course is the obeying of existing law and its enforcement where necessary until reasonable agreement can be secured on changes that will improve it. It is essentially futile to argue that, *if* men were rational and virtuous, social conflicts and problems would disappear. Words like "rationality" and "virtue" merely point to the problem the heart of which is to define them. But they cannot be defined in relation to the realities in such a way that, even if the qualities named could somehow be implanted in all men, a "solution" would result. For a "static" society, living under laws assumed to be immutable and hence universally known, rationality and virtue had a fairly definite meaning and a large degree of logical applicability. But in a society dedicated to freedom and progress, and to truth critically conceived, they merely indicate the problem, which is to agree "intelligently" on ideals to be progressively realized and on the forms of associative action required. This is the perpetual task of man in his life on the earth, in so far as he believes in freedom and intelligence rather than in "freezing" his conduct into a rigid and unchanging pattern. Would we wish it otherwise? If all truth were discovered and known and all possible beauty and other goods achieved, what would we do then? What would we live for?

As a last word, the root of modern man's discontents is his unwillingness to live with the facts of life. But this he "must" do, hard, unpleasant, and nasty as the facts often are—until they can be changed for the better by intelligent action. Idealistic wishing is necessary, but wishful thinking is futile and, if acted upon, will certainly do more harm than good. We "must" preserve life and a civilization in which men can rationally cherish ideals and work toward their achievement; this will constantly involve their own redefinition and "improvement." It is questionable how far it is useful even to consider ideals beyond what reasonably seems possible, and action certainly must not aim at anything else. The impossible includes any strict impartiality. As the world is, men must give first consideration to themselves and their families, both as to living and as to living progressively better. These interests must of course be constantly weighed against those of "others," but the preservation and advance of civilization as it exists must come first. For "others" include the whole human race, born and unborn, from the Eskimos and Tierra del Fuegians to the headhunters and the savages of the tropical jungle; and even beyond them the human race, for the animals—those that know pain and fear and frustration—have a right to "due" consideration. We must indeed be "wise as serpents" but *not* harmless as doves or like little children. Man's wish must exceed his grasp —but not too much. We must respect the interests of others, and even their opinions, no matter how "wrong" we

know them to be; and we must trust people a little further than they probably deserve—but not much further. "Measure in all things," as the Greeks taught; virtue is a mean, and going too far in any direction becomes a vice or some mixture of vice and error. The treatment of that distinction has largely dominated the history of the West since the downfall of classical civilization and is still with us as a problem. And the current tendency is for new knowledge to make the problem even more complex by replacing both error and sin by mental disease or defect.

DIALOGUE: SCIENCE AND HUMANITIES

MALIN, in writing, commented on the uniqueness of history and its relation to ethical values. When history has been referred to in this symposium, it has been lumped off as a social science. In so doing, of course, the orthodox United States interpretation of history is meant—that version described in Volumes LIV (1946) and LXIV (1954) of the *Social Science Research Council Bulletin*. The philosophy behind such a point of view is in the tradition of John Dewey, Charles Beard, and Carl Becker—a pragmatic or subjective relativism. The history derived from this philosophical ancestry is functional and deals only with the "usable" past. The criteria for determining what is "usable" past are set up by a frame of reference arising out of the historian's present, and this fluctuates with the changing purpose. If the premises are granted, then there is no escape from the conclusions about relativism of ethics in the spirit of Protagoras and the Greek Sophists—the ethical nihilism prior to Socrates. Ethics, according to such a system, is the product of "education."

The conception of history as unique is in contrast, in an absolute sense, with social science history. History is not a science. The individual human person is unique in an absolute sense. Like-wise, each historical event and situation is unique—absolutely. Further-more, each human culture is unique. The historian is interested for its own sake in the great body of discoverable knowledge about the past. It possesses a value in its own right as an object of study. In the social science sense, all this is useless, because it is not functional. But history as defined above is neither science nor functional. The individual man or woman is not inferior, superior, or equal to any other man or woman. Those terms are social science constructs, not properties of the individual. Each human person is unique. The ethical principles derived from this property of uniqueness are positive and absolute and involve the inviolability of the dignity of this unique individual. Respect for the dignity of the unique person is good; violation of that dignity is evil. The same principle applies to the status of each unique cultural group. Thus each individual and each culture derives its freedom, and its right to exercise and to defend it, from the property of uniqueness—a property inherent in individuality.

It seemed to GUTKIND that he had heard a great deal on the conservation of the soil but nothing about the conservation of the soul. This symposium may establish certain facts, but it has differed sincerely and wholeheartedly in their interpretations. Those who are more interested in the human side of the problem would challenge all scientists as to whether they wish to continue as the pampered and adored children of our technical civilization. It is absolutely impossible for this technical civilization in which we are living to continue to develop on the same scale with the same intensity without destroying the most valuable thing—the human substance. Perhaps the process of the disintegration of the creative spirit of man in all things which are not

technical is already beginning. Not one fundamental change has taken place since the "urban revolution." All that followed after have been only differences of degree, not of principle.

STEWART disagreed with Seidenberg's idea that we have become scientific. The scientific had been overemphasized, leaving out a very important variable—the problem of religion. If religion plays a role in the United States and Europe, it plays a much greater role in some other parts of the world. Our scientific plans on how to reduce the birth rate in India or how to reduce its death rate may be developed, but religion may completely frustrate all our ideas to help the people of India.

DARWIN took up the point of permanence of conditions and how rapidly they change. Now in past history, undoubtedly, one of the most important things has been religion. If we take only the Christian religion, which we know best, we find that it has been very, very different at different periods of time. Perhaps the important thing in a religion is the fact that people are ready to die for it. In A.D. 1100, during the Crusades, the one important thing was to conquer the Saracens and to occupy Jerusalem. Three to four hundred years later it was the Reformation. Today, most of us would not be ready to die for anything of that kind. These "creeds," or doctrines of life, have a quality of heredity, but they do not last for periods of more than four hundred years. If that is so, we are just about due for another one. MUMFORD commented that this theory was in keeping with that of the Scotsman J. Stuart Lenny, who in 1870 introduced the notion of a cyclical recurrence in civilization at intervals of about five hundred years.

HEICHELHEIM felt that Darwin's remarks had been much too polite and moderate. A memorable shaft of light was his expression that man needs something to die for. The "possible" of Chairman Mumford's introduction might be expressed as: "Man stays alive only if he is able to live dangerously." Women do this by bearing children and sacrificing themselves for the upkeep of their offspring; men, by changing and experimenting with their physical environment and their social order. Even in the so-called "static civilizations," the element of danger is always in existence. In the future are all men to be happy? Are no uncalculated risks to be taken? Is everything to proceed nicely? Or would such an environment be one in which man could not live. The directors of change, HEICHELHEIM felt, were not to be the conservationists but the adventurers— the Vikings of the future.

BANKS asked: "Who is going to control the vast forces being unleashed?" "The man who loves danger," may be a good answer, but, if so, then who selects him, and what training for leadership has he had for the post?

To look at our future as people who try to handle the earth better, and to see what happens to man while he does so, meant for WITTFOGEL: "What kind of a man are we going to have when we get into all these developments which previously have been so ably outlined?"

Huzayyin had spoken for the East when he expressed the feeling that there was and is a difference between the Western and the Eastern worlds. He is not alone in feeling that there are many things that are problematic in the modern industrial world of the West; there are many in the West who think similarly.

In Central Europe after World War I, socialism seemed the natural solution, with big private property being the most evil institution that had to be overcome in one way or another. Marx was partly responsible for this attitude.

But professional study of hydraulic civilizations, based upon great governmental agencies built up in certain parts of the world, has given awareness of another man and another thesis: it was Lord Acton who said that absolute power corrupts absolutely. And Acton's thesis seems to hold up better than Marx's.

Law is not enough; it just formulates something. Many laws express only a one-sided relationship of man to man in which one side dictates and the other subordinates itself. Confucius, with all his subtlety, said: "The attitude of the ruler is like the wind going over the grass. When the wind blows, the grass has to bend." Life is a great value, but not the only value, and sometimes not the last. Are there not times when death is preferable to living as a slave? Total submission must be fought. But the competitive capitalism of twentieth-century society is tame by comparison with ugly totalitarian bureaucratic despotism.

TUKEY raised the question whether in the discussions enough care had been spent in distinguishing science, a way toward knowledge and understanding, from technology, a way toward doing things. The objectivity of scientists also had been discussed. If we looked at how scientists really work, we would find that they depend very much upon non-objective ideas. The contrast Seidenberg had made was much too black and white. One characteristic of science as it ought to be is that its final test is what happens when it is tried. Contrary to Stewart's suggestion, it would not be scientific to plan ahead without taking into account religious considerations and cultural inertia. To do so would be perpetrating bad science.

TUKEY, in writing, pointed out that Mumford had said: "For historic man the future presents a dimension that science, because of its methodological restrictions, cannot admit: it is the realm of the potential and the possible." And later: "There is a difference, then, between the scientific prediction of probabilities and the humanistic anticipation of possibilities, which often gather force as reactions against the dominant institutions." By these words Mumford claims for the humanities all anticipation of novel possibilities. But TUKEY avowed that this claim should not be allowed to stand; no informed court would grant it. Much of science may be pedestrian, some as dry as dust, but there have been, are, and will continue to be aspects of science which are imaginative, which reach out far into the possible, and which effectively react against dominant institutions. Why these have been overlooked by Mumford and by others in this symposium is difficult to see. Have they confused science and engineering? Have they associated only with the more pedestrian scientists? Do they believe that effective science must be restricted to fields safely distant from the humanities?

In the physical sciences, where science has built up now for centuries—which ought therefore to be the very model of science—it is easy to give examples of imagination extending to possibilities far beyond experience and institutions. To be sure, this imagination has often come in stages, but so have the imaginative gains of the humanities —else why the historians of ideas?

The atomic bomb and the hydrogen bomb might come to mind, but they are hardly perfect examples. The opposition might argue that astronomers have studied the interiors of stars, that stars are dominant institutions, and that their study is immediate experience. (Yet how much less immediate are the insights of the humanists?)

The stored-program automatic computer—the machine which rearranges and converts its own orders as the computation proceeds—is as long a jump into possibility and as wide a deviation from existing institutions as any leap of man's mind. It comes just midway between the human mind, *free to rearrange* its orders and instructions, and the Jacquard loom, carrying out *explicitly* given orders to manufacture a preassigned pattern. The insight that recognized this midway possibility and the values which would stem from its realization was surely not mere routine extrapolation. When the present growth in scope and depth and facility of use has reached the shoulder of the hill, we will be able to see just what this insight has done to dominant institutions. There are other examples, but this should serve to make the point.

It seemed to DODDS that there was even an ecological dimension to war, although the subject had scarcely been mentioned, let alone discussed. Another point was that man is not man in a vacuum; he is men. He is not a set of chessmen to be moved about on an ecological "chessboard." Any consideration that omits his psychological, cultural, and moral dimensions is to that extent incomplete. STEWART enlarged upon Dodds's remarks about the dangers of talking about man instead of considering men as different types of people developed under different cultural conditions.

HUZAYYIN spoke on material and technological development versus the non-material aspects of human life. The West is accustomed to thinking of its civilization as the first real technological development in human history. This fact must be corrected with the knowledge of the technological inventions in man's history. How to make fire was perhaps the most important invention that the human brain developed. And then would be included the invention or evolution of crop cultivation, animal domestication, brickmaking, etc. We must remember that civilizations like those of ancient Egypt, ancient Greece, and ancient Rome had great technological developments.

Antithetical to this is the non-technical side of man. We are more accustomed to distinguish man from the animal on the basis of his mind—the brain. But man shares the brain with other animals; he shares sentiment and instinct with most other creatures. However, that something in man which is not shared by any other creature is conscience. Perhaps we are thinking solely of the future in the material sense. After all, we must live physically; but human life, as distinct from the usual biologic life, requires something more—spiritual values.

If we look at the past, the people of Egyptian pharaonic civilization were not backward. They lived for something and died for something. Life was not limited to the physical existence of the short period that one lived on earth; people looked for something after death. In the ancient East, with technological development there was always some spiritual contribution. When it came to a clash between the spirit and the material, the spirit usually won. In the case of Islam, the Bedouins who came out of the desert did not have any stronger material means than the Persians or the Byzantines, but in the end the struggle was won by the stronger spiritual side.

We in the Orient look on Europe with rather a sense of pity, in that this great continent has contributed so much to the technological development of humanity and contributed so little toward the spiritual advancement of man. It is important that in the future we should aim at the balance between the material and the spiritual—the balance between the mind and the conscience.

BURKE presented a hypothesis to explain why Westerners think the way they do and the extent to which their concepts are not related to spiritual values or anything other than material values. That we in the Western world do not recognize some of the values to which Huzayyin referred relates to two basically different points of view. One of these is an intuitive understanding of what goes on in the surrounding world, in which the kind of society, the religious values, and most of those things that have to do with a way of living are tied directly to the facts of life as lived over millenniums.

About two thousand years ago Socrates and Aristotle worked out a line of reasoning which provided an empirical approach to working out problems, which has taken the Western world away from a good many of the facts of life that are tied to the religious values, moral concepts, and ethical concepts visualized in the rest of the world.

In non-Western cultures very complex societies have been built up which reflect rather different values from our own. But, in the Hopi or the Navaho cultures, many of the values that are reflected in the lives of the people are directly tied to the affairs of their everyday life—the facts of life around them. Their body of intuitive knowledge is very much part of the environment in which they live. Their religion, their moral values, and their ethical values are tied to their everyday lives.

On the other hand, the Western world had originally a basic body of intuitive knowledge on which we began to predicate hypotheses. On the basis of our success in predicating a hypothetical situation in which life would be better if we subscribed to the values of that situation, we began building another set of hypotheses which had a number of alternatives. Gradually, in the process of doing all this, we have grown away from the basic values in our life that at one time were part of our religious values and which made moral and ethical sense in terms of tying us to the environment in which we lived. We in the Western world have built up a concept of the world around us which is not directly related to this body of intuitive knowledge that was once a part of our background and is still a part of the background of a good many non-Western peoples.

Religious values, moral values, and ethical values are all tied to the reality of the world around people in the so-called "backward" parts of the world. There are less conflicts for these people; they do not recognize divisions between the various parts of their lives. They do not consciously have to strive to keep soils in good shape, for example, because keeping soils in good shape is part of the moral and ethical standards to which they are still tied by the way they live. In the Western world, technology separates us from reality. Science has been substituted for common sense, and we are farther removed from the realities of the world around us than the people who have to live very close to them.

A very important question is whether man is a part of nature or exists apart from nature. Some years ago, BURKE said, a Navaho friend explained to him, as simply as he could, the theological concepts by which the Navaho live. He drew a circle, and on this circle he put all those things which make up the Navaho world—spiritual things as well as material things. One had to do with his religion, one had to do with animals, one with plants. But the point was that one of the items on this ring of the universe was man. Man was on a higher level of the order of things than the rest of the items in the ring, but, nevertheless, man was a part of this ring, and, in order for there to be harmony in the universe, man had to be part of this ring which made up the whole universe around him. To illustrate the Western concept, the Navaho drew another circle with the same set of relationships; only in this case he had man sitting in the middle of the circle. The big difference, he said, between his culture, in which man was a part of things that created a harmony in the universe, and that of Western man was that we recognized that man sat in the middle, so as to be served by all things. And he pointed out that this was impossible, because man could not be served by these things until he recognized that he was a part of them too.

But, however much we may admire the efforts of a group of people to maintain their integrity, it is an impossible situation—the most unreal of all approaches—for there never has been a time in human history when any culture has been able to resist the encroachments of any other. There has always been a give and take in every case where cultures have met. The goal is to find an area of compromise. Conservationists hope that the best area of compromise is found where the most that is good is preserved. What concerned BURKE in Tax's example (see pp. 952–54) was that there was just as inflexible an attitude on the part of the Indians as that which is usually attributed to whites. Between the two there must be give and take, not simply give by one and take by the other. SEIDENBERG asked whether the same process of cultural impact were not happening in Tibet. The question is to know why one culture dominates another.

NORTHROP referred to the formula with which Sears had begun the session on "Commercial Economies" (p. 423),

$$\frac{R}{P} = f(C) ,$$

"The sum total of resources and the population among which the resources have to be divided are a function of the pattern of culture." Now, what is culture? Man is never responding to his environment but to his concept of his environment. A common culture exists when people respond to an environment conceived with a common set of meanings such as the Hindu, the Buddhist, the Navaho. For a people trained in biochemistry, environment means carbon dioxide–oxygen cycle and thermodynamical conceptual analysis.

To be a spiritual creature is to be guided by ideas, but that the modern West is a technological civilization without values is nonsense. That is, one culture is exactly as spiritual as the other; the only thing is that the content of its conceptual meanings is different.

A common law means common norms and ways of conceiving of what a human being is, what other human beings are, what plants, animals, vegetables, the motions of the seasons are—in other words, a common conceptual system and a common meaning. The real reason why the Navaho become disrupted is not that other peoples force things on them; it is that other ideas come in and corrupt their meaning system, and then they cannot co-operate with one another. Unless there is a common meaning system, there cannot be a common cultural or historical community. These common values may be, as the anthropologists say, explicit or implicit. For example, most people in the United States do not know the role of John Locke's theory of the state and of Marshall's and Jevons' theory of economic analysis. Though these have been made explicit in publications and are gone into in our universities, for most people these represent implicit meanings which order our society.

We can use the word "technological" for any kind of tool, and in this sense, then, every society is a technological society. But one very fundamental thing arose uniquely in the world with the first Greek mathematical physicist. If we analyze conceptual meaning, there are two sources for concepts. The word "blue," in the sense of color, is an in-tuitive concept which anybody can feel with immediacy in his own experience. But there is also another concept of "blue," in the sense of the number for the wave length in mathematical physics. This is blue in the non-intuitive sense; it is an electromagnetic wave which has certain formal properties specified by a mathematician. When people in a society publicly conceive of their environment by the latter instead of the former type of concept, then a non-intuitive type of civilization results. This does not mean that the latter person is any less a part of nature than the former. He is just a part of nature in a different way. We are just as much a part of nature as the Navaho is, but it is nature understood in a different way. The real difference between a non-technological and a technological civilization is whether the tools come from a way of thinking about nature conceptually that goes back to intuitive inductive concepts or to axiomatically, mathematically constructed ones. This has a prodigious effect on attitudes. Breaking away from intuitive concepts means breaking away from an ethics for a society which is family- and tribal-centered. Inductively, individuals are different. If they have a different skin color, this is a fact, and good conduct must recognize it.

But when the Greek mathematical physicists shifted to an axiomatically constructed nature known hypothetically, this was the beginning of the shift which Sir Henry Maine, in his *Ancient Law*, describes as a shift from status to contract. In contract all men are born equal; this does not mean biologically identical but represents a law-of-contract statement which is agreed upon. This is important in the contemporary world, because India is introducing a law-of-contract constitution to take the place of the old law-of-status ethics of an intuitively oriented conceptual system in which family values and differences in color or caste values are ethically primary. The discovery of hypothetically proposed, axiomatically constructed, concepts passed over from Greek mathematics through Greek philosophy into Stoic Rome and led to the idea of a law of contract. Under this law men can have a common community if they accept the same constitutional postulates for ordering their social relations with one another. In this, the color of the skin or the family or tribe a person belongs to is irrelevant; the only thing that is relevant is consent. Contracts are not valid unless consent is given to them.

When utopias are guided with a technical knowledge of science, this is just as spiritual a society as an intuitive one. It is just that, in operating, different meanings are used. The problem of our world is to take people immersed in the values of an intuitive conceptual system and bring to them a law-of-contract type of knowing and all the technical, scientific meanings coming out of that way of knowing. It is in this direction that a real advance in the realm of the spiritual is to be made.

HEICHELHEIM doubted that man is going to live by reason and by the law of contract; man is different. NORTHROP replied that we cannot get away from what is known, and physicists, mathematicians, and biologists *have* experimentally verified certain knowledge. To ignore this is to live in a fool's paradise. Under the law of contract we accept only what we accept. There is nothing about rationality that forces us to accept anything other than what seems reasonable.

One general theme of the symposium seemed to TUKEY to be that commercial economies should come to terms with their environments by becoming, on a world scale, subsistence economies. Northrop had related the original transition from (micro-)subsistence

economy to the transition from status law to contract law. Is it reasonable to conjecture that, if our commercial economy is to be converted into a (macro-) subsistence economy, it may be necessary to convert from contract law to status law, at least in the relation of social man to his environment?

GOUROU, in writing, did not think that Asian civilizations of today have spiritual superiority over the West. They are different but not superior. He felt that the claim of superiority was a sort of "psychic compensation." Neither, however, did he feel, were they inferior. One of the great problems at this time is to give technology to Asians without destroying their moral and spiritual traditions. While some think that technology is inseparable from Western civilization, GOUROU did not think so; but it was important for the future to investigate the point.

ULLMAN recognized that we obviously want to change things; we need not only criteria for change but criteria that match our values. Obviously, now, they do not match, because the measures that we use do not fit the values. As an example, in deciding whether to build a reclamation project in the arid West, we calculate a benefit-cost ratio. If the benefits exceed the cost, the project will pay, and it is built. Yet, at the same time, the benefit-cost ratios are not computed for all other alternative projects throughout the country, even though many would have a higher figure. But this problem, though fantastically difficult, is simple compared with the real alternative opportunities with which we are confronted. For instance, should society build superhighways or double teachers' salaries? An engineer can easily compute the savings in gasoline, rubber, and travel time and can prove that almost any superhighway will pay. But no one has produced a method for proving that better salaries for schoolteachers would pay. The rational world is unable to measure and compare its values on a rational basis. MUMFORD commented that Emerson had a generalized answer to the problem: "Save on the low levels and spend on the high ones." All we need to define is the difference between the low and the high.

GLIKSON considered that there are apparently two ways out of the present situation of societal disorganization and that both are ways of planning or organization.

First is the one to which Brown looks forward—ever more inventions. If, in Seidenberg's analysis, man has to change himself in the course of time into a tool of an ever more complete machine, does this mean that man is entering into a new stage of serfdom?

Second is a sort of organization which is often called "planning." It seems that, in the stage into which we have come in this specific moment of our development, the only intellectual way out is by comprehensive planning of our ways of life. This way of planning not only has to consider change of the physical environment, not only economic rehabilitation, but also has to consider fully the human factors.

The instances which Tax has given are not just a scientific attempt to look upon primitive people but a beginning of a way to introduce these people into the development of our times.

The way of the future seems to lie in success in establishing in fact the connection between our whole intellectual and scientific development and the basis of life. We should look upon human life not as distinct from biological life but as its highest form.

GRAHAM referred to the fact that since the time of Marsh there had been a progressively greater destruction of environment than there was in his time. In our cultivated lands and our forests and our grasslands a great deal of devastation has taken place; there has been

a further impact on our physical and biological environment, to say nothing of the socioeconomic aspects of our existence. As part of man's reaction to this destruction, five professional fields have arisen during the last fifty years in the United States which did not exist in Marsh's time and some not even so long ago as a generation. These are soil conservation, forestry, range management, wildlife management, and modern agronomy, each of which is now a profession, in the sense that there are trained workers, that there are organizations which represent them, that there are state and federal government bureaus that support their activities, etc. The significant thing is that, in spite of a highly technological world, man has reacted to the mechanistic destructive capacity of his society by developing these new disciplines for taking action. For example, in each state of the United States, locally organized groups —soil-conservation districts—have been formed in which people who live and work on the land organize themselves to accept the best in modern ecological technology. Amazingly, though these local organizations began only in 1937, today some 85 per cent of our agricultural land is now included in soil-conservation districts. We need only to fly over the country to see a transformation in the landscape which reveals not only changes in the way land is worked but also changes in the people's attitudes toward it. The land is being re-created in a manner that twenty-five or fifty years ago would have been thought impossible.

LEOPOLD pointed out that, in centralized governments today, the higher administrative units have considerable ability to form or alter public opinion to create demands for their services. However, for example, the administrative units of government which are engaged in changing the forms of river valleys have certain social responsibilities to the public which are not now being met. The initial development of river-valley systems is comparable to the mining of ores. Just as economic considerations led to mining the best ores first, so the best water projects are going to be developed first. Sooner or later, only second-rate units will be left for development. Eventually, the point is reached at which a forced public demand is created for the continuation of a service which originally was a social good. Reclamation in the West has already built upon the best sites; now marginal sites are being built. Yet within the administrative units of government there remains a sufficiently centralized control which is able to create public demand for a thing the public thinks it wants but for which it does not have access to information to know whether it is a good thing. When the scientist is involved in actually creating public demand for something, he had better be sure he is right.

Tukey commented that the research director of Oak Ridge National Laboratory, one of America's largest atomic research laboratories, had said that the time was in sight when problems in the nuclear field of a scale requiring such large laboratories for their solution soon would be solved.[1] Perhaps one function of this present symposium was to organize and redirect opinion, so that large-scale research could be undertaken on the problems here outlined.

The discussion had indicated that perhaps it might be good for humanity to try to look for a unified future for human beings in whatever part of the earth they may be living. But Huzayyin begged to differ; he felt that, in spite of the existence of certain unified

1. Alvin W. Weinberg, in a talk on "Future Aims of Large-Scale Research," presented on March 2, 1955, at the Pittsburgh Conference on Analytical Chemistry and Applied Spectroscopy, as published in *The News* (Oak Ridge National Laboratory, Tennessee), June 10 and 17, 1955.

lines, for the future of humanity we should always maintain diversity. We should not look here for solutions for different segments of humanity; we should never try to put the human race into one mold, either materially or spiritually. It is, perhaps, most important always to maintain the balance between unity and diversity and between the material and spiritual. We should keep our own personality, at the same time realizing that we should live in harmony with other personalities, with which we have something in common.

Stewart brought out that the Western world has a very unusual culture pattern which holds culture change in technical things as a high value. We like new styles in clothes and in automobiles, but we do not like new styles in government or new styles in religion. We are only partly for change, even in our own culture pattern. In the world as a whole, however, the pattern of not-change is very much stronger than it is in the United States. We have developed a very unusual culture pattern in approving change and holding it at a high value. The fact is that most of the world still holds at a very high value those things which do not change and considers change itself bad in all areas.

We should appreciate cultural diversity in what people value as important and good and realize that we are dealing with a world of many different patterns. Changes, if they do occur, do so at different rates. We have no bases in our experiences upon which to predict what people of other cultures will appreciate and how they will change.

Anderson, in commenting that the United States is getting itself and the world into a terrible mess by not being able to face the facts of life, pointed to the need for a searching of hearts among Westerners before action is being taken for the supposed benefit of other civilizations. An individual who denies the world as it is to himself is psychotic. A civilization which will not face the first fact of human existence is psychotic. On this criterion, the United States not only belongs to the most psychotic of all civilizations but also is the most psychotic of countries in that civilization. The two outstanding things about life are that we get old and we die; birth we did not know about, but death we face. But people in the United States prefer to say, "I'm just as young as I ever was." The outstanding fact of human existence is death, which in the United States is ignored. Americans are not half so wise as those in other civilizations, yet missionaries of all kinds are sent to other civilizations.

Several speakers from countries outside the United States had expressed concern at the spread of Western technology and urban values into the so-called "undeveloped" areas. EVANS expressed delight at the real concern of most of the American members of the symposium as to the ethics of this policy of expansion. The problem is whether American scientists can win over big business and government to this view.

DIALOGUE: PLANNING AND
FREE CHOICE

CLARK regarded planners as rather suspiciously akin to missionaries and said that he preferred a world in which there are a number of ways of living and loving and eating and drinking and building and planting and playing and singing and worshiping and thinking. Perhaps the most serious thing happening to us is the very heavy erosion of all these different ways of doing things.

If we were, in fact, obtaining a hybrid vigor from hybridization of culture, we might be in better shape; but technological advance has granted to a very few the power—through war or propaganda or material success—to override and eliminate a very great many of these ways of doing things. A

uniform world of forty billion Hopi or of Communists or of Israelis or of white Protestant Anglo-Saxon Republicans would be hell on earth—a world that would be neither worth living nor worth dying for.

To illustrate the futility of planning (and also of race suicide), KNIGHT told the following little story: "Once upon a time, there was a reflective individual who decided that the human race was a hopeless mess. Human history was a succession of horrors. It would be very simple to put a stop to the whole business by persuading people not to have children for one generation. So he began the propaganda, and, being a good propagandist, he was successful. Being also a tough bird, he was the last human being left alive. As he was walking along the seashore between the woods and the waters contemplating with great satisfaction the termination of his life's work, what should he see but a bunch of big gray apes come out of the woods onto the sand and proceed to build a fire."

★   ★   ★

TAX thought that the divisions among the participants of the discussion had not been between scientists and humanists but a division established by those who regard others as thinking they know all the answers. All probably share a common value that we should not take advantage of any power that we may have unless we have no alternative and have to make a decision. All realize that we cannot know everything that is necessary in order to act with certainty. Certainty of knowledge that we know what is best without the willingness to say, "Just possibly we're wrong," is something that we cannot and should not tolerate.

MUMFORD, in addressing those who are confident of their future predictions, added the classic words of Cromwell: "Brethren, bethink ye. By the bowels of Christ ye may be wrong."

The Unstable Equilibrium of Man in Nature

Are the Earth and Life Unique?

How Many People on Earth?

The Human Reaction

Some "One World" Consequences

And So the Story Continues

Dr. Harrison Brown, as Chairman for the last discussion session, expressed the hope that remaining deliberations would take both the long view and the broad view. He began by presenting his own perspective concerning the problem, stressing the new view that had emerged during the last two decades of the relation of the earth and of life on the earth to the exterior universe.

ARE THE EARTH AND LIFE UNIQUE?

In the light of what is known, the process of solar-system formation is not an unusual thing. It appears to be related to the process of double-star formation. As we know, double stars exist in our universe in numbers which far exceed those which would be expected solely on the basis of chance or random comings-together. Indeed, we can look upon our own solar system as almost a double-star system, in which Jupiter, the largest planet, did not become quite large enough to be a star in its own right.

This view has considerable consequences: of the 1,000,000,000,000,000,-000,000 (10^{21}) or so stars which can be seen through the Mount Palomar telescope, something like 1,000,000,000,-000,000 (10^{15}) may have components which are not stars (being too small to generate thermonuclear reactions) but

are what we call "planets." The concept of the existence of perhaps a million billion planets is a breath-taking thought—something quite new that has emerged from research during the course of the last two decades.

Life emerged on earth, we know not how. But the question arises: Is life unique, or, if given the opportunity, would life emerge wherever the chemical-physical environment was conducive to the emergence of those chemical reactions necessary for life-processes? If a planet possessed what we might call "chemical flexibility"; that is, if it were not so hot that complicated compounds could not form; if it were not so cold that things could not move; if it were not so large, like Jupiter, as to be composed almost entirely of hydrogen and helium; if it were not so small as the moon or Mercury that it contained no atmosphere; but if the planet had characteristics in between—would life emerge as a natural end product of chemical processes?

With one case (the earth) out of one possibility our statistics are poor. Another intriguing possibility is Mars, which has a remarkable blue-green area that appears to shrink in the Martian summer and to expand in the Martian spring. The infrared reflection spectrogram of this area is very different from that of the background; the color effects are exceedingly difficult if not impossible to explain on a purely inorganic basis. It seems quite possible that what we see on Mars is some form of plant life existing under very rugged conditions. And there are on Mars carbon dioxide and water—the ingredients for photosynthesis.

If life exists on Mars, then there are two cases out of two possibilities. Keeping in mind that we have possibly a million billion (10^{15}) solar systems and pessimistically guessing that only one out of a thousand has its planets not too close to its sun, is not too far away, not too large and not too small for conditions in which life could emerge, there still would be a thousand billion (10^{12}) planets possessing life. This long view permits consideration of an incredible variation of life-forms that puts to shame the variety of life-forms on earth.

On our own earth, life is a very, very thin film. All living substances could be wadded into a ball of a size in relation to the earth as a mosquito is to a melon. And within that thin film of life, which started perhaps two billion years ago, there has been ceaseless change. We have rather good evidence that the earth itself started four and a half billion years ago. It took a very long time before the life which did emerge learned how to precipitate calcium as shells and eventually bones. All life that has existed since the beginning of the Cambrian occupies but one-eighth of the total time span for the earth as a whole. Man emerged about a million years ago, so that all the history of man is really but a point in the geologic time scale. Measured in this manner, historic man occupies a point that scarcely exists.

Throughout the span of time in which life has been on earth, there has been evolution of new species and extinction of old. A species comes into existence; it fills a niche; then its environment changes, either for external reasons or because the living species itself changes its environment, and the species becomes extinct. Man, geologically speaking, is very young, yet he has come to effect most conspicuous changes in his environment. The questions we must ask are: Are creatures possessed of the power of conceptual thought here to stay on earth, or, like other species around him, is man doomed to extinction? If so, by what mechanisms and when?

Of course these questions are markedly involved with the whole factor of culture. In India, New Delhi, Madras, Calcutta, or Bombay might be wiped out, and this would not have the slightest effect upon the people in the remoter villages. It might even be twenty years before they heard about it. Contrast that situation with the United States, where the wiping-out of even one city might have a marked effect upon the whole country. In an industrial society the wiping-out of half the cities does not result in having half the country left. As in an ecological network, everything is directly and indirectly linked to everything else; if one thing is affected in the network, the whole equilibrium is upset. So in the web of industrial production, all is directly or indirectly linked to everything else, and the wiping-out of but a relatively small fraction of our industrial civilization could well result in the breakdown of the whole.

Also there must be kept in mind the distinction between two environments. First is the natural environment in which man emerged—which, in effect, molded man by determining his biological characteristics—and in which man is intimately a part of nature. Second is the environment which man is creating with his technological activity. How is this new environment affecting mankind's existence? And here in our discussion it is important to stress again the difference between what we think will happen and what we hope will happen.

Man's existence on this earth, from the point of view of technological civilization, requires a great deal of "food" in the form of ores and in the form of fuel. The first men who used metal tools picked up pieces of pure copper ore, which is rather thinly distributed over the earth's surface. The first man who used coal picked it up near the surface of the ground. As time has gone on, we have had to dig ever more deeply for leaner ores at the expense of requiring a great deal of technology. It takes much more technology to drill an oil well five miles deep than one a hundred feet in depth. This process of increasing complexity can be continued so long as our tools and our elaborate technological network are maintained. But imagine a world of Neolithic men which had been denuded by a previous technological civilization. Could metals and external sources of energy again come into use without easily available coal seams and easily available copper and iron? Are we so changing our environment by eating up these easily available ores and fuels that if the boat is rocked (biologically, or by hydrogen bombs, or by other ways) it would be difficult for a technological civilization to start again? DARWIN added that, in the long eons of time before us, the process will at some time decay and that therefore our present civilization, however long we keep it going, is doomed.

DARWIN also pointed out that Brown did not go as far as he might to have our flesh really creeping. The "hydrogen" bomb we now have is fortunately not of hydrogen but of deuterium. If it were a true hydrogen bomb composed of protons, and if we knew how to set it off, we should get enormously more energy; but it is extremely probable that such an act would set fire to the whole sea. There would appear a blaze of the brilliance of the sun for something like three weeks or three months, and then it would be over. We know that there have been two or three of these supernovae in the galaxy during historic time. Thus, since the galaxy is but a "limited" part of the universe, statistics suggest that about every five hundred years, on the average, one of these thousand billion (10^{12}) planets with life has developed not the deuterium bomb but the hydrogen bomb! May we hope that we do not discover it.

Chairman BROWN thought that, in addition, we should look rather intensively into the biological effects of industrial civilization. What is industrial civilization doing to man biologically and, from a long-range point of view, genetically? The term "industrial civilization" was here used in the broad sense to mean the use of energy and tools within a framework of any culture pattern—not necessarily that of America or of Western Europe. The use of energy and tools is spreading to the Orient, and, barring a world catastrophe, it is inevitable that countries such as India and China will develop high levels of industrial activity. This is as inevitable as was the spread of agriculture over the world which superseded the previous world of hunters and food-gatherers.

HOW MANY PEOPLE ON EARTH?

DARWIN stated that he was an absolutely convinced Malthusian. It was the custom for a long time, though much less so now, to decry Malthus by saying that none of the terrible things he foretold came to pass during the last one hundred and fifty years. But there were two sides to the Malthus equation: population and subsistence.

Malthus was demonstrably and absolutely right over the first and most important part of his thesis. He foretold the geometrical increase of population which happened. The population of England *has* quadrupled in a century. Now, quantities of experiments have been done on colonies of insects which, even when they are provided any quantity of food and the water closet is cleaned out every day, reach in some curious way a peak of population and then do not continue to increase. Yet there is nothing as far as can be seen in the Malthusian principle to prevent their increase. However, man is not that kind of insect. At any rate, until he gets very thick, man certainly is an example of the Malthusian system.

Where Malthus went wrong was on the supply side—the other side of the balance of his equation. What he could not foresee in 1799 was the development of transportation, including the railways, which made possible the rapid filling-up of North America, so as to remove the population pressure from Europe both by emigration and by the transport of food. The great open spaces of the New World for a hundred years have fed the Old World and kept it going. This has been a unique period in history, when the subsistence side of the Malthusian balance developed so rapidly that it could offset the rate of growth of humanity. Furthermore, Malthus could not foresee the great developments in science leading to the technological improvements which have made it easy for men to live together at so much greater densities.

Now that there are few empty spaces left, the second part of Malthus' equation—the supply of food—is assuming importance. Malthus, of course, spoke only of food production; today, Ordway and Brown speak of mineral and fuel consumption. Many of the quite common minerals—essential industrial "foods"—are beginning to go short. These must be included in the Malthus equation, because the level of our civili-

zation and its ability to sustain great concentrations of populations at that level depend on such things as copper for electric motors.

The subject that looms importantly large for humanity is the question of population increase. At a conference on population held in Rome in 1954, it was quite apparent from the calculations of all the demographers that, do whatever we can, short of a real catastrophe, the population of the world in a hundred years will be not the present two billion four hundred million but will be six billion. This population increase can be supported, but only if agriculture everywhere, including the undeveloped countries, is developed to its fullest. But there would have to be something quite revolutionary in the way of agriculture to get beyond a six billion population. Even an error in this estimate by a factor of two merely postpones the evil day when agriculture is defeated by population another fifty or sixty years. We have got to face the fact that over the long ages population must decrease as well as increase. This has not been our experience for two centuries now, and most people are therefore inclined to regard this fantastically abnormal period of world history as though it were normal. The necessity for periods of decrease may be demonstrated by some simple arithmetic. We know that population now will double in a century. If we then work it out, at the end of two thousand years there would be on the land surfaces of the earth only standing room for the mass of people and no room for them to lie down.

Actually, population has been doubling much faster; standing room will more likely be reached in one thousand years rather than two. This is a fantastically exceptional period in human history in which to be living. It cannot possibly continue. Would not three billion or four billion living in comparative comfort make a better world than six billion living in squalor? Do we not want to have more than just standing room for our population? The point is that human experiments take a long time. If we want to discover how to limit population, practically any experiment we do on it cannot really be complete under the minimum of forty years. It is not enough to change the birth rate; before we can be satisfied that we have done any good, we must know what kinds of people are the result of that change in birth rate, and this cannot be known until they are thirty or forty years old.

It is impossible to exaggerate the urgency with which anyone who believes that anything can be done about the problem should start dealing with it. There are two sides to the process: the social and the biological. On the social side experience shows that considerable changes in the population numbers can be made by legislation and by economics. For instance, France, by a system of family allowances, has built up its population quite a bit; something similar has been done in Sweden. Finding that they were decreasing, each group was able to reverse the trend. On the other hand, economic depressions led to lower numbers of children being born. On the social side there are not only legal economic stimuli but, most disturbing of all, the possibilities merely of fashion. Twenty years ago among the better-to-do classes there were rather likely to be two children in a family. A good deal of that, perhaps, was that Mrs. Jones thought that Mr. and Mrs. Smith were being a bit voluptuous and licentious when they had four or five children. Now, on the other hand, it is going the other way round: Mrs. Jones sees all the little Smith children playing round in the garden; she is certain that all her children are much superior to the little Smith children; and so she insists on

having more than the Smiths. It may seem surprising, but the most menacing increase of population in the world at the present time is found in the United States.

On the biological side there is the question of contraceptives. They are not very successful, but the small amount of effort—reflected in money spent—devoted to this problem is ludicrous. Three or four hundred thousand dollars recently have been devoted to the study of contraceptives, whereas something like twenty million dollars a year is being spent in the United States on cancer. It is a fantastic upset in the proportion of importance between those two subjects in terms of world problems. DARWIN did not believe that we will succeed in the long run in stopping population increase from being purely automatic, but, he admonished, "Do not let us be blamed by our descendants for not trying."

BANKS discussed the changing pattern of disease as seen in his own lifetime. In 1904 the infant mortality rate in England was 153 per thousand, but it has now dropped to about 26, whereas the expectation of life from birth has risen within our lifetime by about thirty years. In our own lifetime, almost while we watched, the pattern of disease has changed out of all recognition. The great killing diseases of infancy and adolescence have given place now to cancer, which is the current first killing disease, and to degenerative diseases of the cardiovascular system. The second thing which has emerged is the increasing proportion of mental illness. Nearly 50 per cent of all hospital beds in England and the United States are given over to mental patients. In England, 21 per cent of the patients in those hospitals are over sixty-five years of age.

We are entering a period of very delicate equilibrium with a smaller proportion of healthy children and a larger proportion of healthy adults. The picture has changed from a state when disease was almost a normal pattern and complete health abnormal to a state now when health is normal and disease is an abnormal interlude. But what is going to happen in the future with industrial hazards of which we know very little: the unknown effect on heredity of these compounds which affect not only the genes but the germinating tissues and the early critical months of the fetus *in utero*. Although it looks, in the long view, as though we are on the verge of a utopia, with a community so healthy that it can go right ahead with all its projects, the equilibrium is still an extremely unstable one.

OSBORN continued by saying that he believed in the tendency of the Malthusian principle. But it is a tendency that is very liable to work, not a fact that must work. The opinions of world agriculturists that the food needs of six billion persons can be met are highly questionable prophecies. We are not in one context now in meeting the world needs for food—not just the basic quantity, but the quality of food which is desirable for a minimum optimum nutritional diet. The relevance of a poor nutritional diet for health, energy, and creative impulses in man is too well known to dwell upon. We have no reference to what food production is in the world except for the appraisals and status reports produced by the Food and Agriculture Organization of the United Nations. Are these statements as accurate as perhaps they might be theoretically?

There is a fundamental need for a harmless, effective, simple, economic check to human fertility. A study is now being made of the social and political effects that may occur if, as, and when such a harmless control is discovered. Various reports by the governments of India, Japan, Jamaica, etc.,

constitute extraordinary signs that population increase is being recognized as a critical and vital problem.

LEOPOLD spoke on the question of time in population dynamics. The study of population in birds and animals has been concerned for a long time with the question of population eruptions. There are many species—quail, grouse, rabbits, deer, and others—whose populations are characterized by rapid fluctuations up and down. For example, in quail, the maximum density which can be supported over a long period of time is one bird per acre (regardless of the fact that they live in coveys, not as individuals). The eruption is characterized by supersaturation, which is unstable. The cutting-down of the supersaturated population in birds and mammals can be related, as far as we know, to such things as disease and food. Yet there are also indications that in certain species there are psychological-physiological changes which might be operative but of which next to nothing is yet known. From what little has been discovered, the decrease in population seems to be related to quality of food rather than to quantity. Time presumably has not been long enough to indicate whether these principles might be operative in human populations. It is not impossible, however, that they are; the rapid increase in mental disease might actually be one of the symptoms comparable to the kinds of things that are being shown in the new research in the population dynamics of birds and animals.

Assuming that practicable means can be found to restrict the number of human beings, EGLER, in writing, mentioned one factor that has not yet directly appeared to thwart such means but which in his opinion would appear just as soon as population controls appeared imminent. He referred to pressures from *organized industry*. Industry, particularly American industry, has in recent years become a relatively independent facet of society, bearing many aspects of the "organism" of holistic thought. It is becoming increasingly aggressive for its own interests, even when these appear to conflict with other interests of society. There are two major ways for industry to grow, which it clearly recognizes. One way is to sell more goods to the same people. In this respect, they raise the "standard of living," and most Americans think that they are better off. The entire applied-psychology field of "motivation research" is directed toward these ends, and every possible weakness of gullible buyers is exploited. The other way is to sell goods to *additional* people, and, for this purpose, industry is openly anticipating future increases in population with all the eagerness of a hungry animal drooling at the prospects of a big meal. It was EGLER's thought that, *if* any suitable means are found to limit human populations, organized industry will rise in an opposition that is more effective than that now provided by religious motivations.

GOUROU, in writing, did not think it scientifically practicable to be preoccupied with world population. Changes of world population are the result of combinations of local changes. It is these local changes that ought to be made the object of scientific studies. What would be necessary and profitable are studies of types of demographic evolution (not theoretical types, but real types, such as for the Indian Republic, northwestern Europe, the United States, and Japan).

THE HUMAN REACTION

GALDSTON stated that he did not share Darwin's pessimism about the world, perhaps because Sir Charles was a physicist, and he, a psychiatrist. Perhaps the pessimism Darwin had voiced dealt not with the universe but with man. It is possible to accept Malthus as a good scientist but not as a prophet; there is too much of a self-regulatory mechanism operating in mankind. There has been a good deal of talk about man not being logical—the implication thereby being that man was therefore illogical—but this is wrong. Man has many more important things to do than to bother eternally about logic. The reason for this is that life itself is not logical. Most of the truly important things in life have no logical explanation or no logical warrant for them. Life is not logical; it is biological. Is it logical to produce children and, as Francis Bacon had said, "give a pledge to all eternity"? Life transcends logic. Man has a much more important thing to do on earth, and that is to fulfil his destiny. But let us shed the word "destiny" and use something more scientifically acceptable, such as "man has a commitment to fulfil his architectonic." When the sperm and ovum unite to form a fertilized ovum, there is initiated a drama which embraces the total destiny of man and which involves the realization of his architectonic. The architectonic is reflected in a time-bound scheme of eventuation. In nine months, if the calendar is counted correctly, a human being results. The fetus which matures during this period and comes forth as a human being is the carrier of an architectonic which it will, with some variations, follow. This architectonic is both very definite and very beautiful. We know that it will grow, by accretion, following certain metabolic processes, controlled by certain factors, from seven pounds to a hundred and some. Thus, just as soon as the essential growth by accretion has been completed, the gonadic functions take over, epiphassal cartilage disappears, longitudinal growth is no longer possible, and now the organism is prepared for the operation which is no longer growth by accretion but growth by reproduction or, as we might say, by "procretion."

Two individuals of opposite sex then unite to effect the process of childbearing. This involves a tremendously complicated physical, endocrinological, physiological, emotional, and social reorientation. The individual's innate architectonic can be disrupted. The individual can be subjected to some degree of duress, but, if pressed beyond a given degree, the creature does not change; it curls up and dies. This innate architectonic has been built up over hundreds of thousands of years. It has been subjected in the last three hundred years to a pressure such as never before witnessed in history. In physical ways (food, health), the environment has been improved as a consequence of the industrial revolution; psychologically, perhaps, we have not caught up at all. Maybe a good portion of the mentally sick persons who occupy 50 per cent of our total of beds are there not so much because they are mentally sick as because the world is sick. When we take a look at some schizophrenics and listen to them, one is at times persuaded that their logic is a lot better than ours. They do not like the world; the world is wrong, and perhaps there is a great deal of reason in that. Man has a self-regulatory mechanism, but he can be pushed only so far.

Man has been thrown into severe disequilibrium by the industrial revolution and by its concomitants, but perhaps the "self-righting principle" will make us aware of some of the untoward effects and sharpen our enterprises to correct them. Art and science should facilitate man's living in and with nature. It should reconcile man to nature and not alienate him. For this we need, on the one hand, an awareness of what science both promises and threatens and, on the other hand, a basic concept of the innate architectonic of man which is not only physical

but psychological. This architectonic may operate to balance out overproduction, overmisery, overthreat, and anything else which threatens to liquidate the universe in the glorious fire of the seas.

HEICHELHEIM remarked that the Hellenistic and Roman worlds also suffered from mental disorganization, just as does our own time. With the psychiatrist, Dr. Alfred Storch, Heichelheim had analyzed genuine dreams found in the Serapeum at Memphis and believed he proved that the feeling of psychological insecurity at that time was unusual—even when compared to today's in Storch's experience. But the healing force for this was the rise of Christianity. For example, when a person went over to the new religion of Christianity, he came into conflict with such a law as that which forbade the taking-home of babies which had been exposed by their parents to die. Greek and Roman law made it possible for a father to say whether he would accept a child; if he did not, it was exposed to die, and a law made it illegal to save such babies. There is no doubt that this horrible custom came to an end by the interference of Christians, who secretly took these children home and brought them up as members of Christian families. As a result, the population increased. When we meet modern movements of this kind, which of course cannot be exactly like those of the first post-Christian centuries, perhaps it is important that we think more carefully about whether there is not a healing process of our civilization in these movements before we try to impede them.

SEIDENBERG stated that the basic problem confronting us is not technology but culture in relation to technology. We are in danger of a cultural break now under our present system of technology. Technology has certain social implications, the main one perhaps being that technology implies an increasingly organized world. Such a system favors the kind of people for whom an organized world is the proper habitat. Galdston has reminded us of the increase in the number of maladjusted people in a maladjusted civilization. This means that, at least in the long run, there may be an elimination of these maladjusted people as an influence upon the system. In that event the values of technological civilization will prevail. Is it not possible that the "adjusted" people will become totally dominant, so that we reach neither a point of collapse nor the mountaintops but a plateau existence? This would be a long-range final adjustment in which we are not going to realize those high spiritual values that the past has given us.

Tax thought that man as a species is facing perhaps the second great crisis in human history. The first was when man as an animal became conscious and realized his individual mortality. The reconciliation of people to the fact that their egos are going to be destroyed was a great human achievement which in part gave rise to a great deal of what we think of as culture. Every individual has to make the reconciliation, but the culture now provides him some tools and some support. The reconciliation of the individual is made by thinking either of immortality or of the self-fulfilment of the individual, or both.

In accordance with Brown's presentation of the future, the problem with which man is now faced for the first time appears to be that not only is he as an individual, a species, mortal but so, too, is the planet. The beginning of reconciliation to this, of course, is the thought that there are many millions of other planets with people—that we are not alone—and so all will not die with us. But, unless communication with some other planet is achieved, we can-

not fulfil the great human desire to pass on our collective ego. Of course, man can always fall back upon the basic religious notion of immortality, which also is a way of reconciliation; but the reconciliation that seems to be taking shape is that, though man's days be numbered, he should do the best he can, just as an individual should in the time he has.

It is a remarkable thing to be living in an era when such a basic revolution occurs. We have come to the point where it appears to be possible that man's life on earth can be ended much sooner. As man faces reconciliation to this, he has again to look at the duality of human existence, one side of which is represented by the general notion of progress, the other side of which is identification with the universe. The two prototypes of ways of reconciliation are the Western and the Indian ways of looking at things. Will mankind be satisfied to exist on the earth without attempting to communicate with some other planets? In the building of space ships our engineers happily take leadership. The other reconciliation is to develop within ourselves the fulfilment of a total existence. The bridging of this fundamental dichotomy might be what is necessary for man to continue to exist on the planet as a whole psychological being.

Clark did not think it particularly useful to focus attention on man's imminent end, which is becoming a fascination. It probably does not lie within our power to do very much about it. Meanwhile, he earnestly hoped we would not try to communicate with other planets, because essentially our problem is the degree and facility of intercommunication among men. It is possible to interpret the history of cultural development in terms of media of communications, both from one generation to the next and from one man, tribe, city, or larger political unit to another. Our desperate illness—a severe social and ecological pathology—has come not because we know too little of what others are doing but because we are bombarded with information about it. There are perhaps certain optimum rates of cultural absorption, and these rates have been far surpassed. We have probably far too many people, and we are far too closely identified with too many of our fellows. It is said that we cannot resist the one-world tendency, but, if we must plan for the future, let us have a deliberate reduction of intercommunication. We really ought to stop worrying about making all men and all gods over into our own images. The question is, really, what our discernible ends may be. Not many of us could distinguish the superior from the inferior, outside of our own particular group. So let us establish local option that lets people breed and live and die in their own way and make fools of themselves if they want to.

GLIKSON spoke about hopes and possibilities for the future equilibrium of man and resources. We are not limited only to observing streams of development in nature and in society, but we are enabled by our intelligence to act to the benefit of the human race and the earth. We have arrived at a certain point of crisis where decisions have to be made. This moment of decision-making is also a moment of great chance for realization of improvement. In order to realize an improvement in life, we need positive cultural and ethical goals. We should never take these aims and goals as world wide; every part of the world does not have to act in the same way or use the same means in order to solve the problems of its emergency.

We should not look for abstract total conceptions of world-wide development but should rather try to make small steps in different parts of the world, in order to begin improvement

of man-nature relations. The intelligent and ethical action of planning requires thought not in terms of this year or next but in terms of future generations over long-range periods. Also there must be change in thought about our scale of space as a consequence of development of communications and transportation all over the world. Specific regions and populations are to be considered in relation to total earth space.

BURKE followed on Galdston's earlier comment with the thought that environmental disorientation perhaps has led to mental illness. The extent to which a society is out of kilter with the ecological realities, whether biological or social, and of the world around it is a disorientation which may be reflected in basic illnesses.

STEINBACH observed that much of the environment that technological man creates for himself and which should be fitted into his sense of values comes essentially from an "as if" philosophy. For example, if we today wiped away all our knowledge of the control and application of antibiotics, ten years from now we would have no use for our store of those antibiotics, for they would not be effective, and we would have all the old diseases right back again. There tends to be an acceptance of the fruits of technology without a realization that they stem from man's really greatest resource—his imagination and ability to use it in a way that we call "scientific."

KLIMM added that man has always been able to get into trouble with his environment but that there are societal as well as physical aspects to that environment. BURKE continued that Clark's decrying that many millions of people cannot pursue their own destiny seems to be a product of an environment in which there is a large margin of resources that can be wasted. Glikson's comment about the need for planning to assure an adequate existence reflects an environment in which there is a small margin of resources. If we are living in a psychotic civilization, and if we have disregard for what we leave our offspring, this does not help matters the more. It has been said that it does not make a bit of difference what kind of world is left to coming generations: What they did not know would not hurt them, for they would simply adapt to their environment despite its differences from our time. But such an attitude overlooks that we are passing on to them classical traditions and other ideas about the good life which presupposes a world that they might not have. We are setting up problems for our offspring that we cannot as yet begin to visualize as problems.

It also seems that, if any valid work is to be done in the sciences and carried through to fruition, it cannot be carried on in a vacuum. In a society in which the bulk of the population possesses the right to vote on what will be carried out and contributes support for scientific work, we can operate only on the assumption that there is a need for more communication, not less.

SCHAEFER rose to speak as an optimist. Man is an adaptable creature, and a few at least resist efforts of enforced conformity. The current tendency of business to elevate management to a pedestal and to attempt techniques for large-scale control of man's actions is leading rapidly to a pattern of conformity which militates against free will, discourages new ideas, and drives away the brilliant and unorthodox thinkers so important for developing new ideas and concepts. The encouraging feature of this new development is the exit of the nonconformists to universities, small businesses, and laboratories and the rise of the individual consultant, who often sells his skills, abilities, or services to the same group which drove him away by their inflexible rules and organization. So long as such readjustments are feasible and continue to occur, we may take heart in the continuation of freedom and advance in our understanding of the world.

WITTFOGEL noted that speakers were dealing with the future of mankind on two levels: one, the far-distant future; the other, the operational future, which is near by. It is very important to develop something different from the prevailing mood of shallow optimism that man gets better and better and more clever and more harmonious all the time. It is very important for both the wisdom and the dignity of man to build and develop into one's self an element of stoicism. Actually, man knows only a very small part of the cosmos. Let us not lose ourselves in the long perspective. Our task is to concentrate on the near-by future.

The crisis of our time occurs on many levels—in religion, in political science, and in values. Where are we going? There is a self-critical attitude which is negativist and defeatist, paralyzes us, and prevents our going ahead. Some have said that the early despotic empires, where commercial competitions played no role, enjoyed harmonious human relations. But, if we study the facts carefully, we find that this is not the case. There is much talk about alienation—people feel lonely. But the critics do not realize that the great second industrial revolution which we are now experiencing is not only the destroyer of old forms but the builder of new forms of community life.

The partial alienation of man, which we know, is sometimes bitter, but it cannot be compared with the total alienation under total power. There the individual is completely broken away from his fellows because distrust and fear stalk unchecked. There he can become alienated even from his conscience by being brain-washed and completely blotted out as an autonomous human being.

We can observe the crisis in the schools. The youngsters in graduate school ask, "Where are we going? Are there no values? Are we really nothing?" Perhaps we citizens of the West are not so good as the great tradition we inherited. We inherited unique traditions of freedom which we shall develop the better, the better we understand their unique value.

PFEIFER agreed that the present situation is unpleasant but that perhaps it is not the technological factor but the political factor that makes it so. We live in a divided world whose parts are technologically and culturally unequal and with economical-political and social-political tendencies on the part of some to enforce development of other parts. Among other things, the flow of food supply is disrupted. Questions of man's future are discussed altogether too much from the basis of the Western world experiences during the last few centuries. We of the West inherited the old traditions of the classical world; we have somehow renewed them, partly embodying the things of practical times, and made them into something new. Happily, there are still human reservoirs of mankind with other cultures. Perhaps they suffer now from the impact of our overwhelming Western society, but what will they do with our achievements? It is certain that the Indians, the Chinese, and the Africans will embody our ideas and techniques with new features when they take them over, even though with perhaps the loss of certain things which we think important to our society.

SOME "ONE WORLD" CONSEQUENCES

ANDERSON stressed the importance of what is known in technical genetics as the "Sewall Wright effect." Evolution is most rapid in small, semi-isolated populations. That is, rapid progress in the shuffling-together of innate differences to produce something that fits a little better into the environment demands a small, semi-isolated population. One of the troubles in the modern world and its future is the breakup of small, semi-isolated populations. Hybridization of human beings is a very good thing, but the immediate result—the production of hybrid vigor—poses special problems. One example is the American propensity toward action rather than toward contemplation. Another part of the world where the problem of hybrid vigor looms larger than elsewhere is Israel. Bringing together into one nation hybrids from many parts of the world will produce a tremendous vitality.

Wherever variation in evolution ultimately may come from, it is produced many times faster during hybridization. The percentage of useful mutations is extremely small. Therefore, all the extremes of human variation should be treasured. By analogy, plant-breeders of two generations ago began to improve maize very rapidly; only at the insistence of the hybrid-corn companies has the New World been combed for the kinds of funny, old, no-good corn at which the plant-breeders turned up their noses. Thus, for a geneticist, the greatest treasure that *Homo sapiens* has are the little people who are off in a corner and are different.

STEINBACH, also, felt that, in the biologist's view, there is every reason why any plans for the future should involve a minimum of control as regards organisms and especially as regards human beings. There is an absolute scientific necessity to maintain a large pool of genetic material floating around, because, until we have definite control of such things as numbers, we can never hope to select, say, all big blond people and end up with a good group of people. It is absolutely essential, according to biological theory, that we have large, essentially natural populations and keep them as natural as we can for such time as we can see into the future.

TUKEY, in writing, indicated that we must face up to certain consequences for *Homo sapiens* of the coming unification of the world.

In the Neolithic and earlier times, communities of *Homo sapiens* were small but many in number. Now they are larger but fewer in number. Soon, perhaps, there will be but one community. This quantitative change has quantitative consequences. From the point of view of survival of the species, planning and conservation become more important as "one world" is approached. If a Neolithic community or even a small state of the Middle Ages destroyed itself by destroying its environment, the species went on with little disturbance. If "one world" destroys its environment, the species is gone.

As Anderson brought out, biological evolution proceeded rather continuously in undisturbed habitats and made jumps in disturbed ones. If we dare to extrapolate this to social evolution and believe that when and if "one world" arrives there will no longer be disturbed habitats, then we face a situation in which social evolution will be only continuous, where jumps are ruled out. In so far as various interesting social systems are separated by barriers not likely to be crossed by continuous variation, we shall be locked into some of these systems when "one world" arises. The years between are "years of most crucial decision."

Some years ago Arnold Toynbee gave a public lecture at Princeton in which he stressed two points: that the great religions of the world had arisen at points of contact among differing cultures and that many cultures were today in intimate contact. (Why he did not draw the logical conclusion is an interesting question.) If his first point

is true, then the forthcoming "years of most crucial decision" not only will be the last years in which such developments are likely but will be years in which new developments are very probable indeed. To what extent will these new religious and ethical systems include the ideas discussed at this symposium?

AND SO THE STORY CONTINUES

BATEMAN spoke as a geologist accustomed to looking back millions of years in following the development of life on the earth—the passage of species and the rising of new ones. He expressed faith in the ingenuity of man to meet problems in the future as he had in the past. For many of the materials of which we see a growing scarcity, the future may not be quite so black as we now contemplate.

BROWN expressed the idea that not many people have doubted man's technological ingenuity. Indeed, that the sky is the limit has been admitted. What has been questioned is man's cultural ingenuity.

HUZAYYIN noticed that several speakers had expressed an underlying faith in man's continuity. If we admit the existence of a creative power behind the universe and behind our planet, it is impossible to ignore the idea of continuity. To be sure, there will be changing continuity both in time and in space.

The human story has been a matter of successive civilizations. From cultures connected with limited areas, there arose a number of cultural areas, each having contact with the neighboring areas but not with far ones; for instance, Egypt had contact with Persia or with Greece but very little or hardly any with China. Later, after the time of Alexander, there was the first rise of the idea of universality of humanity. Unfortunately, Western culture, when it looked back to its roots, only went as far as Rome and Greece and did not choose to look as much as it should have to the heritages of other cultures. As a result Western culture appears to be a superstructure not sufficiently linked with deeper structures in the human edifice as a whole. We can imagine that in a thousand years' time, perhaps, a historian evaluating the British Empire will designate the greatest contribution of the British people to be not technical development but such things as the Boy Scout movement and sports, which contributed to the development of human spirit and the spirit of comradeship between man and man. It is pleasing to note that, when the United States came out of its long and unnatural isolationist situation, it began to look to the human origins, not only in Western Europe, but also in Greece, in the Middle East, and even in India and other parts of the world.

Connections in space between man and man are also to be intensified and improved. The idea of so-called "underdeveloped" countries or peoples has been touched upon in this symposium. But "underdevelopment" is all relative. Some of the so-called "underdeveloped" people are far more developed in certain aspects of their life than some who consider themselves the most developed. For example, think how far music of African derivation has succeeded in the United States in supplanting classical music brought from Europe. By taking other values—spiritual or moral—we can correct these notions of developed, underdeveloped, overdeveloped, and so on, only by viewing humanity as a whole for its spiritual and moral values toward which all human beings have something to contribute. MURPHY thought Huzayyin tended to limit far too much the heritage of the West. Not mentioned was the creative and artistic heritage of the West, which goes back fifty thousand years to the time when

Altamira, Lascaux, Les Trois Frères, and the other great caves of Western Europe received on their walls the first expression of man's leisure and creative possibilities. The chain has been continuous ever since that time.

ULLMAN spoke with an optimistic viewpoint that man's golden age exists right now and that we are in it. He spoke primarily in an economic sense and, specifically, with the thought that there are fewer human slaves, and, though we do not have as many servants as before, we are spreading the benefits to everyone. This appears to be a greater good for a greater number. From the standpoint of economic well-being, we in the United States are embarrassingly well off.

MALIN, in writing, expressed the view that the proponents of extremes—the millennial perfectibility and its opposite, the Malthusian starvation—appear to assume that their syllogisms must necessarily run out in a straight line to the bitter end. Three considerations are in order to put both of those extreme philosophies into perspective. The net effect may be a version of Stoicism, but what of it?

In the nineteenth century, chemists assumed that certain chemical reactions ran out to the end and, in consequence, found themselves in difficulties about applications to particular problems. Subsequently, mathematical theory opened the way for recognition of the principle of chemical reversals and provided the requisite theoretical explanations. Some ecologists, without benefit of corresponding mathematical formulations, have insisted upon a tendency toward biological compensations in the direction of equilibrium. The behavior of man has been subject to even less explicit formulation of theoretical principles, but the possibilities in that direction cannot be ruled out arbitrarily. Neither the straight-line process nor the principle of reversal as applied to man has been proved. Both share the same hypothetical status.

A second consideration involves the concept of orders of magnitude. In any given state of culture, society operates on the basis of relations suitable to the particular level of technology attained and in the tradition of that particular society. In the broadest aspect, of course, the traditional periodization of human culture into Stone Age (with subdivisions), Bronze Age, and Iron Age, etc., are cases in point. But something more specific is desirable. In England, for example, early railroads used horses and stationary engines with ropes. These soon reached the limits of efficiency, became cumbersomely complex, and were threatened with collapse from sheer giganticism. In 1829 the newly designed "rocket" steam locomotive proved highly successful. Quickly a new simplicity in organization and operation of railroad business was effected through the instrumentality of the steam locomotive—a breakthrough to a new order of magnitude in land communications. This is only a single instance of what occurs from time to time on an even larger scale in the succession of technological levels. The limits of the possibilities of such orders of magnitude are not known, but in the foreseeable future there is no reason to assume that the process should not continue—not in a straight-line process or by ascending or descending series but by unpredictable transitions in orders of magnitude.

The third consideration, that of ecological succession, is more formidable. Of course the idea of succession leading to climax is out. It is unrealistic. In the series of succession states, all the factors entering into the ecosystem are different—plants, animals, soil, climatic impact, etc. Thus, for instance, plants of one ecological state may not be able to grow in the next state, and plants in the second state could not have grown in the first. Each state is unique and irreversible. Geological processes appear to be only long-term versions of some such succession processes. Species, families, and orders of plants and animals have become extinct, making way for innovators. Possibly man is only another example of this succession. In that case, the inexorable consequences of change will work themselves out. If such is the ultimate reality of human existence, then the outcome is not in human hands.

A careful evaluation of the three foregoing considerations places in perspective the particular forms of doom forecast by the Malthusians or by the atomic scientists. Under either of the first two considerations (the principles of reversals and order of magnitude) the Malthusian doom might be postponed or even canceled out without conscious intervention of human planning. In the last instance the extinction of man by the ecological formula would be effected by factors other than mere numbers and food supply, and the palliatives of limitation of numbers would effect nothing in the long run. No one should deny that man's mismanagement might entail atomic doom, but self-extinction also might occur in consequence of other products of the contriving brain and the skilful hand of man. Science and technology per se are always amoral, and successive ages of man have always sounded warnings about man's misuse of them. The major philosophical principles should not be confused by this derivative question of the ethics of man's contrivances.

But let there be no mistake about the facts of this discussion, which is neither history, nor science, nor social science. It is philosophy. History deals with the past in all its uniqueness, and only with the past. Even were the assumption made that the sciences can deal with such predictions about the future, no adequate factual basis is available upon which to predicate scientific operations of requisite magnitude. The only procedure available is speculative, and the direction of the philosophy suggested is possibly a version of Stoicism, which all strictly intellectual operations must necessarily be. Only by stating clearly the issues can liberation of men be effected from those philosophies of extremes, the ideas of "progress" and of "Malthusian doom," which have so largely dominated and contaminated Western thought since the eighteenth century—a captivity of the mind to the miscalled "Enlightenment." Within the finite limits of man's understanding of his relations with the earth, the irrepressible "contriving brain" constitutes the unique active principle in translating continuously the latent properties of the earth into unpredictable resources for man's use or misuse. Beyond these finite limits, obviously, the fate of man in the ecological succession processes of the universe is not in his hands.

Between an inborn optimism and a Damoclean Darwinism, DARLING suggested that there is room for a re-strained pessimism depending on the fallibility of man. The time factor is important, because, the longer the time that we have, the greater the possibility for reversal of the process for the future outlined by Darwin.

Clearly there are optimists, and clearly there are pessimists, Chairman BROWN concluded. He himself shared Darwin's pessimism but not his view as to the inevitability of the world which is to come upon us. The task that confronts us is to walk the tightrope—to fall off neither on the one side into Darwin's world nor on the other into Seidenberg's world. The ultimate answer seems to lie not so much in the improvability of the human being as in the improvability of human culture. And BROWN also agreed with the words of William Shakespeare:

> . . . What is a man,
> If his chief good and market of his time
> Be but to sleep and feed? A beast, no more.
> Sure he that made us with such large
>   discourse,
> Looking before and after, gave us not
> That capability and godlike reason
> To fust in us unused. . . .

Hamlet, Act IV, Scene IV

Part IV
Summary Remarks

Retrospect

Process

Prospect

Summary Remarks

Retrospect

CARL O. SAUER

The time has come to wrap it up and put it away. I shall not attempt to cast up the accounts in due form. As participating observer, I do wish to give my impression of the mode and mood of the conference.

I think we are all pretty full of well-shared discussion, and the point of fatigue is near, if it has not already arrived. Also, the older one gets, the more one finds that fewer words are necessary or relevant. I do not have a great many words coming up that ask for expression.

I do want to say about words, however, that I think you did remarkably well in avoiding intricate and secret language. The communication was very satisfactory on that level. I understood, at least as to words, almost everything that was said. By way of comment for a possible future, some of our members from other lands have had a certain amount of difficulty with some of the things that we have said. That is a matter that Americans need especially to keep in mind. We drop into a vernacular, into a handy idiom, that aids informality but confuses persons from elsewhere. By personal experience of work in Latin America, I can attest to such bewilderment by regional, intimate idioms. We succeeded well in avoiding professional jargon. Should we meet again in international conference, we might keep in mind the possibilities of plain English.

At times I felt during this conference, as at times I have felt about life, that I would not have missed it but would not want to go through it again. This, however, is not my final attitude toward either. I am grateful to have been one of you.

We, or most of us, went into this thing cold. Even we three co-chairmen were quite uninitiated. The nature of the conference and the manner of its setting-up and of its operation are as new to me as they have been to you. This is an original specialty in procedure, not a first-run experiment, on the part of the Wenner-Gren Foundation, to which belongs all credit for the conception and manner of conduct of the conference. I was doubtful for some time as to whether they, the Foundation, knew what they were about, but I am persuaded that they did. For a group of this size and diversity this has been the most relaxed and uninhibited, if not always the most sharply focused, conference in my experience. Digression was not blocked off, nor could it have been restrained except by loss of the self-determining course of the discussions.

In the first preliminary assembly the criticism was voiced that the conference was both too much and too little, too broad and unprecise, and that the range of disciplines was unbalanced. Both criticisms are true; yet, I think, the conference stands pretty well vindicated in both respects. Now that we are at its end I feel assured that it has been what we hoped it might be and that it was made, as we had hoped, by you its members, spontaneously and collectively. If that is true, it has been a very real accomplishment and is a high compliment to all of you.

The participants were not selected as representatives of particular disciplines. This is one of the first items on which we agreed. You are not here because you represent biochemistry or economics. We wanted you here because we wanted you as individuals, and I think that that is a premise for which we do not need to make apology.

The formal disciplinary alliances that may divide academic meetings of broad scope, in so far as we were able, we disregarded completely. As the conference wore on, less and less was said in defense or in support of a particular disciplinary association.

Another matter of interest is that this is a conference of amateurs. The "pros" —to our Continental friends, the hardy and adept professionals who enter tournaments in series—were hardly considered in the makeup of the group. Those who were committed by official positions to declared policies were omitted. Thereby we lost smoothness of performance, but I think that, in the end, these options were properly taken and paid off handsomely. Professor Wittfogel, who is a gracious example of a multicultural hybrid, yesterday asked this question: "Are there any blind dates in this group?" Now, that is a most American query and idiom. The answer is that the "blind dates"—the invitations by "hunch"—were the luckiest things that happened. The selection involved a good deal of guessing as to who might fit. In retrospect over what this conference did, I think we were just "plain," providentially lucky in the over-all list of people that we came up with and in what you have contributed.

We did try deliberately to get people from significantly different and wide backgrounds. Again, I am saying, not from specific disciplines. One of the results has been that you could not talk a great deal of esoteric "shop" in the meeting, as you might have done within narrower selections. There was an apparent tendency for the members to despecialize themselves and think more readily in a wider or over-all context as the meeting developed.

I say very earnestly that I am most happy that we got as many people from abroad as we did. I wish there might have been even more. Our constituents from outside of the United States added more than I can acknowledge to the content and direction of this conference.

Frank Darling made some comment about the difficult, even unhappy, situation in which a member of a minority finds himself. Perhaps we selectors, without planning to do so, inclined to minorities in and out of the United States. We certainly thought of the members from abroad as adding salt and seasoning that we should have missed otherwise, and in this we have not been disappointed. (I find myself getting into an aside I cannot drop.) Whether or not Frank Darling thinks of himself as a member of a minority, I seem in one way or another to have been all my life a member of some cultural minority in these United States, but I had better not become autobiographical but get on with the matter.

We are touching upon a very serious topic that Americans, with their emphasis on acculturation, Americanization, and so forth, have never explored properly. Our own cultural minorities, living and surviving, persisting in some of their own attitudes of values and consciences, have a seminal as well as a historical significance as long as they resist absorption into the general pattern, but we pay little attention to them. This started because I was talking about our participants from abroad. The American group, it has been intimated, in its selection is somewhat atypical, and these remarks, therefore, do not refer specifically to the Americans present.

Perhaps because of our national size and vigor, and also evangelistic tradition, we have an inclination to universalize ourselves. Perhaps no people today is more likely to assume itself to be the norm—that we are indeed the people of the Middle Kingdom. This becomes especially characteristic when we concern ourselves with the behaviors and attitudes of the rest of mankind. Thus, I am not content with what our social science and history are about in their current predilections and theories, because postulates, inferences, and suppositions of "universality" are too often assumed and derived from ourselves. Culture history is interested in the plurality of cultures and is rather alien to our learning.

The enrichment of the conference from a number of different cultural backgrounds has been, from the first meeting on, manifest to all.

Incidentally, about this matter of universalizing ourselves as Americans, there was reference to American activities in guiding the "development" of other parts of the world, even an appeal to us to help others find the right way. I have had a fair amount of experience in at least one part of the world with this sort of thing. Edgar Anderson's attribute of American hybrid vigor is a metaphor that describes this drive to spread "the American way." In large measure I see in it an effect of the frontier tradition, with which is joined our evangelistic background, which is very strong, very deep, and very confident. It is distressing and depressing that we send people out who may be government officials, professors, or technicians—but, in any case, they are bent on particular missions—to realize a

predesigned end. How rare it is when one is in such an "underprivileged," "backward" country, or wherever life is alien to ours—think of the gall of these almost official designations—to find one of us who is there in order to learn of other ways and options instead of working for the adoption of our own. That such intervention increases or introduces ecologic unbalances receives little notice.

That is a peculiarly contemporary American trait, concerning which the beneficiaries have been most gentle with us. What opportunities of understanding have been lost because we presume to know better, instead of seeing that this is our chance to find out how other people live, what their ways are, how they go about getting their satisfactions out of life. In this meeting our attention has been called to other cultural values, to other attitudes concerning "resource development," to the reasonableness of letting other folk live their own way.

In the later sessions a print of the future was presented to us, a prospect of the shape of things to come such as may be expected from the lately found mastery over matter. We were shown the new industrial revolution that may leave the world we have known and liked only antiquarian relics. Thus are we brought in 1955 to a revised version of Aldous Huxley's "brave new world" of the twenties—to a faceless, mindless, countless multitude managed from the cradle to the grave by a brilliant elite of madmen obsessed with accelerating technologic progress. The original of these fantasies was composed by an Englishman, but the reality is being undertaken especially in this country. The social prospect in growing regimentation, in loss of individual freedom as we have known it, in elimination of unplanned variation, lead to questioning the technologic-economic system that is in the making. Was some of this in the mind of Einstein when he said that he would be a plumber if he were starting life over again?

Since we have taken over the role of Providence, our present and prospective conditions must needs become the principal ethical concern of those most informed and wisest. What sort of a world is it that we want, and can we get it? Some of the best young men and minds, and perhaps more and more of them, are saying today that they will have nothing to do with physical science or even with social science, because of the uses to which these are being put. Have the humanities anything left to say?

It was shocking but salutary that we had this sort of thing put up to us. We should be thinking about the lost innocence of science. I do not think that we can say any longer that all extension of knowledge is its own justification. I cannot, nor do I care to, argue the difference between pursuit and use of knowledge. We must not forget that there are a lot of young people who will be facing up to that issue.

One of the cheering things—I think what saved my spirit yesterday—was Dr. Galdston standing up, as he has on several brief occasions, with his deep insight into the nature of man, and saying not to worry too much about this impending superorganization, because man cannot bear biologically in the long run what is contemplated technologically for him. His contributions to the discussion appear to me so fine that I pray earnestly he may expand them at least into a brief essay for the summary of the proceedings. What he said as a psychiatrist meant as much to me as anything that was said, and there were some very important things said.

Now, did we attain our general objectives which were left unprecise by choice? Again, I do not believe I am

speaking *pro domo* by saying, and saying warmly, "Yes."

The papers prepared beforehand represented large and sustained industry and include a high number of remarkable contributions. They bear their own recommendation. I think it was apparent—there was an opposite opinion expressed—that the dross was far outweighed by distinguished learning and original insights. These contributions have added a good deal to my understanding, and I am very sure that they will be read and read again, especially by a lot of youngsters who will find in them an introduction to certain phases of inquiry that are hardly accessible.

You recall that the first paper, presented and distributed first as an earnest of the nature of the conference, was Anderson's genial presentation of his problem of man-plant relations. The last one to come in was also botanical, by H. H. Bartlett. That finished the series. The whole series was completed much as originally planned, which, I think, is itself exceptional. Bartlett's contribution undoubtedly contains the understatement of the conference, for to his paper he added an appendix, entitled "Annotated Bibliography," of six hundred pages. Although this is not included in the volume, it has been issued by the University of Michigan and will have a wide circulation as a remarkable handbook and commentary on tropical vegetation as influenced by man.

Next, as to the discussions that we have just ended. We started out on the first afternoon in wobbly fashion. Darling, I thought, made a magnificent save on that first afternoon, and afterward things began to run more and more smoothly as interchange began to flow.

I think everyone will carry with him his own luminous memories of high points. I was much moved by Edgar

Anderson's statement of the scholar's faith and relation to his fellows, made at the beginning of his session, as I was also by Alan Gregg's reminiscent *envoi* at the end of another session.

The risks of running out of relevant matter and the equal ones of being wound up in a confusion of irrelevant talk were present in the free-wheeling, loose design of the conference. That nothing of the sort happened was due, of course, only to yourselves and your readiness to get the ball back into play. A thoroughly and all-the-time disciplined mind might well be irritated by some of the undisciplined zigs and zags and wags and wogs that took place. To me these were desirable and at times delightful.

Some members of the conference are gifted by nature, or by the advantage of English training, in an elegance and precision of speech which the rest of us cannot match or can acquire only at great effort. It does not matter; style is not the man. There were things said stumblingly that were very important to say. The group was generously responsive to substance rather than to manner and thus invited, and got, free and open expressions.

The tangents added lighter touches at times but also opened new directions. In the end, I think, knowledge was communicated in abundant measure, and insights were developed by spontaneous interplay. This was not a didactic symposium, although each of us was instructed in matters previously unknown or unconsidered. The conference was a different sort of intercommunication, an attempt at comparison, synthesis, and query. A reference was made to it as of "ships that pass in the night," but methinks the ships sailed in good contact and toward a common port, at least more did so than one might have anticipated.

I have a strong feeling that ideas formed out of the discussion which came together out of an unsegregated, undifferentiated mass. Anderson said something to this effect which I trust has been captured on the record. There was (I cannot express it any better than this), every once in a while, some sort of a creative process that took place. Something was not there at one moment, and shortly it took form and found expression.

Now, if that is true, then all this unsystematic wandering about was well worthwhile. Moreover, I do not think that a narrower selection of people as to their interests and experiences would have given as much of such cross-fertilizing as we got. The wide ranks of the participants, I think, were necessary in order to get out of this meeting what we did. The Foundation was right in wishing for as wide an assembly as it asked.

I cannot speak about most of the terrace conferences or the table talks. Some of these probably were as important as anything that happened in the discussions. I hope that all of you had as good fortune as I did in meeting with the right companions at the right moment of proper reduction of inhibitions.

It is not proper for me to elaborate upon the personal, intimate communications that took place, of new friendships formed and old ones resumed. I do feel happy and a bit sentimental about the end result of our having been together. The thing that I should like most to say is that you will remain in my memories as a lot of the very best for the reason that you have been so simply natural and so without pretensions and so ready to give your best.

Process

MARSTON BATES

Any attempt at summarizing, at weaving together into a pattern, all the diverse threads that have been developed in the course of this conference is obviously out of the question. The three of us who have acted as co-chairmen have thought it wiser not even to attempt to co-ordinate our concluding remarks but rather, separately, to comment upon some of the impressions that have formed in our minds while listening to the unfolding discussions.

I find even this difficult, as my impressions have varied so much from day to day, from speaker to speaker: each argument, each point of view, appearing equally plausible, equally persuasive and important, as it was presented. I long ago became reconciled with this weather-vane aspect of my mind; but it does make for difficulty in exposition, since it prevents me from developing any consistent theme or from holding any single point of view. The weather-vane mind has only one advantage—it keeps the holder out of fights. Much of the trouble of the world, it seems to me, is caused by the cult of consistency, by the worship of integrity, by the tendency of right-thinking people to hold grimly to their beliefs. That, at least, is my method of rationalizing what is probably a deplorable defect of character.

The swings of my mind, in listening to the discussions here, have been particularly strong as I have listened, on the one hand, to speakers developing the concept of equilibrium, of the necessity of adapting to the processes that maintain equilibrium, and, on the other hand, to speakers expounding the importance of change, of development, of progress. I think I had never really posed to myself the question of change versus equilibrium before attending this conference. Yet, as I have listened here, I have come to wonder whether this is not a very basic question, underlying many of the arguments and differences in diverse fields of both the biological and the social sciences.

In the social sciences the advocates of the ever expanding economy are obviously thinking in terms of the processes of change. The extreme conservationists, characterized by Kenneth Boulding as people willing to freeze to death while sitting on top of a coal mine, are obviously preoccupied with the processes of equilibrium.

In the biological sciences the ecologists, it seems, are predominantly concerned with processes of equilibrium. The ecological word "climax" implies equilibrium, stability. The students of evolution, on the other hand, are necessarily preoccupied with processes of change. In geological terms nothing is stable; there is no climax.

Here, clearly, the difference is a matter of time scale. Or perhaps one could better say that whether equilibrium dominates or change dominates depends on the time perspective in which the particular phenomena are viewed. But I have often had a rather vague feeling that the findings of the students of ecology and of the students of evolution did not mesh as well as they should; and I wonder now whether this is a consequence of this differing emphasis.

Again, as someone has pointed out in the course of the discussion, in physiology we have an emphasis on homeostasis, on equilibriums, or steady states. Yet the whole history of the individual, from conception through

1136

growth to final death, is a history of change. Thus we are impressed everywhere in nature, when we look in a given cross-section of time, with the balances, the buffer mechanisms, the cycles, that maintain equilibriums. But, when we look longitudinally in time, the changes, whether apparently random or directed, impress us the most; and the system of nature appears to be in disequilibrium rather than in equilibrium.

I have come to wonder, then, whether many of the sharp differences of opinion that occur among students of human affairs—and among students of nature—may not be explicable in terms of these differences in emphasis. Perhaps we are happier in studying equilibriums, which fit more neatly into the way the human mind works; but perhaps the equilibriums are essentially illusions of these minds of ours.

This has relevance to the questions of survival that have so frequently crept into our discussions—questions of the survival of our species, of our various cultures, of ideas, of all sorts of things. Again, humanly, we want to survive, and we tend to want our particular way of life to survive; and survival seems to depend on the maintenance of equilibriums, so we are led to concentrate on the study of steady states.

In thinking about this, we rapidly find ourselves involved in the question of man and nature—a question that frequently turned up in our discussions. Is man a part of nature, or is he something different, apart from nature, a kind of organism with some control over his own destinies?

This surely is partly a semantic question, a matter of words. But it is also partly a problem of the nature of culture, which has not come in for much attention in the course of our discussions. I firmly believe that there is an essential continuity among physical, biological, and cultural processes, from the workings of the solar system to the workings of the Parent-Teacher Association in the Ann Arbor school system. Which means that I believe that man is a part of nature.

But this human culture is undeniably quite different in many essential ways from anything else known in nature; and man, as a culture-bearing animal, has then many unique aspects. One unique aspect is that man has the illusion, at least, of having some control over his destiny, which leads him to organize conferences like the present one. Even the most convinced of determinists, I notice, still write books about what they think should happen, still try to influence the course of human events; and this surely is "good."

Perhaps it is just as well that we avoided getting sidetracked into discussion of free will or determinism. I do not know what profit we could have got from such discussion, though the topic did lurk just below the surface many times during the week. Of course we have to hope that we have some control over our destinies; that, by better understanding of the present and the past, we can achieve a more satisfactory future.

We have been looking at the future frequently, sometimes with hope and sometimes with despair. In this connection I would like to say something about the kind of analogy that seems to me most appropriate for probing this future.

The history of cultures—of civilizations—has frequently been compared with the history of the individual. By this analogy, we may speak of youth, maturity, senescence, perhaps even of rejuvenation. The analogy is certainly dismal and, it seems to me, misleading. Iago Galdston spoke this morning about the marvelous architectonics of life, about the mysterious plan that seems to unfold in the development of every individual, which seems, indeed, to show that the course of development is predetermined.

This is true enough for the individual, but there does not seem to be any corresponding architectonic for the culture—or for the species. Cultures—civilizations—seem then to be comparable, not with individuals, but with species. When we look back over human history or geological history, we see some cultures, some species, and some organic types that have flourished briefly and disappeared and others that have persisted over long stretches of historic or geologic time. We find no signs of prior determination of fate for either the culture or the species.

Of course, as individuals we are going to die, as a culture we are going to disappear, and as a species we are going to become extinct. But, while this fate is predictable within rather narrow limits for the individual, it is outside the range of possible prediction for the culture or for the species.

When we try to draw a lesson from this analogy, we get back to the equilibrium business again. The species that has achieved the most satisfactory equilibrium with environmental forces is most apt to persist—as long as the environmental forces remain constant. But the environment is always changing, when looked at over any long stretch of time, and the species with the greater plasticity, with the ability to adapt to change, persists the longer. These same principles, surely, apply to cultures.

Equilibrium and change, culture and environment—these are words, surely very poor instruments for probing reality. But they are the only instruments we have except in the limited areas in which we have been able to develop mathematical forms of symbolism. When thinking or talking about problems such as those we have dealt with in this conference, I often have the feeling of being caught and bound by the nature of these word symbols. Perhaps the whole idea of "environment" is fallacious, misleading. But we are caught by our vocabulary, and escape, if not impossible, is at least very difficult.

Someone suggested that the conference was deficient in that there was no psychologist among us. The conference was not planned as a meeting of ambassadors from different disciplines; but perhaps a psychologist or, more specifically, a student of perception would have been a useful member to remind us from time to time of the extent to which the environment of man is the creation, perceptually, of man himself.

I have heard Hadley Cantril remark that we should try never to think of the individual and the environment as separate, definable entities but that rather we should try to think in terms of transactions between processes—that there is a continuing modification of one by the other.

We have talked about all sorts of realities here, but it has often enough been apparent that each of us was looking at these realities through his own cultural spectacles—that the realities were in part, at least, a function of his way of seeing. I was reminded, sometimes, in listening, of Cantril's account of some psychological experiments.

Spectacles were devised which distort vertical lines, making them slant. In one experiment well-trained sailors, properly indoctrinated with Navy protocol, were tested. When a sailor looked at a shipmate through these spectacles, he was seen as slanting, considerably out of the vertical stance. When a man in an ensign's uniform was looked at, he was still seen as slanting, though at a smaller angle from the vertical. A man in an admiral's uniform, despite the spectacles, was always perceived as standing straight.

Cantril told about another experiment with married couples. A newly married man, with these spectacles, tended to see his wife standing straight; but a man who had been married for several years would see his wife, as he should with the optical properties of the spectacles, leaning at a considerable angle from the vertical.

This, I think, is inescapable: the world we see depends upon the experience through which we are seeing it. Most of us here have been looking at the world through the experience of contemporary Western civilization. We have among us enough non-Westerners, and enough deculturized anthropologists, to keep reminding us of this bias, yet it constantly intruded into our discussions. I was most aware of these Western spectacles that we were wearing during recent days when the talk turned to technology or to science and technology.

We did not, of course, cover everything in this conference. But I do wish now that we could have taken a little time to explore the question of the nature of science and of the relation between science and technology. As a scientist, I have become increasingly aware of the limitations of science and increasingly doubtful about its utility as a tool for solving all human problems. I have consequently been somewhat distressed at finding some of us here talking as though we regarded science as a sort of white magic, an answer to all problems, a direct road to truth—objective, factual, certain.

It would hardly be appropriate, even if there were time, for me to enlarge on my concept of science here at the end of the conference; yet perhaps I may interpose a few words. It seems to me that science is only one of man's approaches to the understanding of the universe and of himself. By understanding, I suppose I mean trying to make sense out of the apparent chaos of the outer world in terms of the symbol systems of the human mind. This might be considered the function of all art; and in that case I am led, half-seriously, to call science the characteristic art form of Western civilization.

Man's various attempts at finding form and pattern in the universe, at finding "meaning," fall into a sort of scale in terms of objectivity. The scientist, always trying to adapt the symbols of thought to the events that he perceives in the world around him, represents the objective end of the scale. But the scientist can never attain any absolute objectivity, since he must always also deal with the mind of the observer. The impressionistic painter or poet, toward the other extreme in the scale, is primarily concerned with the symbols of the mind; but he, again, can never attain any absolute subjectivity, since his constructions always involve some perceived reality. Weston La-Barre, in dealing with this same line of thought, has suggested that the psychotic represents the subjective extreme, completely lost in the workings of his mind, with no contact left with reality.

This sort of discussion is pertinent to the ever present question, in our modern world, of the relations between the sciences and the humanities. If there is any logic in my reasoning, the sciences and the humanities form a false dichotomy, because science is one of the humanities. The need for relating science more closely to the broad stream of man's intellectual activities is being felt increasingly by our scientists and is reflected in the curricular experiments of many of our technical institutions. This is shown, for instance, in the educational experiments at the Massachusetts Institute of Technology, where they are said to be making efforts to "humanize the sciences." Someone has made the remark that the neighboring institution up the Charles River, not to be outdone, has taken to "Simonizing the humanities."

Man, in his present numbers, clearly requires science and its concomitant technology for survival. Yet, if science itself is to survive, it looks as though we shall have to find some way of "humanizing" it. Several times in the course of our discussions here the frightening aspects of a scientific world have been mentioned. The increase in psychoses and neuroses has been pointed out—and the possibility that human beings may not be able to withstand the stresses of the very environment that they are creating. Both Mr. Mumford and Mr. Sauer have pointed out that there may be a self-correcting mechanism here, in that it seems that the sciences are having increasing difficulties in recruiting scientists to carry the technical load of society. Perhaps our Western world, so proud of its technical advantages, is starting a sort of process of suicide through its failure to assimilate science into its general culture or as a curious consequence of the scientist's own self-important attitude.

We have mentioned these things in our discussions, though we have not explored them in any detail. We could not; yet I am sure that all of us have caught ideas and gained interests that will lead to a continuing development of thought about this aspect of man's role in changing himself and the landscape in which he lives.

I want to touch on one other topic that has frequently bobbed up in our discussions but that has had no formal place on our agenda—war. In this case, I wish now that we could have had a background paper on war as one of the ways in which man has changed the earth's landscape, because, certainly,

war has been a tremendously important agency in this process.

Even though we have talked about war so little, clearly it has been hanging over our minds all through our discussions, as it hangs over the minds of all men in the Western world these days.

War surely is a soluble problem. To treat it as an inevitable part of human nature seems to me foolish. This, of course, takes us back to the question of human nature and its biological and cultural components and to the nature of change in these components. The biological components change on the scale of geologic time. But war, as we see it, seems to me a purely cultural phenomenon, whatever its remote, "instinctive" sources may be; and cultural phenomena sometimes change with remarkable speed. It is not human nature to fly, and yet we managed to learn to do that. To say that we cannot solve the problem of how to avoid killing each other on a mass scale, when we have solved the problem of flying around in the air, seems a fatal pessimism.

But if we start talking about war—if I started to develop the subject here—the theme would rapidly shift from "process" that is supposed to be my preoccupation to "prospect" that is Mr. Mumford's province.

War, because it moves so obviously from process to prospect, seems a good place for me to stop. The war that worries us now is the war of the future. It is with a good deal of satisfaction that I turn the problems of the future over to Mr. Mumford, because I am very glad to see that here they are in the hands of a humanist rather than in those of a scientist.

Prospect

LEWIS MUMFORD

By the mere accident of my position, it seems appropriate that I should bring the discussion of man's role in shaping the face of the earth to a head, not in the sense of settling any of the questions we have raised, but rather showing what is implied in our different and sometimes divergent attitudes toward both man and the earth, despite the underlying unity achieved through science.

In passing from the past to the future, we pass from memory and reflection to observation and current practice and thence to anticipation and prediction. As usually conceived, this is a movement from the known to the unknown, from the probable to the possible, from the domain of necessity to the open realm of choice. But in fact these aspects of time and experience cannot be so neatly separated. Some part of the past is always becoming present in the future; and some part of the future is already present in the past. Instead of thinking of these three segments of time in serial order, we would do well to take the view of a mathematician like A. N. Whitehead and narrow the time band to a tenth of a second before and the tenth of a second after any present event. When one does this, one understands that the past, the present, and the future are in that living moment almost one; and, if our minds were only capable of holding these three elements together in consciousness over a wider span of time, we should deal with our problems in a more organic fashion, doing justice not merely to the succession of events but to their virtual coexistence through anticipation and memory.

Now part of the future we face has already been determined, and we have no control over it. To begin at the physical level, we are limited by the forces of inertia; at the biological level, by the facts of organic inheritance. At the social level we must reckon with institutional persistences which, if not so ingrained as biological structures, cannot be suddenly altered; even at the highest level of the human personality, memory and habit tend to keep our actions in a groove. We do well to reckon with these constant factors and their sluggish ways: if they fetter our creativity, they also tend to limit the possibility of chaos. For good or bad, a part of our future is given; and, like a Christmas gift, we must accept it gracefully, before we try to exchange it for something that fits us better.

We might, for example, in view of the special role that sexuality and love were to play in man's life, have wished that nature—sometime about the point when the structure of the frog was under consideration—had put the reproductive organs and the organs of excretion in different parts of the body. But we cannot hope that this fatal topographical mistake will be corrected. We have many similar commitments that carry over from the past. Some of us now wish, it seems, to feed the growing population of the earth with a synthetic concentrate; but if they succeed with the concentrate—I for one do not wish them well!—they will still have to furnish people with some bulk-producing jelly, as we do a sick person who has been on a liquid diet, in order to keep their bowels functioning; and they may even find it necessary, despite man's inordinate adaptability, to create some illusion of gustatory pleasure, lest the appetite for life itself should wane.

So again the fact that man has been

an active, roaming, searching, prying animal, never at ease when he feels imprisoned or involuntarily hemmed in, should make us think twice, it seems to me, before we make any estimate of possible or desirable populations for the planet. Before we convert our rocks and rills and templed hills into one spreading mass of low-grade urban tissue, under the delusion that, because we accomplish this degradation with the aid of bulldozers and atomic piles and electronic computers, we are advancing civilization, we might ask what all this implies in terms of the historic nature of man.

Already there are metropolitan bathing beaches and "wild" recreation areas, where, on a Sunday afternoon in summer, the sign "Standing Room Only" describes the facilities available. Perhaps some of the perversity and criminal mischief exhibited in our cities, particularly by the more muscular types, may be due to this very constriction of space. Are we prepared to breed legless men, satisfied in their urban pens, as we now breed almost wingless fowl? If not, should we wonder that a race that flourished for some five hundred thousand years or more with a population density of perhaps ten per square mile may not find life altogether satisfactory at a constant density of four hundred per acre?

In calling attention to these constants, I am trying to emphasize what the French philosopher Raymond Ruyer, in his book *Neo-finalisme*,[1] characterizes as the fibrous structure of history. Just because of the nature of time, memory, and inheritance, we cannot make sensible plans for the future without doing justice to the threads and fibers that run through every past stage of man's development and will follow through the future as well. In dealing with man's history, it is convenient to

1. Paris: Presses Universitaires de France, 1952. 272 pp.

cut it off into stages and periods; so we speak as though the Stone Age were represented in our society only by museum showcases of axes and arrowheads. But the fact is that about four-fifths of the planet's population are still living under conditions that approximate those of a Neolithic village, certainly far closer than they touch those of a twentieth-century metropolis. And when the other day some of our friends here said, almost a little contemptuously, "Don't let us go back to Paleolithic society," I was tempted to ask them how far they thought they could express that idea without using one of the tools of Paleolithic society, namely, language.

To sum up this point: the future is not a blank page; and neither is it an open book. The current notion that one has only to measure existing trends and to project, on a grander scale, the forces and institutions that dominate our present-day society in order to give a true picture of the future is based on another kind of illusion—the statistical illusion. This method overweights those elements in the present which are observable and measurable and seemingly powerful, and it overlooks many other elements that are hidden, unmeasured, irrational. In the third century A.D. an objective observer might well have predicted, on the basis of the imperial public works program, an increase in the number of baths, gladiatorial arenas, garrison towns, and aqueducts. But he would have had no anticipation of the real future, which was the product of a deep subjective rejection of the whole classic way of life and so moved not merely away from it but in the opposite direction. Within three centuries the frontier garrisons were withdrawn, the Roman baths were closed, and some of the great Roman buildings were either being used as Christian churches or treated as quarries for building new structures. Can anyone who remembers this historic transformation believe that the rate of scientific and technological change must accelerate indefinitely or that this technological civilization will inevitably remain dominant and will absorb all the energies of life for its own narrow purposes—profit and power?

Often the most significant factors in determining the future are the irrationals. By "irrational" I do not mean subjective or neurotic, because from the standpoint of science any small quantity or unique occasion may be considered as an irrational, since it does not lend itself to statistical treatment and repeated observation. Under this head, we must allow, when we consider the future, for the possibility of miracles, on the grounds developed by Charles Babbage in the *Ninth Bridgewater Treatise* and by James Clerk Maxwell in his famous letter on singular points. By a miracle, we mean not something outside the order of nature but something occurring so infrequently and bringing about such a radical change that one cannot include it in any statistical prediction.

Maxwell's doctrine gives exactly the insight needed into the situation to correct our usual view of the human prospect. He pointed out that even in physical systems, no less than in life generally, there occur, at rare unpredictable intervals, moments when an infinitesimally small force, because of its character and its position in the whole constellation of events, was able to effect a very large transformation. This doctrine allows for the direct impact of the human personality in history, not only by organized movements and group actions, but by individuals who are sufficiently alert to intervene at the right time and the right place for the right purpose. At such moments—they were obviously present and were seized in the founding of Buddhism, Christianity, and Islam—a single human personality may overcome the inertia of formidable institutions.

Even though one must realize, on further consideration, that this doctrine of singular points admits of negative miracles, too, and that, with hydrogen bombs in world-wide production, such a negative miracle is quite possible, I find that the doctrine makes an important qualification in our faith in purely statistical predictions. For, as Maxwell pointed out, the higher and more complex the system, the more often do singular points occur in it; so that there are more such points among living organisms than among crystals and more in the human personality than among animals. Our sense of the probable future of the earth, therefore, must make some allowance for extravagant improbabilities—even for changes that exist as yet only as fantasies in the minds of individual men. And note this: singular points, even when they radically change human events, are not easy to detect until they have done their work. Possibly the decision that will save mankind from nuclear warfare has already been taken. Though that fact would profoundly change all our calculations, we may not be able to pin down that moment until centuries have passed.

This brings me to another doctrine that qualifies and completes that which does justice to the fibrous structure of history. I refer to the doctrine of emergence. By emergence there is signified the change that comes about when a structure or organism alters, not in this or that part, but as a whole; when the new emergent possibilities that did not exist at a lower level of existence become visible and operative. Let me illustrate this on the simplest level—the predictions made in the periodic table. Thanks to Mendeleev, it was possible to predict the atomic weight and many of the other characteristics of elements that had not yet been discovered and even to name their total number—

ninety-two. What made this prediction possible was not merely their rhythmic order but their essential stability. This applied equally to radium. Everything about radium could be predicted except its emergent quality, namely, its radio-activity, its radical instability, which gave the first hint that the atom itself might have some of the characteristics of the organism. As a result, though the number of stable elements is still limited, even when allowing for isotopes, the theoretic number of unstable elements has possibly astronomical dimensions.

Now it seems to me that complex social transformations, capable of affecting every part of society, are often true emergents and are as undiscoverable in advance, on the basis of past observation, as was radium. No matter how fully we know the facts, we cannot predict the new dynamic pattern into which they will fall when they reach the moment of emergence. So the best observer of Neolithic society could not have predicted the new type of large-scale, wide-reaching urban organization that grew out of it in Egypt, Babylonia, and China. Nor yet can the most exact student of national organizations and mechanical collectives predict the nature of the world community that may emerge in our time and, by the very act of emergence, alter our current values and habits. Yet many of the most difficult problems we face today, like that of overpopulation, which remain insoluble so long as men face each other in competing political and religious units, may be simplified, or become nonexistent, once a world culture comes into existence.

All in all, there is no simple formula for dealing with either probabilities or possibilities in human society. Even if we had full knowledge of all the constants and variables—and, of course, we are far from that—we would still be in need of something more important in order to make wise decisions; and that is a theory of human development. The lack of any common notions here has been one of the most serious handicaps to our discussion of the future. Because of our failure here, we tend to make false goals out of the processes that we control; so the increase of quantity, or the promotion of change for the sake of change, like the actions of a bored child turning from one toy to another, constitutes our only directive. As a result of our failure, there are anthropologists and psychologists who look upon the whole experiment of civilization as a mistake or who, even if they do not go so far, treat each culture as a confined, self-subsistent entity, with no other goal than that of continuing in its ancient "way of life." But surely we cannot make good use of the earth unless we have some notion as to what is "good" and what is "useful," what is aimless change and what is a goal-directed transformation. And how can we arrive at these concepts unless we have some definite understanding of man's nature, his development, and his goals?

The evolution theory, as set forth by the great Victorians, was an attempt to give a meaningful interpretation of organic development. You will recall that, even before the great Darwin, Herbert Spencer had begun the modest work of synthesizing all knowledge on the basis of the evolutionary formula. His synthetic philosophy posited a continuous process of change, from indefinite simple homogeneity to definite complex heterogeneity. This plausible formula turned out to be inadequate for many reasons. The process of evolution was not a straight-line movement but one full of twists and turnings, of false starts, strategic retreats, and tangential explorations. By making mere survival a test of organic development, this theory tacitly placed some of the most primitive organisms, like the amoeba, on the same plane as man, for both have survived; and, on the same terms, parasites, which have lost their heterogeneity and complexity, deserved a higher rank than highly developed creatures that did not survive.

Now, the fact is that we cannot derive direction and purpose for any random succession of events; and the attempt to superimpose evolution on the framework of seventeenth-century science, which had deliberately eliminated the attributes of life from the bare framework of mass and motion, was doomed to failure. That failure now vitiates a large part of our thinking, even in the biological sciences. In our effort to reduce complex phenomena to the simplest terms, we inevitably end up with life in a state of organic decomposition, in a formless, purposeless, dehumanized world, with man himself nothing more than a collection of cheap chemicals.

To correct for this physically accurate but one-sided interpretation, we should, I submit, begin with the most highly developed forms and work downward; for only in a scheme dominated by the attributes of life and personality—order, direction, purpose, intelligence, selectivity, sensitiveness, autonomy, self-transformation, consciousness—can we find any criterion for development lower in the scale.

In dealing with the physical world, this elimination of the phenomena of life and mind pays off. We get along much more rapidly if we reduce all factors to their simplest terms, paying attention to the quantitative and repeatable elements and eliminating, as Galileo and Kepler agreed, the secondary and subjective qualities like color, form, and pattern. But, when all events are subjected to this process of reduction and isolation, the most obvious characteristics of organic life disappear from view, namely, the fact that the organism is an autonomous, self-perpetuat-

ing, self-transforming being, in dynamic equilibrium, but with a definite cycle of growth; and, the higher the scale of life, the more plainly does growth record itself in superorganic forms and creative activities, detached from mere survival. Instead of being a passive victim of external forces, living creatures, as Iago Galdston has wisely reminded us, have their own trajectory of growth; and, the higher the rank of organism, the more remote and the more comprehensive are its goals. It is not enough for man to live in the purely physiological sense; he must live the good life, that is, he must expand the realm of significance, value, and form. On any sound reading of biological evolution or human history, it seems to me, development is often at odds with immediate security or ultimate survival. All higher life is precarious, as the highest states of life are themselves fleeting and evanescent.

As man has gone on with his own development, he has become more conscious both of the general process of organic transformation and of the important role he himself has come to play. Instead of bowing himself out of the picture, as he did when he followed the canons of seventeenth-century science, he now takes a central position on the stage, knowing that the performance itself, in the theater of consciousness at least, cannot go on without him. He begins as an actor, singling himself out from his animal colleagues, already something of a prima donna, but uncertain of what part he shall learn. In time he becomes a scene-painter, modifying the natural background and finding himself modified by it, too; and he is driven to be a stagehand likewise, shifting the properties to make his entrances and his exits more manageable. It is only after much practice in all these roles, as actor, scene-painter, stagehand, costumer, that he discovers that his main function is to write the drama, using many of the old plots left by nature, but giving them a new turn of the imagination and working the events up to a climax that nature without his aid might not have blundered upon in another hundred million years.

Just because man has now become the dominant species on the planet, he needs both the knowledge of the external world, independent of his wishing, that science provides him and a knowledge of his own inner life, detached from the operation of extraneous forces and institutions, directed toward goals he himself projects. What will happen to this earth depends very largely upon man's capacities as a dramatist and a creative artist, and that in turn depends in no slight measure upon the estimate he forms of himself. What he proposes to do to the earth, utilizing its soils, its mineral resources, its water, its flow of energies, depends largely upon his knowledge of his own historic nature and his plans for his own further self-transformations. As the dominant biological species, man now has a special responsibility to his fellow-creatures as well as to himself. Will he turn the cosmic energies at his disposal to higher ends, or will he, wilfully or carelessly, exterminate life and bring his own existence to a premature end? If he thinks of himself as an insignificant bag of chemicals, he may wantonly reduce all forms and structures to mere dust and rubble.

If you force me to talk about probabilities, not about possibilities, still less hopes, I would say that man's future seems black, though perhaps a shade lighter than it was five years ago; for even if the nations now armed with nuclear weapons agree not to exterminate each other, even though provoked by a sense of intolerable outrage, the forces still dominant in our age are moving in the direction so keenly analyzed by Roderick Seidenberg, whose picture of *Posthistoric Man*[2] is to me even more frightening than either Aldous Huxley's or George Orwell's somewhat melodramatized versions. The difficulty is that our machine technology and our scientific methodology have reached a high pitch of perfection at a moment when other important parts of our culture, particularly those that shape the human personality—religion, ethics, education, the arts—have become inoperative or, rather, share in the general disintegration and help to widen it. Objective order has gone hand in hand with subjective disorder and formlessness. We seem to be forgetting the art of creating whole human beings, immunized to pathological temptations. The widening wave of neuroticism and criminality, so visible in every advanced society, indicates, it would seem, some lack in the human nutrients needed to create full human beings—a lack that no increased production of snakeroot, for use in psychotherapy, will make up for. If we are to achieve some degree of ecological balance, we must aim at human balance too.

Too much of our discussion here, I am afraid, has dealt with proposals for man's exercising control over nature without reference to the kind of control he must exercise over himself. But, plainly, the greater the quantity of energy at man's disposal, the more important becomes the old Roman question: *Quis custodiet custodies?* which may be loosely translated as: "Who is to control the controller?" At the moment that is a life-and-death question; and Marston Bates has rightly brought up the deep concern we must all feel over the manner in which government agencies in every big country have gone about exploiting our new powers. Atomic energy by itself is a neutral thing, obviously. It promises nothing; it threatens nothing. It is we who do

2. Chapel Hill: University of North Carolina Press, 1950. 246 pp.

the promising; it is we who exert the threat. What makes nuclear power a danger is the fact that it has been released in a world savagely demoralized by two world wars, the last of which turned into a war of unlimited annihilation; and the moral nihilism, first preached and enacted by the Fascist powers, has now been taken over by every person and agency that subscribes to the conception of total war—or, in plain English, unlimited extermination. The danger we face today was prophetically interpreted a century ago by Herman Melville in his great classic of the sea, *Moby-Dick*. In that epic the mad Captain Ahab drives his ship and his crew to destruction in his satanic effort to conquer the white whale—the symbol of all the powers outside man that would limit or lame him. Toward the end, as his mad purpose approaches its climax, Ahab has a sudden moment of illumination and says to himself: "All my means are sane; my motives and object mad." In some such terms, one may characterize the irrational applications of science and technology today. But we have yet to find our moment of self-confrontation and illumination.

By now the wartime threat of nuclear power is obvious even to those who still cling to the idea of using it. For the sake of gaining momentary victory over a transient enemy, they would be ready to bring human history and perhaps all life on this planet to an end. But in recoiling from this ultimate madness, in acknowledging that coexistence is better than nonexistence, we are not necessarily out of the woods; for even the peacetime uses of atomic energy should give us grave concern. On this score, I am not at all reassured by the sedative explanations that our own Atomic Energy Commission has put out. Certainly the history of ordinary industrial pollution gives us no ground for confidence: our childish shortsightedness under the excitement of novelty, our con-

tempt for health when profits are at stake, our lack of reverence for life, even our own life, continue to poison the atmosphere in every industrial area and to make the streams and rivers, as well as the air we breathe, unfit for organic life. The people who are now proposing to use atomic energy on a vast scale are the same people who have not yet made an effort, technologically, to dispose of the lethal carbon monoxide exhaust of the motorcar, the same people whose factories expose the inhabitants of industrial areas to air polluted with virtually the entire number of known cancer-producing substances.

For all our apparent concern to lower the death rate, we have scarcely yet begun to cope with the problems of ordinary industrial pollution. Yet, without even a prudent look over their shoulders, our governmental and industrial leaders are now proposing to manufacture atomic energy on a vast scale, before they have the slightest notion of how to dispose of the fissioned waste products.

This is one of those moments when it is well to remember the life-wisdom of the fairy tales before we turn the latest gift of science into a horror story. When some deep-seated human wish is gratified by magic in these stories, there is usually some fatal catch attached to the gift, which either makes it do just the opposite of what is hoped or suddenly deprives the recipient of the promised boon, as Gilgamesh, in the Babylonian epic, is robbed by the serpent of the plant that would give him immortality. This catch is already visible in atomic energy. We know how to turn nuclear fission on, but, once we have created a radioactive element, we must wait for nature to turn it off if we cannot use it in a further reaction. If once we raised the ceiling of radiation above the critical level, we could not undo that fatal mistake.

Now I am not saying that the problems presented by the peacetime exploitation of atomic energy cannot be overcome. What I am saying is that the problem of atomic pollution must be faced, not at the last possible moment, when irreparable damage has already been done, but at the earliest possible moment. Already, as John Bugher has pointed out, the indiscriminate use of radium paint for the instrument dials of a plane constitutes an occupational hazard for the pilot. We do not know yet whether a technical solution is possible or whether the solution will have to be a political one that will ban nuclear energy except in laboratory quantities. Before we can have any notion of the long-term effects of atomic radiation, even in such relatively small amounts as have been released during the last ten years, we should, in all prudence, put atomic energy under strict probation. Our haste to exploit it betrays a frivolous sense of irresponsibility, which casts doubts on the fitness of our present leaders to exercise these powers.

On this matter, the Atomic Energy Commission can speak with no authority whatever, for it lacks the only data that would be convincing, namely, that provided by time—and only by time. Our knowledge of radioactivity, if one takes it back to the discovery of the Becquerel rays, covers only some sixty years, or two generations; our large-scale production of fissioned materials covers only a decade. If in ordinary engineering calculations one multiplies by two as a factor of safety, in atomic calculations one should multiply by many times that number. We simply do not know enough about the long-term effects of atomic energy in even minor quantities to justify the risks we are already taking. But we know enough about the nature of radiation itself, beginning with the records we have of injury and death to early radiologists, to

know that the risks are serious. In view of that fact, we have a right to demand humility and prudence, not cockiness and indecent haste, in even the peacetime exploitation of atomic energy, no less than a total veto on its large-scale use in war. The compulsive aspect about our peaceful exploitation of atomic energy should itself put us on our guard. It seems, indeed, almost neurotically compulsive, perhaps because it is bound up with our repressed sense of guilt. What will all our atomic power profit us if it radically undermines the balance of nature or the basis of human life?

Now we come to a point where I feel obliged to put a terminal question: What has this conference disclosed to us?

I cannot presume to voice the sense of the meeting on this matter, for it has disclosed many different things to each one of us; and perhaps some of the most important things we shall carry away from our papers and discussions may not become visible until long after we have separated, though they have already seeded themselves in our minds. But to me the conference confirmed a belief that has long been growing more definite; namely, that the still dominant pattern of seventeenth-century science, with its dismembered and isolated data, with its preference for single-factor analysis, with its strict separation of quantity and quality, with its reductive technique, must be supplemented in dealing with the phenomena of life with a method that does justice to the essential nature of life: the autonomy and integrity of organisms, with their selective and purposive behavior. We must abandon the semantic hoax of reducing organic behavior to "mechanisms," for a machine is an arrangement of predetermined parts for serving a specific human end; and the conception of a machine reintroduces the very element of teleology that causal analysis attempts in vain to eliminate from the world of life.

Now, when one deals with human beings, neither Cartesian causality nor Aristotelian teleology, no matter how we reinterpret and refine these concepts, sufficiently accounts for the transformations of man in history. For human behavior is not merely purposive and goal-seeking but conscious; not merely tied to existing ecological associations but capable of projecting a whole new pattern of relations in which both man's objective knowledge of nature and his subjective projection of dream and wish and imagined purpose modify natural processes and bring them to a different destination. That which distinguishes the superorganic processes of culture from organic processes is precisely what man himself, in his cumulative acts of self-nurture, self-education, and self-transformation, has contributed to nature's original gifts. And, if this is the case, one cannot hope to find out what man can do or should do in shaping the earth without canvassing something more than his present knowledge of origins, processes, and stages.

To command the forces now at man's disposal and direct them toward organic and human development, man must be capable of directing his actions toward ideal ends, imaginatively conceived and rationally criticized. The formulation of these ends does not come within the province of science, so long as it remains faithful to its own salutary discipline; it is rather the product of the arts and the humanities, of religious visions and moral aspirations. I come back, accordingly, to the need for a common philosophy of human development that will do justice to all our partial historic formulations. Until we have that, we cannot make enlightened choices and project appro-

priate goals. Because truth itself is a formative influence, scientific knowledge must enter into such a formulation, to replace the sometimes inspired guesswork of early religions; but there comes a moment when knowledge must be applied to action, when action must be guided by rational plans, when plans must be laid out in terms of an ideal goal, and when the ideal goal must be chosen consciously with a view to the kind of self we are trying to produce, and therewith to the kind of facilities—geographic, economic, cultural—that self needs for carrying through its purposes and its whole life-course.

In most of our prognoses about man's relations with the earth we have tended, I am afraid, simply to carry forward processes now observable, with such acceleration as may be expected from the cumulative nature of scientific and technical changes, provided that these remain constant and undisturbed. Thus, we have taken technological civilization as a base line and have assumed that its spread to more primitive technological cultures will continue, with results similar to those now visible in highly industrialized countries. In these predictions we overlook the effects of human consciousness, of human reactions, of human purposes that would possibly project a different destination; some of us, if we do not regard human nature as fixed, treat it as a dependent variable, entirely governed by the machine. Surely, only by regarding man's own self-transformation as negligible would anyone think it worthwhile to speculate, as some of us have done, on the transformations of energy that might make the earth capable of sustaining as many as thirty billion people. That increase of population could not in fact be accomplished without a wholesale regimentation of humanity, so limiting its field of action, so curtailing its choices, so adapting it to merely physiological criteria of survival —with no thought of development— that the result would no longer be recognizable as man but as an inferior creature with an inferior planet to work and play in.

Now the facts are, I submit, quite different from those assumed to operate under this too simple assumption. As I suggested in my little introductory note to the whole section on the future, "within the limit of earth's resources and man's biological nature, there are as many different possible futures as there are ideals, systems of values, goals and plans, and social, political, educational, and religious organizations for bringing about their realization." To assume that there is only one possibility left, that represented by our now-dominant technological civilization, is an act of religious faith, committed by those who believe in this civilization, and in no sense an objective scientific judgment. All our present statistical curves may be deflected and altered in the real future by human choice and human contrivance; and in making these choices our normative ideas and ideals—indeed, our unconscious resistances and drives—will play no less a part than our knowledge.

Let me illustrate. There are, for example, large areas of the United States in national and state parks that might have been gutted out for industrial purposes had not the ideas and values of the romantic movement, as expressed by Henry Thoreau, Frederick Law Olmsted, and George Perkins Marsh, resulted in appropriate political action. Those of us who assume that the one-sided exploitation of the machine, for profit, power, and prestige, without any regard for the quality of life, is fated to go on and become more compulsive are, consciously or covertly, casting their vote for what Roderick Seidenberg calls "posthistoric man." There would be only one virtue in that kind

of society—adjustment—and only one reward—security. And the only freedom left would be that extolled by Karl Marx: "the conscious acceptance of necessity."

In the United States, no less than in Russia, we are moving uncomfortably near such a society; indeed, its main outlines have already been sketched in. If the production of posthistoric man were to become the dominant purpose of our culture, not a few of the problems we have been discussing would be automatically disposed of. If the goal is uniformity, why should we seek to preserve any of the richness of environmental and cultural individuality that still exists on the earth and, in turn, widens the range of human choice? Why should we not, on these terms, create by mechanical processes one single climate, uniform from the pole to the equator? Why should we not grind down the mountains, whether to obtain granite and uranium and soil, or just for the pleasure of bulldozing and grinding, until the whole round earth becomes planed down to one level platform. Then let us, if we need trees at all, reduce them to a few marketable varieties, as we have already reduced the six hundred varieties of pear that were commonly cultivated in the United States only a century ago. Let us remove, as a constant temptation for man to sin against his god, the machine, any memory of things that are wild and untamable, pied and dappled, unique and precious: mountains one might be tempted to climb, deserts where one might seek solitude and inner peace, jungles whose living creatures would remind us of nature's original prodigality in creating a grand diversity of habitats and habits of life out of the primeval protoplasm with which it began.

If the goal is a uniform type of man, reproducing at a uniform rate, in a uniform environment, kept at a constant temperature, pressure, and humidity, living a uniform life, without internal change or choice, from incubator to incinerator, most of our historic problems concerning man's relation to the earth will disappear. Only one problem will remain: Why should anyone, even a machine, bother to keep this kind of creature alive?

If this is not to be mankind's fate, how are we to save ourselves from it? The simple answer reduces itself to a platitude: We must throw overboard this childishly inadequate picture of man's nature and destiny and resume the functions of men. The greatest of these functions, capable of dominating all others, is that of conscious self-fabrication. We shall be ill prepared to meet the real challenges of the future if we imagine that our present institutions, because of the extraordinary successes of the machine economy in production, have congealed into a final mold from which man can never hope to escape. There is rather plenty of evidence at this moment to indicate that man may, as Teilhard de Chardin's paper suggested, be on the point of emerging onto a new plane. For the first time man may, as a conscious, interrelated comprehensive group, take possession of the whole planet. For the last century, not merely have we been able to think of the world as a whole, in time and space, but we have been able through our manifold inventions to act in the same fashion. Yet both our thinking and our acting have been crude, not to say primitive, because we have not yet created the sort of self, freed from nationalistic and ideological obsessions, capable of acting within this global theater.

I cannot, with the brief space that remains at my disposal, begin to characterize this new self, this "one world" self, as one might be tempted to call it; for it has as yet only begun to emerge. But if one of man's main tasks in the future will be to resettle and recultivate the earth, for the sake of human education and vital enjoyment, primarily, rather than for the sake of power, some of the characteristics of this self may be defined in advance. Though it will cherish the skills and talents associated with professional training, it will be multi-occupational as well as multi-environmental; it will demand, wherever it settles or moves, the largest possible variety of opportunities and choices. To exercise all the functions of a man will become more important than to wear the identifying badge of a nation or an office; for the day will come, as Emerson once said, when no badge, uniform, or star will be worn. The members of this conference, Carl Sauer has told us, were chosen not as representatives of a discipline, an institution, or a country but for their qualities as thinking human beings. So, in our meetings we have had, in a happy degree, a foretaste of what world culture and unified man would be. On such a basis, one need not fear posthistoric uniformity. When we begin the cultivation of the earth as a whole for more deeply human purposes, we may look forward rather to a flowering of individuality.

Certainly we can hardly hope to block the seemingly inexorable march of posthistoric man by clinging to obsolete institutions and archaic forms of the human self, fabricated by earlier cultures. To fight against the worldwide tendency toward mechanical uniformity and human nullity by trying to reserve some small segment of our life for an individuated development would be to surrender any hope of final victory. What we need to confront the threatening omniscience and omnipotence of posthistoric man is to cultivate powers equally godlike in a quite different part of the personality. Must we not cultivate a force that came late even in man's conception of godhood—the force that Henry Adams prophetically summoned up in opposition to the dynamo? I mean the force of love. And I mean love in all its meanings: love as erotic desire and procreativeness; love as passion and aesthetic delight, lingering over its images of beauty; love as fellow-feeling and neighborly helpfulness, bestowing its gifts on all who need it; love as parental solicitude and sacrifice; love as the miraculous capacity for overvaluing its own object and, thereby, glorifying it and transfiguring it, releasing for life something that only the lover can see. We need such a redeeming and all-embracing love at this moment to rescue the earth itself and all the creatures that inhabit it from the insensate forces of hate, violence, and destruction.

In evoking something so far outside the accepted province of a scientific conference as the works of love, I feel for a moment as if I were speaking with the voice of another man, a man whom we sorely miss, the voice of Father Teilhard de Chardin. Perhaps not so much the co-discoverer of Peking man, though love of truth is itself one manifestation of love, but the Chardin who belonged to a great Catholic order and who expressed the Christian reverence for life. To those who are quickened by love, every part of the earth has meaning and value; and no man is so humble, be he only a Micronesian islander or a Japanese fisherman, as not to be immune, as of right, from threat of injury or wanton extermination. There has been a palpable undercurrent of love all through this conference; we shall not easily forget John Davis' love of the seashore and the waters that touch the shore, William Albrecht's love of the soil, Fraser Darling's love of the ecological pattern, Soliman Huzayyin's love of the Nile Valley, Gottfried Pfeifer's love of the peasant economy, Sol Tax's love of a primitive Indian community, Edgar Anderson's love of hybrid vigor, to mention all too invidiously—alas!—only a few of these whose love was as conspicuous as their immense scientific competence.

The awful omniscience and the omnipotence of our science and techniques would turn out to be more self-destructive than ignorance and impotence if the compensating processes of life did not foster a new kind of personality, whose all-lovingness will in time offset these dangerous tendencies. We are now at a point where over two billion people have become our neighbors, and we shall have to learn all over again, without going back to our Stone Age ancestors, what the love of neighbors means. We can communicate with them at the speed of light; we can cooperate with them, to our common advantage, in long-term works of dressing and keeping the earth—or we can exterminate them, if we should be so vicious or so reckless, as surely as an electrocutioner, by a press of the button, can kill a condemned man. If we approach the earth and man in a spirit of love, we shall respect their individuality and treasure the gifts to personality that organic variety itself brings with it. We shall beware of all uniformities, unless, like the animal reflexes, they are agents of a higher life. Of every invention, of every organization, of every fresh political or economic proposal, we must dare to demand: Has it been conceived in love and does it further the purposes of love?

Much that we now do would not survive such a question. But much that is still open to man's creative acts of self-transformation would at last become possible. Not power but power directed by love into the forms of beauty and truth is what we need for our further development. Only when love takes the lead will the earth, and life on earth, be safe again. And not until then.

List of Participants*

Dr. WILLIAM A. ALBRECHT, Professor of Soils and Chairman of Department, University of Missouri.

Dr. HARRY ALPERT, Program Director for Anthropological and Related Sciences, National Science Foundation.

Dr. EDGAR ANDERSON, Director, Missouri Botanical Gardens, St. Louis; Engelmann Professor of Botany, Washington University, St. Louis.

Mr. EUGENE AYRES, Consultant, Gulf Research & Development Company, Pittsburgh.

Dr. A. LESLIE BANKS, Professor of Human Ecology and Head of Department, University of Cambridge, Cambridge, England.

Mr. H. H. BARTLETT, Director, Botanical Gardens, University of Michigan.

Dr. ALAN M. BATEMAN, Silliman Professor of Geology and Chairman of Department, Yale University; Editor, *Journal of Economic Geology.*

Dr. MARSTON BATES, Professor of Zoölogy, University of Michigan.

Dr. DAVID I. BLUMENSTOCK, Lecturer in Geography, Rutgers University.

Dr. KENNETH BOULDING, Professor of Economics, University of Michigan.

Dr. HARRISON BROWN, Professor of Geochemistry, California Institute of Technology.

Dr. JOHN C. BUGHER, Director, Division of Biology and Medicine, United States Atomic Energy Commission, Washington, D.C.

Mr. ALBERT E. BURKE, Lecturer in Geography and Director of Graduate Studies, Conservation Program, Yale University.

Dr. ANDREW H. CLARK, Professor of Geography, University of Wisconsin.

Dr. JOHN T. CURTIS, Professor of Botany, University of Wisconsin.

Dr. H. C. DARBY, Professor of Geography and Head of Department, University College, London, University of London, London, England.

Dr. F. FRASER DARLING, Senior Lecturer in Ecology and Conservation, University of Edinburgh, Edinburgh, Scotland.

Sir CHARLES GALTON DARWIN, Newnham Grange, Cambridge, England.

Dr. JOHN H. DAVIS, Professor of Botany, University of Florida.

Dr. JOHN W. DODDS, Professor of English and Director of Special Programs in the Humanities, Stanford University.

Dr. FRANK E. EGLER, American Museum of Natural History, New York.

Dr. E. ESTYN EVANS, Professor of Geography and Head of Department, Queen's University, Belfast, Northern Ireland.

Dr. IAGO GALDSTON, Secretary, Committee on Medical Information, The New York Academy of Medicine, New York.

Dr. CLARENCE J. GLACKEN, Assistant Professor of Geography, University of California, Berkeley.

Mr. ARTUR GLIKSON, Director, Planning Department, Housing Division, Ministry of Labour, Israel.

Dr. PIERRE GOUROU, Director, Institute of Geography, University of Brussels, Brussels, Belgium; Professor of Tropical Geography, Collège de France, Paris, France.

---

* Titles and affiliations given are those in effect at the time of the symposium in June, 1955.

1153

DR. EDWARD H. GRAHAM, Director of Plant Technology, Soil Conservation Service, United States Department of Agriculture.

†MR. MICHAEL GRAHAM, Director of Fishery Research in England and Wales, Gunton Dell, Lowestoft, Suffolk, England.

MR. GEORGE W. GRAY, Special Research Writer, Rockefeller Foundation, New York.

DR. ALAN GREGG, Vice-President, Rockefeller Foundation, New York.

DR. E. A. GUTKIND, 103 Corringham Road, London, N.W. 11, England.

DR. CHAUNCY D. HARRIS, Professor of Geography and Dean, Division of the Social Sciences, University of Chicago.

DR. EMIL W. HAURY, Professor of Anthropology and Head of Department, University of Arizona; Director, Arizona State Museum, Tucson.

DR. FRITZ M. HEICHELHEIM, Assistant Professor in Greek and Roman History, University of Toronto, Toronto, Canada; Honorary Full Professor of Ancient Economic History, Hochschule Giessen, Giessen, Germany.

DR. J. A. HISLOP, Department of Human Ecology, University of Cambridge, Cambridge, England.

MR. CHARLES B. HITCHCOCK, Director, American Geographical Society, New York.

DR. SOLIMAN HUZAYYIN, Professor of Geography, University of Cairo, Cairo, Egypt.

DR. EDAVALETH K. JANAKI AMMAL, Director, Central Botanical Laboratory of India, Lucknow, India.

DR. STEPHEN B. JONES, Professor of Geography, Yale University.

DR. LESTER E. KLIMM, Professor of Geography, Wharton School of Finance and Commerce, University of Pennsylvania.

† Prepared a background paper for discussion but did not attend the symposium.

DR. FRANK H. KNIGHT, Professor of Economics, University of Chicago.

DR. HELMUT LANDSBERG, Chief of Climatic Service, United States Weather Bureau, Washington, D.C.

DR. LUNA B. LEOPOLD, Research Division, Water Supply Section, United States Geological Survey, Washington, D.C.

DR. JAMES C. MALIN, Professor of History, University of Kansas.

MR. ALBERT MAYER, Mayer and Whittlesey, New York.

†DR. DONALD H. MCLAUGHLIN, President, Homestake Mining Company, San Francisco.

†DR. RADHAKAMAL MUKERJEE, Director, Institute of Sociology, Ecology, and Human Relations; Vice-Chancellor, University of Lucknow, Lucknow, India.

MR. LEWIS MUMFORD, Professor of City and Land Planning, University of Pennsylvania.

DR. ROBERT CUSHMAN MURPHY, Lamont Curator of Birds, Emeritus, American Museum of Natural History, New York.

†DR. KARL J. NARR, Scientific Assistant, Seminar für Ur- und Frühgeschichte, University of Göttingen, Göttingen, Germany.

DR. F. S. C. NORTHROP, Sterling Professor of Philosophy and Law, Yale University.

MR. SAMUEL H. ORDWAY, JR., Executive Vice-President, The Conservation Foundation, New York.

DR. FAIRFIELD OSBORN, President, The Conservation Foundation, New York; President, New York Zoölogical Society, New York.

DR. GOTTFRIED PFEIFER, Professor of Geography and Director, Geographical Institute, University of Heidelberg, Heidelberg, Germany.

†DR. RICHARD J. RUSSELL, Professor of Geography and Dean, Graduate School, Louisiana State University.

DR. CARL O. SAUER, Professor of Geography, University of California, Berkeley.

Mr. Charles A. Scarlott, Manager, Technical Information Services, Stanford Research Institute.

Dr. Vincent J. Schaefer, Director of Research, The Munitalp Foundation, Inc., Schenectady, New York.

Dr. Paul B. Sears, Professor of Botany and Chairman, Conservation Program, Yale University.

Mr. Roderick Seidenberg, Pipersville, Bucks County, Pennsylvania.

Dr. J. Russell Smith, Professor Emeritus of Economic Geography, Columbia University.

Dr. Alexander Spoehr, Director, Bernice P. Bishop Museum, Honolulu.

Dr. H. Burr Steinbach, Professor of Zoology, University of Minnesota.

Dr. Omer C. Stewart, Professor of Anthropology, University of Colorado.

Dr. Arthur N. Strahler, Associate Professor of Geomorphology, Columbia University.

Dr. Sol Tax, Professor of Anthropology, University of Chicago; Editor, *American Anthropologist*.

†Dr. Pierre Teilhard de Chardin, Research Associate, Wenner-Gren Foundation for Anthropological Research, Inc. New York.

Dr. Harold E. Thomas, United States Geological Survey, Salt Lake City.

Dr. Warren S. Thompson, Director Emeritus, Scripps Foundation for Research in Population Problems, Miami University.

Dr. C. W. Thornthwaite, Director, The Laboratory of Climatology, Centerton, New Jersey; Professor of Climatology, Drexel Institute of Technology, Philadelphia.

Dr. John W. Tukey, Professor of Mathematics, Princeton University; Bell Telephone Laboratories, Inc., Murray Hill, New Jersey.

Dr. Edward L. Ullman, Professor of Geography, University of Washington.

Dr. Joseph H. Willits, Director, The Educational Survey, University of Pennsylvania.

Dr. Hermann von Wissmann, Professor of Geography and Head of Department, University of Tübingen, Tübingen, Germany.

Dr. Karl A. Wittfogel, Professor of Chinese History, University of Washington; Director, Chinese History Project, Columbia University.

†Dr. Abel Wolman, Professor of Sanitary Engineering, Johns Hopkins University.

CONVERSION SCALES

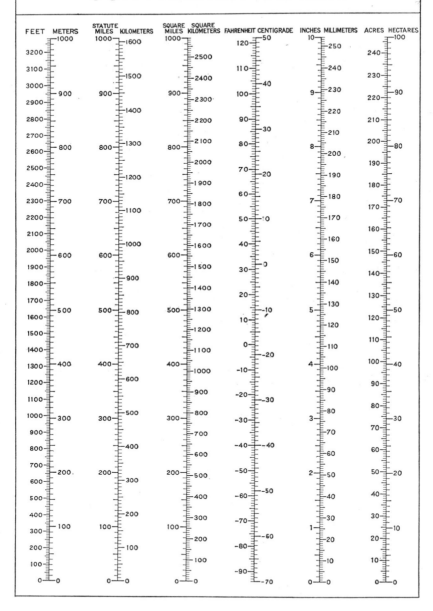

Index of Contributors to Symposium Discussions

General Index

[All numbers refer to pages. Numbers in roman (101) refer to text; numbers in italics (*102*) refer to figures or tables.]